		8A (18)

						8A (18)
						Helium 2 **He** 4.0026
	3A (13)	4A (14)	5A (15)	6A (16)	7A (17)	
	Boron 5 **B** 10.811	Carbon 6 **C** 12.011	Nitrogen 7 **N** 14.0067	Oxygen 8 **O** 15.9994	Fluorine 9 **F** 18.9984	Neon 10 **Ne** 20.1797
2B (12)	Aluminum 13 **Al** 26.9815	Silicon 14 **Si** 28.0855	Phosphorus 15 **P** 30.9738	Sulfur 16 **S** 32.066	Chlorine 17 **Cl** 35.4527	Argon 18 **Ar** 39.948
Zinc 30 **Zn** 65.38	Gallium 31 **Ga** 69.723	Germanium 32 **Ge** 72.61	Arsenic 33 **As** 74.9216	Selenium 34 **Se** 78.96	Bromine 35 **Br** 79.904	Krypton 36 **Kr** 83.80
Cadmium 48 **Cd** 112.411	Indium 49 **In** 114.818	Tin 50 **Sn** 118.710	Antimony 51 **Sb** 121.760	Tellurium 52 **Te** 127.60	Iodine 53 **I** 126.9045	Xenon 54 **Xe** 131.29
Mercury 80 **Hg** 200.59	Thallium 81 **Tl** 204.3833	Lead 82 **Pb** 207.2	Bismuth 83 **Bi** 208.9804	Polonium 84 **Po** (208.98)	Astatine 85 **At** (209.99)	Radon 86 **Rn** (222.02)
Copernicium 112 **Cn** (285)	Ununtrium 113 **Uut** Discovered 2004	Ununquadium 114 **Uuq** Discovered 1999	Ununpentium 115 **Uup** Discovered 2004	Ununhexium 116 **Uuh** Discovered 1999	Ununseptium 117 **Uus** Discovered 2010	Ununoctium 118 **Uuo** Discovered 2002

Terbium 65 **Tb** 158.9254	Dysprosium 66 **Dy** 162.50	Holmium 67 **Ho** 164.9303	Erbium 68 **Er** 167.26	Thulium 69 **Tm** 168.9342	Ytterbium 70 **Yb** 173.054	Lutetium 71 **Lu** 174.9668
Berkelium 97 **Bk** (247.07)	Californium 98 **Cf** (251.08)	Einsteinium 99 **Es** (252.08)	Fermium 100 **Fm** (257.10)	Mendelevium 101 **Md** (258.10)	Nobelium 102 **No** (259.10)	Lawrencium 103 **Lr** (262.11)

Standard Colors for Atoms in Molecular Models

 carbon atoms

 hydrogen atoms

 oxygen atoms

 nitrogen atoms

 chlorine atoms

Chemistry and Chemical Reactivity

Volume II

Eighth Edition

Kotz / Treichel / Townsend

CENGAGE
Learning™

Australia • Brazil • Japan • Korea • Mexico • Singapore • Spain • United Kingdom • United States

CENGAGE
Learning™

Chemistry and Chemical Reactivity: Volume II, Eighth Edition

Chemistry and Chemical Reactivity, 8th Edition
Kotz / Treichel / Townsend

© 2012 Cengage Learning. All rights reserved.

Executive Editors:
Maureen Staudt
Michael Stranz

Senior Project Development Manager:
Linda deStefano

Marketing Specialist:
Courtney Sheldon

Senior Production/Manufacturing Manager:
Donna M. Brown

PreMedia Manager:
Joel Brennecke

Sr. Rights Acquisition Account Manager:
Todd Osborne

Cover Image:
Getty Images*

*Unless otherwise noted, all cover images used by Custom Solutions, a part of Cengage Learning, have been supplied courtesy of Getty Images with the exception of the Earthview cover image, which has been supplied by the National Aeronautics and Space Administration (NASA).

For product information and technology assistance, contact us at
Cengage Learning Customer & Sales Support, 1-800-354-9706

For permission to use material from this text or product,
submit all requests online at **cengage.com/permissions**
Further permissions questions can be emailed to
permissionrequest@cengage.com

Compilation © 2010 Cengage Learning
ISBN-13: 978-1-133-15450-1

ISBN-10: 1-133-15450-6

Cengage Learning
5191 Natorp Boulevard
Mason, Ohio 45040
USA
Cengage Learning is a leading provider of customized learning solutions with office locations around the globe, including Singapore, the United Kingdom, Australia, Mexico, Brazil, and Japan. Locate your local office at:
international.cengage.com/region.

Cengage Learning products are represented in Canada by Nelson Education, Ltd.
For your lifelong learning solutions, visit **www.cengage.com/custom.**
Visit our corporate website at **www.cengage.com.**

Printed in the United States of America

Custom Contents: Volume II

The authors of this book have many years of experience teaching general chemistry and other areas of chemistry at the college level. Although we have been at different institutions, both large and small, during our careers, we share several goals. One is to provide a broad overview of the principles of chemistry, the reactivity of the chemical elements and their compounds, and the applications of chemistry. To reach that goal with our students, we have tried to show the close relation between the observations chemists make of chemical and physical changes in the laboratory and in nature and the way these changes are viewed at the atomic and molecular level.

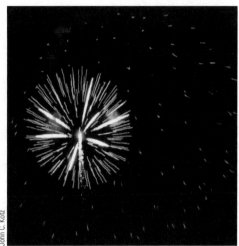

John C. Kotz

Another of our goals has been to convey a sense that chemistry not only has a lively history but is also dynamic, with important new developments occurring every year. Furthermore, we want to provide some insight into the chemical aspects of the world around us. Indeed, a major objective of this book is to provide the tools needed for you to function as a chemically literate citizen. Learning about the chemical world is just as important as understanding some basic mathematics and biology and as important as having an appreciation for history, music, and literature. For example, you should know what materials are important to our economy, some of the reactions in plants and animals and in our environment, and the role that chemists play in protecting the environment. In this regard, one growing area of chemistry, highlighted throughout this edition, is "green" or sustainable chemistry.

These goals have been translated into *Chemistry & Chemical Reactivity*, a book that has been used by more than 1 million students in its first seven editions. The first edition had a copyright date of 1987, and the copyright date for this edition is 2012. So, **this is the 25th anniversary of the book**. It is its silver (Ag) anniversary!

Looking back over the previous editions, we can see how the book has changed. There have been many new and exciting additions to the content of the book. In addition, there have been significant advances in the technology of communicating information, and we have tried to take advantage of those new approaches. A desire to make the book even better for our students has been the impetus behind the preparation of each new edition. With this edition, you will see a new approach to problem solving, new ways to describe contemporary uses of chemistry, new technologies, and improved integration with existing technologies.

Emerging Developments in Content Usage and Delivery: OWL, Go Chemistry®, and the Cengage *YouBook*

Our ongoing challenge as authors and educators is to use multimedia to engage students and to help them reach a higher level of conceptual understanding. More than 15 years ago we incorporated electronic media into this text with the first edition of our *Interactive General Chemistry* CD, a learning tool used by thousands of students worldwide.

As technology has advanced, we have made major changes in our integrated media program. Through several editions we redesigned the media so that students can interact with simulations, tutorials, active figures, and end-of-chapter questions, first through the *Interactive General Chemistry* CD and then with **OWL (Online Web Learning)**. OWL, which was developed at the University of Massachusetts, has been used by hundreds of thousands of students in the past few years.

More recently, we developed and integrated **Go Chemistry** tutorial videos into the seventh edition and more fully into this new edition. These tutorials are 5- to 10-minute mini lectures on topics such as solving equilibrium problems, features of the periodic table, naming compounds, polar molecules, writing net ionic equations, and identifying intermolecular forces.

What's New in This Edition

1. All **Example problems** in the book illustrate a **NEW approach to problem solving**. Each Example problem is broken down into the following categories: Problem, What Do You Know?, Strategy, Solution, Think About Your Answer, and Check Your Understanding. The "Check Your Understanding" questions are largely a revision of the Exercises from previous editions. Being included in the Example format should make them a more useful tool.

2. **NEW Interactive Examples in OWL** allow students to work approximately 70 examples from the book multiple times in slightly different versions to encourage thinking their way through the example instead of passively reading through to the solution.

3. At the end of almost every section in a chapter there are **NEW multiple choice Review & Check questions**. These are meant to be done in a few minutes to check the understanding of the section. In the Cengage *YouBook* these questions are interactive quizzes with feedback. (These questions could also be used in class by instructors to assess student understanding through electronic student response systems.)

4. **Strategy Maps** are a **NEW** feature of this edition. There are approximately 60 maps accompanying Example problems throughout the book. These are visual representations of the pathways to solving problems.

5. Except for Chapter 1, each chapter has **NEW extended Study Questions called *Applying Chemical Principles***. These help students apply principles learned across several chapters to real-world problems. Topics include the discovery of the noble gases, the discovery of elements on the sun, antacids, gunpowder, the rare earth elements, dating meteorites, and lighter-than-air ships.

General Strategy Map

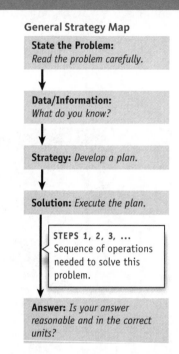

State the Problem:
Read the problem carefully.

Data/Information:
What do you know?

Strategy: *Develop a plan.*

Solution: *Execute the plan.*

STEPS 1, 2, 3, ...
Sequence of operations needed to solve this problem.

Answer: *Is your answer reasonable and in the correct units?*

6. There are 2210 end-of-chapter **Study Questions** in the book in addition to the Check Your Understanding, Review & Check, and Applying Chemical Principles questions. Over 1900 of these questions are available in OWL, more than double the number of questions available in OWL in the previous edition.

7. Another **NEW** feature is a discussion of the Principles of **Green Chemistry** are noted in Chapter 1. This is followed by 10 articles on green chemistry throughout the book. See, for example, an explanation of atom economy (page 168), the synthesis of ibuprofen (page 385), and lithium and green cars (page 586). The development of this NEW feature was assisted by Professor Michael Cann of the University of Scranton, a green chemistry authority.

8. This edition of the book is also available as a Cengage *YouBook*, a digital textbook. This includes all the same content as the print book, but it also has clickable videos, animations, Guided Tours of figures with

tutorials, three-dimensional molecular models, and quick quiz Review & Check questions. Those who choose the Cengage *YouBook* will also have access to strategy maps with audio/video explanations done by one of the authors or by Salman Khan, who has published hundreds of video tutorials on the Internet in many areas of science.

9. The **Interchapters** on energy, biochemistry, materials chemistry, and the environment have been revised to bring them up to date with the latest developments.

10. There are 10 **NEW chapter opening stories**. See, for example, essays on gold (page 1), energy and diet (page 208), rubies and sapphires (page 300), chocolate (page 438), and green cars (page 582).

11. A total of **17 NEW Case Studies** have been added. These include the story of Ötzi, the Iceman of the Alps (page 58); free radicals and hair dye (page 363); methane hydrates and the Gulf of Mexico oil spill (page 538); a pet food catastrophe (page 565); and exploding lakes and Diet Cokes (page 629).

12. ***Reorganization/addition/revision of material:***
    - A short introduction to energy has been moved from Chapter 5 to Chapter 1, and the units used in thermochemistry are introduced in the *Let's Review* portion of Chapter 1. This will assist instructors who wish to use this book in an "atoms-first" approach.
    - The material on metallic bonding and semiconductors has been moved from the materials interchapter into the chapter on solid-state chemistry (Chapter 13).
    - A short discussion on activities has been added to the equilibrium chapter (Chapter 16).
    - Many of the illustrations have been updated and/or redone.
    - New Study Questions have been added to a number of the chapters.

In addition, an entirely new *digital textbook—the* Cengage *YouBook*—has been developed for this edition. The Cengage *YouBook* is a fully electronic, full-color version of the book with extensive interactivity. You can use it with your desktop or laptop computer, to read the text, access useful databases, watch videos of chemical reactions, take a Guided Tour of a book figure, and much more.

Audience for *Chemistry & Chemical Reactivity* and OWL

The textbook (both as a printed book and the Cengage *YouBook* digital version) and OWL are designed for introductory courses in chemistry for students interested in further study in science, whether that science is chemistry, biology, engineering, geology, physics, or related subjects. Our assumption is that students beginning this course have had some preparation in algebra and in general science. Although undeniably helpful, a previous exposure to chemistry is neither assumed nor required.

Philosophy and Approach of the *Chemistry & Chemical Reactivity* Program

We have had several major, but not independent, objectives since the first edition of the book. The first was to write a book that students would enjoy reading and that would offer, at a reasonable level of rigor, chemistry and chemical principles in a format and organization typical of college and university courses today. Second, we wanted to convey the utility and importance of chemistry by introducing the properties of the elements, their compounds, and their reactions as early as possible and by focusing the discussion as much as possible on these subjects. Finally, with the **Go Chemistry** modules and complete integration of *OWL*, we have incorporated electronic tools to bring students to a higher level of conceptual understanding.

Flame colors by salts of boron, sodium, and strontium.

© Cengage Learning/Charles D. Winters

The American Chemical Society has been urging educators to put "chemistry" back into introductory chemistry courses. We agree wholeheartedly. Therefore, we have tried to describe the elements, their compounds, and their reactions as early and as often as possible by:

- Bringing **material on the properties of elements and compounds** as early as possible into the Examples and Study Questions (and especially the *Applying Chemical Principles* questions) and to introduce new principles using realistic chemical situations.
- Using numerous **color photographs** of the elements and common compounds, of chemical reactions, and of common laboratory operations and industrial processes.
- Introducing each chapter with a **problem in practical chemistry**—for example, a short discussion of the energy in common foods or the source of lithium in car batteries—that is relevant to the chapter.
- Using numerous *Case Studies* and introducing new *Applying Chemical Principles* study questions that delve into practical chemistry.

General Organization of the Book

Chemistry & Chemical Reactivity has two broad themes: *Chemical Reactivity* and *Bonding and Molecular Structure*. The chapters on *Principles of Reactivity* introduce the fac-

tors that lead chemical reactions to be successful in converting reactants to products. Under this topic there is a discussion of common types of reactions, the energy involved in reactions, and the factors that affect the speed of a reaction. One reason for the enormous advances in chemistry and molecular biology in the last several decades has been an understanding of molecular structure. Therefore, sections of the book on *Principles of Bonding and Molecular Structure* lay the groundwork for understanding these developments. Particular attention is paid to an understanding of the structural aspects of such biologically important molecules as DNA.

Flexibility of Chapter Organization

A glance at the introductory chemistry texts currently available shows that there is a generally common order of topics used by educators. With only minor variations, we have followed that order. That is not to say that the chapters in our book cannot be used in some other order. We have written this book to be as flexible as possible. An example is the **flexibility of covering the behavior of gases** (Chapter 11). It has been placed with chapters on liquids, solids, and solutions (Chapters 12–14) because it logically fits with those topics. However, it can easily be read and understood after covering only the first four chapters of the book.

Similarly, chapters on atomic and molecular structure (Chapters 6–9) could be used in an **atoms-first approach** before the chapters on stoichiometry and common reactions (Chapters 3 and 4). To facilitate this, we have moved an introduction to energy and its units to Chapter 1.

Also, the chapters on chemical equilibria (Chapters 16–18) can be covered before those on solutions and kinetics (Chapters 14 and 15).

Organic chemistry (Chapter 10) is often left to one of the final chapters in chemistry textbooks. However, we believe the importance of organic compounds in biochemistry and in consumer products means that material should be presented earlier in the sequence of chapters. Therefore, it follows the chapters on structure and bonding because organic chemistry illustrates the application of models of chemical bonding and molecular structure. However, one can use the remainder of the book without including this chapter.

The order of topics in the text was also devised to introduce as early as possible the background required for the laboratory experiments usually performed in introductory chemistry courses. For this reason, chapters on chemical and physical properties, common reaction types, and stoichiometry begin the book. In addition, because an understanding of energy is so important in the study of chemistry, energy and its units are introduced in Chapter 1 and thermochemistry is introduced in Chapter 5.

Interchapters

In addition to the regular chapters, uses and applications of chemistry are described in more detail in supplemental chapters on *The Chemistry of Fuels and Energy Sources; Milestones in the Development of Chemistry and the Modern View of Atoms and Molecules; The Chemistry of Life: Biochemistry; The Chemistry of Modern Materials;* and *The Chemistry of the Environment.*

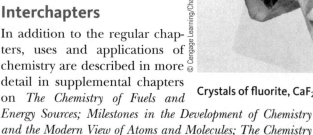

Crystals of fluorite, CaF_2.

Organization and Purposes of the Sections of the Book

Part One: The Basic Tools of Chemistry

The basic ideas and methods that are the basis of all chemistry are introduced in Part One. Chapter 1 defines important terms, and the accompanying *Let's Review* section reviews units and mathematical methods. Chapter 2 introduces atoms, molecules, and ions, and the most important organizational device in chemistry, the periodic table. In Chapters 3 and 4 we begin to discuss the principles of chemical reactivity and to introduce the numerical methods used by chemists to extract quantitative information from chemical reactions. Chapter 5 is an introduction to the energy involved in chemical processes. The supplemental chapter *The Chemistry of Fuels and Energy Sources* follows Chapter 5 and uses the concepts developed in the preceding chapters.

Part Two: The Structure of Atoms and Molecules

The goal of this section is to outline the current theories of the arrangement of electrons in atoms (Chapters 6 and 7). This discussion is tied closely to the arrangement of elements in the periodic table and to periodic properties. In Chapter 8 we discuss the details of chemical bonding and the properties of these bonds. In addition, we show how to derive the three-dimensional structure of simple molecules. Finally, Chapter 9 considers the major theories of chemical bonding in more detail.

This part of the book is completed with a discussion of organic chemistry (Chapter 10), primarily from a structural point of view.

This section includes the interchapter on *Milestones in the Development of Chemistry and the Modern View of Atoms and Molecules.* It also includes *The Chemistry of Life: Biochemistry* to provide an overview of some of the

most important aspects of biochemistry.

Part Three: States of Matter

The behavior of the three states of matter—gases, liquids, and solids—is described in Chapters 11–13. The discussion of liquids and solids is tied to gases through the description of intermolecular forces in Chapter 12, with particular attention given to liquid and solid water. In Chapter 14 we describe the properties of solutions, intimate mixtures of gases, liquids, and solids.

Designing and making new materials with useful properties is one of the most exciting areas of modern chemistry. Therefore, this section includes the interchapter *The Chemistry of Modern Materials.*

Part Four: The Control of Chemical Reactions

This section is wholly concerned with the *Principles of Reactivity.* Chapter 15 examines the rates of chemical processes and the factors controlling these rates. Next, we move to Chapters 16–18, which describe chemical reactions at equilibrium. After an introduction to equilibrium in Chapter 16, we highlight the reactions involving acids and bases in water (Chapters 17 and 18) and reactions leading to slightly soluble salts (Chapter 18). To tie together the discussion of chemical equilibria, we again explore thermodynamics in Chapter 19. As a final topic in this section we describe in Chapter 20 chemical reactions involving the transfer of electrons and the use of these reactions in electrochemical cells.

The Chemistry of the Environment supplemental chapter is at the end of Part Four. This chapter uses ideas from kinetics and chemical equilibria, in particular, as well as principles described in earlier chapters in the book.

Part Five: The Chemistry of the Elements and Their Compounds

Although the chemistry of the various elements is described throughout the book, Part Five considers this topic in a more systematic way. Chapter 21 is devoted to the chemistry of the main group elements, whereas Chapter 22 is a discussion of the transition elements and their compounds. Finally, Chapter 23 is a brief discussion of nuclear chemistry.

Features of the Book

Several years ago a student of one of the authors, now an accountant, shared an interesting perspective with us. He said that, while general chemistry was one of his hardest subjects, it was also the most useful course he had taken because it taught him how to solve problems. We were gratified by this perspective. We have always thought that, for many students, an important goal in general chemistry was not only to teach students chemistry but also to help them learn critical thinking and problem-solving skills. Many of the features of the book are meant to support those goals.

Problem-Solving Approach: Organization and Strategy Maps

Worked-out examples are an essential part of each chapter. To better assist students in following the logic of a solution, these problems are now organized around the following outline:

PROBLEM
This is the statement of the problem.

WHAT DO YOU KNOW?
You outline what information you have and begin to think about a solution.

STRATEGY
You combine the information available with the objective to devise a pathway to solution.

SOLUTION
You work through the steps, both logical and mathematical, to the answer.

THINK ABOUT YOUR ANSWER
You ask if the answer is reasonable or what it means.

CHECK YOUR UNDERSTANDING
This is a similar problem for you to try. Solutions to the problems are in Appendix O.

For many problems, a **strategy map** can be a useful tool in solving the problem. For example, on pages 42–44, we ask how thick the oil layer would be if you spread a given mass of oil on the surface of water in a dish. The density of the oil is also given. To help see the logic of the problem, the Example is accompanied by the strategy map given here.

There are approximately 60 strategy maps in the book accompanying Example problems. Many of the strategy maps in the Cengage *YouBook* digital textbook are accompanied by an audio explanation.

Strategy Map for Example 5

PROBLEM
How thick will an oil layer be when a **given mass** covers a **given area**?

DATA/INFORMATION
Mass and **density** of the oil and **diameter** of the circular surface to be covered.

STEP 1. Calculate the **volume** of oil from **mass** and **density**.

Volume of oil in **cm³**

STEP 2. Calculate the **surface area** from the **diameter**.

Area to be covered in **cm²**

STEP 3. Divide the oil **volume** by the **surface area** to calculate the thickness in **cm**.

Thickness of oil layer in **cm.**

Review & Check: New Quick Review Questions

We have also added new, multiple choice questions at the end of almost every section. Students can check their understanding of the section by attempting these brief questions. Answers to the questions are in Appendix P. In the Cengage *YouBook* digital textbook the questions are clickable so you can quickly check to see if you know the correct answer.

Chapter Goals/Revisited

The learning goals for each chapter are listed on the first page of each chapter and then are revisited on the last page. There the revisited goals are given in more detail. These goals are of great use in studying. Students can go through the goals and ask themselves if they have met each one. Furthermore, specific end-of-chapter Study Questions are listed that help students determine if they have met those goals.

End-of-Chapter Study Questions

There are 50 to over 100 Study Questions for each chapter. They are grouped as follows:

Practicing Skills
These questions are grouped by the topic covered by the questions.

General Questions
There is no indication regarding the type of question.

In the Laboratory
These are problems that may be encountered in a laboratory experiment on the chapter material.

Summary and Conceptual Questions
These questions use concepts from the current chapter as well as preceding chapters.

Applying Chemical Principles
These questions are preceded by a short description giving the background necessary to address the problem.

Study Questions have been available in the OWL Online Web Learning system for the last two editions. In this edition, we have more than doubled the number available. The OWL system now has over 1900 of the roughly 2200 Study Questions in the book.

Finally, note that some questions are marked with a small red triangle (▲). These are meant to be somewhat more challenging than other questions.

Boxed Essays

As in the seventh edition, we continue to include boxed essays titled *A Closer Look* (for a more in-depth look at relevant material), and *Problem Solving Tips*. We have added or revised a number of the *Case Studies*, some of which deal with "green" or sustainable chemistry.

A Word About the Cengage *YouBook*

The Cengage *YouBook* is an interactive digital version of the complete book and retains the paging integrity of the printed textbook. Either the digital version or the printed version of the book can be used in class.

The Cengage *YouBook* has clickable videos of reactions, Guided Tours of book figures, three-dimensional molecular models, searchable databases of chemical information, and the end-of-section Review & Check questions have clickable answers.

A unique feature of the Cengage *YouBook* is the **audio versions of the strategy maps**. For many of the maps in the book, one of the book authors will give a step-by-step audio explanation of the Example problem and explain some of the details of the strategy and solution.

Some of the audio strategy maps have been done by Salman Khan, who has recently been recognized around the world for his online tutorials, not only in chemistry but also in biology, linear algebra, geometry, trigonometry, statistics, pre-calculus, economics, money and banking, finance, and others. The web address for these tutorials is

www.khanacademy.org

All of Khan's tutorials are free and are on YouTube. The Cengage *YouBook* will link to those videos that Mr. Khan has done specifically for *Chemistry & Chemical Reactivity*. However, students should also explore all of the others for chemistry and for other areas of interest.

Changes for the Eighth Edition

Significant additions to the book, such as a new problem-solving format, strategy maps, essays on green chemistry, and *Applying Chemical Principles* problems, have been outlined in the section on "What's New." In addition, we have produced many new photos and new illustrations and have continually tried to improve the writing throughout. The following chapter-by-chapter listing indicates more specific changes from the seventh edition of the book to this edition.

Chapter 1 Basic Concepts of Chemistry

- New opening story: Gold!
- New opening section: we now outline the forensic investigation of the Iceman of the Alps.
- New *Closer Look:* Careers in Chemistry. Features a former student who is now a forensic chemist.
- New Section 1.2, Sustainability and Green Chemistry. Green chemistry is a theme used throughout the book.
- New *Closer Look:* Principles of Green Chemistry.
- New *Closer Look:* Element Names and Symbols.
- New Section 1.8: Energy: Some Basic Principles. Introduction to energy moved into this chapter from Chapter 5.

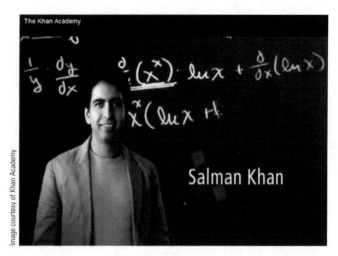

Salman Khan of the Khan Academy.

- New *Case Study:* CO_2 in the Oceans.
- Twelve new or revised Study Questions (out of 46).

Let's Review: The Tools of Quantitative Chemistry

- New: Energy units introduced. (This was in Chapter 5 in the seventh edition.)
- Strategy maps introduced into the book for the first time.
- Six new or revised Study Questions (out of 67).

Chapter 2 Atoms, Molecules, and Ions

- New *Case Study:* Using Isotopes: Ötzi, the Iceman of the Alps.
- New *Case Study:* Mummies, Bangladesh, and the Formula of Compound 606.
- Fourteen new Study Questions (out of 165).
- *Applying Chemical Principles:* Argon—An Amazing Discovery.

Chapter 3 Chemical Reactions

- New figure (Figure 3.9) to predict the species present in aqueous solution.
- Updated *Closer Look:* Sulfuric Acid.
- Twelve new Study Questions (out of 93).
- *Applying Chemical Principles:* Superconductors.

Chapter 4 Stoichiometry: Quantitative Information about Chemical Reactions

- New opening story: The Chemistry of Pyrotechnics.
- New *Case Study:* Green Chemistry and Atom Economy.
- Three new Study Questions (out of 139).
- *Applying Chemical Principles:* Antacids.

Chapter 5 Principles of Chemical Reactivity: Energy and Chemical Reactions

- New opening story: Energy and Your Diet.
- Section on basic principles of heat (pp. 209–211 in seventh edition) moved to Chapter 1 Let's Review.
- Ten new Study Questions (out of 110).
- *Applying Chemical Principles:* Gunpowder.

A device used to ignite gas burners. Depends on rare earth elements.

Chapter 6 The Structure of Atoms

- New opening story: Fireworks.
- Boxed essay on orbitals rewritten and slightly expanded.
- Section on introduction to wave mechanics rewritten.
- Three new Study Questions (out of 84).
- *Applying Chemical Principles:* Chemistry of the Sun.

Chapter 7 The Structure of Atoms and Periodic Trends

- New opening story: Rubies and Sapphires—Pretty Stones.
- Rewritten discussion of effective nuclear charge with new figures.
- Expanded discussion of configurations of transition metal electron configurations, especially Cr and Cu.
- New *Closer Look:* Orbital Energies, Z^*, and Electron Configurations.
- Clarified relation of electron attachment enthalpy and electron affinity.
- *Applying Chemical Principles:* The Not-So-Rare Earths.

Chapter 8 Bonding and Molecular Structure

- New *Closer Look:* A Scientific Controversy—Are There Double Bonds in Sulfate and Phosphate Ions?
- New *Case Study:* Hydroxyl Radicals, Atmospheric Chemistry, and Hair Dyes.
- Electrostatic potential maps were introduced in the seventh edition. We have slightly enlarged the use of these figures for this edition and are using the industry standard software to create them.

- New *Case Study:* Ibuprofen, A Study in Green Chemistry.
- Eleven new or revised Study Questions (out of 96).
- *Applying Chemical Principles:* Linus Pauling and Electronegativity.

Chapter 9 Bonding and Molecular Structure: Orbital Hybridization and Molecular Orbitals

- Updated discussion of molecular orbital theory.
- New *Case Study:* Green Chemistry, Safe Dyes, and Molecular Orbitals.
- New *Closer Look:* Three-Center Bonds and Hybrid Orbitals with *d* Orbitals.
- Thirteen new or revised Study Questions (out of 80).
- *Applying Chemical Principles:* Probing Molecules with Photoelectron Spectroscopy.

Chapter 10 Carbon: Not Just Another Element

- New opening story: The Food of the Gods.
- New *Case Study:* An Awakening with L-DOPA.
- New *Closer Look:* Copolymers and Engineering Plastics for Lego Bricks and Tattoos.
- New *Closer Look:* Green Chemistry: Recycling PET.
- New *Case Study:* Green Adhesives.
- Deleted boxed essays on fats and oils, biofuels, dyes, and "super diapers," but some information on fats and oils was incorporated into the biochemistry interchapter.
- Fifteen new or revised Study Questions (out of 109).
- *Applying Chemical Principles:* Biodiesel—An Attractive Fuel for the Future?

White phosphorus.

Chapter 11 Gases and Their Properties

- New *Closer Look:* SCUBA Diving—An Application of the Gas Laws.
- New *Case Study:* What to Do with All of That CO_2? More on Green Chemistry.
- Six new or rewritten Study Questions (out of 108).
- *Applying Chemical Principles:* The Goodyear Blimp.

Chapter 12 Intermolecular Forces and Liquids

- New opening story: Geckos Can Climb Up der Waals.
- New *Case Study:* Hydrogen Bonding & Methane Hydrates: Opportunities and Problems. This is about the 2010 oil release in the Gulf of Mexico.
- New *Case Study:* A Pet Food Catastrophe.
- New *Closer Look:* Supercritical CO_2 and Green Chemistry.
- Seven new or rewritten Study Questions (out of 67).
- *Applying Chemical Principles:* Chromatography.

Chapter 13 The Chemistry of Solids

- New opening story: Lithium and "Green Cars."
- New *Case Study:* High-Strength Steels and Unit Cells.
- New Section 13.3, Bonding in Metals and Semiconductors. This was moved to Chapter 13 from the Interchapter on materials.
- New *Case Study:* Graphene—The Hottest New Network Solid.
- Eighteen new or rewritten Study Questions (out of 62).
- *Applying Chemical Principles:* Tin Disease.

Chapter 14 Solutions and Their Behavior

- New opening story: Survival at Sea.
- New *Case Study:* Exploding Lakes and Diet Cokes.
- New *Closer Look:* Reverse Osmosis for Pure Water.
- Four new or rewritten Study Questions (out of 106).
- *Applying Chemical Principles:* Distillation.

Chapter 15 Chemical Kinetics: The Rates of Chemical Reactions

- Four new Study Questions (out of 88).
- *Applying Chemical Principles:* Kinetics and Mechanisms: A 70-Year-Old Mystery Solved.

Chapter 16 Principles of Chemical Reactivity: Equilibria

- New *Closer Look:* Activities and Units of *K*.
- Eight new or rewritten Study Questions (out of 72).
- *Applying Chemical Principles:* Trivalent Carbon.

Chapter 17 Principles of Chemical Reactivity: The Chemistry of Acids and Bases

- New *Case Study:* Would You Like Some Belladonna Juice in Your Drink?
- Rearranged the sections on Polyprotic Acids and Bases (Section 17.9) and Molecular Structure, Bonding, and Acid–Base Behavior (Section 17.10).
- Some of the 121 Study Questions were reorganized.

Samples of cobalt metal.

- *Applying Chemical Principles:* The Leveling Effect, Nonaqueous Solvents, and Superacids.

Chapter 18 Principles of Chemical Reactivity: Other Aspects of Aqueous Equilibria

- New opening story: Nature's Acids.
- New *Case Study:* Chemical Equilibria in the Oceans.
- Several new and modified Study Questions (out of 112).
- *Applying Chemical Principles:* Everything That Glitters. . . .

Chapter 19 Principles of Chemical Reactivity: Entropy and Free Energy

- New opening story: Hydrogen for the Future?
- Given the key role of thermodynamics in chemistry, this chapter was carefully revised. Sections on free energy were reorganized.
- Three modified or new Study Questions (out of 84).
- *Applying Chemical Principles:* Are Diamonds Forever?

Chapter 20 Principles of Chemical Reactivity: Electron Transfer Reactions

- New opening story: Battery Power.
- Problem Solving Tip on balancing equations for reactions in basic solution was revised.
- Fourteen new Study Questions (out of 103).
- *Applying Chemical Principles:* Sacrifice!

Chapter 21 The Chemistry of the Main Group Elements

- Six new Study Questions (out of 106).
- *Applying Chemical Principles:* van Arkel Triangles and Bonding.

Chapter 22 The Chemistry of the Transition Elements

- *Applying Chemical Principles:* Green Catalysts.

Chapter 23 Nuclear Chemistry

- The *Closer Look:* The Search for New Elements was updated with the newest discoveries.
- Study Questions were reorganized.
- *Applying Chemical Principles:* The Age of Meteorites.

Alternate Versions

Cengage *YouBook* with OWL

The Cengage *YouBook* is a Flash-based, interactive, and customizable eBook version available with OWL. The instructor text edit feature allows for modification of the narrative by adding notes, re-ordering entire sections and chapters, and hiding content. Additional assets include animated figures, video clips, and student highlighting and note tools. See the OWL description below for more details.

Chemistry & Chemical Reactivity, Eighth Edition, Hybrid Version with OWL

ISBN-10: 1-111-57498-7; ISBN-13: 978-111-57498-7

This briefer version of *Chemistry & Chemical Reactivity* does not contain the end-of-chapter problems, which can be assigned in OWL. Access to OWL and the Cengage *YouBook* is packaged with the hybrid version.

Supporting Materials

◍WL

OWL for General Chemistry

Instant Access OWL with Cengage *YouBook* (6 months)
ISBN-10: 1-111-30524-2; ISBN-13: 978-1-111-30524-6

Instant Access OWL with Cengage *YouBook* (24 months)
ISBN-10: 1-111-30521-8; ISBN-13: 978-1-111-30521-5

By Roberta Day and Beatrice Botch of the University of Massachusetts, Amherst, and William Vining of the State University of New York at Oneonta.

OWL Online Web Learning offers more assignable, gradable content (including end-of-chapter questions specific to this textbook) and more reliability and flexibility than any other system. OWL's powerful course management tools allow instructors to control due dates, number of attempts, and whether students see answers or receive feedback on how to solve problems. OWL includes the Cengage *YouBook*, a Flash-based eBook that is interactive and customizable. It features a text edit tool that allows instructors to modify the textbook narrative as needed. With the Cengage *YouBook*, instructors can quickly re-order entire sections and chapters or hide any content they don't teach to create an eBook that perfectly matches their syllabus. Instructors can further customize the Cengage *YouBook* by publishing web links. Additional media assets include animated figures, video clips, highlighting, notes, and more.

Developed by chemistry instructors for teaching chemistry, OWL is the only system specifically designed to support **mastery learning**, where students work as long as they need to master each chemical concept and skill. OWL has already helped hundreds of thousands of students master chemistry through a wide range of assignment types, including tutorials, interactive simulations, and algorithmically generated homework questions that provide instant, answer-specific feedback.

OWL is continually enhanced with online learning tools to address the various learning styles of today's students such as:

- **Quick Prep** review courses that help students learn essential skills to succeed in General and Organic Chemistry
- **Jmol** molecular visualization program for rotating molecules and measuring bond distances and angles
- **Go Chemistry**® mini video lectures on key concepts that students can play on their computers or download to their video iPods, smart phones, or personal video players
- For this text, OWL includes **How Do I Solve It** problem-solving exercises, new **Interactive Example** assignments, as well as parameterized end-of-chapter questions and **Student Self Assessment** questions

In addition, when you become an OWL user, you can expect service that goes far beyond the ordinary. For more information or to see a demo, please contact your Cengage Learning representative or visit us at **www.cengage.com/owl**.

FOR THE INSTRUCTOR

Supporting instructor materials are available to qualified adopters. Please consult your local Cengage Learning, Brooks/Cole representative for details. Visit **login.cengage.com** and search for this book to access the Instructor's Companion Site, where you can

- See samples of materials
- Request a sample copy
- Locate your local representative
- Download digital files of the ExamView test bank and other helpful materials for instructors and students

PowerLecture Instructor's CD/DVD Package with JoinIn® and ExamView®

ISBN-10: 1-111-42719-4; ISBN-13: 978-1-111-42719-1

This digital library and presentation tool that includes:

- **PowerPoint® lecture slides**, written specially for *Chemistry & Chemical Reactivity*, which instructors can customize by importing their own lecture slides or other materials.
- Image libraries that contain **digital files for all text art, most photographs, all numbered tables, and multimedia animations** in a variety of digital formats. These files can be used to print transparencies, create your own PowerPoint slides, and supplement your lectures.

- Digital files of the complete **Instructor's Resource Manual** and **ExamView test bank.**
- Sample chapters from the **Student Solutions Manual** and **Study Guide.**
- **ExamView testing software** that enables you to create, deliver, and customize tests using the more than 1250 test bank questions written specifically for this text by David Treichel, Nebraska Wesleyan University.
- **JoinIn student response (clicker) questions** written for this book for use with the classroom response system of the instructor's choice.

Instructor's Companion Site

Go to **login.cengage.com** and search for this book to access the Instructor's Companion site, which has resources such as a Blackboard version of ExamView.

Instructor's Resource Manual

by John Vincent, The University of Alabama

ISBN-10: 1-111-42697-X; ISBN-13: 978-1-111-42697-2

Available both on the PowerLecture Instructor's Resource DVD and in print, this comprehensive resource contains worked-out solutions to *all* end-of-chapter Study Questions and features ideas for instructors on how to fully utilize resources and technology in their courses. It provides questions for electronic response (clicker) systems, suggests classroom demonstrations, and emphasizes good and innovative teaching practices.

Transparencies

ISBN-10: 1-111-57489-8; ISBN-13: 978-1-111-57489-5

A collection of 150 full-color transparencies of key images selected from the text by the authors. The PowerLecture Instructor's Resource DVD also gives instructors access to all text art and many photos to help in preparing transparencies for material not present in this set.

FOR THE STUDENT

Visit CengageBrain.com

At **www.cengagebrain.com** you can access additional course materials as well as purchase Cengage products, including those listed below. Search by ISBN using the list below or find this textbook's ISBN on the back cover of your book. Instructors can log in at **login.cengage.com**.

Student Companion Site

This site includes a glossary, flashcards, an interactive periodic table, and samples of the Study Guide and Student Solutions Manual, which are all accessible from **www.cengagebrain.com**.

⊘WL
Quick Prep for General Chemistry
Instant Access OWL Quick Prep for General Chemistry (90 days)
ISBN-10: 0-495-56030-8; ISBN-13: 978-0-495-56030-2

Quick Prep is a self-paced online short course that helps students succeed in general chemistry. Students who completed Quick Prep through an organized class or self-study averaged almost a full letter grade higher in their subsequent general chemistry course than those who did not. Intended to be taken prior to the start of the semester, Quick Prep is appropriate for both underprepared students and for students who seek a review of basic skills and concepts. Quick Prep features an assessment quiz to focus students on the concepts they need to study to be prepared for general chemistry. Quick Prep is approximately 20 hours of instruction delivered through OWL with no textbook required and can be completed at any time in the student's schedule. Professors can package a printed access card for Quick Prep with the textbook or students can purchase instant access at **www.cengagebrain.com**. To view an OWL Quick Prep demonstration and for more information, visit **www.cengage.com/chemistry/quickprep**.

Go Chemistry® for General Chemistry
ISBN-10: 0-495-38228-0; ISBN-13: 978-0-495-38228-7

Pressed for time? Miss a lecture? Need more review? Go Chemistry for General Chemistry is a set of 27 downloadable mini video lectures, accessible via the printed access card packaged with your textbook or available for purchase separately. Developed by one of this book's authors, Go Chemistry helps you quickly review essential topics—whenever and wherever you want! Each video contains animations and problems and can be downloaded to your computer desktop or portable video player (e.g., iPod or iPhone) for convenient self-study and exam review. Selected Go Chemistry videos have e-Flashcards to briefly introduce a key concept and then test student understanding with a series of questions. The Cengage *YouBook* in OWL contains Go Chemistry. Professors can package a printed access card for Go Chemistry with the textbook. Students can enter the ISBN above at **www.cengagebrain.com** to download two free videos or to purchase instant access to the 27-video set or individual videos.

CengageBrain.com App

Now students can prepare for class anytime and anywhere using the CengageBrain.com application developed specifically for the Apple iPhone® and iPod touch®, which allows students to access free study materials—book-specific quizzes, flashcards, related Cengage Learning materials and more—so they can study the way they want, when they want to . . . even on the go. For more information about this complementary application, please visit **www.cengagebrain.com**. Available on the iTunes App Store.

Student Solutions Manual

by Alton J. Banks, North Carolina State University

ISBN-10: 1-111-42698-8; ISBN-13: 978-1-111-42698-9

Improve your performance at exam time with this manual's detailed solutions to the blue-numbered end-of-chapter Study Questions found in the text. This comprehensive guide helps you develop a deeper intuitive understanding of chapter material through constant reinforcement and practice. Solutions match the problem-solving strategies used in the text. Sample chapters are available for review on the PowerLecture Instructor's DVD and on the student companion website, which is accessible from **www.cengagebrain.com**.

Study Guide

by Michael J. Moran and John R. Townsend, West Chester University of Pennsylvania

ISBN-10: 1-111-42699-6; ISBN-13: 978-1-111-42699-6

With learning tools explicitly linked to the Chapter Goals introduced in each chapter, this guide helps ensure that you are well prepared for class and exams. It includes chapter overviews, key terms and definitions, expanded commentary, study tips, worked-out examples, and direct references back to the text. Sample chapters are available for review on the student companion website, which is accessible from **www.cengagebrain.com**.

Essential Math for Chemistry Students, Second Edition

by David W. Ball, Cleveland State University

ISBN-10: 0-495-01327-7; ISBN-13: 978-0-495-01327-3

This short book is intended to help you gain confidence and competency in the essential math skills you need to succeed in general chemistry. Each chapter focuses on a specific type of skill and has worked-out examples to show how these skills translate to chemical problem solving. The book includes references to the OWL learning system where you can access online algebra skills exercises.

Survival Guide for General Chemistry with Math Review, Second Edition

by Charles H. Atwood, University of Georgia

ISBN-10: 0-495-38751-7; ISBN-13: 978-0-495-38751-0

Intended to help you practice for exams, this survival guide shows you how to solve difficult problems by dissecting them into manageable chunks. The guide includes three levels of proficiency questions—A, B, and minimal—to quickly build confidence as you master the knowledge you need to succeed in your course.

For the Laboratory
CENGAGE LEARNING Brooks/Cole Lab Manuals

Cengage Learning offers a variety of printed manuals to meet all general chemistry laboratory needs. Visit **www.cengage.com/chemistry** for a full listing and description of these laboratory manuals and laboratory notebooks. All of our lab manuals can be customized for your specific needs.

Signature Labs . . . for the Customized Laboratory

Signature Labs is Cengage Learning's digital library of tried-and-true labs that help you take the guesswork out of running your chemistry laboratory. Select just the experiments you want from hundreds of options and approaches. Provide your students with only the experiments they will conduct and know you will get the results you seek. Visit **www.signaturelabs.com** to begin building your manual today.

ACKNOWLEDGMENTS

Preparing this new edition of *Chemistry & Chemical Reactivity* took over two years of continuous effort. As in our work on the first seven editions, we have had the support and encouragement of our families and of wonderful friends, colleagues, and students.

A Special Acknowledgment: John Vondeling

The publication of this book, with its copyright of 2012, marks its 25th anniversary. The first edition had a copyright date of 1987 and was the result of a collaboration with our publisher, the late John Vondeling of Saunders College Publishing. John literally invented many of the practices now considered standard among companies publishing college science textbooks. He was responsible for publishing some of the classic textbooks in chemistry, physics, and astronomy. The success of this book in its various editions owes much to John. It may not have become a reality without his confidence that it would be a worthwhile addition to the library of science texts. He was also a good friend, and we miss his humanity, his sense of humor, and his colorful personality.

CENGAGE LEARNING Brooks/Cole

The seventh edition of this book was published by the Brooks/Cole group of Cengage Learning, and we continue with the same excellent team we have had in place for the previous several years.

The seventh edition of the book was very successful, in large part owing to the work of Lisa Lockwood as our executive editor. She has an excellent sense of the market and has helped guide the new edition.

Peter McGahey has been our the Development Editor since he joined us to work on the fifth edition. Peter is blessed with energy, creativity, enthusiasm, intelligence, and good humor. He is a trusted friend and confidant who cheerfully answers our many questions during almost-daily phone calls.

No book can be successful without proper marketing. Nicole Hamm was a great help in marketing the seventh edition, and she is back in that role for this edition. She is knowledgeable about the market and has worked tirelessly to bring the book to everyone's attention.

Our team at Brooks/Cole is completed with Teresa Trego, Production Manager; Lisa Weber and Stephanie VanCamp, Media Editors; Julie Stefani, Marketing Coordinator; and Elizabeth Woods, Assistant Editor. Schedules are very demanding in textbook publishing, and Teresa has helped to keep us on schedule. We certainly appreciate her organizational skills. Lisa was involved in the development of the Go Chemistry modules and our expanded use of OWL. Stephanie handles the Cengage *YouBook,* and Liz also oversees the development of the ancillaries, such as the PowerPoint notes that accompany text.

Megan Greiner of Graphic World Inc. guided the book through its almost year-long production, and Andy Vosburgh of that company was enormously helpful in getting us through the use of new software. Scott Rosen of the Bill Smith Studio directed the photo research for the book and was successful in filling our sometimes offbeat requests for particular photos.

Photography, Art, and Design

Most of the color photographs for this edition were beautifully created by Charles D. Winters. He produced several dozen new images for this book, always with a creative eye. Charlie's work gets better with each edition. We have worked with Charlie for more than 20 years and have become close friends. We listen to his jokes, both new and old—and always forget them.

When the fifth edition was being planned, we brought in Patrick Harman as a member of the team. Pat designed the first edition of our *Interactive General Chemistry* CD (published in the 1990s), and we believe its success is in no small way connected to his design skill. For the fifth, sixth, and seventh editions of the book, Pat went over almost every figure, and almost every word, to bring a fresh perspective to ways to communicate chemistry. Once again he has worked on designing and producing new illustrations for this edition, and his creativity is obvious in their clarity. In addition, he has been an enormous help in designing and producing media for the *YouBook.* Pat has also become a good friend, and we share interests not only in books but in music.

Other Collaborators

We have been fortunate to have a number of other colleagues who have played valuable roles in this project.

- Bill Vining (State University of New York, Oneonta) was a co-author of the *Interactive GeneralChemistry* CD and has authored many of the media assets in OWL. He has been a friend for many years and recently took the place of one of the authors on the faculty at SUNY–Oneonta. Bill has again applied his considerable energy and creativity in preparing many more OWL questions with tutorials and some of the assets in the Cengage *YouBook*.

- Barbara Stewart (University of Maine) authored the new Interactive Examples in OWL.

- Alton Banks (North Carolina State University) has also been involved for a number of editions preparing the *Student Solutions Manual*. Alton has been very helpful in ensuring the accuracy of the Study Question answers in the book, as well as in their respective manuals.

- Michael Moran (West Chester University) has again updated and revised the *Study Guide* for this text. Our textbook has had a history of excellent study guides, and this manual follows that tradition.

- Jay Freedman was the development editor for the first edition of the book and played an important role in its success. For several editions of the book Jay has also done a masterful job compiling the index/glossary for this edition.

- Donnie Byers (Johnson County Community College) has been a long-time user of the book and a member of our Advisory Board. For this edition she coordinated the revisions of the end-of-chapter changes for the international edition.

- David Treichel (Nebraska Wesleyan University) wrote the *Applying Chemical Principles* problems, did the accuracy review, and developed the test bank.

- John Vincent (The University of Alabama–Tuscaloosa) wrote the *Instructor's Resource Manual*, did several reviews, and did an accuracy review.

- Barbara Mowrey, York College of Pennsylvania, also was an accuracy reviewer of the page proofs.

- Michael C. Cann (University of Scranton) helped identify ways in which green chemistry content could be incorporated.

- Salman Khan worked with us on developing audio/video tutorials of some of the book's Example problems. He is making significant contributions to education in the United States and elsewhere. See his website (**www.khanacademy.org**) for the extensive list of free tutorials he has done in all fields of science as well as in mathematics, economics, and finance.

- John Emsley (University of Cambridge) wrote the interchapter on the history of the development of chemistry.

- Jeffrey J. Keaffaber (University of Florida) wrote the Case Study *A Healthy Aquarium and the Nitrogen Cycle* in Chapter 21.

- Eric Scerri (University of California, Los Angeles) wrote the *A Closer Look: The Story of the Periodic Table* in Chapter 2.

Reviewers for the Eighth Edition

As we began to develop the new edition we had helpful input from the following reviewers:

- Gerald M. Korenowski, Rensselaer Polytechnic Institute

- Robert LaDuca, Michigan State University

- Jeffrey Mack, California State University, Sacramento

- Armando Rivera, East Los Angeles College

- Daniel Williams, Kennesaw State University

- Steven Wood, Brigham Young University

- Roger A. Hinrichs, Weill Cornell Medical College in Qatar, reviewed the energy interchapter

- Leonard Interrante, Rensselaer Polytechnic Institute, reviewed the materials interchapter

- Trudy E. Thomas-Smith, SUNY College at Oneonta, reviewed the environment interchapter

- John Vincent, The University of Alabama, reviewed the environment interchapter

Advisory Board for the Eighth Edition

As the new edition was being planned, this board listened to some of our ideas and made other suggestions. We hope to continue our association with these energetic and creative chemical educators.

- Donnie Byers, Johnson County Community College

- Elizabeth Dorland, Washington University of St. Louis

- Michael Finnegan, Washington State University

- Greg Gellene, Texas Tech University

- Milton Johnson, University of South Florida

- Jeffrey Mack, California State University, Sacramento

- Sara McIntosh, Rensselaer Polytechnic Institute

- MaryKay Orgill, University of Nevada, Las Vegas

- Don Siegel, Rutgers University

- Eric Simanek, Texas A&M University

Reviewers for the Seventh Edition

- Gerald M. Korenowski, Rensselaer Polytechnic Institute

- Robert L. LaDuca, Michigan State University

- Jeffrey Alan Mack, California State University, Sacramento

- Armando M. Rivera-Figueroa, East Los Angeles College

- Daniel J. Williams, Kennesaw State University

- Steven G. Wood, Brigham Young University

- Roger A. Hinrichs, Weill Cornell Medical College in Qatar (reviewed the Energy interchapter)

- Leonard Fine, Columbia University (reviewed the Materials interchapter)

Advisory Board for the Seventh Edition

As the seventh edition was being planned, this board listened to some of our ideas and made other suggestions. We hope to continue our association with these energetic and creative chemical educators.

- Donnie Byers, Johnson County Community College

- Sharon Fetzer Gislason, University of Illinois, Chicago

- Adrian George, University of Nebraska

- George Grant, Tidewater Community College, Virginia Beach Campus

- Michael Hampton, University of Central Florida

- Milton Johnston, University of South Florida

- Jeffrey Alan Mack, California State University, Sacramento

- William Broderick, Montana State University

- Shane Street, University of Alabama

- Martin Valla, University of Florida

John C. Kotz, a State University of New York Distinguished Teaching Professor, Emeritus, at the College at Oneonta, was educated at Washington and Lee University and Cornell University. He held National Institutes of Health post-doctoral appointments at the University of Manchester Institute for Science and Technology in England and at Indiana University. He has coauthored three text-books in several editions (*Inorganic Chemistry, Chemistry & Chemical Reactivity*, and *The Chemical World*) and the *General ChemistryNow CD*. His research in inorganic chemistry and electrochemistry also has been published. He was a Fulbright Lecturer and Research Scholar in Portugal in 1979 and a Visiting Professor there in 1992. He was also a Visiting Professor at the Institute for Chemical Education (University of Wisconsin, 1991–1992), at Auckland University in New Zealand (1999), and at Potchefstroom University in South Africa in 2006. He has been an invited speaker on chemical education at conferences in South Africa, New Zealand, and Brazil. He also served four years as a mentor for the U.S. National Chemistry Olympiad Team. He has received several awards, among them a State University of New York Chancellor's Award (1979), a National Catalyst Award for Excellence in Teaching (1992), the Estee Lecturership at the University of South Dakota (1998), the Visiting Scientist Award from the Western Connecticut Section of the American Chemical Society (1999), the Distinguished Education Award from the Binghamton (NY) Section of the American Chemical Society (2001), the SUNY Award for Research and Scholarship (2005), and the Squibb Lectureship in Chemistry at the University of North Carolina-Asheville (2007). He may be contacted by email at kotzjc@oneonta.edu.

Left to right: Paul Treichel, John Townsend, and John Kotz.

Paul M. Treichel, received his B.S. degree from the University of Wisconsin in 1958 and a Ph.D. from Harvard University in 1962. After a year of postdoctoral study in London, he assumed a faculty position at the University of Wisconsin–Madison. He served as department chair from 1986 through 1995 and was awarded a Helfaer Professorship in 1996. He has held visiting faculty positions in South Africa (1975) and in Japan (1995). Retiring after 44 years as a faculty member in 2007, he is currently Emeritus Professor of Chemistry. During his faculty career he taught courses in general chemistry, inorganic chemistry, organometallic chemistry, and scientific ethics. Professor Treichel's research in organometallic and metal cluster chemistry and in mass spectrometry, aided by 75 graduate and under-graduate students, has led to more than 170 papers in scientific journals. He may be contacted by email at treichel@chem.wisc.edu.

John R. Townsend, Professor of Chemistry at West Chester University of Pennsylvania, completed his B.A. in Chemistry as well as the Approved Program for Teacher Certification in Chemistry at the University of Delaware. After a career teaching high school science and mathematics, he earned his M.S. and Ph.D. in biophysical chemistry at Cornell University, where he also received the DuPont Teaching Award for his work as a teaching assistant. After teaching at Bloomsburg University, he joined the faculty at West Chester University, where he coordinates the chemistry education program for prospective high school teachers and the general chemistry lecture program for science majors. He has been the university supervisor for more than 50 prospective high school chemistry teachers during their student teaching semester. His research interests are in the fields of chemical education and biochemistry. He may be contacted by email at jtownsend@wcupa.edu.

11 Gases and Their Properties

©Davis Barber/PhotoEdit

The Atmosphere and Altitude Sickness

Some of you may have dreamed of climbing to the summits of the world's tallest mountains, or you may be an avid skier and visit high-mountain ski areas. In either case, "acute mountain sickness" (AMS) is a possibility. AMS is common at higher altitudes and is characterized by a headache, nausea, insomnia, dizziness, lassitude, and fatigue. It can be prevented by a slow ascent, and its symptoms can be relieved by a mild pain reliever.

AMS and more serious forms of high-altitude sickness are generally due to oxygen deprivation, also called *hypoxia*. The oxygen concentration in Earth's atmosphere is 21%. As you go higher into the atmosphere, the concentration remains 21%, but the atmospheric pressure drops. When you reach 3000 m (the altitude of some ski resorts), the barometric pressure is about 70% of that at sea level. At 5000 m, barometric pressure is only 50% of sea level, and on the summit of Mt. Everest, it is only 29% of the sea level pressure. At sea level, your blood is nearly saturated with oxygen,

but as the partial pressure of oxygen [$P(O_2)$] drops, the percent saturation drops as well. At $P(O_2)$ of 50 mm Hg, hemoglobin in the red blood cells is about 80% saturated. Other saturation levels are given in the table (for a pH of 7.4).

$P(O_2)$(mm Hg)	Approximate Percent Saturation
90	95%
80	92%
70	90%
60	85%
50	80%
40	72%

For more information on the atmosphere, see page 528.

Questions:

1. Assume a sea level pressure of 1 atm (760 mm Hg). What are the O_2 partial pressures at a 3000-m ski resort and on top of Mt. Everest?
2. What are the approximate blood saturation levels under these conditions?

Answers to these questions are available in Appendix N.

CHAPTER GOALS

See Chapter Goals Revisited (page 537) for Study Questions keyed to these goals.

- Understand the basis of the gas laws and know how to use those laws (Boyle's law, Charles's law, Avogadro's hypothesis, Dalton's law).

- Use the ideal gas law.

- Apply the gas laws to stoichiometric calculations.

- Understand kinetic-molecular theory as it is applied to gases, especially the distribution of molecular speeds (energies).

- Recognize why gases do not behave like ideal gases under some conditions.

OWL

Sign in to OWL at **www.cengage.com/owl** to view tutorials and simulations, develop problem-solving skills, and complete online homework assigned by your professor.

go Chemistry

Download mini lecture videos for key concept review and exam prep from OWL or purchase them from **www.cengagebrain.com**

Hot air balloons, SCUBA diving tanks, and automobile air bags (Figure 11.1) depend on the properties of gases. Aside from understanding how these work, there are other reasons for studying gases. First, some common elements and compounds (such as oxygen, nitrogen, and methane) exist in the gaseous state under normal conditions of pressure and temperature. Second, atmospheric gases provide one means of transferring energy and material throughout the globe, and they are a source of life-sustaining chemicals. In addition, the question of "global warming" is one of the major debates of our time, and gases such as carbon dioxide and methane play a role in this apparent problem.

But there is yet another reason for studying gases. Of the three states of matter, the behavior of gases is reasonably simple when viewed at the molecular level, and, as a result, it is well understood. It is possible to describe the properties of gases *qualitatively* in terms of the behavior of the molecules that make up the gas. Even more impressive, it is possible to describe the properties of gases *quantitatively* using simple mathematical models. One objective of scientists is to develop precise mathematical and conceptual models of natural phenomena, and a study of gas behavior

Don Johnston/Getty images

FIGURE 11.1 Automobile air bags. Most automobiles are now equipped with air bags to protect the driver and passengers in the event of a head-on or side crash. Such bags are inflated with nitrogen gas, which is generated by the explosive decomposition of sodium azide (in the presence of KNO_3 and silica):

$$2 \text{ NaN}_3(s) \rightarrow 2 \text{ Na}(s) + 3 \text{ N}_2(g)$$

The air bag is fully inflated in about 0.050 s. This is important because the typical automobile collision lasts about 0.125 s.

FIGURE 11.2 A barometer. The pressure of the atmosphere on the surface of the mercury in the dish is balanced by the downward pressure exerted by the column of mercury. The barometer was invented in 1643 by Evangelista Torricelli (1608–1647). A unit of pressure called the *torr* in his honor is equivalent to 1 mm Hg.

will introduce you to this approach. A remarkably accurate description of most gases requires knowing only four quantities: the pressure (P), volume (V), and temperature (T, kelvins) of the gas, and its amount (n, mol).

11.1 Gas Pressure

Pressure is the force exerted on an object divided by the area over which it is exerted, and a barometer is a device used to measure atmospheric pressure. A barometer can be made by filling a tube with a liquid, often mercury, and inverting the tube in a dish containing the same liquid (Figure 11.2). If the air has been removed completely from the vertical tube, the liquid in the tube assumes a level such that the pressure exerted by the mass of the column of liquid in the tube is balanced by the pressure of the atmosphere pressing down on the surface of the liquid in the dish.

Pressure is often reported in units of **millimeters of mercury (mm Hg)**, the height (in mm) of the mercury column in a mercury barometer above the surface of the mercury in the dish. At sea level, this height is about 760 mm. Pressures are also reported as **standard atmospheres (atm)**, a unit defined as follows:

1 standard atmosphere (1 atm) = 760 mm Hg (exactly)

The SI unit of pressure is the **pascal (Pa)**.

1 pascal (Pa) = 1 newton/meter^2

(The newton is the SI unit of force.) Because the pascal is a very small unit compared with ordinary pressures, the unit kilopascal (kPa) is more often used. Another unit used for gas pressures is the **bar**, where 1 bar = 100,000 Pa. To summarize, the units used in science for pressure are

1 atm = 760 mm Hg (exactly) = 101.325 kilopascals (kPa) = 1.01325 bar

or

1 bar = 1 × 10^5 Pa (exactly) = 1 × 10^2 kPa = 0.9872 atm

EXAMPLE 11.1   Pressure Unit Conversions

Problem Convert a pressure of 635 mm Hg into its corresponding value in units of atmospheres (atm), bars, and kilopascals (kPa).

What Do You Know? You will need the following conversion factors:

1 atm = 760 mm Hg = 1.013 bar   760 mm Hg = 101.3 kPa

Strategy Use the relationships between millimeters of Hg, atmospheres, bars, and pascals described in the text. (The use of dimensional analysis, page 39, is highly recommended.)

Solution

(a) Convert pressure in units of mm Hg to units of atm.

$635 \text{ mm Hg} \times \dfrac{1 \text{ atm}}{760 \text{ mm Hg}} = \boxed{0.836 \text{ atm}}$

(b) Convert pressure in units of atm to units of bar.

$0.836 \text{ atm} \times \dfrac{1.013 \text{ bar}}{1 \text{ atm}} = \boxed{0.846 \text{ bar}}$

(c) Convert pressure in units of mm Hg to units of kilopascals.

$635 \text{ mm Hg} \times \dfrac{101.3 \text{ kPa}}{760 \text{ mm Hg}} = \boxed{84.6 \text{ kPa}}$

Measuring Gas Pressure

Pressure is the force exerted on an object divided by the area over which the force is exerted:

Pressure = force/area

This book, for example, weighs more than 4 lb and has an area of 85 in², so it exerts a pressure of about 0.05 lb/in² when it lies flat on a surface. (In metric units, the pressure is about 320 Pa.)

Now consider the pressure that the column of mercury exerts on the mercury in the dish in the barometer shown in Figure 11.2. This pressure exactly balances the pressure of the atmosphere. Thus, the pressure of the atmosphere (or of any other gas) can be measured by relating it to the height of the column of mercury (or any other liquid) the gas can support.

Mercury is the liquid of choice for barometers because of its high density. A barometer filled with water would be over 10 m in height. [The water column is about 13.6 times as high as a column of mercury because mercury's density (13.53 g/cm³) is

13.6 times that of water (density = 0.997 g/cm³, at 25 °C).]

In the laboratory, we often use a U-tube manometer, which is a mercury-filled, U-shaped glass tube. The closed side of the tube has been evacuated so that no gas remains to exert pressure on the mercury on that side. The other side is open to the gas whose pressure we want to measure. When the gas presses on the mercury in the open side, the gas pressure is read directly (in mm Hg) as the difference in mercury levels on the closed and open sides.

You may have used a tire gauge to check the pressure in your car or bike tires. In the United States, such gauges usually indicate the pressure in pounds per square inch (psi) where 1 atm = 14.7 psi. Some newer gauges give the pressure in kilopascals as well. Be sure to recognize that the reading on the scale refers to the pressure *in excess of atmospheric pressure*. (A flat tire is not a vacuum; it contains air at atmospheric pressure.) For example, if the gauge reads 35 psi (2.4 atm), the pressure in the tire is actually about 50 psi or 3.4 atm.

Think about Your Answer The original pressure, 635 mm Hg, is less than 1 atm, so the pressure is also less than 1 bar and less than 100 kPa.

Check Your Understanding

Rank the following pressures in decreasing order of magnitude (from largest to smallest): 75 kPa 250 mm Hg, 0.83 bar, and 0.63 atm.

REVIEW & CHECK FOR SECTION 11.1

1. In a lab experiment you measure a gas pressure of 120 mm Hg. This pressure in units of kPa is approximately

    (a) 12 kPa   (b) 16 kPa   (c) 900 kPa

2. Suppose you construct a barometer filled with an oil (d = 1.25 g/cm³) instead of mercury (d = 13.5 g/cm³) in the vertical tube. If the atmosphere has a pressure of 0.95 atm, what is the approximate height of the oil in the tube?

    (a) 7.2 m   (b) 7.8 m   (c) 8.3 m

11.2 Gas Laws: The Experimental Basis

Boyle's Law: The Compressibility of Gases

When you pump up the tires of your bicycle, the pump squeezes the air into a smaller volume. This shows that a gas is compressed into a smaller volume when the pressure is increased. While studying the compressibility of gases, the Englishman Robert Boyle (1627–1691) (see page 518) observed that the volume of a fixed amount of gas at a given temperature is inversely proportional to the pressure exerted by the gas. All gases behave in this manner, and we now refer to this relationship as **Boyle's law**.

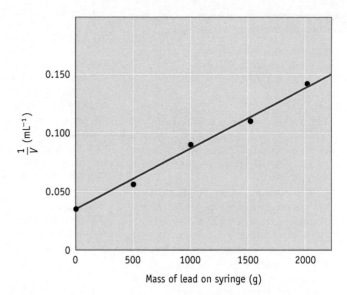

A plot of 1/V (volume of air in the syringe) versus P (as measured by the mass of lead) is a straight line.

A syringe filled with air was sealed. Pressure was applied by adding lead shot to the beaker on top of the syringe. As the mass of lead increased, the pressure on the air in the sealed syringe increased, and the gas was compressed.

FIGURE 11.3 An experiment to demonstrate Boyle's law.

Boyle's law can be demonstrated in many ways. In Figure 11.3, a hypodermic syringe is filled with air (n moles) and sealed. When pressure is applied to the movable plunger of the syringe, the air inside is compressed. As the pressure (P) increases on the syringe, the gas volume in the syringe (V) decreases. When $1/V$ of the gas in the syringe is plotted as a function of P (as measured by mass of lead), a straight line results. This type of plot demonstrates that the pressure and volume of the gas are inversely proportional; that is, they change in opposite directions.

Mathematically, we can write Boyle's law as:

$$P \propto \frac{1}{V} \quad \text{when } n \text{ (= amount of gas) and } T \text{ are constant}$$

where the symbol $\propto$ means "proportional to."

When two quantities are proportional to each other, they can be equated if a *proportionality constant*, here called C_B, is introduced.

$$P = C_B \times \frac{1}{V} \quad \text{or} \quad PV = C_B \text{ at constant } n \text{ and } T$$

This form of Boyle's law expresses the fact that *the product of the pressure and volume of a gas sample is a constant at a given temperature*, where the constant C_B is determined by the amount of gas (in moles) and its temperature (in kelvins). Because the PV product is always equal to C_B [assuming no change in the number of moles of gas (n) and the temperature (T)], it follows that, if PV is known for a gas sample under one set of conditions (P_1 and V_1), then it is known for another set of conditions (P_2 and V_2).

$$P_1V_1 = P_2V_2 \text{ at constant } n \text{ and } T \tag{11.1}$$

This form of **Boyle's law** is useful when we want to know, for example, what happens to the volume of a given amount of gas when the pressure changes at a constant temperature.

⦶WL   **INTERACTIVE EXAMPLE 11.2**   Boyle's Law

Strategy Map 11.2

Problem A bicycle pump has a volume of 1400 cm³. If a sample of air in the pump has a pressure of 730 mm Hg, what is the pressure when the volume is reduced to 170 cm³?

What Do You Know? This is a Boyle's law problem because you are dealing with changes in pressure and/or volume of a given amount of gas at constant temperature. Here the original pressure and volume of gas (P_1 and V_1) and the new volume (V_2) are known, but the final pressure (P_2) is not known. Both volumes are in the same unit so no unit changes are necessary.

Initial Conditions	Final Conditions
P_1 = 730 mm Hg	P_2 = ?
V_1 = 1400 cm³	V_2 = 170 cm³

Strategy Use Boyle's law, Equation 11.1.

Solution You can solve this problem by substituting data into a rearranged version of Boyle's law.

$$P_2 = P_1 (V_1/V_2)$$

$$P_2 = (730 \text{ mm Hg}) \times \frac{1400 \text{ cm}^3}{170 \text{ cm}^3} = 6.0 \times 10^3 \text{ mm Hg}$$

Think about Your Answer You know P and V change in opposite directions. In this case, the volume has decreased, so the new pressure (P_2) must be greater than the original pressure (P_1). The answer of about 6000 mm Hg is reasonable because the volume decreased by a factor of more than 8.

PROBLEM

Calculate the **pressure** when the *volume of a gas* is **reduced**.

DATA/INFORMATION

- *Initial* pressure
- *Initial* volume
- *Final* volume

Rearrange **Boyle's law** (Equation 11.1) to calculate **final pressure** (P_2).

Pressure (P_2) after reducing the volume

Check Your Understanding

A large balloon contains 65.0 L of helium gas at 25 °C and a pressure of 745 mm Hg. The balloon ascends to 3000 m, at which the external pressure has decreased by 30.%. What would be the volume of the balloon, assuming it expands so that the internal and external pressures are equal. (Assume the temperature is still 25 °C.)

The Effect of Temperature on Gas Volume: Charles's Law

In 1787, the French scientist Jacques Charles (1746–1823) discovered that the volume of a fixed quantity of gas at constant pressure decreases with decreasing temperature. The demonstration in Figure 11.4 shows a dramatic decrease in volume with temperature, but Figure 11.5 illustrates more quantitatively how the volumes of two different gas samples change with temperature (at a constant pressure). When

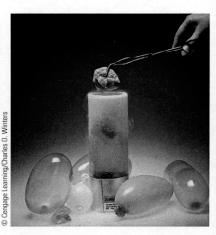

(a) Air-filled balloons are placed in liquid nitrogen (77 K). The volume of the gas in the balloons is dramatically reduced at this temperature.

(b) Here all of the balloons have been placed in the flask of liquid nitrogen.

(c) When the balloons are removed they warm to room temperature and reinflate to their original volume.

FIGURE 11.4 A dramatic illustration of Charles's law.

T (°C)	T (K)	Vol. H_2 (mL)	Vol. O_2 (mL)
300	573	47.0	21.1
200	473	38.8	17.5
100	373	30.6	13.8
0	273	22.4	10.1
−100	173	14.2	6.39
−200	73	6.00	—

FIGURE 11.5 Charles's law. The solid lines represent the volumes of samples of hydrogen (0.00100 mol) and oxygen (0.000450 mol) at a pressure of 1.00 atm but at different temperatures. The volumes decrease as the temperature is lowered (at constant pressure). These lines, if extended, intersect the temperature axis at approximately −273 °C.

the plots of volume versus temperature are extrapolated to lower temperatures, they all reach zero volume at the same temperature, −273.15 °C. (Of course, gases will not actually reach zero volume; they liquefy above that temperature.) This temperature is significant, however. William Thomson (1824–1907), also known as Lord Kelvin, proposed a temperature scale—now known as the Kelvin scale—for which the zero point is −273.15 °C (◄ page 26).

When Kelvin temperatures are used with volume measurements, the volume–temperature relationship is

$$V = C_c \times T$$

where C_c is a proportionality constant (which depends on the amount of gas and its pressure). This is **Charles's law**, which states that if a given amount of gas is held at a constant pressure, its volume is directly proportional to the Kelvin temperature.

Writing Charles's law another way, we have $V/T = C_c$; that is, the volume of a gas divided by the temperature of the gas (in kelvins) is constant for a given sample of gas at a specified pressure. Therefore, if we know the volume and temperature of a given quantity of gas (V_1 and T_1), we can find the volume, V_2, at some other temperature, T_2, using the equation

$$\frac{V_1}{T_1} = \frac{V_2}{T_2} \quad \text{at constant } n \text{ and } P \tag{11.2}$$

A calculation using Charles's law is illustrated by the following example. Be sure to notice that the temperature T *must always be expressed in kelvins*.

EXAMPLE 11.3 Charles's Law

Problem A sample of CO_2 in a gas-tight syringe (as in Figure 11.3) has a volume of 25.0 mL at room temperature (20.0 °C). What is the final volume of the gas if you hold the syringe in your hand to raise its temperature to 37 °C?

What Do You Know? This is a Charles's law problem: There is a change in volume of a gas sample with temperature at constant pressure. You know the original volume and temperature, and you want to know the volume at a new temperature. Be sure to recall that, to use Charles's law, the temperature must be expressed in kelvins.

Initial Conditions	Final Conditions
$V_1 = 25.0$ mL	$V_2 = ?$
$T_1 = 20.0 + 273.2 = 293.2$ K	$T_2 = 37 + 273 = 310.$ K

Strategy Use Charles's Law, Equation 11.2.

Solution Rearrange Equation 11.2 to solve for V_2:

$$V_2 = V_1 \times \frac{T_2}{T_1} = 25.0 \text{ mL} \times \frac{310. \text{ K}}{293.2 \text{ K}} = 26.4 \text{ mL}$$

Think about Your Answer While the temperature increase in degrees Celsius seemed large, the change in volume is small. Mathematically, this is because the change depends on the *ratio* of Kelvin temperatures, which is only slightly greater than 1.

Check Your Understanding

A balloon is inflated with helium to a volume of 45 L at room temperature (25 °C). If the balloon is cooled to −10 °C, what is the new volume of the balloon? Assume that the pressure does not change.

Combining Boyle's and Charles's Laws: The General Gas Law

You now know that the volume of a given amount of gas is inversely proportional to its pressure at constant temperature (Boyle's law) and directly proportional to the Kelvin temperature at constant pressure (Charles's law). But what if you need to know what happens to the gas when two of the three parameters (*P, V,* and *T*) change? For example, what would happen to the pressure of a sample of nitrogen in an automobile air bag if the same amount of gas were placed in a smaller bag and heated to a higher temperature? You can deal with this situation by combining the two equations that express Boyle's and Charles's laws.

$$\frac{P_1 V_1}{T_1} = \frac{P_2 V_2}{T_2} \text{ for a given amount of gas, } n \qquad\qquad \textbf{(11.3)}$$

This equation is sometimes called the **general gas law** or **combined gas law**. It applies specifically to situations in which the *amount of gas does not change.*

⊙WL INTERACTIVE EXAMPLE 11.4 General Gas Law

Problem Helium-filled balloons are used to carry scientific instruments high into the atmosphere. Suppose a balloon is launched when the temperature is 22.5 °C and the barometric pressure is 754 mm Hg. If the balloon's volume is 4.19×10^3 L (and no helium escapes from the balloon), what will the volume be at a height of 20 miles, where the pressure is 76.0 mm Hg and the temperature is −33.0 °C?

What Do You Know? Here you know the initial volume, temperature, and pressure of the gas. You want to know the volume of the same amount of gas at a new pressure and temperature.

Initial Conditions	Final Conditions
$V_1 = 4.19 \times 10^3$ L	$V_2 = ?$ L
$P_1 = 754$ mm Hg	$P_2 = 76.0$ mm Hg
$T_1 = 22.5$ °C (295.7 K)	$T_2 = -33.0$ °C (240.2 K)

Strategy It is most convenient to use Equation 11.3, the general gas law.

Solution You can rearrange the general gas law to calculate the new volume V_2:

$$V_2 = \left(\frac{T_2}{P_2}\right) \times \left(\frac{P_1 V_1}{T_1}\right) = V_1 \times \frac{P_1}{P_2} \times \frac{T_2}{T_1}$$

$$= 4.19 \times 10^3 \text{ L} \times \left(\frac{754 \text{ mm Hg}}{76.0 \text{ mm Hg}}\right) \times \left(\frac{240.2 \text{ K}}{295.7 \text{ K}}\right) = 3.38 \times 10^4 \text{ L}$$

Strategy Map 11.4

PROBLEM

Calculate the **volume** of a gas sample after it undergoes a change in *T* and *P.*

DATA/INFORMATION

- *Initial* pressure, volume, and temperature
- *Final* pressure and temperature

Rearrange the **general gas law** (Equation 11.3) to calculate **final volume** (V_2).

Volume (V_2) after change in *T* and *P*

A weather balloon is filled with helium. As it ascends into the troposphere, does the volume increase or decrease?

Think about Your Answer The pressure decreased by almost a factor of 10, which should lead to about a ten-fold volume increase. This increase is partly offset by a drop in temperature that leads to a volume decrease. On balance, the volume increases because the pressure has dropped so substantially.

Check Your Understanding

You have a 22-L cylinder of helium at a pressure of 150 atm (above atmospheric pressure) and at 31 °C. How many balloons can you fill, each with a volume of 5.0 L, on a day when the atmospheric pressure is 755 mm Hg and the temperature is 22 °C?

The general gas law leads to other, useful predictions of gas behavior. For example, if a given amount of gas is held in a closed container, the pressure of the gas will increase with increasing temperature.

$$\frac{P_1}{T_1} = \frac{P_2}{T_2} \text{ when } V_1 = V_2, \text{ so } P_2 = P_1 \times \frac{T_2}{T_1}$$

That is, when T_2 is greater than T_1, P_2 will be greater than P_1. In fact, this is the reason tire manufacturers recommend checking tire pressures when the tires are cold. After driving for some distance, friction warms a tire and increases the internal pressure. Filling a warm tire to the recommended pressure may lead to an underinflated tire.

Avogadro's Hypothesis

Front and side air bags are now common in automobiles. In the event of an accident, a bag is rapidly inflated with nitrogen gas generated by a chemical reaction. The air bag unit has a sensor that is sensitive to sudden deceleration of the vehicle and will send an electrical signal that will trigger the reaction (Figures 11.1 and 11.6). In many types of air bags, the explosion of sodium azide generates nitrogen gas.

$$2 \text{ NaN}_3(s) \rightarrow 2 \text{ Na}(s) + 3 \text{ N}_2(g)$$

(The sodium produced in the reaction is converted to harmless salts by adding KNO_3 and silica to the mixture.) Driver-side air bags inflate to a volume of about 35–70 L, and passenger air bags inflate to about 60–160 L. The final volume of the bag will depend on the amount of nitrogen gas generated.

The relationship between volume and amount of gas was first noted by Amedeo Avogadro. In 1811, he used work on gases by the chemist (and early experimenter with hot air balloons) Joseph Gay-Lussac (1778–1850) to propose that *equal volumes of gases under the same conditions of temperature and pressure have equal numbers of particles* (either molecules or atoms, depending on the composition of

When a car decelerates in a collision, an electrical contact is made in the sensor unit. The propellant (green solid) detonates, releasing nitrogen gas, and the folded nylon bag explodes out of the plastic housing.

Driver-side air bags inflate with 35–70 L of N_2 gas, whereas passenger air bags hold about 60–160 L.

FIGURE 11.6 Automobile air bags.

The bag deflates within 0.2 second, the gas escaping through holes in the bottom of the bag.

the gas). This idea is now called **Avogadro's hypothesis**. Stated another way, the volume of a gas at a given temperature and pressure is directly proportional to the amount of gas in moles:

$$V \propto n \quad \text{at constant } T \text{ and } P$$

EXAMPLE 11.5   Avogadro's Hypothesis

Problem Ammonia can be made directly from the elements:

$$N_2(g) + 3 H_2(g) \rightarrow 2 NH_3(g)$$

If you begin with 15.0 L of $H_2(g)$, what volume of $N_2(g)$ is required for complete reaction (both gases being at the same T and P)? What is the theoretical yield of NH_3, in liters, under the same conditions?

What Do You Know? From Avogadro's hypothesis, you know that gas volume is proportional to the amount of gas. You know the volume of hydrogen, and, from the balanced equation, you know the stoichiometric factors that relate the known amount of H_2 to the unknown amounts of N_2 and NH_3.

Strategy This is a stoichiometry problem where you can substitute gas volumes for moles. That is, you can calculate the volumes of N_2 required and NH_3 produced (here in liters) by multiplying the volume of H_2 available by a stoichiometric factor obtained from the chemical equation.

Solution

$$V (N_2 \text{ required}) = (15.0 \text{ L } H_2 \text{ available})\left(\frac{1 \text{ L } N_2 \text{ required}}{3 \text{ L } H_2 \text{ available}}\right) = 5.00 \text{ L } N_2 \text{ required}$$

$$V (NH_3 \text{ produced}) = (15.0 \text{ L } H_2 \text{ available})\left(\frac{2 \text{ L } NH_3 \text{ produced}}{3 \text{ L } H_2 \text{ available}}\right) = 10.0 \text{ L } NH_3 \text{ produced}$$

Think about Your Answer The balanced equation informs you that the amount of N_2 required is only 1/3 of the amount of H_2 present, and the amount of NH_3 produced is 2/3 of the amount of H_2.

Check Your Understanding

Methane burns in oxygen to give CO_2 and H_2O, according to the balanced equation

$$CH_4(g) + 2 O_2(g) \rightarrow CO_2(g) + 2 H_2O(g)$$

If 22.4 L of gaseous CH_4 is burned, what volume of O_2 is required for complete combustion? What volumes of CO_2 and H_2O are produced? Assume all gases have the same temperature and pressure.

REVIEW & CHECK FOR SECTION 11.2

1. A sample of a gas has a volume of 222 mL at 695 mm Hg and 0 °C. What is the volume of this same sample of gas if it is measured at 333 mm Hg and 0 °C?

   (a) 894 mL   (b) 463 mL   (c) 657 mL   (d) 359 mL

2. The volume of a gas sample is 235 mL at a temperature of 25 °C. At what temperature would that same gas sample have a volume of 310. mL, if the pressure of the gas sample is held constant?

   (a) −47.0 °C   (b) 69.4 °C   (c) 33.1 °C   (d) 120. °C

3. A gas at 25 °C in a 10.0-L tank has a pressure of 1.00 atm. The gas is transferred to a 20.0-L tank at 0 °C. Which statement is true?

   (a) The pressure of the gas is halved.   (c) The gas pressure is 1.00 atm
   (b) The pressure in the tank is doubled.   (d) None of the above

A CLOSER LOOK

Studies on Gases—Robert Boyle and Jacques Charles

Robert Boyle (1627–1691) was born in Ireland as the 14th and last child of the first Earl of Cork. In his book *Uncle Tungsten*, Oliver Sacks tells us that "Chemistry as a true science made its first emergence with the work of Robert Boyle in the middle of the seventeenth century. Twenty years [Isaac] Newton's senior, Boyle was born at a time when the practice of alchemy still held sway, and he maintained a variety of alchemical beliefs and practices, side by side with his scientific ones. He believed gold could be created, and that he had succeeded in creating it (Newton, also an alchemist, advised him to keep silent about this)."

Boyle examined crystals, explored color, devised an acid–base indicator from the syrup of violets, and provided the first modern definition of an element. He was also a physiologist and was the first to show that the healthy human body has a constant temperature. Today, Boyle is best known for his studies of gases, which were described in his book *The Sceptical Chymist*, published in 1680.

The French chemist and inventor Jacques Alexandre César Charles began his career as a clerk in the finance ministry, but his real interest was science. He developed several inventions and was best known in his lifetime for inventing the hydrogen balloon. In August 1783, Charles exploited his recent studies on hydrogen gas by inflating a balloon with this gas. Because hydrogen would escape easily from a paper bag, he made a silk bag coated with rubber. Inflating the bag took several days and required nearly 225 kg of sulfuric acid and 450 kg of iron to produce the H_2 gas. The balloon stayed aloft for almost 45 minutes and traveled about 15 miles. When it landed in a village, however, the people were so terrified they tore it to shreds. Several months later, Charles and a passenger flew a new hydrogen-filled balloon some distance across the French countryside and ascended to the then-incredible altitude of 2 miles.

See K. R. Williams, "Robert Boyle: Founder of Modern Chemistry," *Journal of Chemical Education*, Vol. 86, page 148, 2009.

Robert Boyle (1627–1691).
Oesper Collection in the History of Chemistry, University of Cincinnati

Jacques Alexandre César Charles (1746–1823).
Image Courtesy of the Library of Congress

Jacques Charles and Aivé Roberts ascended over Paris on December 1, 1783, in a hydrogen-filled balloon.
Smithsonian National Air & Space Museum

11.3 The Ideal Gas Law

Four interrelated quantities can be used to describe a gas: pressure, volume, temperature, and amount (moles). We know from experiments that the following gas laws can be used to describe the relationship of these properties (Section 11.2).

Boyle's Law	Charles's Law	Avogadro's Hypothesis
$V \propto (1/P)$	$V \propto T$	$V \propto n$
(constant T, n)	(constant P, n)	(constant T, P)

If all three laws are combined, the result is

$$V \propto \frac{nT}{P}$$

This can be made into a mathematical equation by introducing a proportionality constant, now labeled **R**. This constant, called the **gas constant**, is a *universal constant*, a number you can use to interrelate the properties of any gas:

$$V = R\left(\frac{nT}{P}\right)$$

or

$$PV = nRT \qquad (11.4)$$

The equation $PV = nRT$ is called the **ideal gas law**. It describes the behavior of a so-called ideal gas. As you will learn in Section 11.8, however, there is no such thing as an "ideal" gas. Nonetheless, real gases at pressures around one atmosphere or less and temperatures around room temperature usually behave close enough to the ideal that $PV = nRT$ adequately describes their behavior.

To use the equation $PV = nRT$, we need a value for R. This is readily determined experimentally. By carefully measuring P, V, n, and T for a sample of gas, we can calculate the value of R from these values using the ideal gas law equation. For example, under conditions of **standard temperature and pressure (STP)** (a gas temperature of 0 °C or 273.15 K and a pressure of 1 atm), 1 mol of an ideal gas occupies 22.414 L, a quantity called the **standard molar volume**. Substituting these values into the ideal gas law gives a value for R:

$$R = \frac{PV}{nT} = \frac{(1.0000 \text{ atm})(22.414 \text{ L})}{(1.0000 \text{ mol})(273.15 \text{ K})} = 0.082057 \frac{\text{L} \cdot \text{atm}}{\text{K} \cdot \text{mol}}$$

With a value for R, we can now use the ideal gas law in calculations.

• **Properties of an Ideal Gas** For ideal gases, it is assumed that there are no forces of attraction between molecules and that the molecules themselves occupy no volume.

• **STP—What Is It?** A gas is at STP, or standard temperature and pressure, when its temperature is 0 °C or 273.15 K and its pressure is 1 atm. Under these conditions, exactly 1 mol of an ideal gas occupies 22.414 L.

⊘WL INTERACTIVE EXMPLE 11.6   Ideal Gas Law

Problem The nitrogen gas in an automobile air bag, with a volume of 65 L, exerts a pressure of 829 mm Hg at 25 °C. What amount of N_2 gas (in moles) is in the air bag?

What Do You Know? You are given P, V, and T for a gas sample and want to calculate the amount of gas (n). P = 829 mm Hg, V = 65 L, T = 25 °C, n = ? You also know R = 0.082057 L · atm/K · mol.

Strategy Use the ideal gas law, Equation 11.4.

Solution To use the ideal gas law with R having units of L · atm/K · mol, the pressure must be expressed in atmospheres and the temperature in kelvins. Therefore, you should first convert the pressure and temperature to values with these units.

$$P = 829 \text{ mm Hg} \left(\frac{1 \text{ atm}}{760 \text{ mm Hg}} \right) = 1.09 \text{ atm}$$

$$T = 25 + 273 = 298 \text{ K}$$

Now substitute the values of P, V, T, and R into the ideal gas law, and solve for the amount of gas, n:

$$n = \frac{PV}{RT} = \frac{(1.09 \text{ atm})(65 \text{ L})}{(0.082057 \text{ L} \cdot \text{atm/K} \cdot \text{mol})(298 \text{ K})} = 2.9 \text{ mol}$$

Notice that units of atmospheres, liters, and kelvins cancel to leave the answer in units of moles.

Think about Your Answer You know that 1 mol of an ideal gas at STP occupies about 22.4 L, so it is reasonable to guess that 65 L of gas (under only slightly different conditions) would be about 3 mol.

Strategy Map 11.6

PROBLEM

Calculate the amount of a gas using the **ideal gas law.**

↓

DATA/INFORMATION

• **Pressure** of the gas
• **Volume** of the gas
• **Temperature** of the gas

Rearrange the **ideal gas law** (Equation 11.4) to calculate the **amount** (n).

Amount of gas, n

Check Your Understanding

The balloon used by Jacques Charles in his historic balloon flight in 1783 (see page 518) was filled with about 1300 mol of H_2. If the temperature of the gas was 23 °C and the gas pressure was 750 mm Hg, what was the volume of the balloon?

The Density of Gases

The density of a gas at a given temperature and pressure is a useful quantity (Figure 11.7). Because the amount (n, mol) of any compound is given by its mass (m) divided by its molar mass (M), we can substitute m/M for n in the ideal gas equation.

$$PV = \left(\frac{m}{M} \right) RT$$

FIGURE 11.7 Gas density.
(a) The balloons are filled with nearly equal amounts of gas at the same temperature and pressure. One yellow balloon contains helium, a low-density gas ($d = 0.179$ g/L at STP). The other balloons contain air, a higher density gas ($d = 1.29$ g/L).
(b) A hot-air balloon rises because the heated air in the balloon has a lower density than the surrounding air.

(a)

(b)

Density (d) is defined as mass divided by volume (m/V). We can rearrange the form of the gas law above to give the following equation, which has the term (m/V) on the left. This is the density of the gas.

$$d = \frac{m}{V} = \frac{PM}{RT} \tag{11.5}$$

Gas density is directly proportional to the pressure and molar mass and inversely proportional to the temperature. Equation 11.5 is useful because gas density can be calculated from the molar mass, or the molar mass can be found from a measurement of gas density at a given pressure and temperature.

EXAMPLE 11.7 Density and Molar Mass

Problem Calculate the density of CO_2 at STP. Is CO_2 more or less dense than air (whose density is 1.29 g/L at STP)?

What Do You Know? The known quantities are molar mass of CO_2 ($M = 44.0$ g/mol), gas pressure (P) = 1.00 atm, temperature (T) = 273.15 K, and the gas constant (R). The density of CO_2 gas (d) is unknown.

Strategy Use Equation 11.5, the equation relating gas density and molar mass.

Solution The known values are substituted into Equation 11.5, which is then solved for density (d):

$$d = \frac{PM}{RT} = \frac{(1.00 \text{ atm})(44.0 \text{ g/mol})}{(0.082057 \text{ L} \cdot \text{atm/K} \cdot \text{mol})(273 \text{ K})} = \boxed{1.96 \text{ g/L}}$$

Think about Your Answer The density of CO_2 is considerably greater than that of dry air at STP (1.29 g/L). (See Figure 11.8.)

Check Your Understanding

The density of an unknown gas is 5.02 g/L at 15.0 °C and 745 mm Hg. Calculate its molar mass.

FIGURE 11.8 Gas density. Because carbon dioxide from fire extinguishers is denser than air, it settles on top of a fire and smothers it. (When CO_2 gas is released from the tank, it expands and cools significantly. The white cloud is condensed moisture from the air.)

Gas density has practical implications. From the equation $d = PM/RT$, we recognize that the density of a gas is directly proportional to its molar mass. Dry air, which has an average molar mass of about 29 g/mol, has a density of about 1.29 g/L at 1 atm and 25 °C. Gases or vapors with molar masses greater than 29 g/mol have densities larger than 1.3 g/L under these same conditions (1 atm and 25 °C). Therefore, gases such as CO_2, SO_2, and gasoline vapor settle along the ground if released into the atmosphere (Figure 11.8). Conversely, gases such as H_2, He, CO, CH_4 (methane), and NH_3 rise if released into the atmosphere.

Calculating the Molar Mass of a Gas from *P*, *V*, and *T* Data

When a new compound is isolated in the laboratory, one of the first things to be done is to determine its molar mass. If the compound is easily volatilized, a classical method of determining the molar mass is to measure the pressure and volume exerted by a given mass of the gas at a given temperature.

⊍WL   **INTERACTIVE EXAMPLE 11.8**   Calculating the Molar Mass
of a Gas from *P*, *V*, and *T* Data

Problem You are trying to determine, by experiment, the formula of a gaseous compound you made to replace chlorofluorocarbons in air conditioners. You have determined the empirical formula is CHF_2, but now you want to know the molecular formula. You therefore do an experiment to determine its molar mass and find that a 0.100-g sample of the compound exerts a pressure of 70.5 mm Hg in a 256-mL container at 22.3 °C. What is the molar mass of the compound? What is its molecular formula?

What Do You Know? You know the mass of a gas in a given volume at a known pressure and temperature. The molar mass of the gas, *M*, is unknown.

m = mass of gas = 0.100 g P = 70.5 mm Hg, or 0.0928 atm

V = 256 mL, or 0.256 L T = 22.3 °C, or 295.5 K

Strategy The quotient of the mass of the gas and its volume gives its density, and this is related to the molar mass through Equation 11.5. Alternatively, the *P*, *V*, and *T* data can be used to calculate the amount of gas (moles). The molar mass is then the quotient of the mass of gas and its amount.

Solution The density of the gas is the mass of the gas divided by the volume.

$$d = \frac{0.100 \text{ g}}{0.256 \text{ L}} = 0.391 \text{ g/L}$$

Use this value of density along with the values of pressure and temperature in Equation 11.5 ($d = PM/RT$), and solve for the molar mass (*M*).

$$M = \frac{dRT}{P} = \frac{(0.391 \text{ g/L})(0.082057 \text{ L} \cdot \text{atm/K} \cdot \text{mol})(295.5 \text{ K})}{0.0928 \text{ atm}} = \boxed{102 \text{ g/mol}}$$

With this result, you can compare the experimentally determined molar mass with the mass of a mole of gas having the empirical formula CHF_2.

$$\frac{\text{Experimental molar mass}}{\text{Mass of 1 mol CHF}_2} = \frac{102 \text{ g/mol}}{51.0 \text{ g/formula unit}} = 2 \text{ formula units of CHF}_2 \text{ per mole}$$

Therefore, the formula of the compound is $\boxed{C_2H_2F_4}$.

In the alternative approach, you use the ideal gas law to calculate the amount of gas, *n*.

$$n = \frac{PV}{RT} = \frac{(0.0928 \text{ atm})(0.256 \text{ L})}{(0.082057 \text{ L} \cdot \text{atm/K} \cdot \text{mol})(295.5 \text{ K})} = 9.80 \times 10^{-4} \text{ mol}$$

You now know that 0.100 g of gas is equivalent to 9.80×10^{-4} mol. Therefore,

$$\text{Molar mass} = \frac{0.100 \text{ g}}{9.80 \times 10^{-4} \text{ mol}} = 102 \text{ g/mol}$$

Think about Your Answer If the calculated molar mass is not the same as that for the empirical formula or a simple multiple of that value, then you can assume that there is an error somewhere.

Strategy Map 11.8

PROBLEM

Calculate the molar mass of a gas using the **ideal gas law**.

↓

DATA/INFORMATION

• **Pressure** of the gas
• **Volume** of the gas
• **Temperature** of the gas

↓

STEP 1. Rearrange the **ideal gas law** (Equation 11.4) to calculate the **amount** (*n*).

Amount of gas, *n*

↓

STEP 2. Divide the **mass** of gas by its **amount** (*n*).

Molar mass of gas

Check Your Understanding

A 0.105-g sample of a gaseous compound has a pressure of 561 mm Hg in a volume of 125 mL at 23.0 °C. What is its molar mass?

REVIEW & CHECK FOR SECTION 11.3

1. Which gas has the greatest density at 25 °C and 1.00 atm pressure?

   (a) O_2 (b) N_2 (c) H_2 (d) CO_2 (e) Xe

2. Gas A is in a 2-L flask with a pressure of 1 atm at 298 K. Gas B is in a 4-L flask with a pressure of 0.5 atm at 273 K. Which gas is present in greater amount, A or B?

   (a) A   (b) B

3. Measured at a pressure of 1.0 atm and 298 K, gas C has a density of 2.0 g/L. The density of gas D, measured at a pressure of 0.5 atm and 298 K, is 1.3 g/L. Which gas, C or D, has the larger molar mass?

   (a) C   (b) D

11.4 Gas Laws and Chemical Reactions

Many industrially important reactions involve gases. Two examples are the combination of nitrogen and hydrogen to produce ammonia,

$$N_2(g) + 3\ H_2(g) \rightarrow 2\ NH_3(g)$$

and the electrolysis of aqueous NaCl to produce hydrogen and chlorine,

$$2\ NaCl(aq) + 2\ H_2O(\ell) \rightarrow 2\ NaOH(aq) + H_2(g) + Cl_2(g)$$

If we want to understand the quantitative aspects of such reactions, we need to carry out stoichiometry calculations. The scheme in Figure 11.9 connects these calculations for gas reactions with the stoichiometry calculations in Chapter 4.

Strategy Map 11.9

PROBLEM

Calculate the **mass of reactant** needed to produce a gas at a known *P*, *V*, and *T*.

↓

DATA/INFORMATION

- **Pressure** of the gas
- **Volume** of the gas
- **Temperature** of the gas
- Balanced equation

STEP 1. Calculate the *amount of gas (n)* using the **ideal gas law**.

Amount of gas, *n*

STEP 2. Use **stoichiometric factor** to relate *amount of gas (n)* to *amount of reactant* required.

Amount of reactant

STEP 3. Calculate **mass of reactant** from its amount.

Mass of reactant

⊘WL INTERACTIVE EXAMPLE 11.9 Gas Laws and Stoichiometry

Problem You are asked to design an air bag for a car. You know that the bag should be filled with gas with a pressure higher than atmospheric pressure, say 829 mm Hg, at a temperature of 22.0 °C. The bag has a volume of 45.5 L. What quantity of sodium azide, NaN_3, should be used to generate the required quantity of gas? The gas-producing reaction is

$$2\ NaN_3(s) \rightarrow 2\ Na(s) + 3\ N_2(g)$$

What Do You Know? You know the pressure, volume, and temperature of the N_2 gas to be produced, and you know the balanced equation that connects the reactant, NaN_3, to the product, N_2.

$$P = 829\ \text{mm Hg}\ (1\ \text{atm}/760\ \text{mm Hg}) = 1.09\ \text{atm}$$

$$V = 45.5\ \text{L}$$

$$T = 22.0\ °\text{C, or }295.2\ \text{K}$$

You want to know the mass of NaN_3 required to produce a given amount of N_2. This will require the molar mass of NaN_3.

Strategy The general logic to be used here follows a pathway in Figure 11.9 and in the Strategy Map in the margin. First, use $PV = nRT$ with gas data to calculate the amount of N_2 required. Then use that amount with a stoichiometric factor to calculate the amount of NaN_3 required. Finally, use the molar mass of NaN_3 to calculate the mass of NaN_3 required.

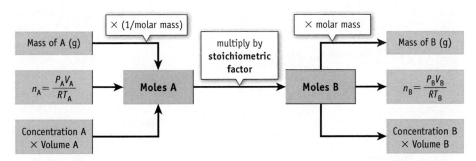

FIGURE 11.9 A scheme for stoichiometry calculations. Here, A and B may be either reactants or products. The amount of A (mol) can be calculated from its mass in grams and its molar mass, from the concentration and volume of a solution, or from *P*, *V*, and *T* data by using the ideal gas law. Once the amount of B is determined, this value can be converted to a mass or solution concentration or volume, or to a property of a gas using the ideal gas law.

Solution

Step 1: Find the amount (mol) of gas required.

$$n = N_2 \text{ required (mol)} = \frac{PV}{RT}$$

$$n = \frac{(1.09 \text{ atm})(45.5 \text{ L})}{(0.082057 \text{ L} \cdot \text{atm/K} \cdot \text{mol})(295.2 \text{ K})} = 2.05 \text{ mol } N_2$$

Step 2: Calculate the quantity of sodium azide that will produce 2.05 mol of N_2 gas.

$$\text{Mass of NaN}_3 = 2.05 \text{ mol } N_2 \left(\frac{2 \text{ mol NaN}_3}{3 \text{ mol } N_2} \right) \left(\frac{65.01 \text{ g}}{1 \text{ mol NaN}_3} \right) = \boxed{88.8 \text{ g NaN}_3}$$

Think about Your Answer You know that at STP, 1 mol of an ideal gas has a volume of 22.4 L. While not at STP exactly, the conditions are close to it, so a volume of 45.5 L should correspond to about 2 mol of N_2. Based on the stoichiometry of the reaction, you will need 2/3 of this amount of NaN_3, or about 1.4 mol. Based on the molar mass of NaN_3 (65 g/mol) this will be about 90 g. The amount of N_2 produced is substantial, so it is reasonable that around 90 g of sodium azide is required.

Check Your Understanding

If you need 25.0 L of N_2 gas, at $P = 1.10$ atm and 25.0 °C, what mass of Na will be produced?

EXAMPLE 11.10 Gas Laws and Stoichiometry

Problem You wish to prepare some deuterium gas, D_2, for use in an experiment. One way to do this is to react heavy water, D_2O, with an active metal such as lithium.

$$2 \text{ Li(s)} + 2 \text{ D}_2O(\ell) \rightarrow 2 \text{ LiOD(aq)} + D_2(g)$$

What amount of D_2 (in moles) can be prepared from 0.125 g of Li metal combined with 15.0 mL of D_2O ($d = 1.11$ g/mL). If dry D_2 gas is captured in a 1450-mL flask at 22.0 °C, what is the pressure of the gas in mm Hg? (Deuterium, D, has an atomic weight of 2.0147 g/mol.)

What Do You Know? You know the quantities of each of the two reactants, which you can use to calculate the amount of D_2 gas that can be produced. Based on the amount (moles) of D_2 gas, its temperature, and the volume of the flask, you can calculate the pressure.

Strategy You are combining two reactants with no guarantee they are in the correct stoichiometric ratio. Therefore, you should approach this as a limiting reactant problem. Once the limiting reactant is known, the amount of D_2 produced can be calculated. From this value, and the values of *V* and *T*, the pressure is calculated using the ideal gas law, *PV* = *nRT*.

Lithium metal (in the spoon) reacts with drops of water, H_2O, to produce LiOH and hydrogen gas, H_2. If heavy water, D_2O, is used, deuterium gas, D_2, can be produced.

Solution

Step 1. Calculate the amounts (mol) of Li and of D_2O:

$$0.125 \ \text{g Li} \left(\frac{1 \ \text{mol Li}}{6.941 \ \text{g Li}} \right) = 0.0180 \ \text{mol Li}$$

$$15.0 \ \text{mL } D_2O \left(\frac{1.11 \ \text{g } D_2O}{1 \ \text{mL } D_2O} \right) \left(\frac{1 \ \text{mol } D_2O}{20.03 \ \text{g } D_2O} \right) = 0.831 \ \text{mol } D_2O$$

Step 2. Decide which reactant is the limiting reactant:

$$\text{Ratio of moles of reactants available} = \frac{0.831 \ \text{mol } D_2O}{0.0180 \ \text{mol Li}} = \frac{46.2 \ \text{mol } D_2O}{1 \ \text{mol Li}}$$

The balanced equation shows that the ratio should be 1 mol of D_2O to 1 mol of Li. From the calculated values, we see that D_2O is in large excess, and so Li is the limiting reactant. Therefore, further calculations are based on the amount of Li available.

Step 3. Use the limiting reactant to calculate the amount of D_2 produced:

$$0.0180 \ \text{mol Li} \left(\frac{1 \ \text{mol } D_2 \ \text{produced}}{2 \ \text{mol Li}} \right) = 0.00900 \ \text{mol } D_2 \ \text{produced}$$

Step 4. Calculate the pressure of D_2:

$P = ?$ $T = 22.0 \ °C$, or 295.2 K

$V = 1450 \ \text{mL}$, or 1.45 L $n = 0.00900 \ \text{mol } D_2$

$$P = \frac{nRT}{V} = \frac{(0.00900 \ \text{mol})(0.082057 \ \text{L} \cdot \text{atm/K} \cdot \text{mol})(295.2 \ \text{K})}{1.45 \ \text{L}} = \boxed{0.150 \ \text{atm}}$$

Think about Your Answer Be sure to recognize that this is a limiting reactant problem. The two reactants were not present in the correct stoichiometric ratio.

Check Your Understanding

Gaseous ammonia is synthesized by the reaction

$$N_2(g) + 3 \ H_2(g) \rightarrow 2 \ NH_3(g)$$

Assume that 355 L of H_2 gas at 25.0 °C and 542 mm Hg is combined with excess N_2 gas. What amount of NH_3 gas, in moles, can be produced? If this amount of NH_3 gas is stored in a 125-L tank at 25.0 °C, what is the pressure of the gas?

REVIEW & CHECK FOR SECTION 11.4

Diborane reacts with O_2 to give boric oxide and water vapor.

$$B_2H_6(g) + 3 \ O_2(g) \rightarrow B_2O_3(s) + 3 \ H_2O(g)$$

1. What mass of O_2 gas is required to react completely with 1.5 L of B_2H_6 at 25 °C and 0.15 atm?

     (a) 0.29 g   (b) 0.59 g   (c) 0.44 g   (d) 0.88 g

2. If you mix 1.5 L of B_2H_6 with 4.0 L of O_2, each at 0 °C and a pressure of 1.0 atm, what amount of water is produced?

     (a) 0.18 mol   (b) 0.067 ml   (c) 0.060 mol   (d) 0.25 mol

---

11.5 Gas Mixtures and Partial Pressures

The air you breathe is a mixture of nitrogen, oxygen, argon, carbon dioxide, water vapor, and small amounts of other gases (Table 11.1). Each of these gases exerts its own pressure, and atmospheric pressure is the sum of the pressures

Table 11.1 Major Components of Atmospheric Dry Air

Constituent	Molar Mass*	Mole Percent	Partial Pressure at STP (atm)
N_2	28.01	78.08	0.7808
O_2	32.00	20.95	0.2095
Ar	39.95	0.934	0.00934
CO_2	44.01	0.0385	0.00039

*The average molar mass of dry air = 28.960 g/mol.

exerted by each gas. The pressure of each gas in the mixture is called its **partial pressure**.

John Dalton (1766–1844) was the first to observe that the pressure of a mixture of ideal gases is the sum of the partial pressures of the different gases in the mixture. This observation is now known as **Dalton's law of partial pressures** (Figure 11.10). Mathematically, we can write Dalton's law of partial pressures as

$$P_{total} = P_1 + P_2 + P_3 \ldots \tag{11.6}$$

where P_1, P_2, and P_3 are the pressures of the different gases in a mixture, and P_{total} is the total pressure.

In a mixture of gases, each gas behaves independently of all others in the mixture. Therefore, we can consider the behavior of each gas in a mixture separately. As an example, take a mixture of three ideal gases, labeled A, B, and C. There are n_A moles of A, n_B moles of B, and n_C moles of C. Assume that the mixture ($n_{total} = n_A + n_B + n_C$) is contained in a given volume (V) at a given temperature (T). We can calculate the pressure exerted by each gas from the ideal gas law equation:

$$P_A V = n_A RT \qquad P_B V = n_B RT \qquad P_C V = n_C RT$$

where each gas (A, B, and C) is in the same volume V and is at the same temperature T. According to Dalton's law, the total pressure exerted by the mixture is the sum of the pressures exerted by each component:

$$P_{total} = P_A + P_B + P_C = n_A\left(\frac{RT}{V}\right) + n_B\left(\frac{RT}{V}\right) + n_C\left(\frac{RT}{V}\right)$$

$$P_{total} = (n_A + n_B + n_C)\left(\frac{RT}{V}\right)$$

$$P_{total} = (n_{total})\left(\frac{RT}{V}\right) \tag{11.7}$$

FIGURE 11.10 Dalton's law.

In a 1.0-L flask at 25 °C, 0.010 mol of N_2 exerts a pressure of 186 mm Hg, and 0.0050 mol of O_2 in a 1.0-L flask at 25 °C exerts a pressure of 93 mm Hg.

The N_2 and O_2 samples are both placed in a 1.0-L flask at 25 °C. The total pressure, 279 mm Hg, is the sum of the pressures that each gas alone exerts in the flask.

For mixtures of gases, it is convenient to introduce a quantity called the **mole fraction**, **X**, which is defined as the number of moles of a particular substance in a mixture divided by the total number of moles of all substances present. Mathematically, the mole fraction of a substance A in a mixture with B and C is expressed as

$$X_A = \frac{n_A}{n_A + n_B + n_C} = \frac{n_A}{n_{total}}$$

Now we can combine this equation (written as $n_{total} = n_A/X_A$) with the equations for P_A and P_{total}, and derive the equation

$$P_A = X_A P_{total} \tag{11.8}$$

This equation tells us that *the pressure of a gas in a mixture of gases is the product of its mole fraction and the total pressure of the mixture.* In other words, the partial pressure of a gas is directly related to the fraction of particles of that gas in the mixture. For example, the mole fraction of N_2 in air is 0.78, so, at STP, its partial pressure is 0.78 atm or 590 mm Hg.

Strategy Map 11.11

PROBLEM

Calculate the **partial pressure** of two gases in a mixture.

↓

DATA/INFORMATION

- **Mass** of each gas
- **Total pressure**

> **STEP 1.** Calculate *amount (n)* of each gas from its **mass**.

Amount of each gas, *n*

> **STEP 2.** Calculate **mole fraction** of each gas, **X**.

Mole fraction of each gas, **X**

> **STEP 3.** Calculate **partial pressure** of gases using Equation 11.8.

Partial pressure of each gas

ⓌWL   INTERACTIVE EXAMPLE 11.11   Partial Pressures of Gases

Problem Halothane, $C_2HBrClF_3$, is a nonflammable, nonexplosive, and nonirritating gas that is commonly used as an inhalation anesthetic. The total pressure of a mixture of 15.0 g of halothane vapor and 23.5 g of oxygen gas is 855 mm Hg. What is the partial pressure of each gas?

What Do You Know? You know the identity and mass of each gas, so you can calculate the amount of each. You also know the total pressure of the gas mixture.

Strategy The partial pressure of a gas is given by the total pressure of the mixture multiplied by the mole fraction of the gas (Equation 11.8). Because you can calculate the amount of each gas, you can determine the total amount (moles) of gas and thus the mole fraction of each.

Solution

Step 1. Calculate mole fractions.

$$\text{Amount of } C_2HBrClF_3 = 15.0 \text{ g} \left(\frac{1 \text{ mol}}{197.4 \text{ g}}\right) = 0.0760 \text{ mol}$$

$$\text{Amount of } O_2 = 23.5 \text{ g} \left(\frac{1 \text{ mol}}{32.00 \text{ g}}\right) = 0.734 \text{ mol}$$

$$\text{Total amount of gas} = 0.0760 \text{ mol } C_2HBrClF_3 + 0.734 \text{ mol } O_2 = 0.810 \text{ mol}$$

$$\text{Mole fraction of } C_2HBrClF_3 = \frac{0.0760 \text{ mol } C_2HBrClF_3}{0.810 \text{ total moles}} = 0.0938$$

Because the sum of the mole fraction of halothane and of O_2 must equal 1.0000, this means that the mole fraction of oxygen is 0.906.

$$X_{halothane} + X_{oxygen} = 1.0000$$

$$0.0938 + X_{oxygen} = 1.0000$$

$$X_{oxygen} = 0.906$$

Step 2. Calculate partial pressures.

$$\text{Partial pressure of halothane} = P_{halothane} = X_{halothane} \cdot P_{total}$$

$$P_{halothane} = 0.0938 \cdot P_{total} = 0.0938 \,(855 \text{ mm Hg})$$

$$P_{halothane} = \boxed{80.2 \text{ mm Hg}}$$

The total pressure of the mixture is the sum of the partial pressures of the gases in the mixture.

$$P_{halothane} + P_{oxygen} = 855 \text{ mm Hg}$$

```
  F   Br
  |   |
F—C — C—H
  |   |
  F   Cl
```

1,1,1-trifluorobromochloroethane, halothane

and so

$$P_{oxygen} = 855 \text{ mm Hg} - P_{halothane}$$

$$P_{oxygen} = 855 \text{ mm Hg} - 80.2 \text{ mm Hg} = \boxed{775 \text{ mm Hg}}$$

Think about Your Answer The amount of halothane is about 1/10th of the amount of oxygen so we would expect the ratio of partial pressures of the two gases to be in a similar ratio.

Check Your Understanding

The halothane–oxygen mixture described in this Example is placed in a 5.00-L tank at 25.0 °C. What is the total pressure (in mm Hg) of the gas mixture in the tank? What are the partial pressures (in mm Hg) of the gases?

REVIEW & CHECK FOR SECTION 11.5

Acetylene reacts with O_2 to give carbon dioxide and water vapor.

$$2 \text{ C}_2\text{H}_2(g) + 5 \text{ O}_2(g) \rightarrow 4 \text{ CO}_2(g) + 2 \text{ H}_2\text{O}(g)$$

If you mix C_2H_2 and O_2 in the correct stoichiometric ratio, and if the total pressure of the mixture is 140. mm Hg, what are the partial pressures of the gases before the reaction occurs?

(a)   100. mm Hg C_2H_2 and 40. mm Hg O_2

(b)   140. mm Hg C_2H_2 and 700. mm Hg O_2

(c)   40. mm Hg C_2H_2 and 100. mm Hg O_2

(d)   140. mm Hg C_2H_2 and 56.0 mm Hg O_2

FIGURE 11.11 **A molecular view of gases and liquids.** The fact that a large volume of N_2 gas can be condensed to a small volume of liquid indicates that the distance between molecules in the gas phase is very large as compared with the distances between molecules in liquids.

11.6 The Kinetic-Molecular Theory of Gases

So far, we have discussed the macroscopic properties of gases, properties such as pressure and volume that result from the behavior of a system with a large number of particles. Now we turn to the kinetic-molecular theory (◄ page 7) for a description of the behavior of matter at the molecular or atomic level. Hundreds of experimental observations have led to the following postulates regarding the behavior of gases.

Module 16: Gas Laws and the Kinetic Molecular Theory covers concepts in this section.

- Gases consist of particles (molecules or atoms) whose separation is much greater than the size of the particles themselves (Figure 11.11).
- The particles of a gas are in continual, random, and rapid motion. As they move, they collide with one another and with the walls of their container, but they do so in a way in which the total energy is unchanged.
- The average kinetic energy of gas particles is proportional to the gas temperature. *All gases, regardless of their molecular mass, have the same average kinetic energy at the same temperature.*

Let us discuss the behavior of gases from this point of view.

Molecular Speed and Kinetic Energy

If your friend walks into your room carrying a pizza, how do you know it? In scientific terms, we know that the odor-causing molecules of food enter the gas phase and drift through space until they reach the cells of your body that react to odors. The same thing happens in the laboratory when bottles of aqueous ammonia (NH_3) and hydrochloric acid (HCl) sit side by side (Figure 11.12). Molecules of the two compounds enter the gas phase and drift along until they encounter one another, at which time they react and form a cloud of tiny particles of solid ammonium chloride (NH_4Cl).

If you change the temperature of the environment of the containers in Figure 11.12 and measure the time needed for the cloud of ammonium chloride to form, you would find the time would be longer at lower temperatures. The rea-

FIGURE 11.12 **The movement of gas molecules.** Open dishes of aqueous ammonia and hydrochloric acid are placed side by side. When molecules of NH_3 and HCl escape from solution to the atmosphere and encounter one another, a cloud of solid ammonium chloride, NH_4Cl, is observed.

© Cengage Learning/Charles D. Winters

The Earth's Atmosphere

Earth's atmosphere is a fascinating mixture of gases in more or less distinct layers with widely differing temperatures.

Up through the troposphere, there is a gradual decline in temperature (and pressure) with altitude. The temperature climbs again in the stratosphere due to the absorption of energy from the sun by stratospheric ozone, O_3.

Above the stratosphere, the pressure declines because there are fewer molecules present. At still higher altitudes, we observe a dramatic increase in temperature in the thermosphere. This is an illustration of the difference between *temperature* and *thermal energy*. The temperature of a gas reflects the average kinetic energy of the molecules of the gas, whereas the thermal energy present in an object is the *total* kinetic energy of the molecules. In the thermosphere, the few molecules present have a very high temperature, but the thermal energy is exceedingly small because there are so few molecules.

Gases within the troposphere are well mixed by convection. Pollutants that are evolved on Earth's surface can rise up to the stratosphere, but it is said that the stratosphere acts as a "thermal lid" on the troposphere and prevents significant mixing of polluting gases into the stratosphere and beyond.

The pressure of the atmosphere declines with altitude, and so the partial pressure of O_2 declines. The figure shows why climbers have a hard time breathing on Mt. Everest, where the altitude is 29,028 ft (8848 m) and the O_2 partial pressure is only 29% of the sea level partial pressure. With proper training, a climber could reach the summit without supplemental oxygen. However, this same feat would not be possible if Everest were farther north. Earth's atmosphere thins toward the poles, and so the O_2 partial pressure would be even less if Everest's summit were in the northern part of North America, for example.

See G. N. Eby, *Environmental Geochemistry*, Cengage Learning/Brooks/Cole, 2004.

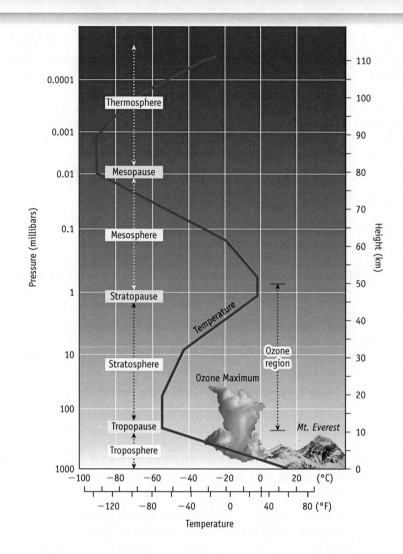

Average Composition of Earth's Atmosphere to a Height of 25 km

Gas	Volume %	Source	Gas	Volume %	Source
N_2	78.08	Biologic	He	0.0005	Radioactivity
O_2	20.95	Biologic	H_2O	0 to 4	Evaporation
Ar	0.93	Radioactivity	CH_4	0.00017	Biologic
CO_2	0.0385	Biologic, industrial	N_2O	0.00003	Biologic, industrial
Ne	0.0018	Earth's interior	O_3	0.000004	Photochemical

son for this is that the speed at which molecules move depends on the temperature. Let us expand on this idea.

The molecules in a gas sample do not all move at the same speed. Rather, as illustrated in Figure 11.13 for O_2 molecules, there is a distribution of speeds. Figure 11.13 shows the number of particles in a gas sample that are moving at certain speeds at a given temperature, and there are two important observations we can make. First, at a given temperature some molecules in a sample have high speeds,

FIGURE 11.13 The distribution of molecular speeds. A graph of the number of molecules with a given speed versus that speed shows the distribution of molecular speeds. The red curve shows the effect of increased temperature. Even though the curve for the higher temperature is "flatter" and broader than the one at a lower temperature, the areas under the curves are the same because the number of molecules in the sample is fixed.

and others have low speeds. Most of the molecules, however, have some intermediate speed, and their most probable speed corresponds to the maximum in the curve. For oxygen gas at 25 °C, for example, most molecules have speeds in the range from 200 m/s to 700 m/s, and their most probable speed is about 400 m/s. (These are very high speeds, indeed. A speed of 400 m/s corresponds to about 900 miles per hour!)

A second observation regarding the distribution of speeds is that as the temperature increases the most probable speed increases, and the number of molecules traveling at very high speeds increases greatly.

The kinetic energy of a single molecule of mass m in a gas sample is given by the equation

$$KE = \frac{1}{2}(mass)(speed)^2 = \frac{1}{2}mu^2$$

where u is the speed of that molecule. We can calculate the kinetic energy of a single gas molecule from this equation but not of a collection of molecules because not all of the molecules in a gas sample are moving at the same speed. However, we can calculate the average kinetic energy of a collection of molecules by relating it to other averaged quantities of the system. In particular, the average kinetic energy of a mole of molecules in a gas sample is related to the average speed:

$$\overline{KE} = \frac{1}{2}N m \overline{u^2}$$

where N is Avogadro's number. (The horizontal bar over the symbols $\overline{KE}$ and $\overline{u}$ indicate an average value.) The product of the mass per molecule and Avogadro's constant is the molar mass, so we can write

$$\overline{KE} = \frac{1}{2}M \overline{u^2}$$

where the molar mass (M) has units of kg/mol (and KE is in joules). This equation states that the average kinetic energy of the molecules in a gas sample, $\overline{KE}$, is related to $\overline{u^2}$, the average of the squares of their speeds (called the "mean square speed").

Experiments also show that the average kinetic energy, $\overline{KE}$, of a mole of gas molecules is directly proportional to temperature with a proportionality constant of $\frac{3}{2}R$,

$$\overline{KE} = \frac{3}{2}RT$$

where R is the gas constant expressed in SI units (8.314472 J/K · mol).

• **Maxwell-Boltzmann Curves**
Plots such as those in Figures 11.13 and 11.14 are often referred to as Maxwell-Boltzmann curves. They are named for two scientists who studied the physical properties of gases: James Clerk Maxwell (1831–1879) and Ludwig Boltzmann (1844–1906).

FIGURE 11.14 The effect of molecular mass on the distribution of speeds. At a given temperature, molecules with higher masses have lower speeds.

The two kinetic energy equations can be combined to yield an equation that relates mass, average speed, and temperature (Equation 11.9).

$$\sqrt{\overline{u^2}} = \sqrt{\frac{3RT}{M}} \tag{11.9}$$

Here, the square root of the mean square speed ($\sqrt{\overline{u^2}}$, called the **root-mean-square speed**, or **rms speed**), the temperature (T, in kelvins), and the molar mass (M) are related. This equation shows that the speeds of gas molecules are indeed related to the temperature (Figure 11.13). The rms speed is a useful quantity because of its relationship to the average kinetic energy and because it is very close to the true average speed for a sample. (The average speed is 92% of the rms speed.)

All gases have the same average kinetic energy at the same temperature. However, if you compare a sample of one gas with another, say compare O_2 and N_2, this does not mean the molecules have the same rms speed (Figure 11.14). Instead, Equation 11.9 shows that the smaller the molar mass of the gas the greater the rms speed.

EXAMPLE 11.12 Molecular Speed

Problem Calculate the rms speed of oxygen molecules at 25 °C.

What Do You Know? You know the molar mass of O_2 and the temperature, the main determinants of speed.

Strategy Use Equation 11.9 with M in units of kg/mol. The reason for this is that R is in units of J/K · mol, and $1\,J = 1\,kg · m^2/s^2$.

Solution The molar mass of O_2 is 32.0×10^{-3} kg/mol.

$$\sqrt{\overline{u^2}} = \sqrt{\frac{3(8.3145 \text{ J/K} \cdot \text{mol})(298 \text{ K})}{32.0 \times 10^{-3} \text{ kg/mol}}} = \sqrt{2.32 \times 10^5 \text{ J/kg}}$$

To obtain the answer in meters per second, use the relation $1\,J = 1\,kg · m^2/s^2$. This means you have

$$\sqrt{\overline{u^2}} = \sqrt{2.32 \times 10^5 \text{ kg} \cdot \text{m}^2/(\text{kg} \cdot \text{s}^2)} = \sqrt{2.32 \times 10^5 \text{ m}^2/\text{s}^2} = 482 \text{ m/s}$$

Think about Your Answer The calculated speed is equivalent to about 1100 miles per hour! This is somewhat greater than the speed of sound in air, 343 m/s.

Check Your Understanding

Calculate the rms speeds of helium atoms and N_2 molecules at 25 °C.

Kinetic-Molecular Theory and the Gas Laws

The gas laws, which come from experiment, can be explained by the kinetic-molecular theory. The starting place is to describe how pressure arises from collisions of gas molecules with the walls of the container holding the gas (Figure 11.15). Remember that pressure is related to the force of the collisions (Section 11.1).

$$\text{Gas pressure} = \frac{\text{force of collisions}}{\text{area}}$$

The force exerted by the collisions depends on the number of collisions and the average force per collision. When the temperature of a gas is increased, we know the average kinetic energy of the molecules increases. This causes the average force of the collisions with the walls to increase as well. (This is much like the difference in the force exerted by a car traveling at high speed versus one moving at only a few kilometers per hour.) Also, because the speed of gas molecules increases with temperature, more collisions occur per second. Thus, the collective force per square centimeter is greater, and the pressure increases. Mathematically, this is related to the direct proportionality between P and T when n and V are fixed, that is, $P = (nR/V)T$.

Increasing the number of molecules of a gas at a fixed temperature and volume does not change the average collision force, but it does increase the number of collisions occurring per second. Thus, the pressure increases, and we can say that P is proportional to n when V and T are constant, that is, $P = n(RT/V)$.

If the pressure is to remain constant when either the number of molecules of gas or the temperature is increased, then the volume of the container (and the area over which the collisions can take place) must increase. This is expressed by stating that V is proportional to nT when P is constant [$V = nT(R/P)$], a statement that is a *combination of Avogadro's hypothesis and Charles's law.*

Finally, if the temperature is constant, the average impact force of molecules of a given mass with the container walls must be constant. If n is kept constant while the volume of the container is made smaller, the number of collisions with the container walls per second must increase. This means the pressure increases, and so P is proportional to $1/V$ when n and T are constant, as stated by *Boyle's law,* that is, $P = (1/V)(nRT)$.

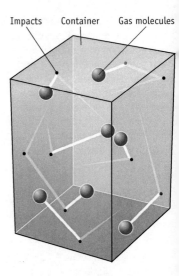

Impacts   Container   Gas molecules

FIGURE 11.15 Gas pressure. According to the kinetic-molecular theory, gas pressure is caused by gas molecules bombarding the container walls.

REVIEW & CHECK FOR SECTION 11.6

The species identified with each curve in the Maxwell-Boltzmann plot below are: (Assume all gases are at the same temperature.)

(a) $A = Xe$, $B = O_2$, $C = Ne$, and $D = He$

(b) $A = Xe$, $B = He$, $C = Ne$, and $D = O_2$

(c) $A = He$, $B = Ne$, $C = O_2$, and $D = Xe$

(d) $A = He$, $B = O_2$, $C = Ne$, and $D = Xe$

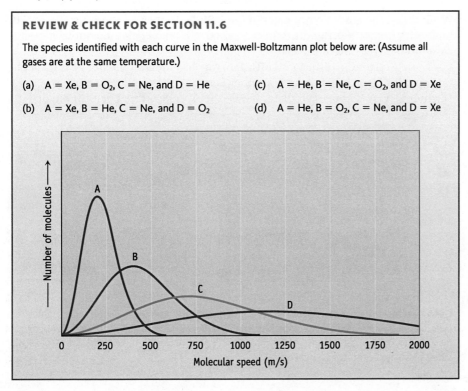

FIGURE 11.16 Gaseous diffusion. Here bromine diffuses out of a flask and mixes with air in the bottle over time. **(a)** Liquid bromine, Br_2, was placed in a small flask inside a larger container. **(b)** The cork was removed from the flask, and, with time, bromine vapor diffused into the larger container. Bromine vapor is now distributed evenly in the containers.

(a)   time →   (b)

11.7 Diffusion and Effusion

When a warm pizza is brought into a room, the volatile aroma-causing molecules vaporize into the atmosphere, where they mix with the oxygen, nitrogen, carbon dioxide, water vapor, and other gases present. Even if there were no movement of the air in the room caused by fans or people moving about, the odor would eventually reach everywhere in the room. This mixing of molecules of two or more gases due to their random molecular motions is the result of **diffusion**. Given time, the molecules of one component in a gas mixture will thoroughly and completely mix with all other components of the mixture (Figure 11.16).

Diffusion is also illustrated by the experiment in Figure 11.17. Here, we have placed cotton moistened with hydrochloric acid at one end of a U-tube and cotton moistened with aqueous ammonia at the other end. Molecules of HCl and NH_3 diffuse into the tube, and, when they meet, they produce white, solid NH_4Cl (just as in Figure 11.12).

$$HCl(g) + NH_3(g) \rightarrow NH_4Cl(s)$$

We find that the gases do not meet in the middle. Rather, because the heavier HCl molecules diffuse less rapidly than the lighter NH_3 molecules, the molecules meet closer to the HCl end of the U-tube.

Closely related to diffusion is **effusion**, which is the movement of gas through a tiny opening in a container into another container where the pressure is very low (Figure 11.17). Thomas Graham (1805–1869), a Scottish chemist, studied the

NH₄Cl
NH₃ — — HCl

Gaseous diffusion. Here, HCl gas (from hydrochloric acid) and ammonia gas (from aqueous ammonia) diffuse from opposite ends of a glass U-tube. When they meet, they produce white, solid NH_4Cl. It is clear that the NH_4Cl is formed closer to the end from which the HCl gas begins because HCl molecules move slower, on average, than NH_3 molecules.

Before effusion

● N₂
● H₂

Vacuum

Porous barrier

During effusion

Gaseous effusion. H_2 and N_2 gas molecules effuse through the pores of a porous barrier. Lighter molecules (H_2) with higher average speeds strike the barrier more often and pass more often through it than heavier, slower molecules (N_2) at the same temperature. According to Graham's law, H_2 molecules effuse 3.72 times faster than N_2 molecules.

FIGURE 11.17 Gaseous diffusion and effusion.

effusion of gases and found that the rate of effusion of a gas—the amount of gas moving from one place to another in a given amount of time—is inversely proportional to the square root of its molar mass. Based on these experimental results, the rates of effusion of two gases can be compared:

$$\frac{\text{Rate of effusion of gas 1}}{\text{Rate of effusion of gas 2}} = \sqrt{\frac{\text{molar mass of gas 2}}{\text{molar mass of gas 1}}} \qquad \text{(11.10)}$$

The relationship in Equation 11.10—now known as **Graham's law**—is readily derived from Equation 11.9 by recognizing that the rate of effusion depends on the speed of the molecules. The ratio of the rms speeds is the same as the ratio of the effusion rates:

$$\frac{\text{Rate of effusion of gas 1}}{\text{Rate of effusion of gas 2}} = \frac{\sqrt{u^2 \text{ of gas 1}}}{\sqrt{u^2 \text{ of gas 2}}} = \frac{\sqrt{3RT/(M \text{ of gas 1})}}{\sqrt{3RT/(M \text{ of gas 2})}}$$

Canceling out like terms gives the expression in Equation 11.10.

EXAMPLE 11.13 Using Graham's Law of Effusion to Calculate a Molar Mass

Problem Tetrafluoroethylene, C_2F_4, effuses through a barrier at a rate of 4.6×10^{-6} mol/h. An unknown gas, consisting only of boron and hydrogen, effuses at the rate of 5.8×10^{-6} mol/h under the same conditions. What is the molar mass of the unknown gas?

What Do You Know? You have two gases, one with a known molar mass (C_2F_4, 100.0 g/mol) and the other unknown. The rate of effusion for both gases is known.

Strategy Substitute the experimental data into Graham's law equation (Equation 11.10).

Solution

$$\frac{5.8 \times 10^{-6} \text{ mol/h}}{4.6 \times 10^{-6} \text{ mol/h}} = 1.3 = \sqrt{\frac{100.0 \text{ g/mol}}{M \text{ of unknown}}}$$

To solve for the unknown molar mass, square both sides of the equation and rearrange to find M for the unknown.

$$1.6 = \frac{100.0 \text{ g/mol}}{M \text{ of unknown}}$$

$$M = \boxed{63 \text{ g/mol}}$$

Think about Your Answer From Graham's law, we know that a light molecule will effuse more rapidly than a heavier one. Because the unknown gas effuses more rapidly than C_2F_4 ($M = 100.0$ g/mol), the unknown must have a molar mass less than 100 g/mol. A boron–hydrogen compound corresponding to this molar mass is B_5H_9, called *pentaborane*.

Check Your Understanding

A sample of pure methane, CH_4, is found to effuse through a porous barrier in 1.50 minutes. Under the same conditions, an equal number of molecules of an unknown gas effuses through the barrier in 4.73 minutes. What is the molar mass of the unknown gas?

REVIEW & CHECK FOR SECTION 11.7

In Figure 11.17, ammonia gas and hydrogen chloride are introduced from opposite ends of a glass U-tube. The gases react to produce white, solid NH_4Cl. What are the relative root mean square speeds of HCl and NH_3?

(a) rms for HCl/rms for NH_3 = 2.2

(b) rms for HCl/rms for NH_3 = 1.5

(c) rms for HCl/rms for NH_3 = 0.68

(d) rms for HCl/rms for NH_3 = 0.46

SCUBA Diving—An Applicaton of the Gas Laws

Diving with a self-contained underwater breathing apparatus (SCUBA) is exciting. If you want to dive much beyond about 60 ft (18 m), however, you need to take special precautions.

When you breathe air from a SCUBA tank, the pressure of the gas in your lungs is equal to the pressure exerted on your body. When you are at the surface, atmospheric pressure is about 1 atm, and, because air has an oxygen concentration of 21%, the partial pressure of O_2 is about 0.21 atm. If you are at a depth of about 33 ft, the water pressure is 2 atm. This means the oxygen partial pressure is double the surface partial pressure, or about 0.4 atm. Similarly, the partial pressure of N_2, which is about 0.8 atm at the surface, doubles to about 1.6 atm at a depth of 33 ft. The solubility of gases in water (and in blood) is directly proportional to pressure. Therefore, more oxygen and nitrogen dissolve in blood under these conditions, and this can lead to several problems.

Nitrogen narcosis, also called *rapture of the deep* or the *martini effect*, results from the toxic effect on nerve conduction of N_2 dissolved in blood. Its effect is comparable to drinking a martini on an empty stomach or taking laughing gas (nitrous oxide, N_2O) at the dentist; it makes you slightly giddy. In severe cases, it can impair a diver's judgment and even cause a diver to take

Image copyright © Jon Milnes. Used under license from Shutterstock.com

the regulator out of his or her mouth and hand it to a fish! Some people can go as deep as 130 ft with no problem, but others experience nitrogen narcosis at 80 ft.

Another problem with breathing air at depths beyond 100 ft or so is oxygen toxicity. Our bodies are regulated for a partial pressure of O_2 of 0.21 atm. At a depth of 130 ft, the

SCUBA diving. Ordinary recreational dives can be made with compressed air to depths of about 60 feet. With a gas mixture called *Nitrox* (which has up to 36% O_2), one can stay at such depths for a longer period. To go even deeper, however, divers must breathe special gas mixtures such as Trimix. This is a breathing mixture consisting of oxygen, helium, and nitrogen.

partial pressure of O_2 is comparable to breathing 100% oxygen at sea level. These higher partial pressures can harm the lungs and cause central nervous system damage. Oxygen toxicity is the reason deep dives are done not with compressed air but with gas mixtures with a much lower percentage of O_2, say about 10%.

Because of the risk of nitrogen narcosis, divers going beyond about 130 ft, such as those who work for offshore oil drilling companies, use a mixture of oxygen and helium. This solves the nitrogen narcosis problem, but it introduces another. If the diver has a voice link to the surface, the diver's speech sounds like Donald Duck! Speech is altered because the velocity of sound in helium is different from that in air.

11.8 Nonideal Behavior of Gases

If you are working with a gas at approximately room temperature and a pressure of 1 atm or less, the ideal gas law is remarkably successful in relating the amount of gas and its pressure, volume, and temperature. At higher pressures or lower temperatures, however, deviations from the ideal gas law occur. The origin of these deviations is explained by the breakdown of the assumptions used when describing ideal gases, specifically the assumptions that the particles have no size and that there are no forces between them.

At standard temperature and pressure (STP), the volume occupied by a single molecule is *very* small relative to its share of the total gas volume. Relatively speaking, a helium atom with a radius of 31 pm has about the same space to move about as a pea has inside a basketball. Now suppose the pressure is increased significantly, to 1000 atm. The volume available to each molecule is a sphere with a radius of only about 200 pm, which means the situation is now like that of a pea inside a sphere a bit larger than a Ping-Pong ball.

The kinetic-molecular theory and the ideal gas law are concerned with the volume available to the molecules to move about, not the total volume of the container. For example, suppose you have a flask marked with a volume of 500 mL. This does not mean the space available to molecules is 500 mL. Rather, the available volume is less than 500 mL because the molecules themselves occupy some of the volume. At low pressures, the volume occupied by the gas molecules in the container is so small in comparison to the space available that neglecting to subtract it

• **How Much Space Does a Molecule Take Up?** The volume of a methane (CH_4) molecule is 3.31×10^{-23} cm³. Suppose you have 1.00 mol of CH_4 gas in a 22.4-L flask at 273 K. The pressure would be high, 22.4 atm, and 19.9 cm³ of the space in the flask would be occupied by CH_4 molecules or about 0.09% of the flask volume.

from the total volume does not introduce significant error. The problem is that the volume occupied by gas molecules is not negligible at higher pressures.

Another assumption of the kinetic-molecular theory is that the atoms or molecules of the gas never stick to one another by some type of intermolecular force. This is clearly not true as well. All gases can be liquefied—although some gases require a very low temperature (Figure 11.11)—and the only way this can happen is if there are forces between the molecules. When a molecule is about to strike the wall of its container, other molecules in its vicinity exert a slight pull on the molecule and pull it away from the wall. The effect of the intermolecular forces is that molecules strike the wall with less force than in the absence of intermolecular attractive forces. Thus, because collisions between molecules in a real gas and the wall are softer, the observed gas pressure is less than that predicted by the ideal gas law. This effect can be particularly pronounced when the temperature is low (near the condensation temperature).

The Dutch physicist Johannes van der Waals (1837–1923) studied the breakdown of the ideal gas law equation and developed an equation to correct for the errors arising from nonideality. This equation is known as the **van der Waals equation**:

observed pressure   container V

$$\left(P + a\left[\frac{n}{V}\right]^2\right)(V - bn) = nRT \tag{11.11}$$

correction for intermolecular forces   correction for molecular volume

where a and b are experimentally determined constants (Table 11.2). Although Equation 11.11 might seem complicated at first glance, the terms in parentheses are those of the ideal gas law, each corrected for the effects discussed previously. The pressure correction term, $a(n/V)^2$, accounts for intermolecular forces. Owing to intermolecular forces, the observed gas pressure is lower than the ideal pressure ($P_{observed} < P_{ideal}$ where P_{ideal} is calculated using the equation $PV = nRT$). Therefore, the term $a(n/V)^2$ is *added* to the observed pressure. The constant a typically has values in the range 0.01 to 10 atm · L^2/mol^2.

The actual volume available to the molecules is smaller than the volume of the container because the molecules themselves take up space. Therefore, an amount is *subtracted* from the container volume ($= bn$) to take this into account. Here, n is the number of moles of gas, and b is an experimental quantity that corrects for the molecular volume. Typical values of b range from 0.01 to 0.1 L/mol, roughly increasing with increasing molecular size.

As an example of the importance of these corrections, consider a sample of 4.00 mol of chlorine gas, Cl_2, in a 4.00-L tank at 100.0 °C. The ideal gas law would lead you to expect a pressure of 30.6 atm. A better estimate of the pressure, obtained from the van der Waals equation, is 26.0 atm, about 4.6 atm less than the ideal pressure!

Table 11.2 **van der Waals Constants**

Gas	a Values (atm·L^2/mol^2)	b Values (L/mol)
He	0.034	0.0237
Ar	1.34	0.0322
H_2	0.244	0.0266
N_2	1.39	0.0391
O_2	1.36	0.0318
CO_2	3.59	0.0427
Cl_2	6.49	0.0562
H_2O	5.46	0.0305

A flask of helium gas for filling party balloons. The tank holds about 15 cubic feet (about 425 L) of helium. (*Note:* These tanks are not designed to be reused! Dispose of them properly. Also, use helium sparingly. The supply of the gas on the planet is not limitless.)

REVIEW & CHECK FOR SECTION 11.8

You can purchase tanks of helium at a party store to fill balloons. Such a tank may hold 343 mol of He in a volume of 473 L. Use van der Waals's equation to calculate the pressure in the tank at 25 °C.

(a) 18.0 atm   (b) 17.7 atm   (c) 17.3 atm

What to Do with All of That CO_2? More on Green Chemistry

Most scientists, including the authors of this book, believe that global warming is occurring and that it is a problem. They also believe this increase is related to the increase in the percentage of greenhouse gases, especially CO_2, in the atmosphere. The percentage of CO_2 in the atmosphere has been on the rise since the beginning of the Industrial Revolution and is projected to continue to rise in the future. Are there ways to stabilize the concentration of CO_2 at the current level, or at least limit its future increase? This in turn focuses attention on the obvious source of CO_2 in the atmosphere, the combustion of fossil fuels.

What is wrong with CO_2 in the atmosphere? After all, it is used by plants as their carbon source, and the oceans can absorb the gas, much of which ends up incorporated in corals. But there is a danger these "sinks" could be overwhelmed.

The United States obtains over half its electricity from coal-fired power plants. So, one question is why not capture and dispose of the CO_2 from power plants. In fact, this is being considered. One way of removing CO_2 generated by burning fossil fuels involves geological sequestration, a process in which CO_2 is pumped into rock formations thou-

sands of feet underground. There, it would presumably remain trapped for thousands of years.

An experiment is underway at the Mountaineer Power Plant in New Haven, West Virginia, to do just that. For this process to succeed, however, the CO_2 to be sequestered needs to be pure, free of impurities. This is accomplished in two steps. The flue gas from the coal-based electricity generating plant is first routed through a scrubber, to remove most of the SO_2, a typical contaminant produced in coal combustion. The gas stream is then cooled to about 35 °F and introduced under pressure into a cooled slurry of ammonium carbonate, $(NH_4)_2CO_3$. As set up in this pilot program, a portion of the CO_2 reacts with the slurry to form ammonium hydrogen carbonate, $NH_4(HCO_3)$:

$$(NH_4)_2CO_3 + CO_2 + H_2O \rightleftharpoons$$
$$2\ NH_4(HCO_3)$$

The remaining flue gases, mainly N_2 and unreacted CO_2, exit the system. The slurry is then separated and heated, reversing the chemical process, giving back pure CO_2 and

regenerating $(NH_4)_2CO_3$ which is recycled back into the system. The pure CO_2 is then pumped underground.

The pilot project is currently set up to remove about 100,000 tons of CO_2 annually. This is only about 1.5% of CO_2 from the exhaust gases, but it is believed that the process could be scaled up to remove as much as 90% of the CO_2 in the future if the method proves economically feasible.

Questions:
1. A large coal-fired plant can burn 10,000 tons of coal a day. We will make the assumption for this problem that the coal is pure carbon, so this is about 9.1×10^9 g of carbon. What mass of CO_2 will be generated?
2. What mass of ammonium carbonate is needed to remove 1.0 million grams of CO_2 per day?

Answers to these questions are available in Appendix N.

Reference:
New York Times, p. A1, September 22, 2009.

Captured, Then Buried

A coal-fired electricity plant in West Virginia plans to capture some of the carbon dioxide it emits and inject it underground. Some environmentalists are wary.

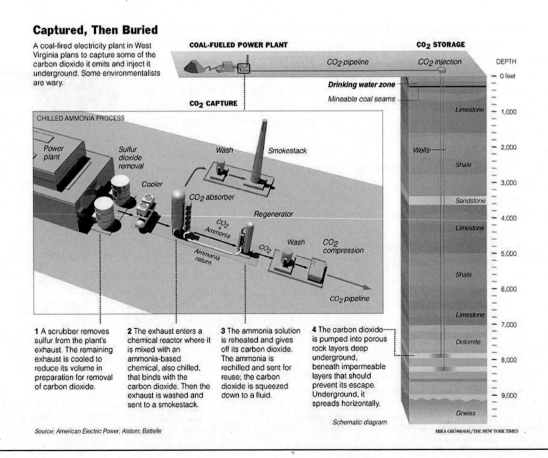

1 A scrubber removes sulfur from the plant's exhaust. The remaining exhaust is cooled to reduce its volume in preparation for removal of carbon dioxide.

2 The exhaust enters a chemical reactor where it is mixed with an ammonia-based chemical, also chilled, that binds with the carbon dioxide. Then the exhaust is washed and sent to a smokestack.

3 The ammonia solution is reheated and gives off its carbon dioxide. The ammonia is rechilled and sent for reuse; the carbon dioxide is squeezed down to a fluid.

4 The carbon dioxide is pumped into porous rock layers deep underground, beneath impermeable layers that should prevent its escape. Underground, it spreads horizontally.

Source: American Electric Power; Alstom; Battelle

Schematic diagram

MIKA GRÖNDAHL/THE NEW YORK TIMES

CHAPTER GOALS REVISITED

Now that you have studied this chapter, you should ask whether you have met the chapter goals. In particular, you should be able to:

Understand the basis of the gas laws and how to use those laws (Boyle's law, Charles's law, Avogadro's hypothesis, Dalton's law)

a. Describe how pressure measurements are made and the units of pressure, especially atmospheres (atm) and millimeters of mercury (mm Hg) (Section 11.1). **Study Questions: 1, 3.**

b. Understand the basis of the gas laws and how to apply them (Section 11.2). **Study Questions: 6, 8, 10, 12, 14–16.**

Use the ideal gas law

a. Understand the origin of the ideal gas law and how to use the equation (Section 11.3). **Study Questions: 17–24, 59, 63, 77, 85, 102.**

b. Calculate the molar mass of a compound from a knowledge of the pressure of a known quantity of a gas in a given volume at a known temperature (Section 11.3). **Study Questions: 25–30, 66, 89, 90.**

Apply the gas laws to stoichiometric calculations

a. Apply the gas laws to a study of the stoichiometry of reactions (Section 11.4). **Study Questions: 31–36, 65, 79, 82.**

b. Use Dalton's law of partial pressures (Section 11.5). **Study Questions: 39, 40, 70, 80, 87.**

Understand kinetic-molecular theory as it is applied to gases, especially the distribution of molecular speeds (energies)

a. Apply the kinetic-molecular theory of gas behavior at the molecular level (Section 11.6). **Study Questions: 41–46, 107, and Go Chemistry Module 16.**

b. Understand the phenomena of diffusion and effusion and how to use Graham's law (Section 11.7). **Study Questions: 47–50, 75, 76.**

Recognize why gases do not behave like ideal gases under some conditions

a. Appreciate the fact that gases usually do not behave as ideal gases. Deviations from ideal behavior are largest at high pressure and low temperature (Section 11.8). **Study Questions: 51, 52.**

and

Sign in at **www.cengage.com/owl** to:
- View tutorials and simulations, develop problem-solving skills, and complete online homework assigned by your professor.
- For quick review and exam prep, download Go Chemistry mini lecture modules from OWL (or purchase them at **www.cengagebrain.com**)

Access **How Do I Solve It?** tutorials on how to approach problem solving using concepts in this chapter.

Key Equations

Equation 11.1 (page 512) Boyle's law (where *P* is the pressure and *V* is the volume).

$$P_1V_1 = P_2V_2 \text{ at constant } n \text{ and } T$$

Equation 11.2 (page 514) Charles's law (where *T* is the Kelvin temperature).

$$\frac{V_1}{T_1} = \frac{V_2}{T_2} \text{ at constant } n \text{ and } P$$

Equation 11.3 (page 515) General gas law (combined gas law).

$$\frac{P_1V_1}{T_1} = \frac{P_2V_2}{T_2} \text{ for a given amount of gas, } n$$

Equation 11.4 (page 518) Ideal gas law (where *n* is the amount of gas in moles and *R* is the universal gas constant, 0.082057 L · atm/K · mol).

$$PV = nRT$$

Equation 11.5 (page 520) Density of gases (where *d* is the gas density in g/L and *M* is the molar mass of the gas).

$$d = \frac{m}{V} = \frac{PM}{RT}$$

Equation 11.6 (page 525) Dalton's law of partial pressures. The total pressure of a gas mixture is the sum of the partial pressures of the component gases (P_n).

$$P_{total} = P_1 + P_2 + P_3 + \ldots$$

Equation 11.7 (page 525) The total pressure of a gas mixture is equal to the total number of moles of gases multiplied by (RT/V).

$$P_{total} = (n_{total})\left(\frac{RT}{V}\right)$$

Equation 11.8 (page 526) The pressure of a gas (A) in a mixture is the product of its mole fraction (X_A) and the total pressure of the mixture.

$$P_A = X_A P_{total}$$

Equation 11.9 (page 530) The rms speed ($\sqrt{u^2}$) depends on the molar mass of a gas *(M)* and its temperature *(T)*.

$$\sqrt{u^2} = \sqrt{\frac{3RT}{M}}$$

Equation 11.10 (page 533) Graham's law. The rate of effusion of a gas is inversely proportional to the square root of its molar mass.

$$\frac{\text{Rate of effusion of gas 1}}{\text{Rate of effusion of gas 2}} = \sqrt{\frac{\text{molar mass of gas 2}}{\text{molar mass of gas 1}}}$$

Equation 11.11 (page 535) The van der Waals equation, which relates pressure, volume, temperature, and amount of gas for a nonideal gas.

$$\left(P + a\left[\frac{n}{V}\right]^2\right)(V - bn) = nRT$$

observed pressure   container *V*

correction for intermolecular forces

correction for molecular volume

Study Questions

Practicing Skills

Pressure
(See Section 11.1 and Example 11.1.)

1. The pressure of a gas is 440 mm Hg. Express this pressure in units of (a) atmospheres, (b) bars, and (c) kilopascals.

2. The average barometric pressure at an altitude of 10 km is 210 mm Hg. Express this pressure in atmospheres, bars, and kilopascals.

3. Indicate which represents the higher pressure in each of the following pairs:
   (a) 534 mm Hg or 0.754 bar
   (b) 534 mm Hg or 650 kPa
   (c) 1.34 bar or 934 kPa

4. Put the following in order of increasing pressure: 363 mm Hg, 363 kPa, 0.256 atm, and 0.523 bar.

Boyle's Law and Charles's Law
(See Section 11.2 and Examples 11.2 and 11.3.)

5. A sample of nitrogen gas has a pressure of 67.5 mm Hg in a 500.-mL flask. What is the pressure of this gas sample when it is transferred to a 125-mL flask at the same temperature?

6. A sample of CO_2 gas has a pressure of 56.5 mm Hg in a 125-mL flask. The sample is transferred to a new flask, where it has a pressure of 62.3 mm Hg at the same temperature. What is the volume of the new flask?

7. You have 3.5 L of NO at a temperature of 22.0 °C. What volume would the NO occupy at 37 °C? (Assume the pressure is constant.)

8. A 5.0-mL sample of CO_2 gas is enclosed in a gas-tight syringe (Figure 11.3) at 22 °C. If the syringe is immersed in an ice bath (0 °C), what is the new gas volume, assuming that the pressure is held constant?

The General Gas Law
(See Section 11.2 and Example 11.4.)

9. You have 3.6 L of H_2 gas at 380 mm Hg and 25 °C. What is the pressure of this gas if it is transferred to a 5.0-L flask at 0.0 °C?

10. You have a sample of CO_2 in flask A with a volume of 25.0 mL. At 20.5 °C, the pressure of the gas is 436.5 mm Hg. To find the volume of another flask, B, you move the CO_2 to that flask and find that its pressure is now 94.3 mm Hg at 24.5 °C. What is the volume of flask B?

11. You have a sample of gas in a flask with a volume of 250 mL. At 25.5 °C, the pressure of the gas is 360 mm Hg. If you decrease the temperature to −5.0 °C, what is the gas pressure at the lower temperature?

12. A sample of gas occupies 135 mL at 22.5 °C; the pressure is 165 mm Hg. What is the pressure of the gas sample when it is placed in a 252-mL flask at a temperature of 0.0 °C?

13. One of the cylinders of an automobile engine has a volume of 400. cm^3. The engine takes in air at a pressure of 1.00 atm and a temperature of 15 °C and compresses the air to a volume of 50.0 cm^3 at 77 °C. What is the final pressure of the gas in the cylinder? (The ratio of before and after volumes—in this case, 400:50 or 8:1—is called the *compression ratio.*)

14. A helium-filled balloon of the type used in long-distance flying contains 420,000 ft^3 (1.2×10^7 L) of helium. Suppose you fill the balloon with helium on the ground, where the pressure is 737 mm Hg and the temperature is 16.0 °C. When the balloon ascends to a height of 2 miles, where the pressure is only 600. mm Hg and the temperature is −33 °C, what volume is occupied by the helium gas? Assume the pressure inside the balloon matches the external pressure. Comment on the result.

Avogadro's Hypothesis
(See Section 11.2 and Example 11.5.)

15. Nitrogen monoxide reacts with oxygen to give nitrogen dioxide.
$$2\ NO(g) + O_2(g) \rightarrow 2\ NO_2(g)$$
(a) You wish to react NO and O_2 in the correct stoichiometric ratio. The sample of NO has a volume of 150 mL. What volume of O_2 is required (at the same pressure and temperature)?
(b) What volume of NO_2 (at the same pressure and temperature) is formed in this reaction?

16. Ethane burns in air to give H_2O and CO_2.
$$2\ C_2H_6(g) + 7\ O_2(g) \rightarrow 4\ CO_2(g) + 6\ H_2O(g)$$
What volume of O_2 (L) is required for complete reaction with 5.2 L of C_2H_6? What volume of H_2O vapor (L) is produced? Assume all gases are measured at the same temperature and pressure.

Ideal Gaw Law
(See Section 11.3 and Example 11.6.)

17. A 1.25-g sample of CO_2 is contained in a 750.-mL flask at 22.5 °C. What is the pressure of the gas?

18. A balloon holds 30.0 kg of helium. What is the volume of the balloon if its pressure is 1.20 atm and the temperature is 22 °C?

19. A flask is first evacuated so that it contains no gas at all. Then, 2.2 g of CO_2 is introduced into the flask. On warming to 22 °C, the gas exerts a pressure of 318 mm Hg. What is the volume of the flask?

20. A steel cylinder holds 1.50 g of ethanol, C_2H_5OH. What is the pressure of the ethanol vapor if the cylinder has a volume of 251 cm^3 and the temperature is 250 °C? (Assume all of the ethanol is in the vapor phase at this temperature.)

21. A balloon for long-distance flying contains 1.2×10^7 L of helium. If the helium pressure is 737 mm Hg at 25 °C, what mass of helium (in grams) does the balloon contain? (See Study Question 14.)

22. What mass of helium, in grams, is required to fill a 5.0-L balloon to a pressure of 1.1 atm at 25 °C?

Gas Density and Molar Mass
(See Section 11.3 and Examples and 11.7 and 11.8.)

23. Forty miles above Earth's surface, the temperature is 250 K, and the pressure is only 0.20 mm Hg. What is the density of air (in grams per liter) at this altitude? (Assume the molar mass of air is 28.96 g/mol.)

24. Diethyl ether, $(C_2H_5)_2O$, vaporizes easily at room temperature. If the vapor exerts a pressure of 233 mm Hg in a flask at 25 °C, what is the density of the vapor?

25. A gaseous organofluorine compound has a density of 0.355 g/L at 17 °C and 189 mm Hg. What is the molar mass of the compound?

26. Chloroform is a common liquid used in the laboratory. It vaporizes readily. If the pressure of chloroform vapor in a flask is 195 mm Hg at 25.0 °C and the density of the vapor is 1.25 g/L, what is the molar mass of chloroform?

27. A 1.007-g sample of an unknown gas exerts a pressure of 715 mm Hg in a 452-mL container at 23 °C. What is the molar mass of the gas?

28. A 0.0125-g sample of a gas with an empirical formula of CHF_2 is placed in a 165-mL flask. It has a pressure of 13.7 mm Hg at 22.5 °C. What is the molecular formula of the compound?

29. A new boron hydride, B_xH_y, has been isolated. To find its molar mass, you measure the pressure of the gas in a known volume at a known temperature. The following experimental data are collected:

    Mass of gas = 12.5 mg   Pressure of gas = 24.8 mm Hg

    Temperature = 25 °C   Volume of flask = 125 mL

    Which formula corresponds to the calculated molar mass?
    (a) B_2H_6
    (b) B_4H_{10}
    (c) B_5H_9
    (d) B_6H_{10}
    (e) $B_{10}H_{14}$

30. Acetaldehyde is a common liquid compound that vaporizes readily. Determine the molar mass of acetaldehyde from the following data:

    Sample mass = 0.107 g   Volume of gas = 125 mL

    Temperature = 0.0 °C   Pressure = 331 mm Hg

Gas Laws and Chemical Reactions
(See Section 11.4 and Examples 11.9 and 11.10.)

31. Iron reacts with hydrochloric acid to produce iron(II) chloride and hydrogen gas:

    $$Fe(s) + 2 HCl(aq) \rightarrow FeCl_2(aq) + H_2(g)$$

    The H_2 gas from the reaction of 2.2 g of iron with excess acid is collected in a 10.0-L flask at 25 °C. What is the pressure of the H_2 gas in this flask?

32. Silane, SiH_4, reacts with O_2 to give silicon dioxide and water:

    $$SiH_4(g) + 2 O_2(g) \rightarrow SiO_2(s) + 2 H_2O(\ell)$$

    A 5.20-L sample of SiH_4 gas at 356 mm Hg pressure and 25 °C is allowed to react with O_2 gas. What volume of O_2 gas, in liters, is required for complete reaction if the oxygen has a pressure of 425 mm Hg at 25 °C?

33. Sodium azide, the explosive compound in automobile air bags, decomposes according to the following equation:

    $$2 NaN_3(s) \rightarrow 2 Na(s) + 3 N_2(g)$$

    What mass of sodium azide is required to provide the nitrogen needed to inflate a 75.0-L bag to a pressure of 1.3 atm at 25 °C?

34. The hydrocarbon octane (C_8H_{18}) burns to give CO_2 and water vapor:

    $$2 C_8H_{18}(g) + 25 O_2(g) \rightarrow 16 CO_2(g) + 18 H_2O(g)$$

    If a 0.048-g sample of octane burns completely in O_2, what will be the pressure of water vapor in a 4.75-L flask at 30.0 °C? If the O_2 gas needed for complete combustion was contained in a 4.75-L flask at 22 °C, what would its pressure be?

35. Hydrazine reacts with O_2 according to the following equation:

    $$N_2H_4(g) + O_2(g) \rightarrow N_2(g) + 2 H_2O(\ell)$$

    Assume the O_2 needed for the reaction is in a 450-L tank at 23 °C. What must the oxygen pressure be in the tank to have enough oxygen to consume 1.00 kg of hydrazine completely?

36. A self-contained underwater breathing apparatus uses canisters containing potassium superoxide. The superoxide consumes the CO_2 exhaled by a person and replaces it with oxygen.

    $$4 KO_2(s) + 2 CO_2(g) \rightarrow 2 K_2CO_3(s) + 3 O_2(g)$$

    What mass of KO_2, in grams, is required to react with 8.90 L of CO_2 at 22.0 °C and 767 mm Hg?

Gas Mixtures and Dalton's Law
(See Section 11.5 and Example 11.11.)

37. What is the total pressure in atmospheres of a gas mixture that contains 1.0 g of H_2 and 8.0 g of Ar in a 3.0-L container at 27 °C? What are the partial pressures of the two gases?

38. A cylinder of compressed gas is labeled "Composition (mole %): 4.5% H_2S, 3.0% CO_2, balance N_2." The pressure gauge attached to the cylinder reads 46 atm. Calculate the partial pressure of each gas, in atmospheres, in the cylinder.

39. A halothane–oxygen mixture ($C_2HBrClF_3 + O_2$) can be used as an anesthetic. A tank containing such a mixture has the following partial pressures: P (halothane) = 170 mm Hg and P (O_2) = 570 mm Hg.
    (a) What is the ratio of the number of moles of halothane to the number of moles of O_2?
    (b) If the tank contains 160 g of O_2, what mass of $C_2HBrClF_3$ is present?

40. A collapsed balloon is filled with He to a volume of 12.5 L at a pressure of 1.00 atm. Oxygen, O_2, is then added so that the final volume of the balloon is 26 L with a total pressure of 1.00 atm. The temperature, which remains constant throughout, is 21.5 °C.
    (a) What mass of He does the balloon contain?
    (b) What is the final partial pressure of He in the balloon?
    (c) What is the partial pressure of O_2 in the balloon?
    (d) What is the mole fraction of each gas?

Kinetic-Molecular Theory
(See Section 11.6 and Example 11.12.)

41. You have two flasks of equal volume. Flask A contains H_2 at 0 °C and 1 atm pressure. Flask B contains CO_2 gas at 25 °C and 2 atm pressure. Compare these two gases with respect to each of the following:
    (a) average kinetic energy per molecule
    (b) root mean square speed
    (c) number of molecules
    (d) mass of gas

42. Equal masses of gaseous N_2 and Ar are placed in separate flasks of equal volume at the same temperature. Tell whether each of the following statements is true or false. Briefly explain your answer in each case.
    (a) There are more molecules of N_2 present than atoms of Ar.
    (b) The pressure is greater in the Ar flask.
    (c) The Ar atoms have a greater rms speed than the N_2 molecules.
    (d) The N_2 molecules collide more frequently with the walls of the flask than do the Ar atoms.

43. If the rms speed of an oxygen molecule is 4.28×10^4 cm/s at 25 °C, what is the rms speed of a CO_2 molecule at the same temperature?

44. Calculate the rms speed for CO molecules at 25 °C. What is the ratio of this speed to that of Ar atoms at the same temperature?

45. Place the following gases in order of increasing rms speed at 25 °C: Ar, CH_4, N_2, CH_2F_2.

46. The reaction of SO_2 with Cl_2 gives dichlorine oxide, which is used to bleach wood pulp and to treat wastewater:

$$SO_2(g) + 2\ Cl_2(g) \rightarrow OSCl_2(g) + Cl_2O(g)$$

All of the compounds involved in the reaction are gases. List them in order of increasing rms speed.

Diffusion and Effusion
(See Section 11.7 and Example 11.13.)

47. In each pair of gases below, tell which will effuse faster:
(a) CO_2 or F_2
(b) O_2 or N_2
(c) C_2H_4 or C_2H_6
(d) two chlorofluorocarbons: $CFCl_3$ or $C_2Cl_2F_4$

48. Argon gas is 10 times denser than helium gas at the same temperature and pressure. Which gas is predicted to effuse faster? How much faster?

49. A gas whose molar mass you wish to know effuses through an opening at a rate one third as fast as that of helium gas. What is the molar mass of the unknown gas?

50. ▲ A sample of uranium fluoride is found to effuse at the rate of 17.7 mg/h. Under comparable conditions, gaseous I_2 effuses at the rate of 15.0 mg/h. What is the molar mass of the uranium fluoride? (*Hint:* Rates must be converted to units of moles per time.)

Nonideal Gases
(See Section 11.8)

51. In the text, it is stated that the pressure of 4.00 mol of Cl_2 in a 4.00-L tank at 100.0 °C should be 26.0 atm if calculated using the van der Waals equation. Verify this result, and compare it with the pressure predicted by the ideal gas law.

52. You want to store 165 g of CO_2 gas in a 12.5-L tank at room temperature (25 °C). Calculate the pressure the gas would have using (a) the ideal gas law and (b) the van der Waals equation. (For CO_2, $a = 3.59$ atm $\cdot$ L^2/ mol^2 and $b = 0.0427$ L/mol.)

General Questions

These questions are not designated as to type or location in the chapter. They may combine several concepts.

53. Complete the following table:

	atm	mm Hg	kPa	bar
Standard atmosphere	___	___	___	___
Partial pressure of N_2 in the atmosphere	___	593	___	___
Tank of compressed H_2	___	___	___	133
Atmospheric pressure at the top of Mount Everest	___	___	33.7	___

54. On combustion, 1.0 L of a gaseous compound of hydrogen, carbon, and nitrogen gives 2.0 L of CO_2, 3.5 L of H_2O vapor, and 0.50 L of N_2 at STP. What is the empirical formula of the compound?

55. ▲ You have a sample of helium gas at −33 °C, and you want to increase the rms speed of helium atoms by 10.0%. To what temperature should the gas be heated to accomplish this?

56. If 12.0 g of O_2 is required to inflate a balloon to a certain size at 27 °C, what mass of O_2 is required to inflate it to the same size (and pressure) at 5.0 °C?

57. Butyl mercaptan, C_4H_9SH, has a very bad odor and is among the compounds added to natural gas to help detect a leak of otherwise odorless natural gas. In an experiment, you burn 95.0 mg of C_4H_9SH and collect the product gases (SO_2, CO_2, and H_2O) in a 5.25-L flask at 25 °C. What is the total gas pressure in the flask, and what is the partial pressure of each of the product gases?

58. A bicycle tire has an internal volume of 1.52 L and contains 0.406 mol of air. The tire will burst if its internal pressure reaches 7.25 atm. To what temperature, in degrees Celsius, does the air in the tire need to be heated to cause a blowout?

59. The temperature of the atmosphere on Mars can be as high as 27 °C at the equator at noon, and the atmospheric pressure is about 8 mm Hg. If a spacecraft could collect 10. m^3 of this atmosphere, compress it to a small volume, and send it back to Earth, how many moles would the sample contain?

60. If you place 2.25 g of solid silicon in a 6.56-L flask that contains CH_3Cl with a pressure of 585 mm Hg at 25 °C, what mass of dimethyldichlorosilane, $(CH_3)_2SiCl_2(g)$, can be formed?

$$Si(s) + 2\ CH_3Cl(g) \rightarrow (CH_3)_2SiCl_2(g)$$

What pressure of $(CH_3)_2SiCl_2(g)$ would you expect in this same flask at 95 °C on completion of the reaction? (Dimethyldichlorosilane is one starting material used to make silicones, polymeric substances used as lubricants, antistick agents, and water-proofing caulk.)

61. $Ni(CO)_4$ can be made by reacting finely divided nickel with gaseous CO. If you have CO in a 1.50-L flask at a pressure of 418 mm Hg at 25.0 °C, along with 0.450 g of Ni powder, what is the theoretical yield of $Ni(CO)_4$?

62. Ethane burns in air to give H_2O and CO_2.

$$2\ C_2H_6(g) + 7\ O_2(g) \rightarrow 4\ CO_2(g) + 6\ H_2O(g)$$

(a) Four gases are involved in this reaction. Place them in order of increasing rms speed. (Assume all are at the same temperature.)
(b) A 3.26-L flask contains C_2H_6 at a pressure of 256 mm Hg and a temperature of 25 °C. Suppose O_2 gas is added to the flask until C_2H_6 and O_2 are in the correct stoichiometric ratio for the combustion reaction. At this point, what is the partial pressure of O_2 and what is the total pressure in the flask?

63. You have four gas samples:
    1. 1.0 L of H_2 at STP
    2. 1.0 L of Ar at STP
    3. 1.0 L of H_2 at 27 °C and 760 mm Hg
    4. 1.0 L of He at 0 °C and 900 mm Hg
    (a) Which sample has the largest number of gas particles (atoms or molecules)?
    (b) Which sample contains the smallest number of particles?
    (c) Which sample represents the largest mass?

64. Propane reacts with oxygen to give carbon dioxide and water vapor.

    $$C_3H_8(g) + 5\ O_2(g) \rightarrow 3\ CO_2(g) + 4\ H_2O(g)$$

    If you mix C_3H_8 and O_2 in the correct stoichiometric ratio, and if the total pressure of the mixture is 288 mm Hg, what are the partial pressures of C_3H_8 and O_2? If the temperature and volume do not change, what is the pressure of the water vapor?

65. Iron carbonyl can be made by the direct reaction of iron metal and carbon monoxide.

    $$Fe(s) + 5\ CO(g) \rightarrow Fe(CO)_5(\ell)$$

    What is the theoretical yield of $Fe(CO)_5$ if 3.52 g of iron is treated with CO gas having a pressure of 732 mm Hg in a 5.50-L flask at 23 °C?

66. Analysis of a gaseous chlorofluorocarbon, CCl_xF_y, shows that it contains 11.79% C and 69.57% Cl. In another experiment, you find that 0.107 g of the compound fills a 458-mL flask at 25 °C with a pressure of 21.3 mm Hg. What is the molecular formula of the compound?

67. There are five compounds in the family of sulfur–fluorine compounds with the general formula S_xF_y. One of these compounds is 25.23% S. If you place 0.0955 g of the compound in a 89-mL flask at 45 °C, the pressure of the gas is 83.8 mm Hg. What is the molecular formula of S_xF_y?

68. A miniature volcano can be made in the laboratory with ammonium dichromate. When ignited, it decomposes in a fiery display.

    $$(NH_4)_2Cr_2O_7(s) \rightarrow N_2(g) + 4\ H_2O(g) + Cr_2O_3(s)$$

    If 0.95 g of ammonium dichromate is used and the gases from this reaction are trapped in a 15.0-L flask at 23 °C, what is the total pressure of the gas in the flask? What are the partial pressures of N_2 and H_2O?

Thermal decomposition of $(NH_4)_2Cr_2O_7$.

69. The density of air 20 km above Earth's surface is 92 g/m³. The pressure of the atmosphere is 42 mm Hg, and the temperature is −63 °C.
    (a) What is the average molar mass of the atmosphere at this altitude?
    (b) If the atmosphere at this altitude consists of only O_2 and N_2, what is the mole fraction of each gas?

70. A 3.0-L bulb containing He at 145 mm Hg is connected by a valve to a 2.0-L bulb containing Ar at 355 mm Hg (see figure below). Calculate the partial pressure of each gas and the total pressure after the valve between the flasks is opened.

71. Chlorine dioxide, ClO_2, reacts with fluorine to give a new gas that contains Cl, O, and F. In an experiment, you find that 0.150 g of this new gas has a pressure of 17.2 mm Hg in a 1850-mL flask at 21 °C. What is the identity of the unknown gas?

72. A xenon fluoride can be prepared by heating a mixture of Xe and F_2 gases to a high temperature in a pressure-proof container. Assume that xenon gas was added to a 0.25-L container until its pressure reached 0.12 atm at 0.0 °C. Fluorine gas was then added until the total pressure reached 0.72 atm at 0.0 °C. After the reaction was complete, the xenon was consumed completely, and the pressure of the F_2 remaining in the container was 0.36 atm at 0.0 °C. What is the empirical formula of the xenon fluoride?

73. Which of the following is *not* correct?
    (a) Diffusion of gases occurs more rapidly at higher temperatures.
    (b) Effusion of H_2 is faster than effusion of He (assume similar conditions and a rate expressed in units of mol/h).
    (c) Diffusion will occur faster at low pressure than at high pressure.
    (d) The rate of effusion of a gas (mol/h) is directly proportional to molar mass.

74. The ideal gas law is least accurate under conditions of high pressure and low temperature. In those situations, using the van der Waals equation is advisable.
    (a) Calculate the pressure exerted by 12.0 g of CO_2 in a 500-mL vessel at 298 K, using the ideal gas equation. Then, recalculate the pressure using the van der Waals equation. Assuming the pressure calculated from van der Waal's equation is correct, what is the percent error in the answer when using the ideal gas equation?

(b) Next, cool this sample to -70 °C. Then perform the same calculation for the pressure exerted by CO_2 at this new temperature, using both the ideal gas law and the van der Waals equation. Again, what is the percent error when using the ideal gas equation?

75. Carbon dioxide, CO_2, was shown to effuse through a porous plate at the rate of 0.033 mol/min. The same quantity of an unknown gas, 0.033 moles, is found to effuse through the same porous barrier in 104 seconds. Calculate the molar mass of the unknown gas.

76. In an experiment, you have determined that 0.66 moles of CF_4 effuse through a porous barrier over a 4.8 minute period. How long will it take for 0.66 moles of CH_4 to effuse through the same barrier?

77. A balloon is filled with helium gas to a gauge pressure of 22 mm Hg at 25 °C. The volume of the gas is 305 mL, and the barometric pressure is 755 mm Hg. What amount of helium is in the balloon? (Remember that gauge pressure = total pressure − barometric pressure. See page 511.)

78. If you have a sample of water in a closed container, some of the water will evaporate until the pressure of the water vapor, at 25 °C, is 23.8 mm Hg. How many molecules of water per cubic centimeter exist in the vapor phase?

79. You are given 1.56 g of a mixture of $KClO_3$ and KCl. When heated, the $KClO_3$ decomposes to KCl and O_2,

$$2\ KClO_3(s) \rightarrow 2\ KCl(s) + 3\ O_2(g)$$

and 327 mL of O_2 with a pressure of 735 mm Hg is collected at 19 °C. What is the weight percentage of $KClO_3$ in the sample?

80. ▲ A study of climbers who reached the summit of Mount Everest without supplemental oxygen showed that the partial pressures of O_2 and CO_2 in their lungs were 35 mm Hg and 7.5 mm Hg, respectively. The barometric pressure at the summit was 253 mm Hg. Assume the lung gases are saturated with moisture at a body temperature of 37 °C [which means the partial pressure of water vapor in the lungs is $P(H_2O) = 47.1$ mm Hg]. If you assume the lung gases consist of only O_2, N_2, CO_2, and H_2O, what is the partial pressure of N_2?

81. Nitrogen monoxide reacts with oxygen to give nitrogen dioxide:

$$2\ NO(g) + O_2(g) \rightarrow 2\ NO_2(g)$$

(a) Place the three gases in order of increasing rms speed at 298 K.
(b) If you mix NO and O_2 in the correct stoichiometric ratio and NO has a partial pressure of 150 mm Hg, what is the partial pressure of O_2?
(c) After reaction between NO and O_2 is complete, what is the pressure of NO_2 if the NO originally had a pressure of 150 mm Hg and O_2 was added in the correct stoichiometric amount?

82. ▲ Ammonia gas is synthesized by combining hydrogen and nitrogen:

$$3\ H_2(g) + N_2(g) \rightarrow 2\ NH_3(g)$$

(a) If you want to produce 562 g of NH_3, what volume of H_2 gas, at 56 °C and 745 mm Hg, is required?
(b) Nitrogen for this reaction will be obtained from air. What volume of air, measured at 29 °C and 745 mm Hg pressure, will be required to provide the nitrogen needed to produce 562 g of NH_3? Assume the sample of air contains 78.1 mole % N_2.

83. Nitrogen trifluoride is prepared by the reaction of ammonia and fluorine.

$$4\ NH_3(g) + 3\ F_2(g) \rightarrow 3\ NH_4F(s) + NF_3(g)$$

If you mix NH_3 with F_2 in the correct stoichiometric ratio, and if the total pressure of the mixture is 120 mm Hg, what are the partial pressures of NH_3 and F_2? When the reactants have been completely consumed, what is the total pressure in the flask? (Assume T is constant.)

84. Chlorine trifluoride, ClF_3, is a valuable reagent because it can be used to convert metal oxides to metal fluorides:

$$6\ NiO(s) + 4\ ClF_3(g) \rightarrow 6\ NiF_2(s) + 2\ Cl_2(g) + 3\ O_2(g)$$

(a) What mass of NiO will react with ClF_3 gas if the gas has a pressure of 250 mm Hg at 20 °C in a 2.5-L flask?
(b) If the ClF_3 described in part (a) is completely consumed, what are the partial pressures of Cl_2 and of O_2 in the 2.5-L flask at 20 °C (in mm Hg)? What is the total pressure in the flask?

85. ▲ Relative humidity is the ratio of the partial pressure of water in air at a given temperature to the vapor pressure of water at that temperature. Calculate the mass of water per liter of air under the following conditions:
(a) at 20 °C and 45% relative humidity
(b) at 0 °C and 95% relative humidity

Under which circumstances is the mass of H_2O per liter greater? (See Appendix G for the vapor pressure of water.)

86. How much water vapor is present in a dormitory room when the relative humidity is 55% and the temperature is 23 °C? The dimensions of the room are 4.5 m² floor area and 3.5 m ceiling height. (See Study Question 85 for a definition of relative humidity and Appendix G for the vapor pressure of water.)

In the Laboratory

87. ▲ You have a 550.-mL tank of gas with a pressure of 1.56 atm at 24 °C. You thought the gas was pure carbon monoxide gas, CO, but you later found it was contaminated by small quantities of gaseous CO_2 and O_2. Analysis shows that the tank pressure is 1.34 atm (at 24 °C) if the CO_2 is removed. Another experiment shows that 0.0870 g of O_2 can be removed chemically. What are the masses of CO and CO_2 in the tank, and what is the partial pressure of each of the three gases at 25 °C?

88. ▲ Methane is burned in a laboratory Bunsen burner to give CO_2 and water vapor. Methane gas is supplied to the burner at the rate of 5.0 L/min (at a temperature of 28 °C and a pressure of 773 mm Hg). At what rate must oxygen be supplied to the burner (at a pressure of 742 mm Hg and a temperature of 26 °C)?

89. ▲ Iron forms a series of compounds of the type $Fe_x(CO)_y$. In air, these compounds are oxidized to Fe_2O_3 and CO_2 gas. After heating a 0.142-g sample of $Fe_x(CO)_y$ in air, you isolate the CO_2 in a 1.50-L flask at 25 °C. The pressure of the gas is 44.9 mm Hg. What is the empirical formula of $Fe_x(CO)_y$?

90. ▲ Group 2A metal carbonates are decomposed to the metal oxide and CO_2 on heating:

$$MCO_3(s) \rightarrow MO(s) + CO_2(g)$$

You heat 0.158 g of a white, solid carbonate of a Group 2A metal (M) and find that the evolved CO_2 has a pressure of 69.8 mm Hg in a 285-mL flask at 25 °C. Identify M.

91. One way to synthesize diborane, B_2H_6, is the reaction

$$2 \text{ NaBH}_4(s) + 2 \text{ H}_3PO_4(\ell) \rightarrow$$
$$B_2H_6(g) + 2 \text{ NaH}_2PO_4(s) + 2 \text{ H}_2(g)$$

(a) If you have 0.136 g of $NaBH_4$ and excess H_3PO_4, and you collect the B_2H_6 in a 2.75-L flask at 25 °C, what is the pressure of the B_2H_6 in the flask?
(b) A by-product of the reaction is H_2 gas. If both B_2H_6 and H_2 gas come from this reaction, what is the *total* pressure in the 2.75-L flask (after reaction of 0.136 g of $NaBH_4$ with excess H_3PO_4) at 25 °C?

92. You are given a solid mixture of $NaNO_2$ and NaCl and are asked to analyze it for the amount of $NaNO_2$ present. To do so, you allow the mixture to react with sulfamic acid, HSO_3NH_2, in water according to the equation

$$NaNO_2(aq) + HSO_3NH_2(aq) \rightarrow$$
$$NaHSO_4(aq) + H_2O(\ell) + N_2(g)$$

What is the weight percentage of $NaNO_2$ in 1.232 g of the solid mixture if reaction with sulfamic acid produces 295 mL of dry N_2 gas with a pressure of 713 mm Hg at 21.0 °C?

93. ▲ You have 1.249 g of a mixture of $NaHCO_3$ and Na_2CO_3. You find that 12.0 mL of 1.50 M HCl is required to convert the sample completely to NaCl, H_2O, and CO_2.

$$NaHCO_3(aq) + HCl(aq) \rightarrow$$
$$NaCl(aq) + H_2O(\ell) + CO_2(g)$$

$$Na_2CO_3(aq) + 2 \text{ HCl}(aq) \rightarrow$$
$$2 \text{ NaCl}(aq) + H_2O(\ell) + CO_2(g)$$

What volume of CO_2 is evolved at 745 mm Hg and 25 °C?

94. ▲ A mixture of $NaHCO_3$ and Na_2CO_3 has a mass of 2.50 g. When treated with HCl(aq), 665 mL of CO_2 gas is liberated with a pressure of 735 mm Hg at 25 °C. What is the weight percent of $NaHCO_3$ and Na_2CO_3 in the mixture? (See Study Question 93 for the reactions that occur.)

95. ▲ Many nitrate salts can be decomposed by heating. For example, blue, anhydrous copper(II) nitrate produces the gases nitrogen dioxide and oxygen when heated. In the laboratory, you find that a sample of this salt produced a 0.195-g mixture of gaseous NO_2 and O_2 with a total pressure of 725 mm Hg at 35 °C in a 125-mL flask (and black, solid CuO was left as a residue). What is the average molar mass of the gas mixture? What are the mole fractions of NO_2 and O_2 in the mixture? What amount of each gas is in the mixture? Do these amounts reflect the relative amounts of NO_2 and O_2 expected based on the balanced equation? Is it possible that the fact that some NO_2 molecules combine to give N_2O_4 plays a role?

© Cengage Learning/Charles D. Winters

Heating copper(II) nitrate produces nitrogen dioxide and oxygen gas and leaves a residue of copper(II) oxide.

96. ▲ A compound containing C, H, N, and O is burned in excess oxygen. The gases produced by burning 0.1152 g are first treated to convert the nitrogen-containing product gases into N_2, and then the resulting mixture of CO_2, H_2O, N_2, and excess O_2 is passed through a bed of $CaCl_2$ to absorb the water. The $CaCl_2$ increases in mass by 0.09912 g. The remaining gases are bubbled into water to form H_2CO_3, and this solution is titrated with 0.3283 M NaOH; 28.81 mL is required to achieve the second equivalence point. The excess O_2 gas is removed by reaction with copper metal (to give CuO). Finally, the N_2 gas is collected in a 225.0-mL flask, where it has a pressure of 65.12 mm Hg at 25 °C. In a separate experiment, the unknown compound is found to have a molar mass of 150 g/mol. What are the empirical and molecular formulas of the unknown compound?

97. You have a gas, one of the three known phosphorus–fluorine compounds (PF_3, PF_5, and P_2F_4). To find out which, you have decided to measure its molar mass.
    (a) First, you determine that the density of the gas is 5.60 g/L at a pressure of 0.971 atm and a temperature of 18.2 °C. Calculate the molar mass and identify the compound.
    (b) To check the results from part (a), you decide to measure the molar mass based on the relative rates of effusion of the unknown gas and CO_2. You find that CO_2 effuses at a rate of 0.050 mol/min, whereas the unknown phosphorus fluoride effuses at a rate of 0.028 mol/min. Calculate the molar mass of the unknown gas based on these results.

98. A 1.50 L constant volume calorimeter (Figure 5.12) contains $C_3H_8(g)$ and $O_2(g)$. The partial pressure of C_3H_8 is 0.10 atm and the partial pressure of O_2 is 5.0 atm. The temperature is 20.0 °C. A reaction occurs between the two compounds, forming $CO_2(g)$ and $H_2O(\ell)$. The heat from the reaction causes the temperature to rise to 23.2 °C.
    (a) Write a balanced chemical equation for the reaction.
    (b) How many moles of $C_3H_8(g)$ are present in the flask initially?
    (c) What is the mole fraction of $C_3H_8(g)$ in the flask before reaction?
    (d) After the reaction, the flask contains excess oxygen and the products of the reaction, $CO_2(g)$ and $H_2O(\ell)$. What amount of unreacted $O_2(g)$ remains?
    (e) After the reaction, what is the partial pressure exerted by the $CO_2(g)$ in this system?
    (f) What is the partial pressure exerted by the excess oxygen remaining after the reaction?

Summary and Conceptual Questions

The following questions may use concepts from this and previous chapters.

99. A 1.0-L flask contains 10.0 g each of O_2 and CO_2 at 25 °C.
    (a) Which gas has the greater partial pressure, O_2 or CO_2, or are they the same?
    (b) Which molecules have the greater rms speed, or are they the same?
    (c) Which molecules have the greater average kinetic energy, or are they the same?

100. If equal masses of O_2 and N_2 are placed in separate containers of equal volume at the same temperature, which of the following statements is true? If false, explain why it is false.
    (a) The pressure in the flask containing N_2 is greater than that in the flask containing O_2.
    (b) There are more molecules in the flask containing O_2 than in the flask containing N_2.

101. You have two pressure-proof steel cylinders of equal volume, one containing 1.0 kg of CO and the other containing 1.0 kg of acetylene, C_2H_2.
    (a) In which cylinder is the pressure greater at 25 °C?
    (b) Which cylinder contains the greater number of molecules?

102. Two flasks, each with a volume of 1.00 L, contain O_2 gas with a pressure of 380 mm Hg. Flask A is at 25 °C, and flask B is at 0 °C. Which flask contains the greater number of O_2 molecules?

103. ▲ State whether each of the following samples of matter is a gas. If there is not enough information for you to decide, write "insufficient information."
    (a) A material is in a steel tank at 100 atm pressure. When the tank is opened to the atmosphere, the material suddenly expands, increasing its volume by 1%.
    (b) A 1.0-mL sample of material weighs 8.2 g.
    (c) The material is transparent and pale green in color.
    (d) One cubic meter of material contains as many molecules as 1.0 m^3 of air at the same temperature and pressure.

104. Each of four flasks is filled with a different gas. Each flask has the same volume, and each is filled to the same pressure, 3.0 atm, at 25 °C. Flask A contains 116 g of air, flask B has 80.7 g of neon, flask C has 16.0 g of helium, and flask C has 160. g of an unknown gas.
    (a) Do all four flasks contain the same number of gas molecules? If not, which one has the greatest number of molecules?
    (b) How many times heavier is a molecule of the unknown gas than an atom of helium?
    (c) In which flask do the molecules have the largest kinetic energy? The highest rms speed?

105. You have two gas-filled balloons, one containing He and the other containing H_2. The H_2 balloon is twice the size of the He balloon. The pressure of gas in the H_2 balloon is 1 atm, and that in the He balloon is 2 atm. The H_2 balloon is outside in the snow (-5 °C), and the He balloon is inside a warm building (23 °C).
    (a) Which balloon contains the greater number of molecules?
    (b) Which balloon contains the greater mass of gas?

106. The sodium azide required for automobile air bags is made by the reaction of sodium metal with dinitrogen monoxide in liquid ammonia:

$$3\,N_2O(g) + 4\,Na(s) + NH_3(\ell) \rightarrow$$
$$NaN_3(s) + 3\,NaOH(s) + 2\,N_2(g)$$

    (a) You have 65.0 g of sodium, a 35.0-L flask containing N_2O gas with a pressure of 2.12 atm at 23 °C, and excess ammonia. What is the theoretical yield (in grams) of NaN_3?
    (b) Draw a Lewis structure for the azide ion. Include all possible resonance structures. Which resonance structure is most likely?
    (c) What is the shape of the azide ion?

107. If the absolute temperature of a gas doubles, by how much does the rms speed of the gaseous molecules increase?

108. ▲ Chlorine gas (Cl_2) is used as a disinfectant in municipal water supplies, although chlorine dioxide (ClO_2) and ozone are becoming more widely used. ClO_2 is a better choice than Cl_2 in this application because it leads to fewer chlorinated by-products, which are themselves pollutants.

(a) How many valence electrons are in ClO_2?

(b) The chlorite ion, ClO_2^-, is obtained by reducing ClO_2. Draw a possible electron dot structure for ClO_2^-. (Cl is the central atom.)

(c) What is the hybridization of the central Cl atom in ClO_2^-? What is the shape of the ion?

(d) Which species has the larger bond angle, O_3 or ClO_2^-? Explain briefly.

(e) Chlorine dioxide, ClO_2, a yellow-green gas, can be made by the reaction of chlorine with sodium chlorite:

$$2\ NaClO_2(s)\ +\ Cl_2(g)\ \rightarrow\ 2\ NaCl(s)\ +\ 2\ ClO_2(g)$$

Assume you react 15.6 g of $NaClO_2$ with chlorine gas, which has a pressure of 1050 mm Hg in a 1.45-L flask at 22 °C. What mass of ClO_2 can be produced?

Applying Chemical Principles

The Goodyear Blimp

Goodyear blimps are a familiar sight at sporting events. They hover at altitudes between 1000–3000 feet, providing a stable platform for television cameras. The outer surface, or envelope, of a Goodyear blimp is constructed of polyester fabric impregnated with neoprene rubber. The envelope contains the lighter-than-air gas helium. Within the fore and aft sections of the envelope are two air-filled structures called ballonets, which serve two purposes. As the blimp changes altitude, the ballonets are inflated or deflated with air to maintain a helium pressure within the envelope that is similar to the external air pressure. The ballonets also are used to keep the craft level. The pilot and passengers ride in the gondola, which is attached to the bottom of the envelope.

One of the Goodyear blimps has a gross weight of 12,840 lbs (5820 kg), and the volume of the inner envelope is 202,700 ft³ (5740 m³). The ballonets, when both fully inflated with air, occupy a total of 18,000 ft³ (510 m³) of the envelope. Helium is neither added nor removed from the envelope during operation. Loss of helium through the rubber impregnated polyester fabric is slow, at approximately 10,000 ft³ (280 m³) per month.

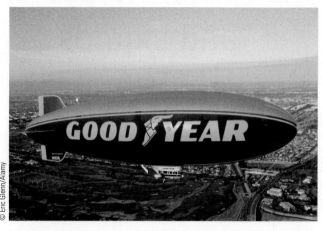

Goodyear blimp. Here the blimp flies over a packed stadium at Ohio State University.

Questions:

1. At sea level, atmospheric pressure is 1.00 atm. Calculate the density (in g/L) of helium at this pressure and 25 °C.
2. Use the data provided in Table 11.1 to calculate the density of dry air at 1.00 atm and 25 °C.
3. To stay aloft, a blimp must achieve neutral buoyancy; that is, its density must equal that of the surrounding air. The density of the blimp is its total weight (blimp, helium and air, passengers, and ballast) divided by its volume. Assume that the gross weight of the blimp includes the blimp's structure and the helium, but does not include the air in the ballonets or the weights of the passengers and ballast. If the ballonets are filled with 12,000 ft³ (340 m³) of air at 1.00 atm and 25 °C, what additional weight (of passengers and ballast) is required for neutral buoyancy?

12 Intermolecular Forces and Liquids

Geckos Can Climb Up der Waals

Just like the comic-book hero Spiderman, a little lizard, the gecko, can climb walls and hang from the ceiling.

This fact intrigued Kellar Autumn, a professor of biology at Lewis and Clark College in Portland, Oregon. An interdisciplinary team of Autumn and his students, along with scientists and engineers from Stanford University, and the Universities of California at Berkeley and Santa Barbara, realized that gecko toes are covered with an array of stiff hairlike setae. Each of these is about as long as the thickness of a human hair or about 0.1 mm long. But each seta is further divided into about 1000 even more minute pads called *spatulae*. And these are only about 200 nm wide, a distance smaller than the wavelength of visible light!

The design of gecko feet is the secret to their wall-crawling abilities. Autumn said, "We discovered that the seta is 10 times more adhesive than predicted from prior measurements on whole animals. In fact, the adhesive is so strong that a single seta can lift the weight of an ant. A million setae, which could easily fit onto the area of a dime, could lift a 45-pound child. Our discovery explains why the gecko can support its entire body weight with only a single finger."

"When the gecko attaches itself to a surface, it uncurls its toes like a party favor that uncurls when you blow into it," Autumn says. "But," he adds, "getting yourself to stick isn't really that difficult. It's getting off the surface that is the major problem. When a gecko runs, it has to attach and detach its feet 15 times a second."

But what is the "adhesive effect" that allows a gecko to climb a wall? It is an intermolecular force, called a *van der Waals force*. This is ordinarily a weak force that operates only over a very short distance. However, each spatula of the millions in each toe experiences an attractive van der Waals force with the surface. It has been calculated that the force between each spatula and the surface is about 0.4 μN (micronewtons). But given that there are millions of spatula in each toe, the total force can easily be 10 N or more.

One of the topics in this chapter is the importance of van der Waals forces. As you learn about this, think about the possibilities of using the design of gecko feet to make even more useful adhesives.

References:

1. www.kellarautumn.com/photography/Welcome.html
2. geckolab.lclark.edu/dept/AutumnLab/ Welcome.html

A Tokay gecko. This is a nocturnal arboreal gecko found from northeast India to southeast Asia.

A close-up of a gecko foot. Notice the adhesive lamellae at the end of each toe. The lamellae consist of arrays of setae.

Rows of setae. Each is about 75 μm long. Each seta is composed of millions of spatulae, the basis of the gecko's stickiness.

Image Courtesy of Professor Kellar Autumn

CHAPTER GOALS

See Chapter Goals Revisited (page 574) for Study Questions keyed to these goals.

- Describe intermolecular forces and their effects.
- Understand the importance of hydrogen bonding.
- Understand the properties of liquids.

I n the last chapter, we studied gases, one of the states of matter. Most of the time we were able to assume that the attractions between the molecules, intermolecular forces, were negligible and so we could ignore them. At the end of that chapter, however, we saw that at high pressures and/or low temperatures this assumption did not work as well; we had to consider intermolecular forces when dealing with the nonideal behavior of gases. In the other two states of matter, the liquid and solid states, intermolecular forces play a major role. In order to describe these states of matter, we will first need to explore the different types and relative strengths of intermolecular forces.

The primary objectives of this chapter are to examine the intermolecular forces that allow molecules to interact and then to look at liquids, a state of matter that results from such interactions. You will find this a useful chapter because it explains, among other things, why your body is cooled when you sweat and why ice can float on liquid water, a property shared by very few other substances.

12.1 States of Matter and Intermolecular Forces

The kinetic-molecular theory of gases (◀ Section 11.6) assumes that gas molecules or atoms are widely separated and that these particles can be considered to be independent of one another. Consequently, we can relate the properties of gases under most conditions by the ideal gas law equation, $PV = nRT$ (◀ Equation 11.4). In real gases, however, there are intermolecular forces between molecules. If these forces are strong enough, the gas can condense to a liquid and eventually to a solid. The existence of intermolecular forces in liquids makes the picture more complex, and it is not possible to create a simple "ideal liquid equation."

How different are the states of matter at the particulate level? We can get a sense of this by comparing the volumes occupied by equal numbers of molecules of a material in different states. Figure 12.1a shows a flask containing about 300 mL of liquid nitrogen. If all of the liquid were allowed to evaporate, the gaseous nitrogen, at 1 atm and room temperature, would fill a large balloon (more than 200 L). A great amount of space exists between molecules in a gas, whereas in liquids the molecules are much closer together.

The increase in volume when converting liquids to gases is strikingly large. In contrast, no dramatic change in volume occurs when a solid is converted to a liquid. Figure 12.1b shows the same amount of liquid and solid benzene, C_6H_6, side by side.

OWL

Sign in to OWL at **www.cengage.com/ owl** to view tutorials and simulations, develop problem-solving skills, and complete online homework assigned by your professor.

go Chemistry

Download mini lecture videos for key concept review and exam prep from OWL or purchase them from **www.cengagebrain.com**

Nitrogen gas

Liquid nitrogen

(a) When a 300-mL sample of liquid nitrogen evaporates, it will produce more than 200 L of gas at 25 °C and 1.0 atm. In the liquid phase, the molecules of N_2 are close together; in the gas phase, they are far apart.

© Cengage Learning/Charles D. Winters

Liquid benzene   Solid benzene

(b) The same volume of liquid benzene, C_6H_6, is placed in two test tubes, and one tube *(right)* is cooled, freezing the liquid. The solid and liquid states have almost the same volume, showing that the molecules are packed together almost as tightly in the liquid state as they are in the solid state.

© Cengage Learning/Charles D. Winters

FIGURE 12.1 Contrasting gases, liquids, and solids.

They are not appreciably different in volume. This means the molecules in the liquid are packed together about as tightly as the molecules in the solid phase.

Intermolecular forces influence chemistry in many ways:

- They are directly related to properties such as melting point, boiling point, and the energy needed to convert a solid to a liquid or a liquid to a vapor.
- They are important in determining the solubility of gases, liquids, and solids in various solvents.
- They are crucial in determining the structures of biologically important molecules such as DNA and proteins.

Bonding in ionic compounds depends on the electrostatic forces of attraction between oppositely charged ions (▶ Section 13.4). Similarly, the intermolecular forces attracting one molecule to another are electrostatic. The energy associated with the attractive forces between the ions in ionic compounds are usually in the range of 700 to 1100 kJ/mol, and most covalent bond energies are in the range of 100 to 400 kJ/mol (◀ Table 8.9). As a rough guideline, intermolecular forces are generally less than about 15% of the values of covalent bond energies. Nonetheless, these interactions can have a profound effect on molecular properties.

Collectively, forces between molecules are called **van der Waals forces**, and these include the attractive and repulsive forces between

- molecules with permanent dipoles (dipole-dipole forces, Section 12.3)
- polar molecules and nonpolar ones (dipole-induced dipole forces, Section 12.4)
- nonpolar molecules (induced dipole-induced dipole forces, also known as *London forces*, Section 12.4)

12.2 Interactions between Ions and Molecules with a Permanent Dipole

Module 17: Intermolecular Forces
covers concepts in this section.

Many molecules are polar, a result of the polarity of individual bonds and a nonsymmetrical geometry (Section 8.7). Conceptually, we can view polar molecules as having positive and negative ends. What happens when a polar molecule encounters an ionic compound? The negative end of the dipole is attracted to a positive cation (Figure 12.2). Similarly, the positive end of the dipole is attracted to a negative anion. Forces of attraction between a positive or negative ion and polar molecules—ion–dipole forces—are less than those for ion–ion attractions, but they are greater than other types of forces between molecules, whether polar or nonpolar.

Ion–dipole attractions can be evaluated using Coulomb's law (◀ Equation 2.3), which informs us that the force of attraction between two charged objects depends

Table 12.1 Radii and Enthalpies of Hydration of Alkali Metal Ions

Cation	Ion Radius (pm)	Enthalpy of Hydration (kJ/mol)
Li^+	78	−515
Na^+	98	−405
K^+	133	−321
Rb^+	149	−296
Cs^+	165	−263

water surrounding
a cation

water surrounding
an anion

FIGURE 12.2 Ion–dipole interactions. When an ionic compound such as NaCl is placed in water, the polar water molecules surround the cations and anions.

on the product of their charges divided by the square of the distance between them (Section 2.7). Therefore, when a polar molecule encounters an ion, the attractive forces depend on three factors:

- The distance between the ion and the dipole. The closer they are, the stronger the attraction.
- The charge on the ion. The higher the ion charge, the stronger the attraction.
- The magnitude of the dipole. The greater the magnitude of the dipole, the stronger the attraction.

The formation of hydrated ions in aqueous solution is one of the most important examples of the interaction between an ion and a polar molecule (Figure 12.2). The enthalpy change associated with the hydration of ions—which is generally called the *enthalpy of solvation* or, for ions in water, the *enthalpy of hydration*—is substantial. The solvation enthalpy for an individual ion cannot be measured directly, but values can be estimated. For example, the hydration of sodium ions is described by the following reaction:

$$Na^+(g) + water \rightarrow Na^+(aq) \qquad \Delta_{hydration}H° = -405 \text{ kJ/mol}$$

The enthalpy of hydration depends on the charge of the ion and on $1/d$, where d is the distance between the center of the ion and the oppositely charged "pole" of the dipole.

The effect of ion radius is illustrated by the enthalpies of hydration of the alkali metal cations in Table 12.1, and the effects of radius *and* charge by $\Delta_{hydration}H°$ for Mg^{2+}, Li^+, and K^+ (Figure 12.3). It is interesting to compare these values with the enthalpy of hydration of the H^+ ion, estimated to be −1090 kJ/mol. This extraordinarily large value is due to the tiny size of the H^+ ion.

● **Coulomb's Law** The force of attraction between oppositely charged particles depends directly on the product of their charges and inversely on the square of the distance (d) between the ions ($1/d^2$) (◀ Equation 2.3, page 76). The energy of the attraction is also proportional to the charge product, but it is inversely proportional to the distance between them ($1/d$).

EXAMPLE 12.1 Hydration Energy

Problem Explain why the enthalpy of hydration of Na^+ (−405 kJ/mol) is more exothermic than that of Cs^+ (−263 kJ/mol), whereas that of Mg^{2+} is much more exothermic (−1922 kJ/mol) than that of either Na^+ or Cs^+.

What Do You Know? You know the ion charges and their sizes (◀ Figure 7.12): Na^+ = 98 pm, Cs^+ = 165 pm, and Mg^{2+} = 79 pm.

Strategy The energy associated with ion–dipole attractions depends directly on the size of the ion charge and the magnitude of the dipole, and inversely on the distance between them. Here the water dipole is a constant factor, so the answer depends on ion size and charge.

Solution From the ion sizes, we can predict that the distances between the center of the positive charge of the ion and the water dipole will vary in this order: $Mg^{2+} < Na^+ < Cs^+$. The hydration energy varies in the reverse order (with the hydration energy of Mg^{2+} being the most negative value). Notice also that Mg^{2+} has a 2+ charge, whereas the other ions are 1+. The greater charge on Mg^{2+} leads to a much greater force of ion–dipole attraction than for the other two ions, which have only a 1+ charge. As a result, the hydration energy for Mg^{2+} is much more negative than for the other two ions.

FIGURE 12.3 Enthalpy of hydration. The energy evolved when an ion is hydrated depends on the dipole moment of water, the ion charge, and the distance d between centers of the ion and the polar water molecule. The distance d increases as ion size increases.

K^+, $r = 133$ pm
$\Delta H = -321$ kJ/mol

Li^+, $r = 78$ pm
$\Delta H = -515$ kJ/mol

Mg^{2+}, $r = 79$ pm
$\Delta H = -1922$ kJ/mol

Increasing force of attraction; more exothermic enthalpy of hydration

Thinking about Your Answer The charge difference between Mg^{2+} and the other ions has a much greater effect than the size difference. The values for hydration energies for the three ions are $Mg^{2+}(aq) = -1922$ kJ/mol (from Table 12.1), $Na^+(aq) = -405$ kJ/mol, and $Cs^+(aq) = -263$ kJ/mol.

Check Your Understanding

Which should have the more negative hydration energy, F^- or Cl^-? Explain briefly.

REVIEW & CHECK FOR SECTION 12.2

Which should have the more negative enthalpy of hydration?

(a) $MgCl_2$ (b) $AlCl_3$

12.3 Interactions between Molecules with a Dipole

Dipole–Dipole Forces

When a polar molecule encounters another polar molecule, of the same or a different kind, the positive end of one molecule is attracted to the negative end of the other polar molecule. This is called a **dipole-dipole interaction**.

For polar molecules, dipole–dipole attractions influence, among other things, the evaporation of a liquid and the condensation of a gas (Figure 12.4). An energy change occurs in both processes. Evaporation requires the input of energy, specifically the enthalpy of vaporization ($\Delta_{vap}H°$) [see Sections 5.3 and 12.6]. The value for the enthalpy of vaporization has a positive sign, indicating that evaporation is an endothermic process. The enthalpy change for the condensation process—the reverse of evaporation—has a negative value.

The greater the forces of attraction between molecules in a liquid, the greater the energy that must be supplied to separate them. Thus, we expect polar compounds to have a higher value for their enthalpy of vaporization than nonpolar compounds with similar molar masses. For example, notice in Table 12.2 that $\Delta_{vap}H°$ for polar molecules is greater than for nonpolar molecules of approximately the same size and mass.

The boiling point of a liquid also depends on intermolecular forces of attraction. As the temperature of a substance is raised, its molecules gain kinetic energy. Eventually, when the boiling point is reached, the molecules have sufficient kinetic

A CLOSER LOOK

Hydrated Salts

Solid salts with waters of hydration are common. The formulas of these compounds are given by appending a specific number of water molecules to the end of the formula, as in $BaCl_2 \cdot 2\ H_2O$. Sometimes, the water molecules simply fill in empty spaces in a crystalline lattice, but often the cation in these salts is directly bound to water molecules. For example, the compound $CrCl_3 \cdot 6\ H_2O$ is better written as $[Cr(H_2O)_4Cl_2]Cl \cdot 2\ H_2O$. Four of the six water molecules are bound to the Cr^{3+} ion by ion–dipole attractive forces; the remaining two water molecules are in the lattice. Common examples of hydrated salts are listed in the table.

© Cengage Learning/Charles D. Winters

Compound	Common Name	Uses
$Na_2CO_3 \cdot 10\ H_2O$	Washing soda	Water softener
$Na_2S_2O_3 \cdot 5\ H_2O$	Hypo	Photography
$MgSO_4 \cdot 7\ H_2O$	Epsom salt	Cathartic, dyeing and tanning
$CaSO_4 \cdot 2\ H_2O$	Gypsum	Wallboard
$CuSO_4 \cdot 5\ H_2O$	Blue vitriol	Biocide

Hydrated cobalt(II) chloride, $CoCl_2 \cdot 6\ H_2O$. In the solid state, the compound is best described by the formula $[Co(H_2O)_4Cl_2] \cdot 2\ H_2O$. The cobalt(II) ion is surrounded by four water molecules and two chloride ions in an octahedral arrangement. In water, the ion is completely hydrated, now being surrounded by six water molecules. Cobalt(II) ions and water molecules interact by ion–dipole forces. This is an example of a coordination compound, a class of compounds discussed in detail in Chapter 22.

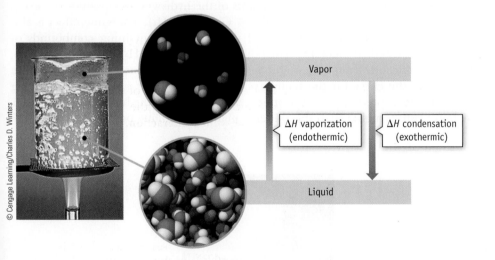

© Cengage Learning/Charles D. Winters

Vapor

ΔH vaporization (endothermic)

ΔH condensation (exothermic)

Liquid

FIGURE 12.4 Evaporation at the molecular level. Energy must be supplied to separate molecules in the liquid state against intermolecular forces of attraction.

energy to escape the forces of attraction of their neighbors. For molecules of similar molar mass, the greater the polarity, the higher the temperature required for the liquid to boil. In Table 12.2, you see that the boiling point for polar ICl is greater than that for nonpolar Br_2, for example.

Intermolecular forces also influence solubility. A qualitative observation on solubility is that "like dissolves like." In other words, polar molecules are likely to dissolve in a polar solvent, and nonpolar molecules are likely to dissolve in a nonpolar solvent (Figure 12.5) (◀ Chapter 8). The converse is also true; that is, it is unlikely that polar molecules will dissolve in nonpolar solvents or that nonpolar molecules will dissolve in polar solvents.

For example, water and ethanol (C_2H_5OH) can be mixed in any ratio to give a homogeneous mixture. In contrast, water does not dissolve in gasoline to an appreciable extent. The difference in these two situations is that ethanol and water are

Table 12.2 Molar Masses, Boiling Points, and $\Delta_{vap}H°$ of Nonpolar and Polar Substances

	Nonpolar				Polar		
	M (g/mol)	BP (°C)	$\Delta_{vap}H°$ (kJ/mol)		M (g/mol)	BP (°C)	$\Delta_{vap}H°$ (kJ/mol)
N_2	28	−196	5.57	CO	28	−192	6.04
SiH_4	32	−112	12.10	PH_3	34	−88	14.06
GeH_4	77	−90	14.06	AsH_3	78	−62	16.69
Br_2	160	59	29.96	ICl	162	97	—

polar molecules, whereas the hydrocarbon molecules in gasoline (e.g., octane, C_8H_{18}) are nonpolar. The water–ethanol interactions are strong enough that the energy expended in pushing water molecules apart to make room for ethanol molecules is compensated for by the energy of attraction between the two kinds of polar molecules. In contrast, water–hydrocarbon attractions are weak. The hydrocarbon molecules cannot disrupt the stronger water–water attractions.

Hydrogen Bonding

Hydrogen fluoride, water, ammonia, and many other compounds with O—H and N—H bonds have exceptional properties, and we can see that by looking at the boiling points for hydrogen compounds of elements in Groups 4A through 7A in Figure 12.6. Generally, the boiling points of related compounds increase with molar mass, and this trend is seen in the boiling points of the hydrogen compounds of Group 4A elements, for example ($CH_4 < SiH_4 < GeH_4 < SnH_4$). The same effect is also operating for the heavier molecules of the hydrogen-containing compounds of Group 5A, 6A, and 7A elements. The boiling points of NH_3, H_2O, and HF, however, deviate significantly from what might be expected based on molar mass alone. If we extrapolate the curve for the boiling points of H_2Te, H_2Se, and H_2S, the boiling point of water is predicted to be around −90 °C. However, the boiling point of water is almost 200 °C higher than this value! Similarly, the boiling points of NH_3 and HF

(a) Ethylene glycol ($HOCH_2CH_2OH$), a polar compound used as antifreeze in automobiles, dissolves in water.

(b) Nonpolar motor oil (a hydrocarbon) dissolves in nonpolar solvents such as gasoline or CCl_4. It will not dissolve in a polar solvent such as water, however. Commercial spot removers use nonpolar solvents to dissolve oil and grease from fabrics.

FIGURE 12.5 "Like dissolves like."

FIGURE 12.6 The boiling points of some simple hydrogen compounds. The effect of hydrogen bonding is apparent in the unusually high boiling points of H_2O, HF, and NH_3. (Also, notice that the boiling point of HCl is somewhat higher than expected based on the data for HBr and HI. It is apparent that some degree of hydrogen bonding also occurs in liquid HCl.)

are much higher than would be expected based on molar mass. Because the temperature at which a substance boils depends on the attractive forces between molecules, the extraordinarily high boiling points of H_2O, HF, and NH_3 indicate strong intermolecular attractions.

Why should H_2O, NH_3, and HF have such strong intermolecular forces? The answer starts with the electronegativities of N (3.0), O (3.5), and F (4.0), which are among the highest of all the elements, whereas the electronegativity of hydrogen is much lower (2.2). This large difference in electronegativity means that N—H, O—H, and F—H bonds are very polar. In bonds between H and N, O, or F, the more electronegative element takes on a significant negative charge (◄ Figure 8.11), and the hydrogen atom acquires a significant positive charge.

There is an unusually strong attraction between an electronegative atom with a lone pair of electrons (most often, an N, O, or F atom in another molecule or even in the same molecule) and the hydrogen atom of the N—H, O—H, or F—H bond. This type of interaction is known as a **hydrogen bond**. Hydrogen bonds are an extreme form of dipole–dipole interaction where one atom involved is always H and the other atom is highly electronegative, most often O, N, or F. A hydrogen bond can be represented as

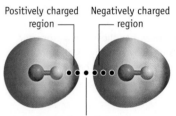

Positively charged region   Negatively charged region

Hydrogen bond

Hydrogen bonding between HF molecules. The partially negative F atom of one HF molecule interacts through hydrogen bonding with a neighboring HF molecule. (Red regions of the molecule are negatively charged, whereas blue regions are positively charged. For more on electrostatic potential surfaces, ◄ page 378.)

$$\underset{X-H}{\overset{\delta^-\quad\delta^+}{\bullet\!-\!\bullet}} - - - \underset{Y-H}{\overset{\delta^-\quad\delta^+}{\bullet\!-\!\bullet}}$$

The hydrogen atom becomes a bridge between the two electronegative atoms X and Y, and the dashed line represents the hydrogen bond. The most pronounced effects of hydrogen bonding occur where both X and Y are N, O, or F. Energies associated with most hydrogen bonds involving these elements are in the range of 5 to 30 kJ/mol.

Types of Hydrogen Bonds [X—H - - - :Y]

N—H - - - :N—	O—H - - - :N—	F—H - - - :N—
N—H - - - :O—	O—H - - - :O—	F—H - - - :O—
N—H - - - :F—	O—H - - - :F—	F—H - - - :F—

Hydrogen bonding has important implications for any property of a compound that is influenced by intermolecular forces of attraction. For example,

● **The Importance of H Atom Charge Density in Hydrogen Bonding** Not only are the bonds between H and O, N, and F significantly polar, but the H atom has an extraordinarily small radius. This means that the partial charge on the H atom is concentrated in a small volume; that is, it has a high charge density. The result is that it is strongly attractive to the negative charge on a neighboring molecule.

FIGURE 12.7 Hydrogen bonding. Two acetic acid molecules can interact through hydrogen bonds. This photo shows partly solid glacial acetic acid. Notice that the solid is denser than the liquid, a property shared by virtually all substances, the notable exception being water.

hydrogen bonding affects the structures of molecular solids. In solid acetic acid, CH_3CO_2H, for example, two molecules are joined to one another by hydrogen bonding (Figure 12.7).

EXAMPLE 12.2   The Effect of Hydrogen Bonding

Problem Ethanol, CH_3CH_2OH, and dimethyl ether, CH_3OCH_3, have the same molecular formula but a different arrangement of atoms. Predict which of these compounds has the higher boiling point.

ethanol, CH_3CH_2OH dimethyl ether, CH_3OCH_3

What Do You Know? You know the molecular structures for the two compounds and that the compound with the stronger intermolecular forces will have the higher boiling point.

Strategy Inspect the structure of each molecule to decide whether each is polar and, if polar, whether hydrogen bonding is possible.

Solution Although these two compounds have identical masses, they have different structures. Ethanol possesses a polar O—H group and so can participate in hydrogen bonding. Dimethyl ether is a polar molecule, and the O atom has a partial negative charge. However, no H atom is attached to the O atom. Thus, there is no opportunity for hydrogen bonding in dimethyl ether. We can predict, therefore, that intermolecular forces will be larger in ethanol than in dimethyl ether and that ethanol will have the higher boiling point.

polar O–H bond

$$CH_3CH_2-\ddot{O}: \cdots H - \ddot{O}:$$
$$\qquad\quad | \qquad\qquad |$$
$$\qquad\quad H \qquad\quad CH_2CH_3$$

hydrogen bonding in ethanol, CH_3CH_2OH

Think about Your Answer According to the literature, ethanol boils at 78.3 °C, whereas dimethyl ether has a boiling point of −24.8 °C, more than 100 °C lower. Under similar conditions (room temperature and 1 atm pressure), dimethyl ether is a gas, whereas ethanol is a liquid.

Check Your Understanding

Using structural formulas, describe the hydrogen bonding between methanol (CH_3OH) molecules. What physical properties of methanol are likely to be affected by hydrogen bonding?

Hydrogen Bonding and the Unusual Properties of Water

One of the most striking differences between our planet and others in our solar system is the presence of large amounts of water on Earth. Three fourths of the planet is covered by oceans; the polar regions are vast ice fields; and even soil and rocks hold large amounts of water. Although we tend to take water for granted, almost no other substance behaves in a similar manner. Water's unique features are a consequence of the ability of H_2O molecules to cling tenaciously to one another by hydrogen bonding.

The unusually high intermolecular forces of attraction between water molecules are a result of the fact that each water molecule can participate in *four* hydrogen bonds. An individual water molecule has two polar O—H bonds and two lone pairs. Both hydrogen atoms are available to hydrogen bond to oxygen atoms in adjacent water molecules. In addition, the oxygen lone pairs can participate in hydrogen bonding to the hydrogen atoms in two other water molecules (Figure 12.8a).

Earth from space. Three quarters of the earth is covered by water, and vast amounts of water are locked in the polar ice caps. Many of the unique properties of water depend on the presence of hydrogen bonding in water.

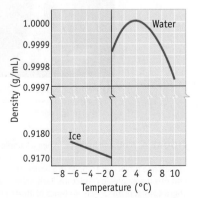

(a) Electrostatic potential surfaces for two water molecules shows the hydrogen bond involving the negatively charged O atom of one molecule and the positively charged H atom of a neighboring molecule.

(b) The oxygen atom of a water molecule attaches itself to two other water molecules by hydrogen bonds. Notice that the four groups that surround an oxygen atom are arranged as a distorted tetrahedron. Each oxygen atom is covalently bonded to two hydrogen atoms and hydrogen bonded to hydrogen atoms from two other molecules. The hydrogen bonds are longer than the covalent bonds.

(c) In ice, the structural unit shown in part (b) is repeated in the crystalline lattice. This computer-generated structure shows a small portion of the extensive lattice. Notice the six-member, hexagonal rings. The vertices of each hexagon are O atoms, and each side is composed of two oxygen atoms with a hydrogen atom in between. One of the oxygen atoms is covalently bonded to the hydrogen atom, and the other is attracted to it by a hydrogen bond.

FIGURE 12.8 Hydrogen bonding in water and the structure of ice.

The result, seen particularly in ice, is a tetrahedral arrangement for the hydrogen atoms around each oxygen, involving two covalently bonded hydrogen atoms and two hydrogen-bonded hydrogen atoms.

As a consequence of the regular arrangement of water molecules linked by hydrogen bonding, ice has an open-cage structure with lots of empty space (Figure 12.8c). The result is that ice has a density about 10% less than that of liquid water, which explains why ice floats. (In contrast, virtually all other solids sink in their liquid phase.) We can also see in this structure that the oxygen atoms are arranged at the corners of puckered, hexagonal rings. Snowflakes are always based on six-sided figures (◀ page 68), a reflection of this internal molecular structure of ice.

When ice melts at 0 °C, the regular structure imposed on the solid state by hydrogen bonding breaks down, and a relatively large increase in density occurs (Figure 12.9). Another surprising thing occurs when the temperature of liquid water is raised from 0 °C to 4 °C: The density of water increases. For almost every other substance known, density decreases as the temperature is raised. Once again, hydrogen bonding is the reason for water's seemingly odd behavior. At a temperature just above the melting point, some of the water molecules continue to cluster in ice-like arrangements, which require extra space. As the temperature is raised from 0 °C to 4 °C, the final vestiges of the ice structure disappear, and the volume contracts further, giving rise to the increase in density. Water's density reaches a maximum at about 4 °C. From this point, the density declines with increasing temperature in the normal fashion.

Because of the way that water's density changes as the temperature approaches the freezing point, lakes do not freeze from the bottom up in the winter. When lake water cools with the approach of winter, its density increases, the cooler water sinks, and the warmer water rises. This "turn over" process continues until all the water reaches 4 °C, the maximum density. (This is the way oxygen-rich water moves to the lake bottom to restore the oxygen used during the summer and nutrients are brought to the top layers of the lake.) As the temperature decreases further, the

FIGURE 12.9 The temperature dependence of the densities of ice and water.

CASE STUDY

Hydrogen Bonding & Methane Hydrates: Opportunities and Problems

Cold water under pressure begins to form complex solid structures at temperatures above 273 K. These are unstable networks of hydrogen-bonded water molecules with large, open cavities. If a small "guest" molecule of the right size is present, however, it can be trapped in the cavities, and the network does not collapse to form the usual ice structure. This phenomenon is most often observed when cold water is saturated with methane, and the result is methane hydrate (Figure A).

Methane hydrates have been known for years, but interest in them has increased because vast deposits of hydrate were recently discovered deep within sediments on the floor of the oceans. It is estimated that global methane hydrate deposits contain approximately 10^{13} tons of carbon, or about twice the combined amount in all known reserves of coal, oil, and natural gas. Methane hydrate is also an efficient energy storehouse; a cubic meter of methane hydrate releases about 160 cubic meters of methane gas.

If methane is to be captured from hydrates and used as a fuel, there are problems to be solved. One significant problem is how to bring commercially useful quantities to the surface from deep in the ocean. Yet another is the possibility of a large, uncontrolled release of methane. Methane is a very effective greenhouse gas, so the release of a significant quantity into the atmosphere could damage the earth's climate. (Indeed, some believe a massive release of methane from hydrates about 55 million years ago led to significant global warming.)

In May 2010 methane hydrates may have led to an environmental catastrophe. The Deepwater Horizon rig used for drilling for oil in very deep water in the Gulf of Mexico was destroyed by a fire triggered by a methane explosion. There is a strong suggestion that the ultimate cause may have been the explosive release of the gas from methane hydrates under the sea bed. The methane shot to the surface through the drilling pipe and was ignited. This then led to an uncontrolled leak of oil from the well, followed by attempts to shut it down. The first attempt to cap the well was to lower a 100-ton steel and concrete dome over the well, which would contain the oil and allow it to be pumped to the surface (Figure B). This was a failure because methane coming from the rupture formed a slush of methane hydrate. The "crystals" of hydrate were trapped in the dome, increased its buoyancy, and prevented it from being anchored to the sea floor.

© Chris Graythen/Getty Images

FIGURE B A containment dome used to control the oil leak in the Gulf of Mexico, May, 2010. The first containment dome that was tried did not work because methane hydrate prevented it from being anchored to the sea floor.

The realization that methane hydrates may be the cause of a significant accident will surely lead to reassessment of oil exploration in very deep water. But it may also renew interest in using more accessible methane hydrates as an energy source. For example, in Alaska's North Slope there are recoverable deposits of 2400 billion cubic meters of methane, roughly the equivalent of four years of U.S. natural gas production And there are extensive deposits in other places in the world. Indeed, the deepest oceans may be a better source of methane than of oil.

Questions:

1. In a methane hydrate the methane molecule is trapped in a cage of water molecules. Describe the structure: (a) how many water molecules make up the cage, (b) how many hydrogen bonds are involved, and (c) how many faces does the cage have?

2. One cubic meter of methane hydrate has 164 m^3 of CH_4 (at STP). If you burn the methane in 1.00 m^3 of hydrate [to give $CO_2(g)$ and $H_2O(g)$], how much energy can be obtained?

Answers to these questions are available in Appendix N

Reference:

A good article on methane hydrates is: E. Suess, G. Bohrmann, J. Greinert, and E. Lausch, *Scientific American*, November 1999, pp. 76–83.

Jim Pinkston and Laura Stern/U.S. Geological Survey/ *Science News*/ 11/9/96

(a) Methane hydrate burns as methane gas escapes from the solid hydrate.

(b) Methane hydrate consists of a lattice of water molecules with methane molecules trapped in the cavity.

FIGURE A Methane hydrate. When a sample is brought to the surface from the depths of the ocean, the methane oozes out of the solid, and the gas readily burns. The structure of the solid methane hydrate consists of methane molecules trapped in a lattice of water molecules. The lattice shown here is a common structural unit of a more complex structure. Each point of the lattice shown here is an O atom of an H_2O molecule. The edges consist of an O—H—O series of atoms connected by a hydrogen bond and covalent bond. (Other, more complex structural units are known.) Such structures are often called "clathrates."

colder water stays on the top of the lake, because water cooler than 4 °C is less dense than water at 4 °C. With further heat loss, ice can then begin to form on the surface, floating there and protecting the underlying water and aquatic life from further heat loss.

Extensive hydrogen bonding is also the origin of the extraordinarily high heat capacity of water. Although liquid water does not have the regular structure of ice, hydrogen bonding still occurs. When the temperature is raised, there must be a significant input of energy to disrupt the intermolecular forces and to raise the temperature even a small amount.

The high specific heat capacity of water is, in large part, why oceans and lakes have such an enormous effect on weather. In autumn, when the temperature of the air is lower than the temperature of the ocean or lake, water transfers energy as heat to the atmosphere, moderating the drop in air temperature. Furthermore, so much energy is available to be transferred for each degree drop in temperature that the decline in water temperature is gradual. For this reason, the temperature of the ocean or of a large lake is generally higher than the average air temperature until late in the autumn.

REVIEW & CHECK FOR SECTION 12.3

1. In which of the following substances would hydrogen bonding be expected?

    (a) CH_4 (b) CH_3OH (c) H_3COCH_3 (d) $H_2C{=}CH_2$

2. Which compound has the strongest intermolecular forces?

    (a) H_2O (b) H_2S (c) H_2Se (d) H_2Te

12.4 Intermolecular Forces Involving Nonpolar Molecules

Many important molecules such as O_2, N_2, and the halogens are not polar. Why, then, does O_2 dissolve in polar water? Why can the N_2 of the atmosphere be liquefied? Some intermolecular forces must be acting between O_2 and water and between N_2 molecules, but what is their nature?

Dipole-Induced Dipole Forces

Polar molecules such as water can induce, or create, a dipole in molecules that do not have a permanent dipole. To see how this can happen, picture a polar water molecule approaching a nonpolar molecule such as O_2 (Figure 12.10). The electron cloud of an isolated (gaseous) O_2 molecule is symmetrically distributed between the two oxygen atoms. As the negative end of the polar H_2O molecule approaches, however, the O_2 electron cloud becomes distorted. In this process, the O_2 molecule itself becomes polar; that is, a dipole is *induced* in the otherwise nonpolar O_2 molecule. The result is that H_2O and O_2 molecules are now attracted to one another, albeit only weakly. Oxygen can dissolve in water because a force of attraction exists between water's permanent dipole and the induced dipole in O_2. Chemists refer to such interactions as **dipole-induced dipole interactions**.

The process of inducing a dipole is called **polarization**, and the degree to which the electron cloud of an atom or a molecule can be distorted depends on the **polarizability** of that atom or molecule. The electron cloud of an atom or molecule with a large, extended electron cloud such as I_2 can be polarized more readily than the electron cloud in a much smaller atom or molecule, such as He or H_2, in which the valence electrons are close to the nucleus and more tightly held. In general, for an analogous series of substances, say the halogens or alkanes (such as CH_4, C_2H_6, C_3H_8, and so on), the higher the molar mass, the greater the polarizability of the molecule.

(a) A polar molecule such as water can induce a dipole in nonpolar O_2 by distorting the molecule's electron cloud.

The dipole of water induces a dipole in O_2 by distorting the O_2 electron cloud.

(b) Nonpolar I_2 dissolves in polar ethanol (C_2H_5OH). The intermolecular force involved is a dipole-induced dipole force.

Polar ethanol (C_2H_5OH) induces a dipole in nonpolar I_2.

© Cengage Learning/Charles D. Winters

FIGURE 12.10 Dipole-induced dipole interaction.

The solubilities of common gases in water illustrate the effect of interactions between a dipole and an induced dipole. In Table 12.3, you see a trend to higher solubility with increasing mass of the nonpolar gas. As the molar mass of the gas increases, the polarizability of the electron cloud increases and the strength of the dipole-induced dipole interaction increases.

London Dispersion Forces: Induced Dipole-Induced Dipole Forces

Iodine, I_2, is a solid and not a gas around room temperature and pressure, illustrating that nonpolar molecules must also experience intermolecular forces. An indication of the magnitude of these forces is provided by the enthalpy of vaporization of the substance at its boiling point. The data in Table 12.4 suggest that these forces can range from very weak (N_2, O_2, and CH_4 with low enthalpies of vaporization and very low boiling points) to more substantial (I_2 and benzene).

To understand how two nonpolar molecules can attract each other, recall that the electrons in atoms or molecules are in a state of constant motion. When two atoms or nonpolar molecules approach each other, attractions or repulsions between their electrons and nuclei can lead to distortions in their electron clouds (Figure 12.11).

Table 12.3 **The Solubility of Some Gases in Water***

	Molar Mass (g/mol)	Solubility at 20 °C (g gas/100 g water)†
H_2	2.01	0.000160
N_2	28.0	0.00190
O_2	32.0	0.00434

*Data taken from J. Dean: *Lange's Handbook of Chemistry*. 14th Ed., pp. 5.3–5.8, New York, McGraw-Hill, 1992.

†Measured under conditions where pressure of gas + pressure of water vapor = 760 mm Hg.

Table 12.4 **Enthalpies of Vaporization and Boiling Points of Some Nonpolar Substances**

	$\Delta_{vap}H°$ (kJ/mol)	Element/Compound BP (°C)
N_2	5.57	−196
O_2	6.82	−183
CH_4 (methane)	8.2	−161.5
Br_2	29.96	+58.8
C_6H_6 (benzene)	30.7	+80.1
I_2	41.95	+185

A CLOSER LOOK

Hydrogen Bonding in Biochemistry

It is arguable that our world is what it is because of hydrogen bonding in water and in biochemical systems. Perhaps the most important occurrence is in DNA and RNA where the organic bases adenine, cytosine, guanine, and thymine (in DNA) or uracil (in RNA) are attached to sugar-phosphate chains (**Figure A**). The chains in DNA are joined by the pairing of bases, adenine with thymine and guanine with cytosine.

Figure B illustrates the hydrogen bonding between adenine and thymine. These models show that the molecules naturally fit together to form a six-sided ring, where two of the six sides involve hydrogen bonds. One side consists of a N · · · H—N grouping, and the other side is N—H · · · O. Here, the electrostatic potential surfaces show that the N atoms of adenine and the O atoms of thymine bear partial negative charges, and the H atoms of the N—H groups bear a positive charge. These charges and the geometry of the bases lead to these very specific interactions.

The fact that base pairing through hydrogen bonding leads to the joining of the sugar-phosphate chains of DNA, and to the double helical form of DNA, was first recognized by James Watson and Francis Crick on the basis of experimental work by Rosalind Franklin and Maurice Wilkins in the 1950s. Determination of the DNA structure was a key development in the molecular biology revolution in the last part of the 20th century. (See page 387 for more on these scientists.)

FIGURE A Hydrogen bonding in DNA. With the four bases in DNA, the usual pairings are adenine with thymine and guanine with cytosine. This pairing is promoted by hydrogen bonding.

FIGURE B Hydrogen bonding between adenine and thymine. Electrostatic potential surfaces depict the hydrogen bonding interactions between adenine and thymine. The polar N—H bond on one molecule can hydrogen bond to an electronegative N or O atom in a neighboring molecule.

Two nonpolar atoms or molecules (depicted as having an electron cloud that has a time-averaged spherical shape).

Momentary attractions and repulsions between nuclei and electrons in neighboring molecules lead to induced dipoles.

Correlation of the electron motions between the two atoms or molecules (which are now polar) leads to a lower energy and stabilizes the system.

FIGURE 12.11 Induced dipole-induced dipole interactions or London dispersion forces. Momentary attractions and repulsions between nuclei and electrons create induced dipoles and lead to a net stabilization due to attractive forces. Nonpolar Br_2 and I_2 both exemplify such forces. They are a liquid and a solid, respectively, indicating that there are forces between the molecules sufficient to cause them to be in a condensed phase.

© Cengage Learning/Charles D. Winters

Br_2 I_2

That is, dipoles can be induced momentarily in neighboring atoms or molecules, and these *induced* dipoles lead to intermolecular attractions. The intermolecular force of attraction in liquids and solids composed of nonpolar molecules is an **induced dipole-induced dipole force**. Chemists often call them **London dispersion forces**. *Dispersion forces actually arise between all molecules, both nonpolar and polar, but dispersion forces are the only intermolecular forces between nonpolar molecules.*

EXAMPLE 12.3　Intermolecular Forces

Problem Suppose you have a mixture of solid iodine, I_2, and the liquids water and carbon tetrachloride (CCl_4). What intermolecular forces exist between each possible pair of compounds?

What Do You Know? Iodine, I_2, is a nonpolar molecule composed of large iodine atoms. It has an extensive electron cloud and is polarizable. CCl_4 is a symmetrical tetrahedral molecule and is not polar. Polar H_2O could be involved in hydrogen bonding with other water molecules or with other molecules with highly polar groups.

Strategy You know whether each substance is polar or nonpolar so you need only to determine the types of intermolecular forces that can exist between the different pairs.

Solution Nonpolar iodine, I_2, is easily polarized, and iodine can interact with polar water molecules by dipole-induced dipole forces. Nonpolar carbon tetrachloride can interact with nonpolar iodine only by dispersion forces. Water and CCl_4 could interact by dipole-induced dipole forces.

Think about Your Answer The photos here show the result of mixing these three compounds. Iodine does dissolve to a small extent in water to give a brown solution. When this brown solution is added to a test tube containing CCl_4, the liquid layers do not mix. (Polar water does not dissolve in nonpolar CCl_4.) (Notice the more dense CCl_4 layer [$d = 1.58$ g/mL] is underneath the less dense water layer.) When the test tube is shaken, nonpolar I_2 is extracted into nonpolar CCl_4, as evidenced by the disappearance of the color of I_2 in the water layer (top) and the appearance of the purple I_2 color in the CCl_4 layer (bottom).

Nonpolar I_2
Polar H_2O
Nonpolar CCl_4

Shake the test tube

Polar H_2O
Nonpolar CCl_4 and I_2

© Cengage Learning/Charles D. Winters

Check Your Understanding

You mix water, CCl_4, and hexane ($CH_3CH_2CH_2CH_2CH_2CH_3$). What type of intermolecular forces can exist between each pair of these compounds?

REVIEW & CHECK FOR SECTION 12.4

1. In which of the following solids are the component particles attracted to each other only by induced dipole-induced dipole forces?

   (a) ice

   (b) solid NH_3 at low temperature

   (c) NaCl

   (d) I_2

2. Which of the following compounds has the largest intermolecular forces?

   (a) pentane, C_5H_{12}

   (b) hexane, C_6H_{14}

   (c) heptane, C_7H_{16}

   (d) octane, C_8H_{18}

Table 12.5 Summary of Intermolecular Forces (in descending order of strength)

Type of Interaction	Factors Responsible for Interaction	Example
Ion–dipole	Ion charge, magnitude of dipole	$Na^+ \ldots H_2O$
Hydrogen bonding, X—H . . . :Y	Very polar X—H bond and atom Y with lone pair of electrons (where X and Y = F, N, O). Typical energy = 20 kJ/mol.	$H_2O \ldots H_2O$
Dipole–dipole . . . $(CH_3)_2O$	Dipole moment (depends on electronegativities and molecular structure). Typical energy = 5–20 kJ/mol.	$(CH_3)_2O \ldots (CH_3)_2O$
Dipole-induced dipole	Dipole moment of polar molecule and polarizability of nonpolar molecule. Typical energy <2 kJ/mol.	$H_2O \ldots I_2$
Induced dipole-induced dipole (London dispersion forces)	Polarizability	$I_2 \ldots I_2$

12.5 A Summary of van der Waals Intermolecular Forces

Van der Waals intermolecular forces involve molecules that are polar or those in which polarity can be induced (Table 12.5). It is important to recognize that

- several types of intermolecular forces contribute to the overall ability of a molecule (Figure 12.12) to interact with another of the same or different kind.
- induced dipole-induced dipole forces can be quite substantial, even in polar molecules (Figure 12.12).

EXAMPLE 12.4   Intermolecular Forces

Problem Decide which are the most important intermolecular forces between each of the following and compare the strength of the interactions: (a) between molecules in liquid methane, CH_4; (b) between molecules of water and methanol (CH_3OH) in a mixture of these species; and (c) between molecules of bromine and water in a mixture of these compounds.

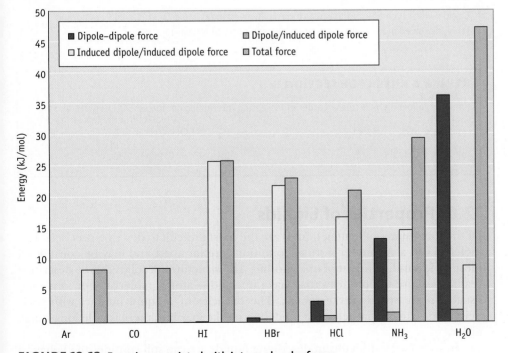

FIGURE 12.12 Energies associated with intermolecular forces.

Hydrogen bonding involving methanol (CH_3OH) and water.

What Do You Know? Methane, CH_4, is a symmetrical, tetrahedral molecule and so is not polar. Both water and methanol are polar, and both have $-OH$ groups that can be involved in hydrogen bonding. Bromine, Br_2, is nonpolar, but it is a large molecule and has an extensive, polarizable electron cloud.

Strategy Determine the type of interaction possible between pairs of molecules based on the structure and characteristics of each species. To evaluate their relative importance, consult Table 12.5 on relative strengths of interactions.

Solution

(a)   Methane is not polar. Therefore, the only way methane molecules can interact with one another is through induced dipole-induced dipole forces (dispersion forces).

(b)   Both water and methanol are polar, and both have an $O-H$ bond. They therefore interact through the special dipole–dipole force called hydrogen bonding as well as dispersion forces.

(c)   Nonpolar molecules of bromine, Br_2, and polar water molecules interact through dipole-induced dipole forces (and dispersion forces). (This is similar to the I_2–ethanol interaction in Figure 12.10.)

In order of increasing strength, the likely order of interactions is

$$\text{liquid } CH_4 \;<\; H_2O \text{ and } Br_2 \;<\; H_2O \text{ and } CH_3OH$$

Think about Your Answer The fact that CH_4 is a liquid only at very low temperatures suggests it has the weakest attractive forces. We would expect the highest forces of attraction to be those involving hydrogen bonding. Thus, the strongest interaction is expected to be between H_2O and CH_3OH, whereas the weakest interaction occurs between two nonpolar molecules of CH_4.

Check Your Understanding

Decide which type of intermolecular force is involved in (a) liquid O_2; (b) liquid CH_3OH; and (c) N_2 dissolved in H_2O. Place the interactions in order of increasing strength.

REVIEW & CHECK FOR SECTION 12.5

Rank the following molecules in order of increasing intermolecular forces: SO_2, CH_3OH, and He.

(a) $He < SO_2 < CH_3OH$ (c) $CH_3OH < He < SO_2$

(b) $He < CH_3OH < SO_2$ (d) $SO_2 < CH_3OH < He$

12.6 Properties of Liquids

Of the three states of matter, liquids are the most difficult to describe precisely. The molecules in a gas under normal conditions are far apart and may be considered more or less independent of one another. The structures of solids can be described readily because the particles that make up solids—atoms, molecules, or ions—are usually in an orderly arrangement. The particles of a liquid interact with their neighbors, like the particles in a solid, but, unlike in solids, there is little long-range order.

In spite of the difficulty in describing liquids, we can still consider the behavior of liquids at the molecular level. Here we want to look further at the process of va-

CASE STUDY

A Pet Food Catastrophe

In early 2007 pet owners all over the United States reported pets becoming seriously ill or dying from eating apparently adulterated food. Dogs and cats developed symptoms of kidney failure, which included loss of appetite, vomiting, extreme thirst, and lethargy. Many ultimately died. Round, greenish-brown kidney stones were also found to be clogging the kidneys of stricken pets. This was mysterious at first, but, within two months, chemists and toxicologists traced the ailments to two compounds in the pet food: melamine and cyanuric acid.

Melamine   Cyanuric acid

Melamine is used to make plastics and fertilizers. It is not approved for food use. Cyanuric acid is used to stabilize chlorine in swimming pools and to sanitize food processing equipment. The acid is sometimes formed as a by-product in the manufacture of melamine, so melamine samples can be contaminated with cyanuric acid.

But why was melamine in pet food in the first place? A U.S. manufacturer of pet food, which also supplied other companies that in turn distributed the food under their brand names, had purchased wheat gluten from a supplier in China. Wheat gluten is a concentrated vegetable protein used as a thickener and binder in pet food. The speculation is that the Chinese supplier had added melamine to the wheat gluten to raise the apparent nitrogen content. When products are tested for protein content, any nitrogen found is assumed to come from protein. Adding melamine is an inexpensive way to deceive

Image copyright © Eric Isselée. Used under license from Shutterstock.com

the buyer into thinking that the product contains a higher percentage of protein.

Melamine and cyanuric acid by themselves are not toxic, but when they are present together they are. The reason is hydrogen bonding! Mixing melamine and cyanuric acid in water produces insoluble crystals of melamine cyanurate.

The structure above shows only the hydrogen bonding between two molecules. How-

ever, additional hydrogen bonding to other molecules is possible, and the result is further aggregation of cyanuric acid and melamine to form an insoluble material.

The behavior of the hydrogen-bonded complex depends on pH. In the stomach, a very acidic medium with a low pH, hydrogen bonding does not occur between these compounds, and the compounds are soluble. The body seeks to get rid of these chemicals through the kidneys, however, and there the compounds encounter a near neutral pH. Hydrogen bonding can then occur, and the molecules aggregate to form solid melamine cyanurate.

The adulteration of food with melamine was not limited to the pet food industry. In 2008, a year after the pet food adulteration scandal, melamine was found in milk products including infant formula. Several thousand babies in China became ill, having suffered acute kidney failure, and several fatalities resulted. These babies had been fed formula milk contaminated with melamine.

Questions:

1. Calculate the weight percent of nitrogen in melamine and cyanuric acid and compare this value to the average percent of nitrogen in protein (14%).
2. An infant formula was found to have 0.14 ppm melamine. (ppm stands for parts per million. This means, for example, there is 1 g of a substance per million grams of the product.) What mass of melamine is there in a package of infant formula with a mass of 454 g (one pound)?

Answers to these questions are available in Appendix N.

---

porization, at the vapor pressure of liquids, at their boiling points and critical properties, and at surface tension, capillary action, and viscosity.

Vaporization and Condensation

Vaporization or evaporation is the process in which a substance in the liquid state becomes a gas. In this process, molecules escape from the liquid surface and enter the gaseous state.

To understand evaporation, we have to look at molecular energies. Molecules in a liquid have a range of energies (Figure 12.13) that resembles the distribution of energies for molecules of a gas (◄ Figure 11.14). As with gases, the average energy for molecules in a liquid depends only on temperature: The higher the

FIGURE 12.13 The distribution of energy among molecules in a liquid sample. T_2 is a higher temperature than T_1, and at the higher temperature, there are more molecules with an energy greater than E.

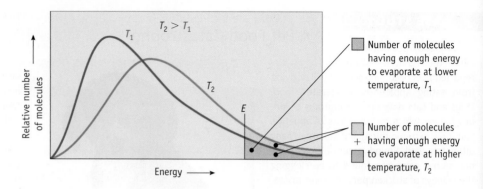

temperature, the higher the average energy and the greater the relative number of molecules with high kinetic energy. In a sample of a liquid, at least a few molecules have more kinetic energy than the potential energy of the intermolecular attractive forces holding the liquid molecules to one another. If these high-energy molecules are at the surface of the liquid and if they are moving in the right direction, they can break free of their neighbors and enter the gas phase (Figure 12.14).

Vaporization is an endothermic process because energy is required to overcome the intermolecular forces of attraction holding the molecules together. The energy required to vaporize a sample is often given as the standard **molar enthalpy of vaporization**, $\Delta_{vap}H°$ (in units of kilojoules per mole; see Tables 12.4 and 12.6 and Figure 12.4).

$$\text{liquid} \xrightarrow[\substack{\text{energy absorbed} \\ \text{by liquid}}]{\text{vaporization}} \text{vapor} \qquad \Delta_{vap}H° = \text{molar enthalpy of vaporization}$$

A molecule in the gas phase can transfer some of its kinetic energy by colliding with slower gaseous molecules and solid objects. If this molecule loses sufficient energy and comes in contact with the surface of the liquid, it can reenter the liquid phase in the process called **condensation**.

$$\text{vapor} \xrightarrow[\substack{\text{energy released} \\ \text{by vapor}}]{\text{condensation}} \text{liquid} \qquad -\Delta_{vap}H° = \text{molar enthalpy of condensation}$$

Condensation is the reverse of vaporization and so is an exothermic process. Energy is transferred to the surroundings. *The enthalpy change for condensation is equal but opposite in sign to the enthalpy of vaporization.* For example, the enthalpy change for the vaporization of 1.00 mol of water at 100 °C is +40.7 kJ. On condensing 1.00 mol of water vapor to liquid water at 100 °C, the enthalpy change is −40.7 kJ.

In the discussion of intermolecular forces, we pointed out the relationship between the $\Delta_{vap}H°$ values for various substances and the temperatures at which they

FIGURE 12.14 Evaporation. Some molecules at the surface of a liquid have enough energy to escape the attractions of their neighbors and enter the gaseous state. At the same time, some molecules in the gaseous state can reenter the liquid.

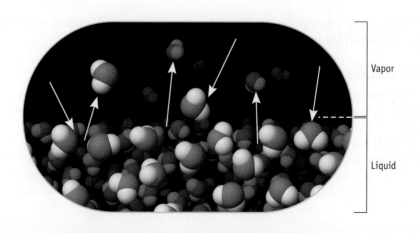

Table 12.6 Molar Enthalpies of Vaporization and Boiling Points for Common Substances*

Compound	Molar Mass (g/mol)	$\Delta_{vap}H°$ (kJ/mol)†	Boiling Point (°C) (Vapor Pressure = 760 mm Hg)
Polar Compounds			
HF	20.0	25.2	19.7
HCl	36.5	16.2	−84.8
HBr	80.9	19.3	−66.4
HI	127.9	19.8	−35.6
NH_3	17.0	23.3	−33.3
H_2O	18.0	40.7	100.0
SO_2	64.1	24.9	−10.0
Nonpolar Compounds			
CH_4 (methane)	16.0	8.2	−161.5
C_2H_6 (ethane)	30.1	14.7	−88.6
C_3H_8 (propane)	44.1	19.0	−42.1
C_4H_{10} (butane)	58.1	22.4	−0.5
Monatomic Elements			
He	4.0	0.08	−268.9
Ne	20.2	1.7	−246.1
Ar	39.9	6.4	−185.9
Xe	131.3	12.6	−108.0
Diatomic Elements			
H_2	2.0	0.90	−252.9
N_2	28.0	5.6	−195.8
O_2	32.0	6.8	−183.0
F_2	38.0	6.6	−188.1
Cl_2	70.9	20.4	−34.0
Br_2	159.8	30.0	58.8

*Data taken from D. R. Lide: *Basic Laboratory and Industrial Chemicals*, Boca Raton, FL, CRC Press, 1993.
†$\Delta_{vap}H°$ is measured at the normal boiling point of the liquid.

boil (Table 12.6). Both properties reflect the attractive forces between particles in the liquid. The boiling points of nonpolar liquids (e.g., the hydrocarbons, atmospheric gases, and the halogens) increase with increasing atomic or molecular mass, a reflection of increased intermolecular dispersion forces. The alkanes (such as methane) listed in Table 12.6 show this trend clearly. Similarly, the boiling points and enthalpies of vaporization of the heavier hydrogen halides (HX, where X = Cl, Br, and I) increase with increasing molecular mass. For these molecules, dispersion forces and ordinary dipole–dipole forces account for their intermolecular attractions (Figure 12.12). Because dispersion forces become increasingly important with increasing mass, the enthalpies of vaporization and the boiling points are in the order HCl < HBr < HI. Among the hydrogen halides HF is the exception; the high enthalpy of vaporization and boiling point are a direct result of extensive hydrogen bonding.

⊙WL   INTERACTIVE EXAMPLE 12.5   Enthalpy of Vaporization

Problem You put 925 mL of water (about 4 cupsful) in a pan at 100 °C, and the water slowly evaporates. How much energy is transferred as heat to vaporize all the water?

What Do You Know? You know the volume of water and wish to know the energy required for evaporation. Three pieces of information are needed to solve this problem:

1. $\Delta_{vap}H°$ for water = +40.7 kJ/mol at 100 °C.

2. Density of water at 100 °C = 0.958 g/cm³.

3. Molar mass of water = 18.02 g/mol.

Strategy Map 12.5

PROBLEM
Calculate the **energy** required to **evaporate** water sample.

↓

DATA/INFORMATION
- Enthalpy of vaporization at boiling point
- Volume of water

STEP 1. Use **density** and **molar mass** to convert **volume** of water to **amount** (mol).

Amount of sample

STEP 2. Multiply **amount** of sample by **molar enthalpy**.

Energy required (kJ) to evaporate sample at boiling point

FIGURE 12.15 Rainstorms release an enormous quantity of energy. When water vapor condenses, energy is transferred to the surroundings. The enthalpy of condensation of water is large, so a large quantity of energy is released in a rainstorm.

Strategy $\Delta_{vap}H°$ has units of kilojoules per mole, so you first must find the mass of water and then the amount. Finally, use the enthalpy of vaporization (in kJ/mol) to calculate the energy required as heat.

Solution Using the density of water at this temperature, we find that 925 mL of water is equivalent to 886 g, and this mass is in turn equivalent to 49.2 mol of water.

$$925 \text{ mL} \left(\frac{0.958 \text{ g}}{1 \text{ mL}} \right) \left(\frac{1 \text{ mol}}{18.02 \text{ g}} \right) = 49.2 \text{ mol H}_2\text{O}$$

Therefore, the amount of energy required is

$$49.2 \text{ mol H}_2\text{O} \left(\frac{40.7 \text{ kJ}}{\text{mol}} \right) = 2.00 \times 10^3 \text{ kJ}$$

Think about Your Answer 2000 kJ is equivalent to the energy obtained by burning about 60 g of carbon.

Check Your Understanding

The molar enthalpy of vaporization of methanol, CH_3OH, is 35.2 kJ/mol at 64.6 °C. How much energy is required to evaporate 1.00 kg of methanol at 64.6 °C?

Liquid water is an exceptional substance; an enormous amount of energy as heat is required to convert liquid water to water vapor. This fact is important to your own physical well-being. When you exercise vigorously, your body responds by sweating. Energy from your body is transferred to sweat in the process of evaporation, and your body is cooled.

Enthalpies of vaporization and condensation of water also play a role in weather (Figure 12.15). For example, if enough water condenses from the air to fall as an inch of rain on an acre of ground, the energy released exceeds 2.0×10^8 kJ! This is equivalent to about 50 tons of exploded dynamite, the energy released by a small bomb.

Vapor Pressure

If you put some water in an open beaker, it will eventually evaporate completely. Air movement and gas diffusion remove the water vapor from the vicinity of the liquid surface, so many water molecules are not able to return to the liquid.

If you put water in a sealed flask (Figure 12.16), however, the water vapor cannot escape, and some will recondense to form liquid water. Eventually, the masses of liquid and vapor in the flask remain constant. This is another example of a **dynamic equilibrium** (◄ page 116).

$$\text{liquid} \rightleftharpoons \text{vapor}$$

FIGURE 12.16 Vapor pressure. A volatile liquid is placed in an evacuated flask *(left)*. At the beginning, no molecules of the liquid are in the vapor phase. After a short time, however, some of the liquid evaporates, and the molecules now in the vapor phase exert a pressure. The pressure of the vapor measured when the liquid and the vapor are in equilibrium is called the *equilibrium vapor pressure (right)*.

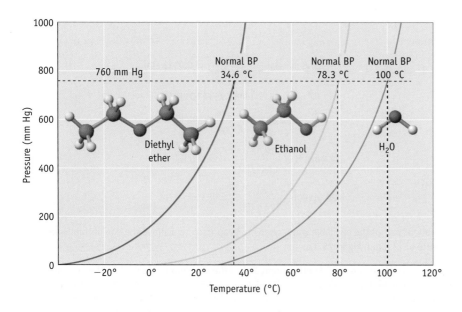

FIGURE 12.17 Vapor pressure curves for diethyl ether [(C_2H_5)$_2$O], ethanol (C_2H_5OH), and water. Each curve represents conditions of T and P at which the two phases, liquid and vapor, are in equilibrium. These compounds exist as liquids for temperatures and pressures to the left of the curve and as gases under conditions to the right of the curve.

Molecules still move continuously from the liquid phase to the vapor phase and from the vapor phase back to the liquid phase. At equilibrium, the rate at which molecules move from liquid to vapor is the same as the rate at which they move from vapor to liquid; thus, there is no net change in the masses of the two phases.

When a liquid–vapor equilibrium has been established, the equilibrium vapor pressure (often just called the vapor pressure) can be measured. The **equilibrium vapor pressure** of a substance is the pressure exerted by the vapor in equilibrium with the liquid phase. Conceptually, the vapor pressure of a liquid is a measure of the tendency of its molecules to escape from the liquid phase and enter the vapor phase at a given temperature. This tendency is referred to qualitatively as the **volatility** of the compound. The higher the equilibrium vapor pressure at a given temperature, the more volatile the substance.

As described previously (Figure 12.13), the distribution of molecular energies in the liquid phase is a function of temperature. At a higher temperature, more molecules have sufficient energy to escape the surface of the liquid. The equilibrium vapor pressure must, therefore, increase with temperature.

It is useful to represent vapor pressure as a function of temperature. Figure 12.17 shows the vapor pressure curves for several liquids as a function of temperature. *All points along the vapor pressure versus temperature curves represent conditions of pressure and temperature at which liquid and vapor are in equilibrium.* For example, at 60 °C the vapor pressure of water is 149 mm Hg. (Vapor pressures of water at various temperatures are given in Appendix G.) If water is placed in an evacuated flask that is maintained at 60 °C, liquid water will evaporate until the pressure exerted by the water vapor is 149 mm Hg (assuming enough water is in the flask so that some liquid remains when equilibrium is reached).

⏀WL INTERACTIVE EXAMPLE 12.6 Using Vapor Pressure

Problem You place 2.00 L of water in an open container in your dormitory room; the room has a amount of 4.25×10^4 L. You seal the room and wait for the water to evaporate. Will all of the water evaporate at 25 °C? (At 25 °C the density of water is 0.997 g/mL, and its vapor pressure is 23.8 mm Hg.)

What Do You Know? You know the volume of water, the density of the water, the volume of the room, and the vapor pressure of the water at 25 °C.

Strategy One approach to solving this problem is to use the ideal gas law to calculate the amount of liquid water that must evaporate for the vapor produced to exert a pressure of 23.8 mm Hg in a volume of 4.25×10^4 L at 25 °C. Next, determine the volume of liquid water from the amount and compare the answer to the 2.00 L of water available.

Strategy Map 12.6

PROBLEM

Will a sample of water **evaporate completely** in a given volume at known *T*?

↓

DATA/INFORMATION

- Volume of water
- Density of water
- Vapor pressure at *T*

↓

STEP 1. Use **ideal gas law** to calculate *amount of water vapor* needed to have a **P** equal to vapor pressure in *given volume*.

↓

Amount of water (mol) in the vapor phase to achieve **P** equal to the vapor pressure at given **T**.

↓

STEP 2. Convert **amount of water** to a **volume of liquid water** using *molar mass* and *density*.

↓

Volume of water that evaporated to achieve the **vapor pressure** at given **T**.

↓

STEP 3. **Compare** *volume of water evaporated* to *volume available before evaporation*.

↓

Volume of water that evaporated is *less* than that available.
Some liquid water remains.

Solution

$$P = 23.8 \text{ mm Hg} \left(\frac{1 \text{ atm}}{760 \text{ mm Hg}} \right) = 0.0313 \text{ atm}$$

$$n = \frac{PV}{RT} = \frac{(0.0313 \text{ atm})(4.25 \times 10^4 \text{ L})}{\left(0.082057 \dfrac{\text{L} \cdot \text{atm}}{\text{K} \cdot \text{mol}} \right)(298 \text{ K})} = 54.4 \text{ mol}$$

$$54.4 \text{ mol H}_2\text{O} \left(\frac{18.02 \text{ g}}{1 \text{ mol H}_2\text{O}} \right) = 980. \text{ g H}_2\text{O}$$

$$980. \text{ g H}_2\text{O} \left(\frac{1 \text{ mL}}{0.997 \text{ g H}_2\text{O}} \right) = 983 \text{ mL}$$

Only about half of the available water needs to evaporate to achieve the equilibrium water vapor pressure of 23.8 mm Hg at 25 °C.

Think about Your Answer Another approach to the problem is to calculate the pressure exerted if all of the water had evaporated. The answer would be 48.4 mm Hg. This is about twice the equilibrium vapor pressure at 25 °C, so only about half of the water needs to evaporate, as you found in the other approach.

Check Your Understanding

Examine the vapor pressure curve for ethanol in Figure 12.17.

(a) What is the approximate vapor pressure of ethanol at 40 °C?

(b) Are liquid and vapor in equilibrium when the temperature is 60 °C and the pressure is 600 mm Hg? If not, does liquid evaporate to form more vapor, or does vapor condense to form more liquid?

Vapor Pressure, Enthalpy of Vaporization, and the Clausius–Clapeyron Equation

Plotting the vapor pressure for a liquid at a series of temperatures results in a curved line (Figure 12.17). However, the German physicist R. Clausius (1822–1888) and the Frenchman B. P. E. Clapeyron (1799–1864) showed that, for a pure liquid, a linear relationship exists between the reciprocal of the Kelvin temperature $(1/T)$ and the logarithm of the vapor pressure $(\ln P)$ (Figure 12.18).

$$\ln P = -(\Delta_{\text{vap}}H^\circ/RT) + C \tag{12.1}$$

Here, $\Delta_{\text{vap}}H^\circ$ is the enthalpy of vaporization of the liquid, R is the ideal gas constant $(8.314472 \text{ J/K} \cdot \text{mol})$, and C is a constant characteristic of the liquid in question. This equation, now called the **Clausius–Clapeyron equation**, provides a method of obtaining values for $\Delta_{\text{vap}}H^\circ$. The equilibrium vapor pressure of a liquid can be measured at several different temperatures, and the logarithm of these pressures is plotted versus $1/T$. The result is a straight line with a slope of $-\Delta_{\text{vap}}H^\circ/R$. For example, plotting data for water (Figure 12.18), we find the slope of the line is -4.90×10^3 K^{-1}, which gives $\Delta_{\text{vap}}H^\circ = 40.7 \text{ kJ/mol}$.

As an alternative to plotting $\ln P$ versus $1/T$, we can write the following equation that allows us to calculate $\Delta_{\text{vap}}H^\circ$ if we know the vapor pressure of a liquid at two different temperatures.

$$\ln P_2 - \ln P_1 = \left[\frac{-\Delta_{\text{vap}}H^\circ}{RT_2} + C \right] - \left[\frac{-\Delta_{\text{vap}}H^\circ}{RT_1} + C \right]$$

This can be simplified to

$$\ln \frac{P_2}{P_1} = -\frac{\Delta_{\text{vap}}H^\circ}{R} \left[\frac{1}{T_2} - \frac{1}{T_1} \right] \tag{12.2}$$

Ethylene glycol has a vapor pressure of 14.9 mm Hg (P_1) at 373 K (T_1), and a vapor pressure of 49.1 mm Hg (P_2) at 398 K (T_2). Using Equation 12.2, we can calculate the enthalpy of vaporization, 59.0 kJ/mol.

$$\ln\left(\frac{49.1 \text{ mm Hg}}{14.9 \text{ mm Hg}}\right) = -\frac{\Delta_{vap}H^\circ}{0.0083145 \text{ kJ/K}\cdot\text{mol}}\left[\frac{1}{398 \text{ K}} - \frac{1}{373 \text{ K}}\right]$$

$$1.192 = -\frac{\Delta_{vap}H^\circ}{0.0083145 \text{ kJ/K}\cdot\text{mol}}\left(-\frac{0.000168}{K}\right)$$

$$\Delta_{vap}H^\circ = 59.0 \text{ kJ/mol}$$

Boiling Point

If you have a beaker of water open to the atmosphere, the atmosphere presses down on the surface. If enough energy is added, a temperature is eventually reached when the vapor pressure of the liquid equals the atmospheric pressure. At this temperature, bubbles of the liquid's vapor will not be crushed by the atmospheric pressure. Instead, bubbles can rise to the surface, and the liquid boils (Figure 12.19).

The boiling point of a liquid is the temperature at which its vapor pressure is equal to the external pressure. If the external pressure is 760 mm Hg, this temperature is called the **normal boiling point**. This point is highlighted on the vapor pressure curves for the substances in Figure 12.17.

The normal boiling point of water is 100 °C, and in a great many places in the United States, water boils at or near this temperature. If you live at higher altitudes, however, such as in Salt Lake City, Utah, where the barometric pressure is about 650 mm Hg, water will boil at a noticeably lower temperature. The curve in Figure 12.17 shows that a pressure of 650 mm Hg corresponds to a boiling temperature of about 95 °C. Food, therefore, has to be cooked a little longer in Salt Lake City to achieve the same result as in New York City at sea level.

Critical Temperature and Pressure

On first thought, it might seem that vapor pressure–temperature curves (such as shown in Figure 12.17) should continue upward without limit, but this is not so. Instead, when a high enough temperature and pressure are reached, the interface between the liquid and the vapor disappears at the **critical point**. The temperature at which this occurs is the **critical temperature, T_c**, and the corresponding pressure is the **critical pressure, P_c** (Figure 12.20). The substance that exists under these conditions is called a **supercritical fluid**. It is like a gas under such a high pressure that its density resembles that of a liquid, while its viscosity (resistance to flow) remains close to that of a gas.

Consider what the substance looks like at the molecular level under these conditions. The molecules have been forced almost as close together as they are in the liquid state, but, unlike the situation in liquids, each molecule in the supercritical fluid has enough kinetic energy to exceed the forces holding molecules together.

For most substances, the critical point is at a very high temperature and pressure (Table 12.7). Water, for instance, has a critical temperature of 374 °C and a critical pressure of 217.7 atm.

Supercritical fluids can have beneficial uses, such as the ability to extract caffeine from coffee beans. As described in *A Closer Look: Supercritical CO₂ and Green Chemistry* (page 574), this property can also be useful in our movement to "green chemistry."

Surface Tension, Capillary Action, and Viscosity

Molecules in the interior of a liquid interact with molecules all around them (Figure 12.21). In contrast, molecules on the surface of a liquid are affected only by those molecules located at or below the surface layer. This leads to a net inward force of attraction on the surface molecules, contracting the surface area and making the liquid behave as though it had a skin. The toughness of this skin is measured

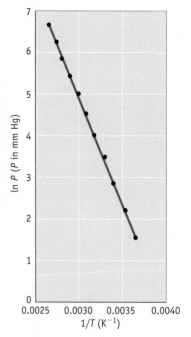

FIGURE 12.18 Clausius–Clapeyron equation. When the natural logarithm of the vapor pressure (ln P) of water at various temperatures (T) is plotted against 1/T, a straight line is obtained. The slope of the line equals $-\Delta_{vap}H^\circ/R$. Values of T and P for water are from Appendix G.

FIGURE 12.19 Vapor pressure and boiling. When the vapor pressure of the liquid equals the atmospheric pressure, bubbles of vapor begin to form within the body of liquid, and the liquid boils.

The separate phases of CO_2 are seen through the window in a high-pressure vessel.

As the sample warms and the pressure increases, the meniscus becomes less distinct.

Once the critical T and P are reached, distinct liquid and vapor phases are no longer in evidence. This homogeneous phase is "supercritical CO_2."

FIGURE 12.20 Critical temperature and pressure for CO_2. The pressure versus temperature curve representing equilibrium conditions for liquid and gaseous carbon dioxide ends at the critical point; above that temperature and pressure, water becomes a supercritical fluid.

TABLE 12.7 Critical Temperatures and Pressures for Common Compounds*

Compound	T_c (°C)	P_c (atm)
CH_4 (methane)	−82.6	45.4
C_2H_6 (ethane)	32.3	49.1
C_3H_8 (propane)	96.7	41.9
C_4H_{10} (butane)	152.0	37.3
CCl_2F_2 (CFC-12)	111.8	40.9
NH_3	132.4	112.0
H_2O	374.0	217.7
CO_2	30.99	72.8
SO_2	157.7	77.8

*Data taken from D. R. Lide: *Basic Laboratory and Industrial Chemicals,* Boca Raton, FL, CRC Press, 1993.

by its **surface tension**—the energy required to break through the surface or to disrupt a liquid drop and spread the material out as a film. Surface tension causes water drops to be spheres and not little cubes, for example (Figure 12.22a), because a sphere has a smaller surface area than any other shape of the same volume.

Capillary action is closely related to surface tension. When a small-diameter glass tube is placed in water, the water rises in the tube, just as water rises in a piece of paper in water (Figures 12.22b and 12.22c). Because polar Si—O bonds are present on the surface of glass, polar water molecules are attracted to the surface by **adhesive forces**. These forces are strong enough that they can compete with the **cohesive forces** between the water molecules themselves. Thus, some water molecules can adhere to the walls; other water molecules are attracted to them by cohesive forces and build a "bridge" back into the liquid. The adhesive forces between the water and the glass are great enough that the water level rises in the tube. The rise will continue until the attractive forces—adhesion between water and glass, cohesion between water molecules—are balanced by the force of gravity pulling down on the water column. These forces lead to the characteristic concave, or downward-curving, meniscus seen with water in a test tube (Figure 12.22c).

In some liquids, cohesive forces (high surface tension) are much greater than adhesive forces with glass. Mercury is one example. Mercury does not climb the walls of a glass capillary. In fact, when it is in a glass tube, mercury will form a convex, or upward-curving, meniscus (Figure 12.22c).

One other important property of liquids in which intermolecular forces play a role is **viscosity**, the resistance of liquids to flow. When you turn over a glassful of water, it empties quickly. In contrast, it takes much more time to empty a glassful of olive oil or honey. Olive oil consists of molecules with long chains of carbon atoms,

Water molecules on the surface are not completely surrounded by other water molecules.

Water molecules under the surface are completely surrounded by other water molecules.

FIGURE 12.21 **Intermolecular forces in a liquid.** Forces acting on a molecule at the surface of a liquid are different than those acting on a molecule in the interior of a liquid.

and it is about 70 times more viscous than ethanol, a small molecule with only two carbons and one oxygen. Longer chains have greater intermolecular forces because there are more atoms to attract one another, with each atom contributing to the total force. Honey (a concentrated aqueous solution of sugar molecules), however, is also a viscous liquid, even though the size of the molecules is fairly small. In this case, the sugar molecules have numerous —OH groups. These lead to greater forces of attraction due to hydrogen bonding.

REVIEW & CHECK FOR SECTION 12.6

1. *Vapor pressure:* Suppose 0.50 g of pure water is sealed in an evacuated 5.0-L flask and the whole assembly is heated to 60 °C. Will any liquid water be left in the flask or does all of the water evaporate?

   (a)   liquid is left   (b)   all the water evaporates

2. *Using the Clausius-Clapeyron equation:* Calculate the enthalpy of vaporization of diethyl ether, $(C_2H_5)_2O$ (Figure 12.17). This compound has vapor pressures of 57.0 mm Hg and 534 mm Hg at −22.8 °C and 25.0 °C, respectively.

   (a)   29.0 kJ/mol   (b)   122 kJ/mol   (c)   2.44 kJ/mol

FIGURE 12.22 **Adhesive and cohesive forces.**

(a) A series of photographs showing the different stages when a water drop falls. The drop was illuminated by a strobe light of 5-ms duration. (The total time for this sequence was 0.05 second.) Water droplets take a spherical shape because of surface tension.

(b) Capillary action. Polar water molecules are attracted to the — OH bonds in paper fibers, and water rises in the paper. If a line of ink is placed in the path of the rising water, the different components of the ink are attracted differently to the water and paper and are separated in a process called paper chromatography.

(c) Water (top layer) forms a concave meniscus, while mercury (bottom layer) forms a convex meniscus. The different shapes are determined by the adhesive forces of the molecules of the liquid with the walls of the tube and the cohesive forces between molecules of the liquid.

S.R. Nagel, James Frank Institute, University of Chicago

© Cengage Learning/Charles D. Winters

© Cengage Learning/Charles D. Winters

Supercritical CO₂ and Green Chemistry

Much has been written recently about CO₂, particularly its role as a greenhouse gas. But there are useful sides to this molecule: one is as a solvent when its physical state is a supercritical fluid.

Carbon dioxide is widely available, essentially nontoxic, nonflammable, and inexpensive. Importantly, it is relatively easy to reach its critical temperature of 30.99 °C and critical pressure of 72.8 atm. In the supercritical state, the molecules are in close proximity, so the substance behaves as a liquid. However, because the kinetic energy of CO₂ molecules is greater than the energy associated with the forces of attraction between molecules, supercritical CO₂ has some properties of a gas. As a result, the supercritical fluid has the density of a liquid but the low viscosity of a gas.

One use of supercritical CO₂ is to extract caffeine from coffee. Coffee beans are treated with steam to bring the caffeine to the surface. The beans are then immersed in supercritical CO₂, which selectively dissolves the caffeine but leaves intact the compounds that give flavor to coffee. (Decaffeinated coffee contains less than 3% of the original caffeine.) The solution of caffeine in supercritical CO₂ is poured off, and the CO₂ is evaporated, trapped, and reused.

Supercritical CO₂ is also being used more and more as a replacement for organic solvents used to clean parts during the manufacture of electronic devices and for

Image courtesy of SiOx Machines AB

Liquid CO₂ inside high-pressure chamber

dry cleaning clothing. This is an important advance because the organic solvents used for these purposes are often atmospheric pollutants.

Solvents such as alcohols and toluene (C₆H₅CH₃) are classified as VOCs (volatile organic compounds). To give you an idea of the scale of their use, it has been estimated that, between the United States and Canada, 26 million tons of VOCs are released into the atmosphere each year.

In addition to VOCs, there are halogenated compounds such as perchloroethylene (PERC) used in dry cleaning. Replacing VOCs and halogen-bearing solvents with supercritical CO₂ would help our environment greatly. Simply replacing VOCs, PERC, and related compounds with liquid or supercritical CO₂ won't work, however, because grease and dirt do not dis-

solve in CO₂. Fortunately, the problem was solved by Professor J. DeSimone of the University of North Carolina. His solution was to add a surfactant, just as you find in detergents in the kitchen. A surfactant is generally a long chain organic molecule with one end that can bind to an organic particle such as grease and another end that is soluble in the bulk solvent, in this case CO₂.

"CO₂-phobic" hydrocarbon head

"CO₂-philic" fluorocarbon tail

The "CO₂-phobic" ends of these molecules surround the grease or dirt to be removed while the "CO₂-philic" ends extend into the supercritical fluid. The dirt is taken into the solvent and washed away, leaving no toxic chemicals behind. The CO₂ is evaporated and recovered, and the dirt is collected.

Reference:
Real World Cases in Green Chemistry, M. C. Cann and M. E. Connelly, American Chemical Society, Washington, DC, 2000.

OWL and **go Chemistry**

Sign in at **www.cengage.com/owl** to:
- View tutorials and simulations, develop problem-solving skills, and complete online homework assigned by your professor.
- For quick review and exam prep, download Go Chemistry mini lecture modules from OWL (or purchase them at **www.cengagebrain.com**)

Access **How Do I Solve It?** tutorials on how to approach problem solving using concepts in this chapter.

CHAPTER GOALS REVISITED

Now that you have studied this chapter, you should ask whether you have met the chapter goals. In particular, you should be able to:

Describe intermolecular forces and their effects
a. Describe the various intermolecular forces found in liquids and solids (Sections 12.3 and 12.4). **Study Questions: 1–10, 29–32, 34, 36, 43, and Go Chemistry Module 17.**
b. Tell when two molecules can interact through a dipole–dipole attraction and when hydrogen bonding may occur. The latter occurs most strongly when H is attached to O, N, or F (Section 12.3). **Study Questions: 1–8.**
c. Identify instances in which molecules interact by induced dipoles (dispersion forces) (Section 12.4). **Study Questions: 1–8.**

Understand the importance of hydrogen bonding
a. Explain how hydrogen bonding affects the properties of water (Section 12.3). **Study Questions: 1–8.**

Understand the properties of liquids
a. Explain the processes of evaporation and condensation, and use the enthalpy of vaporization in calculations (Section 12.6). **Study Questions: 11, 12, 18, 35, 57.**

b. Define the equilibrium vapor pressure of a liquid, and explain the relationship between the vapor pressure and boiling point of a liquid (Section 12.6). **Study Questions: 14, 15, 17, 19, 20, 33, 42, 54.**

c. Describe the phenomena of the critical temperature, T_c, and critical pressure, P_c, of a substance (Section 12.6). **Study Questions: 23, 24, 53.**

d. Describe how intermolecular interactions affect the cohesive forces between identical liquid molecules, the energy necessary to break through the surface of a liquid (surface tension), capillary action, and the resistance to flow, or viscosity, of liquids (Section 12.6). **Study Questions: 25, 26, 27, 28, 45, 46.**

e. Use the Clausius–Clapeyron equation, which connects temperature, vapor pressure, and enthalpy of vaporization for liquids (Section 12.6). **Study Questions: 21, 22, 38, 39.**

Key Equations

Equation 12.1 (page 570) The Clausius–Clapeyron equation relates the equilibrium vapor pressure, P, of a volatile liquid to the molar enthalpy of vaporization ($\Delta_{vap}H°$) at a given temperature, T. (R is the universal constant, 8.314472 J/K · mol.)

$$\ln P = -(\Delta_{vap}H°/RT) + C$$

Equation 12.2 (page 570) This modification of the Clausius–Clapeyron equation allows you to calculate $\Delta_{vap}H°$ if you know the vapor pressures at two different temperatures.

$$\ln \frac{P_2}{P_1} = -\frac{\Delta_{vap}H°}{R}\left[\frac{1}{T_2} - \frac{1}{T_1}\right]$$

Study Questions

⭕WL Interactive versions of these questions are assignable in OWL.

▲ denotes challenging questions.

Blue-numbered questions have answers in Appendix R and fully worked solutions in the *Student Solutions Manual*.

Practicing Skills

Intermolecular Forces
(See Sections 12.1–12.5 and Examples 12.1–12.4.)

1. What intermolecular force(s) must be overcome to perform the following?
    (a) melt ice
    (b) sublime solid I_2
    (c) convert liquid NH_3 to NH_3 vapor

2. What type of forces must be overcome when solid I_2 dissolves in methanol, CH_3OH? What type of forces must be disrupted between CH_3OH molecules when I_2 dissolves? What type of forces exist between I_2 and CH_3OH molecules in solution?

3. What type of intermolecular forces must be overcome in converting each of the following from a liquid to a gas?
    (a) liquid O_2 (c) CH_3I (methyl iodide)
    (b) mercury   (d) CH_3CH_2OH (ethanol)

4. What type of intermolecular forces must be overcome in converting each of the following from a liquid to a gas?
    (a) CO_2 (c) $CHCl_3$
    (b) NH_3 (d) CCl_4

5. Rank the following atoms or molecules in order of increasing strength of intermolecular forces in the pure substance. Which of these substances exists as a gas at 25 °C and 1 atm?
    (a) Ne   (c) CO
    (b) CH_4 (d) CCl_4

6. Rank the following in order of increasing strength of intermolecular forces in the pure substances. Which substance exists as a gas at 25 °C and 1 atm?
    (a) $CH_3CH_2CH_2CH_3$ (butane)
    (b) CH_3OH (methanol)
    (c) He

7. Which of the following compounds would be expected to form intermolecular hydrogen bonds in the liquid state?
    (a) CH_3OCH_3 (dimethyl ether)
    (b) CH_4
    (c) HF
    (d) CH_3CO_2H (acetic acid)
    (e) Br_2
    (f) CH_3OH (methanol)

8. Which of the following compounds would be expected to form intermolecular hydrogen bonds in the liquid state?
    (a) H_2Se
    (b) HCO_2H (formic acid)
    (c) HI
    (d) acetone (see structure below)

$$\begin{array}{c} O \\ \| \\ H_3C-C-CH_3 \end{array}$$

9. In each pair of ionic compounds, which is more likely to have the more negative enthalpy of hydration? Briefly explain your reasoning in each case.
   (a) LiCl or CsCl
   (b) $NaNO_3$ or $Mg(NO_3)_2$
   (c) RbCl or $NiCl_2$

10. When salts of Mg^{2+}, Na^+, and Cs^+ are placed in water, the ions are hydrated. Which of these three cations is most strongly hydrated? Which one is least strongly hydrated?

Liquids
(See Section 12.6 and Examples 12.5 and 12.6.)

11. Ethanol, CH_3CH_2OH, has a vapor pressure of 59 mm Hg at 25 °C. What quantity of energy as heat is required to evaporate 125 mL of the alcohol at 25 °C? The enthalpy of vaporization of the alcohol at 25 °C is 42.32 kJ/mol. The density of the liquid is 0.7849 g/mL.

12. The enthalpy of vaporization of liquid mercury is 59.11 kJ/mol. What quantity of energy as heat is required to vaporize 0.500 mL of mercury at 357 °C, its normal boiling point? The density of mercury is 13.6 g/mL.

13. Answer the following questions using Figure 12.17:
   (a) What is the approximate equilibrium vapor pressure of water at 60 °C? Compare your answer with the data in Appendix G.
   (b) At what temperature does water have an equilibrium vapor pressure of 600 mm Hg?
   (c) Compare the equilibrium vapor pressures of water and ethanol at 70 °C. Which is higher?

14. Answer the following questions using Figure 12.17:
   (a) What is the equilibrium vapor pressure of diethyl ether at room temperature (approximately 20 °C)?
   (b) Place the three compounds in Figure 12.17 in order of increasing intermolecular forces.
   (c) If the pressure in a flask is 400 mm Hg and if the temperature is 40 °C, which of the three compounds (diethyl ether, ethanol, and water) are liquids, and which are gases?

15. Assume you seal 1.0 g of diethyl ether (Figure 12.17) in an evacuated 100.-mL flask. If the flask is held at 30 °C, what is the approximate gas pressure in the flask? If the flask is placed in an ice bath, does additional liquid ether evaporate, or does some ether condense to a liquid?

16. Refer to Figure 12.17 to answer these questions:
   (a) You put some water at 60 °C in a plastic milk bottle and seal the top very tightly so gas cannot enter or leave the carton. What happens when the water cools?
   (b) If you put a few drops of liquid diethyl ether on your hand, does it evaporate completely or remain a liquid?

17. Which member of each of the following pairs of compounds has the higher boiling point?
   (a) O_2 or N_2 (c) HF or HI
   (b) SO_2 or CO_2 (d) SiH_4 or GeH_4

18. Place the following four compounds in order of increasing boiling point:
   (a) SCl_2 (c) C_2H_6
   (b) NH_3 (d) Ne

19. Vapor pressure curves for CS_2 (carbon disulfide) and CH_3NO_2 (nitromethane) are drawn here.
   (a) What are the approximate vapor pressures of CS_2 and CH_3NO_2 at 40 °C?
   (b) What type(s) of intermolecular forces exist in the liquid phase of each compound?
   (c) What is the normal boiling point of CS_2? Of CH_3NO_2?
   (d) At what temperature does CS_2 have a vapor pressure of 600 mm Hg?
   (e) At what temperature does CH_3NO_2 have a vapor pressure of 60 mm Hg?

20. You are comparing three different substances, A, B, and C, all liquids. The vapor pressure at 25 °C for substance A is less than the vapor pressure for B at this temperature. Substance C has the highest boiling point of the three substances. List the three substances A, B, or C in order of the strength of intermolecular forces, from least to greatest.

21. Equilibrium vapor pressures of benzene, C_6H_6, at various temperatures are given in the table.

Temperature (°C)	Vapor Pressure (mm Hg)
7.6	40.
26.1	100.
60.6	400.
80.1	760.

   (a) What is the normal boiling point of benzene?
   (b) Plot these data so that you have a graph resembling the one in Figure 12.17. At what temperature does the liquid have an equilibrium vapor pressure of 250 mm Hg? At what temperature is the vapor pressure 650 mm Hg?
   (c) Calculate the molar enthalpy of vaporization for benzene using the the Clausius–Clapeyron equation.

22. Vapor pressure data are given here for octane, C_8H_{18}.

Temperature (°C)	Vapor Pressure (mm Hg)
25	13.6
50.	45.3
75	127.2
100.	310.8

Use the Clausius–Clapeyron equation to calculate the molar enthalpy of vaporization of octane and its normal boiling point.

23. Can carbon monoxide (T_c = 132.9 K; P_c = 34.5 atm) be liquefied at or above room temperature? Explain briefly.

24. Methane (CH_4) cannot be liquefied at room temperature, no matter how high the pressure. Propane (C_3H_8), another simple hydrocarbon, has a critical pressure of 42 atm and a critical temperature of 96.7 °C. Can this compound be liquefied at room temperature?

25. What is surface tension? Give an example illustrating the phenomenon of surface tension. Explain why surface tension is the consequence of intermolecular forces.

26. What factors affect the viscosity of a substance? Which of the following substances, water (H_2O), ethanol (CH_3CH_2OH), ethylene glycol ($HOCH_2CH_2OH$), and glycerol ($HOCH_2CH(OH)CH_2OH$), is expected to have the highest viscosity? Should viscosity of a substance be affected by temperature? Explain your answers.

27. If a piece of filter paper (an absorbent paper used in laboratories) is suspended above a beaker of water and just touching the surface, water will slowly climb up the paper. What is the name given to this phenomenon, and how is this behavior explained?

28. When water is placed in a buret it forms a concave meniscus at the surface. In contrast, mercury (in a manometer for example) forms a convex meniscus (Figure 12.22). Explain why this phenomenon occurs, and why the two liquids give different results. Predict the meniscus shape if the buret is filled with ethylene glycol ($HOCH_2CH_2OH$).

General Questions

These questions are not designated as to type or location in the chapter. They may combine several concepts.

29. Rank the following substances in order of increasing strength of intermolecular forces: (a) Ar, (b) CH_3OH, and (c) CO_2.

30. What types of intermolecular forces are important in the liquid phase of (a) C_2H_6 and (b) $(CH_3)_2CHOH$.

31. Which of the following salts, Li_2SO_4 or Cs_2SO_4, is expected to have the more exothermic enthalpy of hydration?

32. Select the substance in each of the following pairs that should have the higher boiling point:
(a) Br_2 or ICl
(b) neon or krypton
(c) CH_3CH_2OH (ethanol) or C_2H_4O (ethylene oxide, structure below)

$$H_2C — CH_2$$
$$\diagdown \; / $$
$$O$$

33. Use the vapor pressure curves illustrated here to answer the questions that follow.

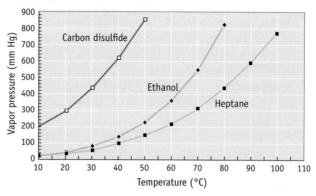

(a) What is the vapor pressure of ethanol, C_2H_5OH, at 60 °C?
(b) Considering only carbon disulfide (CS_2) and ethanol, which has the stronger intermolecular forces in the liquid state?
(c) At what temperature does heptane (C_7H_{16}) have a vapor pressure of 500 mm Hg?
(d) What are the approximate normal boiling points of each of the three substances?
(e) At a pressure of 400 mm Hg and a temperature of 70 °C, is each substance a liquid, a gas, or a mixture of liquid and gas?

34. Which of the following ionic compounds will have the most negative enthalpy of hydration?
(a) $Fe(NO_3)_2$ (c) NaCl
(b) $CoCl_2$ (d) $Al(NO_3)_3$

35. Rank the following compounds in order of increasing molar enthalpy of vaporization: CH_3OH, C_2H_6, HCl.

36. Rank the following molecules in order of increasing intermolecular forces: CH_3Cl, HCO_2H (formic acid), and CO_2.

37. Mercury and many of its compounds are dangerous poisons if breathed, swallowed, or even absorbed through the skin. The liquid metal has a vapor pressure of 0.00169 mm Hg at 24 °C. If the air in a small room is saturated with mercury vapor, how many atoms of mercury vapor occur per cubic meter?

38. ▲ The following data are the equilibrium vapor pressure of limonene, $C_{10}H_{16}$, at various temperatures. (Limonene is used as a scent in commercial products.)

Temperature (°C)	Vapor Pressure (mm Hg)
14.0	1.0
53.8	10.
84.3	40.
108.3	100.
151.4	400.

(a) Plot these data as ln P versus $1/T$ so that you have a graph resembling the one in Figure 12.18.
(b) At what temperature does the liquid have an equilibrium vapor pressure of 250 mm Hg? At what temperature is it 650 mm Hg?
(c) What is the normal boiling point of limonene?
(d) Calculate the molar enthalpy of vaporization for limonene using the the Clausius–Clapeyron equation.

In the Laboratory

39. You are going to prepare a silicone polymer, and one of the starting materials is dichlorodimethylsilane, $SiCl_2(CH_3)_2$. You need its normal boiling point and to measure equilibrium vapor pressures at various temperatures.

Temperature (°C)	Vapor Pressure (mm Hg)
−0.4	40.
+17.5	100.
51.9	400.
70.3	760.

(a) What is the normal boiling point of dichlorodimethylsilane?

(b) Plot these data as ln P versus $1/T$ so that you have a plot resembling the one in Figure 12.18. At what temperature does the liquid have an equilibrium vapor pressure of 250 mm Hg? At what temperature is it 650 mm Hg?

(c) Calculate the molar enthalpy of vaporization for dichlorodimethylsilane using the Clausius–Clapeyron equation.

40. A "hand boiler" can be purchased in toy stores or at science supply companies. If you cup your hand around the bottom bulb, the volatile liquid in the boiler boils, and the liquid moves to the upper chamber. Using your knowledge of kinetic molecular theory and intermolecular forces, explain how the hand boiler works.

© Cengage Learning/Charles D. Winters

41. ▲ The photos below illustrate an experiment you can do yourself. Place 10 mL of water in an empty soda can, and heat the water to boiling. Using tongs or pliers, turn the can over in a pan of cold water, making sure the opening in the can is below the water level in the pan.

© Cengage Learning/Charles D. Winters

(a)　　　　(b)

(a) Describe what happens, and explain it in terms of the subject of this chapter.

(b) Prepare a molecular level sketch of the situation inside the can before heating and after heating (but prior to inverting the can).

42. If you place 1.0 L of ethanol (C_2H_5OH) in a small laboratory that is 3.0 m long, 2.5 m wide, and 2.5 m high, will all the alcohol evaporate? If some liquid remains, how much will there be? The vapor pressure of ethyl alcohol at 25 °C is 59 mm Hg, and the density of the liquid at this temperature is 0.785 g/cm³.

Summary and Conceptual Questions

The following questions may use concepts from this and previous chapters.

43. Acetone, CH_3COCH_3, is a common laboratory solvent. It is usually contaminated with water, however. Why does acetone absorb water so readily? Draw molecular structures showing how water and acetone can interact. What intermolecular force(s) is(are) involved in the interaction?

$$H_3C - \overset{\overset{\textstyle O}{\|}}{C} - CH_3$$

44. Cooking oil floats on top of water. From this observation, what conclusions can you draw regarding the polarity or hydrogen-bonding ability of molecules found in cooking oil?

45. Liquid ethylene glycol, $HOCH_2CH_2OH$, is one of the main ingredients in commercial antifreeze. Do you predict its viscosity to be greater or less than that of ethanol, CH_3CH_2OH?

46. Liquid methanol, CH_3OH, is placed in a glass tube. Is the meniscus of the liquid concave or convex? Explain briefly.

47. Account for these facts:

(a) Although ethanol (C_2H_5OH) (bp, 80 °C) has a higher molar mass than water (bp, 100 °C), the alcohol has a lower boiling point.

(b) Mixing 50 mL of ethanol with 50 mL of water produces a solution with a volume slightly less than 100 mL.

48. Rationalize the observation that $CH_3CH_2CH_2OH$, 1-propanol, has a boiling point of 97.2 °C, whereas a compound with the same empirical formula, methyl ethyl ether ($CH_3CH_2OCH_3$), boils at 7.4 °C.

49. Cite two pieces of evidence to support the statement that water molecules in the liquid state exert considerable attractive force on one another.

50. During thunderstorms in the Midwest, very large hailstones can fall from the sky. (Some are the size of golf balls!) To preserve some of these stones, we put them in the freezer compartment of a frost-free refrigerator. Our friend, who is a chemistry student, tells us to use an older model that is not frost-free. Why?

51. Refer to Figure 12.12 to answer the following questions:
    (a) Of the three hydrogen halides (HX), which has the largest total intermolecular force?
    (b) Why are the dispersion forces greater for HI than for HCl?
    (c) Why are the dipole–dipole forces greater for HCl than for HI?
    (d) Of the seven molecules in Figure 12.12, which involves the largest dispersion forces? Explain why this is reasonable.

52. ▲ What quantity of energy is evolved (in joules) when 1.00 mol of liquid ammonia cools from −33.3 °C (its boiling point) to −43.3 °C? (The specific heat capacity of liquid NH_3 is 4.70 J/g · K.) Compare this with the quantity of heat evolved by 1.00 mol of liquid water cooling by exactly 10 °C. Which evolves more heat per mole on cooling 10 °C, liquid water or liquid ammonia? *(The underlying reason for the difference in energy evolved is scientifically illuminating and interesting. You can learn more by searching the Internet for specific heat capacity and its dependence on molecular properties.)*

53. A fluorocarbon, CF_4, has a critical temperature of −45.7 °C and a critical pressure of 37 atm. Are there any conditions under which this compound can be a liquid at room temperature? Explain briefly.

54. ▲ The figure below is a plot of vapor pressure versus temperature for dichlorodifluoromethane, CCl_2F_2. The enthalpy of vaporization of the liquid is 165 kJ/g, and the specific heat capacity of the liquid is about 1.0 J/g · K.

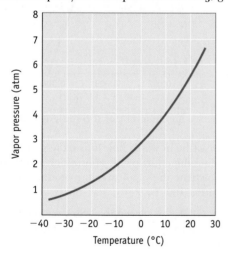

(a) What is the approximate normal boiling point of CCl_2F_2?
(b) A steel cylinder containing 25 kg of CCl_2F_2 in the form of liquid and vapor is set outdoors on a warm day (25 °C). What is the approximate pressure of the vapor in the cylinder?
(c) The cylinder valve is opened, and CCl_2F_2 vapor gushes out of the cylinder in a rapid flow. Soon, however, the flow becomes much slower, and the outside of the cylinder is coated with ice frost. When the valve is closed and the cylinder is re-weighed, it is found that 20 kg of CCl_2F_2 is still in the cylinder. Why is the flow fast at first? Why does it slow down long before the cylinder is empty? Why does the outside become icy?

(d) Which of the following procedures would be effective in emptying the cylinder rapidly (and safely)? (1) Turn the cylinder upside down, and open the valve. (2) Cool the cylinder to −78 °C in dry ice, and open the valve. (3) Knock off the top of the cylinder, valve and all, with a sledgehammer.

55. Acetaminophen is used in analgesics. A model of the molecule is shown here with its electrostatic potential surface. Where are the most likely sites for hydrogen bonding?

56. Shown here are models of two bases in DNA with the electrostatic potential surfaces: cytosine and guanine. What sites in these molecules are involved in hydrogen bonding with each other? Draw molecular structures showing how cytosine can hydrogen bond with guanine.

cytosine

guanine

57. List four properties of liquids that are directly determined by intermolecular forces.

58. List the following ions in order of hydration energies: Na^+, K^+, Mg^{2+}, Ca^{2+}. Explain how you determined this order.

59. Compare the boiling points of the various isomeric hydrocarbons shown in the table below. Notice the relationship between boiling point and structure; branched-chain hydrocarbons have lower boiling points than the unbranched isomer. Speculate on possible reasons for this trend. Why might the intermolecular forces be slightly different in these compounds?

Compound	Boiling point (°C)
Hexane	68.9
3-Methylpentane	63.2
2-Methylpentane	60.3
2,3-Dimethylbutane	58.0
2,2-Dimethylbutane	49.7

60. An 8.82 g sample of Br_2 is placed in an evacuated 1.00 L flask and heated to 58.8 °C, the normal boiling point of bromine. Describe the contents of the flask under these conditions.

61. Polarizability is defined as the extent to which the electron cloud surrounding an atom or molecule can be distorted by an external charge. Rank the halogens (F_2, Cl_2, Br_2, I_2) and the noble gases (He, Ne, Ar, Kr, Xe) in order of polarizability (from least polarizable to most polarizable). What characteristics of these substances could be used to determine this ranked order?

62. In which of the following organic molecules might we expect hydrogen bonding to occur?
    (a) methyl acetate, $CH_3CO_2CH_3$
    (b) acetaldehyde (ethanal), CH_3CHO
    (c) acetone (2-propanone) (see Question 8)
    (d) benzoic acid ($C_6H_5CO_2H$)
    (e) acetamide (CH_3CONH_2 an amide formed from acetic acid and ammonia)
    (f) N,N-dimethylacetamide [$CH_3CON(CH_3)_2$, an amide formed from acetic acid and dimethylamine]

63. A pressure cooker (a kitchen appliance) is a pot on which the top seals tightly, allowing pressure to build up inside. You put water in the pot and heat it to boiling. At the higher pressure, water boils at a higher temperature and this allows food to cook at a faster rate. Most pressure cookers have a setting of 15 psi, which means that the pressure in the pot is 15 psi above atmospheric pressure (1 atm = 14.70 psi). Use the Clausius–Clapeyron equation to calculate the temperature at which water boils in the pressure cooker.

64. Vapor pressures of $NH_3(\ell)$ at several temperatures are given in the table below. Use this information to calculate the enthalpy of vaporization of ammonia.

Temperature (°C)	Vapor Pressure (atm)
−68.4	0.132
−45.4	0.526
−33.6	1.000
−18.7	2.00
4.7	5.00
25.7	10.00
50.1	20.00

65. Chemists sometimes carry out reactions in liquid ammonia as a solvent. With adequate safety protection these reactions can be done at temperatures above ammonia's boiling point in a sealed, thick-walled glass tube. If the reaction is being carried out at 20 °C, what is the pressure of ammonia inside the tube? (Use data from the previous question to answer this question.)

66. The data in the following table were used to create the graph shown below (vp = vapor pressure of ethanol (CH_3CH_2OH) expressed in mm Hg, T = kelvin temperature)

ln(vp)	1/T (K⁻¹)
2.30	0.00369
3.69	0.00342
4.61	0.00325
5.99	0.00297
6.63	0.00285

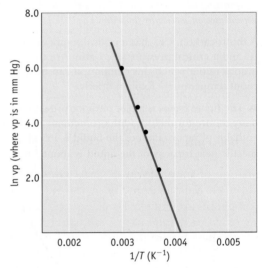

(a) Derive an equation for the straight line in this graph.
(b) Describe in words how to use the graph to determine the enthalpy of vaporization of ethanol.
(c) Calculate the vapor pressure of ethanol at 0.00 °C and at 100 °C.

67. Water (10.0 g) is placed in a thick walled glass tube whose internal volume is 50.0 cm³. Then all the air is removed, the tube is sealed, and then the tube and contents are heated to 100 °C.
    (a) Describe the appearance of the system at 100 °C.
    (b) What is the pressure inside the tube?
    (c) At this temperature, liquid water has a density of 0.958 g/cm³. Calculate the volume of liquid water in the tube.
    (d) Some of the water is in the vapor state. Determine the mass of water in the gaseous state.

Applying Chemical Principles

Chromatography

Separation of mixtures into pure components is important in both the synthesis and the analysis of chemical compounds. A variety of methods are used for separations, including distillation, precipitation, and filtration. However, the most common means of separation of mixtures is chromatography, and the photo on page 4 shows a forensic chemist using an instrument called a high performance liquid chromatograph.

Chromatography is a general term for a collection of related separation methods. It entails using a mobile phase (commonly a liquid or gas) to move a sample (that is, the components in a mixture) through an immiscible stationary phase (usually a liquid or solid). The mobile and stationary phases are chosen so that the components in the mixture distribute themselves to varying degrees between the two phases. The rate at which components in a mixture move through the stationary phase is dependent on their intermolecular interactions with the mobile and stationary phases. Components that interact weakly with the stationary phase move more quickly through the stationary phase than the components that interact more strongly with that phase.

In one common form of chromatography, called partition chromatography, both the mobile and stationary phases are liquids. For example, a polar mobile phase (such as a mixture of methanol and water) is passed through a very thin column containing a nonpolar stationary phase. A common stationary phase is nonpolar octadecane. The linear, eighteen-carbon chain (referred to as C-18) is usually covalently bonded to a solid support, such as small silica particles, to immobilize it inside the column. As the mixture passes through the C-18 column, the components continuously move back and forth between the two liquid phases, with the less polar components spending more time in the nonpolar phase than the more polar components. In an ideal separation, the components that emerge from the column (that is, the eluents) are completed separated.

Questions:

1. Assume that a mixture of the three molecules below are separated on a C-18 column using a methanol/water mixture as the mobile phase.
    (a) Which of the three molecules is most attracted to the mobile phase? What are the forces that attract the molecule to the water/methanol phase?

© Cengage Learning/Charles D. Winters

The separation of black ink by paper chromatography. Typically, the stationary phase (the paper) is suspended vertically. A spot or line of ink is placed near the bottom of the paper. The liquid phase rises up the paper by capillary action, and carries the various components upward at different rates.

   (b) Which molecule is most attracted to the stationary phase? What are the forces that attract the molecule to the nonpolar phase?
   (c) In what order will the three molecules exit (or "elute from") the column?

1-pentanol   propyl ethyl ether

1,5-pentanediol

2. In gas chromatography the mobile phase is an inert gas such as N_2 or He. A mixture's components must be volatile if they are to move in the mobile phase. As with liquid chromatography, the separation is based upon forces of attraction of the various sample components with the mobile and the stationary phases; greater attractive forces between a compound and the column will result in a longer elution time. Assume that you want to separate a group of hydrocarbons, such as pentane (C_5H_{12}), hexane (C_6H_{14}), heptane (C_7H_{16}), and octane (C_8H_{18}) using a column with a nonpolar stationary phase. Predict the order of elution of these species from the column and explain your answer.

13 The Chemistry of Solids

Lithium and "Green Cars"

The focus of much of this chapter is on metals and metal-containing compounds, the vast majority of which are solids.

You are well aware of the use of metals in our world: copper in electric wiring; aluminum in airplanes and soft drink cans; lead and zinc in batteries; and iron in cars, buses, and bridges. You may be less aware of metals such as the platinum group metals (platinum, palladium, rhodium, iridium, and ruthenium) in the catalytic converter in your car or in the chemicals

Lithium and lithium salts. The high plateau in Bolivia where ground water contains high concentrations of Group 1A salts, among them lithium carbonate. The water is left in the sun to deposit the salts by evaporation.

A sample of lithium met and a view of the solid state structure of lithiur

industry. Approximately 2700 metric tons of these metals is used in cars and another 1000 metric tons in industry annually. Fortunately, many of the platinum group metals are recycled, but scientists are concerned about the depletion of metals such as copper, zinc, gallium, indium, and hafnium. They won't become "extinct" because their atoms are immutable, but they may be increasingly difficult to recover.

One metal that seems, fortunately, to be quite abundant on the earth is lithium. We say "fortunately" because lithium compounds are used in ceramics and glass, in reagents for the production of pharmaceuticals, and in lubricating greases. But their most important and largest use may be in batteries for appliances and most recently in cars. Your laptop computer may have a "lithium ion" battery, and several brands of hybrid cars now use lithium-based batteries.

Much of the world's lithium comes from northern Chile and southern Bolivia. There, groundwater with high concentrations of Group 1A salts is pumped into ponds. The solution slowly evaporates in the intense sun of the high Andes plateau,

and, after about a year, the highly concentrated solution is finally taken to a chemical plant where it is evaporated to give white, powdered lithium carbonate. It is estimated that Bolivia alone has a reserve of about 73 million metric tons of Li_2CO_3. To produce lithium metal, the carbonate is converted to LiCl, which is then electrolyzed to produce the metal.

In 2008 *Forbes* magazine said that "the green-car revolution could make lithium one of the planet's most strategic commodities." This remains to be seen, however. Some automobile companies are planning to continue using nickel-metal hydride batteries well into the future.

Questions:

1. What mass of lithium can be obtained from 73 million metric tons of lithium carbonate? (1 metric ton = 1000 kg.)
2. Describe the unit cell of lithium (see Figure).
3. The lithium unit cell is a cube with sides of 351 pm. Use this information, and a knowledge of unit cells, to calculate the density of lithium metal.
4. In the process of making lithium metal, Li_2CO_3 is converted to LiCl. Suggest a way to do this.

Answers to these questions are available in Appendix N.

CHAPTER GOALS

See Chapter Goals Revisited (page 605) for Study Questions keyed to these goals.

- Understand cubic unit cells.

- Relate unit cells for ionic compounds to formulas.

- Describe bonding in ionic and metallic solids and the nature of semiconductors.

- Describe the properties of solids.

- Interpret phase diagrams.

⚉WL

Sign in to OWL at **www.cengage.com/owl** to view tutorials and simulations, develop problem-solving skills, and complete online homework assigned by your professor.

Many kinds of solids exist in the world around us (Figure 13.1 and Table 13.1). As the description of lithium and lithium-based batteries shows, solid-state chemistry is one of the booming areas of science, especially because it relates to the development of interesting new materials. As we describe various kinds of solids, we hope to provide a glimpse of the reasons this area is exciting.

13.1 Crystal Lattices and Unit Cells

In both gases and liquids, molecules move continually and randomly, and they rotate and vibrate as well. Because of this movement, an orderly arrangement of molecules in the gaseous or liquid state is not possible. In solids, however, the molecules, atoms, or ions cannot change their relative positions (although they vibrate and

go Chemistry

Download mini lecture videos for key concept review and exam prep from OWL or purchase them from **www.cengagebrain.com**

Table 13.1 Structures and Properties of Various Types of Solid Substances

Type	Examples	Structural Units	Forces Holding Units Together	Typical Properties
Ionic	$NaCl$, K_2SO_4, $CaCl_2$, $(NH_4)_3PO_4$	Positive and negative ions; no discrete molecules	Ionic; attractions among charges on positive and negative ions	Hard; brittle; high melting point; poor electric conductivity as solid, good as liquid; often water-soluble
Metallic	Iron, silver, copper, other metals and alloys	Metal atoms (positive metal ions with delocalized electrons)	Metallic; electrostatic attraction among metal ions and electrons	Malleable; ductile; good electric conductivity in solid and liquid; good heat conductivity; wide range of hardness and melting points
Molecular	H_2, O_2, I_2, H_2O, CO_2, CH_4, CH_3OH, CH_3CO_2H	Molecules	Dispersion forces, dipole–dipole forces, hydrogen bonds	Low to moderate melting points and boiling points; soft; poor electric conductivity in solid and liquid
Network	Graphite, diamond, quartz, feldspars, mica	Atoms held in an infinite two- or three-dimensional network	Covalent; directional electron-pair bonds	Wide range of hardness and melting points (three-dimensional bonding > two-dimensional bonding); poor electric conductivity, with some exceptions
Amorphous	Glass, polyethylene, nylon	Covalently bonded networks with no long-range regularity	Covalent; directional electron-pair bonds	Noncrystalline; wide temperature range for melting; poor electric conductivity, with some exceptions

FIGURE 13.1
Some common
solids.

occasionally rotate). Thus, a regular, repeating pattern of atoms or molecules within the structure—a long-range order—is a characteristic of most solids. The beautiful, external (macroscopic) regularity of many crystalline compounds (such as those of salt, Figure 13.1) is a consequence of this internal order.

Structures of solids can be described as three-dimensional lattices of atoms, ions, or molecules. For a crystalline solid, we can identify the **unit cell**, the smallest repeating unit that has all of the symmetry characteristic of the way the atoms, ions, or molecules are arranged in the solid.

To understand unit cells, consider first a two-dimensional lattice model, the repeating pattern of circles shown in Figure 13.2. The yellow square at the left is a unit cell because the overall pattern can be created from a group of these cells by joining them edge to edge. It is also a requirement that unit cells reflect the stoichiometry of the solid. Here, the square unit cell at the left contains one smaller sphere and one fourth of each of the four larger circles, giving a total of one small and one large circle per two-dimensional unit cell.

You may recognize that it is possible to draw other unit cells for this two-dimensional lattice. One option is the square in the middle of Figure 13.2 that fully encloses a single large circle and parts of small circles that add up to one net small circle. Yet another possible unit cell is the parallelogram at the right. Other unit cells can be drawn, but it is conventional to draw unit cells in which atoms or ions are placed at the **lattice points**; that is, at the corners of the cube or other geometric object that constitutes the unit cell.

FIGURE 13.2 Unit cells for a flat, two-dimensional solid made from circular "atoms."
A lattice can be represented as being built from repeating unit cells. This two-dimensional lattice can be built by translating the unit cells throughout the plane of the figure. Each unit cell must move by the length of one side of the cell. In this figure, all unit cells contain a net of one large circle and one small circle. Be sure to notice that several unit cells are possible, with two of the most obvious being squares.

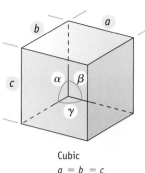

Cubic
$a = b = c$
$\alpha = \beta = \gamma = 90°$

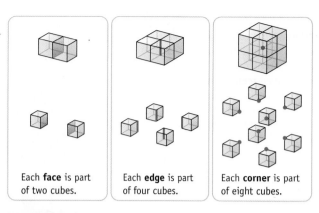

Each **face** is part of two cubes.

Each **edge** is part of four cubes.

Each **corner** is part of eight cubes.

(a) Types of cells. Of the possible unit cells, all are parallelepipeds (except for the hexagonal cell), figures in which opposite sides are parallel. In a cube, all angles (*a-o-c, a-o-b,* and *c-o-b*; where *o* is the origin) are 90°, and all sides are equal. In other cells, the angles and sides may be the same or different. For example, in a tetragonal cell, the angles are 90°, but $a = b \neq c$. In a triclinic cell, the sides have different lengths, the angles are different, and none equals 90°.

(b) Cubic cell. The cube is one of the seven basic unit cells that describe crystal systems. In a cube, all sides are of equal length, and all angles are 90°.

(c) Building a lattice. Stacking cubes to build a crystal lattice. Each crystal face is part of two cubes; each edge is part of four cubes; and each corner is part of eight cubes.

FIGURE 13.3 Unit cells.

The three-dimensional lattices of solids can be built by assembling three-dimensional unit cells much like building blocks (Figure 13.3). The assemblage of these three-dimensional unit cells defines the **crystal lattice**.

To construct crystal lattices, nature can use any of seven three-dimensional unit cells. They differ from one another in that their sides have different relative lengths and their edges meet at different angles. The simplest of the seven crystal lattices is the **cubic unit cell**, a cell with edges of equal length that meet at 90° angles (Figure 13.3). We shall look in detail at only this structure because cubic unit cells are commonly encountered.

Within the cubic class, three cell symmetries occur: **primitive cubic (pc)**, **body-centered cubic (bcc)**, and **face-centered cubic (fcc)** (Figure 13.4). All three have identical atoms, molecules, or ions at the corners of the cubic unit cell. The bcc and

Primitive cubic

Body-centered cubic

Face-centered cubic

FIGURE 13.4 **The three cubic unit cells.** The top row shows the lattice points of the three cells, and the bottom row shows the same cells using space-filling spheres. The spheres in each figure represent identical atoms (or ions) centered on the lattice points. Because eight unit cells share a corner atom, only $\frac{1}{8}$ of each corner atom lies within a given unit cell; the remaining $\frac{7}{8}$ lies in seven other unit cells. Because each face of an fcc unit cell is shared with another unit cell, one half of each atom in the face of a face-centered cube lies in a given unit cell, and the other half lies in the adjoining cell.

FIGURE 13.5 **Metals use four different unit cells.** Three are based on the cube, and the fourth is the hexagonal unit cell (see the next page). (Many metals can crystallize in more than one structure. Mn, for example, can be bcc or fcc, and La exists in all but the primitive unit cell.)

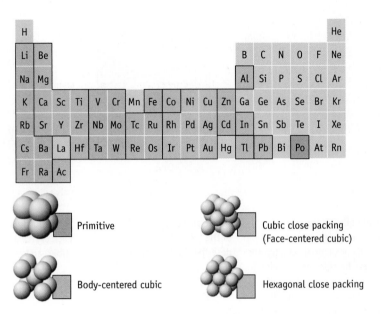

Primitive

Cubic close packing (Face-centered cubic)

Body-centered cubic

Hexagonal close packing

fcc arrangements, however, differ from the primitive cube in that they have additional particles at other locations. The bcc structure is called *body-centered* because it has an additional particle, of the same type as those at the corners, at the center of the cube. The fcc arrangement is called *face-centered* because it has a particle, of the same type as the corner atoms, in the center of each of the six faces of the cube. Examples of each structure are found among the crystal lattices of the metals (Figure 13.5). The alkali metals, for example, are body-centered cubic, whereas nickel, copper, and aluminum are face-centered cubic. Notice that only one metal, polonium, has a primitive cubic lattice.

When the cubes pack together to make a three-dimensional crystal of a metal, the atom at each corner is shared among eight cubes (Figures 13.3, 13.4, and 13.6a). Because of this, only one eighth of each corner atom is actually within a given unit cell. Furthermore, because a cube has eight corners, and because one eighth of the atom at each corner "belongs to" a particular unit cell, the corner atoms contribute a net of one atom to a given unit cell. Thus, *the primitive cubic arrangement has one net atom within the unit cell.*

(8 corners of a cube)($\frac{1}{8}$ of each corner atom within a unit cell) =

1 net atom per unit cell for the primitive cubic unit cell

In contrast to the primitive cubic lattice, a body-centered cube has an additional atom wholly within the unit cell at the cube's center. The center particle is present

FIGURE 13.6 Atom sharing at cube corners and faces.

(a) In any cubic lattice, each corner particle is shared equally among eight cubes, so one eighth of the particle is within a particular cubic unit cell.

(b) In a face-centered lattice, each particle on a cube face is shared equally between two unit cells. One half of each particle of this type is within a given unit cell.

A CLOSER LOOK

Packing Oranges and Marbles

It is a "rule" that nature does things as efficiently as possible. You know this if you have ever tried to stack some oranges into a pile that doesn't fall over and that takes up as little space as possible. How did you do it? Clearly, the pyramid arrangement below on the right works, whereas the cubic one on the left does not.

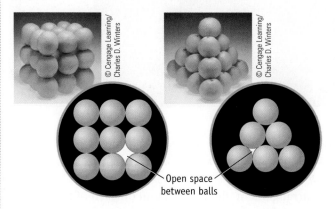

© Cengage Learning/Charles D. Winters

Open space between balls

If you could look inside the pile, you would find that less open space is left in the pyramid stacking than in the cube stacking. Only 52% of the space is filled in the cubic packing arrangement. (If you could stack oranges as a body-centered cube, that would be slightly better; 68% of the space is used.) However, the best method is the pyramid stack, which is really a face-centered cubic arrangement. Oranges, atoms, or ions packed this way occupy 74% of the available space.

To fill three-dimensional space, the most efficient way to pack oranges or atoms is to begin with a hexagonal arrangement of spheres, as in this arrangement of marbles.

© Cengage Learning/Charles D. Winters

Succeeding layers of atoms or ions are then stacked one on top of the other in two different ways. Depending on the stacking pattern (Figure A), you will get either a **cubic close-packed (ccp)** or **hexagonal close-packed (hcp)** arrangement.

In the hcp arrangement, additional layers of particles are placed above and below a given layer, fitting into the same depressions on either side of the middle layer. In a three-dimensional crystal, the layers repeat their pattern in the manner ABABAB. . . . Atoms in each A layer are directly above the ones in another A layer; the same holds true for the B layers.

In the ccp arrangement, the atoms of the "top" layer (A) rest in depressions in the middle layer (B), and those of the "bottom" layer (C) are oriented opposite to those in the top layer. In a crystal, the pattern is repeated ABCABCABC. . . . By turning the whole crystal, you can see that the ccp arrangement is the face-centered cubic structure (Figure B).

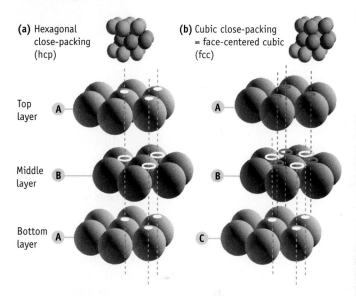

(a) Hexagonal close-packing (hcp)

(b) Cubic close-packing = face-centered cubic (fcc)

Top layer — A

Middle layer — B

Bottom layer — A

Top layer — A

Middle layer — B

Bottom layer — C

FIGURE A Efficient packing. The most efficient ways to pack atoms or ions in crystalline materials are hexagonal close-packing (hcp) and cubic close packing (ccp).

© Cengage Learning/Charles D. Winters

(a) **(b)**

FIGURE B Models of close packing. (a) A model of hexagonal close-packing, where the layers repeat in the order ABABAB. . . . **(b)** A face-centered unit cell (cubic close-packing), where the layers repeat in the order ABCABC. . . . (A kit from which these models can be built is available from the Institute for Chemical Education at the University of Wisconsin at Madison.)

FIGURE 13.7 X-ray crystallography. In the x-ray diffraction experiment, a beam of x-rays is directed at a crystalline solid. The photons of the x-ray beam are scattered by the atoms of the solid. The scattered x-rays are detected by a photographic film or an electronic detector, and the pattern of scattered x-rays is related to the locations of the atoms or ions in the crystal.

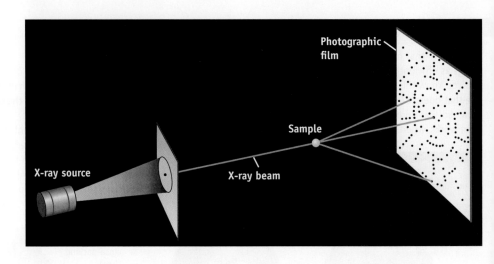

in addition to those at the cube corners, so *the body-centered cubic arrangement has a net of two atoms within the unit cell.*

In a face-centered cubic arrangement, there is an atom on each of the six faces of the cube in addition to those at the cube corners. One half of each atom on a face belongs to a given unit cell (Figure 13.6b). Three net particles are therefore contributed by the particles on the faces of the cube:

(6 faces of a cube)($^1\!/_2$ of an atom within a unit cell) =

3 net face-centered atoms within a face-centered cubic unit cell

Thus, *the face-centered cubic arrangement has a net of four atoms within the unit cell,* one contributed by the corner atoms and another three contributed by the atoms centered in the six faces.

An experimental technique, x-ray crystallography, can be used to determine the structure of a crystalline substance (Figure 13.7). Once the structure is known, the information can be combined with other experimental information to calculate such useful parameters as the radius of an atom (Example 13.1).

⛉WL **INTERACTIVE EXAMPLE 13.1** Determining an Atom Radius from Lattice Dimensions

Problem Aluminum has a density of 2.699 g/cm³, and the atoms are packed in a face-centered cubic crystal lattice. What is the radius of an aluminum atom?

What Do You Know? You are trying to find the radius of an aluminum atom and begin with a knowledge of its unit cell geometry. It is important to recognize the atoms in a face-centered cube do not touch along the cell edges but do so in the faces (as illustrated just below).

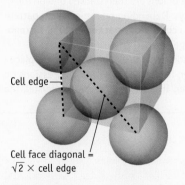

Cell edge ─

Cell face diagonal =
$\sqrt{2}$ × cell edge

One face of a face-centered cubic unit cell. This shows the cell face diagonal, $\sqrt{2}$ × edge, is equal to four times the radius of the atoms in the lattice.

Aluminum metal. The metal has a face-centered cubic unit cell with a net of four Al atoms in each unit cell.

Strategy If you know the cell edge length, you can calculate the diagonal distance across a face, and the illustration above shows the atom radius is one fourth of this distance. So, the problem comes down to finding the length of the cell edge. This dimension is the cube root of the cell volume. But where do you find the cell volume? From the density and mass of the unit cell. The density is given, and the mass of the cell is 4 times the mass of an atom. As described in Chapter 2, the mass of an Al atom can be found from its atomic mass and Avogadro's number. Therefore, you should proceed as follows:

1. Find the mass of a unit cell from the knowledge that it is face-centered cubic.

2. Combine the density of aluminum with the mass of the unit cell to find the cell volume.

3. Find the length of a side of the unit cell from its volume.

4. Calculate the atom radius from the edge dimension.

Solution

1. *Calculate the mass of the unit cell.*

$$\text{Mass of 1 Al atom} = \left(\frac{26.98 \text{ g}}{1 \text{ mol}}\right)\left(\frac{1 \text{ mol}}{6.022 \times 10^{23} \text{ atoms}}\right) = 4.480 \times 10^{-23} \text{ g/atom}$$

$$\text{Mass of unit cell} = \left(\frac{4.480 \times 10^{-23} \text{ g}}{1 \text{ Al atom}}\right)\left(\frac{4 \text{ Al atoms}}{1 \text{ unit cell}}\right) = 1.792 \times 10^{-22} \text{ g/unit cell}$$

2. *Calculate the volume of the unit cell from the unit cell mass and density.*

$$\text{Volume of unit cell} = \left(\frac{1.792 \times 10^{-22} \text{ g}}{\text{unit cell}}\right)\left(\frac{1 \text{ cm}^3}{2.699 \text{ g}}\right) = 6.640 \times 10^{-23} \text{ cm}^3/\text{unit cell}$$

3. *Calculate the length of a unit cell edge.* The length of the unit cell edge is the cube root of the cell volume.

$$\text{Length of unit cell edge} = \sqrt[3]{6.640 \times 10^{-23} \text{ cm}^3} = 4.049 \times 10^{-8} \text{ cm}$$

4. *Calculate the atom radius.* As illustrated in the model above, the diagonal distance across the face of the cell is equal to four times the Al atom radius.

$$\text{Cell face diagonal} = 4 \times (\text{Al atom radius})$$

The cell diagonal is the hypotenuse of a right isosceles triangle, so, using the Pythagorean theorem,

$$(\text{Diagonal distance})^2 = 2 \times (\text{edge})^2$$

Taking the square root of both sides, we have

$$\text{Diagonal distance} = \sqrt{2} \times (\text{cell edge})$$
$$= \sqrt{2} \times (4.049 \times 10^{-8} \text{ cm}) = 5.727 \times 10^{-8} \text{ cm}$$

We divide the diagonal distance by 4 to obtain the Al atom radius in cm.

$$\text{Al atom radius} = \frac{5.727 \times 10^{-8} \text{ cm}}{4} = 1.432 \times 10^{-8} \text{ cm}$$

Atomic dimensions are often expressed in picometers, so we convert the radius to that unit.

$$1.432 \times 10^{-8} \text{ cm}\left(\frac{1 \text{ m}}{100 \text{ cm}}\right)\left(\frac{1 \text{ pm}}{1 \times 10^{-12} \text{ m}}\right) = \boxed{143.2 \text{ pm}}$$

Think about Your Answer The radius in Figure 7.8 was calculated from experimental data as in this Example.

Check Your Understanding

(a) *Determining an Atom Radius from Lattice Dimensions:* Gold has a face-centered unit cell, and its density is 19.32 g/cm³. Calculate the radius of a gold atom.

(b) *The Structure of Solid Iron:* Iron has a density of 7.8740 g/cm³, and the radius of an iron atom is 126 pm. Verify that solid iron has a body-centered cubic unit cell. (Be sure to note that the atoms in a body-centered cubic unit cell touch along the diagonal across the cell. They do not touch along the edges of the cell.) (*Hint:* The diagonal distance across the unit cell = edge × $\sqrt{3}$.)

Strategy Map 13.1

PROBLEM

What is the **radius** of **Al** in solid Al?

↓

DATA/INFORMATION
- Al unit cell is **FCC** with $d = 2.699$ g/cm³
- Need Al *atomic weight*
- Need *Avogadro's number*

↓

STEP 1. Calculate **mass** of unit cell (= 4 Al atoms).

↓

Mass of Al atom, **mass** of unit cell

↓

STEP 2. Calculate **volume** of unit cell from mass and density.

↓

Volume of unit cell

↓

STEP 3. Calculate **length** of unit cell *edge* from cell volume.

↓

Length of unit cell edge

↓

STEP 4. Relate **atom radius** to **unit cell edge length**.

↓

Radius of atom

A portion of the solid state structure of potassium.

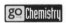

Module 18: The Solid State covers concepts in this section.

REVIEW & CHECK FOR SECTION 13.1

1. A portion of the crystalline lattice for potassium is illustrated in the margin. In what type of unit cell are the K atoms arranged?

   (a)   primitive cubic   (c)   face-centered cubic

   (b)   body-centered cubic

2. If one edge of the potassium unit cell is 533 pm, what is the density of potassium?

   (a)   0.858 g/cm³   (b)   1.17 g/cm³   (c)   0.428 g/cm³

13.2 Structures and Formulas of Ionic Solids

The lattices of many ionic compounds are built by taking a primitive cubic or face-centered cubic lattice of ions of one type and placing ions of opposite charge in the holes within the lattice. This produces a three-dimensional lattice of regularly placed ions. The smallest repeating unit in these structures is, by definition, the unit cell for the ionic compound.

The choice of the lattice and the number and location of the holes in the lattice that are filled are the keys to understanding the relationship between the lattice structure and the formula of a salt. Consider, for example, the ionic compound cesium chloride, CsCl (Figure 13.8). The structure of CsCl has a primitive cubic unit cell of chloride ions. The cesium ion fits into a hole in the center of the cube. (An equivalent unit cell has a primitive cubic unit cell of Cs^+ ions with a Cl^- ion in the center of the cube.)

Next, consider the structure for NaCl. An extended view of the lattice and one unit cell are illustrated in Figures 13.9a and 13.9b, respectively. The Cl^- ions are arranged in a face-centered cubic unit cell, and the Na^+ ions are arranged in a regular manner between these ions. Notice that each Na^+ ion is surrounded by six Cl^- ions in an octahedral geometry. Thus, the Na^+ ions are said to be in **octahedral holes** (Figure 13.9c).

The formula of an ionic compound must always be reflected in the composition of its unit cell; therefore, the formula can always be derived from the unit cell structure. The formula for NaCl can be related to this structure by counting the number of cations and anions contained in one unit cell. A face-centered cubic lattice of Cl^- ions has a net of four Cl^- ions within the unit cell. There is one Na^+ ion in the center of the unit cell, contained totally within the unit cell. In addition, there are 12 Na^+ ions along the edges of the unit cell. Each of these Na^+ ions is shared among four unit cells, so each contributes one fourth of an Na^+ ion to the unit cell, giving three additional Na^+ ions within the unit cell.

(1 Na^+ ion in the center of the unit cell) + ($\frac{1}{4}$ of a Na^+ ion in each edge × 12 edges)

= net of 4 Na^+ ions in NaCl unit cell

This accounts for all of the ions contained in the unit cell: four Cl^- and four Na^+ ions. Thus, a unit cell of NaCl has a 1:1 ratio of Na^+ and Cl^- ions, as the formula requires.

FIGURE 13.8 Cesium chloride (CsCl) unit cell. The unit cell of CsCl may be viewed in two ways. The only requirement is that the unit cell must have a net of one Cs^+ ion and one Cl^- ion. Either way, it is a primitive cubic unit cell of ions of one type (Cl^- on the left or Cs^+ on the right). Generally, ionic lattices are assembled by placing the larger ions (here Cl^-) at the lattice points and placing the smaller ions (here Cs^+) in the lattice holes.

Cl^-, radius = 181 pm Cs^+, radius = 165 pm

Cl^- ions at each cube corner = 1 net Cl^- ion in the unit cell.

Cl^- lattice and Cs^+ in lattice hole

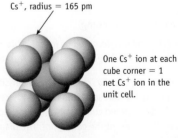

One Cs^+ ion at each cube corner = 1 net Cs^+ ion in the unit cell.

Cs^+ lattice and Cl^- in lattice hole

NaCl unit cell (expanded)

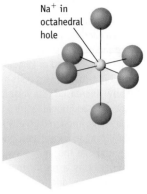

1 hole of this kind
in the center of the
unit cell

12 holes of this kind in the 12
edges of the unit cell
(a net of 3 holes)

(a) Cubic NaCl. The solid is based on a face-centered cubic unit cell of Na^+ and Cl^- ions.

(b) Expanded view of the NaCl lattice. (The lines are not bonds; they are there to help visualize the lattice.) The smaller Na^+ ions (silver) are packed into a face-centered cubic lattice of larger Cl^- ions (yellow).

(c) Octahedral holes. A view showing the octahedral holes in the lattice.

FIGURE 13.9 Sodium chloride.

Another common unit cell has a different placement of ions. Again, there are ions of one type in a face-centered cubic unit cell. Ions of the other type are located in **tetrahedral holes**, wherein each ion is surrounded by four oppositely charged ions. As illustrated in Figure 13.10, there are eight tetrahedral holes in a face-centered cubic unit cell. In ZnS (zinc blende), the sulfide ions (S^{2-}) form a face-centered cubic unit cell. The zinc ions (Zn^{2+}) then occupy one half of the tetrahedral holes, and each Zn^{2+} ion is surrounded by four S^{2-} ions. The unit cell has four S^{2-} ions (making up the fcc lattice) and four Zn^{2+} ions contained wholly within the unit cell (in tetrahedral holes). This 1:1 ratio of ions matches the ratio in the formula.

In summary, compounds with the formula MX commonly form one of three possible crystal structures:

1. M^{n+} ions occupying the cubic hole in a primitive cubic X^{n-} lattice. Example: CsCl.
2. M^{n+} ions in all the octahedral holes in a face-centered cubic X^{n-} lattice. Example: NaCl.
3. M^{n+} ions occupying half of the tetrahedral holes in a face-centered cube lattice of X^{n-} ions. Example: ZnS.

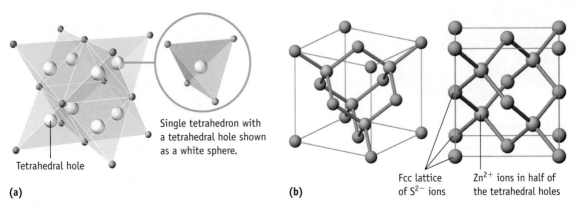

Tetrahedral hole

Single tetrahedron with a tetrahedral hole shown as a white sphere.

Fcc lattice of S^{2-} ions

Zn^{2+} ions in half of the tetrahedral holes

(a)

(b)

FIGURE 13.10 Tetrahedral holes and two views of the ZnS (zinc blende) unit cell. **(a)** The tetrahedral holes in a face-centered cubic lattice. **(b)** This unit cell is an example of a face-centered cubic lattice of ions of one type with ions of the opposite type in one half of the tetrahedral holes.

© Cengage Learning/Charles D. Winters

CASE STUDY

High-Strength Steel and Unit Cells

A few decades ago if you rolled a car over or suffered a front end or side collision, you were likely to be seriously injured or killed. In recent years, though, the use of seat belts and air bags has greatly increased survivability. However, there is an additional factor—the steels used in cars have improved greatly and have led to both stronger frames and energy-absorbing front ends. At the same time cars are lighter and, partly as a result, more fuel-efficient. Much of this is due to the "design" of better steel.

Iron and steel are still made the same way they have always been: First, iron ore is reduced with carbon to produce raw iron. This is then heated in a "basic oxygen furnace" to remove impurities (▶ Chapter 22). Stronger steels were traditionally produced by adding very small amounts of other metals at this point to produce alloys that have very specific properties, but this can be expensive. So, the steel industry has developed new methods for producing steels that are less expensive.

When steel is produced, it is not a single, large crystal of iron atoms neatly arranged in a lattice. Rather, it consists of grains or crystallites of iron in various forms as well as carbon. The characteristics of this material can be changed by rolling a slab at room temperature, by annealing, or by quenching. Quenching refers to a process in which the steel slab is rolled at room temperature, heated to a high temperature, and then rapidly cooled or "quenched" in cold water.

FIGURE A Modern high-strength steels can save the lives of passengers in serious accidents such as rollovers.

Ferrite has a unit cell consisting only of iron atoms (Figure C); carbon atoms are not part of in the lattice. However, when the steel is heated, the lattice can rearrange, and carbon atoms become part of the unit cell. This new form with an embedded carbon atom is called the *austinite form*. When the steel is then quenched, another rearrangement occurs, this time to the martensite form, still with an embedded carbon atom.

Steel that has gone through this process will consist of crystallites of ferrite, austenite, and martensite. Depending on the precise conditions used, the proportion of these can vary, and so can the strength of the steel. For example, steel with a high proportion of martensite is very strong and is used in car bumpers.

Some steels may have added boron, which gives an ultra-high-strength steel that can be used in door pillars and beams. The lives of passengers can be saved in the event of a rollover.

Questions:
1. What is the unit cell of ferrite?
2. Describe the unit cell of austenite.
3. What change has occurred on going from the austenite form to the martensite form?

Answers to these questions are available in Appendix N.

Reference:
New York Times, September 25, 2009, page D1.

□ Ultra-High-Strength Steel
■ High-Strength Steel
■ Boron Steel

FIGURE B Steels used in a recent automobile.

Iron atom   Carbon atom

ferrite   austenite   martensite

FIGURE C The transformation that occurs on treating ferrite in steel.

Chemists and geologists in particular have observed that the sodium chloride or "rock salt" structure is adopted by many ionic compounds, most especially by all the alkali metal halides (except CsCl, CsBr, and CsI), all the oxides and sulfides of the alkaline earth metals, and all the oxides of formula MO of the transition metals of the fourth period.

EXAMPLE 13.2   Ionic Structure and Formula

Problem One unit cell of the common mineral perovskite is illustrated in the margin. This compound is composed of calcium and titanium cations and oxide anions. Based on the unit cell, what is the formula of perovskite?

What Do You Know? The cell is composed of the ions Ca^{2+}, Ti^{4+}, and O^{2-}. The Ca^{2+} ion is wholly within the cell, the Ti^{4+} ions are at the corners of the cell, and the O^{2-} ions are in the cell edges. From this you can decide how many net ions are within the unit cell and thus know the formula.

Strategy Based on the locations of the ions, decide on the net number of ions of each kind in the cell.

Solution

Number of Ti^{4+} ions:

(8 Ti^{4+} ions at cube corners) $\times$ ($\frac{1}{8}$ of each ion inside unit cell) = 1 net Ti^{4+} ion

Number of Ca^{2+} ions:

One ion is in the cube center = 1 net Ca^{2+} ion

Number of O^{2-} ions:

(12 O^{2-} ions in cube edges) $\times$ ($\frac{1}{4}$ of each ion inside unit cell) = 3 net O^{2-} ions

Thus, the formula of perovskite is $CaTiO_3$.

Think about Your Answer $CaTiO_3$ is a reasonable formula. One Ca^{2+} ion and three O^{2-} ions would require a titanium ion with a 4+ charge, a reasonable value because titanium is in Group 4B of the periodic table.

Check Your Understanding

If an ionic solid has an fcc lattice of anions (X) and all of the tetrahedral holes are occupied by metal cations (M), is the formula of the compound MX, MX_2, or M_2X?

Ti^{4+} O^{2-} Ca^{2+}

The unit cell of the mineral perovskite. See Example 13.2.

EXAMPLE 13.3   The Relation of the Density of an Ionic Compound and Its Unit Cell Dimensions

Problem Magnesium oxide has a face-centered cubic unit cell of oxide ions with magnesium ions in octahedral holes. If the radius of Mg^{2+} is 79 pm and the density of MgO is 3.56 g/cm³, what is the radius of an oxide ion?

What Do You Know? This is similar to Example 13.1 in that you wish to know the size of one ion or atom in the cell. You are given the density of the compound and the fact that the unit cell is face-centered cubic. In addition, you know the radius of a Mg^{2+} ion.

Strategy You can use the atomic masses of Mg and O and Avogadro's number to calculate the mass of one formula unit of MgO. You know that the unit cell is face-centered cubic. Because the lattice points are O^{2-} ions, this tells you that there are 4 O^{2-} ions within the cell. There are Mg^{2+} ions in the octahedral holes, so you know there are also 4 Mg^{2+} ions within the cell. The unit cell thus contains 4 MgO units. This, along with the mass per formula unit, can be used to calculate the mass per unit cell. The density of the cell relates the mass of the cell and the cell volume, so you can now calculate the volume of the unit cell and from this the length of one edge (Length = volume$^{1/3}$). As illustrated in the margin, the edge of the unit cell is twice the radius of a Mg^{2+} ion (2 $\times$ 79 pm) plus twice the radius of an O^{2-} ion (the unknown).

(a)

Mg^{2+} O^{2-}

(b)

Magnesium oxide. (a) A unit cell showing oxide ions in a face-centered cubic lattice with magnesium ions in the octahedral holes. **(b)** One face of the cell.

Solution

1. *Calculate the mass of the unit cell.* An ionic compound of formula MX (here MgO) and based on a face-centered cubic lattice of X^- ions with M^+ ions in the octahedral holes has 4 MX units per unit cell.

$$\text{Unit cell mass} = \left(\frac{40.304 \text{ g}}{1 \text{ mol MgO}}\right)\left(\frac{1 \text{ mol MgO}}{6.022 \times 10^{23} \text{ units of MgO}}\right)\left(\frac{4 \text{ MgO units}}{1 \text{ unit cell}}\right)$$

$$= 2.677 \times 10^{-22} \text{ g/unit cell}$$

2. *Calculate the volume of the unit cell from the unit cell mass and density.*

$$\text{Unit cell volume} = \left(\frac{2.667 \times 10^{-22} \text{ g}}{\text{unit cell}}\right)\left(\frac{1 \text{ cm}^3}{3.56 \text{ g}}\right) = 7.52 \times 10^{-23} \text{ cm}^3/\text{unit cell}$$

3. *Calculate the edge dimension of the unit cell in pm.*

$$\text{Unit cell edge} = (7.52 \times 10^{-23} \text{ cm}^3)^{1/3} = 4.22 \times 10^{-8} \text{ cm}$$

$$\text{Unit cell edge} = 4.22 \times 10^{-8} \text{ cm}\left(\frac{1 \text{ m}}{100 \text{ cm}}\right)\left(\frac{1 \times 10^{12} \text{ pm}}{1 \text{ m}}\right) = 422 \text{ pm}$$

4. *Calculate the oxide ion radius.*

One face of the MgO unit cell is shown on the previous page. The O^{2-} ions define the lattice, and the Mg^{2+} and O^{2-} ions along the cell edge just touch one another. This means that one edge of the cell is equal to one O^{2-} radius (x) plus twice the Mg^{2+} radius plus one more O^{2-} radius.

$$\text{MgO unit cell edge} = x \text{ pm} + 2(79 \text{ pm}) + x \text{ pm} = 422 \text{ pm}$$

$$x = \boxed{\text{oxide ion radius} = 132 \text{ pm}}$$

Think about Your Answer Chemists often check the chemical literature to judge the reasonableness of an answer. The calculated result here is very close to the value in Table 7.12 (140 pm).

Check Your Understanding

Potassium chloride has the same unit cell as NaCl. Using the ion sizes in Figure 7.12, calculate the density of KCl.

Unit cell of silicon carbide, SiC.

REVIEW & CHECK FOR SECTION 13.2

1. The unit cell of silicon carbide, SiC, is illustrated in the margin. In what type of unit cell are the (dark gray) C atoms arranged?

   (a)   primitive cubic   (c)   face-centered cubic

   (b)   body-centered cubic

2. If one edge of the silicon carbide unit cell is 436.0 pm, what is the calculated density of this compound?

   (a)   0.803 g/cm³   (b)   0.311 g/cm³   (c)   3.21 g/cm³

13.3 Bonding in Metals and Semiconductors

Molecular orbital (MO) theory was introduced in Chapter 9 to rationalize covalent bonding in molecules, but it can also be used to describe metallic bonding. A metal is a kind of "supermolecule," and to describe the bonding in a metal we have to look at all the atoms in a given sample.

Even a tiny piece of metal contains a very large number of atoms and an even larger number of valence orbitals. In 1 mol of lithium atoms, for example, there are 6×10^{23} atoms. Considering only the $2s$ valence orbitals of lithium, there are 6×10^{23} atomic orbitals, from which 6×10^{23} molecular orbitals can be created

FIGURE 13.11 Bands of molecular orbitals in a metal crystal. Here, the 2s valence orbitals of Li atoms are combined to form molecular orbitals. As more and more atoms with the same valence orbitals are added, the number of molecular orbitals grows until the orbitals are so close in energy that they merge into a band of molecular orbitals. If 1 mol of Li atoms, each with its 2s valence orbital, is combined, 6×10^{23} molecular orbitals are formed. However, only 1 mol of electrons, or 3×10^{23} electron pairs, is available, so only half of these molecular orbitals are filled. (See Section 9.3 for the discussion of molecular orbital theory.)

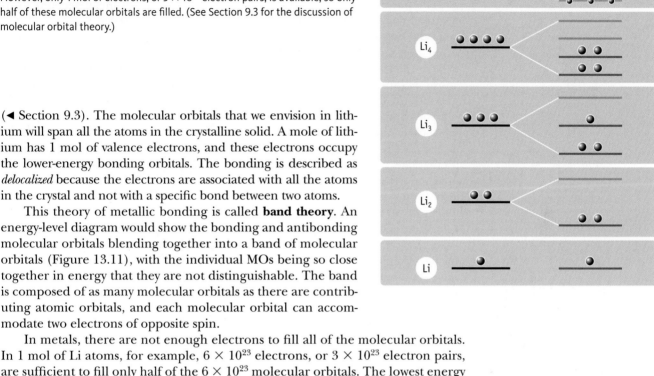

(◄ Section 9.3). The molecular orbitals that we envision in lithium will span all the atoms in the crystalline solid. A mole of lithium has 1 mol of valence electrons, and these electrons occupy the lower-energy bonding orbitals. The bonding is described as *delocalized* because the electrons are associated with all the atoms in the crystal and not with a specific bond between two atoms.

This theory of metallic bonding is called **band theory.** An energy-level diagram would show the bonding and antibonding molecular orbitals blending together into a band of molecular orbitals (Figure 13.11), with the individual MOs being so close together in energy that they are not distinguishable. The band is composed of as many molecular orbitals as there are contributing atomic orbitals, and each molecular orbital can accommodate two electrons of opposite spin.

In metals, there are not enough electrons to fill all of the molecular orbitals. In 1 mol of Li atoms, for example, 6×10^{23} electrons, or 3×10^{23} electron pairs, are sufficient to fill only half of the 6×10^{23} molecular orbitals. The lowest energy for a system occurs with all electrons in orbitals with the lowest possible energy, but this is reached only at 0 K. The highest filled level at 0 K is called the **Fermi level** (Figure 13.12).

Metals. The highest filled level at 0 K is referred to as the *Fermi level*.

Semiconductors. In contrast to metals, the band of filled levels (the valence band) is separated from the band of empty levels (the conduction band) by a band gap. In insulators, the energy of the band gap is large.

FIGURE 13.12 Band theory applied to metals, semiconductors, and insulators. The bonding in metals and semiconductors can be described using molecular orbital theory. Molecular orbitals are constructed from the valence orbitals on each atom and are delocalized over all the atoms.

In metals at temperatures above 0 K, thermal energy will cause some electrons to occupy orbitals above the Fermi level. Even a small input of energy (for example, raising the temperature a few degrees above 0 K) will cause electrons to move from filled orbitals to higher-energy orbitals. For each electron promoted, two singly occupied levels result: a negative electron in an orbital above the Fermi level and a positive "hole"—from the absence of an electron—below the Fermi level.

The positive holes and negative electrons in a piece of metal account for its electrical conductivity. Electrical conductivity arises from the movement of electrons and holes in singly occupied states in the presence of an applied electric field. When an electric field is applied to the metal, negative electrons move toward the positive side, and the positive "holes" move to the negative side. (Positive holes "move" because an electron from an adjacent atom can move into the hole, thereby creating a fresh "hole.")

The band of energy levels in a metal is essentially continuous, that is, the energy gaps between levels are extremely small. A consequence of this is that a metal can absorb energy of nearly any wavelength, causing an electron to move to a higher energy state. The now-excited system can immediately emit a photon of the same energy as the electron returns to the original energy level. This rapid and efficient absorption *and* reemission of light make polished metal surfaces be reflective and appear lustrous (shiny).

The molecular orbital picture for metallic bonding provides an interpretation for other physical characteristics of metals. For example, most metals are malleable and ductile, meaning they can be rolled into sheets and drawn into wires. In these processes, the metal atoms must be able to move fairly freely with respect to their nearest neighbors. This is possible because metallic bonding is delocalized—that is, nondirectional. The layers of atoms can slip past one another relatively easily (as if the delocalized electrons were ball bearings that facilitate this motion), while at the same time the layers are bonded through coulombic attractions between the nuclei and the electrons.

In contrast to metals, rigid network solids such as diamond, silicon, and silica (SiO_2) have localized bonding, which anchors the component atoms or ions in fixed positions. Movement of atoms in these structures relative to their neighbors requires breaking covalent bonds. As a result, such substances are typically hard and brittle. They will not deform under stress as metals do, but instead tend to cleave along crystal planes.

Semiconductors

Semiconducting materials are at the heart of all solid-state electronic devices, including such well-known devices as computer chips and diode lasers. Semiconductors do not conduct electricity easily but can be encouraged to do so by the input of energy. This property allows devices made from semiconductors to essentially have "on" and "off" states, which form the basis of the binary logic used in computers. We can understand how semiconductors function by looking at their electronic structure, following the band theory approach used for metals.

Bonding in Semiconductors: The Band Gap

The Group 4A elements carbon (in the diamond form), silicon, and germanium have similar structures. Each atom is surrounded by four other atoms at the corners of a tetrahedron (Figure 13.13). Using the band model of bonding, the orbitals of each atom are combined to form molecular orbitals that are delocalized over the solid. Unlike metals, however, the result for carbon, silicon, and germanium is two bands, a lower-energy valence band and a higher-energy conduction band. In metals, there is only a small energy barrier for an electron to go from the filled molecular orbitals to empty molecular orbitals, and electricity can flow easily. However, in electrical insulators, such as diamond, and in semiconductors, such as silicon and germanium, the valence and conduction bands are separated from each other resulting in a **band gap**, a barrier to the promotion of electrons to higher energy levels (Figure 13.12). In the Group 4A elements, the orbitals of the valence band are completely filled, but the conduction band is empty.

FIGURE 13.13 The structure of diamond, an insulator. The structures of silicon and germanium, semiconductors, are similar in that each atom is bound tetrahedrally to four others.

Semiconductors can conduct a current because thermal energy is sufficient to promote a few electrons from the valence band, across the band gap, to the conduction band (Figure 13.14). Conduction then occurs when the electrons in the conduction band migrate in one direction and the positive holes in the valence band migrate in the opposite direction.

The band gap in diamond is 580 kJ/mol—so large that electrons are trapped in the filled valence band and cannot make the transition to the conduction band, even at elevated temperatures. Thus, it is not possible to create positive "holes," and so diamond is an insulator, a nonconductor. Semiconductors, in contrast, have a smaller band gap. For common semiconducting materials, this band gap is usually in the range of 10 to 240 kJ/mol. (The band gap is 106 kJ/mol in silicon, whereas it is 68 kJ/mol in germanium.) The magnitude of the band gap in semiconductors is such that these substances are able to conduct small quantities of current under ambient conditions, but, as their name implies, they are much poorer conductors than metals.

Pure silicon and germanium are called **intrinsic semiconductors**, with the name referring to the fact that this is an intrinsic or naturally occurring property of the pure material. In intrinsic semiconductors, the number of electrons in the conduction band is determined by the temperature and the magnitude of the band gap. The smaller the band gap, the smaller the energy required to promote a significant number of electrons. As the temperature increases, more electrons are promoted into the conduction band, and a higher conductivity results.

There are also **extrinsic semiconductors**. The conductivity of these materials is controlled by adding small numbers of different atoms (typically 1 in 10^6 to 1 in 10^8) called *dopants*. That is, the characteristics of semiconductors can be changed by altering their chemical makeup.

Suppose a few silicon atoms in the silicon lattice are replaced by aluminum atoms (or atoms of some other Group 3A element). Aluminum has only three valence electrons, whereas silicon has four. Four Si-Al bonds are created per aluminum atom in the lattice, but these bonds must be deficient in electrons. According to band theory, the Si-Al bonds form a discrete but empty band at an energy level higher than the valence band but lower than the conduction band. This level is referred to as an *acceptor level* because it can accept electrons from the valence band. The gap between the valence band and the acceptor level is usually quite small, so electrons can be promoted readily to the acceptor level. The positive holes created in the valence band are able to move under the influence of an electric potential, so current results from the hole mobility. Because *positive* holes are created in an aluminum-doped semiconductor, this is called a **p-type semiconductor** (Figure 13.14b, left).

● **Intrinsic and Extrinsic** The term *intrinsic* means something is "essential" or "belongs naturally." The converse, *extrinsic*, means that a property is not part of the essential nature of an object.

FIGURE 13.14 Intrinsic (a) and extrinsic (b) semiconductors.

Now suppose phosphorus atoms (or atoms of some other Group 5A element such as arsenic) are incorporated into the silicon lattice instead of aluminum atoms. This material is also a semiconductor, but it now has extra electrons because each phosphorus atom has one more valence electron than the silicon atom it replaces in the lattice. Semiconductors doped in this manner have a discrete, partially filled donor level that resides just below the conduction band. Electrons can be promoted to the conduction band from this donor band, and electrons in the conduction band carry the charge. Such a material, consisting of *negative* charge carriers, is called an **n-type semiconductor** (Figure 13.14b, right).

One group of materials that have desirable semiconducting properties is the III-V semiconductors, so called because they are formed by combining elements from Group 3A (such as Ga and In) with elements from Group 5A (such as As or Sb).

GaAs is a common semiconducting material that has electrical conductivity properties that are sometimes preferable to those of pure silicon or germanium. The crystal structure of GaAs is similar to that of diamond and silicon; each Ga atom is tetrahedrally coordinated to four As atoms, and vice versa.

It is also possible for Group 2B and 6A elements to form semiconducting compounds, such as CdS. The farther apart the elements are found in the periodic table, however, the more ionic the bonding becomes. As the ionic character of the bonding increases, the band gap will increase, and the material will become an insulator rather than a semiconductor. For example, the band gap in GaAs is 140 kJ/mol, whereas it is 232 kJ/mol in CdS.

These materials can also be modified by substituting other atoms into the structure. For example, in one widely used semiconductor, aluminum atoms are substituted for gallium atoms in GaAs, giving materials with a range of compositions ($Ga_{1-x}Al_xAs$). The importance of this modification is that the band gap depends on the relative proportions of the elements, so it is possible to control the size of the band gap by adjusting the stoichiometry. As Al atoms are substituted for Ga atoms, for example, the band gap energy increases. This consideration is important for the specific uses of these materials in devices such as LEDs (light-emitting diodes).

Gallium arsenide, GaAs. The unit cell of GaAs has Ga atoms in an fcc lattice with As atoms in tetrahedral holes. It is an important semiconductor used in infrared emitting diodes, laser diodes, and solar cells.

REVIEW & CHECK FOR SECTION 13.3

Germanium was one of the first materials used as a semiconductor. Given that it has a band gap of 68 kJ/mol, what is the maximum wavelength of light that can excite an electron transition across the band gap of Ge? To what region of the electromagnetic spectrum does this correspond?

(a) 1800 nm, infrared

(b) 29 nm, ultraviolet

(c) 15×10^6 nm, microwave

13.4 Bonding in Ionic Compounds: Lattice Energy

Ionic compounds typically have high melting points, an indication of the strength of the bonding in the ionic crystal lattice. A measure of that is the lattice energy, the main topic of this section.

Lattice Energy

Ionic compounds have positive and negative ions arranged in a three-dimensional lattice in which there are extensive attractions between ions of opposite charge and repulsions between ions of like charge. Each of these interactions is governed by an equation related to Coulomb's law (◄ page 76). For example, $U_{ion\ pair}$, the energy of attractive interactions between a pair of ions, is given by

$$U_{ion\ pair} = C \times \frac{(n^+e)(n^-e)}{d}$$

The symbol C represents a constant, d is the distance between the ion centers, and e is the charge on an electron. The term n^+e represents the charge on the cation in the ion pair, and the term n^-e is the charge on the negative ion. Because n^-e is negative, the energy will have a negative value. Be sure to notice that *the energy depends directly on the charges on the ions and inversely on the distance between them.*

In an extended ionic lattice, there are multiple cation–anion interactions. Taking NaCl as an example (Figure 13.9), focus on an Na^+ ion in the center of the unit cell. We see it is surrounded by, and attracted to, six Cl^- ions. Just a bit farther away from this Na^+ ion, however, there are 12 Na^+ ions along the edges of the cubes, and there is a force of repulsion between the center Na^+ and these ions. And if we still focus on the Na^+ ion in the "center" of the unit cell, we see there are eight more Cl^- ions at the corners of the cube, and these are attracted to the center Na^+ ion. Taking into account *all* of the interactions between the ions in a lattice, we can calculate the **lattice energy**, $\Delta_{lattice}U$, the energy of formation of one mole of a solid crystalline ionic compound when ions in the gas phase combine (Table 13.2). For sodium chloride, this reaction is

$$Na^+(g) + Cl^-(g) \rightarrow NaCl(s)$$

When dealing with ionic compounds chemists often use **lattice enthalpy**, $\Delta_{lattice}H$. The same trends are seen in both lattice energy and enthalpy, and, because we are dealing with a condensed phase, the numerical values are nearly identical.

We shall focus here on the dependence of lattice enthalpy on ion charges and sizes. As given by Coulomb's law, the higher the ion charges, the greater the attraction between oppositely charged ions, so $\Delta_{lattice}H$ has a larger negative value for more highly charged ions. This is illustrated by the lattice enthalpies of MgO and NaF. The value of $\Delta_{lattice}H$ for MgO (-4050 kJ/mol) is about four times more negative than the value for NaF (-926 kJ/mol) because the charges on the Mg^{2+} and O^{2-} ions $[(2+) \times (2-)]$ are twice as large as those on Na^+ and F^- ions.

Because the attraction between ions is inversely proportional to the distance between them, the effect of ion size on lattice enthalpy is also predictable: A lattice built from smaller ions generally leads to a more negative value for the lattice enthalpy (Table 13.2 and Figure 13.15). For alkali metal halides, for example, the lattice enthalpy for lithium compounds is generally more negative than that for potassium compounds because the Li^+ ion is much smaller than the K^+ cation. Similarly, lattice enthalpies of fluorides are more negative than those for iodides with the same cation.

Calculating a Lattice Enthalpy from Thermodynamic Data

Lattice enthalpies can be calculated using a thermodynamic approach known as a **Born–Haber cycle**, an application of Hess's law (◄ page 230). The relationship of various enthalpy changes is illustrated in Figure 13.16 for solid sodium chloride.

Table 13.2 Lattice Energies of Some Ionic Compounds

Compound	$\Delta_{lattice}U$ (kJ/mol)
LiF	−1037
LiCl	−852
LiBr	−815
LiI	−761
NaF	−926
NaCl	−786
NaBr	−752
NaI	−702
KF	−821
KCl	−717
KBr	−689
KI	−649

Source: D. Cubicciotti: Lattice energies of the alkali halides and electron affinities of the halogens. *Journal of Chemical Physics*, Vol. 31, p. 1646, 1959.

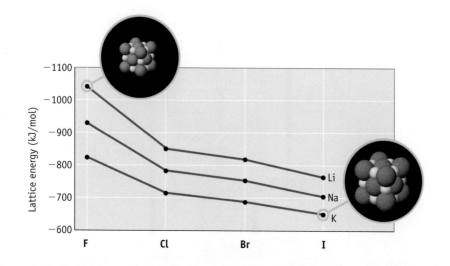

FIGURE 13.15 Lattice energy. $\Delta_{lattice}U$ is illustrated for the formation of the alkali metal halides, MX(s), from the ions $M^+(g) + X^-(g)$.

Steps 1 and 2 in Figure 13.16 involve formation of $Na^+(g)$ and $Cl^-(g)$ ions from the elements; the enthalpy change for each of these steps is known (Appendices F and L). Step 3 in Figure 13.16 gives the lattice enthalpy, $\Delta_{lattice}H$. $\Delta_f H°$ is the standard molar enthalpy of formation of $NaCl(s)$ (Appendix L). The enthalpy values for each step are related by the following equation:

$$\Delta_f H° \, [NaCl(s)] = \Delta H_{Step\ 1a} + \Delta H_{Step\ 1b} + \Delta H_{Step\ 2a} + \Delta H_{Step\ 2b} + \Delta H_{Step\ 3}$$

Because the values for all of these quantities are known except for $\Delta H_{Step\ 3}$ ($\Delta_{lattice}H$), the value for this step can be calculated.

Step 1a.   Enthalpy of formation of $Cl(g)$ $= +121.3$ kJ/mol (Appendix L)
Step 1b. $\Delta H°$ for $Cl(g) + e^- \rightarrow Cl^-(g)$ $= -349$ kJ/mol (Appendix F)
Step 2a.   Enthalpy of formation of $Na(g)$ $= +107.3$ kJ/mol (Appendix L)
Step 2b. $\Delta H°$ for $Na(g) \rightarrow Na^+(g) + e^-$ $= +496$ kJ/mol (Appendix F)

The standard enthalpy of formation of $NaCl(s)$, $\Delta_f H°$, is -411.12 kJ/mol. Combining this with the known values of Steps 1 and 2, we can calculate $\Delta H_{step\ 3}$, which is the lattice enthalpy, $\Delta_{lattice}H$.

Step 3.   Formation of $NaCl(s)$ from the ions in the gas phase $= \Delta H_{step\ 3}$
$$\Delta H_{step\ 3} = \Delta_f H° \, [NaCl(s)] - \Delta H_{Step\ 1a} - \Delta H_{Step\ 1b} - \Delta H_{Step\ 2a} - \Delta H_{Step\ 2b}$$
$$= -411.12 \text{ kJ/mol} - 121.3 \text{ kJ/mol} - (-349 \text{ kJ/mol})$$
$$- 107.3 \text{ kJ/mol} - 496 \text{ kJ/mol}$$
$$= -787 \text{ kJ/mol}$$

REVIEW & CHECK FOR SECTION 13.4

1.   Which sodium halide has the most negative lattice enthalpy?

(a) NaI   (b) NaBr   (c) NaCl   (d) NaF

2.   The lattice enthalpy for NaCl is defined as the enthalpy change for which of the following reactions?

(a) $Na(s) + Cl_2(g) \rightarrow NaCl(s)$ (c) $Na^+(g) + Cl^-(g) \rightarrow NaCl(s)$

(b) $Na(g) + Cl(g) \rightarrow NaCl(s)$ (d) $NaOH(s) + HCl(g) \rightarrow NaCl(s) + H_2O(\ell)$

3.   Calculate the molar enthalpy of formation, $\Delta_f H°$, of solid sodium iodide using the approach outlined in Figure 13.16. The required data can be found in Appendices F and L and in Table 13.2.

(a) +1710 kJ/mol   (c) −287 kJ/mol

(b) −702 kJ/mol   (d) +1120 kJ/mol

FIGURE 13.16 Born–Haber cycle for the formation of NaCl(s) from the elements. The calculation in the text uses enthalpy values, and the value obtained is the lattice enthalpy, $\Delta_{lattice}H$. The difference between $\Delta_{lattice}U$ and $\Delta_{lattice}H$ is generally small and can be corrected for, if desired. (Note that the energy diagram is not to scale.)

Calculation of lattice energies by this procedure (a Born–Haber cycle) is named for Max Born (1882–1970) and Fritz Haber (1868–1934), German scientists who played prominent roles in thermodynamic research.

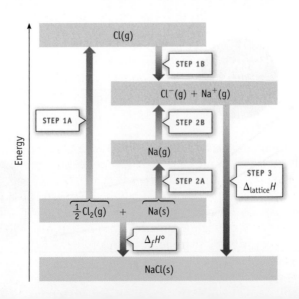

CASE STUDY

Graphene—The Hottest New Network Solid

One of the most interesting developments in chemistry in the last 20 years has been the discovery of new forms of carbon. First, there were buckyballs and then single-wall and multiwall carbon nanotubes.

Common graphite, from which your pencil lead is made, consists of six-member rings of carbon atoms connected in sheets, and the sheets stack one on top of another like cards in a deck. But if carbon compounds are heated under the right conditions, the carbon atoms assemble into sheets, and the sheets close on themselves to form tubes. These are called **nanotubes** because the tubes are only a nanometer or so in diameter. Sometimes they are single tubes, and other times there are tubes within tubes. Carbon nanotubes are at least 100 times stronger than steel but only one sixth as dense, and they conduct heat and electricity far better than copper. Thus, there has been enormous interest in their commercial applications, but it has also been difficult to make them with consistent properties.

Now there is **graphene**, a single sheet of six-member carbon atoms. Researchers in England, Andre Geim and Kostya Novoselov, discovered graphene in a simple way: Put a flake of graphite on Scotch tape, fold the tape over, and then pull it apart. The graphite layers come apart, and, if you do it enough times, only one layer—one C atom thick!—is left on the tape. Now graphene can be made in much

Digital Art/Corbis

Carbon nanotube. These tubes are assembled from six-member rings of carbon atoms and are typically about 1 nm in diameter.

Image courtesy: Dmitriy Dikin (Northwestern University)

Graphene "paper." Researchers at Northwestern University have reassembled graphene sheets to create a tough, flexible, paper-like material.

larger quantities by other methods, and more than 1000 scientific papers have been published on this substance. Chemists and physicists have found that the material is extremely strong and stiff and that it is a better conductor of electrons than any other material at room temperature. It was no surprise when Geim and Novoselov received the 2010 Nobel Prize in physics for their discovery.

Chemical and Engineering News (March 2009) said that although it was "considered a hypothetical curiosity just a few years ago, one-atom-thick graphene has stormed the world of scientific research." Research is proceeding worldwide on its use in electronics and the dream is of making flexible displays. Watch for graphene-based devices to make a difference in your life in the next few years!

Questions:

1. Based on a C–C distance of 139 pm, what is the side-to-side dimension of a planar, C_6 ring?

2. If a graphene sheet has a width of 1.0 micrometer, how many C_6 rings are joined across the sheet?

3. Estimate the thickness of a sheet of graphene (in pm). How did you determine this value?

Answers to these questions are available in Appendix N.

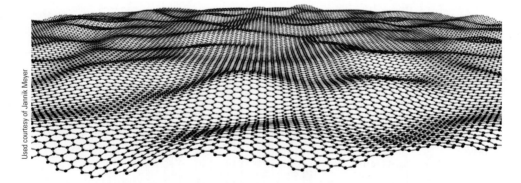

Used courtesy of Jannik Meyer

Graphene is a single sheet of six-member carbon rings. This latest material in the world of carbon chemistry is a faster conductor of electrons than any other material.

are associated with high enthalpies of fusion. Figure 13.19 shows the enthalpies of fusion for the metals of the fourth through the sixth periods. Here we see that transition metals have high enthalpies of fusion, with many of those in the sixth period being extraordinarily high. This trend parallels the trend seen with the melting points for these elements. Tungsten, which has the highest melting point of all the known elements except for carbon, also has the highest enthalpy of fusion among

Table 13.3 Melting Points and Enthalpies of Fusion of Some Elements and Compounds

Element or Compound	Melting Point (°C)	Enthalpy of Fusion (kJ/mol)	Type of Interparticle Forces
Metals			
Hg	−39	2.29	Metal bonding.
Na	98	2.60	
Al	660	10.7	
Ti	1668	20.9	
W	3422	35.2	
Molecular Solids: Nonpolar Molecules			
O_2	−219	0.440	Dispersion forces only.
F_2	−220	0.510	
Cl_2	−102	6.41	
Br_2	−7.2	10.8	
Molecular Solids: Polar Molecules			
HCl	−114	1.99	All three HX molecules have dipole–dipole forces. Dispersion forces increase with size and molar mass.
HBr	−87	2.41	
HI	−51	2.87	
H_2O	0	6.01	Hydrogen bonding, dispersion forces.
Ionic Solids			
NaF	996	33.4	All ionic solids have extended ion–ion interactions. Note the general trend is the same as for lattice energies (see Section 13.4 and Figure 13.15).
NaCl	801	28.2	
NaBr	747	26.1	
NaI	660	23.6	

FIGURE 13.19
Enthalpy of fusion of fourth-, fifth-, and sixth-period metals. Enthalpies of fusion range from 2–5 kJ/mol for Group 1A elements to 35.2 kJ/mol for tungsten. Notice that enthalpies of fusion generally increase for group 4B–8B metals on descending the periodic table.

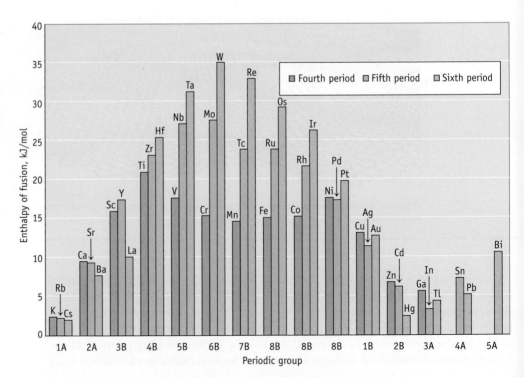

the transition metals. This is the reason tungsten is used for the filaments in incandescent lightbulbs; no other material has been found to work better since the invention of the lightbulb in 1908.

Table 13.3 presents some data for several basic types of substances: metals, polar and nonpolar molecules, and ionic solids. In general, nonpolar substances that form molecular solids have low melting points. Melting points increase within a series of related molecules, however, as the size and molar mass increase. This happens because London dispersion forces are generally larger when the molar mass is larger. Thus, increasing amounts of energy are required to break down the intermolecular forces in the solid, a principle that is reflected in an increasing enthalpy of fusion.

The ionic compounds in Table 13.3 have higher melting points and higher enthalpies of fusion than the molecular solids. This property is due to the strong ion–ion forces present in ionic solids, forces that are reflected in high lattice energies. Because ion–ion forces depend on ion size (as well as ion charge), there is a good correlation between lattice energy and the position of the metal or halogen in the periodic table. For example, the data in Table 13.3 show a decrease in melting point and enthalpy of fusion for sodium salts as the halide ion increases in size. This parallels the decrease in lattice energy seen with increasing ion size.

LED lights. Incandescent lights, with a tungsten filament, may soon be a thing of the past. They can be replaced by LED (light-emitting diode) lamps with a much lower energy consumption. The LED element is a semiconductor that releases light energy when electrons recombine with holes.

Sublimation: Conversion of Solid into Vapor

Molecules can escape directly from the solid to the gas phase by sublimation (Figure 13.20).

$$\text{Solid} \rightarrow \text{gas} \qquad \text{Energy required as heat} = \Delta_{\text{sublimation}}H$$

Sublimation, like fusion and evaporation, is an endothermic process. The energy required as heat is called the **enthalpy of sublimation**. Water, which has a molar enthalpy of sublimation of 51 kJ/mol, can be converted from solid ice to water vapor quite readily. A good example of this phenomenon is the sublimation of frost from grass and trees as night turns to day on a cold morning in the winter.

REVIEW & CHECK FOR SECTION 13.6

1. Which of the following Group 1A halides is expected to have the highest enthalpy of fusion?

   (a) NaCl   (b) KCl   (c) NaBr   (d) KBr

2. Suppose you wanted to cool 100. g of water from 20 °C to 0 °C using dry ice, $CO_2(s)$. The enthalpy of sublimation of $CO_2(s)$ is 25.2 kJ/mol. What mass of dry ice should you need?

   (a) 0.33 g   (b) 15 g   (c) 3.5 g   (d) 150 g

Iodine sublimes when heated.

FIGURE 13.20 Sublimation. Sublimation is the conversion of a solid directly to its vapor. Here, iodine (I_2) sublimes when warmed. If an ice-filled test tube is inserted into the flask, the vapor deposits on the cold surface.

13.7 Phase Diagrams

Depending on the conditions of temperature and pressure, a substance can exist as a gas, a liquid, or a solid. In addition, under certain specific conditions, two (or even three) states can coexist in equilibrium. It is possible to summarize this information in the form of a graph called a **phase diagram**. Phase diagrams are used to illustrate the relationship between phases of matter and the pressure and temperature.

Water

Figure 13.21 illustrates the phase diagram for water. The lines in a phase diagram identify the conditions under which two phases exist at equilibrium. Conversely, all points that do not fall on the lines in the figure represent conditions under which there is only one state that is stable. Line A–B represents conditions for solid-vapor equilibrium, and line A–C for liquid–solid equilibrium. The line from point A to point D, representing the temperature and pressure combination at which the liquid and vapor phases are in equilibrium, is the same curve plotted for water vapor pressure in Figure 12.17. Recall that the normal boiling point, 100 °C in the case of water, is the temperature at which the equilibrium vapor pressure is 760 mm Hg.

Point A, appropriately called the **triple point**, indicates the conditions under which all three phases coexist in equilibrium. For water, the triple point is at $P = 4.6$ mm Hg and $T = 0.01$ °C.

The line A–C shows the conditions of pressure and temperature at which solid–liquid equilibrium exists. (Because no vapor pressure is involved here, the pressure referred to is the external pressure on the liquid.) For water, this line has a negative slope; the change for water is approximately −0.01 °C for each one-atmosphere increase in pressure. That is, the higher the external pressure, the lower the melting point.

The negative slope of the water solid–liquid equilibrium line can be explained from our knowledge of the structure of water and ice. When the pressure on an object increases, common sense tells us that the volume of the object will become smaller, giving the substance a higher density. Because ice is less dense than liquid water (due to the open lattice structure of ice, Figure 12.8), ice and water in equilibrium respond to increased pressure (at constant T) by melting ice to form more water because the same mass of liquid water requires less volume.

Phase Diagrams and Thermodynamics

Let us explore the water phase diagram further by correlating phase changes with thermodynamic data. Suppose we begin with ice at −10 °C and under a pressure of 500 mm Hg (point a on Figure 13.21). As ice is heated (at constant P), it absorbs about 2.1 J/g · K in warming from point a to point b at a temperature between 0 °C and 0.01 °C. At this point, the solid is in equilibrium with liquid water. Solid-liquid equilibrium is maintained until 333 J/g has been transferred to the sample and it has become liquid water at this temperature. If the liquid, still under a pressure of 500 mm Hg, absorbs 4.184 J/g · K, it warms to point c. The temperature at point c is about 89 °C, and equilibrium is established between liquid water and water vapor. The equilibrium vapor pressure of the liquid water is 500 mm Hg. If about 2300 J/g is transferred to the liquid–vapor sample, the equilibrium vapor pressure remains 500 mm Hg until the liquid is completely converted to vapor at 89 °C.

Carbon Dioxide

The features of the phase diagram for CO_2 (Figure 13.22) are generally the same as those for water but with some important differences.

In contrast to water, the CO_2 solid–liquid equilibrium line has a positive slope. Once again, increasing pressure on the solid in equilibrium with the liquid will shift the equilibrium to the more dense phase, but for CO_2 this will be the solid. Because solid CO_2 is denser than the liquid, the newly formed solid CO_2 sinks to the bottom in a container of liquid CO_2.

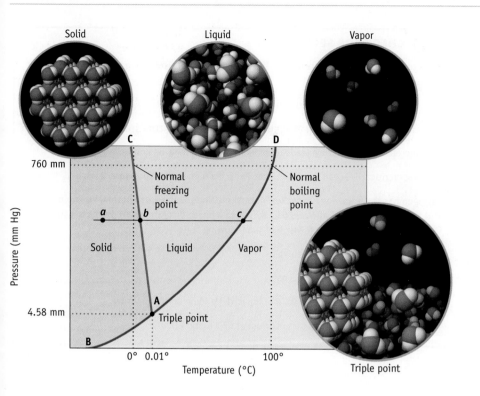

FIGURE 13.21 Phase diagram for water. The scale is intentionally exaggerated to be able to show the triple point and the negative slope of the line representing the liquid–solid equilibrium. (Points a, b, and c are discussed in the text.)

Another feature of the CO_2 phase diagram is the triple point that occurs at a pressure of 5.19 atm (3940 mm Hg) and 216.6 K (−56.6 °C). Carbon dioxide cannot be a liquid at pressures lower than this.

At pressures around normal atmospheric pressure, CO_2 will be either a solid or a gas, depending on the temperature. [At a pressure of 1 atm, solid CO_2 is in equilibrium with the gas at a temperature of 197.5 K (−78.7 °C).] As a result, as solid CO_2 warms above this temperature, it sublimes rather than melts. Carbon dioxide is called *dry ice* for this reason; it looks like water ice, but it does not melt.

From the CO_2 phase diagram, we can also learn that CO_2 gas can be converted to a liquid at room temperature (20–25 °C) by exerting a moderate pressure on the gas. In fact, CO_2 is regularly shipped in tanks as a liquid to laboratories and industrial companies.

Finally, the critical pressure and temperature for CO_2 are 73 atm and 31 °C, respectively. Because the critical temperature and pressure are easily attained in the laboratory, it is possible to observe the transformation to supercritical CO_2 (Figure 12.20).

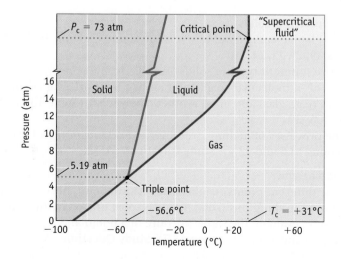

FIGURE 13.22 The phase diagram of CO_2. Notice in particular the positive slope of the solid–liquid equilibrium line. (For more on the critical point, see page 573.)

REVIEW & CHECK FOR SECTION 13.7

1. Refer to the phase diagram for CO_2 in the text. Which of the following statements is *not* true?

   (a) Liquid and gaseous CO_2 exist in equilibrium at approximately 0 °C and 12 atm.

   (b) Liquid CO_2 can only exist at a pressure greater than 5.19 atm.

   (c) Increasing the pressure leads to an increase in the melting point of $CO_2(s)$.

   (d) Supercritical CO_2 can be obtained at 25 °C if a high enough pressure is applied.

2. Nitrogen has the following properties: normal melting point, 63.3 K; normal boiling point, 77.4 K; triple point, 0.123 atm and 63.2 K. Sketch a phase diagram based on these data. Determine from your drawing which of the following statements is *not* correct.

   (a) At 75 K and 0.20 atm N_2 is a gas.

   (b) At 66 K and 0.50 atm N_2 is a gas.

   (c) At 60 K N_2 will be either a solid or a gas, depending on the pressure.

   (d) Solid and liquid coexist at equilibrium at 63.3 K and 1.0 atm.

CHAPTER GOALS REVISITED

Now that you have studied this chapter, you should ask whether you have met the chapter goals. In particular, you should be able to:

Understand cubic unit cells

a. Describe the three types of cubic unit cells: primitive cubic (pc), body-centered cubic (bcc), and face-centered cubic (fcc) (Section 13.1).

b. Relate atom size and unit cell dimensions. **Study Questions: 7, 8, 10, 38, 39, 41, 44, 46, 48, 61, and Go Chemistry Module 18.**

Relate unit cells for ionic compounds to formulas

a. Understand the relation of unit cell structure and formula for ionic compounds. (Section 13.2). **Study Questions: 3, 4, 5, 6, 8, 40, and Go Chemistry Module 18.**

Describe bonding in ionic and metallic solids and the nature of semiconductors.

a. Understand the band theory of bonding in metals and the electrical conductivity of metals. (Section 13.3). **Study Questions: 11, 13.**

b. Understand the nature of semiconductors. (Section 13.3). **Study Questions: 15–18, 51, 53.**

Describe the properties of solids

a. Understand lattice energy and how it is calculated (Section 13.4). **Study Questions: 19, 21, 22, 24, 50.**

b. Characterize different types of solids: metallic (e.g., copper), ionic (e.g., NaCl and CaF_2), molecular (e.g., water and I_2), network (e.g., diamond), and amorphous (e.g., glass and many synthetic polymers) (Table 13.1). **Study Questions: 25–30.**

c. Define the processes of melting, freezing, and sublimation and their enthalpies (Sections 13.6 and 13.7). **Study Questions: 31, 32.**

Interpret phase diagrams

a. Identify the different points (triple point, critical point, normal boiling point, freezing point) and regions (solid, liquid, vapor) of a phase diagram, and use the diagram to evaluate the vapor pressure of a liquid and the relative densities of a liquid and a solid (Section 13.7). **Study Questions: 33–36.**

Study Questions

⦿WL Interactive versions of these questions are assignable in OWL.

▲ denotes challenging questions.

Blue-numbered questions have answers in Appendix R and fully worked solutions in the *Student Solutions Manual*.

Practicing Skills

Metallic and Ionic Solids
(See Sections 13.1 and 13.2 and Examples 13.1–13.3.)

1. Outline a two-dimensional unit cell for the pattern shown here. If the black squares are labeled A and the white squares are B, what is the simplest formula for a "compound" based on this pattern?

2. Outline a two-dimensional unit cell for the pattern shown here. If the black squares are labeled A and the white squares are B, what is the simplest formula for a "compound" based on this pattern?

3. One way of viewing the unit cell of perovskite was illustrated in Example 13.2. Another way is shown here. Prove that this view also leads to a formula of $CaTiO_3$.

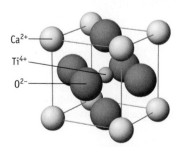

4. Rutile, TiO_2, crystallizes in a structure characteristic of many other ionic compounds. How many formula units of TiO_2 are in the unit cell illustrated here? (The oxide ions marked by an *x* are wholly within the cell; the others are in the cell faces.)

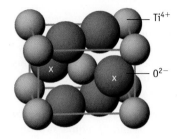

5. Cuprite is a semiconductor. Oxide ions are at the cube corners and in the cube center. Copper ions are wholly within the unit cell.
   (a) What is the formula of cuprite?
   (b) What is the oxidation number of copper?

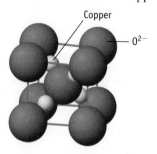

6. The mineral fluorite, which is composed of calcium ions and fluoride ions, has the unit cell shown here.
   (a) What type of unit cell is described by the Ca^{2+} ions?
   (b) Where are the F^- ions located, in octahedral holes or tetrahedral holes?
   (c) Based on this unit cell, what is the formula of fluorite?

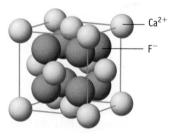

7. Calcium metal crystallizes in a face-centered cubic unit cell. The density of the solid is 1.54 g/cm^3. What is the radius of a calcium atom?

8. The density of copper metal is 8.95 g/cm^3. If the radius of a copper atom is 127.8 pm, is the copper unit cell primitive, body-centered cubic, or face-centered cubic?

9. Potassium iodide has a face-centered cubic unit cell of iodide ions with potassium ions in octahedral holes. The density of KI is 3.12 g/cm^3. What is the length of one side of the unit cell? (Ion sizes are found in Table 7.12.)

10. ▲ A unit cell of cesium chloride is shown on page 590. The density of the solid is 3.99 g/cm^3, and the radius of the Cl^- ion is 181 pm. Calculate the radius of the Cs^+ ion in the center of the cell. (Assume that the Cs^+ ion touches all of the corner Cl^- ions.)

Metals and Semiconductors
(See Section 13.3.)

11. Considering only the molecular orbitals formed by combinations of the $2s$ atomic orbitals, how many molecular orbitals can be formed by 1000 Li atoms? In the lowest energy state, how many of these orbitals will be populated by pairs of electrons and how many will be empty?

12. How many molecular orbitals will be formed by combination of the $3s$ and $3p$ atomic orbitals in 1.0 mol of Mg atoms? At 0 K, what fraction of these orbitals will be occupied by electron pairs (all orbitals filled up to the Fermi level)?

13. Conduction of an electric current is a general property associated with metals. How does the theory for metallic bonding explain conductivity?

14. Most metals are shiny, that is, they reflect light. How does the bonding theory for metals explain this characteristic?

15. Elemental silicon and carbon (in the diamond allotropic form) have the same solid-state structure. However, diamond is an insulator and silicon is a semiconductor. Explain why there is a difference.

16. List the Group 4A elements in order of the size of the band gap.

17. Define the terms intrinsic semiconductor and extrinsic semiconductor. Give an example of each.

18. Explain the conductivity that occurs in an aluminum-doped silicon semiconductor. Is this material a p-type or an n-type semiconductor?

Ionic Bonding and Lattice Energy
(See Section 13.4.)

19. List the following compounds in order from least negative to most negative lattice energy: LiI, LiF, CaO, RbI.

20. Examine the trends in lattice energy in Table 13.2. The value of the lattice energy becomes somewhat more negative on going from NaI to NaBr to NaCl, and all are in the range from -700 to -800 kJ/mol. Suggest a reason for the observation that the lattice energy of NaF ($\Delta_{lattice}U = -926$ kJ/mol) is much more negative than those of the other sodium halides.

21. To melt an ionic solid, energy must be supplied to disrupt the forces between ions so the regular array of ions collapses. If the distance between the anion and the cation in a crystalline solid decreases (but ion charges remain the same), should the melting point decrease or increase? Explain.

22. Which compound in each of the following pairs should have the higher melting point? (See Study Question 21.)
    (a) NaCl or RbCl
    (b) BaO or MgO
    (c) NaCl or MgS

23. Calculate the molar enthalpy of formation, $\Delta_f H°$, of solid lithium fluoride from the lattice energy (Table 13.2) and other thermochemical data. The enthalpy of formation of Li(g), $\Delta_f H°$ [Li(g)] = 159.37 kJ/mol, and other required data can be found in Appendices F and L.

24. Calculate the lattice enthalpy for RbCl. In addition to data in Appendices F and L, you will need the following information:

    $\Delta_f H°$ [Rb(g)] = 80.9 kJ/mol

    $\Delta_f H°$ [RbCl(s)] = -435.4 kJ/mol

Other Types of Solids
(See Section 13.5.)

25. A diamond unit cell is shown here.
    (a) How many carbon atoms are in one unit cell?
    (b) The unit cell can be considered as a cubic unit cell of C atoms with other C atoms in holes in the lattice. What type of unit cell is this (pc, bcc, fcc)? In what holes are other C atoms located, octahedral or tetrahedral holes?

26. The structure of graphite is given in Figure 2.7.
    (a) What type of intermolecular bonding forces exist between the layers of six-member carbon rings?
    (b) Account for the lubricating ability of graphite. That is, why does graphite feel slippery? Why does pencil lead (which is really graphite in clay) leave black marks on paper?

27. We have identified five types of solids (metallic, ionic, molecular, network, amorphous). What particles make up each of these solids and what are the forces of attraction between these particles?

28. List the general properties of each type of solid.

29. Classify each of the following materials as falling into one of the categories listed in Table 13.1. What particles make up these solids and what are the forces of attraction between particles? Give one physical property of each.
    (a) gallium arsenide
    (b) polystyrene
    (c) silicon carbide
    (d) perovskite, $CaTiO_3$

30. Classify each of the following materials as falling into one of the categories listed in Table 13.1. What particles make up these solids, and what are the forces of attraction between particles? Give one physical property of each.
    (a) Si doped with P
    (b) graphite
    (c) benzoic acid, $C_6H_5CO_2H$
    (d) Na_2SO_4

Phase Changes for Solids
(See Section 13.6.)

31. Benzene, C_6H_6, is an organic liquid that freezes at 5.5 °C (◄ Figure 12.1) to form beautiful, feather-like crystals. How much energy is evolved as heat when 15.5 g of benzene freezes at 5.5 °C? (The enthalpy of fusion of benzene is 9.95 kJ/mol.) If the 15.5-g sample is remelted, again at 5.5 °C, what quantity of energy is required to convert it to a liquid?

32. The specific heat capacity of silver is 0.235 J/g · K. Its melting point is 962 °C, and its enthalpy of fusion is 11.3 kJ/mol. What quantity of energy, in joules, is required to change 5.00 g of silver from a solid at 25 °C to a liquid at 962 °C?

Phase Diagrams and Phase Changes
(See Section 13.7.)

33. Consider the phase diagram of CO_2 in Figure 13.22.
    (a) Is the density of liquid CO_2 greater or less than that of solid CO_2?
    (b) In what phase do you find CO_2 at 5 atm and 0 °C?
    (c) Can CO_2 be liquefied at 45 °C?

34. Use the phase diagram given here to answer the following questions:

(a) In what phase is the substance found at room temperature and 1.0 atm pressure?
(b) If the pressure exerted on a sample is 0.75 atm and the temperature is −114 °C, in what phase does the substance exist?
(c) If you measure the vapor pressure of a liquid sample and find it to be 380 mm Hg, what is the temperature of the liquid phase?
(d) What is the vapor pressure of the solid at −122 °C?
(e) Which is the denser phase—solid or liquid? Explain briefly.

35. Liquid ammonia, $NH_3(\ell)$, was once used in home refrigerators as the heat transfer fluid. The specific heat capacity of the liquid is 4.7 J/g · K and that of the vapor is 2.2 J/g · K. The enthalpy of vaporization is 23.33 kJ/mol at the boiling point. If you heat 12 kg of liquid ammonia from −50.0 °C to its boiling point of −33.3 °C, allow it to evaporate, and then continue warming to 0.0 °C, how much energy must you supply?

36. If your air conditioner is more than several years old, it may use the chlorofluorocarbon CCl_2F_2 as the heat transfer fluid. The normal boiling point of CCl_2F_2 is −29.8 °C, and the enthalpy of vaporization is 20.11 kJ/mol. The gas and the liquid have molar heat capacities of 117.2 J/mol · K and 72.3 J/mol · K, respectively. How much energy is evolved as heat when 20.0 g of CCl_2F_2 is cooled from +40 °C to −40 °C?

General Questions

These questions are not designated as to type or location in the chapter. They may combine several concepts.

37. Construct a phase diagram for O_2 from the following information: normal boiling point, 90.18 K; normal melting point, 54.8 K; and triple point, 54.34 K at a pressure of 2 mm Hg. Very roughly estimate the vapor pressure of liquid O_2 at −196 °C, the lowest temperature easily reached in the laboratory. Is the density of liquid O_2 greater or less than that of solid O_2?

38. ▲ Tungsten crystallizes in the unit cell shown here.

316.5 pm

(a) What type of unit cell is this?
(b) How many tungsten atoms occur per unit cell?
(c) If the edge of the unit cell is 316.5 pm, what is the radius of a tungsten atom? (*Hint:* The W atoms touch each other along the diagonal line from one corner of the unit cell to the opposite corner of the unit cell.)

39. Silver crystallizes in a face-centered cubic unit cell. Each side of the unit cell has a length of 409 pm. What is the radius of a silver atom?

40. ▲ The unit cell shown here is for calcium carbide. How many calcium atoms and how many carbon atoms are in each unit cell? What is the formula of calcium carbide? (Calcium ions are silver in color and carbon atoms are gray.)

41. The very dense metal iridium has a face-centered cubic unit cell and a density of 22.56 g/cm³. Use this information to calculate the radius of an atom of the element.

42. Vanadium metal has a density of 6.11 g/cm³. Assuming the vanadium atomic radius is 132 pm, is the vanadium unit cell primitive cubic, body-centered cubic, or face-centered cubic?

43. ▲ Calcium fluoride is the well-known mineral fluorite. Each unit cell contains four Ca^{2+} ions and eight F^- ions. The F^- ions fill all the tetrahedral holes in a face-centered cubic lattice of Ca^{2+} ions. The edge of the CaF_2 unit cell is 5.46295×10^{-8} cm in length. The density of the solid is 3.1805 g/cm³. Use this information to calculate Avogadro's number.

44. ▲ Iron has a body-centered cubic unit cell with a cell dimension of 286.65 pm. The density of iron is 7.874 g/cm³. Use this information to calculate Avogadro's number.

45. ▲ You can get some idea of how efficiently spherical atoms or ions are packed in a three-dimensional solid by seeing how well circular atoms pack in two dimensions. Using the drawings shown here, prove that B is a more efficient way to pack circular atoms than A. The unit cell of A contains portions of four circles and one hole. In B, packing coverage can be calculated by looking at a triangle that contains portions of three circles and one hole. Show that A fills about 80% of the available space, whereas B fills closer to 90% of the available space.

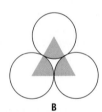

A   B

46. ▲ Assuming that in a primitive cubic unit cell the spherical atoms or ions just touch along the cube's edges, calculate the percentage of empty space within the unit cell. (Recall that the volume of a sphere is $(4/3)\pi r^3$, where r is the radius of the sphere.)

47. ▲ The solid state structure of silicon is shown below.

(a) Describe this crystal as pc, bcc, or fcc. What type of holes are occupied in the lattice?

(b) Calculate the density of silicon in g/cm³ (given that the cube edge has a length of 543.1 pm), and estimate the radius of the silicon atom. (*Note:* The Si atoms on the edges do not touch one another.)

48. ▲ The solid state structure of silicon carbide, SiC, is shown below. Knowing that the Si—C bond length is 188.8 pm (and the Si—C—Si bond angle is 109.5°), calculate the density of SiC.

Unit cell of SiC.

Sample of silicon carbide.

© Cengage Learning/Charles D. Winters

49. Spinels are solids with the general formula AB_2O_4 (where A^{2+} and B^{3+} are metal cations of the same or different metals). The best-known example is common magnetite, Fe_3O_4 [which you can formulate as $(Fe^{2+})(Fe^{3+})_2O_4$]. Another example is the mineral often referred to as *spinel*, $MgAl_2O_4$.

© Cengage Learning/Charles D. Winters

A crystal of the spinel $MgAl_2O_4$.

The oxide ions of spinels form a face-centered cubic lattice. In a *normal spinel*, cations occupy $\frac{1}{8}$ of the tetrahedral sites and $\frac{1}{2}$ of the octahedral sites.

(a) In $MgAl_2O_4$, in what types of holes are the magnesium and aluminum ions found?

(b) The mineral chromite has the formula $FeCr_2O_4$. What ions are involved, and in what types of holes are they found?

50. Using the thermochemical data below and an estimated value of -2481 kJ/mol for the lattice energy for Na_2O, calculate the value for the *second* electron affinity of oxygen $[O^-(g) + e^- \rightarrow O^{2-}(g)]$.

Quantity	Numerical Value (kJ/mol)
Enthalpy of atomization of Na	107.3
Ionization energy of Na	495.9
Enthalpy of formation of solid Na_2O	-418.0
Enthalpy of formation of $O(g)$ from O_2	249.1
First electron attachment enthalpy of O	-141.0

51. The band gap in gallium arsenide is 140 kJ/mol. What is the maximum wavelength of light needed to excite an electron to move from the valence band to the conduction band?

52. The conductivity of an intrinsic semiconductor increases with increasing temperature. How can this be rationalized?

53. Which will show the highest conductivity at 298 K, silicon or germanium?

54. Identify the following as either *p*- or *n*-type semiconductors.
(a) Germanium doped with arsenic
(b) Silicon doped with phosphorus
(c) Germanium doped with indium
(d) Germanium doped with antimony

55. Diamond-based semiconductors are currently of enormous interest in the research community. Although diamond itself is an insulator, the addition of a dopant will narrow the band gap. One semiconductor system has diamond with boron as a dopant. Is this a *p*- or an *n*-type semiconductor?

56. Molecular solids, network solids, and amorphous solids all contain atoms that are joined together by covalent bonds. However, these classes of compounds are very different in overall structure and this leads to different physical properties associated with each group. Describe how the overall structures of these classes of solids differ from each other.

In the Laboratory

57. Like ZnS, lead(II) sulfide, PbS (commonly called *galena*), has a 1:1 empirical formula with a 2+ cation combined with the sulfide anion.

Unit cell of PbS.

Sample of galena.

Does PbS have the same solid structure as ZnS? If different, how are they different? How is the unit cell of PbS related to its formula?

58. $CaTiO_3$, a perovskite, has the structure below.
(a) If the density of the solid is 4.10 g/cm^3, what is the length of a side of the unit cell?
(b) Calculate the radius of the Ti^{4+} ion in the center of the unit cell. How well does your calculation agree with a literature value of 75 pm?

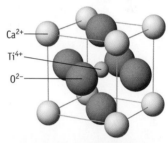

Ca^{2+}
Ti^{4+}
O^{2-}

Unit cell of the perovskite $CaTiO_3$.

A sample of perovskite, $CaTiO_3$.

Summary and Conceptual Questions

The following questions may use concepts from this and previous chapters.

59. ▲ Boron phosphide, BP, is a semiconductor and a hard, abrasion-resistant material. It is made by reacting boron tribromide and phosphorus tribromide in a hydrogen atmosphere at high temperature (>750 °C).
    (a) Write a balanced chemical equation for the synthesis of BP. (*Hint:* Hydrogen is a reducing agent.)
    (b) Boron phosphide crystallizes in a zinc-blend structure, formed from boron atoms in a face-centered cubic lattice and phosphorus atoms in tetrahedral holes. How many tetrahedral holes are filled with P atoms in each unit cell?
    (c) The length of a unit cell of BP is 478 pm. What is the density of the solid in g/cm^3?
    (d) Calculate the closest distance between a B and a P atom in the unit cell. (Assume the B atoms do not touch along the cell edge. The B atoms in the faces touch the B atoms at the corners of the unit cell.)

60. ▲ Why is it not possible for a salt with the formula M_3X (Na_3PO_4, for example) to have a face-centered cubic lattice of X anions with M cations in octahedral holes?

61. ▲ Two identical swimming pools are filled with uniform spheres of ice packed as closely as possible. The spheres in the first pool are the size of grains of sand; those in the second pool are the size of oranges. The ice in both pools melts. In which pool, if either, will the water level be higher? (Ignore any differences in filling space at the planes next to the walls and bottom.)

62. Spinels are described in Study Question 49. Consider two normal spinels, $CoAl_2O_4$ and $SnCo_2O_4$. What metal ions are involved in each? What are their electron configurations? Are the metal ions paramagnetic, and if so how many unpaired electrons are involved?

Applying Chemical Principles

Tin Disease

Organ pipes in northern European cathedrals have been made of tin for several hundred years. It is believed that the metal improves both the tone and appearance of the pipes. Now organ pipes are made of a tin-lead alloy, in part because many old organ pipes have crumbled over time due to "tin disease." Gray splotches appear on the normally shiny metal and over time the metal crumbles to a gray powder. Although it could be assumed that the tin reacted with other elements or compounds to form this gray substance, chemical analysis shows the substance is pure tin.

What is the cause of "tin disease"? Two allotropes of tin exist at atmospheric pressure. The metallic form, known as white tin (or β-tin), is stable at temperatures above 13 °C (Figure 1). This metallic form of tin has a tetragonal crystal structure (Figure 2). Below 13 °C, the metal undergoes a phase transition to a cubic crystal structure that is similar to diamond (page 596). The transition occurs slowly, with a rate that depends on the purity of the tin and the temperature, but the final product is gray tin or α-tin.

The tetragonal structure of white tin has atoms at each corner as well as an atom in four of its six faces and an atom at the center of the lattice. The cubic crystal lattice structure of gray tin has an atom on each of the six faces and four atoms within the unit cell (in addition to atoms at the corners) as in the diamond structure.

The low temperature transformation of white tin to gray tin has been used to explain some famous disasters in history, one apparently true, the other false.

Early in the 20th century, there was great interest in reaching the South Pole, and many tried. The British explorer Robert Scott mounted a large expedition and reached the Pole in January 1912 with a party of five. It was an enormous accomplishment, but he learned to his great disappointment that the Norwegian Roald Amundsen had beaten him by five weeks. Having reached their goal, the Scott party started the 800-mile journey back across the polar ice to the Ross Sea. Along the journey to the Pole they had left food and fuel for use on their

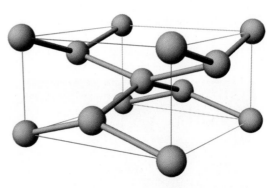

FIGURE 2 A tetragonal unit cell of white of β-tin. The tetragonal unit cell has 90 angles at each corner. Two of the three sides are equal in length (583 pm) while the third side is shorter (318 pm). (Note that the lines connecting atoms are not bonds. They are meant only to show the spatial relationship of the atoms.)

return trip. Both fuel and food were packed in tin cans with tin-soldered joints. Unfortunately, in the extremely low temperature, the tin in the joints turned into gray tin, flaked off, and the fuel leaked out. None was available to use, and all in Scott's party perished.

Another story of tin disease is a myth: the legend of crumbling buttons on the overcoats of French soldiers in 1812. In the winter of 1812, Napoleon's army fought and lost a brutal campaign in Russia. The shiny tin buttons used by the French soldiers are said to have crumbled in the cold Russian climate so they could not keep their clothing around them in the frigid weather. The problem with this story is that the uniform buttons at the time were made of bone.

Questions:

1. How many tin atoms are contained in the tetragonal crystal lattice unit cell of β-tin? How many tin atoms are contained in the cubic crystal lattice unit cell of α-tin?
2. Using the dimensions of the unit cell and the molar mass of tin, calculate the density of white tin (in g/cm^3).
3. The density of gray tin is 5.769 g/cm^3. Determine the dimensions (in pm) of the cubic crystal lattice.
4. Determine the percentage of space occupied by tin atoms in both the tetragonal and cubic crystal lattices. The atomic radius of tin is 141 pm.

References:

1. J. Emsley, *Nature's Building Blocks, An A–Z Guide to the Elements*, Oxford University Press, 2001.
2. P. LeCouteur and J. Burreson, *Napoleon's Buttons*, Penguin Putnam, New York, 2003.

© Cengage Learning/Charles D. Winters

FIGURE 1 A sample of white tin. This common element has a density of 7.31 g/cm^3 and a melting point of 232 °C.

14 Solutions and Their Behavior

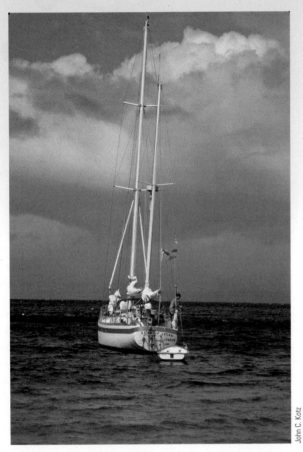

The Seax, an ocean-going yacht, in the Fiji Islands.

Portable reverse osmosis water purifier carried by deep water sailors.

Survival at Sea In the late 1980s, Bill and Simone Butler set off from Florida to sail their 38-foot boat around the world. Everything went well as they sailed through the Panama Canal and into the Pacific Ocean. Somewhere west of Costa Rica, however, on June 15, 1989, their boat was attacked by a school of whales in the middle of the night. The boat was holed and was going to sink. They had only enough time to launch their small life raft, grab some fishing line and a few other supplies, and one other important device: a portable water purifier that worked by reverse osmosis.

The Butlers drifted toward the east in their little raft for 66 days. They subsisted on the raw fish they could catch, but most importantly they had fresh water to drink from the reverse osmosis device. The device was able to produce 2–3 L of pure water a day, which saved their lives. Although they lost some weight, they were in good health when they were rescued by Costa Rican fishermen on August 19, 1989.

Question:

What is the osmotic pressure of seawater at 25 °C with a total dissolved ion concentration of 1.15 M?

The answer to this question is available in Appendix N.

CHAPTER GOALS

See Chapter Goals Revisited (page 646) for Study Questions keyed to these goals.

- Calculate and use the solution concentration units molality, mole fraction, and weight percent.

- Understand the solution process.

- Understand and use the colligative properties of solutions.

- Recognize the properties and importance of colloids

We come into contact with solutions every day: aqueous solutions of ionic salts, gasoline with additives to improve its properties, and household cleaners such as ammonia in water. We purposely make solutions. Adding sugar, flavoring, and sometimes CO_2 to water produces a palatable soft drink. Athletes drink commercial beverages with dissolved salts to match salt concentrations in body fluids precisely, thus allowing the fluid to be taken into the body more rapidly. In medicine, saline solutions (aqueous solutions containing NaCl and other soluble salts) are infused into the body to replace lost fluids.

A **solution** is a homogeneous mixture of two or more substances in a single phase. By convention, the component present in largest amount is identified as the **solvent** and the other component(s) as the **solute**(s) (Figure 14.1). Although other types of solutions exist (such as alloys, solid solutions of metals), the objective in this chapter is to develop an understanding of gases, liquids, and solids dissolved in liquid solvents.

Experience tells you that adding a solute to a pure liquid will change the properties of the liquid. Indeed, that is the reason some solutions are made. For instance, adding antifreeze to the water in your car's radiator prevents the coolant from boiling in the summer and freezing in the winter. The changes that occur in the freezing and boiling points when a substance is dissolved in a pure liquid are two observations we want to examine in detail. These properties, as well as the osmotic pressure of a solution and changes in solvent vapor pressure, are examples of colligative properties. **Colligative properties** are properties of solutions that depend only on the number of solute particles per solvent molecule and not on the identity of the solute.

(a) Copper(II) chloride, the solute, is added to water, the solvent.

(b) Interactions between water molecules and Cu^{2+} and Cl^- ions allow the solid to dissolve. The ions are now sheathed with water molecules.

FIGURE 14.1 Making a solution of copper(II) chloride (the solute) in water (the solvent). When ionic compounds dissolve in water, each ion is surrounded by water molecules. The number of water molecules depends on ion size and charge.

© Cengage Learning/Charles D. Winters

© Cengage Learning/Charles D. Winters

FIGURE 14.2 Preparing 0.100 molal and 0.100 molar solutions. In the flask on the right, 0.100 mol (19.4 g) of K_2CrO_4 was mixed with enough water to make 1.000 L of solution. (The volumetric flask was filled to the mark on its neck, indicating that the volume is 1.000 L. Slightly less than 1.00 L of water was added.) If 1.00 kg of water was added to 0.100 mol of K_2CrO_4 in the flask on the left, the volume of solution is greater than 1.000 L. (The small pile of yellow solid in front of the flasks is 0.100 mol of K_2CrO_4.)

Notice the difference in water levels in the two flasks

0.100 molal solution
Water added to flask = 1.00 kg
Volume of solution > 1.00 L

0.100 molar solution
Water added to flask < 1.00 L
Volume of solution = 1.00 L

© Cengage Learning/Charles D. Winters

14.1 Units of Concentration

To analyze the colligative properties of solutions, we need ways of measuring solute concentrations that reflect the number of molecules or ions of solute per molecule of solvent.

Molarity, a concentration unit useful in stoichiometry calculations, is not useful when dealing with most colligative properties. Recall that molarity (M) is defined as the number of moles of solute per liter of solution (◀ page 173), so using molarity does not allow us to identify the exact amount of solvent used to make the solution. This fact is illustrated in Figure 14.2. The flask on the right contains a 0.100 M aqueous solution of potassium chromate. It was made by adding enough water to 0.100 mol of K_2CrO_4 to make 1.000 L of solution. The amount of solvent (water) that was actually added is not readily known. If 1.00 kg of water had been added to 0.100 mol of K_2CrO_4, as illustrated with the flask on the left in Figure 14.2, the volume of solution would be greater than 1.000 L.

Three concentration units are described here that reflect the number of molecules or ions of solute per solvent molecule: molality, mole fraction, and weight percent.

The **molality**, m, of a solution is defined as the amount of solute (mol) per kilogram of solvent.

$$\text{Concentration } (c, \text{ mol/kg}) = \text{molality of solute} = \frac{\text{amount of solute (mol)}}{\text{mass of solvent (kg)}} \quad (14.1)$$

The molality of K_2CrO_4 in the flask on the left side of Figure 14.2 is 0.100 mol/kg. It was prepared from 0.100 mol (19.4 g) of K_2CrO_4 and 1.00 kg (1.000 L × 1.00 kg/L) of water.

Notice that different quantities of water were used to make the 0.100 M (0.100 molar) and 0.100 m (0.100 molal) solutions of K_2CrO_4. This means the *molarity and the molality of a given solution cannot be the same*, although the difference may be negligibly small when the solution is quite dilute.

The **mole fraction**, X, of a solution component is defined as the amount of that component (n_A) divided by the total amount of all of the components of the mixture ($n_A + n_B + n_C + \ldots$). Mathematically it is represented as

• **Mole Fraction and Gases** The mole fraction of a gas in a mixture of gases was defined on page 526.

$$\text{Mole fraction of A } (X_A) = \frac{n_A}{n_A + n_B + n_C + \ldots} \quad (14.2)$$

Consider a solution that contains 1.00 mol (46.1 g) of ethanol, C_2H_5OH, in 9.00 mol (162 g) of water. The mole fraction of alcohol is 0.100, and that of water is 0.900.

$$X_{ethanol} = \frac{1.00 \text{ mol ethanol}}{1.00 \text{ mol ethanol} + 9.00 \text{ mol water}} = 0.100$$

$$X_{water} = \frac{9.00 \text{ mol water}}{1.00 \text{ mol ethanol} + 9.00 \text{ mol water}} = 0.900$$

Notice that the sum of the mole fractions of the components in the solution equals 1.000, a relationship that must be true, based on how mole fraction is defined.

Weight percent is the mass of one component divided by the total mass of the mixture, multiplied by 100%:

$$\text{Weight \% A} = \frac{\text{mass of A}}{\text{mass of A} + \text{mass of B} + \text{mass of C} + \ldots} \times 100\% \qquad \textbf{(14.3)}$$

The alcohol–water mixture has 46.1 g of ethanol and 162 g of water, so the total mass of solution is 208 g, and the weight % of alcohol is

$$\text{Weight \% ethanol} = \frac{46.1 \text{ g ethanol}}{46.1 \text{ g ethanol} + 162 \text{ g water}} \times 100\% = 22.2\%$$

Weight percent is a common unit in consumer products (Figure 14.3). Vinegar, for example, is an aqueous solution containing approximately 5% acetic acid and 95% water. The label on a common household bleach lists its active ingredient as 6.00% sodium hypochlorite (NaOCl) and 94.00% inert ingredients.

Naturally occurring solutions are often very dilute. Environmental chemists, biologists, geologists, oceanographers, and others frequently use **parts per million (ppm)** to express their concentrations. The unit ppm refers to relative quantities by mass; 1.0 ppm represents 1.0 g of a substance in a sample with a total mass of 1.0 million g or 1 mg in 1000 g.

FIGURE 14.3 Weight percent. The composition of many common products is often given in terms of weight percent. Here, the label on the cat spray indicates it contains 1.15% active ingredients.

© Cengage Learning/Charles D. Winters

EXAMPLE 14.1   Calculating Mole Fractions, Molality, and Weight Percent

Problem Assume you add 1.2 kg of ethylene glycol, $HOCH_2CH_2OH$, as an antifreeze to 4.0 kg of water in the radiator of your car. What are the mole fraction, molality, and weight percent of the ethylene glycol?

What Do You Know? You know the identity and masses of solute and solvent.

Strategy The amount of solute and solvent can be calculated using the mass and molar mass of each material. The masses and amounts of solute and solvent can then be combined to calculate the concentration in each of the desired concentration units using Equations 14.1–14.3.

Solution The 1.2 kg of ethylene glycol (molar mass = 62.1 g/mol) is equivalent to 19 mol, and 4.0 kg of water represents 220 mol.

Mole fraction:

$$X_{glycol} = \frac{19 \text{ mol ethylene glycol}}{19 \text{ mol ethylene glycol} + 220 \text{ mol water}} = \boxed{0.080}$$

Molality:

$$c_{glycol} = \frac{19 \text{ mol ethylene glycol}}{4.0 \text{ kg water}} = 4.8 \text{ mol/kg} = \boxed{4.8 \text{ } m}$$

Weight percent:

$$\text{Weight \%} = \frac{1.2 \times 10^3 \text{ g ethylene glycol}}{1.2 \times 10^3 \text{ g ethylene glycol} + 4.0 \times 10^3 \text{ g water}} \times 100\% = \boxed{23\%}$$

© Cengage Learning/Charles D. Winters

Commercial antifreeze. This solution contains ethylene glycol, $HOCH_2CH_2OH$, an organic alcohol that is readily soluble in water. Regulations specify that the weight percent of ethylene glycol in ethylene glycol–based antifreeze must be at least 75%. (The remainder of the solution can be other glycols and water.)

Think about Your Answer Although the numerical values are very different, the information contained in these values is similar; each relates to the relative numbers of solvent and solute particles.

Check Your Understanding

(a) Mole fraction, molality, and weight percent: If you dissolve 10.0 g (about one heaping tea-spoonful) of sugar (sucrose, $C_{12}H_{22}O_{11}$), in a cup of water (250. g), what are the mole fraction, molality, and weight percent of sugar?

(b) Parts per million: Seawater has a sodium ion concentration of 1.08×10^4 ppm. If the sodium is present in the form of dissolved sodium chloride, what mass of NaCl is in each liter of sea-water? Seawater is denser than pure water because of dissolved salts. Its density is 1.05 g/mL.

REVIEW & CHECK FOR SECTION 14.1

1. You dissolve 1.0 mol of urea (H_2NCONH_2) in 270 g of water. The mole fraction of urea is

    (a) 3.7×10^{-3} (b) 0.063   (c) 16   (d) 1.0

    and its molality is

    (a) 1.0   (b) 3.7   (c) 0.063   (d) 0.27

2. An aqueous solution has 1.0 g of CH_3OH in 50.0 g of water. Which concentration has the largest numerical value for the methanol content?

    (a) weight percent

    (b) mole fraction

    (c) molality

14.2 The Solution Process

• **Unsaturated** The term unsaturated is used when referring to solutions with solute concentrations that are less than that of a saturated solution.

If solid $CuCl_2$ is added to a beaker of water, the salt will begin to dissolve (Figure 14.1). The amount of solid diminishes, and the concentrations of Cu^{2+}(aq) and Cl^-(aq) in the solution increase. If we continue to add $CuCl_2$, however, we will eventually reach a point when no additional $CuCl_2$ seems to dissolve. The concentrations of Cu^{2+}(aq) and Cl^-(aq) will not increase further, and any additional solid $CuCl_2$ added after this point will remain as a solid at the bottom of the beaker. We say that such a solution is **saturated**.

Although no change is observed on the macroscopic level, it is a different matter on the particulate level. The process of dissolving continues, with Cu^{2+} and Cl^- ions leaving the solid state and entering solution. However, at the same time solid $CuCl_2$(s) is being formed from Cu^{2+}(aq) and Cl^-(aq). The rates at which $CuCl_2$ is dissolving and reprecipitating are equal in a saturated solution, so that no net change in the concentration of ions is observed on the macroscopic level.

This process is another example of a dynamic equilibrium (◀ page 118), and we can describe the situation in terms of an equation with substances linked by a set of double arrows ($\rightleftharpoons$):

$$CuCl_2(s) \rightleftharpoons Cu^{2+}(aq) + 2\ Cl^-(aq)$$

A saturated solution gives us a way to define precisely the solubility of a solid in a liquid. **Solubility** is the concentration of solute in equilibrium with undissolved solute in a saturated solution. The solubility of $CuCl_2$, for example, is 70.6 g in 100 mL of water at 0 °C. If we add 100.0 g of $CuCl_2$ to 100 mL of water at 0 °C, we can expect 70.6 g to dissolve, and 29.4 g of solid to remain.

FIGURE 14.4
Miscibility.

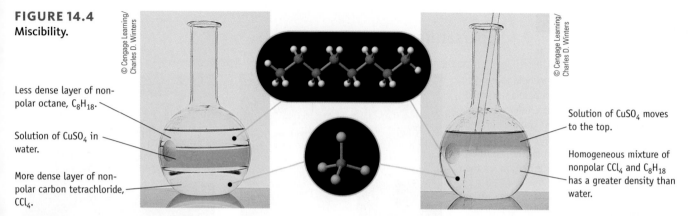

Less dense layer of non-polar octane, C_8H_{18}.

Solution of $CuSO_4$ in water.

More dense layer of non-polar carbon tetrachloride, CCl_4.

Solution of $CuSO_4$ moves to the top.

Homogeneous mixture of nonpolar CCl_4 and C_8H_{18} has a greater density than water.

(a) Before mixing. The colorless, denser bottom layer is nonpolar carbon tetrachloride, CCl_4. The blue middle layer is a solution of $CuSO_4$ in water, and the colorless, less dense top layer is nonpolar octane, C_8H_{18}. This mixture was prepared by carefully layering one liquid on top of another, without mixing.

(b) After mixing. After stirring the mixture, the two nonpolar liquids form a homogeneous mixture. This layer of mixed liquids is under the water layer because the mixture of CCl_4 and C_8H_{18} has a greater density than water.

Liquids Dissolving in Liquids

If two liquids mix to an appreciable extent to form a solution, they are said to be **miscible**. In contrast, **immiscible** liquids do not mix to form a solution; they exist in contact with each other as separate layers (Figure 14.4).

The polar compounds ethanol (C_2H_5OH) and water are miscible in all proportions, as are the nonpolar liquids octane (C_8H_{18}) and carbon tetrachloride (CCl_4). On the other hand, neither C_8H_{18} nor CCl_4 is miscible with water. Observations like these have led to a familiar rule of thumb: *Like dissolves like.* That is, two or more nonpolar liquids frequently are miscible, just as are two or more polar liquids.

What is the molecular basis for the "like dissolves like" guideline? In pure water and pure ethanol, the major force between molecules is hydrogen bonding involving —OH groups. When the two liquids are mixed, hydrogen bonding between ethanol and water molecules also occurs and assists in the solution process. In contrast, molecules of pure octane or pure CCl_4, both of which are nonpolar, are held together in the liquid phase by dispersion forces (◄ Section 12.4). The energy associated with these forces of attraction is similar in value to the energy due to the forces of attraction between octane and CCl_4 molecules when these nonpolar liquids are mixed. Thus, little or no energy change occurs when octane–octane and CCl_4–CCl_4 attractive forces are replaced with octane–CCl_4 forces. The solution process is expected to be nearly energy neutral. So, why do the liquids mix? The answer lies deeper in thermodynamics. As you shall see in Chapter 19, spontaneous changes, such as the mixing of liquids, are accompanied by an increase in entropy, a thermodynamic function that is a measure of the wider dispersal of the energy of the particles in the mixture relative to the pure liquids (Figure 14.5).

In contrast, polar and nonpolar liquids usually do not mix to an appreciable degree; when placed together in a container, they separate into two distinct layers

● **Entropy and the Solution Process**
Although the energetics of solution formation are important, it is generally accepted that entropy is a more important contributor to the solution process. (See Chapter 19 and T. P. Silverstein: "The real reason why oil and water don't mix." *Journal of Chemical Education*, Vol. 75, pp. 116–118, 1998.)

H_2O Separate liquids CH_3OH Mixture

FIGURE 14.5 Driving the solution process— entropy. When two similar liquids—here water and methanol—are mixed, the molecules intermingle, and the energy of the system is more dispersed than in the two, separate pure liquids. A measure of this energy dispersal is entropy, a thermodynamic function described in more detail in Chapter 19.

A CLOSER LOOK

Supersaturated Solutions

Although at first glance it may seem a contradiction, it is possible for a solution to hold more dissolved solute than the amount in a saturated solution. Such solutions are referred to as **supersaturated** solutions. Supersaturated solutions are unstable, and the excess solid eventually crystallizes from the solution until the equilibrium concentration of the solute is reached.

The solubility of substances often decreases if the temperature is lowered. Supersaturated solutions are usually made by preparing a saturated solution at a given temperature and then carefully cooling it. If the rate of crystallization is slow, the solid may not precipitate when the solubility is exceeded. The result is a solution that has more solute than the amount defined by equilibrium conditions; it is supersaturated.

When disturbed in some manner, a supersaturated solution moves toward equilibrium by precipitating solute. This change can occur rapidly, often with the evolution of thermal energy. In fact, supersaturated solutions are used in "heat packs" to apply

Supersaturated solutions. When a supersaturated solution is disturbed, the dissolved salt (here sodium acetate, $NaCH_3CO_2$) rapidly crystallizes.

heat to injured muscles. When crystallization of sodium acetate ($NaCH_3CO_2$) from a supersaturated solution in a heat pack is

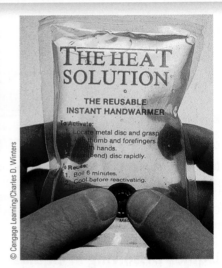

Heat of crystallization. A heat pack relies on the heat evolved by the crystallization of sodium acetate.

initiated, the temperature of the heat pack rises to about 50 °C and crystals of solid sodium acetate are detected inside the bag.

(Figure 14.4). The explanation is complex and involves the interplay of the enthalpy of mixing and entropy. The enthalpy of mixing is zero or nearly so, but mixing dissimilar liquids leads to a decrease in entropy. As explained in Chapter 19, this means that mixing dissimilar liquids is not thermodynamically favorable.

Solids Dissolving in Water

The "like dissolves like" guideline also holds for molecular solids dissolving in liquids. Nonpolar solids such as naphthalene, $C_{10}H_8$, dissolve readily in nonpolar solvents such as benzene, C_6H_6, and hexane, C_6H_{14}. Iodine, I_2, a nonpolar inorganic solid, dissolves in water to some extent, but, given a choice, it dissolves to a larger extent in a nonpolar liquid such as CCl_4 (Figure 14.6). Sucrose (sugar), a polar molecular solid, is not very soluble in nonpolar solvents but is readily soluble in water, a fact that we know well because of its use to sweeten beverages. The presence of O—H groups in the structure of sugar and other substances such as glucose

FIGURE 14.6 Solubility of nonpolar iodine in polar water and nonpolar carbon tetrachloride. When a solution of nonpolar I_2 in water (the brown layer on top in the left test tube) is shaken with nonpolar CCl_4 (the colorless bottom layer in the left test tube), the I_2 transfers preferentially to the nonpolar solvent. Evidence for this is the purple color of the bottom CCl_4 layer in the test tube on the right.

Nonpolar I_2
Polar H_2O

Nonpolar CCl_4

Shake the test tube

Polar H_2O

Nonpolar CCl_4 and I_2

Photos © Cengage Learning/Charles D. Winters

(a) Dissolving NaOH in water is a strongly exothermic process.

(b) A "cold pack" contains solid ammonium nitrate, NH_4NO_3, and a package of water. When the water and NH_4NO_3 are mixed and the salt dissolves, the temperature of the system drops, owing to the endothermic enthalpy of solution of ammonium nitrate ($\Delta_{soln}H° = +25.7$ kJ/mol).

FIGURE 14.7 Dissolving ionic solids and enthalpy of solution.

allows these molecules to interact with polar water molecules through hydrogen bonding.

"Like dissolves like" is a somewhat less effective but still useful guideline when considering the solubility of ionic solids. Thus, we can reasonably predict that ionic compounds, which can be considered extreme examples of polar compounds, will not dissolve in nonpolar solvents. This fact is amply borne out by observation. Sodium chloride, for example, will not dissolve in liquids such as hexane or CCl_4, but it does have a significant solubility in water. Many ionic compounds are soluble in water, but, according to the solubility guidelines on page 122, there are many other ionic solids that are not.

Predicting the solubility of ionic compounds in water is complicated. As mentioned earlier, two factors—enthalpy and entropy—together determine the extent to which one substance dissolves in another. For ionic compounds dissolving in water, entropy usually (but not always) favors solution. A favorable enthalpy factor (negative ΔH) generally leads to a compound being soluble. For example, when sodium hydroxide dissolves in water, the solution warms up (Figure 14.7a), and sodium hydroxide dissolves readily in water. An unfavorable enthalpy factor, however, does not guarantee that an ionic compound will not dissolve. When ammonium nitrate dissolves in water, the solution becomes colder (Figure 14.7b), but ammonium nitrate is still very soluble in water.

Network solids, including graphite, diamond, and quartz sand (SiO_2), do not dissolve in water. (Where would all the beaches be if sand dissolved in water?) The covalent chemical bonding in network solids is simply too strong to be broken; the lattice remains intact when in contact with water.

Enthalpy of Solution

To understand the energetics of the solution process, let us view it at the molecular level. We will use the process of dissolving potassium fluoride, KF, in water to illustrate what occurs, and the energy-level diagram in Figure 14.8 will help us to follow the changes.

Solid potassium fluoride has an ionic crystal lattice with alternating K^+ and F^- ions held in place by attractive forces due to their opposite charges. In water, these ions are separated from each other and *hydrated*; that is, they are surrounded by water molecules (Figure 14.1). Ion–dipole forces of attraction bind water molecules strongly to each ion. The energy change occurring on going from the

OH group

Like dissolves like. Glucose has five —OH groups on each molecule, groups that allow it to form hydrogen bonds with water molecules. As a result, glucose dissolves readily in water.

FIGURE 14.8 Model for energy changes on dissolving KF. An estimate of the magnitude of the energy change on dissolving an ionic compound in water is achieved by imagining it as occurring in two steps at the particulate level. Here, KF is first separated into cations and anions in the gas phase with an expenditure of 821 kJ per mol of KF. These ions are then hydrated, with $\Delta_{hydration}H$ estimated to be -837 kJ. Thus, the net energy change is -16 kJ, a slightly exothermic enthalpy of solution.

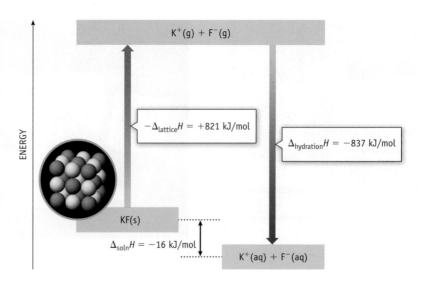

reactant, KF(s), to the products, $K^+(aq)$ and $F^-(aq)$, is the sum of the energies of two individual steps:

1. Energy must be supplied to separate the ions in the lattice against their attractive forces. This is the reverse of the process defining the lattice enthalpy of an ionic compound (◄ page 598), and its value will be equal to $-\Delta_{lattice}H$. Separating the ions from one another is highly endothermic because the attractive forces between ions are strong.

2. Energy is evolved when the individual ions dissolve in water, where each ion becomes surrounded by water molecules. Again, strong forces of attraction (ion–dipole forces) are involved. This process, referred to as **hydration** when water is the solvent, is strongly exothermic.

We can therefore represent the process of dissolving KF in terms of these chemical equations:

Step 1: $KF(s) \longrightarrow K^+(g) + F^-(g)$ $-\Delta_{lattice}H$
Step 2: $K^+(g) + F^-(g) \longrightarrow K^+(aq) + F^-(aq)$ $\Delta_{hydration}H$

The overall reaction is the sum of these two steps. The enthalpy of the overall reaction, called the **enthalpy of solution** ($\Delta_{soln}H$), is the sum of the two enthalpies.

Overall: $KF(s) \longrightarrow K^+(aq) + F^-(aq)$ $\Delta_{soln}H = -\Delta_{lattice}H + \Delta_{hydration}H$

We can use this equation to estimate the value of $\Delta_{hydration}H$. For example, the lattice energy for KF is -821 kJ/mol [calculated using a Born-Haber cycle calculation (◄ page 600)], and the value of $\Delta_{soln}H$ determined by a calorimetry experiment is -16.4 kJ/mol. From these two values, we can determine $\Delta_{hydration}H$ to be -837 kJ/mol.

As a general rule, to be soluble, an ionic compound will have an enthalpy of solution that is exothermic or only slightly endothermic (Figure 14.9). In the latter instance, it is assumed that the enthalpy-disfavored solution process will be balanced by a favorable entropy of solution. If the enthalpy of solution is very endothermic—because of a low hydration energy, for example—then the compound is unlikely to be soluble. We can reasonably speculate that nonpolar solvents would not solvate ions strongly, and that solution formation would thus be energetically unfavorable. We therefore predict that an ionic compound, such as copper(II) sulfate, is not very soluble in nonpolar solvents such as carbon tetrachloride and octane (Figure 14.4).

It is also important to recognize that the enthalpy of solution is the difference between two very large numbers. Small variations in either lattice energy or hydration enthalpies can determine whether a salt dissolves endothermically or exothermically.

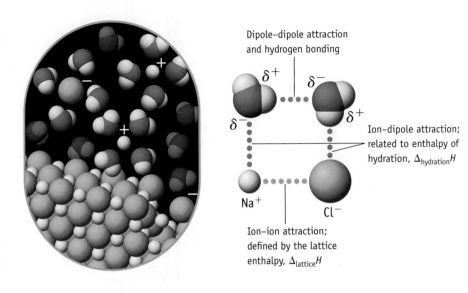

FIGURE 14.9 Dissolving an ionic solid in water. This process is a balance of forces. There are intermolecular forces between water molecules, and ion–ion forces are at work in the ionic crystal lattice. To dissolve, the ion–dipole forces between water and the ions (as measured by $\Delta_{hydration}H$) must overcome the ion–ion forces (as measured by $\Delta_{lattice}H$) and the intermolecular forces in water.

Finally, notice that the two energy quantities, $\Delta_{lattice}H$ and $\Delta_{hydration}H$, are both affected by ion sizes and ion charges (◀ pages 551 and 598). A salt composed of smaller ions is expected to have a greater (more negative) lattice enthalpy because the ions can be closer together and experience higher attractive forces. However, the small size will also allow a closer approach of solvent molecules and a greater solvation enthalpy. The net result is that correlations of solubility with structure (ionic radii) or thermodynamic parameters ($\Delta_{lattice}H$) are generally not successful.

Enthalpy of Solution: Thermodynamic Data

As mentioned earlier, the enthalpy of solution for a salt can be measured using a calorimeter. This is usually done in an open system such as the coffee-cup calorimeter described in Section 5.6. For an experiment run under standard conditions, the resulting measurement produces a value for the standard enthalpy of solution, $\Delta_{soln}H°$, where standard conditions refer to a concentration of 1 molal.

Tables of thermodynamic values often include values for the enthalpies of formation of aqueous solutions of salts. For example, a value of $\Delta_f H°$ for NaCl(aq) of −407.3 kJ/mol is listed in Table 14.1 and Appendix L. This value refers to the formation of a 1 m solution of NaCl from the elements. It may be considered to involve the enthalpies of two steps: (1) the formation of NaCl(s) from the elements Na(s) and Cl_2(g) in their standard states, and (2) the formation of a 1 m solution by dissolving solid NaCl in water:

Formation of NaCl(s):   Na(s) + ½ Cl₂(g) ⟶ NaCl(s) $\Delta_f H° = -411.1$ kJ/mol

Dissolving NaCl: NaCl(s) ⟶ NaCl(aq, 1 m) $\Delta_{soln}H° = +3.8$ kJ/mol

Net process: Na(s) + ½ Cl₂(g) ⟶ NaCl(aq, 1 m) $\Delta_f H° = -407.3$ kJ/mol

Table 14.1
Data for Calculating Enthalpy of Solution

Compound	$\Delta_f H°$ (s) (kJ/mol)	$\Delta_f H°$ (aq, 1 m) (kJ/mol)
LiF	−616.9	−611.1
NaF	−573.6	−572.8
KF	−568.6	−585.0
RbF	−557.7	−583.8
LiCl	−408.7	−445.6
NaCl	−411.1	−407.3
KCl	−436.7	−419.5
RbCl	−435.4	−418.3
NaOH	−425.9	−469.2
NH₄NO₃	−365.6	−339.9

EXAMPLE 14.2   Calculating an Enthalpy of Solution

Problem Determine the enthalpy of solution for NH₄NO₃, the compound used in cold packs.

What Do You Know? The solution process for NH₄NO₃ is represented by the equation

$$NH_4NO_3(s) \longrightarrow NH_4NO_3(aq)$$

The enthalpies of formation of NH₄NO₃ in the solid state (−365.6 kJ/mol) and in solution (−339.9 kJ/mol) are given in Table 14.1.

Strategy Equation 5.6 (page 234) states that the enthalpy change for a process is the difference between the enthalpy of the final state (here the compound in solution) and the initial state (the solid).

Solution The enthalpy change for this process is calculated using Equation 5.6 as follows:

$$\Delta_{soln}H° = \sum[n\Delta_f H° \text{ (product)}] - \sum[n\Delta_f H° \text{ (reactant)}]$$
$$= \Delta_f H° \left[NH_4NO_3(aq)\right] - \Delta_f H° \left[NH_4NO_3(s)\right] \text{ (where } n = 1 \text{ for both)}$$
$$= -339.9 \text{ kJ} - (-365.6 \text{ kJ}) = +25.7 \text{ kJ}$$

Think about Your Answer The process is endothermic, as indicated by the fact that $\Delta_{soln}H°$ has a positive value and as verified by the experiment in Figure 14.7b.

Check Your Understanding

Use the data in Table 14.1 to calculate the enthalpy of solution for NaOH.

REVIEW & CHECK FOR SECTION 14.2

Given the enthalpy of formation data below, calculate $\Delta_{soln}H°$ for LiOH.

$$\Delta_f H° \text{ [LiOH(s)]} = -484.93 \text{ kJ/mol} \qquad \Delta_f H° \text{ [LiOH(aq)]} = -508.48 \text{ kJ/mol}$$

(a) +23.55 kJ/mol   (c) −23.55 kJ/mol

(b) +993.41 kJ/mol   (d) −993.41 kJ/mol

14.3 Factors Affecting Solubility: Pressure and Temperature

Pressure and temperature are two external factors that influence solubility. Both affect the solubility of gases in liquids, whereas only temperature is a factor in the solubility of solids in liquids.

Dissolving Gases in Liquids: Henry's Law

The solubility of a gas in a liquid is directly proportional to the gas pressure. This is a statement of **Henry's law**,

$$S_g = k_H P_g \tag{14.4}$$

where S_g is the gas solubility (in mol/kg), P_g is the partial pressure of the gaseous solute, and k_H is Henry's law constant (Table 14.2), a constant characteristic of the solute and solvent.

Carbonated soft drinks illustrate how Henry's law works. These beverages are packed under pressure in a chamber filled with carbon dioxide gas, some of which dissolves in the beverage. When the can or bottle is opened, the partial pressure of CO_2 above the solution drops, which causes the solubility of CO_2 to drop. Gas bubbles out of the solution (Figure 14.10).

Henry's law has important consequences in SCUBA diving. When you dive, the pressure of the air you breathe must be balanced against the external pressure of the water. In deeper dives, the pressure of the gases in the SCUBA gear must be several atmospheres and, as a result, more gas dissolves in the blood. This can lead to a problem. If you ascend too rapidly, you can experience a painful and potentially lethal condition referred to as "the bends," in which nitrogen gas bubbles form in the blood as the solubility of nitrogen decreases with decreasing pressure. In an effort to prevent the bends, divers may use a helium–oxygen mixture (rather than nitrogen–oxygen) because helium is not as soluble in blood as nitrogen.

We can better understand the effect of pressure on solubility by examining the system at the particulate level. The solubility of a gas is defined as the concentration of the dissolved gas in equilibrium with the substance in the gaseous state. At equilibrium, the rate at which solute gas molecules escape the solution and enter the gaseous state equals the rate at which gas molecules reenter the solution. An increase in pressure

Table 14.2
Henry's Law Constants (25 °C)*

Gas	k_H (mol/kg·bar)
N_2	6.0×10^{-4}
O_2	1.3×10^{-3}
CO_2	0.034

*From http://webbook.nist.gov/chemistry/. *Note:* 1 bar = 0.9869 atm.

FIGURE 14.10 Gas solubility and pressure. Carbonated beverages are bottled under CO_2 pressure. When the bottle is opened, the pressure is released, and bubbles of CO_2 form within the liquid and rise to the surface. After some time, an equilibrium between dissolved CO_2 and atmospheric CO_2 is reached. The beverage tastes flat when most of its dissolved CO_2 is lost.

results in more molecules of gas striking the surface of the liquid and entering solution in a given time. The solution eventually reaches a new equilibrium when the concentration of gas dissolved in the solvent is high enough that the rate of gas molecules escaping the solution again equals the rate of gas molecules entering the solution.

• **Limitations of Henry's Law** Henry's law holds quantitatively only for gases that do not interact chemically with the solvent. It does not accurately predict the solubility of NH_3 in water, for example, because this compound gives small concentrations of NH_4^+ and OH^- in water.

EXAMPLE 14.3   Using Henry's Law

Problem What is the concentration of O_2 in a freshwater stream in equilibrium with air at 25 °C and 1.0 bar? Express the answer in grams of O_2 per kg of solvent.

What Do You Know? You know the total air pressure and temperature, and you can look up the Henry's law constant at the indicated temperature (1.3×10^{-3} mol/kg · bar). (Note that 1 bar is approximately 1 atm; page 510.)

Strategy Because you are trying to find the solubility of O_2, you first must find the partial pressure of O_2 from its mole fraction in air (0.21) and the specified atmospheric pressure (1.0 bar). Then use Henry's Law to calculate its molar solubility.

Solution

(a) The mole fraction of O_2 in air is 0.21, and, assuming the total pressure is 1.0 bar, the partial pressure of O_2 is 0.21 bar.

(b) Using the O_2 partial pressure for P_g in Henry's law, we have:

$$\text{Solubility of } O_2 = k_H P_g = \left(\frac{1.3 \times 10^{-3}\text{ mol}}{\text{kg} \cdot \text{bar}}\right)(0.21\text{ bar}) = 2.7 \times 10^{-4}\text{ mol/kg}$$

(c) Calculate the concentration in g/kg from the concentration in mol/kg and the molar mass of O_2:

$$\text{Solubility of } O_2 = \left(\frac{2.7 \times 10^{-4}\text{ mol}}{\text{kg}}\right)\left(\frac{32.0\text{ g}}{\text{mol}}\right) = 0.0087\text{ g/kg}$$

Think about Your Answer The concentration of O_2 is 8.7 ppm (8.7 mg/1000 g). This concentration is quite low, but it is sufficient to provide the oxygen required by aquatic life.

Check Your Understanding

What is the concentration of CO_2 in water at 25 °C when the partial pressure is 0.33 bar? (Although CO_2 reacts with water to give traces of H_3O^+ and HCO_3^-, the reaction occurs to such a small extent that Henry's law is obeyed at low CO_2 partial pressures.)

Temperature Effects on Solubility: Le Chatelier's Principle

The solubility of all gases in water decreases with increasing temperature. You may realize this from everyday observations such as the appearance of bubbles of air as water is heated below the boiling point.

To understand the effect of temperature on the solubility of gases, let us reexamine the enthalpy of solution. Gases that dissolve to an appreciable extent in water usually do so in an exothermic process

$$\text{Gas + liquid solvent} \xrightleftharpoons{\Delta_{soln}H < 0} \text{saturated solution + energy}$$

FIGURE 14.11
The temperature dependence of the solubility of some ionic compounds in water. Most compounds, such as NH_4Cl, decrease in solubility with decreasing temperature.

(a) Temperature dependence of the solubility of some ionic compounds.

(b) NH_4Cl dissolved in water.

(c) NH_4Cl precipitates when the solution is cooled in ice.

The reverse process, loss of dissolved gas molecules from a solution, requires energy as heat. At equilibrium, the rates of the two processes are the same.

To understand how temperature affects solubility, we turn to **Le Chatelier's principle**, which states that a change in any of the factors determining an equilibrium causes the system to adjust by shifting in the direction that reduces or counteracts the effect of the change. If a solution of a gas in a liquid is heated, for example, the equilibrium will shift to absorb some of the added energy. That is, the reaction

$$\text{Gas + liquid solvent} \underset{\text{Add energy. Equilibrium shifts left.}}{\overset{\substack{\text{Exothermic process}\\ \Delta_{soln}H \text{ is negative.}}}{\rightleftharpoons}} \text{saturated solution + energy}$$

shifts to the left if the temperature is raised because energy is absorbed in the process that produces free gas molecules and pure solvent. This shift corresponds to less gas dissolved and a lower solubility at higher temperature—the observed result.

The solubility of solids in water is also affected by temperature, but, unlike the situation involving solutions of gases, no general pattern of behavior is observed. In Figure 14.11, the solubilities of several salts are plotted versus temperature. The solubility of many salts increases with increasing temperature, but there are notable exceptions. Predictions based on whether the enthalpy of solution is positive or negative work most of the time, but exceptions do occur.

Chemists take advantage of the variation of solubility with temperature to purify compounds. An impure sample of a compound that is more soluble at higher temperatures is dissolved by heating the solution. The solution is then cooled to decrease the solubility (Figure 14.11c). When the limit of solubility is reached at the lower temperature, crystals of the pure compound form. If the process is done slowly and carefully, it is sometimes possible to obtain very large crystals (Figure 14.12).

FIGURE 14.12 Giant crystals of potassium dihydrogen phosphate. The crystal being measured by this researcher at Lawrence Livermore Laboratory in California weighs 318 kg and measures 66 × 53 × 58 cm. The crystals were grown by suspending a thumbnail-sized seed crystal in a 6-foot tank of saturated KH_2PO_4. The temperature of the solution was gradually reduced from 65 °C over a period of about 50 days. The crystals are sliced into thin plates, which are used to convert light from a giant laser from infrared to ultraviolet.

REVIEW & CHECK FOR SECTION 14.3

Soft drinks are carbonated by adding CO_2 under pressure. Assume that CO_2 is added to a bottle of soft drink containing 710 g of diet soda. The pressure of CO_2 is 4.0 bar. (CO_2 obeys Henry's law at pressures up to about 5 bar.) What amount of CO_2 is dissolved in 710 g of diet soda?

(a) 0.14 mol   (b) 0.097 mol   (c) 0.034 mol   (d) 0.13 mol

Exploding Lakes and Diet Cokes

On Thursday, August 21, 1986, people and animals around Lake Nyos in Cameroon, a small nation on the west coast of Africa, suddenly collapsed and died. More than 1700 people and hundreds of animals were dead, but there was no apparent cause—no fire, no earthquake, no storm. What had brought on this disaster?

Some weeks later, the mystery was solved. Lake Nyos and nearby Lake Monoun are crater lakes, which formed when cooled volcanic craters filled with water. Importantly, Lake Nyos contains an enormous amount of dissolved carbon dioxide, which was generated as a result of volcanic activity deep in the earth. Under the high pressure at the bottom of the lake, a very large amount of CO_2 dissolved in the water.

But on that evening in 1986, something disturbed the lake. The CO_2-saturated water at the bottom of the lake was carried to the surface, where, under lower pressure, the gas was much less soluble. About one cubic kilometer of carbon dioxide was released into the atmosphere, much like the explosive release of CO_2 from a can of carbonated beverage that has been shaken. The CO_2 shot up about 260 feet; then, because this gas is more dense than air, it hugged the ground and began to move with the prevailing breeze at about 45 miles per hour. When it reached the villages 12 miles away, vital oxygen was displaced. The result was that both people and animals were asphyxiated.

In most lakes, this situation would not occur because lake water "turns over" as the seasons change. In the autumn, the top layer of water in a lake cools; its density increases; and the water sinks. This process continues, with warmer water coming to the surface and cooler water sinking. Dissolved CO_2 at the bottom of a lake would normally be expelled in this turnover process, but geologists found that the lakes in Cameroon are different. The chemocline, the boundary between deep water, rich in gas and minerals, and the upper layer, full of freshwater, stayed intact. As carbon dioxide continued to enter the lake through vents in the bottom of the lake, the water became saturated with this gas. It is presumed that a minor disturbance—perhaps a small earthquake, a strong wind, or an underwater landslide—caused the lake water to turn over and led to the explosive release of CO_2.

The explosive release of CO_2 that occurred in Lake Nyos is much like what occurs when you drop a candy like a Mentos into a bottle of Diet Coke. Carbonated sodas are bottled under a high pressure of CO_2. Some of the gas dissolves in the soda, but some also remains in the small space above the liquid (called the *headspace*). The pressure of the CO_2 in the headspace is between 2 and 4 atm. When the bottle cap is removed, the CO_2 in the headspace escapes rapidly. Some of the dissolved CO_2 also comes out of solution, and you see bubbles of gas rising to the surface. If the bottle remains open, this continues until equilibrium is established with CO_2 in the atmosphere (where the partial pressure of CO_2 is 3.75×10^{-4} atm),

$$CO_2(solution) \rightleftharpoons CO_2(g)$$

and the soda goes "flat." If the newly opened soda bottle is undisturbed, however, the loss of CO_2 from solution is rather slow because bubble formation is not rapid, and your soda keeps its fizz.

To understand how CO_2 can be released explosively, you have to understand that impurities in the water or the rough surfaces of an ice cube or bottle or drinking glass can serve as "nucleation sites" on which a bubble can form. The more nucleation sites available, the more rapid the bubble formation. The surface of a Mentos apparently has many such sites and pro-

A Mentos was dropped into large bottles of Diet Coke. For more information, see J. E. Baur and M. B. Baur, *Journal of Chemical Education*, Vol. 83, pages 577–580, 2006.

motes very rapid bubble formation. In the case of the African lake, perhaps an earthquake or underwater landslide opened up nucleation sites, and the CO_2 was released explosively.

Questions:
1. If the headspace of a soda is 25 mL and the pressure of CO_2 in the space is 4.0 atm ($\approx$4.0 bar) at 25 °C, what amount of CO_2 is contained in the headspace?
2. If the CO_2 in the headspace escapes into the atmosphere where the partial pressure of CO_2 is 3.7×10^{-4} atm, what volume would the CO_2 occupy (at 25 °C)? By what amount did the CO_2 expand when it was released?
3. What is the solubility of CO_2 in water at 25 °C when the pressure of the gas is 3.7×10^{-4} bar?
4. After opening a 1.0 L soda, what mass of the dissolved CO_2 is released to the atmosphere in order to reach equilibrium? Assume that the CO_2 dissolved in the soda in the sealed bottle was in equilibrium with the CO_2 in the headspace at 4.0 bar pressure.

Answers to these questions are available in Appendix N.

Lake Nyos in Cameroon (western Africa), the site of a natural disaster. In 1986, a huge bubble of CO_2 escaped from the lake and asphyxiated more than 1700 people.

Module 19: Colligative Properties covers concepts in this section.

14.4 Colligative Properties

If you dissolve some salt in water, the vapor pressure of the water over the solution will decrease. In addition, the solution will freeze below 0 °C and boil above 100 °C. These observations refer to the **colligative properties** of the solution, properties that depend on the relative numbers of solute and solvent particles in a solution and not on their identity.

Changes in Vapor Pressure: Raoult's Law

The equilibrium vapor pressure at a particular temperature is the pressure of the vapor when the liquid and the vapor are in equilibrium (◄ page 568). When the vapor pressure of the solvent over a solution is measured at a given temperature, it is experimentally observed that

- The vapor pressure of the solvent over the solution is lower than the vapor pressure of the pure solvent.
- The vapor pressure of the solvent, $P_{solvent}$, is proportional to the relative number of solvent molecules in the solution; that is, the solvent vapor pressure is proportional to the solvent mole fraction, $P_{solvent} \propto X_{solvent}$.

Because solvent vapor pressure is proportional to the relative number of solvent molecules, we can write the following equation for the equilibrium vapor pressure of the solvent over a solution:

$$P_{solvent} = X_{solvent} \, P^\circ_{solvent} \tag{14.5}$$

This equation, called **Raoult's law**, tells us that the vapor pressure of solvent over a solution ($P_{solvent}$) is some fraction of the pure solvent equilibrium vapor pressure ($P^\circ_{solvent}$). For example, if 95% of the molecules in a solution are solvent molecules ($X_{solvent} = 0.95$), then the vapor pressure of the solvent ($P_{solvent}$) is 95% of $P^\circ_{solvent}$.

An ideal solution is one that obeys Raoult's law. However, just as no gas is truly ideal, no solution is ideal. Although Raoult's law describes a simplified model of a solution, it is a good approximation of solution behavior in many instances, especially at low solute concentration.

For Raoult's law to hold, the forces of attraction between solute and solvent molecules must be the same as those between solvent molecules in the pure solvent. This is frequently the case when molecules with similar structures are involved. Solutions of one hydrocarbon in another (hexane, C_6H_{14}, dissolved in octane, C_8H_{18}, for example) follow Raoult's law quite closely. If solvent–solute interactions are stronger than solvent–solvent interactions, the actual vapor pressure will be lower than calculated by Raoult's law. If the solvent–solute interactions are weaker than solvent–solvent interactions, the vapor pressure will be higher.

EXAMPLE 14.4 Using Raoult's Law

Problem You dissolve 651 g of ethylene glycol, $HOCH_2CH_2OH$, in 1.50 kg of water. What is the vapor pressure of the water over the solution at 90 °C? Assume ideal behavior for the solution.

What Do You Know? This is a Raoult's law problem where you want to know $P_{solvent}$. To calculate $P_{solvent}$ you need the mole fraction of solvent and the vapor pressure of the pure solvent. You can calculate the mole fraction of solute from the masses of solute and solvent and the molar masses of these species. The vapor pressure of pure water at 90 °C (= 525.8 mm Hg) is found in Appendix G.

Strategy First calculate the mole fraction of the solvent (water) and then combine that with the vapor pressure of pure solvent at the specified temperature using Raoult's law (Equation 14.5).

Solution

(a) Calculate the amounts of water and ethylene glycol and, from these, the mole fraction of water.

$$\text{Amount of water} = 1.50 \times 10^3 \text{ g} \left(\frac{1 \text{ mol}}{18.02 \text{ g}}\right) = 83.2 \text{ mol water}$$

$$\text{Amount of ethylene glycol} = 651 \text{ g} \left(\frac{1 \text{ mol}}{62.07 \text{ g}}\right) = 10.5 \text{ mol glycol}$$

$$X_{water} = \frac{83.2 \text{ mol water}}{83.2 \text{ mol water} + 10.5 \text{ mol glycol}} = 0.888$$

(b) Next apply Raoult's law.

$$P_{water} = X_{water}P°_{water} = (0.888)(525.8 \text{ mm Hg}) = \boxed{467 \text{ mm Hg}}$$

Think about Your Answer Although a substantial mass of ethylene glycol was added to the water, it led to a decrease in the vapor pressure of the solvent of only 59 mm Hg, or about 11%:

$$\Delta P_{water} = P_{water} - P°_{water} = 467 \text{ mm Hg} - 525.8 \text{ mm Hg} = -59 \text{ mm Hg}$$

Ethylene glycol is ideal for use as antifreeze. It dissolves easily in water, is noncorrosive, and is relatively inexpensive. Because of its high boiling point, it will not evaporate readily. It is, however, toxic to animals, so it is being replaced by less toxic propylene glycol.

Check Your Understanding

Assume you dissolve 10.0 g of sucrose ($C_{12}H_{22}O_{11}$) in 225 mL (225 g) of water and warm the water to 60 °C. What is the vapor pressure of the water over this solution? (Appendix G lists $P°(H_2O)$ at various temperatures.)

Adding a nonvolatile solute to a solvent lowers the vapor pressure of the solvent (Example 14.4). Raoult's law can be modified to calculate directly the lowering of the vapor pressure, $\Delta P_{solvent}$, as a function of the mole fraction of the solute.

$$\Delta P_{solvent} = P_{solvent} - P°_{solvent}$$

Substituting Raoult's law for $P_{solvent}$, we have

$$\Delta P_{solvent} = (X_{solvent} P°_{solvent}) - P°_{solvent} = -(1 - X_{solvent})P°_{solvent}$$

In a solution that has only the volatile solvent and one nonvolatile solute, the sum of the mole fraction of solvent and solute must be 1:

$$X_{solvent} + X_{solute} = 1$$

Therefore, $1 - X_{solvent} = X_{solute}$, and the equation for $\Delta P_{solvent}$ can be rewritten as

$$\Delta P_{solvent} = -X_{solute} P°_{solvent} \tag{14.6}$$

Thus, the *decrease* in the vapor pressure of the solvent is proportional to the mole fraction (the relative number of particles) of solute.

Boiling Point Elevation

Suppose you have a solution of a nonvolatile solute in the volatile solvent benzene. If the solute concentration is 0.200 mol in 100. g of benzene (C_6H_6) (= 2.00 mol/kg), this means that $X_{benzene} = 0.865$. Using $X_{benzene}$ and applying Raoult's law, we can calculate that the vapor pressure of the solvent at 60 °C will drop from 400. mm Hg for the pure solvent to 346 mm Hg for the solution:

$$P_{benzene} = X_{benzene} P°_{benzene} = (0.865)(400. \text{ mm Hg}) = 346 \text{ mm Hg}$$

FIGURE 14.13 Lowering the vapor pressure of benzene by addition of a nonvolatile solute. The curve drawn in red represents the vapor pressure of pure benzene, and the curve in blue represents the vapor pressure of a solution containing 0.200 mol of a solute dissolved in 0.100 kg of solvent (2.00 *m*). This graph was created by doing a series of calculations such as those shown in the text. As an alternative, the graph could be created by measuring various vapor pressures for the solution in a laboratory experiment.

This point is marked on the vapor pressure graph in Figure 14.13. Now, what is the vapor pressure when the temperature of the solution is raised another 10 °C? The vapor pressure of pure benzene, $P°_{benzene}$, becomes larger with increasing temperature, so $P_{benzene}$ for the solution must also become larger. This new point, and additional ones calculated in the same way for other temperatures, define the vapor pressure curve for the solution (the lower curve in Figure 14.13).

An important observation we can make in Figure 14.13 is that the vapor pressure lowering caused by the nonvolatile solute leads to an increase in the boiling point. The normal boiling point of a liquid is the temperature at which its vapor pressure is equal to 1 atm or 760 mm Hg (◄ page 571). In Figure 14.13, we see that the normal boiling point of pure benzene (at 760 mm Hg) is about 80 °C. Tracing the vapor pressure curve for the solution, we also see that the vapor pressure reaches 760 mm Hg at a temperature about 5 °C higher than this value.

An important question is how the boiling point of the solution varies with solute concentration. In fact, a simple relationship exists: the boiling point elevation, ΔT_{bp}, is directly proportional to the molality of the solute.

$$\text{Elevation in boiling point} = \Delta T_{bp} = K_{bp}m_{solute} \qquad (14.7)$$

In this equation, K_{bp} is a proportionality constant called the **molal boiling point elevation constant**. It has the units of degrees/molal (°C/*m*). Values for K_{bp} are determined experimentally, and different solvents have different values (Table 14.3). Formally, the value of K_{bp} corresponds to the elevation in boiling point for a 1 *m* solution.

⊘WL **INTERACTIVE EXAMPLE 14.5** Boiling Point Elevation

Problem Eugenol, a compound found in nutmeg and cloves, has the formula $C_{10}H_{12}O_2$. What is the boiling point of a solution containing 0.144 g of this compound dissolved in 10.0 g of benzene?

What Do You Know? You know the identify and mass of both the solute and the solvent.

Eugenol, $C_{10}H_{12}O_2$, is an important component in oil of cloves, a commonly used spice.

Strategy

- Calculate the solution concentration (molality, m, in mol/kg) from the amount of eugenol and the mass of solvent (kg).

- Calculate the change in boiling point using Equation 14.7 (with a value of K_{bp} from Table 14.3).

- Add the change to the boiling temperature of pure benzene to obtain the new boiling point.

Solution

(a) Solution concentration

$$0.144 \text{ g eugenol}\left(\frac{1 \text{ mol eugenol}}{164.2 \text{ g}}\right) = 8.77 \times 10^{-4} \text{ mol eugenol}$$

$$c_{eugenol} = \frac{8.77 \times 10^{-4} \text{ mol eugenol}}{0.0100 \text{ kg benzene}} = 8.77 \times 10^{-2} \, m$$

(b) Boiling point elevation

$$\Delta T_{bp} = (2.53 \text{ °C}/m)(0.0877 \, m) = 0.222 \text{ °C}$$

Because the boiling point rises relative to that of the pure solvent, the boiling point of the solution is

$$80.10 \text{ °C} + 0.222 \text{ °C} = \boxed{80.32 \text{ °C}}$$

Think about Your Answer Keep in mind that the boiling point elevation is proportional to the solute concentration. At high concentrations, sizable increases in boiling point are possible.

Check Your Understanding

What quantity of ethylene glycol, $HOCH_2CH_2OH$, must be added to 125 g of water to raise the boiling point by 1.0 °C? Express the answer in grams.

Strategy Map 14.5

PROBLEM

Calculate **boiling point** of solution.

DATA/INFORMATION
- **Mass** of *compound* and *solvent*
- K_{bp} and T(bp solvent) from Table 14.3

STEP 1. Calculate c_{solute} = (mol compound/kg solvent).

Concentration of solute (mol/kg)

STEP 2. Use $\Delta T_{bp} = K_{bp}m$.

Change in boiling point (ΔT_{bp})

STEP 3. ΔT_{bp} = T(bp solution) – T(bp solvent).

T(bp solution)

The elevation of the boiling point of a solvent on adding a solute has many practical consequences. One of them is the summer protection your car's engine receives from "all-season" antifreeze. The main ingredient of commercial antifreeze is ethylene glycol, $HOCH_2CH_2OH$. The car's radiator and cooling system are sealed to keep the coolant under pressure, ensuring that it will not vaporize at normal engine temperatures. When the air temperature is high in the summer, however, the radiator could "boil over" if it were not protected with "antifreeze." By adding this nonvolatile liquid, the solution in the radiator has a higher boiling point than that of pure water.

Table 14.3 Some Boiling Point Elevation and Freezing Point Depression Constants

Solvent	Normal Boiling Point (°C) Pure Solvent	K_{bp} (°C/m)	Normal Freezing Point (°C) Pure Solvent	K_{fp} (°C/m)
Water	100.00	+0.5121	0.0	−1.86
Benzene	80.10	+2.53	5.50	−5.12
Camphor	207.4	+5.611	179.75	−39.7
Chloroform ($CHCl_3$)	61.70	+3.63	—	—

FIGURE 14.14 Freezing a solution.

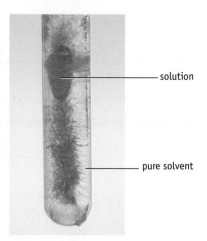

solution

pure solvent

(a) Adding antifreeze to water prevents the water from freezing. Here, a jar of pure water *(left)* and a jar of water to which automobile antifreeze had been added *(right)* were kept overnight in the freezing compartment of a home refrigerator.

(b) When a solution freezes, it is pure solvent that solidifies. To take this photo, a purple dye was dissolved in water, and the solution was frozen slowly. Pure ice formed along the walls of the tube, and the dye stayed in solution. The concentration of the solute increased as more and more solvent was frozen out, and the resulting solution had a lower and lower freezing point. Eventually, the system contains pure, colorless ice that formed along the walls of the tube and a concentrated solution of dye in the center of the tube.

Freezing Point Depression

● **Why Is the Boiling Point of a Solution Elevated and Its Freezing Point Depressed?** The answer to this question is related to entropy, a thermodynamic function discussed in Chapter 19. You can consult a website that has an *extensive* discussion of entropy (entropysite.oxy.edu) or the specific site at which colligative properties are discussed: http://entropysite.oxy.edu/entropy_is_simple/index.html.

Another consequence of dissolving a solute in a solvent is that the freezing point of the solution is lower than that of the pure solvent (Figure 14.14). For an ideal solution, the depression of the freezing point is given by an equation similar to that for the elevation of the boiling point:

$$\text{Freezing point depression} = \Delta T_{fp} = K_{fp} m_{solute} \qquad (14.8)$$

where K_{fp} is the **freezing point depression constant** in degrees Celsius per molal ($°C/m$). Values of K_{fp} for a few common solvents are given in Table 14.3. The values are negative quantities, so the result of the calculation is a negative value for ΔT_{fp}, signifying a decrease in temperature.

The practical aspects of freezing point changes from pure solvent to solution are similar to those for boiling point elevation. The very name of the liquid you add to the radiator in your car, antifreeze, indicates its purpose (Figure 14.14a). The label on the container of antifreeze tells you, for example, to add 6 qt (5.7 L) of antifreeze to a 12-qt (11.4-L) cooling system to lower the freezing point to −34 °C and to raise the boiling point to +109 °C.

EXAMPLE 14.6   Freezing Point Depression

Problem What mass of ethylene glycol, $HOCH_2CH_2OH$, must be added to 5.50 kg of water to lower the freezing point of the water from 0.0 °C to −10.0 °C?

What Do You Know? In some ways this is the reverse of Example 14.5. Here you know the change in freezing point, but wish to know how much solute is needed to produce that value of ΔT.

Strategy The solution concentration (molality, m) can be calculated from ΔT_{fp} and K_{fp} (Table 14.3) using Equation 14.8. Combine the concentration with the mass of solvent to obtain the amount of solute and then its mass.

Solution

(a) Calculate the solute concentration in a solution with a freezing point depression of −10.0 °C.

$$\text{Solute concentration } (m) = \frac{\Delta T_{fp}}{K_{fp}} = \frac{-10.0\ °C}{-1.86\ °C/m} = 5.38\ m$$

(b) Calculate the amount of solute from the concentration and solvent mass.

$$\left(\frac{5.38\ \text{mol glycol}}{1.00\ \text{kg water}}\right)(5.50\ \text{kg water}) = 29.6\ \text{mol glycol}$$

(c) Calculate the mass of the solute, ethylene glycol.

$$29.6\ \text{mol glycol}\left(\frac{62.07\ g}{1\ \text{mol}}\right) = 1840\ g\ \text{glycol}$$

Think about Your Answer The value of K_{fp} tells us that the freezing point of water goes down by 1.86 °C for a 1 molal solution. In this particular problem, the freezing point depression was −10.0 °C, so a molality around 5 m is reasonable. The density of ethylene glycol is 1.11 kg/L, so the volume of glycol to be added is: (1.84 kg)(1 L/1.11 kg) = 1.66 L.

Check Your Understanding

In the northern United States, summer cottages are usually closed up for the winter. When doing so, the owners "winterize" the plumbing by putting antifreeze in the toilet tanks, for example. Will adding 525 g of $HOCH_2CH_2OH$ to 3.00 kg of water ensure that the water will not freeze at −25 °C?

Osmotic Pressure

Osmosis is the movement of solvent molecules through a semipermeable membrane from a region of lower solute concentration to a region of higher solute concentration. This movement can be demonstrated with a simple experiment. The beaker in Figure 14.15 contains pure water, and the bag and tube hold a concentrated sugar

FIGURE 14.15 The process of osmosis.

Height of solution column

time

Pure water

5% sugar 95% water

Semi-permeable membrane

(a) The bag attached to the tube contains a solution that is 5% sugar and 95% water. The beaker contains pure water. The bag is made of a material that is semipermeable, meaning that it allows water, but not sugar molecules, to pass through.

(b) Over time, water flows from the region of low solute concentration (pure water) to the region of higher solute concentration (the sugar solution). Flow continues until the pressure exerted by the column of solution in the tube above the water level in the beaker is great enough to result in equal rates of passage of water molecules in both directions. The height of the column of solution is a measure of the osmotic pressure.

solution. The liquids are separated by a semipermeable membrane, a thin sheet of material (such as a vegetable tissue or cellophane) through which only certain types of molecules can pass. Here, water molecules can pass through the membrane, but larger sugar molecules (or hydrated ions) cannot (Figure 14.16). When the experiment is begun, the liquid levels in the beaker and the tube are the same. Over time, however, the level of the sugar solution inside the tube rises, the level of pure water in the beaker falls, and the sugar solution becomes more dilute. Eventually, no further net change occurs; equilibrium is reached.

From a molecular point of view, the semipermeable membrane does not present a barrier to the movement of water molecules, so they move through the membrane in both directions. Over time, more water molecules pass through the membrane from the pure water side to the solution side than in the opposite direction. The net effect is that water molecules move from regions of low solute concentration to regions of high solute concentration. The same is true for any solvent, as long as the membrane allows solvent molecules but not solute molecules or ions to pass through.

Why does the system eventually reach equilibrium? Clearly, the solution in the tube in Figure 14.15 can never reach zero sugar or salt concentration, which would be required to equalize the number of water molecules moving through the membrane in each direction in a given time. The answer lies in the fact that the solution moves higher and higher in the tube as osmosis continues and water moves into the sugar solution. Eventually, the pressure exerted by this column of solution counterbalances the pressure exerted by the water moving through the membrane from the pure water side, and no further net movement of water occurs. An equilibrium of forces is achieved. The pressure created by the column of solution for the system at equilibrium is called the **osmotic pressure**, Π. A measure of this pressure is the difference between the height of the solution in the tube and the level of pure water in the beaker.

From experimental measurements on dilute solutions, it is known that osmotic pressure and concentration (c) are related by the equation

$$\Pi = cRT \tag{14.9}$$

In this equation, c is the molar concentration (in moles per liter); R is the gas constant; and T is the absolute temperature (in kelvins). Using a value for the gas law constant of $0.082057 \ L \cdot atm/K \cdot mol$ allows calculation of the osmotic pressure Π in atmospheres. This equation is analogous to the ideal gas law ($PV = nRT$), with Π taking the place of P and c being equivalent to n/V.

FIGURE 14.16 Osmosis at the particulate level. Osmotic flow through a membrane that is selectively permeable (semipermeable) to water. Dissolved substances such as hydrated ions or large sugar molecules cannot diffuse through the membrane.

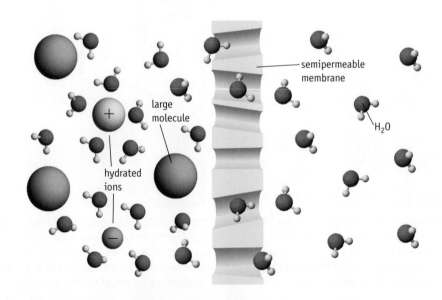

Reverse Osmosis for Pure Water

Finding sources of freshwater for humans and agriculture has been a constant battle for centuries, and, if we continue using Earth's water at the present rate, those problems may increase. Although the earth has abundant water, 97% of it is too salty to drink or to use on crops. A large portion of the remaining 3% is locked in the form of ice in the polar regions and is not easily obtained.

One of the oldest ways to obtain freshwater from seawater is by evaporation. This is, however, very energy-intensive, and the salt and other materials left behind may not be useful.

Reverse osmosis is another method of obtaining freshwater from seawater or groundwater. In this technique a pressure greater than the osmotic pressure of the impure water is applied to force water through a semipermeable membrane from a region of high solute concentration to one of lower solute concentration, that is, in the reverse direction that the water would move by osmosis.

Although reverse osmosis has been known for over 200 years, only in the last few decades has it been exploited. Now some municipalities obtain drinking water that way, and pharmaceutical companies use it to obtain highly purified water. More than 15,000 reverse osmosis plants are in operation or in the planning stage worldwide.

A reverse osmosis plant.

Reverse osmosis. Drinking water can be produced from seawater by reverse osmosis. The osmotic pressure of seawater is approximately 22 atm. To obtain freshwater at a reasonable rate, reverse osmosis requires a pressure of about 50 atm. For comparison, bicycle tires usually have an air pressure of 2–3 atm. (See the portable reverse osmosis device on page 616.)

Even solutions with low solute concentrations have a significant osmotic pressure. For example, the osmotic pressure of a 1.00×10^{-3} M solution at 298K is 18.5 mm Hg. Such pressures are easily and accurately measured. Because of this, the concentrations of very dilute solutions can be determined using this technique. Compare this to the effect of a solute on freezing point, for example. A dilute aqueous solution of similar concentration, 1.00×10^{-3} mol/kg solvent, would be expected to lower the freezing point by about 0.002 °C, too small to measure accurately. For this reason osmosis is a particularly useful technique when dealing with solutions of compounds having a very high molar mass such as polymers and large biomolecules.

Other examples of osmosis are shown in Figure 14.17. In this case, the egg's membrane serves as the semipermeable membrane. Osmosis occurs in one direction if the concentration of solute is greater inside the egg than in the exterior

(a) A fresh egg is placed in dilute acetic acid. The acid reacts with the $CaCO_3$ of the shell but leaves the egg membrane intact.

(b) If the egg, with its shell removed, is placed in pure water, the egg swells.

(c) If the egg, with its shell removed, is placed in a concentrated sugar solution, the egg shrivels.

FIGURE 14.17 An experiment to observe osmosis. You can try this experiment in your kitchen. In the first step, use vinegar as a source of acetic acid.

solution and occurs in the other direction if the concentration solution is less inside the egg than it is in the exterior solution. In both cases, solvent flows from the region of low solute concentration to the region of high solute concentration.

EXAMPLE 14.7 Determining the Osmotic Pressure of a Solution of a Polymer

Problem Polyvinyl alcohol is a water soluble polymer with an average molar mass of 28,000. You dissolve 1.844 g of this polymer in water to give 150. mL of solution. What is the osmotic pressure, measured at 27 °C?

What Do You Know? Osmotic pressure is calculated by Equation 14.9, $\Pi = cRT$. You are given the mass and molar mass of the polymer and the temperature and will need the gas law constant.

Strategy Calculate the concentration of the polymer, c, in mol/L. The temperature must be expressed in kelvins. Substitute these values into Equation 14.9 to solve for the osmotic pressure.

Solution

$$c = 1.844 \text{ g}(1 \text{ mol}/28,000 \text{ g})/(0.150 \text{ L}) = 4.4 \times 10^{-4} \text{ mol/L}$$

$$\Pi = cRT$$

$$\Pi = (4.4 \times 10^{-4} \text{ mol/L})(0.08206 \text{ L atm/mol K})(300 \text{ K})$$

$$\Pi = 0.011 \text{ atm } (= 8.2 \text{ mm Hg})$$

Think about Your Answer If the osmotic pressure is measured in a device similar to that shown in Figure 14.15, the height of the column of aqueous solution supported would be about 110 mm (8.2 mm × 13.5 mm H_2O/mm Hg = 110 mm). This would be easily measurable in the laboratory.

Check Your Understanding

Bradykinin is a small peptide (9 amino acids; 1060 g/mol) that lowers blood pressure by causing blood vessels to dilate. What is the osmotic pressure of a solution of this protein at 20 °C if 0.033 g of the peptide is dissolved in water to give 50.0 mL of solution?

Colligative Properties and Molar Mass Determination

Earlier in this book you learned how to calculate a molecular formula from an empirical formula when given the molar mass. But how do you know the molar mass of an unknown compound? An experiment must be carried out to find this crucial piece of information, and one way to do so is to use a colligative property of a solution of the compound. The strategy map used with Example 14.8 represents the basic approach for each of the colligative properties studied.

⊘WL INTERACTIVE EXAMPLE 14.8 Determining Molar Mass from Boiling Point Elevation

Problem A solution prepared from 1.25 g of oil of wintergreen (methyl salicylate) in 99.0 g of benzene has a boiling point of 80.31 °C. Determine the molar mass of methyl salicylate.

What Do You Know? The molar mass of a compound is the quotient of the mass of a sample (g) and the amount (mol) represented by that sample. Here you know the mass of the sample (1.25 g), so you need to find the amount that corresponds to this mass.

Strategy

- Determine ΔT_{bp} from the given boiling point of the solution. (The boiling point of pure benzene and K_{bp} for benzene are given in Table 14.3.) Use the equation $\Delta T_{bp} = K_{bp} \cdot m$ to calculate the solution concentration in units of mol/kg.

- Knowing the mass of solvent, calculate the amount of solute (mol).

- Combine the mass and amount of solute to give the molar mass [molar mass = mass (g)/amount (mol)].

Solution

(a) Use the boiling point elevation to calculate the solution concentration:

Boiling point elevation $(\Delta T_{bp}) = 80.31\,°C - 80.10\,°C = 0.21\,°C$

$$c_{solute} = \frac{\Delta T_{bp}}{K_{bp}} = \frac{0.21\,°C}{2.53\,°C/m} = 0.083\,m$$

(b) Calculate the amount of solute in the solution from the solution concentration:

$$\text{Amount of solute} = \left(\frac{0.083\,\text{mol}}{1.00\,\text{kg}}\right)(0.099\,\text{kg solvent}) = 0.0082\,\text{mol solute}$$

(c) Combine the amount of solute with its mass to obtain its molar mass.

$$\frac{1.25\,g}{0.0082\,\text{mol}} = 150\,g/mol$$

Think about Your Answer Methyl salicylate has the formula $C_8H_8O_3$ and a molar mass of 152.14 g/mol. Given that ΔT has only two significant figures, the calculated value is acceptably close to the actual value.

Check Your Understanding

An aluminum-containing compound has the empirical formula $(C_2H_5)_2AlF$. Find the molecular formula if 0.448 g of the compound dissolved in 23.46 g of benzene has a freezing point of 5.265 °C.

Strategy Map 14.8

PROBLEM

Calculate **molar mass** of unknown.

DATA/INFORMATION
- **Mass** of unknown and solvent
- **Boiling point** of solution (80.31 °C)

STEP 1. Use $\Delta T_{bp} = K_{bp}m$.

Concentration of solute (mol/kg)

STEP 2. Mol solute = (mol/kg)(kg solvent).

Amount of solute (mol)

STEP 3. Molar mass = g solute/mol solute.

Molar mass of unknown **(g/mol)**

EXAMPLE 14.9   Osmotic Pressure and Molar Mass

Problem Beta-carotene is the most important of the A vitamins. Calculate the molar mass of β-carotene if 10.0 mL of a solution in chloroform containing 7.68 mg of β-carotene has an osmotic pressure of 26.57 mm Hg at 25.0 °C.

What Do You Know? As in Example 14.8, the molar mass of a compound is the quotient of the mass of a sample and the amount represented by that sample. Here you know the mass of the sample (7.68 mg), so you need to find the amount equivalent to this mass.

Strategy

- Use Equation 14.9 to calculate the solution concentration from the osmotic pressure.

- Use the volume and concentration of the solution to calculate the amount of solute.

- Find the molar mass of the solute from its mass and amount.

Solution

(a) Calculate the concentration of β-carotene from Π, R, and T.

$$\text{Concentration (mol/L)} = \frac{\Pi}{RT} = \frac{(26.57\,\text{mm Hg})\left(\dfrac{1\,\text{atm}}{760\,\text{mm Hg}}\right)}{(0.082057\,L\cdot atm/K\cdot mol)(298.2\,K)}$$

$$= 1.429 \times 10^{-3}\,\text{mol/L}$$

(b) Calculate the amount of β-carotene dissolved in 10.0 mL of solvent.

$$(1.429 \times 10^{-3}\,\text{mol/L})(0.0100\,L) = 1.43 \times 10^{-5}\,\text{mol}$$

(c) Combine the amount of solute with its mass to calculate its molar mass:

$$\frac{7.68 \times 10^{-3}\,g}{1.43 \times 10^{-5}\,\text{mol}} = 538\,g/mol$$

Think about Your Answer Beta-carotene is a hydrocarbon with the formula $C_{40}H_{56}$ (molar mass = 536.9 g/mol).

Osmosis and Medicine

Osmosis is of practical significance for people in the health professions. Patients who become dehydrated through illness often need to be given water and nutrients intravenously. Water cannot simply be dripped into a patient's vein, however. Rather, the intravenous solution must have the same overall solute concentration as the patient's blood: the solution must be isoosmotic or **isotonic** (Figure B, middle). If pure water was used, the inside of a blood cell would have a higher solute concentration (lower water concentration), and water would flow into the cell. This hypotonic situation would cause the red blood cells to burst (lyse) (Figure B, right). The opposite situation, hypertonicity, occurs if the intravenous solution is more concentrated than the contents of the blood cell (Figure B, left). In this case, the cell would lose water and shrivel up (crenate). To combat this, a dehydrated patient is rehydrated in the hospital with a sterile saline solution that is 0.16 M NaCl, a solution that is isotonic with the cells of the body.

FIGURE A **An isotonic saline solution.** This solution has the same molality as body fluids.

FIGURE B **Osmosis and living cells.** *(middle)* A cell placed in an isotonic solution. The net movement of water into and out of the cell is zero because the concentration of solutes inside and outside the cell is the same. *(left)* In a hypertonic solution, the concentration of solutes outside the cell is greater than that inside. There is a net flow of water out of the cell, causing the cell to dehydrate, shrink, and perhaps die. *(right)* In a hypotonic solution, the concentration of solutes outside the cell is less than that inside. There is a net flow of water into the cell, causing the cell to swell and perhaps to burst (or lyse).

Check Your Understanding

A 1.40-g sample of polyethylene, a common plastic, is dissolved in enough organic solvent to give 100.0 mL of solution. What is the average molar mass of the polymer if the measured osmotic pressure of the solution is 1.86 mm Hg at 25 °C?

Colligative Properties of Solutions Containing Ions

In the northern United States, it is common practice to scatter salt on snowy or icy roads or sidewalks. When the sun shines on the snow or patch of ice, a small amount melts, and some salt dissolves in the water. As a result of the dissolved solute, the freezing point of the solution is lower than 0 °C. The solution "eats" its way through the ice, breaking it up, and the icy patch is no longer dangerous for drivers or for people walking.

Salt (NaCl) is the most common substance used on roads because it is inexpensive and dissolves readily in water. Its relatively low molar mass means that the effect per gram is large. In addition, salt is especially effective because it is an electrolyte. That is, it dissolves to give ions in solution:

$$NaCl(s) \rightarrow Na^+(aq) + Cl^-(aq)$$

Recall that colligative properties depend not on what is dissolved but *only on the number of particles of solute per solvent particle*. When 1 mol of NaCl dissolves, 2 mol of ions form, which means that the effect on the freezing point of water should be twice as large as that expected for a mole of sugar. A 0.100 *m* solution of

Table 14.4 Freezing Point Depressions of Some Ionic Solutions

Mass %	m (mol/kg)	ΔT_{fp} (measured, °C)	ΔT_{fp} (calculated, °C)	$\dfrac{\Delta T_{fp},\text{ measured}}{\Delta T_{fp},\text{ calculated}}$
NaCl				
0.00700	0.0120	−0.0433	−0.0223	1.94
0.500	0.0860	−0.299	−0.160	1.87
1.00	0.173	−0.593	−0.322	1.84
2.00	0.349	−1.186	−0.649	1.83
Na₂SO₄				
0.00700	0.00493	−0.0257	−0.00917	2.80
0.500	0.0354	−0.165	−0.0658	2.51
1.00	0.0711	−0.320	−0.132	2.42
2.00	0.144	−0.606	−0.268	2.26

NaCl really contains two solutes, 0.100 m Na^+ and 0.100 m Cl^-. What we should use to estimate the freezing point depression is the *total* molality of solute particles:

$$m_{total} = m(Na^+) + m(Cl^-) = (0.100 + 0.100)\text{ mol/kg} = 0.200\text{ mol/kg}$$

$$\Delta T_{fp} = (-1.86\text{ °C}/m)(0.200\ m) = -0.372\text{ °C}$$

To estimate the freezing point depression for an ionic compound, first find the molality of solute from the mass and molar mass of the compound and the mass of the solvent. Then, multiply the molality by the number of ions in the formula: two for NaCl, three for Na_2SO_4, four for $LaCl_3$, five for $Al_2(SO_4)_3$, and so on.

Table 14.4 shows that as the concentration of NaCl decreases, ΔT_{fp} for NaCl approaches but does not quite reach a value that is two times larger than the value determined assuming no dissociation. Likewise, ΔT_{fp} for Na_2SO_4 approaches but does not reach a value that is three times larger. The ratio of the experimentally observed value of ΔT_{fp} to the value calculated, assuming no dissociation, is called the **van't Hoff factor** after Jacobus Henrikus van't Hoff (1852–1911), who studied this phenomenon. The van't Hoff factor is represented by i.

$$i = \frac{\Delta T_{fp},\text{ measured}}{\Delta T_{fp},\text{ calculated}} = \frac{\Delta T_{fp},\text{ measured}}{K_{fp}\ m}$$

or

$$\Delta T_{fp}\text{ measured} = K_{fp} \times m \times i \qquad\qquad \text{(14.10)}$$

The numbers in the last column of Table 14.4 are van't Hoff factors. These values can be used in calculations of any colligative property. Vapor pressure lowering, boiling point elevation, freezing point depression, and osmotic pressure are all larger for electrolytes than for nonelectrolytes of the same molality.

The van't Hoff factor approaches a whole number (2, 3, and so on) only with very dilute solutions. In more concentrated solutions, the experimental freezing point depressions indicate that there are fewer ions in solution than expected. This behavior, which is typical of all ionic compounds, is a consequence of the strong attractions between ions. The result is as if some of the positive and negative ions are paired, decreasing the total molality of particles. Indeed, in more concentrated solutions, and especially in solvents less polar than water, ions are extensively associated in ion pairs and in even larger clusters.

EXAMPLE 14.10 Freezing Point and Ionic Solutions

Problem A 0.0200 m aqueous solution of an ionic compound, $Co(NH_3)_4Cl_3$, freezes at -0.0640 °C. How many moles of ions does 1 mol of the salt produce on being dissolved in water?

What Do You Know? You know the freezing point depression (-0.0640 °C), the solution concentration, and K_{fp}.

Strategy The van't Hoff factor, i, is the ratio of the measured ΔT_{fp} to the calculated freezing point depression. First, calculate ΔT_{fp} expected for a solution in which no ions are produced. Compare this value with the actual value of ΔT_{fp}. The ratio ($= i$) will reflect the number of ions produced.

Solution

(a) Calculate the freezing-point depression expected for a 0.0200 m solution assuming that the salt does not dissociate into ions.

$$\Delta T_{fp} \text{ calculated} = K_{fp}m = (-1.86 \text{ °C})(0.0200 \text{ } m) = -0.0372 \text{ °C}$$

(b) Compare the calculated freezing point depression with the measured depression. This gives the van't Hoff factor:

$$i = \frac{\Delta T_{fp}, \text{ measured}}{\Delta T_{fp}, \text{ calculated}} = \frac{-0.0640 \text{ °C}}{-0.0372 \text{ °C}} = 1.72$$

The i value is much greater that 1 and is approaching 2. Therefore, we assume each molecule affords 2 ions in solution.

Think about Your Answer We find i is approaching 2, meaning that the complex dissociates into two ions: $[Co(NH_3)Cl_2]^+$ and Cl^-. As you will see in Chapter 22, the cation is a Co^{3+} ion surrounded octahedrally by 4 NH_3 molecules and two Cl^- ions.

Check Your Understanding

Calculate the freezing point of 525 g of water that contains 25.0 g of NaCl. Assume i, the van't Hoff factor, is 1.85 for NaCl.

REVIEW & CHECK FOR SECTION 14.4

1. *Vapor pressure:* Arrange the following aqueous solutions in order of increasing vapor pressure at 25 °C: 0.35 m $C_2H_4(OH)_2$ (ethylene glycol, nonvolatile solute); 0.50 m sugar; 0.20 m KBr; and 0.20 m Na_2SO_4.

    (a) $C_2H_4(OH)_2 <$ sugar $<$ KBr $< Na_2SO_4$ (c) sugar $< C_2H_4(OH)_2 <$ KBr $< Na_2SO_4$

    (b) $Na_2SO_4 <$ sugar $<$ KBr $< C_2H_4(OH)_2$ (d) KBr $<$ sugar $< Na_2SO_4 < C_2H_4(OH)_2$

2. One gram (1.00 g) of each of the listed substances is dissolved in 50 g of benzene. Which of the solutions has the lowest freezing point?

    (a) buckyballs, C_{60} (c) trinitrotoluene, $C_7H_5(NO_2)_3$

    (b) acetaminophen, $C_8H_9NO_2$ (d) naphthalene, $C_{10}H_8$

3. Samples of each of the substances listed below are dissolved in 125 g of water. Which of the solutions has the highest boiling point?

    (a) 3.0 g sucrose, $C_{12}H_{22}O_{11}$ (c) 1.0 g propylene glycol, $C_3H_6(OH)_2$

    (b) 1.0 g glycerol, $C_3H_5(OH)_3$ (d) 2.0 g glucose, $C_6H_{12}O_6$

4. *Molar mass:* Erythritol is a compound that occurs naturally in algae and fungi. It is about twice as sweet as sucrose. A solution of 2.50 g of erythritol in 50.0 g of water freezes at -0.762 °C. What is the molar mass of the compound?

    (a) 26.9 g/mol   (c) 122 g/mol

    (b) 35.5 g/mol   (d) 224 g/mol

14.5 Colloids

Earlier in this chapter, we defined a solution broadly as a homogeneous mixture of two or more substances in a single phase. To this definition we should add that, in a true solution, no settling of the solute should be observed and the solute particles should be in the form of ions or relatively small molecules. Thus, NaCl and sugar form true solutions in water. You are also familiar with suspensions, which result, for example, if a handful of fine sand is added to water and shaken vigorously. Sand particles are still visible and gradually settle to the bottom of the beaker or bottle. **Colloidal dispersions**, also called **colloids**, represent a state intermediate between a solution and a suspension (Figure 14.18). Colloids include many of the foods you eat and the materials around you; among them are JELL-O®, milk, fog, and porcelain (Table 14.5).

Around 1860, the British chemist Thomas Graham (1805–1869) found that substances such as starch, gelatin, glue, and albumin from eggs diffused only very slowly when placed in water, compared with sugar or salt. In addition, the former substances differ significantly in their ability to diffuse through a thin membrane: Sugar molecules can diffuse through many membranes, but the very large molecules that make up starch, gelatin, glue, and albumin do not. Moreover, Graham found that he could not crystallize these substances, whereas he could crystallize sugar, salt, and other materials that form true solutions. Graham coined the word "colloid" (from the Greek, meaning "glue") to describe this class of substances that are distinctly different from true solutions and suspensions.

We now know that it is possible to crystallize some colloidal substances, albeit with difficulty, so there really is no sharp dividing line between these classes based on this property. Colloids do, however, have two distinguishing characteristics. First, colloids generally have high molar masses; this is true of proteins such as hemoglobin that have molar masses in the thousands. Second, the particles of a colloid are relatively large (say, 1000 nm in diameter). As a consequence, they exhibit the **Tyndall effect**; they scatter visible light when dispersed in a solvent, making the mixture appear cloudy (Figure 14.19). Third, even though colloidal particles are large, they are not so large that they settle out.

Graham also gave us the words **sol** for a colloidal dispersion of a solid substance in a fluid medium and **gel** for a colloidal dispersion that has a structure that prevents it from being mobile. JELL-O® is a sol when the solid is first mixed with boiling water, but it becomes a gel when cooled. Other examples of gels are the gelatinous precipitates of $Al(OH)_3$, $Fe(OH)_3$, and $Cu(OH)_2$ (Figure 14.20).

Colloidal dispersions consist of finely divided particles that, as a result, have a very high surface area. For example, if you have one millionth of a mole of colloidal particles, each assumed to be a sphere with a diameter of 200 nm, the total surface

FIGURE 14.18 Gold colloid. A water-soluble salt of $[AuCl_4]^-$ is reduced to give colloidal gold metal. The colloidal gold gives the dispersion its red color (when the particles have a length or diameter of less than 100 nm). (Similarly, colloidal gold is used to give a beautiful red color to glass.) Since the days of alchemy, some have claimed that drinking a colloidal gold solution "cleared the mind, increased intelligence and willpower, and balanced the emotions."

Dust in the air scatters the light coming through the trees in a forest along the Oregon coast.

A narrow beam of light from a laser is passed through an NaCl solution *(left)* and then a colloidal mixture of gelatin and water *(right)*.

FIGURE 14.19 The Tyndall effect. Colloidal dispersions scatter light, a phenomenon known as the Tyndall effect.

FIGURE 14.20 Gelatinous precipitates. *(left)* $Al(OH)_3$, *(center)* $Fe(OH)_3$, and *(right)* $Cu(OH)_2$.

Table 14.5 **Types of Colloids**

Type	Dispersing Medium	Dispersed Phase	Examples
Aerosol	Gas	Liquid	Fog, clouds, aerosol sprays
Aerosol	Gas	Solid	Smoke, airborne viruses, automobile exhaust
Foam	Liquid	Gas	Shaving cream, whipped cream
Foam	Solid	Gas	Styrofoam, marshmallow
Emulsion	Liquid	Liquid	Mayonnaise, milk, face cream
Gel	Solid	Liquid	Jelly, JELL-O®, cheese, butter
Sol	Liquid	Solid	Gold in water, milk of magnesia, mud
Solid sol	Solid	Solid	Milkglass

area of the particles would be on the order of 200 million cm^2, or the size of several football fields. It is not surprising, therefore, that many of the properties of colloids depend on the properties of surfaces.

Types of Colloids

Colloids are classified according to the state of the dispersed phase and the dispersing medium. Table 14.5 lists several types of colloids and gives examples of each.

Colloids with water as the dispersing medium can be classified as **hydrophobic** (from the Greek, meaning "water-fearing") or **hydrophilic** ("water-loving"). A hydrophobic colloid is one in which only weak attractive forces exist between the water and the surfaces of the colloidal particles. Examples include dispersions of metals (Figure 14.18) and of nearly insoluble salts in water. When compounds like AgCl precipitate, the result is often a colloidal dispersion. The precipitation reaction occurs too rapidly for ions to gather from long distances and make large crystals, so the ions aggregate to form small particles that remain suspended in the liquid.

Why don't the particles come together (coagulate) and form larger particles? The answer is that the colloidal particles carry electric charges. To see how this happens, suppose AgCl ion pairs come together to form a tiny particle. If Ag^+ ions are still present in substantial concentration in the solution, these positive ions could be attracted to negative Cl^- ions on the surface of the particle. Thus the original clump of AgCl ion pairs becomes positively charged, allowing it to attract a secondary layer of anions. The particles, now surrounded by layers of ions, repel one another and are prevented from coming together to form a precipitate (Figure 14.21).

FIGURE 14.21 Hydrophobic colloids. A hydrophobic colloid is stabilized by positive ions absorbed onto each particle and a secondary layer of negative ions. Because the particles bear similar charges, they repel one another, and precipitation is prevented.

Soil particles are often carried by water in rivers and streams as hydrophobic colloids. When river water carrying large amounts of colloidal particles meets seawater with its high concentration of salts, the particles coagulate to form the silt seen at the mouth of the river (Figure 14.22). Municipal water treatment plants often add salts such as $Al_2(SO_4)_3$ to clarify water. In aqueous solution, aluminum ions exist as $[Al(H_2O)_6]^{3+}$ cations, which neutralize the charge on the hydrophobic colloidal soil particles, causing these particles to aggregate and settle out.

Hydrophilic colloids are strongly attracted to water molecules. They often have groups such as —OH and —NH_2 on their surfaces. These groups form strong hydrogen bonds to water, thereby stabilizing the colloid. Proteins and starch are important examples of hydrophilic colloids, and homogenized milk is the most familiar example.

Emulsions are colloidal dispersions of one liquid in another, such as oil or fat in water. Familiar examples include salad dressing, mayonnaise, and milk. If vegetable oil and vinegar are mixed to make a salad dressing, the mixture quickly separates into two layers because the nonpolar oil molecules do not interact with the polar water and acetic acid (CH_3CO_2H) molecules. So why are milk and mayonnaise apparently homogeneous mixtures that do not separate into layers? The answer is that they contain an **emulsifying agent** such as soap or a protein. Lecithin is a phospholipid found in egg yolks, so mixing egg yolks with oil and vinegar stabilizes the colloidal dispersion known as mayonnaise. To understand this process further, let us look into the functioning of soaps and detergents, substances known as surfactants.

Surfactants

Soaps and detergents are emulsifying agents. Soap is made by heating a fat with sodium or potassium hydroxide, which produces the anions of long chain carboxylic acids, sometimes referred to as fatty acids (◄ page 489). An example is sodium stearate.

sodium stearate, a soap

The fatty acid anion has a split personality: It has a nonpolar, hydrophobic hydrocarbon tail that is soluble in other similar hydrocarbons and a polar, hydrophilic head that is soluble in water.

Oil cannot be readily washed away from dishes or clothing with water because oil is nonpolar and thus insoluble in water. Instead, we add soap to the water to clean away the oil. The nonpolar molecules of the oil interact with the nonpolar hydrocarbon tails of the soap molecules, leaving the polar heads of the soap to interact with surrounding water molecules. The oil and water then mix (Figure 14.23).

FIGURE 14.22 Formation of silt. Silt forms at a river delta as colloidal soil particles come in contact with saltwater in the ocean. Here, the Ashley and Cooper Rivers empty into the Atlantic Ocean at Charleston, South Carolina. The high concentration of ions in seawater causes the colloidal soil particles to coagulate.

FIGURE 14.23 The cleaning action of soap. Soap molecules interact with water through the charged, hydrophilic end of the molecule. The long, hydrocarbon end of the molecule is hydrophobic, but it can bind through dispersion forces with hydrocarbons and other nonpolar substances.

FIGURE 14.24 **Effect of a detergent on the surface tension of water.** Sulfur (density = 2.1 g/cm³) is carefully placed on the surface of water (density, 1.0 g/cm³) *(left)*. The surface tension of the water keeps the denser sulfur afloat. Several drops of detergent are then placed on the surface of the water *(right)*. The surface tension of the water is reduced, and the sulfur sinks to the bottom of the beaker.

 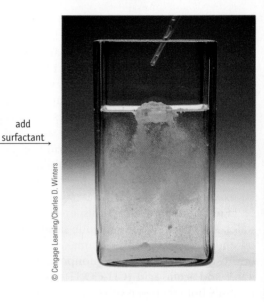

add surfactant →

• **Soaps and Surfactants** A sodium soap is a solid at room temperature, whereas potassium soaps are usually liquids. About 30 million tons of household and toilet soap, and synthetic and soap-based laundry detergents, are produced annually worldwide.

If the oily material on a piece of clothing or a dish also contains some dirt particles, that dirt can now be washed away.

Substances such as soaps that affect the properties of surfaces, and therefore affect the interaction between two phases, are called surface-active agents, or **surfactants**, for short. A surfactant used for cleaning is called a **detergent**. One function of a surfactant is to lower the surface tension of water, which enhances the cleansing action of the detergent (Figure 14.24).

Many detergents used in the home and industry are synthetic. One example is sodium laurylbenzenesulfonate, a biodegradable compound.

$$CH_3CH_2CH_2CH_2CH_2CH_2CH_2CH_2CH_2CH_2CH_2CH_2 \text{—} \bigcirc \text{—} SO_3^- \ Na^+$$

sodium laurylbenzenesulfonate

In general, synthetic detergents use the sulfonate group, $-SO_3^-$, as the polar head instead of the carboxylate group, $-CO_2^-$. The carboxylate anions form an insoluble precipitate with any Ca^{2+} or Mg^{2+} ions present in water. Because hard water is characterized by high concentrations of these ions, using soaps containing carboxylates produces bathtub rings and telltale gray clothing. The synthetic sulfonate detergents have the advantage that they do not form such precipitates because their calcium salts are more soluble in water.

REVIEW & CHECK FOR SECTION 14.5

Figure 14.18 illustrates a gold colloid. Assume the colloidal particles are spherical clumps of gold atoms and are 100 nm in diameter. What is the approximate number of gold atoms that could form such a particle? (The radius of a gold atom is 144 pm.)

(a)   300 atoms   (b)   40 million atoms   (c)   2 billion atoms

---

CHAPTER GOALS REVISITED

Now that you have studied this chapter, you should ask whether you have met the chapter goals. In particular, you should be able to:

Calculate and use the solution concentration units molality, mole fraction, and weight percent

a.   Define the terms solution, solvent, solute, and colligative properties.

b.   Use the following concentration units: molality, mole fraction, and weight percent (Section 14.1) **Study Questions: 1–12.**

c. Understand the distinctions between saturated, unsaturated, and supersaturated solutions (Section 14.2). **Study Questions: 17, 18, 94.**

d. Define and illustrate the terms *miscible* and *immiscible* (Section 14.2). **Study Questions: 13, 96.**

Understand the solution process

a. Describe the process of dissolving a solute in a solvent, including the energy changes that may occur (Section 14.2). **Study Questions: 14–16, 71.**

b. Understand the relationship of lattice enthalpy and enthalpy of hydration to the enthalpy of solution for an ionic solute (Section 14.2). **Study Question: 91.**

c. Describe the effect of pressure and temperature on the solubility of a solute (Section 14.3). **Study Questions: 17, 18.**

d. Use Henry's law to calculate the solubility of a gas in a solvent (Section 14.3). **Study Questions: 19–22, 67, 81, 82.**

e. Apply Le Chatelier's principle to the change in solubility of gases with temperature changes (Section 14.3).

Understand and use the colligative properties of solutions

a. Calculate the mole fraction of a solvent ($X_{solvent}$) and the effect of a solute on solvent vapor pressure ($P_{solvent}$) using Raoult's law (Section 14.4). **Study Questions: 23–26, 73, 74, 98.**

b. Calculate the boiling point elevation or freezing point depression caused by a solute in a solvent (Section 14.4). **Study Questions: 27–34, 45, 53, 60, and Go Chemistry Module 19.**

c. Calculate the osmotic pressure (Π) for solutions (Section 14.4). **Study Questions: 35–38, 78, 88.**

d. Use colligative properties to determine the molar mass of a solute (Section 14.4). **Study Questions: 39–44, 64, 89, 90.**

e. Characterize the effect of ionic solutes on colligative properties (Section 14.4). **Study Questions: 47, 48, 52, 53, 60, 61, 93.**

f. Use the van't Hoff factor, i, in calculations involving colligative properties (Section 14.4). **Study Questions: 45, 46, 62, 63, 75, 77, 79, 80, 102.**

Recognize the properties and importance of colloids (Section 14.5).

Key Equations

Equation 14.1 (page 618) Molality is defined as the amount of solute per kilogram of solvent.

$$\text{Concentration } (c, \text{ mol/kg}) = \text{molality of solute} = \frac{\text{amount of solute (mol)}}{\text{mass of solvent (kg)}}$$

Equation 14.2 (page 618) The mole fraction, X, of a solution component is defined as the number of moles of a given component of a mixture (n_A, mol) divided by the total number of moles of all of the components of the mixture.

$$\text{Mole fraction of A } (X_A) = \frac{n_A}{n_A + n_B + n_C + \ldots}$$

Equation 14.3 (page 619) Weight percent is the mass of one component divided by the total mass of the mixture (multiplied by 100%).

$$\text{Weight \% A} = \frac{\text{mass of A}}{\text{mass of A} + \text{mass of B} + \text{mass of C} + \ldots} \times 100\%$$

Equation 14.4 (page 626) Henry's law: The solubility of a gas, S_g, is equal to the product of the partial pressure of the gaseous solute (P_g) and a constant (k_H) characteristic of the solute and solvent.

$$S_g = k_H P_g$$

Equation 14.5 (page 630) Raoult's law: The equilibrium vapor pressure of a solvent over a solution at a given temperature, $P_{solvent}$, is the product of the mole fraction of the solvent ($X_{solvent}$) and the vapor pressure of the pure solvent ($P°_{solvent}$).

$$P_{solvent} = X_{solvent}\, P°_{solvent}$$

Equation 14.6 (page 631) The decrease in the vapor pressure of the solvent over a solution, $\Delta P_{solvent}$, depends on the mole fraction of the solute (X_{solute}) and the vapor pressure of the pure solvent ($P°_{solvent}$).

$$\Delta P_{solvent} = -X_{solute}\, P°_{solvent}$$

Equation 14.7 (page 632) The elevation in boiling point of the solvent in a solution, ΔT_{bp}, is the product of the molality of the solute, m_{solute}, and a constant characteristic of the solvent, K_{bp}.

$$\text{Elevation in boiling point} = \Delta T_{bp} = K_{bp} m_{solute}$$

Equation 14.8 (page 634) The depression of the freezing point of the solvent in a solution, ΔT_{fp}, is the product of the molality of the solute, m_{solute}, and a constant characteristic of the solvent, K_{fp}.

$$\text{Freezing point depression} = \Delta T_{fp} = K_{fp} m_{solute}$$

Equation 14.9 (page 636) The osmotic pressure, Π, is the product of the solute concentration c (in mol/L), the universal gas constant R (0.082057 L · atm/ K · mol), and the temperature T (in kelvins).

$$\Pi = cRT$$

Equation 14.10 (page 641) This modified equation for freezing point depression accounts for the possible dissociation of a solute. The van't Hoff factor, i, the ratio of the measured freezing point depression and the freezing point depression calculated assuming no solute dissociation, is related to the relative number of particles produced by a dissolved solute.

$$\Delta T_{fp} \text{ measured} = K_{fp} \times m \times i$$

Study Questions

ⓊWL Interactive versions of these questions are assignable in OWL.

▲ denotes challenging questions.

Blue-numbered questions have answers in Appendix R and fully worked solutions in the *Student Solutions Manual*.

Practicing Skills

Concentration

(See Section 14.1 and Example 14.1.)

1. Suppose you dissolve 2.56 g of succinic acid, $C_2H_4(CO_2H)_2$, in 500. mL of water. Assuming that the density of water is 1.00 g/cm³, calculate the molality, mole fraction, and weight percent of acid in the solution.

2. Assume you dissolve 45.0 g of camphor, $C_{10}H_{16}O$, in 425 mL of ethanol, C_2H_5OH. Calculate the molality, mole fraction, and weight percent of camphor in this solution. (The density of ethanol is 0.785 g/mL.)

3. Fill in the blanks in the table. Aqueous solutions are assumed.

Compound	Molality	Weight Percent	Mole Fraction
NaI	0.15	____	____
C_2H_5OH	____	5.0	____
$C_{12}H_{22}O_{11}$	0.15	____	____

4. Fill in the blanks in the table. Aqueous solutions are assumed.

Compound	Molality	Weight Percent	Mole Fraction
KNO_3	____	10.0	____
CH_3CO_2H	0.0183	____	____
$HOCH_2CH_2OH$	____	18.0	____

5. What mass of Na_2CO_3 must you add to 125 g of water to prepare 0.200 *m* Na_2CO_3? What is the mole fraction of Na_2CO_3 in the resulting solution?

6. You want to prepare a solution that is 0.0512 *m* in $NaNO_3$. What mass of $NaNO_3$ must be added to 500. g of water? What is the mole fraction of $NaNO_3$ in the solution?

7. You wish to prepare an aqueous solution of glycerol, $C_3H_5(OH)_3$, in which the mole fraction of the solute is 0.093. What mass of glycerol must you add to 425 g of water to make this solution? What is the molality of the solution?

8. You want to prepare an aqueous solution of ethylene glycol, $HOCH_2CH_2OH$, in which the mole fraction of solute is 0.125. What mass of ethylene glycol, in grams, should you combine with 955 g of water? What is the molality of the solution?

9. Hydrochloric acid is sold as a concentrated aqueous solution. If the molarity of commercial HCl is 12.0 and its density is 1.18 g/cm³, calculate the following:
   (a) the molality of the solution
   (b) the weight percent of HCl in the solution

10. Concentrated sulfuric acid has a density of 1.84 g/cm³ and is 95.0% by weight H_2SO_4. What is the molality of this acid? What is its molarity?

11. The average lithium ion concentration in seawater is 0.18 ppm. What is the molality of Li^+ in seawater?

12. Silver ion has an average concentration of 28 ppb (parts per billion) in U.S. water supplies.
   (a) What is the molality of the silver ion?
   (b) If you wanted 1.0×10^2 g of silver and could recover it chemically from water supplies, what volume of water in liters, would you have to treat? (Assume the density of water is 1.0 g/cm³.)

The Solution Process
(See Section 14.2 and Example 14.2.)

13. Which pairs of liquids will be miscible?
   (a) H_2O and $CH_3CH_2CH_2CH_3$
   (b) C_6H_6 (benzene) and CCl_4
   (c) H_2O and CH_3CO_2H

14. Acetone, CH_3COCH_3, is quite soluble in water. Explain why this should be so.

15. Use the data of Table 14.1 to calculate the enthalpy of solution of LiCl.

16. Use the following data to calculate the enthalpy of solution of sodium perchlorate, $NaClO_4$:

   $\Delta_f H°(s) = -382.9$ kJ/mol   and
   $\Delta_f H°(aq, 1\ m) = -369.5$ kJ/mol

17. You make a saturated solution of NaCl at 25 °C. No solid is present in the beaker holding the solution. What can be done to increase the amount of dissolved NaCl in this solution? (See Figure 14.11.)
   (a) Add more solid NaCl.
   (b) Raise the temperature of the solution.
   (c) Raise the temperature of the solution, and add some NaCl.
   (d) Lower the temperature of the solution, and add some NaCl.

18. Some lithium chloride, LiCl, is dissolved in 100 mL of water in one beaker, and some Li_2SO_4 is dissolved in 100 mL of water in another beaker. Both are at 10 °C, and both are saturated solutions; some solid remains undissolved in each beaker. Describe what you would observe as the temperature is raised. The following data are available to you from a handbook of chemistry:

Compound	Solubility (g/100 mL)	
	10 °C	40 °C
Li_2SO_4	35.5	33.7
LiCl	74.5	89.8

Henry's Law
(See Section 14.3 and Example 14.3.)

19. The partial pressure of O_2 in your lungs varies from 25 mm Hg to 40 mm Hg. What mass of O_2 can dissolve in 1.0 L of water at 25 °C if the partial pressure of O_2 is 40 mm Hg?

20. The Henry's law constant for O_2 in water at 25 °C is given in Table 14.2. Which of the following is a reasonable constant when the temperature is 50 °C? Explain the reason for your choice.
   (a) 6.7×10^{-4} mol/kg · bar   (c) 1.3×10^{-3} mol/kg · bar
   (b) 2.6×10^{-3} mol/kg · bar   (d) 6.4×10^{-2} mol/kg · bar

21. An unopened soda can has an aqueous CO_2 concentration of 0.0506 m at 25 °C. What is the pressure of CO_2 gas in the can?

22. Hydrogen gas has a Henry's law constant of 7.8×10^{-4} mol/kg · bar at 25 °C when dissolving in water. If the total pressure of gas (H_2 gas plus water vapor) over water is 1.00 bar, what is the concentration of H_2 in the water in grams per milliliter? (See Appendix G for the vapor pressure of water.)

Raoult's Law
(See Section 14.4 and Example 14.4.)

23. A 35.0-g sample of ethylene glycol, $HOCH_2CH_2OH$, is dissolved in 500.0 g of water. The vapor pressure of water at 32 °C is 35.7 mm Hg. What is the vapor pressure of the water–ethylene glycol solution at 32 °C? (Ethylene glycol is nonvolatile.)

24. Urea, $(NH_2)_2CO$, which is widely used in fertilizers and plastics, is quite soluble in water. If you dissolve 9.00 g of urea in 10.0 mL of water, what is the vapor pressure of the solution at 24 °C? Assume the density of water is 1.00 g/mL.

25. Pure ethylene glycol, $HOCH_2CH_2OH$, is added to 2.00 kg of water in the cooling system of a car. The vapor pressure of the water in the system when the temperature is 90 °C is 457 mm Hg. What mass of glycol was added? (Assume the solution is ideal. See Appendix G for the vapor pressure of water.)

26. Pure iodine (105 g) is dissolved in 325 g of CCl_4 at 65 °C. Given that the vapor pressure of CCl_4 at this temperature is 531 mm Hg, what is the vapor pressure of the CCl_4–I_2 solution at 65 °C? (Assume that I_2 does not contribute to the vapor pressure.)

Boiling Point Elevation
(See Section 14.4 and Example 14.5.)

27. Verify that 0.200 mol of a nonvolatile solute in 125 g of benzene (C_6H_6) produces a solution whose boiling point is 84.2 °C.

28. What is the boiling point of a solution composed of 15.0 g of urea, $(NH_2)_2CO$, in 0.500 kg of water?

29. What is the boiling point of a solution composed of 15.0 g of $CHCl_3$ and 0.515 g of the nonvolatile solute acenaphthene, $C_{12}H_{10}$, a component of coal tar?

30. A solution of glycerol, $C_3H_5(OH)_3$, in 735 g of water has a boiling point of 104.4 °C at a pressure of 760 mm Hg. What is the mass of glycerol in the solution? What is the mole fraction of the solute?

Freezing Point Depression
(See Section 14.4 and Example 14.6.)

31. A mixture of ethanol, C_2H_5OH, and water has a freezing point of −16.0 °C.
(a) What is the molality of the alcohol?
(b) What is the weight percent of alcohol in the solution?

32. Some ethylene glycol, $HOCH_2CH_2OH$, is added to your car's cooling system along with 5.0 kg of water. If the freezing point of the water–glycol solution is −15.0 °C, what mass of $HOCH_2CH_2OH$ must have been added?

33. You dissolve 15.0 g of sucrose, $C_{12}H_{22}O_{11}$, in a cup of water (225 g). What is the freezing point of the solution?

34. Assume a bottle of wine consists of an 11% solution (by weight) of ethanol (C_2H_5OH) in water. If the bottle of wine is chilled to −20 °C, will the solution begin to freeze?

Osmosis
(See Section 14.4 and Example 14.7.)

35. An aqueous solution contains 3.00% phenylalanine ($C_9H_{11}NO_2$) by mass. Assume the phenylalanine is non-ionic and nonvolatile. Find the following:
(a) the freezing point of the solution
(b) the boiling point of the solution
(c) the osmotic pressure of the solution at 25 °C
In your view, which of these values is most easily measurable in the laboratory?

36. Estimate the osmotic pressure of human blood at 37 °C. Assume blood is isotonic with a 0.154 M NaCl solution, and assume the van't Hoff factor, i, is 1.90 for NaCl.

37. An aqueous solution containing 1.00 g of bovine insulin (a protein, not ionized) per liter has an osmotic pressure of 3.1 mm Hg at 25 °C. Calculate the molar mass of bovine insulin.

38. Calculate the osmotic pressure of a 0.0120 M solution of NaCl in water at 0 °C. Assume the van't Hoff factor, i, is 1.94 for this solution.

Colligative Properties and Molar Mass Determination
(See Section 14.4 and Examples 14.8 and 14.9.)

39. You add 0.255 g of an orange, crystalline compound whose empirical formula is $C_{10}H_8Fe$ to 11.12 g of benzene. The boiling point of the benzene rises from 80.10 °C to 80.26 °C. What are the molar mass and molecular formula of the compound?

40. Butylated hydroxyanisole (BHA) is used in margarine and other fats and oils. (It is used as an antioxidant and prolongs the shelf life of the food.) What is the molar mass of BHA if 0.640 g of the compound, dissolved in 25.0 g of chloroform, produces a solution whose boiling point is 62.22 °C?

41. Benzyl acetate is one of the active components of oil of jasmine. If 0.125 g of the compound is added to 25.0 g of chloroform ($CHCl_3$), the boiling point of the solution is 61.82 °C. What is the molar mass of benzyl acetate?

42. Anthracene, a hydrocarbon obtained from coal, has an empirical formula of C_7H_5. To find its molecular formula, you dissolve 0.500 g in 30.0 g of benzene. The boiling point of pure benzene is 80.10 °C, whereas the solution has a boiling point of 80.34 °C. What is the molecular formula of anthracene?

43. An aqueous solution contains 0.180 g of an unknown, nonionic solute in 50.0 g of water. The solution freezes at −0.040 °C. What is the molar mass of the solute?

44. The organic compound called *aluminon* is used as a reagent to test for the presence of the aluminum ion in aqueous solution. A solution of 2.50 g of aluminon in 50.0 g of water freezes at −0.197 °C. What is the molar mass of aluminon?

Colligative Properties of Ionic Compounds
(See Section 14.4 and Example 14.10.)

45. If 52.5 g of LiF is dissolved in 306 g of water, what is the expected freezing point of the solution? (Assume the van't Hoff factor, i, for LiF is 2.)

46. To make homemade ice cream, you cool the milk and cream by immersing the container in ice and a concentrated solution of rock salt (NaCl) in water. If you want to have a water–salt solution that freezes at −10. °C, what mass of NaCl must you add to 3.0 kg of water? (Assume the van't Hoff factor, i, for NaCl is 1.85.)

47. List the following aqueous solutions in order of increasing melting point. (The last three are all assumed to dissociate completely into ions in water.)
(a) 0.1 m sugar
(b) 0.1 m NaCl
(c) 0.08 m $CaCl_2$
(d) 0.04 m Na_2SO_4

48. Arrange the following aqueous solutions in order of decreasing freezing point. (The last three are all assumed to dissociate completely into ions in water.)
(a) 0.20 m ethylene glycol (nonvolatile, nonelectrolyte)
(b) 0.12 m K_2SO_4
(c) 0.10 m $MgCl_2$
(d) 0.12 m KBr

Colloids
(See Section 14.5.)

49. When solutions of $BaCl_2$ and Na_2SO_4 are mixed, the mixture becomes cloudy. After a few days, a white solid is observed on the bottom of the beaker with a clear liquid above it.
(a) Write a balanced equation for the reaction that occurs.
(b) Why is the solution cloudy at first?
(c) What happens during the few days of waiting?

50. The dispersed phase of a certain colloidal dispersion consists of spheres of diameter 1.0×10^2 nm.
(a) What are the volume ($V = \frac{4}{3}\pi r^3$) and surface area ($A = 4\pi r^2$) of each sphere?
(b) How many spheres are required to give a total volume of 1.0 cm^3? What is the total surface area of these spheres in square meters?

General Questions

These questions are not designated as to type or location in the chapter. They may combine several concepts.

51. Phenylcarbinol is used in nasal sprays as a preservative. A solution of 0.52 g of the compound in 25.0 g of water has a melting point of -0.36 °C. What is the molar mass of phenylcarbinol?

52. (a) Which aqueous solution is expected to have the higher boiling point: 0.10 m Na_2SO_4 or 0.15 m sugar?
(b) For which aqueous solution is the vapor pressure of water higher: 0.30 m NH_4NO_3 or 0.15 m Na_2SO_4?

53. Arrange the following aqueous solutions in order of (i) increasing vapor pressure of water and (ii) increasing boiling point.
(a) 0.35 m $HOCH_2CH_2OH$ (a nonvolatile solute)
(b) 0.50 m sugar
(c) 0.20 m KBr (a strong electrolyte)
(d) 0.20 m Na_2SO_4 (a strong electrolyte)

54. Making homemade ice cream is one of life's great pleasures. Fresh milk and cream, sugar, and flavorings are churned in a bucket suspended in an ice–water mixture, the freezing point of which has been lowered by adding rock salt. One manufacturer of home ice cream freezers recommends adding 2.50 lb (1130 g) of rock salt (NaCl) to 16.0 lb of ice (7250 g) in a 4-qt freezer. For the solution when this mixture melts, calculate the following:
(a) the weight percent of NaCl
(b) the mole fraction of NaCl
(c) the molality of the solution

55. Dimethylglyoxime [DMG, $(CH_3CNOH)_2$] is used as a reagent to precipitate nickel ion. Assume that 53.0 g of DMG has been dissolved in 525 g of ethanol (C_2H_5OH).

© Cengage Learning/Charles D. Winters

The red, insoluble compound formed between nickel(II) ion and dimethylglyoxime (DMG) is precipitated when DMG is added to a basic solution of Ni^{2+}(aq).

(a) What is the mole fraction of DMG?
(b) What is the molality of the solution?
(c) What is the vapor pressure of the ethanol over the solution at ethanol's normal boiling point of 78.4 °C?
(d) What is the boiling point of the solution? (DMG does not produce ions in solution.) (K_{bp} for ethanol $= +1.22$ °C/m)

56. A 10.7 m solution of NaOH has a density of 1.33 g/cm^3 at 20 °C. Calculate the following:
(a) the mole fraction of NaOH
(b) the weight percent of NaOH
(c) the molarity of the solution

57. Concentrated aqueous ammonia has a molarity of 14.8 mol/L and a density of 0.90 g/cm^3. What is the molality of the solution? Calculate the mole fraction and weight percent of NH_3.

58. If you dissolve 2.00 g of $Ca(NO_3)_2$ in 750 g of water, what is the molality of $Ca(NO_3)_2$? What is the total molality of ions in solution? (Assume total dissociation of the ionic solid.)

59. If you want a solution that is 0.100 m in ions, what mass of Na_2SO_4 must you dissolve in 125 g of water? (Assume total dissociation of the ionic solid.)

60. Consider the following aqueous solutions: (i) 0.20 m $HOCH_2CH_2OH$ (nonvolatile, nonelectrolyte); (ii) 0.10 m $CaCl_2$; (iii) 0.12 m KBr; and (iv) 0.12 m Na_2SO_4.
(a) Which solution has the highest boiling point?
(b) Which solution has the lowest freezing point?
(c) Which solution has the highest water vapor pressure?

61. (a) Which solution is expected to have the higher boiling point: 0.20 m KBr or 0.30 m sugar?
(b) Which aqueous solution has the lower freezing point: 0.12 m NH_4NO_3 or 0.10 m Na_2CO_3?

62. The solubility of NaCl in water at 100 °C is 39.1 g/100. g of water. Calculate the boiling point of this solution. (Assume $i = 1.85$ for NaCl.)

63. Instead of using NaCl to melt the ice on your sidewalk, you decide to use $CaCl_2$. If you add 35.0 g of $CaCl_2$ to 150. g of water, what is the freezing point of the solution? (Assume $i = 2.7$ for $CaCl_2$.)

64. The smell of ripe raspberries is due to 4-(*p*-hydroxyphenyl)-2-butanone, which has the empirical formula C_5H_6O. To find its molecular formula, you dissolve 0.135 g in 25.0 g of chloroform, $CHCl_3$. The boiling point of the solution is 61.82 °C. What is the molecular formula of the solute?

65. Hexachlorophene has been used in germicidal soap. What is its molar mass if 0.640 g of the compound, dissolved in 25.0 g of chloroform, produces a solution whose boiling point is 61.93 °C?

66. The solubility of ammonium formate, NH_4CHO_2, in 100. g of water is 102 g at 0 °C and 546 g at 80 °C. A solution is prepared by dissolving NH_4CHO_2 in 200. g of water until no more will dissolve at 80 °C. The solution is then cooled to 0 °C. What mass of NH_4CHO_2 precipitates? (Assume that no water evaporates and that the solution is not supersaturated.)

67. How much N_2 can dissolve in water at 25 °C if the N_2 partial pressure is 585 mm Hg?

68. Cigars are best stored in a "humidor" at 18 °C and 55% relative humidity. This means the pressure of water vapor should be 55% of the vapor pressure of pure water at the same temperature. The proper humidity can be maintained by placing a solution of glycerol [$C_3H_5(OH)_3$] and water in the humidor. Calculate the percent by mass of glycerol that will lower the vapor pressure of water to the desired value. (The vapor pressure of glycerol is negligible.)

69. An aqueous solution containing 10.0 g of starch per liter has an osmotic pressure of 3.8 mm Hg at 25 °C.
    (a) What is the average molar mass of starch? (Because not all starch molecules are identical, the result will be an average.)
    (b) What is the freezing point of the solution? Would it be easy to determine the molecular weight of starch by measuring the freezing point depression? (Assume that the molarity and molality are the same for this solution.)

70. Vinegar is a 5% solution (by weight) of acetic acid in water. Determine the mole fraction and molality of acetic acid. What is the concentration of acetic acid in parts per million (ppm)? Explain why it is not possible to calculate the molarity of this solution from the information provided.

71. Calculate the enthalpies of solution for Li_2SO_4 and K_2SO_4. Are the solution processes exothermic or endothermic? Compare them with LiCl and KCl. What similarities or differences do you find?

Compound	$\Delta_fH°(s)$ (kJ/mol)	$\Delta_fH°(aq, 1\ m)$ (kJ/mol)
Li_2SO_4	−1436.4	−1464.4
K_2SO_4	−1437.7	−1414.0

72. ▲ Water at 25 °C has a density of 0.997 g/cm³. Calculate the molality and molarity of pure water at this temperature.

73. ▲ If a volatile solute is added to a volatile solvent, both substances contribute to the vapor pressure over the solution. Assuming an ideal solution, the vapor pressure of each is given by Raoult's law, and the total vapor pressure is the sum of the vapor pressures for each component. A solution, assumed to be ideal, is made from 1.0 mol of toluene ($C_6H_5CH_3$) and 2.0 mol of benzene (C_6H_6). The vapor pressures of the pure solvents are 22 mm Hg and 75 mm Hg, respectively, at 20 °C. What is the total vapor pressure of the mixture? What is the mole fraction of each component in the liquid and in the vapor?

74. A solution is made by adding 50.0 mL of ethanol (C_2H_5OH, $d = 0.789$ g/mL) to 50.0 mL of water ($d = 0.998$ g/mL). What is the total vapor pressure over the solution at 20 °C? (See Study Question 73.) The vapor pressure of ethanol at 20 °C is 43.6 mm Hg.

75. A 2.0% (by mass) aqueous solution of novocainium chloride ($C_{13}H_{21}ClN_2O_2$) freezes at −0.237 °C. Calculate the van't Hoff factor, i. How many moles of ions are in the solution per mole of compound?

76. A solution is 4.00% (by mass) maltose and 96.00% water. It freezes at −0.229 °C.
    (a) Calculate the molar mass of maltose (which is not an ionic compound).
    (b) The density of the solution is 1.014 g/mL. Calculate the osmotic pressure of the solution.

77. ▲ The following table lists the concentrations of the principal ions in seawater:

Ion	Concentration (ppm)
Cl^-	1.95×10^4
Na^+	1.08×10^4
Mg^{2+}	1.29×10^3
SO_4^{2-}	9.05×10^2
Ca^{2+}	4.12×10^2
K^+	3.80×10^2
Br^-	67

   (a) Calculate the freezing point of seawater.
   (b) Calculate the osmotic pressure of seawater at 25 °C. What is the minimum pressure needed to purify seawater by reverse osmosis?

78. ▲ A tree is exactly 10 m tall.
    (a) What must be the total molarity of the solutes if sap rises to the top of the tree by osmotic pressure at 20 °C? Assume the groundwater outside the tree is pure water and that the density of the sap is 1.0 g/mL. (1 mm Hg = 13.6 mm H_2O.)
    (b) If the only solute in the sap is sucrose, $C_{12}H_{22}O_{11}$, what is its percent by mass?

79. A 2.00% solution of H_2SO_4 in water freezes at -0.796 °C.
    (a) Calculate the van't Hoff factor, i.
    (b) Which of the following best represents sulfuric acid in a dilute aqueous solution: H_2SO_4, $H_3O^+ + HSO_4^-$, or $2\ H_3O^+ + SO_4^{2-}$?

80. A compound is known to be a potassium halide, KX. If 4.00 g of the salt is dissolved in exactly 100 g of water, the solution freezes at -1.28 °C. Identify the halide ion in this formula.

81. The Henry's law constant for N_2O is 2.4×10^{-2} mol/kg · bar. (Nitrous oxide, N_2O, laughing gas, is used as an anesthetic). Determine the mass of N_2O that will dissolve in 500. mL of water, under an N_2O pressure of 1.00 bar. What is the concentration of N_2O in this solution, expressed in ppm (d (H_2O) = 1.00 g/mL)?

82. If a carbonated beverage is bottled under 1.5 bar CO_2 pressure, what will be the concentration of dissolved CO_2 in that beverage? (k_H for CO_2 is 0.034 mol/kg bar.) After the pressure is released what fraction of the dissolved gas will escape before equilibrium with the CO_2 in the atmosphere is reached?

83. You are given a flask filled with a colored liquid. Suggest several tests that would allow you to determine whether this is a solution or a colloid.

84. If one is very careful, it is possible to float a needle on the surface of water. (If the needle is magnetized, it will turn to point north and south and become a makeshift compass.) What would happen to the needle if a drop of liquid soap is added to the solution? Explain the observation.

In the Laboratory

85. ▲ A solution of benzoic acid in benzene has a freezing point of 3.1 °C and a boiling point of 82.6 °C. (The freezing point of pure benzene is 5.50 °C, and its boiling point is 80.1 °C.) The structure of benzoic acid is

    What can you conclude about the state of the benzoic acid molecules at the two different temperatures? Recall the discussion of hydrogen bonding in Section 12.3, and see Figure 12.7.

86. ▲ You dissolve 5.0 mg of iodine, I_2, in 25 mL of water. You then add 10.0 mL of CCl_4 and shake the mixture. If I_2 is 85 times more soluble in CCl_4 than in H_2O (on a volume basis), what are the masses of I_2 in the water and CCl_4 layers after shaking? (See Figure 14.6.)

87. ▲ A solution of 5.00 g of acetic acid in 100. g of benzene freezes at 3.37 °C. A solution of 5.00 g of acetic acid in 100. g of water freezes at -1.49 °C. Find the molar mass of acetic acid from each of these experiments. What can you conclude about the state of the

acetic acid molecules dissolved in each of these solvents? Recall the discussion of hydrogen bonding in Section 12.3 (and see Figure 12.7), and propose a structure for the species in benzene solution.

88. ▲ In a police forensics lab, you examine a package that may contain heroin. However, you find the white powder is not pure heroin but a mixture of heroin ($C_{21}H_{23}O_5N$) and lactose ($C_{12}H_{22}O_{11}$). To determine the amount of heroin in the mixture, you dissolve 1.00 g of the white powdery mixture in water in a 100.0-mL volumetric flask. You find that the solution has an osmotic pressure of 539 mm Hg at 25 °C. What is the composition of the mixture?

89. A newly synthesized compound containing boron and fluorine is 22.1% boron. Dissolving 0.146 g of the compound in 10.0 g of benzene gives a solution with a vapor pressure of 94.16 mm Hg at 25 °C. (The vapor pressure of pure benzene at this temperature is 95.26 mm Hg.) In a separate experiment, it is found that the compound does not have a dipole moment.
    (a) What is the molecular formula for the compound?
    (b) Draw a Lewis structure for the molecule, and suggest a possible molecular structure. Give the bond angles in the molecule and the hybridization of the boron atom.

90. In chemical research we often send newly synthesized compounds to commercial laboratories for analysis. These laboratories determine the weight percent of C and H by burning the compound and collecting the evolved CO_2 and H_2O. They determine the molar mass by measuring the osmotic pressure of a solution of the compound. Calculate the empirical and molecular formulas of a compound, C_xH_yCr, given the following information:
    (a) The compound contains 73.94% C and 8.27% H; the remainder is chromium.
    (b) At 25 °C, the osmotic pressure of a solution containing 5.00 mg of the unknown dissolved in exactly 100 mL of chloroform solution is 3.17 mm Hg.

Summary and Conceptual Questions

The following questions may use concepts from this and previous chapters.

91. When salts of Mg^{2+}, Ca^{2+}, and Be^{2+} are placed in water, the positive ion is hydrated (as is the negative ion). Which of these three cations is most strongly hydrated? Which one is least strongly hydrated?

92. Explain why a cucumber shrivels up when it is placed in a concentrated solution of salt.

93. If you dissolve equal molar amounts of NaCl and $CaCl_2$ in water, the $CaCl_2$ lowers the freezing point of the water almost 1.5 times as much as the NaCl. Why?

94. A 100.-gram sample of sodium chloride (NaCl) is added to 100. mL of water at 0 °C. After equilibrium is reached, about 64 g of solid remains undissolved. Describe the equilibrium that exists in this system at the particulate level.

95. Which of the following substances is/are likely to dissolve in water, and which is/are likely to dissolve in benzene (C_6H_6)?
    (a) $NaNO_3$
    (b) diethyl ether, $CH_3CH_2OCH_2CH_3$
    (c) naphthalene, $C_{10}H_8$ (see page 454 for structure)
    (d) NH_4Cl

96. Account for the fact that alcohols such as methanol (CH_3OH) and ethanol (C_2H_5OH) are quite miscible with water, whereas an alcohol with a long-carbon chain, such as octanol ($C_8H_{17}OH$), is poorly soluble in water.

97. Starch contains C—C, C—H, C—O, and O—H bonds. Hydrocarbons have only C—C and C—H bonds. Both starch and hydrocarbons can form colloidal dispersions in water. Which dispersion is classified as hydrophobic? Which is hydrophilic? Explain briefly.

98. Which substance would have the greater influence on the vapor pressure of water when added to 1000. g of the liquid: 10.0 g of sucrose ($C_{12}H_{22}O_{11}$) or 10.0 g of ethylene glycol ($HOCH_2CH_2OH$)?

99. Suppose you have two aqueous solutions separated by a semipermeable membrane. One contains 5.85 g of NaCl dissolved in 100. mL of solution, and the other contains 8.88 g of KNO_3 dissolved in 100. mL of solution. In which direction will solvent flow: from the NaCl solution to the KNO_3 solution, or from KNO_3 to NaCl? Explain briefly.

100. A protozoan (single-celled animal) that normally lives in the ocean is placed in freshwater. Will it shrivel or burst? Explain briefly.

101. In the process of distillation, a mixture of two (or more) volatile liquids is first heated to convert the volatile materials to the vapor state. Then the vapor is condensed, reforming the liquid. The net result of this liquid→vapor→liquid conversion is to enrich the fraction of a more volatile component in the mixture in the condensate. We can describe how this occurs using Raoult's law. Imagine that you have a mixture of 12% (by weight) ethanol and water (as formed, for example, by fermentation of grapes.)
    (a) What are the mole fractions of ethanol and water in this mixture?
    (b) This mixture is heated to 78.5 °C (the normal boiling point of ethanol). What are the equilibrium vapor pressures of ethanol and water at this temperature, assuming Raoult's law (ideal) behavior? (You will need to derive the equilibrium vapor pressure of water at 78.5 °C from data in Appendix G.)
    (c) What are the mole fractions of ethanol and water in the vapor?
    (d) After this vapor is condensed to a liquid, to what extent has the mole fraction of ethanol been enriched? What is the mass fraction of ethanol in the condensate?

102. Sodium chloride (NaCl) is commonly used to melt ice on roads during the winter. Calcium chloride ($CaCl_2$) is sometimes used for this purpose too. Let us compare the effectiveness of equal masses of these two compounds in lowering the freezing point of water, by calculating the freezing point depression of solutions containing 200. g of each salt in 1.00 kg of water. (An advantage of $CaCl_2$ is that it acts more quickly because it is hygroscopic, that is, it absorbs moisture from the air to give a solution and begin the process. A disadvantage is that this compound is more costly.)

103. Review the trend in values of the van't Hoff factor i as a function of concentration (Table 14.4). Use the following data to calculate the van't Hoff factor for a NaCl concentration of 5.00% (by weight) (for which $\Delta T = -3.05$ °C) and a Na_2SO_4 concentration of 5.00% (by weight) (for which $\Delta T = -1.36$ °C). Are these values in line with your expectations based on the trend in the values given in Table 14.4? Speculate on why this trend is seen.

104. The table below gives experimentally determined values for freezing points of 1.00% solutions (mass %) of a series of acids.
    (a) Calculate the molality of each solution, determine the calculated freezing points, and then calculate the values of the van't Hoff factor i. Fill these values into the table.

Acid (1.00 mass %)	Molality (mol/kg H_2O)	$T_{measured}$ (°C)	$T_{calculated}$ (°C)	i
HNO_3	_____	−0.56	_____	_____
CH_3CO_2H	_____	−0.32	_____	_____
H_2SO_4	_____	−0.42	_____	_____
$H_2C_2O_4$	_____	−0.30	_____	_____
HCO_2H	_____	−0.42	_____	_____
CCl_3CO_2H	_____	−0.21	_____	_____

    (b) Analyze the results, comparing the values of i for the various acids. How does this data relate to acid strengths? (The discussion of strong and weak acids on pages 128–131 will assist you to answer this question.)

105. It is interesting how the Fahrenheit temperature scale was established. One report, given by Fahrenheit in a paper in 1724, stated that the value of 0 °F was established as the freezing temperature of saturated solutions of sea salt. From the literature we find that the freezing point of a 20% by mass solution of NaCl is −16.46 °C (This is the lowest freezing temperature reported for solutions of NaCl.) Does this value lend credence to this story of the establishment of the Fahrenheit scale?

106. The osmotic pressure exerted by seawater at 25 °C is about 27 atm. Calculate the concentration of ions dissolved in seawater that is needed to give an osmotic pressure of this magnitude. (Desalination of seawater is accomplished by reverse osmosis. In this process an applied pressure forces water through a membrane against a concentration gradient. The minimum external force needed for this process will be 27 atm. Actually, to accomplish the process at a reasonable rate, the applied pressure needs to be about twice this value.)

Applying Chemical Principles

Distillation

Distillation is a means of separating components of a mixture based upon differences in volatility. Because petroleum consists of a large number of compounds of widely varying volatility, distillation is a key process used to produce gasoline and related products. How does this process work?

If a mixture is composed of one volatile component and one or more nonvolatile components, a complete separation of the volatile component is possible. But, when two or more components in a mixture have non-zero vapor pressures at the mixture's boiling point, the result of a simple distillation is an incomplete separation.

Fractional distillation uses repetitive evaporation-condensation cycles to improve the separation of volatile compounds. When a mixture is boiled, the vapor above the liquid has a higher concentration of the more volatile components than the liquid. If this vapor is condensed, then boiled again, the resulting vapor is further enriched in more volatile material.

The temperature-composition diagram for a hexane–heptane mixture is shown below. The lower curved line indicates the boiling point of the mixture as a function of the mole fraction of the more volatile component, hexane. The upper curve indicates the mole fraction of hexane in the vapor phase above the boiling solution. The blue line represents the change in composition of the mixture in the course of the fractional distillation of a mixture with an initial hexane mole fraction of 0.20.

Equipment used for fractional distillation of petroleum in an oil refinery.

Paul Rapson/Photo Researchers, Inc.

The solution may be heated until it reaches its boiling point of 90 °C. At this temperature, the mole fraction of hexane in the vapor phase can be determined by drawing a horizontal line at 90 °C that intersects the top curve. This indicates that the vapor phase has a mole fraction of hexane of 0.38 at this temperature.

The efficiency of a fractional distillation column is expressed in terms of *theoretical plates*. Each evaporation-condensation cycle requires one theoretical plate. The greater the number of theoretical plates, the better the separation for most mixtures.

Questions:

1. The blue line on the diagram illustrates the effect of using fractional distillation to separate a mixture of hexane (C_6H_{14}) and heptane (C_7H_{16}). If one starts a fractional distillation with a 0.20 mole fraction of hexane, what is the approximate mole fraction of hexane in the vapor phase after two evaporation-condensation cycles?

2. How many theoretical plates are required to produce a solution with a mole fraction of hexane greater than 0.90?

3. What is the mass percent of hexane in a mixture with heptane if the mole fraction of hexane is 0.20?

4. The vapor pressure of pure heptane is 361.5 mm Hg at 75.0 °C and its normal boiling point is 98.4 °C. Use the Clausius–Clapeyron equation to determine the enthalpy of vaporization of heptane.

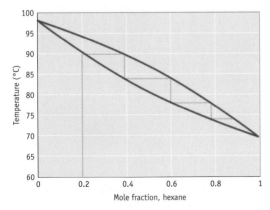

A temperature-composition diagram for hexane (C_6H_{14})-heptane (C_7H_{16}) mixtures.

The Chemistry of Modern Materials

White limestone and the minerals calcite, aragonite, and Iceland spar are all composed of calcium carbonate. So are chalk, eggshells, and seashells. These objects have distinctly different physical characteristics (Figure 1), yet they are composed primarily of the same component ions, Ca^{2+} and CO_3^{2-} ions. What is interesting to chemists, geologists, and biologists is that the differences in the macroscopic characteristics result from small differences in composition (due to the presence of impurities) and in the arrangement of these ions.

FIGURE 1 **Forms of calcium carbonate.** (clockwise from top) The shell of an abalone, a limestone paving block from Europe, crystalline aragonite, common blackboard chalk ($CaCO_3$ and a binder), and transparent Iceland spar.

© Cengage Learning/Charles D. Winters

As defined by the International Union of Pure and Applied Chemistry (IUPAC) the area of materials chemistry "comprises the application of chemistry to the design, synthesis, characterization, processing, understanding and utilization of materials, particularly those with useful, or potentially useful, physical properties." By studying the composition and structure of synthetic and naturally occurring materials, chemists are able to gain insight into what gives each material its properties and to create new materials that are tailored to particular applications and that have predictable behaviors.

This section explores a variety of common materials—except organic polymers, which were described in Section 10.5—and examines the connection between composition, atomic arrangements, and bulk properties.

Alloys: Mixtures of Metals

Alloys, materials formed by addition of one or more elements to a metal, are among the earliest materials made by humans. The Bronze Age, dating back to 3300 BC, is well established in history, and the use of this alloy of copper and tin for tools and decorations was well known. Smelting of iron ore to form an impure iron containing carbon, among other elements, was introduced about 2000 years later (Figure 2). Mercury amalgams (mixtures of mercury and gold, silver, or tin) were used for centuries for gilding objects; a liquid mixture of gold and mercury, an amalgam, was placed on the surface of a metal object that was then heated, vaporizing the mercury and leaving a surface coating of gold (Figure 2).

• **Fiberoptics.** Fibers made of glass are used increasingly to carry information.

FIGURE 2 Uses of iron and gold. *(left)* The top of the iron pillar in the Qutub complex in Delhi, India. The 24-foot tall pillar was made in approximately 400 AD. Although there is a thin film of rust on the pillar, it is largely free of corrosion because there is a significant amount of phosphorus (> 0.1%) in the metal. *(right)* The dome of St. Isaac's Cathedral in St. Petersburg, Russia, is covered with 100 kg of gold. An amalgam of gold and mercury was sprayed onto the surface and then heated to evaporate the mercury. Dozens of workers died as a result of mercury poisoning.

Even though the names we give them are the names of the elements, most "metals" we now use are, in fact, alloys (Table 1). Steel is an alloy of iron with carbon and often other elements.   Adding elements to iron can greatly change its properties, as we noted earlier when discussing special steels used in cars (page 592). Most aluminum contains small amounts of magnesium or silicon.

Gold and silver alloys are familiar to most of us. For example, sterling silver, commonly used for jewelry, is an alloy composed of 92.5% Ag and 7.5% Cu. Pure silver is soft and easily damaged, but the addition of copper makes the metal more rigid. You can confirm that an article of jewelry

Table 1 Some Common Alloys

Sterling silver	92.5% Ag, 7.5% Cu
18 K "yellow" gold	75% Au, 12.5% Ag, 12.5% Cu
Pewter	91% Sn, 7.5% Sb, 1.5% Cu
Low-alloy steel	98.6% Fe, 1.0% Mn, 0.4% C
Carbon steels	Approximately 99% Fe, 0.2–1.5% C
Stainless steel	72.8% Fe, 17.0% Cr, 7.1% Ni, and approximately 1% each of Al and Mn
Alnico magnets	10% Al, 19% Ni, 12% Co, 6% Cu, remainder Fe
Brass	95–60% Cu, 5–40% Zn
Bronze	90% Cu, 10% Sn

is sterling silver by looking for the stamp that says "925," which means 92.5% silver.

Gold used in jewelry is rarely pure (24 carat) gold. More often, you will find 18 K, 14 K, or 9 K stamped on a gold object, referring to alloys that are 18/24, 14/24, or 9/24 gold. "Yellow" gold (18 K) is 75% gold, and the remaining 25% is copper and silver. As with sterling silver, the added metals lead to a harder and more rigid material (and one that is less costly).

Alloys fall into three general classes: solid solutions, which are homogeneous mixtures of two or more elements; heterogeneous mixtures; and intermetallic compounds.

In solid solutions, one element is usually considered the "solute" and the other the "solvent." As with solutions in liquids, the solute atoms are dispersed throughout the solvent such that the bulk structure is homogeneous. Unlike liquid solutions, however, there are limitations on the size of solvent and solute atoms. For a solid solution to form, the solute atoms must be incorporated in such a way that the original crystal structure of the solvent metal is preserved. Solid solutions can be achieved in two ways: with solute atoms as **interstitial** atoms or as **substitutional** atoms in the crystalline lattice. In interstitial alloys, the solute atoms occupy the interstices, the small "holes" between solvent atoms (Figure 3a). The solute atoms must be substantially smaller than the metal atoms making up the lattice to fit into these positions. In substitutional alloys, the solute atoms replace one of the solvent atoms in the original crystal structure (Figure 3b). For this to occur, the solute and solvent atoms must be similar in size.

If the size constraints are not met, then the alloy will likely form a heterogeneous mixture. When viewed under a microscope, regions of different composition and crystal structure can be seen in heterogeneous alloys.

For a solid solution to form, the electronegativities of the alloy components must also be similar. When the two metals have different electronegativities, the possibility exists for intermetallic compounds, substances with a definite stoichiometry and formula. Examples of intermetallic compounds include $CuAl_2$, Mg_2Pb, and $AuCu_3$. In general, intermetallic compounds are likely when one element is relatively electronegative and the other is more electro-

(a) Interstitial atoms   **(b)** Substitutional atoms

FIGURE 3 Alloys. (a) The solute atoms may be interstitial atoms, fitting into holes in the crystal lattice. **(b)** The solute atoms can also substitute for one of the lattice atoms.

© Cengage Learning/Charles D. Winters

FIGURE 4 **Light-emitting diodes (LEDs).** *(left)* A schematic drawing of a typical LED. *(right)* Traffic signs with LED lights require much less energy input than incandescent lights and are now being widely used.

positive. For Mg_2Pb, for example, χ for Pb = 2.3 and χ for Mg = 1.3 ($\Delta\chi$ = 1.0). (For more on this topic, see the *Applying Chemical Principles* question on the van Arkel triangle on page 1015.)

The macroscopic properties of an alloy will vary, depending on the ratio of the elements in the mixture. For example, "stainless" steel is highly resistant to corrosion and is roughly five times stronger than carbon and low-alloy steels. Melting point, electrical resistance, thermal conductivity, ductility, and other properties can be similarly adjusted by changing the composition of the alloys.

Metals and their alloys are good examples of how changes in the atomic composition and structure of a crystalline substance can have profound effects on its macroscopic chemical and physical characteristics. The same is true for semiconductors, the next class of materials we want to explore.

Semiconductors

Semiconducting materials are at the heart of all solid-state electronic devices, including such well-known devices as computer chips and diode lasers. Semiconductors will not conduct electricity easily but can be encouraged to do so by the input of energy. This property allows devices made from semiconductors to essentially have "on" and "off" states, which form the basis of the binary logic used in computers. We can understand how semiconductors function by looking at their electronic structure, following the band theory approach used for metals. (◄ Section 13.3, pages 594–598, for a discussion of the mechanism by which metals and semiconductors can conduct an electric current.)

Applications of Semiconductors: Diodes, LEDs, and Transistors

The combination of *p*- and *n*-type semiconducting materials in a single electronic device launched the microelectronics and computer industries. When a semiconductor is created such that it is *p*-type on one half and *n*-type on the other, a marvelous device known as the *p–n rectifying junction*, or **diode**, results. Diodes, which allow current to flow easily in only one direction when a voltage is applied, are the fundamental building blocks of solid-state electronic devices. They are used for many circuitry applications, such as switching and converting between electromagnetic radiation and electric current.

LEDs, or **light-emitting diodes** (Figure 4), are now used in the lights in the dashboards of cars and in their rear warning lights, in traffic lights, and in toys. These semiconducting devices are made by combining elements such as gallium, phosphorus, arsenic, and aluminum. When attached to a low-voltage (say 6–12 V) source, they emit light with a wavelength that depends on their composition. Furthermore, they emit light with a brightness that rivals standard incandescent lights, and the light can be focused using a tiny plastic lens.

An LED has a simple construction. It consists of a *p*-type semiconductor joined to an *n*-type semiconductor (Figure 5). A voltage is applied to the material, perhaps by hooking the positive terminal of a battery to the *p*-type semiconductor and the negative terminal to the *n*-type semiconductor. Electrons move from the *n*-type to the *p*-type, and positive holes move from the *p*-type to the *n*-type. When an electron moves across the *p–n* junction, it can drop from the conduction band into a hole in the valence band of the *p*-type semiconductor, and energy is released as a photon of electromagnetic radiation. (The mechanism of light emission by an LED is similar to that described for excited atoms in Section 6.3.) If the band gap energy is equivalent to the energy of light in the visible region, light can be observed. Because the band gap energy can be adjusted by changing the composition of the doped semiconductor, the wavelength of the light can also be altered, giving light of different colors.

The same device that forms the LED can be run in reverse to convert light into an electrical signal. Solar panel cells work in this manner (Figure 6). They are generally silicon-based *p–n* junction materials that have a band gap corresponding to the energy of visible light. When sunlight falls on these devices, a current is induced. That current can be used either immediately or stored in batteries for later use.

The *p*- and *n*-type semiconductor materials can also be constructed into a sandwich structure of either *p–n–p* or *n–p–n* composition. This arrangement forms a device known as a **transistor**. A transistor amplifies an electrical signal, making it ideal for powering loudspeakers, for ex-

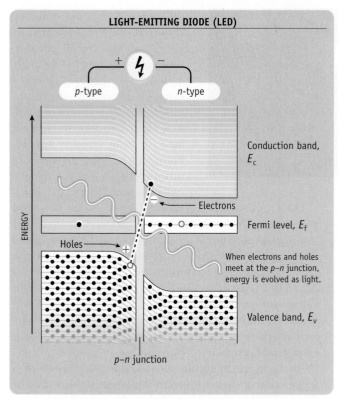

LIGHT-EMITTING DIODE (LED)

p-type   *n*-type

Conduction band, E_c

Electrons

Fermi level, E_f

Holes

When electrons and holes meet at the *p–n* junction, energy is evolved as light.

Valence band, E_v

p–n junction

ENERGY

FIGURE 5 Mechanism for the emission of light from an LED constructed from *n*- and *p*-type semiconductors. When *p*- and *n*-type semiconductors are joined, the energy levels adjust so that the Fermi levels (E_f) are equal. This causes the energy levels of the conduction (E_c) and valence (E_v) bands to "bend." Also, holes flow from the *p* side to the *n* side, and electrons flow from *n* to *p* until equilibrium is reached. No more charge will flow until a voltage is applied. When an electric field is applied, occasionally electrons in the conduction band will move across the band gap and combine with holes in the valence band. Energy is then evolved as light. The energy of the emitted light is approximately equal to the band gap. Therefore, by adjusting the band gap, the color of the emitted light can be altered. (See pages 594–598 for background information on semiconductors. See also S. M. Condren, G. C. Lisensky, A. B. Ellis, K. J. Nordell, T. F. Kuech, and S. A. Stockman: *Journal of Chemical Education*, Vol. 78, pp. 1033–1040, 2001.)

ample. Transistors can also be used for processing and storing information, a critical function for computer chips. By combining thousands of these transistors and diodes, an integrated circuit can be made that is the basis of what we commonly refer to as computer chips, devices for controlling and storing information (Figure 7).

FIGURE 6 Silicon photovoltaic panel.

© Maximilian Weinzierl/Alamy

© Will & Deni McIntyre/Photo Researchers, Inc.

January Hinsch/Photo Researchers, Inc.

FIGURE 7 Integrated circuits. *(left)* A wafer on which a large number of integrated circuits have been printed. *(right)* A close-up of a semiconductor chip showing the complex layering of circuits that is now possible.

Ceramics

Let's go back to our original examples of various forms of $CaCO_3$, including seashells and chalk. Chalk is so soft that it will rub off on the rough surface of a blackboard. In contrast, seashells are inherently tough. They are designed to protect their soft and vulnerable inhabitants from the powerful jaws of sea-borne predators or rough conditions underwater. Chalk, seashells, and the spines of sea urchins (Figure 8) are all ceramics, but they are obviously different from one another. Clearly, there is a great deal of variability in this class of materials.

You may be accustomed to thinking of "ceramics" as the objects that result from high-temperature firing, such as pottery. From a materials chemistry perspective, however,

Jeffrey L. Rotman/Corbis

FIGURE 8 A sea urchin. The spines of the urchin are composed primarily of $CaCO_3$, but a significant amount of $MgCO_3$ is present as well.

other materials such as clay, which largely consists of hydrated silicates of various compositions, are also considered ceramics. **Ceramics** are solid inorganic compounds typically composed of metallic elements combined with nonmetallic elements, and the bonding between atoms ranges from very ionic to covalent (◄ Section 8.1). In general, ceramics are hard, relatively brittle, and inflexible, and they are usually good thermal insulators. Some ceramics can be electrically conductive, but most are electrical insulators. Some, like glass, another type of ceramic, can be optically transparent, whereas other ceramics are completely opaque.

It is also possible to have ceramics in which impurity atoms are included in the composition. As we saw with metals and semiconductors, impurity atoms can have dramatic effects on the characteristics of a material.

Glass: A Disordered Ceramic

An amorphous, or noncrystalline, solid material is generally referred to as a **glass** (◄ Section 13.5). As with alloys, there is a long history of glass making. Glass beads have been found dating back to at least 3500 BC in Egypt and Mesopotamia.

Glasses are formed by melting the raw material and then cooling it from the liquid state rapidly so that the component atoms do not have time to crystallize into a regular lattice structure. A wide range of materials, including metals and organic polymers, can be coaxed into a glassy form. However, the best-known glasses are silicate glasses. These are derived from SiO_2, which is plentiful, inexpensive, and chemically unreactive. Each silicon atom is linked to four oxygen atoms in the solid structure, with a tetrahedral arrangement around each silicon atom. The SiO_2 units are linked together to form a large network of atoms (Figure 9). Over a longer distance, however, the network has no discernible order or pattern.

Glasses can be modified by the presence of alkali metal oxides (such as Na_2O and K_2O) or other metal or nonmetal oxides (such as CaO, B_2O_3, and Al_2O_3). The added impurities change the silicate network and alter the properties of the material. The oxide ions are incorporated into the silicate network structure, and the resultant negative charge is balanced by the interstitial metal cations (Figure 9c). Because the network is changed by such an addition, these network modifiers can dramatically alter the physical characteristics of the material, such as melting point, color, opacity, and strength. Soda-lime glass—made from SiO_2, Na_2O (soda), and CaO (lime)—is a common glass used in windows and for containers. The metal oxides lower the melting temperature by about a thousand degrees from that of pure silica. Pyrex glass, also called *borosilicate glass*, incorporates an additional component, boric oxide. The boric oxide raises the softening temperature and minimizes the coefficient of thermal expansion, enabling the glass to better withstand temperature changes. Because of its excellent thermal properties, this type of glass is used for beakers and flasks in chemistry laboratories and for ovenware for the kitchen.

Colors in glass result from the presence of metal ions (Figure 10). Adding small amounts of iron(II) oxide and chromium(III) oxide results in a green glass (used in some wine bottles), whereas cobalt(III) oxide imparts a blue color. Dishes made from yellow-green uranium glass [glass containing uranium(IV) oxide] were popular in the first half of the 20th century. However, because of the radioactivity associated with uranium, this glass is no longer used.

The presence of particulate materials in glass will also result in colors. Nanoscale particles of selenium give glass a deep red color. A notable example is the inclusion of very small silver halide crystals resulting in a photochromic glass (Figure 11). This glass darkens reversibly when exposed to light, a result of the reduction of the silver halide to metallic silver. This technology was used in early versions of self-darkening eyeglasses.

An important characteristic of some glasses is their optical transparency, which allows them to be used as windows and lenses. Glasses can also be reflective. The combination of transparency and reflectivity is controlled by the material's **index of refraction**. All materials have an index of

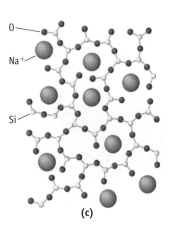

(a) (b) (c)

FIGURE 9 Representation of glass structure. Silica glass (SiO_2) may have some order over a short distance **(a)** but much less order over a larger portion of the solid **(b)**. **(c)** The SiO_2 structure can be modified by adding metal oxides (such as Na_2O), which leads to a lower melting temperature and other desirable properties. (In these simple representations, the gray Si atoms are shown at the center of a planar triangle of red O atoms; in reality, each Si atom is surrounded tetrahedrally by O atoms. The structure is not planar but is three dimensional.)

FIGURE 10 Colored glass. Small amounts of transition metal ions can give color to glass: blue (Co_2O_3); green (FeO or Cr_2O_3); purple (NiO or Co_2O_3); iridescent green (U_2O_3).

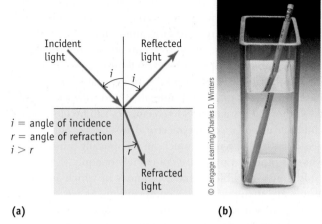

(a)   **(b)**

FIGURE 12 Refraction of light. **(a)** When light enters a different medium, its velocity changes. This causes the path of a photon to change direction in the material. **(b)** Observing an object in a glass of water illustrates the effect of light refraction.

refraction that determines how much a beam of light will change its velocity when entering the material. The index of refraction is defined relative to the speed of light in a vacuum, which is defined as exactly 1. (The index of refraction = velocity of light in a vacuum/velocity in material.) On this basis, dry air has an index of refraction of 1.0003, and typical values for silicate glasses range from 1.5 to 1.9.

The change in the velocity of the electromagnetic wave once it enters the material causes the beam to bend, or change direction within the material. If light hits a surface at some incident angle relative to the line perpendicular to the surface, some of the light will be reflected at the same angle, and some will be transmitted into the material at a refracted angle (Figure 12). Both the incident angle and the index of refraction will affect how much of the light is reflected and the angle at which it bends in the second material. You can observe this effect by putting an object in a glass of water and looking at the apparent bend that results in the object (Figure 12b).

This combination of the transmission and reflection characteristics of glass allowed scientists and engineers to develop optical fibers (Figure 13). Optical fibers are designed to have a property called *total internal reflection,* whereby all the light that enters at one end of the fiber stays within the fiber through reflections with the interior surface as the light trav-

els from one end of the fiber to the other. Total internal reflection in these fibers is achieved by controlling the ratio of the indices of refraction between the fiber's core and its outside surface. Chemically, the index of refraction is controlled by adjusting the quantity and type of cationic network modifiers that are added to the glass. The index of refraction of a glass fiber can be controlled so that it has one value at the core of the fiber but changes smoothly across the radius of the fiber to a different value at the surface. This is accomplished by an ion-exchange process during fiber production in which, for example, K^+ ions are replaced by Tl^+ ions.

Optical fibers are transforming the communications industry in an amazing fashion. Instead of transmitting information using electrons traveling through metallic wires, optical fibers allow communication to occur by transmitting photons through glass fiber bundles. Signal transmission by optical fibers, known as *photonics,* is much faster and more economical than transmission using copper wires and cables. For example, the quantity of copper required to carry the equivalent amount of information

FIGURE 11 Photochromic glass. Glass with embedded silver halide particles darkens reversibly when exposed to sunlight.

FIGURE 13 Optical fibers. Glass fibers transmit light along the axis of the fiber.

FIGURE 14 The deep sea sponge, *Euplectella*. Photographs of sponge's structure at various levels of magnification. **(a)** Photograph of the sponge. **(b)** Fragment of the structure showing the square grid of the lattice with diagonal supports. Scale bar = 1 mm. **(c)** Scanning electron microscope (SEM) image of a single strand showing its ceramic—composite structure. Scale bar = 20 μm. **(d)** SEM image of the surface of a strand showing that it is composed of nanoscale spheres of hydrated silica. Scale bar = 500 nm. **(e)** Scientist Joanna Aizenberg. Dr. Aizenberg's research group at Harvard University also developed the polymeric material shown on the front cover of this book.

transmitted by optical fiber would weigh 300,000 times more than the optical fiber material!

Interestingly, research has led to the discovery that materials with similar structure and optical properties exist in nature. Joanna Aizenberg, now at Harvard University, discovered that a deep sea sponge, made chiefly of silica (SiO_2), has a framework with the same characteristics (Figure 14).

Fired Ceramics for Special Purposes: Cements, Clays, and Refractories

Other classes of ceramics include cements, clays, and refractories. Unlike glasses, these ceramics are processed by shaping, drying, and sometimes firing, without ever melting the solid.

Cements are extremely strong and are commonly used as structural materials. They can be formed into almost any shape. When mixed with water, they produce a paste that can be poured into molds and allowed to dry and harden.

Clays are generally mixtures of hydrated alumina (Al_2O_3) and silica (SiO_2), but they may also contain other ingredients, such as tricalcium silicate ($3\ CaO \cdot SiO_2$), dicalcium silicate ($2\ CaO \cdot SiO_2$), and MgO. Their composition is irregular, and, because they are powders, their crystallinity extends for only short distances.

Clays have the useful property of becoming very plastic when water is added, a characteristic referred to as **hydroplasticity**. This plasticity, and clay's ability to hold its shape during firing, are very important for the forming processes used to create various objects.

The layered molecular structure of clays results in microscopic platelets that can slide over each other easily when wet. The layers consist of SiO_4 tetrahedra joined with AlO_6 octahedra (▶ Section 21.7). In addition to these basic silicon- and aluminum-based structures, different cations can be substituted into the framework to change the properties of the clay. Common substituents include Ca^{2+}, Fe^{2+}, and Mg^{2+}. Different clay materials can then be created by varying the combinations of layers and the substituent cations.

Refractories constitute a class of ceramics that are capable of withstanding very high temperatures without deforming, in some cases up to 1650 °C (3000 °F), and that are thermally insulating. Because of these properties, refractory bricks are used in applications such as furnace linings and in metallurgical operations. These materials are thermally insulating largely because of the porosity of their structure; that is, holes (or pores) are dispersed evenly within the solid. However, while porosity will make a material more thermally insulating, it will also weaken it. As a consequence, refractories are not as strong as cements.

Aerogels

It has been called the "world's lightest solid" and the "best thermal insulator." Even though it is 99.98% air and has a density of only about 1.9 mg/cm^3, it is a light blue solid that, to the touch, feels much like Styrofoam chips that are used in packaging. It is also strong structurally, able to hold over 2000 times its weight (Figure 15a). "It" is a silica aerogel, a low-density substance derived from a gel in which the liquid has been replaced by air. There are

FIGURE 15 Aerogel. (a) A 2.5-kg brick is supported by a piece of silica aerogel weighing about 2 g. (http://stardust.jpl.nasa.gov/photo/aerogel.html) **(b)** Aerogel as an insulator.

(a)

(b)

aerogels based on silicon and carbon as well as aluminum and other metals, but the silicon-based aerogel is the most thoroughly studied. This aerogel is made by polymerizing a compound like $Si(OC_2H_5)_4$ in alcohol. The resulting long-chain molecules form a gel that is bathed in the alcohol. This substance is then placed in supercritical CO_2 (page 574), which causes the alcohol in the nanopores in the gel to be replaced by CO_2. When the CO_2 is vented off as a gas, what remains is a highly porous aerogel with an incredibly low density.

Aerogels have been known for decades but have only recently received a lot of study. They do have amazing properties! Chief among them is their insulating ability, as illustrated in Figure 15b. Aerogels do not allow heat to be conducted through the lattice, and convective heat transfer is also poor because air cannot circulate throughout the lattice. One potential use for these aerogels is in insulating glass. However, before aerogels can be truly useful for this purpose, researchers need to find a way to make one that is completely transparent. (Silica aerogel is very light blue owing to Rayleigh scattering, the same process that makes the sky blue.) Aerogels are also biocompatible and are being studied as possible drug delivery systems.

Aerogel was in the news a few years ago because it was used to catch comet dust in Project Stardust (Figure 16). A spacecraft was sent to intercept a comet in 2004 and returned to Earth in January 2006. On the spacecraft was an array holding blocks of aerogel. As the craft flew through the comet's tail, dust particles impacted the aerogel blocks and were "brought to a standstill as they tunneled through it without much heating or alteration, leaving carrot-shaped tracks." When the spacecraft

was returned to Earth, scientists analyzed the particles and found that there were silicate minerals that seemed to have been formed in the inner regions of the solar system.

Ceramics with Exceptional Properties

In 1880, Pierre Curie and his brother Jacques worked in a small laboratory in Paris to examine the electrical properties of certain crystalline substances. Using nothing more than tinfoil, glue, wire, and magnets, they were able to confirm the presence of surface charges on samples of materials such as tourmaline, quartz, and topaz when they were subjected to mechanical stresses. This phenomenon, now called **piezoelectricity**, is the property that allows a mechanical distortion (such as a slight bending) to induce an electrical current and, conversely, an electrical current to cause a distortion in the material.

Not all crystalline ceramics exhibit piezoelectricity. Those that do have a specific unit cell structure (◄ Section 13.2)

FIGURE 16 Aerogel, a networked matrix of SiO_2. *(left)* NASA's Peter Tsou holds a piece of aerogel. *(right)* Aerogel was used on a NASA mission to collect the particles in comet dust. The particles entered the gel at a very high velocity, but were slowed gradually. Scientists studied the tracks made by the particles and later retrieved the particles and studied their composition.

that can loosely trap an impurity cation. The ion's position shifts when the unit cell is deformed by mechanical stress. This shift causes an induced dipole (◄ Section 12.3) and, therefore, a potential difference across the material that can be converted to an electrical signal.

Materials that exhibit piezoelectricity—such as lead(II) zirconate ($PbZrO_3$) and ammonium dihydrogen phosphate ($NH_4H_2PO_4$)—have a great many applications, ranging from home gadgets to sophisticated medical and scientific applications. One use with which you may be familiar is the ignition systems on some barbecue grills (Figure 17). All digital watch beepers are based on piezoceramics, as are smoke detector alarms. A less familiar application is found in the sensing lever of some atomic force microscopes (AFMs) and scanning-tunneling microscopes (STMs), instruments that convert mechanical vibrations to electrical signals.

Scientists and engineers are always searching for materials with new and useful properties. Perhaps the most dramatic property that has been observed in newly developed ceramics is superconductivity at relatively high temperatures. **Superconductivity** is a phenomenon in which the electrical resistivity of a material drops to nearly zero at a particular temperature referred to as the **critical temperature**, T_c (Figure 18). Most metals naturally have resistivities that decrease with temperature in a constant manner but still have significant resistivity even at temperatures near 0 K.

A few metals and metal alloys have been found to exhibit superconductivity. For metals, however, the critical temperatures are extremely low, between 0 and 20 K. These temperatures are costly to achieve and difficult to maintain. Recent scientific attention has, therefore, focused on a class of ceramics with superconductive critical temperatures (T_c) near

FIGURE 18 **Superconductivity.** Several superconductive disks were cooled in liquid nitrogen (77 K). When a 500 g magnet was brought toward the disks, the magnet induced a magnetic field in the superconductors. The two magnetic fields repelled, causing the magnet to float (or levitate) above the cooled superconductors.

100 K. These materials include $YBa_2Cu_3O_7$, with $T_c = 92$ K (Figure 19), and $HgBa_2Ca_2Cu_2O_3$, with $T_c = 153$ K.

Once again, we see that combining atoms into sometimes complex chemical compositions allows scientists to develop materials with particular properties. In ceramics, which are normally electrically insulating, this includes even the ability to conduct electricity.

Biomaterials: Learning from Nature

Most of the materials described so far in this chapter come from nonliving sources and, in many cases, are the result of laboratory syntheses. However, an important branch of materials research deals with examining, understanding, and even copying materials produced by living systems.

The study of naturally occurring materials has led to the development of synthetic materials that possess important properties. A good example is rubber (◄ Chapter 10, page 476). This natural polymer was initially obtained from certain trees and chemically modified to convert it to a useful material. It was found to be so useful that chemists eventually achieved the synthesis of a structurally identical material. Research on rubber, which spanned more than 200 years, has had important consequences for humans as evidenced by the myriad applications of rubber today.

Today, scientists continue to look to nature to provide new materials and to provide clues to improve the materials we already use. The sea urchin and its ceramic spines (Figure 8) and the sponge whose skeleton has the characteristics of optical fibers (Figure 14) are just two examples where biomaterials research has focused on sea life in a search for new materials.

Scientists have also examined conch shells to understand their incredible fracture strength. They used scan-

FIGURE 17 **Devices that depend on the piezoelectric effect.** These devices work by using a mechanical stress to produce an electric current. Piezoelectric materials are widely used in ignitors and in devices that convert electric impulses to vibrations, such as in the timing circuit of a wristwatch.

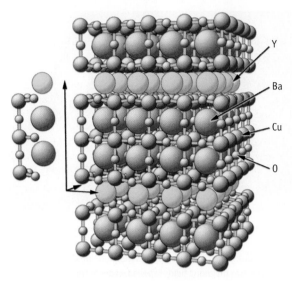

FIGURE 19 The lattice of $YBa_2Cu_3O_7$, a superconductor. Yttrium ions are yellow; barium ions are red; copper ions are green; and oxygen ions are blue. (Reprinted with permission of Dr. Klaus Hermann of the Fritz Haber Institution.)

FIGURE 20 A scanning electron microscope picture of the shell of the conch. (From S. Kamat, X. Su, R. Ballarini, and A. H. Heuer. Structural basis for the fracture toughness of the shell of the conch *Strombus gigas. Nature.* Vol. 405, pp. 1036–1040, 2000.)

ning electron microscopy (SEM) to scrutinize the structure of the shell when it was fractured. What they discovered was a criss-crossed, layered structure that is the equivalent of a "ceramic plywood" (Figure 20). This microarchitecture prevents fractures that occur on the outside surface of the shell from being transferred into the inner layers. The discovery has inspired materials engineers to create materials that are significantly strengthened by incorporating a fibrous ceramic matrix, such as SiC (silicon carbide) whiskers.

Research on adhesive materials represents another area in which sea creatures can provide some clues. Getting things to stick together is important in a multitude of applications. The loss of the space shuttle Columbia in early 2003, caused by loss of some ceramic tiles when a piece of insulating foam that fell off during launch hit them, offered a sobering lesson in adhesive failure under extreme conditions of temperature and humidity. If you look around, you will probably find something with an adhesive label, something with an attached plastic part, something with a rubber seal, or perhaps something taped together. Adhesives have also proven useful for medical applications, where specialized glues help doctors seal tissues within the human body. For every type of sticking application, different properties are needed for the adhesive material.

Nature provides numerous examples of adhesion. Geckos and flies that can walk on glass while completely inverted hold clues to the kind of biologically based adhesion that could be the basis of synthetic analogs (◄ page 548). Marine mussels, which can stick quite well to wood, metal, and rock, also hold great interest for scientists studying adhesion.

Scientists who have researched mussel adhesives have been able to determine that the amino acid 3,4-dihydroxyphenylalanine (DOPA) is the agent primarily responsible for the strength of the adhesion. But DOPA alone cannot explain the incredible strength of the mussel glues. The secret lies in the combination of an Fe^{3+} ion with DOPA to form a cross-linked matrix of the mussel's protein (Figure 21; see also "Green Adhesives" on page 481). The curing process, or hardening of the natural proteinaceous liquid produced by the mussel, is a result of the iron–protein interaction that occurs to form $Fe(DOPA)_3$ cross-links.

The Future of Materials

The modern tools and techniques of chemistry are making it possible for scientists not only to develop novel materials, but also to proceed in new and unforeseen directions. The

FIGURE 21 Strong mussels. *(left)* A common blue mussel can cling to almost any surface, including this Teflon sheet, even underwater. *(right)* The adhesive precursor is a protein interlinked with iron(III) ions. An iron(III) ion binds to the hydroxyl groups (–OH) in three side chains of dihydroxyphenylalanine (DOPA) amino acids in the protein chain.

FIGURE 22 Multi-walled carbon nanotubes (MWNT). Sheets of six-membered carbon rings close on themselves to form tubes. Multi-walled nanotubes, which are presently more easily produced than single-wall tubes, have tubes within tubes.

field of **nanotechnology** is an example. In nanotechnology, structures with dimensions on the order of nanometers are used to carry out specific functions.

Nanotubes (Figure 22) and graphene (page 603), both allotropes of carbon, are among the best known examples of nanomaterials. If carbon or carbon-based compounds are heated under the right conditions, the carbon atoms assemble into sheets of six-member rings, just as in graphite. However, under the right conditions, the sheets close on themselves to form tubes. Because these tubes are only a nanometer or so in diameter, chemists refer to them as *carbon nanotubes* (CNT). Some are single-walled (SWNT), but multi-walled tubes within tubes (MWNT) are also common. The record for their length (as of 2010) is 18 cm!

There is enormous industrial interest in CNTs for a variety of uses: for displays for computers and televisions, molecular wiring in appliances, biosensors, and drug-delivery systems. Thus far, MWNTs are more easily produced, and prices have fallen from thousands of dollars per gram to a few hundred dollars per kilogram. Companies in Asia, Europe, and the United States are being built to produce up to 3000 metric tons per year.

Chemistry is the key to understanding and developing materials. The atomic compositions and long-range structure of different materials fundamentally determine their properties and characteristics. Chemists can use analytical instruments to determine these structures. They can then exploit this knowledge to manipulate or develop materials to achieve different properties for special functions. In many cases, we can look to nature to provide answers and suggestions on how to proceed.

SUGGESTED READINGS

1. Materials chemistry: P. Day, L. V. Interrante, and A. R. West, *Pure and Applied Chemistry*, Vol. 81, page 1707, 2009.
2. X. Su, S. Kamat, and A. H. Heuer: "The structure of sea urchin spines, large biogenic single crystals of calcite." *Journal of Materials Science*, Vol. 35, pp. 5545–5551, 2000.
3. M. J. Sever, J. T. Weisser, J. Monahan, S. Srinivasan, and J. J. Wilker: "Metal-mediated cross-linking in the generation of marine mussel adhesive." *Angewandte Chemie International Edition*, Vol. 43, pp. 447–450, 2004.

STUDY QUESTIONS

Blue-numbered questions have answers in Appendix Q and fully worked solutions in the *Student Solutions Manual*.

1. The degree of magnification is often given when photographing objects with a microscope. Refer to the photos of the skeleton of the sea sponge (Figure 14). What are the degrees of magnification for the pictures in Figures 14b, 14c, and 14d? The length of the scale bar in each figure is 5.0 mm.

2. Which of the following would be good substitutional impurities for an aluminum alloy?
   (a) Sn   (b) P   (c) K   (d) Pb

3. The amount of sunlight striking the surface of the earth (when the sun is directly overhead on a clear day) is approximately 925 watts per square meter (W/m^2). The area of a typical solar cell is approximately 1.0 cm^2. If the cell is running at 25% efficiency, what is its energy output per minute?

4. Using the result of the calculation in Question 3, estimate the number of solar cells that would be needed to power a 700-W microwave oven. If the solar cells were assembled into a panel, what would be the approximate area of the panel?

5. Describe how you could calculate the density of pewter (Table 1) from the densities of the component elements, assuming that pewter is a substitutional alloy. Look up the densities of the constituent elements and carry out this calculation. Densities can be found on a website such as www.webelements.com or www.ptable.com.

6. Calculate an approximate value for the density of aerogel using the fact that it is 99.98% air and the remainder is SiO_2 (density = 2.63 g/cm^3). What is the mass of a 1.0-cm^3 piece of aerogel?

7. Suppose you wish to make a superinsulated window by filling the gap between two sheets of glass with aerogel. What mass of aerogel is needed for a 180-cm × 150-cm window with a gap of 2.0 mm between the glass sheets?

8. Assume that the repeating unit in an aerogel polymer is $OSi(OC_2H_5)_2$. If the polymer is 99.98% air and the density is about 1.9 mg/cm^3, how many silicon atoms are there in 1.0 cm^3 of aerogel?

15 Chemical Kinetics: The Rates of Chemical Reactions

Fading of the color of phenolphthalein with time

(elapsed time about 3 minutes)

Photos © Cengage Learning/Charles D. Winters

Where Did the Indicator Go? The indicator phenolphthalein is often used for the titration of a weak acid using a strong base. A change from colorless to pale pink indicates that the equivalence point in the reaction has been reached (◄ page 183). If more base is added to the solution, the color of the indicator intensifies to a bright red color.

If the solution containing phenolphthalein has a pH higher than about 12, another phenomenon is observed. Slowly, the red color fades, and the solution becomes colorless. This is due to a chemical reaction of the anion of phenolphthalein with hydroxide ion, as shown in the equation. The reaction is slow, and it is easy to measure the rate of this reaction by monitoring the intensity of color of the solution.

This chapter is about a fundamental area of chemistry: *chemical kinetics*. This encompasses the study of reaction rates and their interpretation based on reaction mechanisms. In Study Question 75, you will see some data that will allow you to determine how the rate of the phenolphthalein reaction depends on the hydroxide ion concentration, and you will derive an equation that will allow you to predict the results under other conditions.

The reaction of phenolphthalein and hydroxide ion.

CHAPTER GOALS

See Chapter Goals Revisited (page 706) for Study Questions keyed to these goals.

- Understand rates of reaction and the conditions affecting rates.

- Derive a rate equation, rate constant, and reaction order from experimental data.

- Use integrated rate laws.

- Understand the collision theory of reaction rates and the role of activation energy.

- Relate reaction mechanisms and rate laws.

◐WL

Sign in to OWL at **www.cengage.com/owl** to view tutorials and simulations, develop problem-solving skills, and complete online homework assigned by your professor.

go Chemistry

Download mini lecture videos for key concept review and exam prep from OWL or purchase them from **www.cengagebrain.com**

When carrying out a chemical reaction, chemists are concerned with two issues: the *rate* at which the reaction proceeds and the *extent* to which the reaction is product-favored at equilibrium. Chapter 5 began to address the second question, and Chapters 16 and 19 will develop that topic further. In this chapter, we turn to the first-mentioned question, **chemical kinetics**, a study of the rates of chemical reactions.

The study of kinetics is divided into two parts. The first part is at the *macroscopic level*, which addresses rates of reactions: what reaction rate means, how to determine a reaction rate experimentally, and how factors such as temperature and the concentrations of reactants influence rates. The second part of this subject considers chemical reactions at the *particulate level*. Here, the concern is with the **reaction mechanism**, the detailed pathway taken by atoms and molecules as a reaction proceeds. The goal is to reconcile data in the macroscopic world of chemistry with an understanding of how and why chemical reactions occur at the particulate level—and then to apply this information to control important reactions.

15.1   Rates of Chemical Reactions

You encounter the concept of rates in many nonchemical circumstances. Common examples are the speed of an automobile, given in terms of the distance traveled per unit time (for example, kilometers per hour) and the rate of flow of water from a faucet, given as volume per unit time (perhaps liters per minute). In each case, a change is measured over an interval of time. Similarly, the rate of a chemical reaction refers to the change in concentration of a reactant or product per unit of time.

$$\text{Rate of reaction} = \frac{\text{change in concentration}}{\text{change in time}}$$

Two measurements are made to determine the average speed of an automobile: distance traveled and time elapsed. Average speed is the distance traveled divided by the time elapsed, or $\Delta(\text{distance})/\Delta(\text{time})$. If an automobile travels 3.9 km in 4.5 min (0.075 h), its average speed is (3.9 km/0.075 h), or 52 kph (or 32 mph).

Photos © Cengage Learning/Charles D. Winters

(a) A few drops of blue food dye were added to water, followed by a solution of bleach. Initially, the concentration of dye was about 3.4×10^{-5} M, and the bleach (NaOCl) concentration was about 0.034 M.

(b) The color fades as the dye reacts with the bleach. The absorbance of the solution can be measured at various times using a spectrophotometer (page 188), and these values can be used to determine the concentration of the dye.

FIGURE 15.1 An experiment to measure rate of reaction.

Average rates of chemical reactions can be determined similarly. Two quantities, concentration and time, are measured. Concentrations can be determined in a variety of ways, such as by using a pH meter to determine the concentration of hydronium ion in a solution or by measuring the absorbance of light by a solution, a property that can be related to the concentration of a species in solution (Figure 15.1). The average rate of the reaction is the change in the concentration per unit time—that is, $\Delta(\text{concentration})/\Delta(\text{time})$.

Let's consider the decomposition of N_2O_5 in a solvent. This reaction occurs according to the following equation:

$$N_2O_5 \rightarrow 2\ NO_2 + \tfrac{1}{2}\ O_2$$

Concentrations and time elapsed for a typical experiment done at 30.0 °C are presented as a graph in Figure 15.2.

FIGURE 15.2 A plot of reactant concentration versus time for the decomposition of N_2O_5. The average rate for a 15-minute interval from 40 to 55 minutes is 0.0080 mol/L · min. The instantaneous rate calculated when $[N_2O_5] = 0.34$ M is 0.0014 mol/L · min.

The rate of this reaction for any interval of time can be expressed as the change in concentration of N_2O_5 divided by the change in time:

$$\text{Rate of reaction} = -\frac{\text{change in } [N_2O_5]}{\text{change in time}} = -\frac{\Delta[N_2O_5]}{\Delta t}$$

The minus sign is required because the concentration of N_2O_5 decreases with time (that is, $\Delta[N_2O_5] = [N_2O_5](\text{final}) - [N_2O_5](\text{initial})$ is negative), and rate is always expressed as a positive quantity. Using data from Figure 15.2, the rate of disappearance of N_2O_5 between 40 and 55 minutes is given by

$$\text{Rate} = -\frac{\Delta[N_2O_5]}{\Delta t} = -\frac{(1.10 \text{ mol/L}) - (1.22 \text{ mol/L})}{55 \text{ min} - 40 \text{ min}} = +\frac{0.12 \text{ mol/L}}{15 \text{ min}}$$

$$\text{Rate} = 0.0080 \frac{\text{mol } N_2O_5 \text{ consumed}}{L \cdot \text{min}}$$

Note the units for reaction rates; if concentration is expressed in mol/L, the units for rate will be mol/L · time.

During a chemical reaction, amounts of reactants decrease with time, and amounts of products increase. For the decomposition of N_2O_5, we could also express the rate either as $\Delta[NO_2]/\Delta t$ or as $\Delta[O_2]/\Delta t$. Rates based on changes in concentrations of products will have a positive sign because the concentration is increasing. Furthermore, the numerical values of rates defined in these ways will be different from the value of $\Delta[N_2O_5]/\Delta t$. Note that the rate of decomposition of N_2O_5 is one half the rate of formation of NO_2 and twice the rate of formation of O_2. A rate expression relating all of these rates can be determined by dividing each rate expression by the stoichiometric coefficient of the substance in the balanced chemical equation.

$$\text{Rate of reaction} = -\frac{\Delta[N_2O_5]}{\Delta t} = +\frac{1}{2}\frac{\Delta[NO_2]}{\Delta t} = +2\frac{\Delta[O_2]}{\Delta t}$$

For the 15-minute interval between 40 and 55 minutes, the average rates for the formation of NO_2 and O_2 are

$$\text{Rate} = \frac{\Delta[NO_2]}{\Delta t} = \frac{0.0080 \text{ mol } N_2O_5 \text{ consumed}}{L \cdot \text{min}} \times \frac{2 \text{ mol } NO_2 \text{ formed}}{1 \text{ mol } N_2O_5 \text{ consumed}}$$

$$= 0.016 \frac{\text{mol } NO_2 \text{ formed}}{L \cdot \text{min}}$$

$$\text{Rate} = \frac{\Delta[O_2]}{\Delta t} = \frac{0.0080 \text{ mol } N_2O_5 \text{ consumed}}{L \cdot \text{min}} \times \frac{\frac{1}{2} \text{ mol } O_2 \text{ formed}}{1 \text{ mol } N_2O_5 \text{ consumed}}$$

$$= 0.0040 \frac{\text{mol } O_2 \text{ formed}}{L \cdot \text{min}}$$

The graph of $[N_2O_5]$ versus time in Figure 15.2 does not give a straight line because, as described in Section 15.3, the rate of the reaction changes during the course of the reaction. The concentration of N_2O_5 decreases rapidly at the beginning of the reaction but more slowly near the end. We can verify this by comparing the rate of disappearance of N_2O_5 calculated previously (the concentration decreased by 0.12 mol/L in 15 minutes) to the average rate of reaction calculated for the time interval from 6.5 to 9.0 hours (when the concentration drops by 0.12 mol/L in 150 minutes). The average rate in this later stage of this reaction is only one tenth of the previous value.

$$-\frac{\Delta[N_2O_5]}{\Delta t} = -\frac{(0.10 \text{ mol/L}) - (0.22 \text{ mol/L})}{540 \text{ min} - 390 \text{ min}} = +\frac{0.12 \text{ mol/L}}{150 \text{ min}}$$

$$= 0.00080 \frac{\text{mol}}{L \cdot \text{min}}$$

● **Representing Concentrations** Recall that square brackets around a formula indicate its concentrations in mol/L (Section 4.5).

● **Calculating Changes** When calculating a change in a quantity, we always do so by subtracting the initial quantity from the final quantity: $\Delta c = c_{\text{final}} - c_{\text{initial}}$.

● **Reaction Rates and Stoichiometry** For the general reaction $a A + b B \rightarrow c C + d D$, the international convention defines the reaction rate as

$$\text{Reaction rate} = -\frac{1}{a}\frac{\Delta[A]}{\Delta t} = -\frac{1}{b}\frac{\Delta[B]}{\Delta t}$$
$$= +\frac{1}{c}\frac{\Delta[C]}{\Delta t} = +\frac{1}{d}\frac{\Delta[D]}{\Delta t}$$

Note that this gives us the reaction rate on a "per mole of reaction" basis. For more on this topic, see K. T. Quisenberry and J. Tellinghuisen, *Journal of Chemical Education*, Vol. 83, pp. 510–512, 2006.

● **The Slope of a Line** The instantaneous rate in Figure 15.2 can be determined from an analysis of the slope of the line. See pages 41–42 for more on finding the slope of a line.

The procedure we have used to calculate the reaction rate gives the average rate over the chosen time interval.

We might also ask what the instantaneous rate is at a single point in time. In an automobile, the instantaneous rate can be read from the speedometer. For a chemical reaction, we can extract the instantaneous rate from the concentration–time graph by drawing a line tangent to the concentration–time curve at a particular time (Figure 15.2). The instantaneous rate is obtained from the slope of this line. For example, when $[N_2O_5] = 0.34$ mol/L and $t = 5.0$ hours, the rate is

$$\text{Rate when } [N_2O_5] \text{ is 0.34 M} = -\frac{\Delta[N_2O_5]}{\Delta t} = +\frac{0.20 \text{ mol/L}}{140 \text{ min}}$$

$$= 0.0014 \frac{\text{mol}}{L \cdot \text{min}}$$

At that particular moment in time, ($t = 5.0$ hours), N_2O_5 is being consumed at a rate of 0.0014 mol/L · min.

EXAMPLE 15.1   Relative Rates and Stoichiometry

Problem Relate the rates for the disappearance of reactants and formation of products for the following reaction:

$$4 \, PH_3(g) \rightarrow P_4(g) + 6 \, H_2(g)$$

What Do You Know? The balanced chemical equation for the reaction is given. The stoichiometric coefficients in this equation will be used to evaluate the relative rates for the disappearance of the starting material and formation of the products.

Strategy In this reaction, PH_3 disappears, and P_4 and H_2 are formed. Consequently, the value of $\Delta[PH_3]/\Delta t$ will be negative, whereas $\Delta[P_4]/\Delta t$ and $\Delta[H_2]/\Delta t$ will be positive. To relate the rates to each other, we divide $\Delta[\text{reagent}]/\Delta t$ by its stoichiometric coefficient in the balanced equation.

Solution Because four moles of PH_3 disappear for every one mole of P_4 formed, the numerical value of the rate of formation of P_4 is one fourth of the rate of disappearance of PH_3. Similarly, P_4 is formed at only one sixth of the rate that H_2 is formed.

$$\text{Reaction rate} = -\frac{1}{4}\left(\frac{\Delta[PH_3]}{\Delta t}\right) = +\frac{\Delta[P_4]}{\Delta t} = +\frac{1}{6}\left(\frac{\Delta[H_2]}{\Delta t}\right)$$

Think about Your Answer A general equation to determine the relative rates of disappearance and formation from a balanced chemical equation is given in the margin on page 671.

Check Your Understanding

What are the relative rates of appearance or disappearance of each product and reactant, respectively, in the decomposition of nitrosyl chloride, NOCl?

$$2 \, NOCl(g) \rightarrow 2 \, NO(g) + Cl_2(g)$$

EXAMPLE 15.2   Rate of Reaction

Problem Data collected on the concentration of dye as a function of time (Figure 15.1) are given in the graph below. What is the average rate of change of the dye concentration over the first 2 minutes? What is the average rate of change during the fifth minute (from $t = 4.0$ minutes to $t = 5.0$ minutes)? Estimate the instantaneous rate at 4.0 minutes.

What Do You Know? The concentration of dye as a function of time is presented as a graph. From this curve you can identify the concentration of dye at specific times.

Strategy To find the average rate, calculate the difference in concentration at the beginning and end of a time period ($\Delta c = c_{final} - c_{initial}$) and divide by the elapsed time. To find the instantaneous rate at 4 minutes, draw a line tangent to the graph at the specified time. The negative of the slope of the line is the instantaneous rate.

Solution The concentration of dye decreases from 3.4×10^{-5} mol/L at $t = 0$ minutes to 1.7×10^{-5} mol/L at $t = 2.0$ minutes. The average rate of the reaction in this interval of time is

$$\text{Average rate} = -\frac{\Delta[\text{Dye}]}{\Delta t} = -\frac{(1.7 \times 10^{-5} \text{ mol/L}) - (3.4 \times 10^{-5} \text{ mol/L})}{2.0 \text{ min}}$$

$$\text{Average rate} = \frac{8.5 \times 10^{-6} \text{ mol}}{\text{L} \cdot \text{min}}$$

The concentration of dye decreases from 0.90×10^{-5} mol/L at $t = 4.0$ minutes to 0.60×10^{-5} mol/L at $t = 5.0$ minutes. The average rate of the reaction in this interval of time is

$$\text{Average rate} = -\frac{\Delta[\text{Dye}]}{\Delta t} = -\frac{(0.60 \times 10^{-5} \text{ mol/L}) - (0.90 \times 10^{-5} \text{ mol/L})}{1.0 \text{ min}}$$

$$\text{Average rate} = \frac{3.0 \times 10^{-6} \text{ mol}}{\text{L} \cdot \text{min}}$$

From the slope of the line tangent to the curve, the instantaneous rate at 4 minutes is found to be $+3.5 \times 10^{-6}$ mol/L · min.

Think about Your Answer Notice that the rate of reaction decreases as the concentration of dye decreases. This tells us that the rate of the reaction is related to the concentration of dye. We can also deduce this qualitatively from the fact that graphing concentration vs. time gave a curved line.

Check Your Understanding

Sucrose decomposes to fructose and glucose in acid solution. A plot of the concentration of sucrose as a function of time is given in the margin. What is the rate of change of the sucrose concentration over the first 2 hours? What is the rate of change over the last 2 hours? Estimate the instantaneous rate at 4 hours.

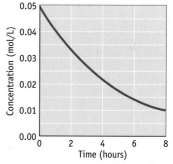

Concentration versus time for the decomposition of sucrose.
("Check Your Understanding" in Example 15.2.)

REVIEW & CHECK FOR SECTION 15.1

1. Compare the rates of disappearance of NO(g) and O_2(g) for the reaction
    $2 \text{ NO(g)} + O_2\text{(g)} \rightarrow 2 \text{ NO}_2\text{(g)}$.

    (a)   The rates are equal.

    (b)   The rate of disappearance of NO(g) is twice the rate of disappearance of O_2(g).

    (c)   The rate of disappearance of NO(g) is one half the rate of disappearance of O_2(g).

    (d)   The rates are not related.

2. Use the graph provided in Example 15.2 to estimate the average rate of disappearance of dye for the period 1-3 minutes.

(a) 0.6 mol/L · min

(c) 0.6×10^{-5} mol/L · min

(b) 1.2×10^{-5} mol/L · min

(d) 1.2 mol/L · min

15.2 Reaction Conditions and Rate

Several factors—reactant concentrations, temperature, and presence of catalysts—affect the rate of a reaction. If the reactant is a solid, the surface area available for reaction is also a factor.

The "iodine clock reaction" (Figure 15.3) illustrates the **effect of concentration and temperature**. The reaction mixture contains hydrogen peroxide (H_2O_2), iodide ion (I^-), vitamin C (ascorbic acid), and starch (which is an indicator of the presence of iodine, I_2). A sequence of reactions begins with the slow oxidation of iodide ion to I_2 by H_2O_2.

$$H_2O_2(aq) + 2\ I^-(aq) + 2\ H_3O^+(aq) \rightarrow 4\ H_2O(\ell) + I_2(aq)$$

As soon as I_2 is formed in the solution, vitamin C rapidly reduces it to I^-.

$$2\ H_2O(\ell) + I_2(aq) + C_6H_8O_6(aq) \rightarrow C_6H_6O_6(aq) + 2\ H_3O^+(aq) + 2\ I^-(aq)$$

When all of the vitamin C has been consumed, I_2 remains in solution and forms a blue-black complex with starch. The time measured represents how long it has taken for the given amount of vitamin C to react. For the first experiment (A in Figure 15.3) the time required is 51 seconds. When the concentration of iodide ion is smaller (B), the time required for the vitamin C to be consumed is longer, 1 minute 33 seconds. Finally, when the concentrations are again the same as in experiment B but the reaction mixture is heated, the reaction occurs more rapidly (56 seconds). This experiment illustrates two features that are true of most reactions:

- If the concentration of a reactant is increased, the reaction rate will often increase as well.
- Chemical reactions occur more rapidly at higher temperatures.

● **Effect of Temperature on Reaction Rate** Cooking involves chemical reactions, and a higher temperature results in foods cooking faster. In the laboratory, reaction mixtures are often heated to make reactions occur faster.

(a) Initial experiment.
The blue color of the starch–iodine complex develops in 51 seconds.

(b) Change concentration.
The blue color of the starch–iodine complex develops in 1 minute 33 seconds when the solution is less concentrated than A.

(c) Change temperature.
The blue color of the starch–iodine complex develops in 56 seconds when the solution is the same concentration as in B but at a higher temperature.

Smaller concentration of I^- than in Experiment A.

Hot bath

Same concentrations as in Experiment B, but at a higher temperature.

Solutions containing vitamin C, H_2O_2, I^-, and starch are mixed.

Photos © Cengage Learning/Charles D. Winters

FIGURE 15.3 The iodine clock reaction. This reaction illustrates the effects of concentration and temperature on reaction rate. (You can do these experiments yourself with reagents available in the supermarket. For details, see S. W. Wright: "The vitamin C clock reaction," *Journal of Chemical Education*, Vol. 79, p. 41, 2002.)

(a) The rate of decomposition of hydrogen peroxide is increased by the catalyst MnO_2. Here, H_2O_2 (as a 30% aqueous solution) is poured onto the black solid MnO_2 and rapidly decomposes to O_2 and H_2O. Steam forms because of the high heat of reaction.

(b) A bombardier beetle uses the catalyzed decomposition of H_2O_2 as a defense mechanism. The energy involved in the reaction lets the insect eject hot water and other irritating chemicals with explosive force.

(c) Enzyme catalysis. Here, the enzyme catalase, found in potatoes, is used to catalyze H_2O_2 decomposition, and bubbles of O_2 gas are seen rising in the solution.

FIGURE 15.4 Catalyzed decomposition of H_2O_2.

Catalysts are substances that accelerate chemical reactions but are not themselves consumed. Consider the effect of a catalyst on the decomposition of hydrogen peroxide, H_2O_2, to form water and oxygen.

$$2\ H_2O_2(aq) \rightarrow O_2(g) + 2\ H_2O(\ell)$$

This decomposition is very slow; a solution of H_2O_2 can be stored for many months with only minimal change in concentration. Adding manganese(IV) oxide, an iodide-containing salt, or a compound called catalase—an example of a biological catalyst or *enzyme*—causes this reaction to occur rapidly, as shown by vigorous bubbling as gaseous oxygen escapes from the solution (Figure 15.4).

The *surface area* of a solid reactant can also affect the reaction rate. Only molecules at the surface of a solid can come in contact with other reactants. The smaller the particles of a solid, the more molecules are found on the solid's surface. With very small particles, the effect of surface area on rate can be quite dramatic (Figure 15.5). Farmers know that explosions of fine dust particles (suspended in the air in an enclosed silo or at a feed mill) represent a major hazard.

REVIEW & CHECK FOR SECTION 15.2

Which of the factors listed below affect the rates of chemical reactions?

(a) catalysts   (c) concentration of reactants   (e) all of the above

(b) temperature   (d) surface area of solid

15.3 Effect of Concentration on Reaction Rate

One important goal in studying the kinetics of a reaction is to determine its mechanism; that is, how the reaction occurs at the molecular level. The place to begin is to learn how concentrations of reactants affect the reaction rate.

The effect of concentration can be determined by evaluating how the rate is affected when the concentrations of the reactants are varied (with the temperature held constant). Consider, for example, the decomposition of N_2O_5 to NO_2 and O_2. Figure 15.2 presented data on the concentration of N_2O_5 as a function of time. We previously calculated that, when $[N_2O_5] = 0.34$ mol/L, the instantaneous rate of disappearance of N_2O_5 is 0.0014 mol/L · min. An evaluation of the instantaneous rate of the reaction when $[N_2O_5] = 0.68$ mol/L reveals a rate of 0.0028 mol/L · min.

(a)

(b)

FIGURE 15.5 The combustion of lycopodium powder. (a) The spores of this common fern burn only with difficulty when piled in a dish. **(b)** If the spores are ground to a fine powder and sprayed into a flame, combustion is rapid.

That is, doubling the concentration of N_2O_5 doubles the reaction rate. A similar exercise shows that if $[N_2O_5]$ is 0.17 mol/L (half of 0.34 mol/L), the reaction rate is also halved. From these results, we know that the rate for this reaction must be directly proportional to the N_2O_5 concentration:

$$N_2O_5 \rightarrow 2\ NO_2 + \tfrac{1}{2}\ O_2$$

$$\text{Rate of reaction} \propto [N_2O_5]$$

where the symbol $\propto$ means "proportional to."

Different relationships between reaction rate and reactant concentration are encountered in other reactions. For example, the reaction rate could be independent of concentration, or it may depend on the reactant concentration raised to some power n (that is, $[\text{reactant}]^n$). If the reaction involves several reactants, the reaction rate may depend on the concentrations of each of them or on only one of them. Finally, the concentration of a catalyst or even the concentrations of the products may affect the rate.

Rate Equations

The relationship between reactant concentration and reaction rate is expressed by an equation called a **rate equation**, or **rate law**. For the decomposition of N_2O_5 the rate equation is

$$N_2O_5(g) \rightarrow 2\ NO_2(g) + \tfrac{1}{2}\ O_2$$

$$\text{Rate of reaction} = -\Delta[N_2O_5]/\Delta t = +(1/2)\Delta[NO_2]/\Delta t = +2\Delta[O_2]/\Delta t = k[N_2O_5]$$

where the proportionality constant, k, is called the **rate constant**. This rate equation tells us that this reaction rate is proportional to the concentration of the reactant. Based on this equation, we can determine that when $[N_2O_5]$ is doubled, the reaction rate doubles (and we know $[N_2O_5]$ decreases twice as fast as $[O_2]$ increases).

Generally, for a reaction such as

$$a\ A + b\ B \rightarrow x\ X$$

the rate equation has the form

$$\text{Rate of reaction} = k[A]^m[B]^n$$

● **Exponents on Reactant Concentrations and Reaction Stoichiometry** It is important to recognize that the exponents m and n are not necessarily the stoichiometric coefficients (a and b) for the balanced chemical equation.

The rate equation expresses the fact that the rate of reaction is proportional to the reactant concentrations, each concentration being raised to some power. The exponents in this equation are often positive whole numbers, but they can also be negative numbers, fractions, or zero, and they are determined by experiment.

If a homogeneous catalyst is present, its concentration might also be included in the rate equation, even though the catalytic species in not a product or reactant in the equation for the reaction. Consider, for example, the decomposition of hydrogen peroxide in the presence of a catalyst such as iodide ion.

$$H_2O_2(aq) \xrightarrow{\ I^-(aq)\ } H_2O(\ell) + \tfrac{1}{2}\ O_2(g)$$

Experiments show that this reaction has the following rate equation:

$$\text{Reaction rate} = -\Delta[H_2O_2]/\Delta t = +\Delta[H_2O]/\Delta t = +2\Delta[O_2]/\Delta t = k[H_2O_2][I^-]$$

● **The Nature of Catalysts** A catalyst does not appear as a reactant in the balanced, overall equation for the reaction, but it may appear in the rate expression. A common practice is to identify catalysts by name or symbol above the reaction arrow, as shown in the example. A homogeneous catalyst is one in the same phase as the reactants. For example, both H_2O_2 and I^- are dissolved in water.

Here, the concentration of I^- appears in the rate law, even though it is not involved in the balanced equation.

The Order of a Reaction

The **order** of a reaction with respect to a particular reactant is the exponent of its concentration term in the rate expression, and the **overall reaction order** is the sum of the exponents on all concentration terms. Consider, for example, the reaction of NO and Cl_2:

$$2\ NO(g) + Cl_2(g) \rightarrow 2\ NOCl(g)$$

The experimentally determined rate equation for this reaction is

$$\text{Reaction rate} = -(1/2)\Delta[\text{NO}]/\Delta t = -\Delta[\text{Cl}_2]/\Delta t = +(1/2)\Delta[\text{NOCl}]/\Delta t = k[\text{NO}]^2[\text{Cl}_2]$$

This reaction is second order in NO, first order in Cl_2, and third order overall. How is this related to the following experimental data for the rate of disappearance of NO?

Experiment	[NO] mol/L	[Cl$_2$] mol/L	Rate mol/L · s
1	0.250	0.250	1.43×10^{-6}
	↓ × 2	↓ No change	↓ × 4
2	0.500	0.250	5.72×10^{-6}
3	0.250	0.500	2.86×10^{-6}
4	0.500	0.500	11.4×10^{-6}

- *Compare Experiments 1 and 2:* Here, [Cl$_2$] is held constant, and [NO] is doubled. The change in [NO] leads to a reaction rate increase by a factor of 4; that is, the rate is proportional to the *square* of the NO concentration.
- *Compare Experiments 1 and 3:* In experiments 1 and 3, [NO] is held constant, and [Cl$_2$] is doubled, causing the rate to double. That is, the rate is proportional to [Cl$_2$].
- *Compare Experiments 1 and 4:* Both [NO] and [Cl$_2$] are doubled from 0.250 M to 0.500 M. From previous experiments, we know that doubling [NO] should cause a four-fold increase, and doubling [Cl$_2$] causes a two-fold increase. Therefore, doubling both concentrations should cause an eight-fold increase, as is observed [$(1.43 \times 10^{-6}$ mol/L · s$) \times 8 = 11.4 \times 10^{-6}$ mol/L · s].

● **Time and Rate Constants** The time in a rate constant can be seconds, minutes, hours, days, years, or whatever time unit is appropriate. The fraction 1/time can also be written as time^{-1}. For example, $1/y$ is equivalent to y^{-1}, and $1/s$ is equivalent to s^{-1}.

The decomposition of ammonia on a platinum surface at 856 °C is a zero-order reaction.

$$\text{NH}_3(g) \rightarrow \tfrac{1}{2}\,\text{N}_2(g) + \tfrac{3}{2}\,\text{H}_2(g)$$

This means that the reaction rate is independent of NH$_3$ concentration.

$$\text{Reaction rate} = -\Delta[\text{NH}_3]/\Delta t = +2\Delta[\text{N}_2]/\Delta t = +(2/3)\Delta[\text{H}_2]/\Delta t = k[\text{NH}_3]^0 = k$$

Reaction order is important because it gives some insight into the most interesting question of all—how the reaction occurs. This is described further in Section 15.6.

The Rate Constant, *k*

The rate constant, k, is a proportionality constant that relates rate and concentration at a given temperature. It is an important quantity because it enables you to find the reaction rate for a new set of concentrations. To see how to use k, consider the substitution of Cl$^-$ ion by water in the cancer chemotherapy agent cisplatin, Pt(NH$_3$)$_2$Cl$_2$.

$$\text{Pt(NH}_3)_2\text{Cl}_2(aq) + \text{H}_2\text{O}(\ell) \longrightarrow [\text{Pt(NH}_3)_2(\text{H}_2\text{O})\text{Cl}]^+(aq) + \text{Cl}^-(aq)$$

The rate law for this reaction is

$$\text{Reaction rate} = -\Delta[\text{Pt(NH}_3)_2\text{Cl}_2]\Delta t = k[\text{Pt(NH}_3)_2\text{Cl}_2]$$

and the rate constant, k, is 0.27/h at 25 °C. Knowing k allows you to calculate the rate at a particular reactant concentration—for example, when [Pt(NH$_3$)$_2$Cl$_2$] = 0.018 mol/L:

$$\text{Reaction rate} = (0.27/\text{h})(0.018 \text{ mol/L}) = 0.0049 \text{ mol/L} \cdot \text{h}$$

● **Some Rate Constants**

First Order	k (1/s)
2 N$_2$O$_5$(g) → 4 NO$_2$(g) + O$_2$(g)	3.38×10^{-5} at 25 °C
C$_2$H$_6$(g) → 2 CH$_3$(g)	5.36×10^{-4} at 700 °C
Sucrose(aq, H$_3$O$^+$) → fructose(aq) + glucose(aq)	6.0×10^{-5} at 25 °C

Second Order	k (L/mol · s)
2 NOBr(g) → 2 NO(g) + Br$_2$(g)	0.80 at 10 °C
H$_2$(g) + I$_2$(g) → 2 HI(g)	0.0242 at 400 °C

As noted earlier, reaction rates have units of mol/L · time when concentrations are given as moles per liter. Rate constants must have units consistent with the units for the other terms in the rate equation.

- First-order reactions: The units of k are 1/time.
- Second-order reactions: The units of k are L/mol · time.
- Zero-order reaction: The units of k are mol/L · time.

Determining a Rate Equation

One way to determine a rate equation is by using the "method of initial rates." The initial rate is the instantaneous reaction rate at the start of the reaction (the rate at $t = 0$). An approximate value of the initial rate can be obtained by mixing the reactants and determining the reaction rate after 1% to 2% of the limiting reactant has been consumed. Measuring the rate during the initial stage of a reaction is convenient because initial concentrations are known.

As an example of the determination of a reaction rate by the method of initial rates, let us consider the reaction of sodium hydroxide with methyl acetate to produce acetate ion and methanol.

$$CH_3CO_2CH_3(aq) \quad + \quad OH^-(aq) \quad \longrightarrow \quad CH_3CO_2^-(aq) \quad + \quad CH_3OH(aq)$$

Reactant concentrations and initial rates for this reaction for several experiments at 25 °C are collected in the table below.

Experiment	Initial Concentrations (mol/L)		Initial Reaction Rate
	$[CH_3CO_2CH_3]$	$[OH^-]$	(mol/L · s) at 25 °C
1	0.050	0.050	0.00034
	↓ no change	↓ × 2	↓ × 2
2	0.050	0.10	0.00069
	↓ × 2	↓ no change	↓ × 2
3	0.10	0.10	0.00137

As you can see from the data in the table, when the initial concentration of one reactant (either $CH_3CO_2CH_3$ or OH^-) is doubled while the concentration of the other reactant is held constant, the initial reaction rate doubles. This rate doubling shows that the reaction rate is directly proportional to the concentrations of both $CH_3CO_2CH_3$ and OH^-; thus, the reaction is first order in each of these reactants and second order overall. The rate law that reflects these experimental observations is

$$\text{Reaction rate} = -\Delta[CH_3CO_2H]/\Delta t = k[CH_3CO_2CH_3][OH^-]$$

Using this equation, we can predict that doubling both concentrations at the same time should cause the rate to go up by a factor of 4. What happens, however, if one concentration is doubled and the other is halved? The rate equation tells us the rate should not change!

If the rate equation is known, the value of k, the rate constant, can be found by substituting values for the rate and concentration into the rate equation. Using the data for the methyl acetate/hydroxide ion reaction from the first experiment, we have

$$\text{Reaction rate} = 0.00034 \text{ mol/L} \cdot \text{s} = k(0.050 \text{ mol/L})(0.050 \text{ mol/L})$$

$$k = \frac{0.00034 \text{ mol/L} \cdot \text{s}}{(0.050 \text{ mol/L})(0.050 \text{ mol/L})} = 0.14 \text{ L/mol} \cdot \text{s}$$

⊌WL   INTERACTIVE EXAMPLE 15.3   Determining a Rate Equation

Problem The rate of the reaction between CO and NO_2 at 540 K

$$CO(g) + NO_2(g) \rightarrow CO_2(g) + NO(g)$$

was measured starting with various concentrations of CO and NO_2. Determine the rate equation and the value of the rate constant.

Experiment	Initial Concentrations		Initial Rate
	[CO], mol/L	[NO₂], mol/L	(mol/L · h)
1	5.10×10^{-4}	0.350×10^{-4}	3.4×10^{-8}
2	5.10×10^{-4}	0.700×10^{-4}	6.8×10^{-8}
3	5.10×10^{-4}	0.175×10^{-4}	1.7×10^{-8}
4	1.02×10^{-3}	0.350×10^{-4}	6.8×10^{-8}
5	1.53×10^{-3}	0.350×10^{-4}	10.2×10^{-8}

What Do You Know? The table contains concentrations of the two reactants and initial rates for five experiments.

Strategy For a reaction involving several reactants, the general approach is to keep the concentration of one reactant constant and then decide how the rate of reaction changes as the concentration of the other reagent is varied. Because the rate is proportional to the concentration of a reactant, R, raised to some power n (the reaction order)

$$\text{Rate} \propto [R]^n$$

we can write the general equation for the ratio of rates in two experiments

$$\frac{\text{Rate in experiment 2}}{\text{Rate in experiment 1}} = \frac{\left[R_2\right]^n}{\left[R_1\right]^n} = \left(\frac{\left[R_2\right]}{\left[R_1\right]}\right)^n$$

If [R] is doubled and the rate doubles from experiment 1 to experiment 2, then $n = 1$. If [R], doubles and the rate goes up by 4, then $n = 2$.

Solution In the first three experiments, the concentration of CO is held constant. In the second experiment, the NO_2 concentration has been doubled relative to experiment 1, leading to a two-fold increase in the rate. Thus, $n = 1$ and the reaction is first order in NO_2.

$$\frac{\text{Rate in experiment 2}}{\text{Rate in experiment 1}} = \frac{6.8 \times 10^{-8} \text{ mol/L} \cdot \text{h}}{3.4 \times 10^{-8} \text{ mol/L} \cdot \text{h}} = \left(\frac{0.700 \times 10^{-4}}{0.350 \times 10^{-4}}\right)^n$$

$$2 = (2)^n$$

and so $n = 1$.

This finding is confirmed by experiment 3. Decreasing [NO_2] in experiment 3 to half its original value causes the rate to decrease by half.

The data in experiments 1 and 4 (with constant [NO_2]) show that doubling [CO] doubles the rate, and the data from experiments 1 and 5 show that tripling the concentration of CO triples the rate. These results mean that the reaction is first order in [CO]. Thus, we now know the rate equation is

$$\text{Reaction rate} = -\Delta[CO]/\Delta t = -\Delta[NO_2]/\Delta t = +\Delta[CO_2]/\Delta t = +\Delta[NO]/\Delta t = k[CO][NO_2]$$

The rate constant, k, can be found by inserting data for one of the experiments into the rate equation. Using data from experiment 1, for example,

$$\text{Rate} = 3.4 \times 10^{-8} \text{ mol/L} \cdot \text{h} = k(5.10 \times 10^{-4} \text{ mol/L})(0.350 \times 10^{-4} \text{ mol/L})$$

$$k = 1.9 \text{ L/mol} \cdot \text{h}$$

Think about Your Answer This reaction is first order in each reactant (and second order overall), and you know the value of the rate constant k. The same rate law would apply if the reaction were carried out at a different temperature, but the rate constant k would have a different value.

Strategy Map 15.3

PROBLEM
Derive the **rate equation** and **value of k** for a given reaction.

↓

DATA/INFORMATION
• **5 experiments** measuring *initial rate* as a function of **reactant concentration**

STEP 1. Compare rates for two experiments where the concentration of reactant **A** is *constant* and reactant **B** is *varied*.

Gives the **dependence of rate** on one reactant (**B**)

STEP 2. Compare rates for two experiments where the concentration of reactant **B** is *constant* and reactant **A** is *varied*.

Gives the **dependence of rate** on the other reactant (**A**)

STEP 3. Use the *rate dependence* on **A** and **B** to write the **rate equation**.

Rate = k [A]^n[B]^m

STEP 4. Substitute the **rate data** for one experiment into the **rate equation** to calculate k.

↓

Value of rate constant k

Check Your Understanding

The initial rate of the reaction of nitrogen monoxide and oxygen

$$2 NO(g) + O_2(g) \rightarrow 2 NO_2(g)$$

was measured for various initial concentrations of NO and O_2. Determine the rate equation from these data. What is the value of the rate constant, k, and what are its units?

	Initial Concentrations (mol/L)		Initial Rate for [NO]
Experiment	[NO]	[O₂]	(mol NO/L · s)
1	0.020	0.010	0.028
2	0.020	0.020	0.057
3	0.020	0.040	0.114
4	0.040	0.020	0.227
5	0.010	0.020	0.014

Be sure to note that the reaction rate here is defined as

$$\text{Reaction rate} = -(1/2)\Delta[NO]/\Delta t = -\Delta[O_2]/\Delta t = +(1/2)\Delta[NO_2]/\Delta t = k[NO]^m[O_2]^n$$

EXAMPLE 15.4 Using a Rate Equation to Determine Rates

Problem Using the rate equation and rate constant determined for the reaction of CO and NO_2 at 540 K in Example 15.3, determine the initial rate of the reaction when [CO] = 3.8×10^{-4} mol/L and [NO₂] = 0.650×10^{-4} mol/L.

What Do You Know? The rate law and the value for the rate constant (1.9 L/mol · h) are both known. The concentrations of the two reactants are given.

Strategy A rate equation consists of three parts: a rate, a rate constant (k), and the concentration terms. if two of these parts are known (here k and the concentrations), the third can be calculated.

Solution Substitute k (= 1.9 L/mol · h) and the concentration of each reactant into the rate law determined in Example 15.3.

$$\text{Reaction rate} = k[CO][NO_2] = (1.9 \text{ L/mol} \cdot \text{h})(3.8 \times 10^{-4} \text{ mol/L})(0.650 \times 10^{-4} \text{ m}$$

$$\text{Reaction rate} = 4.7 \times 10^{-8} \text{ mol/L} \cdot \text{h}$$

Think about Your Answer As a check on the calculated result, it is sometimes useful to make an educated guess at the answer before carrying out the mathematical solution. We know that the reaction here is first order in both reactants. Comparing the concentration values given in this problem with the concentration values in experiment 1 in Example 15.3, we notice that [CO] is about three fourths of the concentration value, whereas [NO₂] is almost twice the value. The effects do not precisely offset each other, but we might predict that the difference in rates between this experiment and experiment 1 will be fairly small, with the rate of this experiment being just a little greater. The calculated value bears this out.

Check Your Understanding

The rate constant, k, at 25 °C is 0.27/h for the reaction

$$Pt(NH_3)_2Cl_2(aq) + H_2O(\ell) \rightarrow [Pt(NH_3)_2(H_2O)Cl]^+(aq) + Cl^-(aq)$$

and the rate equation is

$$\text{Reaction rate} = k[Pt(NH_3)_2Cl_2]$$

Calculate the rate of reaction when the concentration of $Pt(NH_3)_2Cl_2$ is 0.020 M.

REVIEW & CHECK FOR SECTION 15.3

The reaction $2 NO(g) + Cl_2(g) \rightarrow 2 NOCl(g)$ is first order in $[Cl_2]$ and second order with respect to $[NO]$. Under a given set of conditions, the initial rate of this reaction is 6.20×10^{-6} mol/L $\cdot$ s. What is the rate of this reaction if the concentration of NO is doubled and the concentration of Cl_2 is reduced to half the original value?

(a) 6.20×10^{-6} mol/L $\cdot$ s

(b) 1.24×10^{-5} mol/L $\cdot$ s

(c) 2.48×10^{-5} mol/L $\cdot$ s

(d) 4.96×10^{-5} mol/L $\cdot$ s

15.4 Concentration–Time Relationships: Integrated Rate Laws

It is often important for a chemist to know how long a reaction must proceed to reach a predetermined concentration of some reactant or product, or what the reactant and product concentrations will be after some time has elapsed. For this reason it would be useful to have a mathematical equation that relates time and concentration—an equation that describes concentration-time curves like the one shown in Figure 15.2—and that can be used to determine this information. With such an equation, we could calculate the concentration at any given time or the length of time needed for a given amount of reactant to react.

Module 20: Chemical Kinetics covers concepts in this section.

First-Order Reactions

Suppose the reaction "$R \rightarrow$ products" is first order. This means the reaction rate is directly proportional to the concentration of R raised to the first power, or, mathematically,

$$-\frac{\Delta[R]}{\Delta t} = k[R]$$

Using calculus, this relationship can be transformed into a very useful equation called an **integrated rate equation** (because integral calculus is used in its derivation).

$$\ln\frac{[R]_t}{[R]_0} = -kt \qquad (15.1)$$

Here, $[R]_0$ and $[R]_t$ are concentrations of the reactant at time $t = 0$ and at a later time, t, respectively. The ratio of concentrations, $[R]_t/[R]_0$, is the fraction of reactant that remains after a given time has elapsed. Notice the negative sign in the equation. The ratio $[R]_t/[R]_0$ is less than 1 because $[R]_t$ is always less than $[R]_0$; the reactant R is consumed during the reaction. This means the logarithm of $[R]_t/[R]_0$ is negative, so the other side of the equation must also bear a negative sign.

Equation 15.1 can be used to carry out the following calculations:

- If $[R]_t/[R]_0$ is measured in the laboratory after some amount of time has elapsed, then k can be calculated.
- If $[R]_0$ and k are known, then the concentration of material remaining after a given amount of time ($[R]_t$) can be calculated.
- If k is known, then the time elapsed until a specific fraction ($[R]_t/[R]_0$) remains can be calculated.

Finally, notice that k for a first-order reaction is independent of concentration; k has units of time^{-1} (y^{-1} or s^{-1}, for example). This means we can choose any convenient unit for $[R]_t$ and $[R]_0$: moles per liter, moles, grams, number of atoms, number of molecules, or gas pressure.

● **Initial and Final Time, t** The time $t = 0$ does not need to correspond to the actual beginning of the experiment. It can be the time when instrument readings were started, for example, even though the reaction may have already begun.

EXAMPLE 15.5   The First-Order Rate Equation

Problem In the past, cyclopropane, C_3H_6, was used in a mixture with oxygen as an anesthetic. (This practice has almost ceased today because the compound is flammable.) When heated, cyclopropane rearranges to propene in a first-order process.

| cyclopropane | propene |

$$\text{Rate} = k[\text{cyclopropane}] \qquad k = 2.42 \text{ h}^{-1} \text{ at } 500 \text{ °C}$$

If the initial concentration of cyclopropane is 0.050 mol/L, how much time (in hours) must elapse for its concentration to drop to 0.010 mol/L?

What Do You Know? The reaction is first order in cyclopropane. You know the rate constant, k, and the initial and final concentrations of this reactant, [R] and [R]$_0$.

Strategy Use Equation 15.1 to calculate the time (t) elapsed to reach a concentration of 0.010 mol/L.

Solution Values for [cyclopropane]$_t$, [cyclopropane]$_0$, and k are substituted into Equation 15.1; t (time) is the unknown:

$$\ln\frac{[0.010]}{[0.050]} = -(2.42 \text{ h}^{-1})t$$

$$t = \frac{-\ln(0.20)}{2.42 \text{ h}^{-1}} = \frac{-(-1.61)}{2.42 \text{ h}^{-1}} = \boxed{0.665 \text{ h}}$$

Think about Your Answer Cycloalkanes with fewer than five carbon atoms are strained because the C—C—C bond angles cannot match the preferred 109.5°. Because of ring strain, the cyclopropane ring opens readily to form propene.

Check Your Understanding

Sucrose, a sugar, decomposes in acid solution to give glucose and fructose. The reaction is first order in sucrose, and the rate constant at 25 °C is $k = 0.21 \text{ h}^{-1}$. If the initial concentration of sucrose is 0.010 mol/L, what is its concentration after 5.0 h?

EXAMPLE 15.6   Using the First-Order Rate Equation

Problem Hydrogen peroxide decomposes in a dilute sodium hydroxide solution at 20 °C in a first-order reaction:

$$H_2O_2(aq) \rightarrow H_2O(\ell) + \tfrac{1}{2} O_2(g)$$
$$\text{Rate} = k[H_2O_2] \text{ with } k = 1.06 \times 10^{-3} \text{ min}^{-1}$$

What is the fraction remaining after 100. min? What is the concentration of H_2O_2 after 100. minutes if the initial concentration of H_2O_2 is 0.020 mol/L??

What Do You Know? This is a first-order reaction. The rate constant k, initial concentration of H_2O_2, and elapsed time are given.

Strategy Because the reaction is first order in H_2O_2, we use Equation 15.1. Here, [H_2O_2]$_0$, k, and t are known, and we are asked to find the value of the fraction remaining. Recall that

$$\frac{[R]_t}{[R]_0} = \text{fraction remaining}$$

Once this value is known, and knowing [H_2O_2]$_0$, we can calculate [H_2O_2]$_t$.

Solution Substitute the known values into Equation 15.1.

$$\ln \frac{[H_2O_2]_t}{[H_2O_2]_0} = -kt = -(1.06 \times 10^{-3}\ \text{min}^{-1})(100.\ \text{min})$$

$$\ln \frac{[H_2O_2]_t}{[H_2O_2]_0} = -0.106$$

Taking the antilogarithm of -0.106 [i.e., the inverse of the logarithm of -0.106 or $e^{-0.106}$], we find the fraction remaining to be 0.90.

$$\text{Fraction remaining} = \frac{[H_2O_2]_t}{[H_2O_2]_0} = 0.90$$

The calculated fraction remaining is 0.90, thus the concentration of H_2O_2 remaining is 90% of the initial concentration.

$$[H_2O_2]_t = 0.90\ [H_2O_2]_0 = 0.90\ (0.020\ \text{mol/L}) = 0.018\ \text{mol/L}$$

Think about Your Answer Although H_2O_2 is unstable, its rate of decomposition is very slow, particularly in a dilute solution. However, sodium hydroxide catalyzes the decomposition. The rate of the reaction can be studied by measuring the volume of O_2 gas evolved as a function of time.

Check Your Understanding

Gaseous azomethane ($CH_3N_2CH_3$) decomposes to ethane and nitrogen when heated:

$$CH_3N_2CH_3(g) \rightarrow CH_3CH_3(g) + N_2(g)$$

The disappearance of azomethane is a first-order reaction with $k = 3.6 \times 10^{-4}\ \text{s}^{-1}$ at 600 K.

(a) A sample of gaseous $CH_3N_2CH_3$ is placed in a flask and heated at 600 K for 150 seconds. What fraction of the initial sample remains after this time?

(b) How long must a sample be heated so that 99% of the sample has decomposed?

Second-Order Reactions

Suppose the reaction "R → products" is second order. The rate equation is

$$-\frac{\Delta[R]}{\Delta t} = k[R]^2$$

Using calculus, this relationship can be transformed into the following equation that relates reactant concentration and time:

$$\frac{1}{[R]_t} - \frac{1}{[R]_0} = kt \tag{15.2}$$

The same symbolism used with first-order reactions applies: $[R]_0$ is the concentration of reactant at the time $t = 0$; $[R]_t$ is the concentration at a later time; and k is the second-order rate constant, which has the units of L/mol · time.

EXAMPLE 15.7   Using the Second-Order Integrated Rate Equation

Problem The gas-phase decomposition of HI

$$HI(g) \rightarrow \tfrac{1}{2}\ H_2(g) + \tfrac{1}{2}\ I_2(g)$$

has the rate equation

$$-\frac{\Delta[HI]}{\Delta t} = k[HI]^2$$

where $k = 30.$ L/mol · min at 443 °C. How much time does it take for the concentration of HI to drop from 0.010 mol/L to 0.0050 mol/L at 443 °C?

What Do You Know? Equation 15.2 is used for a second-order reaction. The rate constant, k, and the initial and final concentrations of HI are given; the elapsed time is the unknown.

Strategy Substitute the values of $[HI]_0$, $[HI]_t$, and k into Equation 15.2, and solve for the unknown, t.

Solution Here, $[HI]_0 = 0.010$ mol/L and $[HI]_t = 0.0050$ mol/L. Using Equation 15.2, we have

$$\frac{1}{0.0050 \text{ mol/L}} - \frac{1}{0.010 \text{ mol/L}} = (30. \text{ L/mol} \cdot \text{min})t$$

$$(2.0 \times 10^2 \text{ L/mol}) - (1.0 \times 10^2 \text{ L/mol}) = (30. \text{ L/mol} \cdot \text{min})t$$

$$t = 3.3 \text{ minutes}$$

Think about Your Answer In the solution of this problem, we kept track of the units for each quantity. This leads to an answer for time elapsed with the unit minutes.

Check Your Understanding

Using the rate constant for HI decomposition given in this Example, calculate the concentration of HI after 12 minutes if $[HI]_0 = 0.010$ mol/L.

Zero-Order Reactions

If a reaction (R → products) is zero order, the rate equation is

$$-\frac{\Delta[R]}{\Delta t} = k[R]^0$$

This equation leads to the integrated rate equation

$$[R]_0 - [R]_t = kt \tag{15.3}$$

where the units of k are mol/L $\cdot$ s.

Graphical Methods for Determining Reaction Order and the Rate Constant

● **Finding the Slope of a Line** See pages 41–42 for a description of methods for finding the slope of a line.

Chemists find it is convenient to determine the order of a reaction and its rate constant using graphical methods. Equations 15.1, 15.2, and 15.3, if rearranged slightly, have the form $y = mx + b$. This is the equation for a straight line, where m is the slope of the line and b is the y-intercept. In these equations, $x = t$ in each case.

Zero order	First order	Second order
$[R]_t = -kt + [R]_0$	$\ln [R]_t = -kt + \ln [R]_0$	$\dfrac{1}{[R]_t} = +kt + \dfrac{1}{[R]_0}$
$y \quad\quad mx \quad b$	$y \quad\quad mx \quad\quad b$	$y \quad\quad mx \quad\quad b$

As an example of the graphical method for determining reaction order, consider the decomposition of azomethane.

$$CH_3N_2CH_3(g) \rightarrow CH_3CH_3(g) + N_2(g)$$

The decomposition of azomethane was followed at 600 K by observing the decrease in its partial pressure with time (Figure 15.6). (Recall from Chapter 11 that pressure is proportional to concentration at a given temperature and volume.) The third column of the data table lists values of $\ln P(CH_3N_2CH_3)$. As shown in Figure 15.6, a graph of $\ln P(CH_3N_2CH_3)$ versus time produces a straight line, which shows that the reaction is first order in $CH_3N_2CH_3$. The slope of the line can be measured, and the negative of the slope equals the rate constant for the reaction, 3.6×10^{-4} s^{-1}.

$t(s)$	$P \times 10^2$ atm	$\ln P$
0	8.20	−2.50
1000	5.72	−2.86
2000	3.99	−3.22
3000	2.78	−3.58
4000	1.94	−3.94

FIGURE 15.6 The decomposition of azomethane, $CH_3N_2CH_3$. If data for the decomposition of azomethane,

$$CH_3N_2CH_3(g) \rightarrow CH_3CH_3(g) + N_2(g)$$

are plotted as the natural logarithm of the $CH_3N_2CH_3$ pressure versus time, the result is a straight line with a negative slope. This indicates a first-order reaction. The rate constant $k = -$slope.

The decomposition of NO_2 is a second-order process.

$$NO_2(g) \rightarrow NO(g) + \tfrac{1}{2} O_2(g)$$
$$\text{Rate} = k[NO_2]^2$$

This fact can be verified by showing that a plot of $1/[NO_2]$ versus time is a straight line (Figure 15.7). Here, the slope of the line is equal to k.

For a zero-order reaction (Figure 15.8 on page 686), a plot of concentration versus time gives a straight line with a slope equal to the negative of the rate constant.

Table 15.1 (on page 686) summarizes the relationships between concentration and time for first-, second-, and zero-order processes.

Half-Life and First-Order Reactions

The **half-life**, $t_{1/2}$, of a reaction is the time required for the concentration of a reactant to decrease to one half its initial value. Half-life is a convenient way to describe the rate at which a reactant is consumed in a chemical reaction: *The longer the half-life, the slower the reaction.* Half-life is used primarily when dealing with first-order processes.

The half-life, $t_{1/2}$, is the time when the fraction of the reactant R remaining is equal to $1/2$.

$$[R]_t = \tfrac{1}{2}[R]_0 \quad \text{or} \quad \frac{[R]_t}{[R]_0} = \tfrac{1}{2}$$

Here, $[R]_0$ is the initial concentration, and $[R]_t$ is the concentration after the reaction is half completed. To evaluate $t_{1/2}$ for a first-order reaction, we substitute $[R]_t/[R]_0 = \tfrac{1}{2}$ and $t = t_{1/2}$ into the integrated first-order rate equation (Equation 15.1),

$$\ln \left(\tfrac{1}{2}\right) = -kt_{1/2} \quad \text{or} \quad \ln 2 = kt_{1/2}$$

Time (min)	$[NO_2]$ (mol/L)	$1/[NO_2]$ (L/mol)
0	0.020	50
0.50	0.015	67
1.0	0.012	83
1.5	0.010	100
2.0	0.0087	115

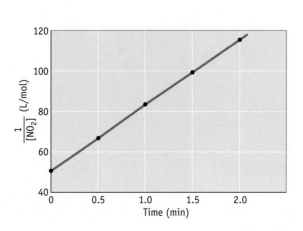

FIGURE 15.7 A second-order reaction. A plot of $1/[NO_2]$ versus time for the decomposition of NO_2,

$$NO_2(g) \rightarrow NO(g) + \tfrac{1}{2} O_2(g)$$

results in a straight line. This confirms this is a second-order reaction. The slope of the line equals the rate constant for this reaction.

Table 15.1 Characteristic Properties of Reactions of the Type "R $\longrightarrow$ Products"

Order	Rate Equation	Integrated Rate Equation	Straight-Line Plot	Slope	k Units
0	$-\Delta[R]/\Delta t = k[R]^0$	$[R]_0 - [R]_t = kt$	$[R]_t$ vs. t	$-k$	mol/L · time
1	$-\Delta[R]/\Delta t = k[R]^1$	$\ln([R]_t/[R]_0) = -kt$	$\ln[R]_t$ vs. t	$-k$	1/time
2	$-\Delta[R]/\Delta t = k[R]^2$	$(1/[R]_t) - (1/[R]_0) = kt$	$1/[R]_t$ vs. t	k	L/mol · time

● **Half-Life and Radioactivity**

Half-life is a term often encountered when dealing with radioactive elements. Radioactive decay is a first-order process, and half-life is commonly used to describe how rapidly a radioactive element decays. See Chapter 23 and Example 15.9.

Rearranging this equation (and calculating that $\ln 2 = 0.693$) provides a useful equation that relates half-life and the first-order rate constant:

$$t_{1/2} = \frac{0.693}{k} \qquad (15.4)$$

This equation identifies an important feature of first-order reactions: $t_{1/2}$ *is independent of concentration.*

To illustrate the concept of half-life, consider again the first-order decomposition of azomethane, $CH_3N_2CH_3$.

$$CH_3N_2CH_3(g) \rightarrow CH_3CH_3(g) + N_2(g)$$

Rate = $k[CH_3N_2CH_3]$ with $k = 3.6 \times 10^{-4}\ s^{-1}$ at 600 K

● **Half-Life Equations for Other Reaction Orders**

For a zero-order reaction, R → products

$$t_{1/2} = \frac{[R]_0}{2k}$$

For a second-order reaction, R → products

$$t_{1/2} = \frac{1}{k[R]_0}$$

Note that in both cases the half-life depends on the initial concentration.

Given a rate constant of $3.6 \times 10^{-4}\ s^{-1}$, we calculate a half-life of 1.9×10^3 s or 32 minutes.

$$t_{1/2} = \frac{0.693}{3.6 \times 10^{-4}\ s^{-1}} = 1.9 \times 10^3\ s\ (\text{or 32 min})$$

The partial pressure of azomethane has been plotted as a function of time in Figure 15.9, and this graph shows that P(azomethane) decreases by half every 32 minutes. The initial pressure was 820 mm Hg, but it dropped to 410 mm Hg in 32 minutes, and then dropped to 205 mm Hg in another 32 minutes. That is, after two half-lives (64 minutes), the pressure is $(\frac{1}{2}) \times (\frac{1}{2}) = (\frac{1}{2})^2 = \frac{1}{4}$ or 25% of the initial pressure. After three half-lives, the pressure has dropped further to 102 mm Hg or 12.5% of the initial value and is equal to $(\frac{1}{2}) \times (\frac{1}{2}) \times (\frac{1}{2}) = (\frac{1}{2})^3 = \frac{1}{8}$ of the initial value.

It can be hard to visualize whether a reaction is fast or slow from the rate constant value. Can you tell from the rate constant, $k = 3.6 \times 10^{-4}\ s^{-1}$, whether the

FIGURE 15.8 Plot of a zero-order reaction. A graph of the concentration of ammonia, $[NH_3]_t$, against time for the decomposition of NH_3.

$$NH_3(g) \rightarrow \frac{1}{2} N_2(g) + \frac{3}{2} H_2(g)$$

on a metal surface at 856 °C is a straight line, indicating that this is a zero-order reaction. The rate constant, k, for this reaction is found from the slope of the line; $k = -$slope. (The points chosen to calculate the slope are given in red.)

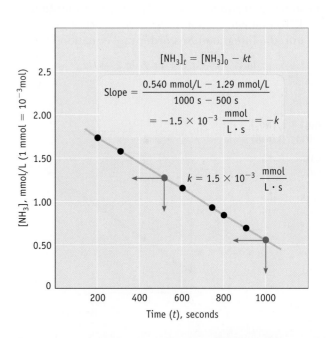

$$[NH_3]_t = [NH_3]_0 - kt$$

$$\text{Slope} = \frac{0.540\ mmol/L - 1.29\ mmol/L}{1000\ s - 500\ s}$$

$$= -1.5 \times 10^{-3}\ \frac{mmol}{L \cdot s} = -k$$

$$k = 1.5 \times 10^{-3}\ \frac{mmol}{L \cdot s}$$

$[NH_3]$, mmol/L (1 mmol = 10^{-3}mol)

Time (t), seconds

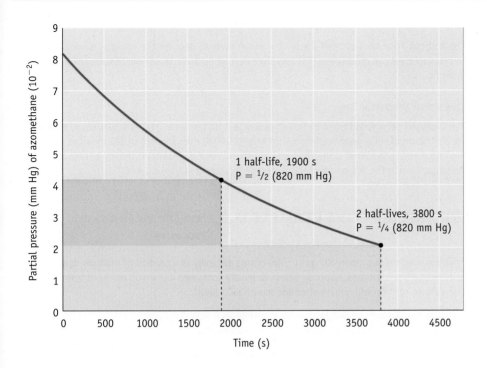

FIGURE 15.9 Half-life of a first-order reaction. The curve is a plot of the pressure of $CH_3N_2CH_3$ as a function of time. (The compound decomposes to CH_3CH_3 and N_2 with $k = 3.6 \times 10^{-4}\ s^{-1}$). The pressure of $CH_3N_2CH_3$ is halved every 1900 seconds (32 minutes). (This plot of pressure versus time is similar in shape to plots of concentration versus time for all other first-order reactions.)

azomethane decomposition will take seconds, hours, or days to reach completion? Probably not, but this can be assessed from the value of the half-life for the reaction (32 minutes). Now we know that we would only have to wait a few hours for the reactant to be essentially consumed.

EXAMPLE 15.8　Half-Life and a First-Order Process

Problem Sucrose, $C_{12}H_{22}O_{11}$, decomposes to fructose and glucose in acid solution with the rate law

$$\text{Rate} = k[C_{12}H_{22}O_{11}] \qquad k = 0.216\ h^{-1} \text{ at } 25\ °C$$

(a) What is the half-life of $C_{12}H_{22}O_{11}$ at this temperature?

(b) What amount of time is required for 87.5% of the initial concentration of $C_{12}H_{22}O_{11}$ to decompose?

What Do You Know? The decomposition of sucrose is a first-order reaction. The rate constant for the reaction (at 25 °C) is given.

Strategy (a) Use Equation 15.4 to calculate the half-life from the rate constant. (b) After 87.5% of the $C_{12}H_{22}O_{11}$ has decomposed, 12.5% (or one eighth of the sample) remains. To reach this point, three half-lives are required.

Half-Life	Fraction Remaining
1	0.5
2	0.25
3	0.125

Therefore, we multiply the half-life calculated in part (a) by 3.

Solution

(a) The half-life for the reaction is

$$t_{1/2} = 0.693/k = 0.693/(0.216\ h^{-1}) = 3.21\ \text{hours}$$

(b) Three half-lives must elapse before the fraction remaining is 0.125, so

$$\text{Time elapsed} = 3 \times 3.21\ h = \boxed{9.63\ \text{hours}}$$

Think about Your Answer Half-life is a convenient way to describe the speed of a reaction. In this example, we can quickly see that complete decomposition of a sample of sucrose requires many hours.

Check Your Understanding

The catalyzed decomposition of hydrogen peroxide is first order in $[H_2O_2]$. It was found that the concentration of H_2O_2 decreased from 0.24 M to 0.060 M over a period of 282 minutes. What is the half-life of H_2O_2? What is the rate constant for this reaction? What is the initial rate of decomposition at the beginning of this experiment (when $[H_2O_2] = 0.24$ M)?

Strategy Map 15.9

PROBLEM

Find the **final number of atoms** of a radioactive isotope after a **given time period**.

↓

DATA/INFORMATION

• Half-life for decay
• Initial number of atoms
• Time elapsed

STEP 1. Use Equation 15.4 to calculate k from $t_{1/2}$.

Value of k

STEP 2. Use Equation 15.1 where k, $[R]_0$, and t are known to calculate $[R]_t$.

Value of $[R]_t$, the **final number of atoms** of radioactive isotope after time **t**.

ⓌL INTERACTIVE EXAMPLE 15.9 Half-Life and First-Order Processes

Problem Radioactive radon-222 gas (^{222}Rn) occurs naturally as a product of uranium decay. The half-life of ^{222}Rn is 3.8 days. Suppose a flask originally contained 4.0×10^{13} atoms of ^{222}Rn. How many atoms of ^{222}Rn will remain after one month (30. days)?

What Do You Know? All radioactive decay processes follow first-order kinetics. The half-life of ^{222}Rn and the number of atoms initially present are known.

Strategy First, the rate constant, k, must be found from the half-life using Equation 15.4. Then, using Equation 15.1, and knowing the number of atoms at the beginning ($[R]_0$), the elapsed time (30. days), and the rate constant, we can calculate the number of atoms remaining ($[R]_t$).

Solution The rate constant, k, is

$$k = \frac{0.693}{t_{1/2}} = \frac{0.693}{3.8 \text{ d}} = 0.18 \text{ d}^{-1}$$

Now use Equation 15.1 to calculate the number of atoms remaining after 30. days.

$$\ln \frac{[Rn]_t}{4.0 \times 10^{13} \text{ atoms}} = -(0.18 \text{ d}^{-1})(30. \text{ d}) = -5.5$$

$$\frac{[Rn]_t}{4.0 \times 10^{13} \text{ atoms}} = e^{-5.5} = 0.0042$$

$$[Rn]_t = 2 \times 10^{11} \text{ atoms}$$

Think about Your Answer Thirty days is approximately 8 half-lives for this element. This means that the number of atoms present at the end of the month is approximately $(\frac{1}{2})^8$ or $\frac{1}{256}$th of the original number.

Check Your Understanding

Americium is used in smoke detectors and in medicine for the treatment of certain malignancies. One isotope of americium, ^{241}Am, has a rate constant, k, for radioactive decay of 0.0016 y^{-1}. In contrast, radioactive iodine-125, which is used for studies of thyroid functioning, has a rate constant for decay of 0.011 d^{-1}.

(a) What are the half-lives of these isotopes?

(b) Which isotope decays faster?

(c) If you are given a dose of iodine-125 containing 1.6×10^{15} atoms, how many atoms remain after 2.0 days?

REVIEW & CHECK FOR SECTION 15.4

1. The decomposition of N_2O_5 is a first-order process. How many half-lives would be required to decompose 99% of the sample?

    (a) 7   (b) between 6 and 7   (c) 5   (d) between 5 and 6

2. Which of the following will confirm that the decomposition of SO_2Cl_2 (to form SO_2 and Cl_2) is a first-order process?

   (a) A graph of $[SO_2Cl_2]$ vs. time gives a curved line.

   (b) A graph of $\ln[SO_2Cl_2]$ vs. time gives a curved line.

   (c) A graph of $1/[SO_2Cl_2]$ vs time gives a straight line.

   (d) A graph of $\ln[SO_2Cl_2]$ vs. time gives a straight line.

3. The equation for the decomposition of $NO_2(g)$ at 573 K is $2\ NO_2(g) \rightarrow 2\ NO(g) + O_2(g)$. Using the concentration-time data below, determine the order of the reaction with respect to $[NO_2]$.

$[NO_2]$, M	time, min
0.20	0
0.095	5
0.063	10
0.047	15

   (a) first order   (b) second order   (c) zero order

15.5 A Microscopic View of Reaction Rates

Throughout this book, we have turned to the particulate level of chemistry to understand chemical phenomena. Rates of reaction are no exception. Looking at the way reactions occur at the atomic and molecular levels can give us some insight into the various influences on rates of reactions.

Let us review the macroscopic observations we have made so far concerning reaction rates. We know that there are wide differences in rates of reactions—from very fast reactions like the explosion that occurs when hydrogen and oxygen are exposed to a spark or flame (◀ Figure 1.16), to slow reactions like the formation of rust that occurs over days, weeks, or years. For a specific reaction, factors that influence reaction rate include the concentrations of the reactants, the temperature of the reaction system, and the presence of catalysts. In this section we want to look at each of these influences in more depth in the context of the **collision theory of reaction rates**, which states that three conditions must be met for a reaction to occur:

1. The reacting molecules must collide with one another.
2. The reacting molecules must collide with sufficient energy to initiate the process of breaking and forming bonds.
3. The molecules must collide in an orientation that can lead to rearrangement of the atoms and the formation of products.

Collision Theory: Concentration and Reaction Rate

Consider the gas-phase reaction of nitric oxide and ozone, an environmentally important reaction:

$$NO(g) + O_3(g) \rightarrow NO_2(g) + O_2(g)$$

The rate law for this product-favored reaction is first order in each reactant: Rate $= k[NO][O_3]$. How can this reaction have this rate law?

Let us consider the reaction at the particulate level and imagine a flask containing a mixture of NO and O_3 molecules in the gas phase. Both kinds of molecules are in rapid and random motion within the flask. They strike the walls of the vessel, but they also collide with other molecules. Thus, it is reasonable to propose that the rate of their reaction should be related to the number of collisions, which is in turn related to their concentrations (Figure 15.10). Doubling the concentration of one reagent in the $NO + O_3$ reaction, say NO, will lead to twice the number of

(a) 1 NO : 16 O₃ — *2 hits/second*.
A single NO molecule, moving among sixteen O₃ molecules, is shown colliding with two of them per second.

(b) 2 NO : 16 O₃ — *4 hits/second*.
If two NO molecules move among 16 O₃ molecules, we would predict that four NO—O₃ collisions would occur per second.

(c) 1 NO : 32 O₃ — *4 hits/second*.
If the number of O₃ molecules is doubled (to 32), the frequency of NO—O₃ collisions is also doubled, to four per second.

FIGURE 15.10 The effect of concentration on the frequency of molecular collisions.

molecular collisions. Figure 15.10a shows a single molecule of one of the reactants (NO) moving randomly among sixteen O_3 molecules. In a given time period, it might collide with two O_3 molecules. The number of NO—O_3 collisions will double, however, if the concentration of NO molecules is doubled (to 2, as shown in Figure 15.10b) or if the number of O_3 molecules is doubled (to 32, as in Figure 15.10c). Thus, we can explain the dependence of reaction rate on concentration: The number of collisions between the two reactant molecules is directly proportional to the concentration of each reactant, and the rate of the reaction shows a first-order dependence on each reactant.

Collision Theory: Temperature and Reaction Rate

In a laboratory or in the chemical industry, a chemical reaction is often carried out at elevated temperatures because this allows the reaction to occur more rapidly. Conversely, it is sometimes desirable to lower the temperature to slow down a chemical reaction (to avoid an uncontrollable reaction or a potentially dangerous explosion). Chemists are very aware of the effect of temperature on the rate of a reaction.

A discussion of the effect of temperature on reaction rate begins with reference to distribution of energies for molecules in a sample of a gas or liquid. Recall from studying gases and liquids that the molecules in a sample have a wide range of energies, described earlier as a Boltzmann distribution of energies (◀ Figure 11.14). In any sample of a gas or liquid, some molecules have very low energies; others have very high energies; but most have some intermediate energy. As the temperature increases, the average energy of the molecules in the sample increases, as does the fraction having higher energies (Figure 15.11).

Collision Theory: Activation Energy

Molecules require some minimum energy to react. Chemists visualize this as an energy barrier that must be surmounted by the reactants for a reaction to occur (Figure 15.12). The energy required to surmount the barrier is called the **activation energy**, E_a. If the barrier is low, the energy required is low, and a high proportion of the molecules in a sample may have sufficient energy to react. In such a case, the reaction will be fast. If the barrier is high, the activation energy is high, and only a few reactant molecules in a sample may have sufficient energy. In this case, the reaction will be slow.

To illustrate an activation energy barrier, consider the high temperature conversion of NO_2 and CO to NO and CO_2 or the reverse reaction (Figure 15.13). At the molecular level, we imagine that the reaction involves the transfer of an O atom

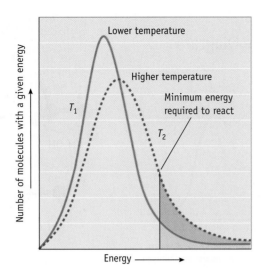

FIGURE 15.11 Energy distribution curve. The vertical axis gives the relative number of molecules possessing the energy indicated on the horizontal axis. The graph indicates the minimum energy required for an arbitrary reaction. At a higher temperature, a larger fraction of the molecules have sufficient energy to react. (Recall Figure 11.14, the Boltzmann distribution function, for a collection of gas molecules.)

from an NO_2 molecule to a CO molecule (or, in the reverse reaction, the transfer of an O atom from CO_2 to NO).

$$NO_2(g) + CO(g) \rightleftharpoons NO(g) + CO_2(g)$$

We can describe this process by using an energy diagram or **reaction coordinate** diagram. The horizontal axis describes the reaction progress as the reaction proceeds, and the vertical axis represents the potential energy of the system during the reaction. When NO_2 and CO approach and O atom transfer begins, an N—O bond is being broken, and a C=O bond is forming. Energy input (the activation energy) is required for this to occur. The energy of the system reaches a maximum at the **transition state**. At the transition state, sufficient energy has been concentrated in the appropriate bonds; bonds in the reactants can now break, and new bonds can form to give products. The system is poised to go on to products. Alternatively, it can return to the reactants. Because the transition state is at a maximum in potential energy, it cannot be isolated. Using computer molecular modeling techniques, however, chemists can describe what the transition state must look like.

In the NO_2 + CO reaction, 132 kJ/mol is required to reach the transition state; that is, the top of the energy barrier. As the reaction continues toward the products—as the N—O bond is finally broken and a C=O bond forms—the reaction evolves energy, 358 kJ/mol. The net energy change involved in this exothermic reaction is −226 kJ/mol.

$$\Delta U = +132 \text{ kJ/mol} + (−358 \text{ kJ/mol}) = −226 \text{ kJ/mol}$$

FIGURE 15.12 An analogy to chemical activation energy. For the volleyball to go over the net, the player must give it sufficient energy.

Reactants   Transition state   Products

$E_a = 132$ kJ/mol

Reactants
NO_2 + CO

$E_a{}' = 358$ kJ/mol

$\Delta H = −226$ kJ/mol

Products
$NO + CO_2$

Reaction progress

FIGURE 15.13 Activation Energy. The reaction of NO_2 and CO (to give NO and CO_2) has an activation energy barrier of 132 kJ/mol. The reverse reaction ($NO + CO_2 \rightarrow NO_2 + CO$) has an activation energy barrier of 358 kJ/mol. The net energy change for the reaction of NO_2 and CO is −226 kJ/mol.

Reaction Coordinate Diagrams

Reaction coordinate diagrams (Figure 15.13) convey a great deal of information. A reaction that would have an energy diagram like that in Figure 15.13 is the substitution of a halogen atom of CH_3Cl by an ion such as F^-. Here, the F^- ion attacks the molecule from the side opposite the Cl substituent. As F^- begins to form a bond to carbon, the C—Cl bond weakens, and the CH_3 portion of the molecule changes shape. As time progresses, the products CH_3F and Cl^- are formed.

FIGURE A **A reaction coordinate diagram for a two-step reaction, a process involving an intermediate.**

The diagram in Figure A describes a reaction that occurs in two steps. An example of such a reaction is the substitution of the —OH group on methanol by a halide ion in the presence of acid. In the first step, an H^+ ion attaches to the O of the C—O—H group in a rapid, reversible reaction. The energy of this protonated species, $CH_3OH_2^+$, a reaction intermediate, is higher than the energies of the reactants and is represented by the dip in the curve shown in Figure A. In the second step, a halide ion, say Br^-, attacks the intermediate to produce methyl bromide, CH_3Br, and water. There is an activation energy barrier in both the first step and second step.

Notice in Figure A, as in Figure 15.13, that the energy of the products is lower than the energy of the reactants. The reaction is exothermic.

What happens if NO and CO_2 are mixed to form NO_2 and CO? Now the reaction requires 358 kJ/mol-rxn to reach the transition state, and 132 kJ/mol-rxn is evolved on proceeding to the product, NO_2 and CO. The reaction in this direction is endothermic, requiring a net input of +226 kJ/mol-rxn.

Collision Theory: Activation Energy and Temperature

The conversion of NO_2 and CO to products at room temperature is slow because only a small fraction of the molecules have enough energy to reach the transition state. The rate can be increased by heating the sample. Raising the temperature increases the reaction rate by increasing the fraction of molecules with enough energy to surmount the activation energy barrier (Figure 15.11).

Collision Theory: Effect of Molecular Orientation on Reaction Rate

Having a sufficiently high energy is necessary, but it is not sufficient to ensure that a given collision of reactants will form products. The reactant molecules must also come together in the correct orientation. For the reaction of NO_2 and CO, we can imagine that the transition state structure has one of the O atoms of NO_2 beginning to bind to the C atom of CO in preparation for O atom transfer (Figure 15.13). The lower the probability of achieving the proper alignment, the smaller the value of k, and the slower the reaction.

Imagine what happens when two or more complicated molecules collide. In only a small fraction of the collisions will the molecules come together in exactly the right orientation. Thus, only a tiny fraction of the collisions can be effective. No wonder some reactions are slow. Conversely, it is amazing that so many are fast!

The Arrhenius Equation

The observation that reaction rates depend on the energy and frequency of collisions between reacting molecules, on the temperature, and on whether the collisions have the correct geometry is summarized by the **Arrhenius equation**:

$$k = \text{rate constant} = \underbrace{A}_{\text{Frequency factor}} \underbrace{e^{-E_a/RT}}_{\substack{\text{Fraction of molecules with minimum} \\ \text{energy for reaction}}} \qquad (15.5)$$

In this equation, k is the rate constant, R is the gas constant with a value of 8.314510×10^{-3} kJ/K · mol, and T is the kelvin temperature. The parameter A is called the **frequency factor**. It is related to the number of collisions and to the fraction of collisions that have the correct geometry; A is specific to each reaction and is temperature dependent. The factor $e^{-E_a/RT}$ represents *the fraction of molecules having the minimum energy required for reaction*; its value is always less than 1. As the table in the margin shows, this fraction changes significantly with temperature.

The Arrhenius equation is significant because

- it can be used to calculate E_a from the temperature dependence of the rate constant.
- it can be used to calculate the rate constant for a given temperature, if E_a and A are known.

If rate constants of a given reaction are measured at several temperatures then one can apply graphical techniques to determine the activation energy of a reaction. Taking the natural logarithm of each side of Equation 15.5, we have

$$\ln k = \ln A + \left(-\frac{E_a}{RT} \right)$$

Rearranging this expression slightly shows that $\ln k$ and $1/T$ are related linearly.

$$\ln k = -\frac{E_a}{R}\left(\frac{1}{T}\right) + \ln A \quad \leftarrow \text{Arrhenius equation} \qquad (15.6)$$

$$\underset{y}{\downarrow} \quad = \quad \underset{mx}{\downarrow} \quad + \underset{b}{\downarrow} \quad \leftarrow \text{Equation for straight line}$$

This means that, if the natural logarithm of k ($\ln k$) is plotted versus $1/T$, the result is a downward-sloping straight line with a slope of $(-E_a/R)$. The activation energy, E_a, can be obtained from the slope of this line ($E_a = -R \times$ slope).

• **E_a, Reaction Rates, and Temperature** An often-used rule of thumb is that reaction rates double for every 10 °C rise in temperature in the vicinity of room temperature.

• **Interpreting the Arrhenius Equation** (a) The exponential term. This gives the fraction of molecules having sufficient energy for reaction and is a function of T.

Temperature (K)	Value of $e^{-E_a/RT}$ for $E_a =$ 40 kJ/mol-rxn
298	9.7×10^{-8}
400	5.9×10^{-6}
600	3.3×10^{-4}

(b) Significance of A. Although a complete understanding of A goes beyond the level of this text, it can be noted that A becomes smaller as the reactants become larger. It reflects the fact that larger molecules have a smaller probability of coming together in the appropriate geometry.

EXAMPLE 15.10 Determination of E_a from the Arrhenius Equation

Problem Using the experimental data shown in the table, calculate the activation energy E_a for the reaction

$$2\,N_2O(g) \rightarrow 2\,N_2(g) + O_2(g)$$

Experiment	Temperature (K)	k (L/mol · s)
1	1125	11.59
2	1053	1.67
3	1001	0.380
4	838	0.0011

What Do You Know? The rate constants are given at several temperatures.

Strategy To solve this problem graphically, we first need to calculate ln k and $1/T$ for each data point. These data are then plotted, and E_a is calculated from the resulting straight line (slope = $-E_a/R$).

Solution First, calculate $1/T$ and ln k.

Experiment	$1/T$ (K^{-1})	ln k
1	8.889×10^{-4}	2.4501
2	9.497×10^{-4}	0.513
3	9.990×10^{-4}	-0.968
4	11.9×10^{-4}	-6.81

Plotting these data gives the graph shown in Figure 15.14. Choosing the large blue points on the graph, the slope is found to be

$$\text{Slope} = \frac{\Delta \ln k}{\Delta(1/T)} = \frac{2.0 - (-5.6)}{(9.0 - 11.5)(10^{-4})K^{-1}} = -3.0 \times 10^4 \text{ K}$$

The activation energy is evaluated from the slope.

$$\text{Slope} = -\frac{E_a}{R} = -\frac{E_a}{8.31 \times 10^{-3} \text{ kJ/K} \cdot \text{mol}} = -3.0 \times 10^4 \text{ K}$$

$$E_a = 250 \text{ kJ/mol}$$

Think about Your Answer Notice the units of the answer. Using the value for $R = 8.31 \times 10^{-3}$ kJ/mol will give an answer with the units kJ/mol.

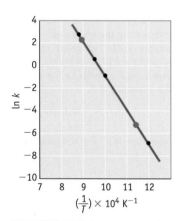

FIGURE 15.14 Arrhenius plot. A plot of ln k versus $1/T$ for the reaction $2 N_2O(g) \rightarrow 2 N_2(g) + O_2(g)$. The slope of the line can be used to calculate E_a. See Example 15.10.

Check Your Understanding

Rate constants were determined for the decomposition of acetaldehyde (CH_3CHO) in the temperature range 700 to 1000 K. Use these data to determine E_a for the reaction using a graphical method.

T (K)	700	760	840	1000
k (L/mol · s)	0.011	0.105	2.17	145

The activation energy, E_a, for a reaction can be obtained algebraically if k is known at two different temperatures. We can write an equation for each set of these conditions:

$$\ln k_1 = -\left(\frac{E_a}{RT_1}\right) + \ln A \quad \text{and} \quad \ln k_2 = -\left(\frac{E_a}{RT_2}\right) + \ln A$$

If one of these equations is subtracted from the other, we have

$$\ln k_2 - \ln k_1 = \ln \frac{k_2}{k_1} = -\frac{E_a}{R}\left[\frac{1}{T_2} - \frac{1}{T_1}\right] \tag{15.7}$$

Example 15.11 demonstrates the use of this equation.

EXAMPLE 15.11   Calculating E_a Numerically

Problem Use values of k determined at two different temperatures to calculate the value of E_a for the decomposition of HI:

$$2 HI(g) \rightarrow H_2(g) + I_2(g)$$

$$k_1 = 2.15 \times 10^{-8} \text{ L/(mol} \cdot \text{s) at } 6.50 \times 10^2 \text{ K } (T_1)$$

$$k_2 = 2.39 \times 10^{-7} \text{ L/(mol} \cdot \text{s) at } 7.00 \times 10^2 \text{ K } (T_2)$$

What Do You Know? Values for the rate constant at two temperatures are given.

Strategy Substitute values of k_1, k_2, T_1, and T_2 into Equation 15.7 and solve for E_a.

Solution

$$\ln \frac{2.39 \times 10^{-7} \text{ L/(mol} \cdot \text{s})}{2.15 \times 10^{-8} \text{ L/(mol} \cdot \text{s})} = -\frac{E_a}{8.315 \times 10^{-3} \text{ kJ/K} \cdot \text{mol}} \times \left[\frac{1}{7.00 \times 10^2 \text{ K}} - \frac{1}{6.50 \times 10^2 \text{ K}} \right]$$

Solving this equation gives $E_a = 180$ kJ/mol.

Think about Your Answer Another way to write the difference in fractions in brackets is

$$\left[\frac{1}{T_2} - \frac{1}{T_1} \right] = \frac{T_1 - T_2}{T_1 T_2}$$

This expression is sometimes easier to use.

Check Your Understanding

The colorless gas N_2O_4 decomposes to the brown gas NO_2 in a first-order reaction.

$$N_2O_4(g) \rightarrow 2 NO_2(g)$$

The rate constant $k = 4.5 \times 10^3$ s^{-1} at 274 K and $k = 1.00 \times 10^4$ s^{-1} at 283 K. What is the activation energy, E_a?

Effect of Catalysts on Reaction Rate

Catalysts are substances that speed up the rate of a chemical reaction. We have seen several examples of catalysts in earlier discussions in this chapter: MnO_2, iodide ion, the enzyme catalase in a potato, and hydroxide ion all catalyze the decomposition of hydrogen peroxide (Figure 15.4).

Catalysts are not consumed in a chemical reaction. They are, however, intimately involved in the details of the reaction at the particulate level. Their function is to provide a different pathway with a lower activation energy for the reaction. To illustrate how a catalyst participates in a reaction, let us consider the isomerization of *cis*-2-butene, to the slightly more stable isomer, *trans*-2-butene.

● **Enzymes: Biological Catalysts** Catalase is an enzyme whose function is to speed up the decomposition of hydrogen peroxide. This enzyme ensures that hydrogen peroxide, which is highly toxic, does not build up in the body.

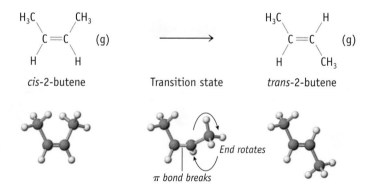

cis-2-butene   Transition state   trans-2-butene

End rotates

π bond breaks

● **Butene Isomerization** Isomerization of *cis*-2-butene is a first-order process with the rate law Rate = k[*cis*-2-butene]. It is suggested to occur by rotation around the carbon–carbon double bond. The rate at which a molecule will isomerize is related to the fraction of molecules that have a high enough energy.

The activation energy for the uncatalyzed conversion is relatively large— 264 kJ/mol—because the π bond must be broken to allow one end of the molecule to rotate into a new position. Because of the high activation energy, this is a slow reaction, and rather high temperatures are required for it to occur at a reasonable rate.

The *cis*- to *trans*-2-butene reaction is greatly accelerated by a catalyst, iodine. In the presence of iodine, this reaction can be carried out at a temperature several hundred degrees lower than for the uncatalyzed reaction. Iodine is not consumed

● **Catalysts and the Economy** "One third of [the] material gross national product in the United States involves a catalytic process somewhere in the production chain." (Quoted in A. Bell, *Science*, Vol. 299, p. 1688, 2003.)

(nor is it a product), and it does not appear in the overall balanced equation. It does appear in the reaction rate law, however; the rate of the reaction depends on the square root of the iodine concentration:

$$\text{Rate} = k[\textit{cis-2-butene}][I_2]^{1/2}$$

The presence of I_2 changes the way the reaction occurs; that is, it changes the mechanism of the reaction (Figure 15.15). The best hypothesis is that iodine molecules first dissociate to form iodine atoms (Step 1). An iodine atom then adds to one of the C atoms of the C=C double bond (Step 2). This converts the double bond between the carbon atoms to a single bond (the π bond is broken) and allows the ends of the molecule to twist freely relative to each other (Step 3). If the iodine atom then dissociates from the intermediate, the double bond can re-form in the *trans* configuration (Step 4). The iodine atom catalyzing the rotation is now free to add to another molecule of *cis*-2-butene. The result is a kind of chain reaction, as one molecule of *cis*-2-butene after another is converted to the *trans* isomer. The chain is broken if the iodine atom recombines with another iodine atom to re-form molecular iodine.

An energy profile for the catalyzed reaction (Figure 15.16) shows that the overall energy barrier is much lower than for the uncatalyzed reaction. Five separate steps are identified for the mechanism in the energy profile. This proposed mechanism also includes a series of chemical species called **reaction intermediates**, species formed in one step of the reaction and consumed in a later step. Iodine atoms are intermediates, as are the free radical species formed when an iodine atom adds to *cis*-2-butene.

Five important points are associated with this mechanism:

- Iodine molecules, I_2, dissociate to atoms and then re-form. On the macroscopic level, the concentration of I_2 is unchanged. Iodine does not appear in the balanced, stoichiometric equation even though it appears in the rate equation. This is generally true of catalysts.
- Both the catalyst I_2 and the reactant *cis*-2-butene are in the gas phase. If a catalyst is present in the same phase as the reacting substance, it is called a *homogeneous catalyst*.
- Iodine atoms and the radical species formed by addition of an iodine atom to a 2-butene molecule are intermediates.

FIGURE 15.15 The mechanism of the iodine-catalyzed isomerization of *cis*-2-butene. *Cis*-2-butene is converted to *trans*-2-butene in the presence of a catalytic amount of iodine. Catalyzed reactions are often pictured in such diagrams to emphasize what chemists refer to as a "catalytic cycle."

FIGURE 15.16 Energy profile for the iodine-catalyzed reaction of *cis*-2-butene. A catalyst accelerates a reaction by altering the mechanism so that the activation energy is lowered. With a smaller barrier to overcome, more reacting molecules have sufficient energy to surmount the barrier, and the reaction occurs more rapidly. The energy profile for the uncatalyzed conversion of *cis*-2-butene to *trans*-2-butene is shown by the black curve, and that for the iodine-catalyzed reaction is represented by the red curve. Notice that the shape of the barrier has changed because the mechanism has changed.

- The activation energy barrier to reaction is significantly lower because the mechanism changed. Dropping the activation energy from 264 kJ/mol for the uncatalyzed reaction to about 150 kJ/mol for the catalyzed process makes the catalyzed reaction 10^{15} times faster!
- The diagram of energy-versus-reaction progress has five energy barriers (five humps appear in the curve). This feature in the diagram means that the reaction occurs in a series of five steps.

What we have described here are two different reaction mechanisms for the isomerization of *cis*-2-butene. The uncatalyzed isomerization reaction is a one-step reaction mechanism, whereas the catalyzed mechanism involves a series of steps. We shall discuss reaction mechanisms in more detail in the next section.

REVIEW & CHECK FOR SECTION 15.5

1. Which of the following graphs will produce a straight line?

   (a) k vs. T (b) $\ln E_a$ vs. T (c) $\ln k$ vs. $1/T$ (d) E_a vs. $1/T$

2. What is the primary reason that increasing the temperature causes an increase in reaction rate?

   (a) An increase in T lowers the activation energy.

   (b) A higher proportion of reactant molecules exceeds the activation energy.

   (c) In a closed vessel, increasing the temperature results in a higher pressure.

   (d) Increasing the temperature provides other reaction pathways.

15.6 Reaction Mechanisms

Rate laws help us understand **reaction mechanisms**, the sequence of bond-making and bond-breaking steps that occurs during the conversion of reactants to products. We want to analyze the changes that molecules undergo when they react. We then want to relate this description back to the macroscopic world, to the experimental observations of reaction rates.

Based on the rate equation for a reaction, and by applying chemical intuition, chemists can often make an educated guess about the mechanism for a reaction. In some reactions, the conversion of reactants to products in a single step is envisioned as the logical mechanism. For example, the uncatalyzed isomerization of *cis*-2-butene to *trans*-2-butene is best described as a single-step reaction (Figure 15.16).

FIGURE 15.17 A reaction mechanism. A representation of the proposed two-step mechanism by which NO and Br_2 are converted to NOBr.

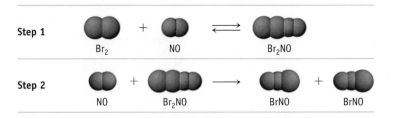

Step 1 Br_2 + NO $\rightleftharpoons$ Br_2NO

Step 2   NO + Br_2NO $\longrightarrow$ BrNO + BrNO

Most chemical reactions occur in a sequence of steps, however. A multiple-step mechanism was proposed for the iodine-catalyzed 2-butene isomerization reaction. Another example of a reaction that occurs in several steps is the reaction of bromine and NO:

$$Br_2(g) + 2\ NO(g) \rightarrow 2\ BrNO(g)$$

A single-step reaction would require that three reactant molecules collide simultaneously in just the right orientation. The probability of this occurring is small; thus, it would be reasonable to look for a mechanism that occurs in a series of steps, with each step involving only one or two molecules. In one possible mechanism, Br_2 and NO might combine in an initial step to produce an intermediate species, Br_2NO (Figure 15.17). This intermediate would then react with another NO molecule to give the reaction products. The equation for the overall reaction is obtained by adding the equations for these two steps:

● **Rate Laws and Mechanisms** Rate laws are derived by experiment; they are macroscopic observations. Mechanisms are schemes we propose that speculate on how reactions occur at the particulate level.

Step 1:	$Br_2(g) + NO(g) \rightleftharpoons Br_2NO(g)$
Step 2:	$Br_2NO(g) + NO(g) \rightarrow 2\ BrNO(g)$
Overall Reaction:	$Br_2(g) + 2\ NO(g) \rightarrow 2\ BrNO(g)$

Each step in a multistep reaction sequence is an **elementary step**, defined by a chemical equation that describes a single molecular event such as the formation or rupture of a chemical bond resulting from a molecular collision. Each step has its own activation energy, E_a, and rate constant, k. Adding the equations for each step must give the balanced equation for the overall reaction, and the time required to complete all of the steps defines the overall reaction rate. The series of steps constitutes a possible reaction mechanism.

Molecularity of Elementary Steps

Elementary steps are classified by the number of reactant molecules (or ions, atoms, or free radicals) that come together. This whole, positive number is called the **molecularity** of the elementary step. When one molecule is the only reactant in an elementary step, the reaction is a **unimolecular** process. A **bimolecular** elementary process involves two molecules, which may be identical (A + A → products) or different (A + B → products). The mechanism proposed for the decomposition of ozone in the stratosphere illustrates the use of these terms.

Step 1:	Unimolecular	$O_3(g) \rightarrow O_2(g) + O(g)$
Step 2:	Bimolecular	$O_3(g) + O(g) \rightarrow 2\ O_2(g)$
Overall Reaction:		$2\ O_3(g) \rightarrow 3\ O_2(g)$

A **termolecular** elementary step involves three molecules, which could be the same or different (3 A → products; 2 A + B → products; or A + B + C → products). Be aware, however, the simultaneous collision of three molecules has a low probability, unless one of the molecules involved is in high concentration, such as a solvent molecule. In fact, most termolecular processes involve the collision of two reactant molecules and a third, inert molecule. The function of the inert molecule is to absorb the excess energy produced when a new chemical bond is formed by the first two molecules. For example, N_2 is unchanged in a termolecular reaction between oxygen molecules and oxygen atoms that produces ozone in the upper atmosphere:

$$O(g) + O_2(g) + N_2(g) \rightarrow O_3(g) + \text{energetic } N_2(g)$$

The probability that four or more molecules will simultaneously collide with sufficient kinetic energy and proper orientation to react is so small that reaction molecularities greater than three are never proposed.

Rate Equations for Elementary Steps

The experimentally determined rate equation for a reaction cannot be predicted from its overall stoichiometry. In contrast, *the rate equation for any elementary step is defined by the reaction stoichiometry.* The rate equation of an elementary step is given by the product of the rate constant for that step and the concentrations of the reactants in that step. We can therefore write the rate equation for any elementary step, as shown by examples in the following table:

Elementary Step	Molecularity	Rate Equation
A → product	Unimolecular	Rate = $k[A]$
A + B → product	Bimolecular	Rate = $k[A][B]$
A + A → product	Bimolecular	Rate = $k[A]^2$
2 A + B → product	Termolecular	Rate = $k[A]^2[B]$

For example, the rate laws for each of the two elementary steps in the decomposition of ozone are

$$\text{Rate for (unimolecular) Step 1} = k[O_3]$$

$$\text{Rate for (bimolecular) Step 2} = k'[O_3][O]$$

When a reaction mechanism consists of two elementary steps, the two steps will likely occur at different rates. The two rate constants (k and k' in this example) are not expected to have the same value (nor the same units, if the two steps have different molecularities).

Molecularity and Reaction Order

A unimolecular elementary step must be first order; a bimolecular elementary step must be second order; and a termolecular elementary step must be third order. Such a direct relation between molecularity and order is emphatically not true for a multistep reaction. If you learn from an experiment that a reaction is first order, you cannot conclude that it occurs in a single, unimolecular elementary step. Similarly, a second-order rate equation does not imply that the reaction occurs in a single, bimolecular elementary step. An illustration of this is the decomposition of N_2O_5:

$$2\ N_2O_5(g) \rightarrow 4\ NO_2(g) + O_2(g)$$

Here, the rate law is "Rate = $k[N_2O_5]$," but chemists are fairly certain the mechanism involves a series of unimolecular and bimolecular steps.

To see how the experimentally observed rate equation for the overall reaction is connected with a possible mechanism or sequence of elementary steps requires some chemical intuition. We will provide only a glimpse of the subject in the next section.

N_2O_5 Decomposition. The first step in the decomposition of N_2O_5 is thought to be the cleavage of one of the N—O bonds in the N—O—N link to give the odd-electron molecules NO_2 and NO_3. These react further to give the final products.

EXAMPLE 15.12   Elementary Steps

Problem The hypochlorite ion undergoes self-oxidation–reduction to give chlorate, ClO_3^-, and chloride ions.

$$3\ ClO^-(aq) \rightarrow ClO_3^-(aq) + 2\ Cl^-(aq)$$

This reaction is thought to occur in two steps:

Step 1: $ClO^-(aq) + ClO^-(aq) \rightarrow ClO_2^-(aq) + Cl^-(aq)$

Step 2: $ClO_2^-(aq) + ClO^-(aq) \rightarrow ClO_3^-(aq) + Cl^-(aq)$

What is the molecularity of each step? Write the rate equation for each reaction step. Show that the sum of these reactions gives the equation for the net reaction.

What Do You Know? A two-step mechanism for the reaction of OCl^- to form Cl^- and ClO_3^- is proposed.

Strategy The molecularity is the number of ions or molecules involved in a reaction step. The rate equation involves the concentration of each ion or molecule in an elementary step, raised to the power of its stoichiometric coefficient.

Solution Because two ions are involved in each elementary step, each step is bimolecular. The rate equation for any elementary step involves the product of the concentrations of the reactants. Thus, in this case, the rate equations are

Step 1: $\qquad$ Rate $= k[ClO^-]^2$

Step 2: $\qquad$ Rate $= k'[ClO_2^-][ClO^-]$

From the equations for the two elementary steps, we see that the ClO_2^- ion is an intermediate, a product of the first step and a reactant in the second step. It therefore cancels out, and we are left with the stoichiometric equation for the overall reaction:

Step 1: $\qquad$ $ClO^-(aq) + ClO^-(aq) \rightarrow ClO_2^-(aq) + Cl^-(aq)$

Step 2: $\qquad$ $ClO_2^-(aq) + ClO^-(aq) \rightarrow ClO_3^-(aq) + Cl^-(aq)$

$\rule{6cm}{0.4pt}$

Sum of steps: $\qquad$ $3\ ClO^-(aq) \rightarrow ClO_3^-(aq) + 2\ Cl^-(aq)$

Think about Your Answer Other mechanisms are possible. The next question to ask is "What is the evidence that will let you decide between several different mechanisms?"

Check Your Understanding

Nitrogen monoxide is reduced by hydrogen to give nitrogen and water:

$$2\ NO(g) + 2\ H_2(g) \rightarrow N_2(g) + 2\ H_2O(g)$$

One possible mechanism for this reaction is

$$2\ NO(g) \rightarrow N_2O_2(g)$$

$$N_2O_2(g) + H_2(g) \rightarrow N_2O(g) + H_2O(g)$$

$$N_2O(g) + H_2(g) \rightarrow N_2(g) + H_2O(g)$$

What is the molecularity of each of the three steps? What is the rate equation for the third step? Identify the intermediates in this reaction; how many different intermediates are there? Show that the sum of these elementary steps gives the equation for the overall reaction.

Reaction Mechanisms and Rate Equations

The dependence of rate on concentration is an experimental fact. Mechanisms, by contrast, are constructs of our imagination, intuition, and good "chemical sense." To describe a mechanism, we need to make a guess (a good guess, we hope) about how the reaction occurs at the particulate level. Several mechanisms can always be proposed that correspond to the observed rate equation, and a postulated mechanism can be wrong. A good mechanism is a worthy goal because it allows us to understand the chemistry better. A practical consequence of a good mechanism is that it allows us to predict, for example, how to control a reaction better and how to design new experiments.

One of the important guidelines of kinetics is that *products of a reaction can never be produced at a rate faster than the rate of the slowest step*. If one step in a multistep reaction is slower than the others, then *the rate of the overall reaction is limited by the combined rates of all elementary steps up through the slowest step in the mechanism*. Often the overall reaction rate and the rate of the slow step are nearly the same. If the slow step determines the rate of the reaction, it is called the **rate-determining step**, or rate-limiting step.

Imagine that a reaction takes place with a mechanism involving two sequential steps, and assume that we know the rates of both steps. The first step is slow and the second is fast:

Elementary Step 1:
$$A + B \xrightarrow[\text{Slow, } E_a \text{ large}]{k_1} X + M$$

Elementary Step 2:
$$M + A \xrightarrow[\text{Fast, } E_a \text{ small}]{k_2} Y$$

Overall Reaction:
$$2A + B \longrightarrow X + Y$$

In the first step, A and B come together and slowly react to form one of the products (X) plus another reactive species, M. Almost as soon as M is formed, however, it is rapidly consumed by reacting with another molecule of A to form the second product Y. The rate-determining elementary step in this example is the first step. That is, the rate of the first step is equal to the rate of the overall reaction. This step is bimolecular and so it has the rate equation:

$$\text{Rate} = k_1[A][B]$$

where k_1 is the rate constant for that step. The overall reaction is expected to have this same second-order rate equation.

Let us apply these ideas to the mechanism of a real reaction: the second-order reaction of nitrogen dioxide with fluorine.

Overall Reaction:
$$2\,NO_2(g) + F_2(g) \rightarrow 2\,FNO_2(g)$$

$$\text{Rate} = k[NO_2][F_2]$$

The rate equation immediately rules out the possibility that the reaction occurs in a single step. If the equation for the reaction represented an elementary step, the rate law would have a second-order dependence on $[NO_2]$. Because a single-step reaction is ruled out, the mechanism must include at least two steps. We can also conclude from the rate law that the rate-determining elementary step must involve NO_2 and F_2 in a 1:1 ratio. One possible mechanism proposes that molecules of NO_2 and F_2 first react to produce one molecule of the product (FNO_2) plus one F atom. In a second step, the fluorine atom produced in the first step reacts with additional NO_2 to give a second molecule of product. If the first, bimolecular step is rate determining, the rate equation would be "Rate $= k_1[NO_2][F_2]$," the same as the experimentally observed rate equation. The experimental rate constant would be the same as k_1.

● **Can You Derive a Mechanism?** At this introductory level, you cannot be expected to derive reaction mechanisms. Given a mechanism, however, you can decide whether it agrees with experimental rate laws.

Elementary Step 1:   Slow
$$NO_2(g) + F_2(g) \xrightarrow{k_1} FNO_2(g) + F(g)$$

Elementary Step 2:   Fast
$$NO_2(g) + F(g) \xrightarrow{k_2} FNO_2(g)$$

Overall Reaction:
$$2\,NO_2(g) + F_2(g) \longrightarrow 2\,FNO_2(g)$$

The fluorine atom formed in the first step of the NO_2/F_2 reaction is a reaction intermediate. It does not appear in the equation describing the overall reaction. Reaction intermediates usually have only a fleeting existence, but occasionally they have long enough lifetimes to be observed. The detection and identification of an intermediate are strong evidence for the proposed mechanism.

CASE STUDY

Enzymes—Nature's Catalysts

Within any living organism, there are untold numbers of chemical reactions occurring, many of them extremely rapidly. In many cases, enzymes, biological catalysts, speed up reactions that would normally move at a snail's pace from reactants to products. Typically, enzyme-catalyzed reactions are 10^7 to 10^{14} times faster than uncatalyzed reactions.

Enzymes are typically large proteins, often containing metal ions such as Zn^{2+}. They are thought to function by bringing the reactants together in just the right orientation in a site where specific bonds can be broken and/or made.

Carbonic anhydrase is one of many enzymes important in biological processes (Figure A). Carbon dioxide dissolves in water to a small extent to produce carbonic acid, which ionizes to give H_3O^+ and HCO_3^- ions.

$$CO_2(g) \rightleftharpoons CO_2(aq) \tag{1}$$

$$CO_2(aq) + H_2O(\ell) \rightleftharpoons H_2CO_3(aq) \tag{2}$$

$$H_2CO_3(aq) + H_2O(\ell)$$
$$\rightleftharpoons H_3O^+(aq) + HCO_3^-(aq) \tag{3}$$

Carbonic anhydrase speeds up reactions 1 and 2. Many of the H_3O^+ ions produced by ionization of H_2CO_3 (reaction 3) are picked up by hemoglobin in the blood as hemoglobin loses O_2. The resulting HCO_3^- ions are transported back to the lungs. When hemoglobin again takes on O_2, it releases H_3O^+ ions. These ions and HCO_3^- re-form H_2CO_3, from which CO_2 is liberated and exhaled.

You can do an experiment that illustrates the effect of carbonic anhydrase. First, add a small amount of NaOH to a cold, aqueous solution of CO_2. The solution becomes basic immediately because there is not enough H_2CO_3 in the solution to use up the NaOH. After some seconds, however, dissolved CO_2 slowly produces more H_2CO_3, which consumes NaOH, and the solution is again acidic.

Now try the experiment again, this time adding a few drops of blood to the solution (Figure A). Carbonic anhydrase in blood speeds up reactions 1 and 2 by a factor of about 10^7, as evidenced by the more rapid reaction under these conditions.

In 1913, Leonor Michaelis and Maud L. Menten proposed a general theory of enzyme action based on kinetic observations. They assumed that the substrate, S (the reactant), and the enzyme, E, form a complex, ES. This complex then breaks down, releasing the enzyme and the product, P.

$$E + S \rightleftharpoons ES$$

$$ES \rightarrow P + E$$

When the substrate concentration is low, the rate of the reaction is first order in S (Figure B). As [S] increases, however, the active sites in the enzyme become saturated with substrate, and the rate reaches its maximum value. Now the kinetics are zero order in substrate.

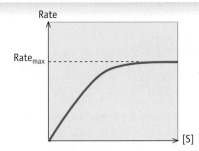

FIGURE B **Rate of enzyme-catalyzed reaction.** This plot of substrate concentration [S] versus reaction velocity is typical of reactions catalyzed by enzymes that follow the Michaelis–Menten model.

Questions:

1. Catalase can decompose hydrogen peroxide to O_2 and water about 10^7 times faster than the uncatalyzed reaction. If the latter requires one year, how much time is required by the enzyme-catalyzed reaction?

2. According to the Michaelis–Menten model, if 1/Rate is plotted versus 1/[S], the intercept of the plot (when 1/[S] = 0) is $1/Rate_{max}$. Find $Rate_{max}$ for a reaction involving carbonic anhydrase.

[S], mol/L	Rate (millimoles/min)
2.500	0.588
1.00	0.500
0.714	0.417
0.526	0.370
0.250	0.256

Answers to these questions are available in Appendix N.

Photos © Cengage Learning/ Charles D. Winters

   (a) $t = 0$ **(b)** $t = 3$ sec   **(c)** $t = 15$ sec   **(d)** $t = 17$ sec   **(e)** $t = 21$ sec

FIGURE A CO_2 in water. **(a)** A few drops of blood are added to a cold solution of CO_2 in water. **(b)** A few drops of a dye (bromthymol blue) are added to the solution, the yellow color indicating an acidic solution. **(c, d)** A less-than-stoichiometric amount of sodium hydroxide is added, converting the H_2CO_3 to HCO_3^- (and CO_3^{2-}). The blue color of the dye indicates a basic solution. **(e)** The blue color begins to fade after some seconds as CO_2 forms more H_2CO_3. The amount of H_2CO_3 formed is finally sufficient to consume the added NaOH, and the solution is again acidic. Blood is a source of the enzyme *carbonic anhydrase*, so the formation of H_2CO_3 is noticeably more rapid than the reaction in the absence of blood.

EXAMPLE 15.13   Elementary Steps and Reaction Mechanisms

Problem Oxygen atom transfer from NO_2 to CO produces nitrogen monoxide and carbon dioxide (Figure 15.13):

$$NO_2(g) + CO(g) \rightarrow NO(g) + CO_2(g)$$

The rate equation for this reaction at temperatures less than 500 K is Rate $= k[NO_2]^2$. Can this reaction occur in one bimolecular step?

What Do You Know? The reaction equation and the rate law for the reaction are given.

Strategy Write the rate law based on the equation for the NO_2 + CO reaction occurring as if it were an elementary step. If this rate law corresponds to the observed rate law, then a one-step mechanism is possible.

Solution If the reaction occurs by the collision of one NO_2 molecule with one CO molecule, the rate equation would be

$$\text{Rate} = k[NO_2][CO]$$

This does not agree with experiment, so the mechanism must involve more than a single step. In one possible mechanism, the reaction occurs in two bimolecular steps, the first one slow and the second one fast:

Elementary Step 1:	Slow, rate-determining	$2\ NO_2(g) \longrightarrow NO_3(g) + NO(g)$

Elementary Step 2:	Fast	$NO_3(g) + CO(g) \longrightarrow NO_2(g) + CO_2(g)$

Overall Reaction:		$NO_2(g) + CO(g) \longrightarrow NO(g) + CO_2(g)$

The first (rate-determining) step has a rate equation that agrees with experiment, so this is a possible mechanism.

Think about Your Answer Because the rate equation is second order in $[NO_2]$, the rate-determining step in this multistep reaction must involve the collision of two NO_2 molecules.

Check Your Understanding

The Raschig reaction produces hydrazine, N_2H_4, an industrially important reducing agent, from NH_3 and OCl^- in basic, aqueous solution. A proposed mechanism is

Step 1: Fast $NH_3(aq) + OCl^-(aq) \rightarrow NH_2Cl(aq) + OH^-(aq)$

Step 2: Slow $NH_2Cl(aq) + NH_3(aq) \rightarrow N_2H_5^+(aq) + Cl^-(aq)$

Step 3: Fast $N_2H_5^+(aq) + OH^-(aq) \rightarrow N_2H_4(aq) + H_2O(\ell)$

(a) What is the overall equation?

(b) Which step of the three is rate determining?

(c) Write the rate equation for the rate-determining elementary step.

(d) What reaction intermediates are involved?

Reaction Mechanisms Involving an Equilibrium Step

A common two-step reaction mechanism involves an initial fast reaction that produces an intermediate, followed by a slower second step in which the intermediate is converted to the final product. The rate of the reaction is determined by the second step, for which a rate law can be written. The rate of that step, however, depends on the concentration of the intermediate. An intermediate, whose concentration will probably not be measurable, cannot appear as a term in the overall rate equation. We must find a way to replace the expression for the intermediate with another expression in terms of quantities measurable in the lab.

The reaction of nitrogen monoxide and oxygen is an example of a two-step reaction where the first step is fast and the second step is rate determining.

$$2\ NO(g) + O_2(g) \rightarrow 2\ NO_2(g)$$

$$Rate = k[NO]^2[O_2]$$

The experimentally determined rate law shows second-order dependence on NO and first-order dependence on O_2. Although this rate law would be correct for a termolecular reaction, experimental evidence indicates that an intermediate is formed in this reaction. A possible two-step mechanism that proceeds through an intermediate is

Elementary Step 1:	Fast, equilibrium	$NO(g) + O_2(g) \underset{k_{-1}}{\overset{k_1}{\rightleftharpoons}} OONO(g)$ intermediate
Elementary Step 2:	Slow, rate-determining	$NO(g) + OONO(g) \overset{k_2}{\rightarrow} 2\ NO_2(g)$
Overall Reaction:		$2\ NO(g) + O_2(g) \rightarrow 2\ NO_2(g)$

The second step of this reaction is the slow step, and the overall rate depends on it. We can write a rate law for the second step:

$$Rate = k_2[NO][OONO]$$

This rate law cannot be compared directly with the experimental rate law because it contains the concentration of an intermediate, OONO. To eliminate the concentration of intermediate from this rate expression, we look at the rapid first step in this reaction sequence that involves an equilibrium between the intermediate species and the reactants.

● **Mechanisms with an Initial Equilibrium** In this mechanism, the forward and reverse reactions in the first elementary step are so much faster than the second elementary step that equilibrium is established before any significant amount of OONO is consumed by NO to give NO_2. The state of equilibrium for the first step remains throughout the lifetime of the overall reaction.

At the beginning of the reaction, NO and O_2 react rapidly and produce the intermediate OONO. The rate of formation can be defined by a rate law with a rate constant k_1:

$$Rate\ of\ production\ of\ OONO = k_1[NO][O_2]$$

Because the intermediate is consumed only very slowly in the second step, it is possible for the OONO to revert to NO and O_2 before it reacts further:

$$Rate\ of\ reverse\ reaction\ (OONO \rightarrow NO + O_2) = k_{-1}[OONO]$$

As NO and O_2 form OONO, their concentrations drop, so the rate of the forward reaction decreases. At the same time, the concentration of OONO builds up, so the rate of the reverse reaction increases. At equilibrium, the rates of the forward and reverse reactions become the same.

$$Rate\ of\ forward\ reaction = rate\ of\ reverse\ reaction$$

$$k_1[NO][O_2] = k_{-1}[OONO]$$

Rearranging this equation, we find

$$\frac{k_1}{k_{-1}} = \frac{[OONO]}{[NO][O_2]} = K$$

Both k_1 and k_{-1} are constants (they will change only if the temperature changes). We can define a new constant K equal to the ratio of these two constants and called the **equilibrium constant**, which is equal to the quotient $[OONO]/[NO][O_2]$. From this, we can derive an expression for the concentration of OONO:

$$[OONO] = K[NO][O_2]$$

Relating Rate Equations and Reaction Mechanisms

The connection between an experimental rate equation and the proposed reaction mechanism is important in chemistry.

1. Experiments must first be performed to determine the experimental rate equation.

2. A mechanism for the reaction is proposed on the basis of the experimental rate equation, the principles of stoichi-

ometry, molecular structure and bonding, general chemical experience, and intuition.

3. The proposed reaction mechanism is used to derive a rate equation. This rate equation can contain only those species present in the overall chemical reaction. If the derived and experimental rate equations are the same, the postulated

mechanism *may* be a reasonable hypothesis of the reaction sequence.

4. If more than one mechanism can be proposed and they all predict derived rate equations in agreement with experiment, then more experiments must be done.

If $K[NO][O_2]$ is substituted for $[OONO]$ in the rate law for the rate-determining elementary step, we have

$$\text{Rate} = k_2[NO][OONO] = k_2[NO]\{K[NO][O_2]\}$$

$$= k_2 K[NO]^2[O_2]$$

Because both k_2 and K are constants, their product is another constant k', and we have

$$\text{Rate} = k'[NO]^2[O_2]$$

This is exactly the rate law derived from experiment. Thus, the sequence of reactions on which the rate law is based may be a reasonable mechanism for this reaction. It is not the only possible mechanism, however. This rate equation is also consistent with the reaction occurring in a single termolecular step. Another possible mechanism is illustrated in Example 15.14.

● **Equilibrium Constant** The important concept of chemical equilibrium was introduced in Chapter 3 and will be described in more detail in Chapters 16–19.

EXAMPLE 15.14   Reaction Mechanism Involving an Equilibrium Step

Problem The $NO + O_2$ reaction described in the text could also occur by the following mechanism:

Elementary Step 1: Fast, equilibrium

$$NO(g) + NO(g) \underset{k_{-1} \text{ intermediate}}{\overset{k_1}{\rightleftharpoons}} N_2O_2(g)$$

Elementary Step 2: Slow, rate-determining

$$N_2O_2(g) + O_2(g) \overset{k_2}{\rightarrow} 2\, NO_2(g)$$

Overall Reaction: $2\, NO(g) + O_2(g) \rightarrow 2\, NO_2(g)$

Show that this mechanism leads to the following experimental rate law: Rate = $k[NO]^2[O_2]$.

What Do You Know? A possible mechanism for the reaction of NO and O_2 is given.

Strategy The rate law for the rate-determining elementary step is

$$\text{Rate} = k_2[N_2O_2][O_2]$$

The intermediate N_2O_2 cannot appear in the final derived rate law. However, we can find an expression relating the concentration of the unknown to the concentrations of the reactants, using the equilibrium constant expression for the first step.

Solution $[N_2O_2]$ and $[NO]$ are related by the equilibrium constant.

$$\frac{k_1}{k_{-1}} = \frac{[N_2O_2]}{[NO]^2} = K$$

Solving this equation for $[N_2O_2]$ gives $[N_2O_2] = K[NO]^2$. When this is substituted into the derived rate law

$$\text{Rate} = k_2\{K[NO]^2\}[O_2]$$

the resulting equation is identical with the experimental rate law where $k_2K = k$.

Think about Your Answer Three mechanisms have been proposed for the $NO + O_2$ reaction. The challenge for chemists is to decide which is correct. In this case, further experimentation detected the species OONO as a short-lived intermediate, thus providing evidence for the mechanism involving this intermediate.

Check Your Understanding

One possible mechanism for the decomposition of nitryl chloride, NO_2Cl, is

Elementary Step 1: Fast, equilibrium $NO_2Cl(g) \underset{k_{-1}}{\overset{k_1}{\rightleftharpoons}} NO_2(g) + Cl(g)$

Elementary Step 2: Slow $NO_2Cl(g) + Cl(g) \overset{k_2}{\rightarrow} NO_2(g) + Cl_2(g)$

What is the overall reaction? What rate law would be derived from this mechanism? What effect does increasing the concentration of the product NO_2 have on the reaction rate?

REVIEW & CHECK FOR SECTION 15.6

1. The rate equation for a reaction $A + B \rightarrow C$ was determined by experiment to be Rate $= k[A][B]$. From this we can conclude

    (a)   the reaction occurs in a single elementary step

    (b)   this reaction might occur in a single elementary step

    (c)   this reaction must involve several elementary steps

2. A reaction is believed to occur by the following mechanism:

    Step 1: $2\,A \rightleftharpoons I$ (Fast, equilibrium)

    Step 2: $I + B \rightarrow C$ (Slow)

    Overall: $2\,A + B \rightarrow C$

    What experimentally determined rate law would lead to this mechanism?

    (a)   Rate $= k[A][B]$ (c)   Rate $= k[A]^2[B]$

    (b)   Rate $= k[A]^2$ (d)   Rate $= k[I][B]$

Sign in at **www.cengage.com/owl** to:
- View tutorials and simulations, develop problem-solving skills, and complete online homework assigned by your professor.
- For quick review and exam prep, download Go Chemistry mini lecture modules from OWL (or purchase them at **www.cengagebrain.com**)

 Access **How Do I Solve It?** tutorials on how to approach problem solving using concepts in this chapter.

CHAPTER GOALS REVISITED

Now that you have studied this chapter, you should ask whether you have met the chapter goals. In particular, you should be able to:

Understand rates of reaction and the conditions affecting rates

a. Explain the concept of reaction rate (Section 15.1).

b. Derive the average and instantaneous rates of a reaction from concentration-time data (Section 15.1). **Study Question: 5.**

c. Describe factors that affect reaction rate (i.e., reactant concentrations, temperature, presence of a catalyst, and the state of the reactants) (Section 15.2). **Study Questions: 8, 9, 10, 66, 80, 81, 85.**

Derive a rate equation, rate constant, and reaction order from experimental data

a. Define the various parts of a rate equation (the rate constant and order of reaction), and understand their significance (Section 15.3). **Study Questions: 12–14.**

b. Derive a rate equation from experimental information (Section 15.3). Study Questions: 11–14, 52, 60.

Use integrated rate laws

a. Describe and use the relationships between reactant concentration and time for zero-order, first-order, and second-order reactions (Section 15.4 and Table 15.1). Study Questions: 15–24, and Go Chemistry Module 20.

b. Apply graphical methods for determining reaction order and the rate constant from experimental data (Section 15.4 and Table 15.1). Study Questions: 31–36, 54, 55, 57.

c. Use the concept of half-life $(t_{1/2})$, especially for first-order reactions (Section 15.4). Study Questions: 25–30, 64, 75.

Understand the collision theory of reaction rates and the role of activation energy

a. Describe the collision theory of reaction rates (Section 15.5).

b. Relate activation energy (E_a) to the rate of a reaction (Section 15.5). Study Question: 40.

c. Use collision theory to describe the effect of reactant concentration on reaction rate (Section 15.5). Study Question: 84.

d. Understand the effect of molecular orientation on reaction rate (Section 15.5).

e. Describe the effect of temperature on reaction rate using the collision theory of reaction rates and the Arrhenius equation (Section 15.5 and Equations 15.5–15.7).Study Question: 84.

f. Use Equations 15.5, 15.6, and 15.7 to calculate the activation energy from rate constants at different temperatures (Section 15.5). Study Questions: 37, 39, 40, 62, 67, 68, 76c.

g. Understand reaction coordinate diagrams (Section 15.5). Study Questions: 41, 42, 47, 87.

Relate reaction mechanisms and rate laws

a. Describe the functioning of a catalyst and its effect on the activation energy and mechanism of a reaction (Section 15.5). Study Questions: 82, 88.

b. Understand the concept of a reaction mechanism (a proposed sequence of bond-making and bond-breaking steps that occurs during the conversion of reactants to products) and the relation of the mechanism to the overall, stoichiometric equation for a reaction (Section 15.6).

c. Describe the elementary steps of a mechanism, and give their molecularity (Section 15.6). Study Questions: 43–48, 78.

d. Define the rate-determining step in a mechanism, and identify any reaction intermediates (Section 15.6). Study Questions: 45, 48, 59, 65, 74, 82, 83.

Key Equations

Equation 15.1 (page 681) Integrated rate equation for a first-order reaction (in which $-\Delta[R]/\Delta t = k[R]$).

$$\ln\frac{[R]_t}{[R]_0} = -kt$$

Here, $[R]_0$ and $[R]_t$ are concentrations of the reactant at time $t = 0$ and at a later time, t. The ratio of concentrations, $[R]_t/[R]_0$, is the fraction of reactant that remains after a given time has elapsed.

Equation 15.2 (page 683) Integrated rate equation for a second-order reaction (in which $-\Delta[R]/\Delta t = k[R]^2$).

$$\frac{1}{[R]_t} - \frac{1}{[R]_0} = kt$$

Equation 15.3 (page 684) Integrated rate equation for a zero-order reaction (in which $-\Delta[R]/\Delta t = k[R]^0$).

$$[R]_0 - [R]_t = kt$$

Equation 15.4 (page 686) The relation between the half-life ($t_{1/2}$) and the rate constant (k) for a first-order reaction.

$$t_{1/2} = \frac{0.693}{k}$$

Equation 15.5 (page 693) Arrhenius equation in exponential form.

$$k = \text{rate constant} = Ae^{-E_a/RT}$$

Frequency factor

Fraction of molecules with minimum energy for reaction

A is the frequency factor; E_a is the activation energy; T is the temperature (in kelvins); and R is the gas constant (= 8.314510×10^{-3} kJ/K · mol).

Equation 15.6 (page 693) Expanded Arrhenius equation in logarithmic form.

$$\ln k = -\frac{E_a}{R}\left(\frac{1}{T}\right) + \ln A \longleftarrow \text{Arrhenius equation}$$

$$y \quad = \quad mx \quad + b \longleftarrow \text{Equation for straight line}$$

Equation 15.7 (page 694) A version of the Arrhenius equation used to calculate the activation energy for a reaction when you know the values of the rate constant at two temperatures (in kelvins).

$$\ln k_2 - \ln k_1 = \ln \frac{k_2}{k_1} = -\frac{E_a}{R}\left[\frac{1}{T_2} - \frac{1}{T_1}\right]$$

Study Questions

OWL Interactive versions of these questions are assignable in OWL.

▲ denotes challenging questions.

Blue-numbered questions have answers in Appendix R and fully worked solutions in the *Student Solutions Manual*.

Practicing Skills

Reaction Rates
(See Section 15.1 and Examples 15.1–15.2.)

1. Give the relative rates of disappearance of reactants and formation of products for each of the following reactions.
   (a) $2 O_3(g) \rightarrow 3 O_2(g)$
   (b) $2 HOF(g) \rightarrow 2 HF(g) + O_2(g)$

2. Give the relative rates of disappearance of reactants and formation of products for each of the following reactions.
   (a) $2 NO(g) + Br_2(g) \rightarrow 2 NOBr(g)$
   (b) $N_2(g) + 3 H_2(g) \rightarrow 2 NH_3(g)$

3. In the reaction $2 O_3(g) \rightarrow 3 O_2(g)$, the rate of formation of O_2 is 1.5×10^{-3} mol/L · s. What is the rate of decomposition of O_3?

4. In the synthesis of ammonia, if $-\Delta[H_2]/\Delta t = 4.5 \times 10^{-4}$ mol/L·min, what is $\Delta[NH_3]/\Delta t$?
   $$N_2(g) + 3 H_2(g) \rightarrow 2 NH_3(g)$$

5. Experimental data are listed here for the reaction $A \rightarrow 2 B$.

Time (s)	[B] (mol/L)
0.00	0.000
10.0	0.326
20.0	0.572
30.0	0.750
40.0	0.890

(a) Prepare a graph from these data; connect the points with a smooth line; and calculate the rate of change of [B] for each 10-second interval from 0.0 to 40.0 seconds. Does the rate of change decrease from one time interval to the next? Suggest a reason for this result.

(b) How is the rate of change of [A] related to the rate of change of [B] in each time interval? Calculate the rate of change of [A] for the time interval from 10.0 to 20.0 seconds.

(c) What is the instantaneous rate, $\Delta[B]/\Delta t$, when [B] = 0.750 mol/L?

6. Phenyl acetate, an ester, reacts with water according to the equation

$$\underset{\text{phenyl acetate}}{CH_3\overset{\displaystyle O}{\overset{\|}{C}}OC_6H_5} + H_2O \longrightarrow \underset{\text{acetic acid}}{CH_3\overset{\displaystyle O}{\overset{\|}{C}}OH} + \underset{\text{phenol}}{C_6H_5OH}$$

The data in the table were collected for this reaction at 5 °C.

Time (s)	[Phenyl acetate] (mol/L)
0	0.55
15.0	0.42
30.0	0.31
45.0	0.23
60.0	0.17
75.0	0.12
90.0	0.085

(a) Plot the phenyl acetate concentration versus time, and describe the shape of the curve observed.

(b) Calculate the rate of change of the phenyl acetate concentration during the period 15.0 seconds to 30.0 seconds and also during the period 75.0 seconds to 90.0 seconds. Why is one value smaller than the other?

(c) What is the rate of change of the phenol concentration during the time period 60.0 seconds to 75.0 seconds?

(d) What is the instantaneous rate at 15.0 seconds?

Concentration and Rate Equations
(See Section 15.3 and Examples 15.3–15.4.)

7. Using the rate equation "Rate = $k[A]^2[B]$," define the order of the reaction with respect to A and B. What is the total order of the reaction?

8. A reaction has the experimental rate equation Rate = $k[A]^2$. How will the rate change if the concentration of A is tripled? If the concentration of A is halved?

9. The reaction between ozone and nitrogen dioxide at 231 K is first order in both [NO$_2$] and [O$_3$].

$$2\ NO_2(g) + O_3(g) \longrightarrow N_2O_5(g) + O_2(g)$$

(a) Write the rate equation for the reaction.

(b) If the concentration of NO$_2$ is tripled (and [O$_3$] is not changed), what is the change in the reaction rate?

(c) What is the effect on reaction rate if the concentration of O$_3$ is halved (with no change in [NO$_2$])?

10. Nitrosyl bromide, NOBr, is formed from NO and Br$_2$:

$$2\ NO(g) + Br_2(g) \longrightarrow 2\ NOBr(g)$$

Experiments show that this reaction is second order in NO and first order in Br$_2$.

(a) Write the rate equation for the reaction.

(b) How does the initial reaction rate change if the concentration of Br$_2$ is changed from 0.0022 mol/L to 0.0066 mol/L?

(c) What is the change in the initial rate if the concentration of NO is changed from 0.0024 mol/L to 0.0012 mol/L?

11. The data in the table are for the reaction of NO and O$_2$ at 660 K. (See "Check Your Understanding" for Example 15.3, page 680.)

$$2\ NO(g) + O_2(g) \longrightarrow 2\ NO_2(g)$$

Reactant Concentration (mol/L)		Rate of Disappearance of NO
[NO]	[O$_2$]	(mol/L · s)
0.010	0.010	2.5×10^{-5}
0.020	0.010	1.0×10^{-4}
0.010	0.020	5.0×10^{-5}

(a) Determine the order of the reaction for each reactant.

(b) Write the rate equation for the reaction.

(c) Calculate the rate constant.

(d) Calculate the rate (in mol/L · s) at the instant when [NO] = 0.015 mol/L and [O$_2$] = 0.0050 mol/L.

(e) At the instant when NO is reacting at the rate 1.0×10^{-4} mol/L · s, what is the rate at which O$_2$ is reacting and NO$_2$ is forming?

12. The reaction

$$2\ NO(g) + 2\ H_2(g) \longrightarrow N_2(g) + 2\ H_2O(g)$$

was studied at 904 °C, and the data in the table were collected.

Reactant Concentration (mol/L)		Rate of Appearance of N$_2$
[NO]	[H$_2$]	(mol/L · s)
0.420	0.122	0.136
0.210	0.122	0.0339
0.210	0.244	0.0678
0.105	0.488	0.0339

(a) Determine the order of the reaction for each reactant.

(b) Write the rate equation for the reaction.

(c) Calculate the rate constant for the reaction.

(d) Find the rate of appearance of N$_2$ at the instant when [NO] = 0.350 mol/L and [H$_2$] = 0.205 mol/L.

13. Data for the reaction $2 NO(g) + O_2(g) \rightarrow 2 NO_2(g)$ are given (for a particular temperature) in the table.

Experiment	Concentration (mol/L) [NO]	[O$_2$]	Initial Rate (mol NO/L · h)
1	3.6×10^{-4}	5.2×10^{-3}	3.4×10^{-8}
2	3.6×10^{-4}	1.04×10^{-2}	6.8×10^{-8}
3	1.8×10^{-4}	1.04×10^{-2}	1.7×10^{-8}
4	1.8×10^{-4}	5.2×10^{-3}	?

(a) What is the rate law for this reaction?
(b) What is the rate constant for the reaction?
(c) What is the initial rate of the reaction in experiment 4?

14. Data for the following reaction are given in the table below.

$$CO(g) + NO_2(g) \rightarrow CO_2(g) + NO(g)$$

Experiment	Concentration (mol/L) [CO]	[NO$_2$]	Initial Rate (mol/L · h)
1	5.0×10^{-4}	0.36×10^{-4}	3.4×10^{-8}
2	5.0×10^{-4}	0.18×10^{-4}	1.7×10^{-8}
3	1.0×10^{-3}	0.36×10^{-4}	6.8×10^{-8}
4	1.5×10^{-3}	0.72×10^{-4}	?

(a) What is the rate law for this reaction?
(b) What is the rate constant for the reaction?
(c) What is the initial rate of the reaction in experiment 4?

Concentration–Time Relationships
(See Section 15.4 and Examples 15.5–15.7.)

15. The rate equation for the hydrolysis of sucrose to fructose and glucose

$$C_{12}H_{22}O_{11}(aq) + H_2O(\ell) \rightarrow 2 C_6H_{12}O_6(aq)$$

is $-\Delta[\text{sucrose}]/\Delta t = k[C_{12}H_{22}O_{11}]$. After 27 minutes at 27 °C, the sucrose concentration decreased from 0.0146 M to 0.0132 M. Find the rate constant, k.

16. The decomposition of N_2O_5 in CCl_4 is a first-order reaction. If 2.56 mg of N_2O_5 is present initially and 2.50 mg is present after 4.26 minutes at 55 °C, what is the value of the rate constant, k?

17. The decomposition of SO_2Cl_2 is a first-order reaction:

$$SO_2Cl_2(g) \rightarrow SO_2(g) + Cl_2(g)$$

The rate constant for the reaction is 2.8×10^{-3} min^{-1} at 600 K. If the initial concentration of SO_2Cl_2 is 1.24×10^{-3} mol/L, how long will it take for the concentration to drop to 0.31×10^{-3} mol/L?

18. The conversion of cyclopropane to propene (see Example 15.5) occurs with a first-order rate constant of 2.42×10^{-2} h^{-1}. How long will it take for the concentration of cyclopropane to decrease from an initial concentration of 0.080 mol/L to 0.020 mol/L?

19. Hydrogen peroxide, $H_2O_2(aq)$, decomposes to $H_2O(\ell)$ and $O_2(g)$ in a reaction that is first order in H_2O_2 and has a rate constant $k = 1.06 \times 10^{-3}$ min^{-1} at a given temperature.
(a) How long will it take for 15% of a sample of H_2O_2 to decompose?
(b) How long will it take for 85% of the sample to decompose?

20. The decomposition of nitrogen dioxide at a high temperature

$$NO_2(g) \rightarrow NO(g) + \tfrac{1}{2} O_2(g)$$

is second order in this reactant. The rate constant for this reaction is 3.40 L/mol · min. Determine the time needed for the concentration of NO_2 to decrease from 2.00 mol/L to 1.50 mol/L.

21. At 573 K, gaseous $NO_2(g)$ decomposes, forming $NO(g)$ and $O_2(g)$. If a vessel containing $NO_2(g)$ has an initial concentration of 2.8×10^{-2} mol/L, how long will it take for 75% of the $NO_2(g)$ to decompose? The decomposition of $NO_2(g)$ is second order in the reactant and the rate constant for this reaction, at 573 K, is 1.1 L/mol · s.

22. The dimerization of butadiene, C_4H_6, to form 1,5-cyclooctadiene is a second-order process that occurs when the diene is heated. In an experiment, a sample of 0.0087 mol of C_4H_6 was heated in a 1.0-L flask. After 600 seconds, 21% of the butadiene had dimerized. Calculate the rate constant for this reaction.

23. The decomposition of ammonia on a metal surface to form N_2 and H_2 is a zero-order reaction (Figure 15.8). At 873 °C, the value of the rate constant is 1.5×10^{-3} mol/L · s. How long it will take to completely decompose 1.0 g of NH_3 in a 1.0-L flask?

24. Hydrogen iodide decomposes when heated, forming $H_2(g)$ and $I_2(g)$. The rate law for this reaction is $-\Delta[\text{HI}]/\Delta t = k[\text{HI}]^2$. At 443 °C, $k = 30$. L/mol · min. If the initial HI(g) concentration is 3.5×10^{-2} mol/L, what concentration of HI(g) will remain after 10. minutes?

Half-Life
(See Section 15.4 and Examples 15.8 and 15.9.)

25. The rate equation for the decomposition of N_2O_5 (giving NO_2 and O_2) is Rate = $k[N_2O_5]$. The value of k is 6.7×10^{-5} s^{-1} for the reaction at a particular temperature.
(a) Calculate the half-life of N_2O_5.
(b) How long does it take for the N_2O_5 concentration to drop to one tenth of its original value?

26. The decomposition of SO_2Cl_2

$$SO_2Cl_2(g) \rightarrow SO_2(g) + Cl_2(g)$$

is first order in SO_2Cl_2, and the reaction has a half-life of 245 minutes at 600 K. If you begin with 3.6×10^{-3} mol of SO_2Cl_2 in a 1.0-L flask, how long will it take for the amount of SO_2Cl_2 to decrease to 2.00×10^{-4} mol?

27. Gaseous azomethane, $CH_3N{=}NCH_3$, decomposes in a first-order reaction when heated:

$$CH_3N{=}NCH_3(g) \rightarrow N_2(g) + C_2H_6(g)$$

The rate constant for this reaction at 600 K is 0.0216 min^{-1}. If the initial quantity of azomethane in the flask is 2.00 g, how much remains after 0.0500 hour? What quantity of N_2 is formed in this time?

28. The compound $Xe(CF_3)_2$ decomposes in a first-order reaction to elemental Xe with a half-life of 30. minutes. If you place 7.50 mg of $Xe(CF_3)_2$ in a flask, how long must you wait until only 0.25 mg of $Xe(CF_3)_2$ remains?

29. The radioactive isotope ^{64}Cu is used in the form of copper(II) acetate to study Wilson's disease. The isotope has a half-life of 12.70 hours. What fraction of radioactive copper(II) acetate remains after 64 hours?

30. Radioactive gold-198 is used in the diagnosis of liver problems. The half-life of this isotope is 2.7 days. If you begin with a 5.6-mg sample of the isotope, how much of this sample remains after 1.0 day?

Graphical Analysis: Rate Equations and *k*
(See Section 15.4.)

31. Data for the decomposition of dinitrogen monoxide

$$N_2O(g) \rightarrow N_2(g) + \tfrac{1}{2} O_2(g)$$

on a gold surface at 900 °C are given below. Verify that the reaction is first order by preparing a graph of ln $[N_2O]$ versus time. Derive the rate constant from the slope of the line in this graph. Using the rate law and value of *k*, determine the decomposition rate at 900 °C when $[N_2O] = 0.035$ mol/L.

Time (min)	$[N_2O]$ (mol/L)
15.0	0.0835
30.0	0.0680
80.0	0.0350
120.0	0.0220

32. Ammonia decomposes when heated according to the equation

$$NH_3(g) \rightarrow NH_2(g) + H(g)$$

The data in the table for this reaction were collected at a high temperature.

Time (h)	$[NH_3]$ (mol/L)
0	8.00×10^{-7}
25	6.75×10^{-7}
50	5.84×10^{-7}
75	5.15×10^{-7}

Plot ln $[NH_3]$ versus time and $1/[NH_3]$ versus time. What is the order of this reaction with respect to NH_3? Find the rate constant for the reaction from the slope.

33. Gaseous NO_2 decomposes at 573 K.

$$NO_2(g) \rightarrow NO(g) + \tfrac{1}{2} O_2(g)$$

The concentration of NO_2 was measured as a function of time. A graph of $1/[NO_2]$ versus time gives a straight line with a slope of 1.1 L/mol · s. What is the rate law for this reaction? What is the rate constant?

34. The decomposition of HOF occurs at 25 °C.

$$HOF(g) \rightarrow HF(g) + \tfrac{1}{2} O_2(g)$$

Using the data in the table below, determine the rate law, and then calculate the rate constant.

[HOF] (mol/L)	Time (min)
0.850	0
0.810	2.00
0.754	5.00
0.526	20.0
0.243	50.0

35. For the reaction $C_2F_4 \rightarrow \tfrac{1}{2} C_4F_8$, a graph of $1/[C_2F_4]$ versus time gives a straight line with a slope of $+0.04$ L/mol · s. What is the rate law for this reaction?

36. Butadiene, $C_4H_6(g)$, dimerizes when heated, forming 1,5-cyclooctadiene, C_8H_{12}. The data in the table were collected.

1,3-butadiene   1,5-cyclooctadiene

$[C_4H_6]$ (mol/L)	Time (s)
1.0×10^{-2}	0
8.7×10^{-3}	200.
7.7×10^{-3}	500.
6.9×10^{-3}	800.
5.8×10^{-3}	1200.

(a) Use a graphical method to verify that this is a second-order reaction.
(b) Calculate the rate constant for the reaction.

Kinetics and Energy
(See Section 15.5 and Examples 15.10 and 15.11.)

37. Calculate the activation energy, E_a, for the reaction

$$2 N_2O_5(g) \rightarrow 4 NO_2(g) + O_2(g)$$

from the observed rate constants: *k* at 25 °C = 3.46×10^{-5} s^{-1} and *k* at 55 °C = 1.5×10^{-3} s^{-1}.

38. If the rate constant for a reaction triples when the temperature rises from 3.00×10^2 K to 3.10×10^2 K, what is the activation energy of the reaction?

39. When heated to a high temperature, cyclobutane, C_4H_8, decomposes to ethylene:

$$C_4H_8(g) \rightarrow 2 C_2H_4(g)$$

The activation energy, E_a, for this reaction is 260 kJ/mol. At 800 K, the rate constant $k = 0.0315$ s^{-1}. Determine the value of *k* at 850 K.

40. When heated, cyclopropane is converted to propene (see Example 15.5). Rate constants for this reaction at 470 °C and 510 °C are $k = 1.10 \times 10^{-4}$ s^{-1} and $k = 1.02 \times 10^{-3}$ s^{-1}, respectively. Determine the activation energy, E_a, from these data.

41. The reaction of H_2 molecules with F atoms

$$H_2(g) + F(g) \rightarrow HF(g) + H(g)$$

has an activation energy of 8 kJ/mol and an enthalpy change of -133 kJ/mol. Draw a diagram similar to Figure 15.13 for this process. Indicate the activation energy and enthalpy change on this diagram.

42. Answer the following questions based on the diagram below.
    (a) Is the reaction exothermic or endothermic?
    (b) Does the reaction occur in more than one step? If so, how many?

Reaction Mechanisms
(See Section 15.6 and Examples 15.12–15.14.)

43. What is the rate law for each of the following elementary reactions?
    (a) $NO(g) + NO_3(g) \rightarrow 2 NO_2(g)$
    (b) $Cl(g) + H_2(g) \rightarrow HCl(g) + H(g)$
    (c) $(CH_3)_3CBr(aq) \rightarrow (CH_3)_3C^+(aq) + Br^-(aq)$

44. What is the rate law for each of the following elementary reactions?
    (a) $Cl(g) + ICl(g) \rightarrow I(g) + Cl_2(g)$
    (b) $O(g) + O_3(g) \rightarrow 2 O_2(g)$
    (c) $2 NO_2(g) \rightarrow N_2O_4(g)$

45. Ozone, O_3, in the earth's upper atmosphere decomposes according to the equation

    $$2 O_3(g) \rightarrow 3 O_2(g)$$

    The mechanism of the reaction is thought to proceed through an initial fast, reversible step followed by a slow, second step.

    Step 1: Fast, reversible $O_3(g) \rightleftharpoons O_2(g) + O(g)$

    Step 2: Slow $O_3(g) + O(g) \rightarrow 2 O_2(g)$

    (a) Which of the steps is rate-determining?
    (b) Write the rate equation for the rate-determining step.

46. The reaction of $NO_2(g)$ and $CO(g)$ is thought to occur in two steps:

    Step 1: Slow $NO_2(g) + NO_2(g) \rightarrow NO(g) + NO_3(g)$

    Step 2: Fast $NO_3(g) + CO(g) \rightarrow NO_2(g) + CO_2(g)$

    (a) Show that the elementary steps add up to give the overall, stoichiometric equation.
    (b) What is the molecularity of each step?
    (c) For this mechanism to be consistent with kinetic data, what must be the experimental rate equation?
    (d) Identify any intermediates in this reaction.

47. A proposed mechanism for the reaction of NO_2 and CO is

    Step 1: Slow, endothermic
    $$2 NO_2(g) \rightarrow NO(g) + NO_3(g)$$

    Step 2: Fast, exothermic
    $$NO_3(g) + CO(g) \rightarrow NO_2(g) + CO_2(g)$$

    Overall Reaction: Exothermic
    $$NO_2(g) + CO(g) \rightarrow NO(g) + CO_2(g)$$

    (a) Identify each of the following as a reactant, product, or intermediate: $NO_2(g)$, $CO(g)$, $NO_3(g)$, $CO_2(g)$, $NO(g)$.
    (b) Draw a reaction coordinate diagram for this reaction. Indicate on this drawing the activation energy for each step and the overall enthalpy change.

48. The mechanism for the reaction of CH_3OH and HBr is believed to involve two steps. The overall reaction is exothermic.

    Step 1: Fast, endothermic
    $$CH_3OH + H^+ \rightleftharpoons CH_3OH_2^+$$

    Step 2: Slow
    $$CH_3OH_2^+ + Br^- \rightarrow CH_3Br + H_2O$$

    (a) Write an equation for the overall reaction.
    (b) Draw a reaction coordinate diagram for this reaction.
    (c) Show that the rate law for this reaction is Rate $= k[CH_3OH][H^+][Br^-]$.

General Questions

These questions are not designated as to type or location in the chapter. They may combine several concepts.

49. A reaction has the following experimental rate equation: Rate $= k[A]^2[B]$. If the concentration of A is doubled and the concentration of B is halved, what happens to the reaction rate?

50. For a first-order reaction, what fraction of reactant remains after five half-lives have elapsed?

51. To determine the concentration dependence of the rate of the reaction

    $$H_2PO_3^-(aq) + OH^-(aq) \rightarrow HPO_3^{2-}(aq) + H_2O(\ell)$$

    you might measure $[OH^-]$ as a function of time using a pH meter. (To do so, you would set up conditions under which $[H_2PO_3^-]$ remains constant by using a large excess of this reactant.) How would you prove a second-order rate dependence for $[OH^-]$?

52. Data for the following reaction are given in the table.

    $$2 NO(g) + Br_2(g) \rightarrow 2 NOBr(g)$$

Experiment	[NO] (M)	[Br₂] (M)	Initial Rate (mol/L · s)
1	1.0×10^{-2}	2.0×10^{-2}	2.4×10^{-2}
2	4.0×10^{-2}	2.0×10^{-2}	0.384
3	1.0×10^{-2}	5.0×10^{-2}	6.0×10^{-2}

What is the order of the reaction with respect to [NO] and [Br₂], and what is the overall order of the reaction?

53. Formic acid decomposes at 550 °C according to the equation

    $$HCO_2H(g) \rightarrow CO_2(g) + H_2(g)$$

    The reaction follows first-order kinetics. In an experiment, it is determined that 75% of a sample of HCO_2H has decomposed in 72 seconds. Determine $t_{1/2}$ for this reaction.

54. Isomerization of CH_3NC occurs slowly when CH_3NC is heated.

$$CH_3NC(g) \rightarrow CH_3CN(g)$$

To study the rate of this reaction at 488 K, data on $[CH_3NC]$ were collected at various times. Analysis led to the graph below.

(a) What is the rate law for this reaction?
(b) What is the equation for the straight line in this graph?
(c) Calculate the rate constant for this reaction.
(d) How long does it take for half of the sample to isomerize?
(e) What is the concentration of CH_3NC after 1.0×10^4 s?

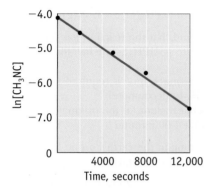

55. When heated, tetrafluoroethylene dimerizes to form octafluorocyclobutane.

$$C_2F_4(g) \rightarrow \tfrac{1}{2} \, C_4F_8(g)$$

To determine the rate of this reaction at 488 K, the data in the table were collected. Analysis was done graphically, as shown below:

$[C_2F_4]$ (M)	Time (s)
0.100	0
0.080	56
0.060	150.
0.040	335
0.030	520.

(a) What is the rate law for this reaction?
(b) What is the value of the rate constant?
(c) What is the concentration of C_2F_4 after 600 s?
(d) How long will it take until the reaction is 90% complete?

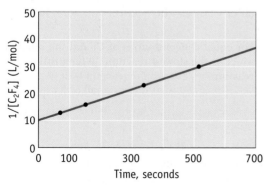

56. Data in the table were collected at 540 K for the following reaction:

$$CO(g) + NO_2(g) \rightarrow CO_2(g) + NO(g)$$

(a) Derive the rate equation.
(b) Determine the reaction order with respect to each reactant.
(c) Calculate the rate constant, giving the correct units for k.

Initial Concentration (mol/L)		Initial Rate
[CO]	[NO$_2$]	(mol/L · h)
5.1×10^{-4}	0.35×10^{-4}	3.4×10^{-8}
5.1×10^{-4}	0.70×10^{-4}	6.8×10^{-8}
5.1×10^{-4}	0.18×10^{-4}	1.7×10^{-8}
1.0×10^{-3}	0.35×10^{-4}	6.8×10^{-8}
1.5×10^{-3}	0.35×10^{-4}	10.2×10^{-8}

57. Ammonium cyanate, NH_4NCO, rearranges in water to give urea, $(NH_2)_2CO$.

$$NH_4NCO(aq) \rightarrow (NH_2)_2CO(aq)$$

Time (min)	[NH$_4$NCO] (mol/L)
0	0.458
4.50×10^1	0.370
1.07×10^2	0.292
2.30×10^2	0.212
6.00×10^2	0.114

Using the data in the table:
(a) Decide whether the reaction is first order or second order.
(b) Calculate k for this reaction.
(c) Calculate the half-life of ammonium cyanate under these conditions.
(d) Calculate the concentration of NH_4NCO after 12.0 hours.

58. Nitrogen oxides, NO_x (a mixture of NO and NO_2 collectively designated as NO_x), play an essential role in the production of pollutants found in photochemical smog. The NO_x in the atmosphere is slowly broken down to N_2 and O_2 in a first-order reaction. The average half-life of NO_x in the smokestack emissions in a large city during daylight is 3.9 hours.
(a) Starting with 1.50 mg in an experiment, what quantity of NO_x remains after 5.25 hours?
(b) How many hours of daylight must have elapsed to decrease 1.50 mg of NO_x to 2.50×10^{-6} mg?

59. At temperatures below 500 K, the reaction between carbon monoxide and nitrogen dioxide

$$CO(g) + NO_2(g) \rightarrow CO_2(g) + NO(g)$$

has the following rate equation: Rate = $k[NO_2]^2$. Which of the three mechanisms suggested here best agrees with the experimentally observed rate equation?

Mechanism 1   Single, elementary step

$$NO_2 + CO \rightarrow CO_2 + NO$$

Mechanism 2   Two steps

Slow $NO_2 + NO_2 \rightarrow NO_3 + NO$

Fast $NO_3 + CO \rightarrow NO_2 + CO_2$

Mechanism 3   Two steps

Slow $NO_2 \rightarrow NO + O$

Fast $CO + O \rightarrow CO_2$

60. ▲ Nitryl fluoride can be made by treating nitrogen dioxide with fluorine:

$$2\ NO_2(g) + F_2(g) \rightarrow 2\ NO_2F(g)$$

Use the rate data in the table to do the following:
(a) Write the rate equation for the reaction.
(b) Indicate the order of reaction with respect to each component of the reaction.
(c) Find the numerical value of the rate constant, k.

	Initial Concentrations (mol/L)			Initial Rate
Experiment	[NO₂]	[F₂]	[NO₂F]	(mol F₂/L · s)
1	0.001	0.005	0.001	2.0×10^{-4}
2	0.002	0.005	0.001	4.0×10^{-4}
3	0.006	0.002	0.001	4.8×10^{-4}
4	0.006	0.004	0.001	9.6×10^{-4}
5	0.001	0.001	0.001	4.0×10^{-5}
6	0.001	0.001	0.002	4.0×10^{-5}

61. The decomposition of dinitrogen pentaoxide

$$N_2O_5(g) \rightarrow 2\ NO_2(g) + \tfrac{1}{2}\ O_2(g)$$

has the following rate equation: Rate = $k[N_2O_5]$. It has been found experimentally that the decomposition is 20.5% complete in 13.0 hours at 298 K. Calculate the rate constant and the half-life at 298 K.

62. The data in the table give the temperature dependence of the rate constant for the reaction $N_2O_5(g)$ → $2\ NO_2(g) + \tfrac{1}{2}\ O_2(g)$. Plot these data in the appropriate way to derive the activation energy for the reaction.

T(K)	k (s⁻¹)
338	4.87×10^{-3}
328	1.50×10^{-3}
318	4.98×10^{-4}
308	1.35×10^{-4}
298	3.46×10^{-5}
273	7.87×10^{-7}

63. The decomposition of gaseous dimethyl ether at ordinary pressures is first order. Its half-life is 25.0 minutes at 500 °C:

$$CH_3OCH_3(g) \rightarrow CH_4(g) + CO(g) + H_2(g)$$

(a) Starting with 8.00 g of dimethyl ether, what mass remains (in grams) after 125 minutes and after 145 minutes?
(b) Calculate the time in minutes required to decrease 7.60 ng (nanograms) to 2.25 ng.
(c) What fraction of the original dimethyl ether remains after 150 minutes?

64. The decomposition of phosphine, PH_3, proceeds according to the equation

$$PH_3(g) \rightarrow \tfrac{1}{4}\ P_4(g) + \tfrac{3}{2}\ H_2(g)$$

It is found that the reaction has the following rate equation: Rate = $k[PH_3]$. The half-life of PH_3 is 37.9 seconds at 120 °C.
(a) How much time is required for three fourths of the PH_3 to decompose?
(b) What fraction of the original sample of PH_3 remains after 1.00 minute?

65. The ozone in the earth's ozone layer decomposes according to the equation

$$2\ O_3(g) \rightarrow 3\ O_2(g)$$

The mechanism of the reaction is thought to proceed through an initial fast equilibrium and a slow step:

Step 1:   Fast, reversible $O_3(g) \rightleftharpoons O_2(g) + O(g)$

Step 2:   Slow $O_3(g) + O(g) \rightarrow 2\ O_2(g)$

Show that the mechanism agrees with this experimental rate law:

$$\text{Rate} = -(1/2)\Delta[O_3]/\Delta t = k\ [O_3]^2/[O_2].$$

66. Hundreds of different reactions can occur in the stratosphere, among them reactions that destroy the earth's ozone layer. The table below lists several (second-order) reactions of Cl atoms with ozone and organic compounds; each is given with its rate constant.

Reaction	Rate Constant (298 K, cm³/molecule · s)
(a) $Cl + O_3 \rightarrow ClO + O_2$	1.2×10^{-11}
(b) $Cl + CH_4 \rightarrow HCl + CH_3$	1.0×10^{-13}
(c) $Cl + C_3H_8 \rightarrow HCl + C_3H_7$	1.4×10^{-10}
(d) $Cl + CH_2FCl \rightarrow HCl + CHFCl$	3.0×10^{-18}

For equal concentrations of Cl and the other reactant, which is the slowest reaction? Which is the fastest reaction?

67. Data for the reaction

$$[Mn(CO)_5(CH_3CN)]^+ + NC_5H_5$$
$$\longrightarrow [Mn(CO)_5(NC_5H_5)]^+ + CH_3CN$$

are given in the table. Calculate E_a from a plot of $\ln k$ versus $1/T$.

T(K)	k(min^{-1})
298	0.0409
308	0.0818
318	0.157

68. The gas-phase reaction

$$2 N_2O_5(g) \longrightarrow 4 NO_2(g) + O_2(g)$$

has an activation energy of 103 kJ/mol, and the rate constant is 0.0900 min^{-1} at 328.0 K. Find the rate constant at 318.0 K.

69. ▲ Egg protein albumin is precipitated when an egg is cooked in boiling (100 °C) water. E_a for this first-order reaction is 52.0 kJ/mol. Estimate the time to prepare a 3-minute egg at an altitude at which water boils at 90 °C.

70. ▲ Two molecules of 1,3-butadiene (C_4H_6) form 1,5-cyclooctadiene, C_8H_{12} at higher temperatures.

$$2 C_4H_6(g) \longrightarrow C_8H_{12}(g)$$

Use the following data to determine the order of the reaction and the rate constant, k. (Note that the total pressure is the pressure of the unreacted C_4H_6 at any time and the pressure of the C_8H_{12}.)

Time (min)	Total Pressure (mm Hg)
0	436
3.5	428
11.5	413
18.3	401
25.0	391
32.0	382
41.2	371

71. ▲ Hypofluorous acid, HOF, is very unstable, decomposing in a first-order reaction to give HF and O_2, with a half-life of 30. minutes at room temperature:

$$HOF(g) \longrightarrow HF(g) + \tfrac{1}{2} O_2(g)$$

If the partial pressure of HOF in a 1.00-L flask is initially 1.00×10^2 mm Hg at 25 °C, what are the total pressure in the flask and the partial pressure of HOF after exactly 30 minutes? After 45 minutes?

72. ▲ We know that the decomposition of SO_2Cl_2 is first order in SO_2Cl_2,

$$SO_2Cl_2(g) \longrightarrow SO_2(g) + Cl_2(g)$$

with a half-life of 245 minutes at 600 K. If you begin with a partial pressure of SO_2Cl_2 of 25 mm Hg in a 1.0-L flask, what is the partial pressure of each reactant and product after 245 minutes? What is the partial pressure of each reactant after 12 hours?

73. ▲ Nitramide, NO_2NH_2, decomposes slowly in aqueous solution according to the following reaction:

$$NO_2NH_2(aq) \rightarrow N_2O(g) + H_2O(\ell)$$

The reaction follows the experimental rate law

$$Rate = \frac{k[NO_2NH_2]}{[H_3O^+]}$$

(a) What is the apparent order of the reaction in a buffered solution?

(b) Which of the following mechanisms is the most appropriate for the interpretation of this rate law? Explain.

Mechanism 1

$$NO_2NH_2 \xrightarrow{k_1} N_2O + H_2O$$

Mechanism 2

$$NO_2NH_2 + H_3O^+ \underset{k_2'}{\overset{k_2}{\rightleftharpoons}} NO_2NH_3^+ + H_2O$$
$$\text{(rapid equilibrium)}$$
$$NO_2NH_3^+ \xrightarrow{k_3} N_2O + H_3O^+ \text{ (rate-limiting step)}$$

Mechanism 3

$$NO_2NH_2 + H_2O \underset{k_4'}{\overset{k_4}{\rightleftharpoons}} NO_2NH^- + H_3O^+$$
$$\text{(rapid equilibrium)}$$
$$NO_2NH^- \xrightarrow{k_5} N_2O + OH^- \text{ (rate-limiting step)}$$
$$H_3O^+ + OH^- \xrightarrow{k_6} 2 H_2O \text{ (very fast reaction)}$$

(c) Show the relationship between the experimentally observed rate constant, k, and the rate constants in the selected mechanism. (Note that when writing the expression for K, the equilibrium constant, $[H_2O]$ is not involved. ▶ Chapter 16.)

(d) Show that hydroxide ions catalyze the decomposition of nitramide.

74. Many biochemical reactions are catalyzed by acids. A typical mechanism consistent with the experimental results (in which HA is the acid and X is the reactant) is

Step 1:   Fast, reversible: $HA \rightleftharpoons H^+ + A^-$

Step 2:   Fast, reversible: $X + H^+ \rightleftharpoons XH^+$

Step 3:   Slow $XH^+ \rightarrow$ products

What rate law is derived from this mechanism? What is the order of the reaction with respect to HA? How would doubling the concentration of HA affect the reaction?

In the Laboratory

75. The color change accompanying the reaction of phenolphthalein with strong base is illustrated on page 668. The change in concentration of the dye can be followed by spectrophotometry (page 188), and some data collected by that approach are given below. The initial concentrations were [phenolphthalein] = 0.0050 mol/L and $[OH^-]$ = 0.61 mol/L. (Data are taken from review materials for kinetics at chemed.chem.purdue.edu.)

(For more details on this reaction see L. Nicholson, *Journal of Chemical Education*, Vol. 66, p. 725, 1989.)

Concentration of Phenolphthalein (mol/L)	Time (s)
0.0050	0.00
0.0045	10.5
0.0040	22.3
0.0035	35.7
0.0030	51.1
0.0025	69.3
0.0020	91.6
0.0015	120.4
0.0010	160.9
0.00050	230.3
0.00025	299.6

(a) Plot the data above as [phenolphthalein] versus time, and determine the average rate from $t = 0$ to $t = 15$ seconds and from $t = 100$ seconds to $t = 125$ seconds. Does the rate change? If so, why?

(b) What is the instantaneous rate at 50 seconds?

(c) Use a graphical method to determine the order of the reaction with respect to phenolphthalein. Write the rate law, and determine the rate constant.

(d) What is the half-life for the reaction?

76. ▲ We want to study the hydrolysis of the beautiful green, cobalt-based complex called *trans*-dichlorobis-(ethylenediamine)cobalt(III) ion,

In this hydrolysis reaction, the green complex ion *trans*–[Co(en)$_2$Cl$_2$]$^+$ forms the red complex ion [Co(en)$_2$(H$_2$O)Cl]$^{2+}$ as a Cl$^-$ ion is replaced with a water molecule on the Co^{3+} ion (en = H$_2$NCH$_2$CH$_2$NH$_2$).

$$trans\text{–}[Co(en)_2Cl_2]^+(aq) + H_2O(\ell) \rightarrow$$
$$\text{green}$$
$$[Co(en)_2(H_2O)Cl]^{2+}(aq) + Cl^-(aq)$$
$$\text{red}$$

The reaction progress is followed by observing the color of the solution. The original solution is green, and the final solution is red, but at some intermediate stage when both the reactant and product are present, the solution is gray.

original solution

intermediate solution

final solution

Photos © Cengage Learning/Charles D. Winters

Changes in color with time as Cl$^-$ ion is replaced by H$_2$O in a cobalt(III) complex. The shape in the middle of the beaker is a vortex that arises because the solutions are being stirred using a magnetic stirring bar in the bottom of the beaker.

Reactions such as this have been studied extensively, and experiments suggest that the initial, slow step in the reaction is the breaking of the Co—Cl bond to give a five-coordinate intermediate. The intermediate is then attacked rapidly by water.

Slow: $trans$–[Co(en)$_2$Cl$_2$]$^+$(aq) →
$$[Co(en)_2Cl]^{2+}(aq) + Cl^-(aq)$$

Fast: [Co(en)$_2$Cl]$^{2+}$(aq) + H$_2$O(aq) →
$$[Co(en)_2(H_2O)Cl]^{2+}(aq)$$

(a) Based on the reaction mechanism, what is the predicted rate law?

(b) As the reaction proceeds, the color changes from green to red with an intermediate stage where the color is gray. The gray color is reached at the same time, no matter what the concentration of the green starting material (at the same temperature). How does this show the reaction is first order in the green form? Explain.

(c) The activation energy for a reaction can be found by plotting ln k versus $1/T$. However, here we do not need to measure k directly. Instead, because $k = -(1/t)\ln([R]/[R]_0)$, the time needed to achieve the gray color is a measure of k. Use the data below to find the activation energy.

Temperature °C	Time Needed to Achieve Gray Colors (for the Same Initial Concentration)
56	156 s
60	114 s
65	88 s
75	47 s

77. The enzyme chymotrypsin catalyzes the hydrolysis of a peptide containing phenylalanine. Using the data below at a given temperature, calculate the maximum rate of the reaction, Rate$_{max}$. (For more information on enzyme catalysis and the Michaelis–Menten model, see page 702.)

Peptide Concentration (mol/L)	Reaction Rate (mol/L · min)
2.5×10^{-4}	2.2×10^{-6}
5.0×10^{-4}	3.8×10^{-6}
10.0×10^{-4}	5.9×10^{-6}
15.0×10^{-4}	7.1×10^{-6}

78. The substitution of CO in $Ni(CO)_4$ by another molecule L [where L is an electron-pair donor such as $P(CH_3)_3$] was studied some years ago and led to an understanding of some of the general principles that govern the chemistry of compounds having metal–CO bonds. (See J. P. Day, F. Basolo, and R. G. Pearson: *Journal of the American Chemical Society*, Vol. 90, p. 6927, 1968.) A detailed study of the kinetics of the reaction led to the following mechanism:

Slow $Ni(CO)_4 \rightarrow Ni(CO)_3 + CO$

Fast $Ni(CO)_3 + L \rightarrow Ni(CO)_3L$

(a) What is the molecularity of each of the elementary reactions?
(b) Doubling the concentration of $Ni(CO)_4$ increased the reaction rate by a factor of 2. Doubling the concentration of L had no effect on the reaction rate. Based on this information, write the rate equation for the reaction. Does this agree with the mechanism described?
(c) The experimental rate constant for the reaction, when L = $P(C_6H_5)_3$, is $9.3 \times 10^{-3}\ s^{-1}$ at 20 °C. If the initial concentration of $Ni(CO)_4$ is 0.025 M, what is the concentration of the product after 5.0 minutes?

Summary and Conceptual Questions

The following questions may use concepts from this and previous chapters.

79. Hydrogenation reactions, processes wherein H_2 is added to a molecule, are usually catalyzed. An excellent catalyst is a very finely divided metal suspended in the reaction solvent. Tell why finely divided rhodium, for example, is a much more efficient catalyst than a small block of the metal.

80. ▲ Suppose you have 1000 blocks, each of which is 1.0 cm on a side. If all 1000 of these blocks are stacked to give a cube that is 10. cm on a side, what fraction of the 1000 blocks have at least one surface on the outside surface of the cube? Next, divide the 1000 blocks into eight equal piles of blocks and form them into eight cubes, 5.0 cm on a side. What fraction of the blocks now have at least one surface on the outside of the cubes? How does this mathematical model pertain to Study Question 79?

81. The following statements relate to the reaction for the formation of HI:

$$H_2(g) + I_2(g) \rightarrow 2\ HI(g) \qquad Rate = k[H_2][I_2]$$

Determine which of the following statements are true. If a statement is false, indicate why it is incorrect.
(a) The reaction must occur in a single step.
(b) This is a second-order reaction overall.
(c) Raising the temperature will cause the value of k to decrease.
(d) Raising the temperature lowers the activation energy for this reaction.
(e) If the concentrations of both reactants are doubled, the rate will double.
(f) Adding a catalyst in the reaction will cause the initial rate to increase.

82. Chlorine atoms contribute to the destruction of the earth's ozone layer by the following sequence of reactions:

$$Cl + O_3 \rightarrow ClO + O_2$$

$$ClO + O \rightarrow Cl + O_2$$

where the O atoms in the second step come from the decomposition of ozone by sunlight:

$$O_3(g) \rightarrow O(g) + O_2(g)$$

What is the net equation on summing these three equations? Why does this lead to ozone loss in the stratosphere? What is the role played by Cl in this sequence of reactions? What name is given to species such as ClO?

83. Describe each of the following statements as true or false. If false, rewrite the sentence to make it correct.
(a) The rate-determining elementary step in a reaction is the slowest step in a mechanism.
(b) It is possible to change the rate constant by changing the temperature.

(c) As a reaction proceeds at constant temperature, the rate remains constant.

(d) A reaction that is third order overall must involve more than one step.

84. Identify which of the following statements are incorrect. If the statement is incorrect, rewrite it to be correct.

(a) Reactions are faster at a higher temperature because activation energies are lower.

(b) Rates increase with increasing concentration of reactants because there are more collisions between reactant molecules.

(c) At higher temperatures, a larger fraction of molecules have enough energy to get over the activation energy barrier.

(d) Catalyzed and uncatalyzed reactions have identical mechanisms.

85. The reaction cyclopropane → propene occurs on a platinum metal surface at 200 °C. (The platinum is a catalyst.) The reaction is first order in cyclopropane. Indicate how the following quantities change (increase, decrease, or no change) as this reaction progresses, assuming constant temperature.

(a) [cyclopropane]
(b) [propene]
(c) [catalyst]
(d) the rate constant, k
(e) the order of the reaction
(f) the half-life of cyclopropane

86. Isotopes are often used as "tracers" to follow an atom through a chemical reaction, and the following is an example. Acetic acid reacts with methanol (Chapter 10).

$$CH_3CO_2H \quad + \quad CH_3OH$$

$$CH_3CO_2CH_3 \quad + \quad H_2O$$

Explain how you could use the isotope ^{18}O to show whether the oxygen atom in the water comes from the —OH of the acid or the —OH of the alcohol.

87. Examine the reaction coordinate diagram given here.

(a) How many steps are in the mechanism for the reaction described by this diagram?

(b) Is the reaction overall exothermic or endothermic?

88. Draw a reaction coordinate diagram for an exothermic reaction that occurs in a single step. Identify the activation energy and the net energy change for the reaction on this diagram. Draw a second diagram that represents the same reaction in the presence of a catalyst, assuming a single step reaction is involved here also. Identify the activation energy of this reaction and the energy change. Is the activation energy in the two drawings different? Does the energy evolved in the two reactions differ?

Applying Chemical Principles

Kinetics and Mechanisms: A 70-Year-Old Mystery Solved

Toward the end of the 19th century, the gas phase reaction of $H_2(g)$ with $I_2(s)$ was shown to be first-order for each reactant.

$$H_2(g) + I_2(g) \rightleftharpoons 2\ HI(g)$$

For approximately 70 years, the accepted mechanism was an elementary bimolecular collision that results in an exchange of atoms.

However, in 1967, John H. Sullivan determined that this single-step mechanism is incorrect. Sullivan provided evidence that the reaction actually occurs in two steps. The first step of the mechanism is the dissociation of elemental iodine into iodine atoms. The dissociation of I_2 is a fast equilibrium process that produces a relatively constant concentration of iodine atoms.

Fast equilibrium $I_2(g) \rightleftharpoons 2\ I(g)$

The second step of the mechanism is a termolecular reaction between two iodine atoms and elemental hydrogen.

Slow $H_2(g) + 2\ I(g) \rightarrow 2\ HI$

What was Sullivan's evidence for the revised mechanism? First, he worked at temperatures too low to allow thermal decomposition of I_2. At these temperatures, little or no hydrogen iodide is formed. Second, he used a technique called *flash photolysis* to create iodine atoms from I_2. In this technique a mixture of hydrogen and iodine was irradiated with a strong pulse of light. Sullivan found that the rate of the reaction was dependent on the square of the concentration of iodine atoms created by flash photolysis, which is consistent with the second elementary step in his reaction mechanism.

The story of the mechanism of the hydrogen-iodine reaction is a good lesson: chemists should not trust a proposed mechanism just because it fits with an experimentally determined reaction order. Verifying mechanisms often requires identifying intermediates during the course of a reaction. Sullivan was not only able to identify an intermediate, he controlled its production.

Colin Cuthbert/Photo Researchers, Inc.

An apparatus for carrying out flash photolysis experiments in the study of kinetics.
(http://www.photophysics.com/chem_react_mech.php)

Questions:

1. Sullivan used 578 nm light to dissociate I_2 molecules to I atoms.
    a) What is the energy (in kJ/mol) of 578 nm light?
    b) Breaking an I_2 bond requires 151 kJ/mol of energy. What is the longest wavelength of light that has enough energy to dissociate I_2?
2. Show that the two-step mechanism proposed by Sullivan yields the correct (overall second-order) rate law.
3. Why is a termolecular elementary step likely to be the slowest in a mechanism?
4. Determine the activation energy for the reaction of H_2 and I_2 to produce HI, given the data in the table.

Temperature (°C)	Rate Constant (M^{-1}s^{-1})
144.7	1.40×10^{-12}
207.5	1.52×10^{-9}
246.9	5.15×10^{-8}

Reference:

J. H. Sullivan, *Journal of Chemical Physics*, Vol. 46, pp. 73–77, 1967.

16 Principles of Chemical Reactivity: Equilibria

Photos © Cengage Learning/Charles D. Winters

Solution of cobalt(II) chloride in dilute hydrochloric acid

Solution in an ice bath

Solution in a boiling water bath

Solution after adding more hydrochloric acid

Solution after adding more water

Dynamic and Reversible! Chemical reactions are dynamic, as proved by experiments in which reactants and products can be interconverted by making small changes in the conditions of the reaction. Dissolving cobalt(II) chloride in dilute hydrochloric acid demonstrates this very well.

$$[Co(H_2O)_6]^{2+}(aq) + 4\ Cl^-(aq) \rightleftharpoons [CoCl_4]^{2-}(aq) + 6\ H_2O(\ell)$$
red   blue

The photo at the top shows a solution that is a mixture of the red cation, $[Co(H_2O)_6]^{2+}$, and the blue anion, $[CoCl_4]^{2-}$. When the solution is placed in ice, the color changes to red, and when it is put in boiling water, the color is blue. Adding more hydrochloric acid also changes the color, as does adding more water.

Questions:

1. Is the conversion of the red cation to the blue anion by changing the temperature exothermic or endothermic?
2. Account for the effect of adding hydrochloric acid and more water.
3. How do these observations prove the reaction is reversible?

Answers to these questions are available in Appendix N.

CHAPTER GOALS

See Chapter Goals Revisited (page 746) for Study Questions keyed to these goals.

- Understand the nature and characteristics of chemical equilibria.

- Understand the significance of the equilibrium constant, *K*, and the reaction quotient, *Q*.

- Understand how to use *K* in quantitative studies of chemical equilibria.

- Predict how a system at equilibrium will respond if the reaction conditions are changed.

The concept of equilibrium is fundamental in chemistry. The general concept was introduced in Chapter 3, and you have already encountered its importance in explaining phenomena such as solubility, acid–base behavior, and changes of state. These preliminary discussions of equilibrium emphasized the following concepts: that chemical reactions are reversible, that chemical reactions proceed spontaneously in the direction that leads toward equilibrium, that in a closed system a state of equilibrium between reactants and products is achieved eventually, and that outside forces can affect the equilibrium. A major result of our further exploration of chemical equilibria in this and the next two chapters will be an ability to describe chemical equilibria in quantitative terms.

16.1 Chemical Equilibrium: A Review

If you mix solutions of $CaCl_2$ and $NaHCO_3$, a chemical reaction is immediately detected: a gas (CO_2) bubbles from the mixture, and white solid (insoluble) $CaCO_3$ forms (Figure 16.1a). The reaction occurring is

$$Ca^{2+}(aq) + 2\ HCO_3^-(aq) \rightarrow CaCO_3(s) + CO_2(g) + H_2O(\ell)$$

If you next add pieces of dry ice to the suspension of $CaCO_3$ (or if you bubble gaseous CO_2 into the mixture), you will observe that the solid $CaCO_3$ dissolves (Figure 16.1b). This happens because a reaction occurs that is the reverse of the reaction that led to precipitation of $CaCO_3$; that is:

$$CaCO_3(s) + CO_2(g) + H_2O(\ell) \rightarrow Ca^{2+}(aq) + 2\ HCO_3^-(aq)$$

Now imagine what will happen if the solution of Ca^{2+} and HCO_3^- ions is in a *closed* container (unlike the reaction in Figure 16.1, which was done in an open container). As the reaction begins, Ca^{2+} and HCO_3^- react to give products at some rate. As the reactants are depleted, the rate of this reaction slows. At the same time, however, the reaction products ($CaCO_3$, CO_2, and H_2O) begin to combine to re-form Ca^{2+} and HCO_3^-. Eventually, the rate of the forward reaction, the formation of $CaCO_3$, and the rate of the reverse reaction, the redissolving of $CaCO_3$, become equal. With $CaCO_3$ being formed and redissolving at the same rate, no further macroscopic change is observed. Equilibrium has been achieved.

We describe an equilibrium system with an equation that connects reactants and products with double arrows. The double arrows, $\rightleftharpoons$, indicate that the reaction is reversible and that the reaction will be studied using the concepts of chemical equilibria.

$$Ca^{2+}(aq) + 2\ HCO_3^-(aq) \rightleftharpoons CaCO_3(s) + CO_2(g) + H_2O(\ell)$$

● **Cave Chemistry** This same chemistry accounts for stalactites and stalagmites in caves. See page 116.

Photos © Cengage Learning/Charles D. Winters

(a) Combining solutions of $NaHCO_3$ and $CaCl_2$ produces solid $CaCO_3$ and CO_2 gas.

(b) Dry ice (the white solid) is added to the slurry of $CaCO_3$ precipitated in (a).

(c) The calcium carbonate dissolves on adding sufficient dry ice (CO_2) to give Ca^{2+}(aq) and HCO_3^-(aq).

FIGURE 16.1 Equilibrium in the $CO_2/Ca^{2+}/H_2O$ system. See Figure 3.5, which shows the same reaction and illustrates the chemistry of the system.

These experiments illustrate an important feature of chemical reactions: *All chemical reactions are reversible, at least in principle.* This was a key point in our earlier discussion of equilibrium (◄ Chapter 3).

Our next step will be to move from a qualitative to a quantitative description of equilibrium systems. Among other things, this will lead us to the subject of product- and reactant-favored reactions (◄ page 118). Recall that a reaction that has a greater concentration of products than reactants once it has reached equilibrium is said to be product-favored. Similarly, a reaction that has a greater concentration of reactants than products at equilibrium is said to be reactant-favored.

REVIEW & CHECK FOR SECTION 16.1

What would happen in the experiment in Figure 16.1c if you added some additional Ca^{2+} ions (in the form of $CaCl_2$)?

(a) More $CaCO_3$ would precipitate.

(c) Nothing would happen.

(b) Some $CaCO_3$ would dissolve.

16.2 The Equilibrium Constant and Reaction Quotient

Chemical equilibria can also be described in a quantitative fashion. The concentrations of reactants and products when a reaction has reached equilibrium are related. For the reaction of hydrogen and iodine to produce hydrogen iodide, for example, a very large number of experiments have shown that at equilibrium the ratio of the square of the HI concentration to the product of the H_2 and I_2 concentrations is a constant.

$$H_2(g) + I_2(g) \rightleftharpoons 2\ HI(g)$$

$$\frac{[HI]^2}{[H_2][I_2]} = \text{constant } (K) \text{ at equilibrium}$$

This constant is always the same within experimental error for all experiments done *at a given temperature.* Suppose, for example, the concentrations of H_2 and I_2 in a flask are each initially 0.0175 mol/L at 425 °C and no HI is present. Over time, the concentrations of H_2 and I_2 will decrease, and the concentration of HI will increase until a state of equilibrium is reached (Figure 16.2). If the gases in

$$H_2(g) + I_2(g) \rightleftharpoons 2HI(g)$$

Reactants proceeding toward equilibrium

FIGURE 16.2 The reaction of H_2 and I_2 reaches equilibrium. The final concentrations of H_2, I_2, and HI depend on the initial concentrations of H_2 and I_2. If one begins with a different set of initial concentrations, the equilibrium concentrations will be different, but the quotient $[HI]^2/[H_2][I_2]$ will always be the same at a given temperature.

the flask are then analyzed, the observed concentrations would be $[H_2] = [I_2] = 0.0037$ mol/L and $[HI] = 0.0276$ mol/L. The following table—which we call an **ICE table for initial, change, and equilibrium concentrations**—summarizes these results:

Equation	$H_2(g)$	+	$I_2(g)$	$\rightleftharpoons$	2 HI(g)
I = *Initial* concentration (M)	0.0175		0.0175		0
C = *Change* in concentration as reaction proceeds to equilibrium (M)	−0.0138		−0.0138		+0.0276
E = *Equilibrium* concentration (M)	0.0037		0.0037		0.0276

● **ICE Table: Initial, Change, and Equilibrium** Throughout our discussions of chemical equilibria, we shall express the quantitative information for reactions in an amounts table or ICE table (◄ Chapter 4, page 159). These tables show what the initial (I) concentrations are, how those concentrations change (C) on proceeding to equilibrium, and what the concentrations are at equilibrium (E). Some students call these **RICE tables**, where R stands for "reaction."

The second line in the table gives the change in concentration of reactants and products on proceeding to equilibrium. Changes are always equal to the difference between the equilibrium and initial concentrations.

Change in concentration = equilibrium concentration − initial concentration

Putting the equilibrium concentration values from the ICE table into the expression for the constant (K) gives a value of 56 (to two significant figures).

$$\frac{[HI]^2}{[H_2][I_2]} = \frac{(0.0276)^2}{(0.0037)(0.0037)} = 56$$

Other experiments can be done on the H_2/I_2 reaction with different concentrations of reactants, or done using mixtures of reactants and products. Regardless of the initial amounts, when equilibrium is achieved, the ratio $[HI]^2/[H_2][I_2]$ is always the same, 56, at this temperature.

The observation that the product and reactant concentrations for the H_2 and I_2 reaction are always in the same ratio can be generalized to other reactions. For the general chemical reaction

$$aA + bB \rightleftharpoons cC + dD$$

we can define the equilibrium constant, K.

When the reaction is at equilibrium

$$\text{Equilibrium constant} = K = \frac{[C]^c[D]^d}{[A]^a[B]^b} \qquad (16.1)$$

Equation 16.1 is called the **equilibrium constant expression**. If the ratio of products to reactants as defined by Equation 16.1 matches the equilibrium constant value, the system is known to be at equilibrium. Conversely, if the ratio has a

© Cengage Learning/Charles D. Winters

FIGURE 16.3 Burning sulfur. Elemental sulfur burns in oxygen with a beautiful blue flame to give SO_2 gas.

different value, the system is not at equilibrium, and, as you will see later in this section, we can predict in which direction the reaction will proceed to reach equilibrium.

Writing Equilibrium Constant Expressions

In an equilibrium constant expression,

- all concentrations are equilibrium values.
- product concentrations appear in the numerator, and reactant concentrations appear in the denominator.
- each concentration is raised to the power of its stoichiometric coefficient in the balanced chemical equation.
- the value of the constant K depends on the particular reaction and on the temperature.
- values of K are dimensionless.

Reactions Involving Solids

The oxidation of solid, yellow sulfur produces colorless sulfur dioxide gas in a product-favored reaction (Figure 16.3).

$$S(s) + O_2(g) \rightleftharpoons SO_2(g)$$

The general principle when writing an equilibrium constant expression is to place product concentrations in the numerator and reactant concentrations in the denominator. In reactions involving solids, however, experiments show that the equilibrium concentrations of other reactants or products—here, O_2 and SO_2—do not depend on the amount of solid present (as long as some solid is present at equilibrium). Therefore, the concentration of a solid such as sulfur is not included in the equilibrium constant expression.

$$K = \frac{[SO_2]}{[O_2]}$$

In general, *the concentrations of any solid reactants and products are not included in the equilibrium constant expression.*

Reactions in Solution

There are also special considerations for reactions occurring in solution, particularly aqueous solutions in which water is either a reactant or a product. Consider ammonia, which is a weak base owing to its incomplete reaction with water.

$$NH_3(aq) + H_2O(\ell) \rightleftharpoons NH_4^+(aq) + OH^-(aq)$$

Because the water concentration is very high in a dilute ammonia solution, the concentration of water is essentially unchanged by the reaction. The general rule *for reactions in aqueous solution is that the molar concentration of water is not included in the equilibrium constant expression.* Thus, for aqueous ammonia we write

$$K = \frac{[NH_4^+][OH^-]}{[NH_3]}$$

● **K_c and K_p** The subscript "c" (K_c) indicates that the numerical values of concentrations in the equilibrium constant expression have units of mol/L. A subscript "p" (K_p) indicates that partial pressures of gaseous reactants and products were used in calculating the equilibrium constant. In this chapter, we will sometimes write simply K for K_c but will always write K_p to indicate that partial pressures were used.

Reactions Involving Gases: K_c and K_p

Concentration data can be used to calculate equilibrium constants for both aqueous and gaseous systems. In these cases, the symbol K is sometimes given the subscript "c" for "concentration," as in K_c. For gases, however, equilibrium constant expressions can be written in another way—in terms of partial pressures of reactants and products. If you rearrange the ideal gas law, $[PV = nRT]$, and recognize that the "gas concentration," (n/V), is equivalent to P/RT, you see that the partial pressure of a gas is proportional to its concentration $[P = (n/V)RT]$. If reactant and

A CLOSER LOOK

Activities and Units of *K*

In the text we state that "Values of *K* are dimensionless." After all our care in using units, this might seem sloppy. However, advanced thermodynamics informs us that equilibrium constants should really be calculated from the "activities" of reactants and products and not from their concentrations or partial pressures. Activities can be thought of as "effective" concentrations or partial pressures.

The activity of a substance in solution is obtained by calculating the ratio of its concentration, [X], relative to a standard concentration (1 M) and then multiplying this ratio by a correction factor called an *activity coefficient*. Because it involves a ratio of concentrations, the activity is dimensionless. (Likewise, the activity of a gas is obtained from the ratio of its partial pressure, P_X, relative to a standard pressure (1 atm or 1 bar) and then multiplying by an activity coefficient.) In general chemistry, we assume all the activity coefficients are equal to 1 and so the activity of a solute or a gas is numerically the same as its concentration or partial pressure, respectively. This assumption is best met for solutes in very dilute solutions or gases at low pressures. Regardless of the values of activity coefficients, values of *K* are properly calculated using dimensionless quantities and so they have no units.

Another consequence of using activities is that the "concentration" of solids does not appear in the *K* expression. This is because the activity of a solid is 1. Similarly, water or other solvent is not included because its activity is 1.

---

product quantities are given in partial pressures (in atmospheres or in bars), then *K* is given the subscript "p," as in K_p.

$$H_2(g) + I_2(g) \rightleftharpoons 2\ HI(g)$$

$$K_p = \frac{P_{HI}^2}{P_{H_2} P_{I_2}}$$

Notice that the basic form of the equilibrium constant expression is the same as for K_c. In some cases, the numerical values of K_c and K_p are the same, but they are different when the numbers of moles of gaseous reactants and products are different. *A Closer Look: Equilibrium Constant Expressions for Gases—K_c and K_p* shows how K_c and K_p are related and how to convert from one to the other.

EXAMPLE 16.1 Writing Equilibrium Constant Expressions

Problem Write the equilibrium constant expressions for the following reactions.

(a) $N_2(g) + 3\ H_2(g) \rightleftharpoons 2\ NH_3(g)$

(b) $H_2CO_3(aq) + H_2O(\ell) \rightleftharpoons HCO_3^-(aq) + H_3O^+(aq)$

What Do You Know? You have balanced chemical equations, from which you can write the equilibrium constant expressions.

Strategy Product concentrations always appear in the numerator and reactant concentrations appear in the denominator. Each concentration should be raised to a power equal to the stoichiometric coefficient in the balanced equation. In reaction (b), the water concentration does not appear in the equilibrium constant expression.

Solution

(a) $K = \dfrac{[NH_3]^2}{[N_2][H_2]^3}$

(b) $K = \dfrac{[HCO_3^-][H_3O^+]}{[H_2CO_3]}$

Think about Your Answer Always check to make sure you have the products in the numerator and reactants in the denominator. Confusing these is a common source of student error.

Check Your Understanding

Write the equilibrium constant expression for each of the following reactions in terms of concentrations.

(a) $CO_2(g) + C(s) \rightleftharpoons 2\ CO(g)$

(b) $[Cu(NH_3)_4]^{2+}(aq) \rightleftharpoons Cu^{2+}(aq) + 4\ NH_3(aq)$

(c) $CH_3CO_2H(aq) + H_2O(\ell) \rightleftharpoons CH_3CO_2^-(aq) + H_3O^+(aq)$

A CLOSER LOOK

Equilibrium Constant Expressions for Gases—K_c and K_p

Many metal carbonates, such as limestone, decompose on heating to give the metal oxide and CO_2 gas.

$$CaCO_3(s) \rightleftharpoons CaO(s) + CO_2(g)$$

The equilibrium constant for this reaction can be expressed either in terms of the number of moles per liter of CO_2, $K_c = [CO_2]$, or in terms of the pressure of CO_2, $K_p = P_{CO_2}$. From the ideal gas law, you know that

$$P = (n/V)RT =$$
(concentration in mol/L) $\times RT$

For this reaction, we can therefore say that $P_{CO_2} = [CO_2]RT = K_p$. Because $K_c = [CO_2]$, we find that $K_p = K_c(RT)$. That is, the values of K_p and K_c are not the same; for the decomposition of calcium carbonate, K_p is the product of K_c and the factor RT.

Consider the equilibrium constant for the reaction of N_2 and H_2 to produce ammonia in terms of partial pressures, K_p.

$$N_2(g) + 3 H_2(g) \rightleftharpoons 2 NH_3(g)$$

$$K_p = \frac{(P_{NH_3})^2}{(P_{N_2})(P_{H_2})^3}$$

Does K_c, the equilibrium constant in terms of concentrations, have the same value as, or a different value than, K_p? We can answer this question by substituting for each pressure in K_p the equivalent expression $[C](RT)$. That is,

$$K_p = \frac{\{[NH_3](RT)\}^2}{\{[N_2](RT)\}\{[H_2](RT)\}^3} =$$

$$\frac{[NH_3]^2}{[N_2][H_2]^3} \times \frac{1}{(RT)^2} = \frac{K_c}{(RT)^2}$$

or $K_p = K_c(RT)^{-2}$

Once again, you see that K_p and K_c are not the same but are related by some function of RT.

Looking carefully at this example and others, we find that

$$K_p = K_c(RT)^{\Delta n}$$

where Δn is the change in the number of moles of gas on going from reactants to products.

$\Delta n =$ total moles of gaseous products $-$ total moles of gaseous reactants

For the decomposition of $CaCO_3$,

$$\Delta n = 1 - 0 = 1$$

whereas the value of Δn for the ammonia synthesis is

$$\Delta n = 2 - 4 = -2$$

The Meaning of the Equilibrium Constant, K

Table 16.1 lists a few equilibrium constants for different kinds of reactions. A large value of K means that the concentrations of the products are higher than the concentrations of the reactants at equilibrium. That is, the products are favored over the reactants at equilibrium.

> **K > 1: Reaction is product-favored at equilibrium.** The concentrations of products are greater than the concentrations of the reactants at equilibrium.

Table 16.1 Selected Equilibrium Constant Values

Reaction	Equilibrium Constant, K (at 25 °C)	Product- or Reactant-Favored at Equilibrium
Combination Reaction of Nonmetals		
$S(s) + O_2(g) \rightleftharpoons SO_2(g)$	4.2×10^{52}	$K > 1$; product-favored
$2 H_2(g) + O_2(g) \rightleftharpoons 2 H_2O(g)$	3.2×10^{81}	$K > 1$; product-favored
$N_2(g) + 3 H_2(g) \rightleftharpoons 2 NH_3(g)$	3.5×10^8	$K > 1$; product-favored
Ionization of Weak Acids and Bases		
$HCO_2H(aq) + H_2O(\ell) \rightleftharpoons HCO_2^-(aq) + H_3O^+(aq)$ formic acid	1.8×10^{-4}	$K < 1$; reactant-favored
$CH_3CO_2H(aq) + H_2O(\ell) \rightleftharpoons CH_3CO_2^-(aq) + H_3O^+(aq)$ acetic acid	1.8×10^{-5}	$K < 1$; reactant-favored
$H_2CO_3(aq) + H_2O(\ell) \rightleftharpoons HCO_3^-(aq) + H_3O^+(aq)$ carbonic acid	4.2×10^{-7}	$K < 1$; reactant-favored
$NH_3(aq) + H_2O(\ell) \rightleftharpoons NH_4^+(aq) + OH^-(aq)$ ammonia	1.8×10^{-5}	$K < 1$; reactant-favored
Dissolution of "Insoluble" Solids		
$CaCO_3(s) \rightleftharpoons Ca^{2+}(aq) + CO_3^{2-}(aq)$	3.8×10^{-9}	$K < 1$; reactant-favored
$AgCl(s) \rightleftharpoons Ag^+(aq) + Cl^-(aq)$	1.8×10^{-10}	$K < 1$; reactant-favored

Product-favored (K > 1)

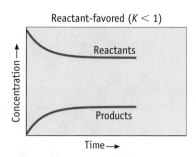

Reactant-favored (K < 1)

FIGURE 16.4 The difference between reactions that are product-favored or reactant-favored at equilibrium.

(a) The concentrations of products exceeds the concentrations of reactants at equilibrium, and the reaction is product-favored.

(b) The reactant concentrations exceed the product concentrations at equilibrium, and the reaction is reactant-favored.

An example is the reaction of nitrogen monoxide and ozone.

$$NO(g) + O_3(g) \rightleftharpoons NO_2(g) + O_2(g)$$

$$K = \frac{[NO_2][O_2]}{[NO][O_3]} = 6 \times 10^{34} \text{ at } 25 \,°C$$

The very large value of K indicates that, at equilibrium, $[NO_2][O_2] >> [NO][O_3]$. If stoichiometric amounts of NO and O_3 are mixed and allowed to come to equilibrium, virtually none of the reactants will be found (Figure 16.4a). Essentially, all will have been converted to NO_2 and O_2. A chemist would say that "the reaction has gone to completion."

Conversely, a small value of K means that very little of the products exists when equilibrium has been achieved (Figure 16.4b). That is, the reactants are favored over the products at equilibrium.

$K < 1$: Reaction is reactant-favored at equilibrium. Concentrations of reactants are greater than concentrations of products at equilibrium.

This is true for the formation of ozone from oxygen.

$$3/2 \, O_2(g) \rightleftharpoons O_3(g)$$

$$K = \frac{[O_3]}{[O_2]^{3/2}} = 2.5 \times 10^{-29} \text{ at } 25 \,°C$$

The very small value of K indicates that, at equilibrium, $[O_3] << [O_2]^{3/2}$. If O_2 is placed in a flask, very little O_2 will have been converted to O_3 when equilibrium has been achieved.

When K is close to 1, it may not be immediately clear whether the reactant concentrations are larger than the product concentrations, or vice versa. It will depend on the form of K and thus on the reaction stoichiometry. Calculations of the concentrations will have to be done.

The Reaction Quotient, Q

The equilibrium constant, K, for a reaction has a particular numerical value when the reactants and products are at equilibrium. When the reactants and products in a reaction are not at equilibrium, however, it is convenient to calculate the reaction quotient, Q. For the general reaction of A and B to give C and D,

$$aA + bB \rightleftharpoons cC + dD$$

the reaction quotient is defined as

$$\text{Reaction quotient} = Q = \frac{[C]^c[D]^d}{[A]^a[B]^b} \tag{16.2}$$

(a) Not at equilibrium. $Q = 4/3 < K$.

Here, four isobutane molecules and three butane molecules are present. Reaction will proceed to convert butane into isobutane to reach equilibrium.

(b) At equilibrium. $Q = 5/2 = K$.

Here, five isobutane molecules and two butane molecules are present. Reaction is at equilibrium.

(c) Not at equilibrium. $Q = 6/1 > K$.

Here, six isobutane molecules and one butane molecule are present. Reaction will proceed to convert isobutane into butane to reach equilibrium.

FIGURE 16.5 The interconversion of isobutane and butane. Only when the concentrations of isobutane and butane are in the ratio [isobutane]/[butane] = 2.5 is the system at equilibrium (b). With any other ratio of concentrations, there will be a net conversion of one compound into the other until equilibrium is achieved.

This expression appears to be just like the expression for the equilibrium constant, K, in Equation 16.1, but it is not. In calculating K, the concentrations must be those present *at equilibrium.* The concentrations of reactants and products in the expression for Q are those that occur at any point as the reaction proceeds from reactants to an equilibrium mixture. Only when the system is at equilibrium does $Q = K$. For the reaction of H_2 and I_2 to give HI (Figure 16.2), any combination of reactant and product concentrations before equilibrium is achieved will give a value of Q different than K.

Determining a reaction quotient is useful for two reasons. First, it will tell you whether a system is at equilibrium (when $Q = K$) or is not at equilibrium (when $Q \neq K$). Second, by comparing Q and K, we can predict what changes will occur in reactant and product concentrations as the reaction proceeds to equilibrium.

● **Comparing Q and K**

Relative Magnitude	Direction of Reaction
$Q < K$	Reactants → Products
$Q = K$	Reaction at equilibrium
$Q > K$	Reactants ← Products

- $Q < K$: If Q is less than K, some reactants must be converted to products for the reaction to reach equilibrium. This will decrease the reactant concentrations and increase the product concentrations. (This is the case for the system in Figure 16.5a.)
- $Q > K$: If Q is greater than K, some products must be converted to reactants for the reaction to reach equilibrium. This will increase the reactant concentrations and decrease the product concentrations (Figure 16.5c).

To illustrate these points, let us consider a reaction such as the transformation of butane to isobutane (2-methylpropane).

Butane $\rightleftharpoons$ Isobutane

$$CH_3CH_2CH_2CH_3 \quad \rightleftharpoons \quad CH_3\overset{\displaystyle CH_3}{\underset{\displaystyle |}{CH}}CH_3$$

$$K_c = \frac{[\text{isobutane}]}{[\text{butane}]} = 2.50 \text{ at } 298 \text{ K}$$

Any mixture of butane and isobutane, whether at equilibrium or not, can be represented by the reaction quotient Q ($=$ [isobutane]/[butane]). Suppose you have a mixture composed of 3.0 mol/L of butane and 4.0 mol/L of isobutane (at 298 K) (Figure 16.5a). This means that the reaction quotient, Q, is

$$Q = \frac{[\text{isobutane}]}{[\text{butane}]} = \frac{4.0}{3.0} = 1.3$$

This set of concentrations clearly does not represent an equilibrium system because $Q < K$. To reach equilibrium, some butane molecules must be transformed into molecules of isobutane, thereby lowering [butane] and raising [isobutane]. This transformation will continue until the ratio [isobutane]/[butane] = 2.5; that is, until $Q = K$ (Figure 16.5b).

What happens when there is too much isobutane in the system relative to the amount of butane? Suppose [isobutane] = 6.0 mol/L but [butane] is only 1.0 mol/L (Figure 16.5c). Now the reaction quotient Q is greater than K ($Q > K$), and the system is again not at equilibrium. It will proceed to equilibrium by converting isobutane molecules to butane molecules.

⦿WL   INTERACTIVE EXAMPLE 16.2   The Reaction Quotient

Problem The brown gas nitrogen dioxide, NO_2, can exist in equilibrium with the colorless gas N_2O_4. $K = 170$ at 298 K for the reaction

$$2\ NO_2(g) \rightleftharpoons N_2O_4(g) \quad K = 170$$

Suppose that, at a specific time, the concentration of NO_2 is 0.015 M and the concentration of N_2O_4 is 0.025 M. Is Q larger than, smaller than, or equal to K? If the system is not at equilibrium, in which direction will the reaction proceed to achieve equilibrium?

What Do You Know? You are given the balanced chemical equation, the value of the equilibrium constant K_c, and concentrations of reactant and product.

Strategy

- Write the expression for the reaction quotient, Q, from the balanced equation.

- Substitute concentrations of reactant and product into the expression and calculate Q.

- Decide if Q is greater than, less than, or equal to K_c and in which direction the reaction will proceed.

Solution

$$Q = \frac{[N_2O_4]}{[NO_2]^2} = \frac{(0.025)}{(0.015)^2} = 110$$

The value of Q is less than the value of K ($Q < K$), so the reaction is not at equilibrium. The system proceeds to equilibrium by converting NO_2 to N_2O_4, increasing [N_2O_4], and decreasing [NO_2] until $Q = K$.

Think about Your Answer When calculating Q, make sure that you raise each concentration to the power corresponding to the stoichiometric coefficient.

Check Your Understanding

Answer the following questions regarding the butane $\rightleftharpoons$ isobutane equilibrium ($K = 2.50$ at 298 K).

(a) Is the system at equilibrium when [butane] = 0.97 M and [isobutane] = 2.18 M? If not, in which direction will the reaction proceed to achieve equilibrium?

(b) Is the system at equilibrium when [butane] = 0.75 M and [isobutane] = 2.60 M? If not, in which direction will the reaction proceed to achieve equilibrium?

Strategy Map 16.2

PROBLEM

Is a reaction at **equilibrium**? If not, which way does it proceed? Calculate **Q**.

$\downarrow$

DATA/INFORMATION KNOWN

- Balanced equation
- Value of **K**
- Concentrations of **reactant** and **product**

STEP 1. Write **Q** expression and calculate **Q**.

Calculated **Q** from reactant and product concentrations

STEP 2. Compare **Q** and **K**.

Q (110) < **K** (170) More product forms from reactant to reach equilibrium.

REVIEW & CHECK FOR SECTION 16.2

1. Which of the following is the correct form of the equilibrium constant expression for the reaction below?

$$2\ SO_3(g) \rightleftharpoons 2\ SO_2(g) + O_2(g)$$

   (a) $K = [SO_2][O_2]/[SO_3]$

   (b) $K = [SO_2]^2[O_2]/[SO_3]^2$

   (c) $K = [SO_3]^2/[SO_2]^2[O_2]$

   (d) $K = [SO_2][O_2]^2$

2. At 2000 K the equilibrium constant for the formation of NO(g) is 4.0×10^{-4}.

$$N_2(g) + O_2(g) \rightleftharpoons 2\ NO(g)$$

   You have a flask in which, at 2000 K, the concentration of N_2 is 0.50 mol/L, that of O_2 is 0.25 mol/L, and that of NO is 4.2×10^{-3} mol/L. Is the system at equilibrium?

   (a) Yes, it is at equilibrium.

   (b) No, it is not at equilibrium, and the reaction proceeds further to the right.

   (c) No, it is not at equilibrium, and the reaction proceeds to the left, turning products into reactants.

16.3 Determining an Equilibrium Constant

When the experimental values of the concentrations of all of the reactants and products are known at equilibrium, an equilibrium constant can be calculated by substituting the data into the equilibrium constant expression. Consider this concept as it applies to the oxidation of sulfur dioxide.

$$2\ SO_2(g) + O_2(g) \rightleftharpoons 2\ SO_3(g)$$

In an experiment done at 852 K, the equilibrium concentrations are found to be $[SO_2] = 3.61 \times 10^{-3}$ mol/L, $[O_2] = 6.11 \times 10^{-4}$ mol/L, and $[SO_3] = 1.01 \times 10^{-2}$ mol/L. Substituting these data into the equilibrium constant expression, we can calculate the value of K.

$$K = \frac{[SO_3]^2}{[SO_2]^2[O_2]} = \frac{(1.01 \times 10^{-2})^2}{(3.61 \times 10^{-3})^2(6.11 \times 10^{-4})} = 1.28 \times 10^4 \text{ at 852 K}$$

(Notice that K has a large value; at equilibrium, the oxidation of sulfur dioxide is product-favored at 852 K.)

More commonly, an experiment will provide information on the initial quantities of reactants and the concentration at equilibrium of only one of the reactants or of one of the products. The equilibrium concentrations of the rest of the reactants and products must then be inferred from the reaction stoichiometry. As an example, again consider the oxidation of sulfur dioxide to sulfur trioxide. Suppose that 1.00 mol of SO_2 and 1.00 mol of O_2 are placed in a 1.00-L flask, this time at 1000 K. When equilibrium has been achieved, 0.925 mol of SO_3 has been formed. Let us use this information to calculate the equilibrium constant for the reaction. After writing the equilibrium constant expression in terms of concentrations, we set up an ICE table (page 723) showing the initial concentrations, the changes in those concentrations on proceeding to equilibrium, and the concentrations at equilibrium.

Equation	$2\ SO_2(g)$	+	$O_2(g)$	$\rightleftharpoons$	$2\ SO_3(g)$
Initial (M)	1.00		1.00		0
Change (M)	$-2x$		$-x$		$+2x$
Equilibrium (M)	$1.00 - 2x$		$1.00 - x$		$2x$
	$1.00 - 0.925 = 0.075$		$1.00 - 0.925/2 = 0.54$		$= 0.925$

The quantities in the ICE table result from the following analysis:

- Line 1: Original concentrations.
- Line 2: The amount of O_2 consumed is designated as $-x$ mol/L. We give it a minus sign because O_2 is consumed. It then follows from the reaction stoichiometry that the amount of SO_2 consumed is $-2x$, and the amount of SO_3 produced is $+2x$.
- Lines 3 and 4:
  - (a) We know from experiment that $[SO_3]$ at equilibrium is 0.925 M. Therefore, $2x = 0.925$ M.
  - (b) The equilibrium concentration of SO_2 is equal to the initial concentration minus what was consumed. Therefore, $[SO_2]$ is $(1.00 - 2x)$ M or 0.075 M.
  - (c) The amount of O_2 consumed is half of the amount of SO_3 produced or x ($= 0.463$ mol/L). Therefore, the equilibrium concentration of O_2 is 0.54 M.

With the equilibrium concentrations now known, it is possible to calculate K.

$$K = \frac{[SO_3]^2}{[SO_2]^2[O_2]} = \frac{(0.925)^2}{(0.075)^2(0.54)} = 2.8 \times 10^2 \text{ at 1000 K}$$

⬚WL   INTERACTIVE EXAMPLE 16.3   Calculating an Equilibrium Constant (K_c) Using Concentrations

Problem In aqueous solution iron(III) ions react with iodide ions to give iron(II) ions and triiodide ions, I_3^-. Suppose the initial concentration of Fe^{3+} ions is 0.200 M, the initial I^- ion concentration is 0.300 M, and the equilibrium concentration of I_3^- ions is 0.0866 M. What is the value of K_c?

$$2\,Fe^{3+}(aq) + 3\,I^-(aq) \rightleftharpoons 2\,Fe^{2+}(aq) + I_3^-(aq)$$

What Do You Know? You are given the balanced equation (from which the equilibrium constant expression can be written), initial concentrations of the reactants, and the concentration of one product (I_3^-) after equilibrium has been reached.

Strategy

- Set up an ICE table and enter the initial concentrations.

- Decide how each concentration changes. Let us begin by saying that x mol/L of I_3^- ions are produced on proceeding to equilibrium. Based on the reaction stoichiometry, this means that $2x$ mol/L of Fe^{2+} must also be produced, $2x$ mol/L of Fe^{3+} ions are consumed, and $3x$ mol/L of I^- ions are consumed.

- The equilibrium concentration of I_3^- is known (0.0866 M), so this is the quantity x.

- Knowing that $x = 0.0866$ M, calculate the equilibrium concentrations for each species.

- Enter the equilibrium concentrations of reactants and products into the equilibrium constant expression and solve for K_c.

Solution The strategy outlined leads to the ICE table below.

Equation	2 Fe^{3+}	+	3 I^-	$\rightleftharpoons$	2 Fe^{2+}	+	I_3^-
Initial (M)	0.200		0.300		0		0
Change (M)	$-2x$		$-3x$		$+2x$		$+x$
Equilibrium (M)	0.200 − 2(0.0866)		0.300 − 3(0.0866)		2(0.0866)		0.0866
	= 0.027		= 0.040		= 0.173		

The concentration of each substance at equilibrium is now known, and K can be calculated.

$$K_c = \frac{[Fe^{2+}]^2[I_3^-]}{[Fe^{3+}]^2[I^-]^3} = \frac{(0.173)^2(0.0866)}{(0.027)^2(0.040)^3} = 5.6 \times 10^4$$

Strategy Map 16.3

PROBLEM

Calculate K_c for reaction of Fe^{3+} with I^- to give Fe^{2+} and I_3^-.

↓

DATA/INFORMATION KNOWN

- Balanced equation
- **Initial concentrations** of reactants
- **Equilibrium concentration** of one product

STEP 1. Organize information.

Write K_c expression, set up **ICE table**, and enter **known concentrations** in the table.

STEP 2. Enter **concentration changes** in ICE table and derive **equilibrium concentrations**.

Complete **ICE table** with equilibrium concentrations known.

STEP 3. Enter **equilibrium concentrations** in K_c expression and solve for K_c.

Value of K_c

Think about Your Answer The key to this problem is that the concentration of one product, I_3^-, was known at equilibrium. The concentrations of the other product and of the reactants could be derived from this based on the reaction stoichiometry. Also notice that the calculated K is much greater than one, so the reaction is product-favored at equilibrium. This is consistent with the equilibrium concentrations calculated in the ICE table.

Check Your Understanding

A solution is prepared by dissolving 0.050 mol of diiodocyclohexane, $C_6H_{10}I_2$, in the solvent CCl_4. The total solution volume is 1.00 L. When the reaction

$$C_6H_{10}I_2 \rightleftharpoons C_6H_{10} + I_2$$

has come to equilibrium at 35 °C, the concentration of I_2 is 0.035 mol/L.

(a) What are the concentrations of $C_6H_{10}I_2$ and C_6H_{10} at equilibrium?

(b) Calculate K_c, the equilibrium constant.

EXAMPLE 16.4   Calculating an Equilibrium Constant (K_p) Using Partial Pressures

Problem Suppose a tank initially contains H_2S at a pressure of 10.00 atm and a temperature of 800 K. When the reaction has come to equilibrium, the partial pressure of S_2 vapor is 0.020 atm. Calculate K_p.

$$2\ H_2S(g) \rightleftharpoons 2\ H_2(g) + S_2(g)$$

What Do You Know? You are given the balanced equation (from which the equilibrium constant expression for K_p can be written), the initial pressure of the reactant (H_2S), and the pressure of one product (S_2) after equilibrium has been reached.

Strategy

- Set up an ICE table and enter the initial pressures of H_2S, H_2, and S_2.

- Define the change in S_2 concentration as $+x$.

- From the reaction stoichiometry you know that the change in the partial pressure of H_2 is twice that of S_2 ($= +2x$ atm) and that the change in H_2S partial pressure is $-2x$.

- The equilibrium partial pressure of S_2 is given, so you know that $x = 0.020$ atm. From this calculate the equilibrium partial pressures for H_2S and H_2.

- Enter the equilibrium pressures of reactants and products into the equilibrium constant expression and solve for K_p.

Solution Following the strategy outlined gives the ICE table below.

Equation	$2\ H_2S(g)$	$\rightleftharpoons$	$2\ H_2(g)$	$+$	$S_2(g)$
Initial (atm)	10.00		0		0
Change (atm)	$-2x$		$+2x$		$+x$
Equilibrium (atm)	$10.00 - 2x$		$2(0.020)$		0.020
	$10.00 - 0.040 = 9.96$		$= 0.040$		

Now that the partial pressures of all of the reactants and products are known, K_p can be calculated.

$$K_p = \frac{(P_{H_2})^2 P_{S_2}}{(P_{H_2S})^2} = \frac{(0.040)^2(0.020)}{(9.96)^2} = 3.2 \times 10^{-7}$$

Think about Your Answer The value of K_p calculated is much less than 1, therefore this reaction is reactant-favored at equilibrium, as also indicated by the concentrations calculated in the ICE table. The value of K_p is the same as the value of K_c only when the number of moles of gaseous reactants is the same as the number of moles of gaseous products. This is not true here, so $K_p \neq K_c$. (See *A Closer Look*, page 726).

Check Your Understanding

Pure PCl_5 gas is placed in a 2.00-L flask. After heating to 250 °C the pressure of PCl_5 is initially 2.000 atm. However, the gas slowly but only partially decomposes to gaseous PCl_3 and Cl_2. When equilibrium is reached, the partial pressure of Cl_2 is 0.814 atm. Calculate K_p for the decomposition.

REVIEW & CHECK FOR SECTION 16.3

You place 0.010 mol of $N_2O_4(g)$ in a 2.0-L flask at 200 °C. After reaching equilibrium, $[N_2O_4] = 0.0042$ M. Calculate K_c for the following reaction: $N_2O_4(g) \rightleftharpoons 2\ NO_2(g)$

(a) 1640

(c) 3.1×10^{-4}

(b) 6.1×10^{-4}

(d) 8.8×10^{-6}

16.4 Using Equilibrium Constants in Calculations

In many cases, the value of K and the initial concentrations of reactants are known, and you want to know the concentrations present at equilibrium. As we look at several examples of this situation, we will again use ICE tables that summarize the initial conditions, the changes occurring on proceeding to equilibrium, and the final conditions.

⊘WL   **INTERACTIVE EXAMPLE 16.5**   Calculating Equilibrium Concentrations

Problem The equilibrium constant K_c ($= 55.64$) for

$$H_2(g) + I_2(g) \rightleftharpoons 2\ HI(g)$$

has been determined at 425 °C. If 1.00 mol each of H_2 and I_2 is placed in a 0.500-L flask at 425 °C, what are the concentrations of H_2, I_2, and HI when equilibrium has been achieved?

What Do You Know? You are given the balanced equation (from which the equilibrium constant expression can be written), the value of K, and the initial amounts of the reactants and the volume of the container (from which initial concentrations of the reactants can be calculated).

Strategy

*   Write the equilibrium constant expression and set up an ICE table.

*   Enter the initial concentrations of H_2 and I_2 on the first line (I).

*   Assign the variable x to represent changes in concentration. Based on the reaction stoichiometry the change in $[H_2]$ and $[I_2]$ is $-x$ and the change in [HI] is $+2x$. Enter these values into the change (C) line of the table.

*   Enter the expressions for the final equilibrium concentrations of all three species on the third line (E) of the ICE table, and then transfer these expressions to the equilibrium constant expression and solve for x.

*   Use the calculated value of x to solve for the final concentration of each species.

Strategy Map 16.5

PROBLEM

What are the **equilibrium concentrations** of H_2, I_2, and **HI** in formation of HI from H_2 and I_2?

↓

DATA/INFORMATION KNOWN

*   Balanced equation
*   Value of K_c
*   **Initial concentrations** of reactants

↓

⟨ **STEP 1.** Organize information.

↓

Write K_c expression, set up **ICE table**, and enter **known concentrations** in the table.

⟨ **STEP 2.** Enter **concentration changes** in ICE table and derive **equilibrium concentrations** in terms of unknown quantity x.

↓

Equilibrium concentrations of H_2, I_2, and **HI** are defined in terms of the unknown quantity x.

⟨ **STEP 3.** Enter **equilibrium concentrations** in K_c expression and solve for x.

↓

Value of x

⟨ **STEP 4.** Use value of x to derive **equilibrium concentrations**.

↓

Values of equilibrium concentrations

Module 21: Chemical Equilibrium
covers concepts in this section.

Solution Write the equilibrium constant expression

$$K = \frac{[\text{HI}]^2}{[\text{H}_2][\text{I}_2]} = 55.64$$

and then set up the ICE table as outlined in the Strategy.

Equation	$\text{H}_2\text{(g)}$	+	$\text{I}_2\text{(g)}$	$\rightleftharpoons$	2 HI(g)
Initial (M)	1.00 mol/0.500 L = 2.00 M		1.00 mol/0.500 L = 2.00 M		0
Change (M)	$-x$		$-x$		$+2x$
Equilibrium (M)	$2.00 - x$		$2.00 - x$		$2x$

Now the expressions for the equilibrium concentrations can be substituted into the equilibrium constant expression.

$$55.64 = \frac{(2x)^2}{(2.00 - x)(2.00 - x)} = \frac{(2x)^2}{(2.00 - x)^2}$$

In this case, you can solve for the unknown quantity x by taking the square root of both sides of the equation,

$$\sqrt{K} = 7.459 = \frac{2x}{2.00 - x}$$
$$7.459\,(2.00 - x) = 14.9 - 7.459x = 2x$$
$$14.9 = 9.459x$$
$$x = 1.58$$

With x known, you can solve for the equilibrium concentrations of the reactants and products.

$$[\text{H}_2] = [\text{I}_2] = 2.00 - x = 0.42 \text{ M}$$

$$[\text{HI}] = 2x = 3.16 \text{ M}$$

Think about Your Answer It is always wise to verify the answer by substituting the value of each concentration back into the equilibrium expression to see if your calculated K agrees with the one given in the problem. In this case, $(3.16)^2/(0.42)^2 = 57$. The slight discrepancy with the given value, $K = 55.64$, occurs because we know $[\text{H}_2]$ and $[\text{I}_2]$ to only two significant figures.

Check Your Understanding

At some temperature, $K_c = 33$ for the reaction

$$\text{H}_2\text{(g)} + \text{I}_2\text{(g)} \rightleftharpoons 2 \text{ HI(g)}$$

Assume the initial concentrations of both H_2 and I_2 are 6.00×10^{-3} mol/L. Find the concentration of each reactant and product at equilibrium.

Calculations Where the Solution Involves a Quadratic Expression

Suppose you are studying the decomposition of PCl_5 to form PCl_3 and Cl_2. You know that $K = 1.20$ at a given temperature.

$$\text{PCl}_5\text{(g)} \rightleftharpoons \text{PCl}_3\text{(g)} + \text{Cl}_2\text{(g)}$$

If the initial concentration of PCl_5 is 1.60 M, what will be the concentrations of reactant and products when the system reaches equilibrium? Following the procedures outlined in Example 16.5, you would set up an ICE table to define the equilibrium concentrations of reactants and products.

Reaction	$\text{PCl}_5\text{(g)}$	$\rightleftharpoons$	$\text{PCl}_3\text{(g)}$	+	$\text{Cl}_2\text{(g)}$
Initial (M)	1.60		0		0
Change (M)	$-x$		$+x$		$+x$
Equilibrium (M)	$1.60 - x$		x		x

Substituting into the equilibrium constant expression, we have

$$K = 1.20 = \frac{[PCl_3][Cl_2]}{[PCl_5]} = \frac{(x)(x)}{1.60 - x}$$

Expanding the algebraic expression results in a quadratic equation,

$$x^2 + 1.20x - 1.92 = 0$$

Using the quadratic formula (Appendix A; $a = 1$, $b = 1.20$, and $c = -1.92$), we find two roots to the equation: $x = 0.91$ and -2.11. Because a negative value of x (which represents a negative concentration) is not chemically meaningful, the answer is $x = 0.91$. Therefore, at equilibrium we have

$$[PCl_5] = 1.60 - 0.91 = 0.69 \text{ M}$$

$$[PCl_3] = [Cl_2] = 0.91 \text{ M}$$

Although a solution to a quadratic equation can always be obtained using the quadratic formula, in many instances an acceptable answer can be obtained by using a realistic approximation to simplify the equation. To illustrate this, consider another equilibrium, the dissociation of I_2 molecules to form I atoms, for which $K = 5.6 \times 10^{-12}$ at 500 K.

$$I_2(g) \rightleftharpoons 2 I(g)$$

$$K = \frac{[I]^2}{[I_2]} = 5.6 \times 10^{-12}$$

Assuming the initial I_2 concentration is 0.45 M and setting up the ICE table in the usual manner, we have

Reaction	$I_2(g)$	$\rightleftharpoons$	$2 I(g)$
Initial (M)	0.45		0
Change (M)	$-x$		$+2x$
Equilibrium (M)	$0.45 - x$		$2x$

For the equilibrium constant expression, we again arrive at a quadratic equation.

$$K = 5.6 \times 10^{-12} = \frac{(2x)^2}{(0.45 - x)}$$

Although we could solve this equation using the quadratic formula, there is a simpler way to reach an answer. Notice that the value of K is very small, indicating that the amount of I_2 that will be dissociated ($= x$) is very small. In fact, K is so small that subtracting x from the original reactant concentration (0.45 mol/L) in the denominator of the equilibrium constant expression will leave the denominator essentially unchanged. That is, $(0.45 - x)$ is essentially equal to 0.45. Thus, we drop x in the denominator and have a simpler equation to solve.

$$K = 5.6 \times 10^{-12} = \frac{(2x)^2}{(0.45)}$$

The solution to this equation gives $x = 7.9 \times 10^{-7}$. From this value, we can determine that $[I_2] = 0.45 - x = 0.45$ mol/L and $[I] = 2x = 1.6 \times 10^{-6}$ mol/L. Notice that the answer to the I_2 dissociation problem confirms the assumption the dissociation of I_2 is so small that $[I_2]$ at equilibrium is essentially equal to the initial concentration.

When is it possible to simplify a quadratic equation? The decision depends on both the value of the initial concentration of the reactant and the value of x, which is in turn related to the value of K. Consider the general reaction

$$A \rightleftharpoons B + C$$

● **Solving Quadratic Equations**
Quadratic equations are usually solved using the quadratic formula (Appendix A). An alternative is the *method of successive approximations*, also outlined in Appendix A. Most equilibrium expressions can be solved quickly by this method, and you are urged to try it. This will remove the uncertainty of whether K expressions need to be solved exactly. (There are, however, rare cases in which this does not work.)

When Do You Need to Use the Quadratic Equation?

In most equilibrium calculations, the quantity x may be neglected in the denominator of the equation $K = x^2/([A]_0 - x)$ if x is less than 10% of the quantity of reactant initially present. The guideline presented in the text for making the approximation that $[A]_0 - x = [A]_0$ when $100 \times K < [A]_0$ reflects this fact.

In general, when K is about 1 or greater, the approximation cannot be made. If K is much less than 1 and $100 \times K < [A]_0$ (you will see many such cases in Chapter 17), the approximate expression ($K = x^2/[A]_0$) gives an acceptable answer. If you are not certain, then first make the assumption that the unknown (x) is small, and solve the approximate expression ($K = (x)^2/[A]_0$). Next, compare the "approximate" value of x with $[A]_0$. If x has a value equal to or less than 10% of $[A]_0$, then there is no need to solve the full equation using the quadratic formula.

where $K = [B][C]/[A]$. Assume you know K and the initial concentration of A ($= [A]_0$) and wish to find the equilibrium concentrations of B and C ($= x$). The equilibrium constant expression now is

$$K = \frac{[B][C]}{[A]} = \frac{(x)(x)}{[A]_0 - x}$$

When K is very small, the value of x will be much less than $[A]_0$, so $[A]_0 - x \cong [A]_0$. Therefore, we can write the following expression.

$$K = \frac{[B][C]}{[A]} \approx \frac{(x)(x)}{[A]_0} \tag{16.3}$$

If $100 \times K < [A]_0$, the approximate expression will give acceptable values of equilibrium concentrations (to two significant figures). For more about this useful guideline, see *Problem Solving Tip 16.1*.

Strategy Map 16.6

PROBLEM

What are the **equilibrium concentrations** of N_2, O_2, and **NO** in formation of NO from N_2 and O_2?

↓

DATA/INFORMATION KNOWN

- Balanced equation
- Value of K_c
- **Initial concentrations** of reactants

STEP 1. Enter *concentration changes* in ICE table and derive **equilibrium concentrations** in terms of unknown quantity **x**.

↓

Equilibrium concentrations of N_2, O_2, and **NO** are defined in terms of the unknown quantity **x**.

STEP 2. Enter **equilibrium concentrations** in K_c **expression** and solve for **x**.

↓

Value of **x**

STEP 3. Use value of **x** to derive **equilibrium concentrations**.

↓

Values of equilibrium concentrations

⬤**WL** **INTERACTIVE EXAMPLE 16.6** Calculating Equilibrium Concentrations Using an Equilibrium Constant

Problem The reaction

$$N_2(g) + O_2(g) \rightleftharpoons 2\,NO(g)$$

contributes to air pollution whenever a fuel is burned in air at a high temperature, as in a gasoline engine. At 1500 K, $K = 1.0 \times 10^{-5}$. Suppose a sample of air has $[N_2] = 0.80$ mol/L and $[O_2] = 0.20$ mol/L before any reaction occurs. Calculate the equilibrium concentrations of reactants and products after the mixture has been heated to 1500 K.

What Do You Know? As in Example 16.5, you know the value of K and can write the equilibrium expression from the balanced equation. You also know the initial concentrations of the reactants and can define the equilibrium concentrations in terms of the amounts of N_2 and O_2 consumed ($= x$).

Strategy Set up an ICE table, and then substitute the equilibrium concentrations into the equilibrium constant expression. The result will be a quadratic equation. This expression can be solved using the methods outlined in Appendix A or by using the guideline in the text to simplify the calculation.

Solution We first set up an ICE table where the amounts of N_2 and O_2 consumed are designated as x.

Equation	$N_2(g)$	+	$O_2(g)$	⇌	2 NO(g)
Initial (M)	0.80		0.20		0
Change (M)	$-x$		$-x$		$+2x$
Equilibrium (M)	$0.80 - x$		$0.20 - x$		$2x$

Next, the equilibrium concentrations are substituted into the equilibrium constant expression.

$$K = 1.0 \times 10^{-5} = \frac{[NO]^2}{[N_2][O_2]} = \frac{[2x]^2}{(0.80 - x)(0.20 - x)}$$

We refer to the guideline (Equation 16.3) to decide whether an approximate solution is possible. Here, $100 \times K (= 1.0 \times 10^{-3})$ is smaller than either of the initial reactant concentrations (0.80 and 0.20). This means we can use the approximate expression

$$K = 1.0 \times 10^{-5} = \frac{[NO]^2}{[N_2][O_2]} = \frac{(2x)^2}{(0.80)(0.20)}$$

Solving this expression, we find

$$1.6 \times 10^{-6} = 4x^2$$

$$x = 6.3 \times 10^{-4}$$

Therefore, the reactant and product concentrations at equilibrium are

$$[N_2] = 0.80 - 6.3 \times 10^{-4} \approx 0.80 \text{ M}$$

$$[O_2] = 0.20 - 6.3 \times 10^{-4} \approx 0.20 \text{ M}$$

$$[NO] = 2x = 1.3 \times 10^{-3} \text{ M}$$

Think about Your Answer The value of x obtained using the approximation is the same as that obtained from the quadratic formula. If the full equilibrium constant expression is expanded, we have

$$(1.0 \times 10^{-5})(0.80 - x)(0.20 - x) = 4x^2$$

$$(1.0 \times 10^{-5})(0.16 - 1.00x + x^2) = 4x^2$$

$$\underbrace{(4 - 1.0 \times 10^{-5})x^2}_{ax^2} + \underbrace{(1.0 \times 10^{-5})x}_{bx} - \underbrace{0.16 \times 10^{-5}}_{c} = 0$$

The two roots to this equation are:

$$x = 6.3 \times 10^{-4} \text{ or } x = -6.3 \times 10^{-4}$$

The only meaningful root is identical to the approximate answer obtained above. The approximation is indeed valid in this case.

Check Your Understanding

The decomposition of $PCl_5(g)$ to form $PCl_3(g)$ and $Cl_2(g)$ has $K_c = 33.3$ at a high temperature. If the initial concentration of PCl_5 is 0.1000 M, what are the equilibrium concentrations of the reactants and products?

REVIEW & CHECK FOR SECTION 16.4

Graphite and carbon dioxide are kept at constant volume at 1000 K until the reaction

$$C(graphite) + CO_2(g) \rightleftharpoons 2 CO(g)$$

has come to equilibrium. At this temperature, $K = 0.021$. The initial concentration of CO_2 is 0.012 mol/L. Calculate the equilibrium concentration of CO.

(a) 0.012 M

(c) 0.0057 M

(b) 0.011 M

16.5 More about Balanced Equations and Equilibrium Constants

Chemical equations can be balanced using different sets of stoichiometric coefficients. For example, the equation for the oxidation of carbon to give carbon monoxide can be written

$$C(s) + \tfrac{1}{2} O_2(g) \rightleftharpoons CO(g)$$

In this case, the equilibrium constant expression would be

$$K_1 = \frac{[CO]}{[O_2]^{1/2}} = 4.6 \times 10^{23} \text{ at } 25\ °C$$

You can write the chemical equation equally well, however, as

$$2\ C(s) + O_2(g) \rightleftharpoons 2\ CO(g)$$

and the equilibrium constant expression would now be

$$K_2 = \frac{[CO]^2}{[O_2]} = 2.1 \times 10^{47} \text{ at } 25\ °C$$

When you compare the two equilibrium constant expressions you find that $K_2 = (K_1)^2$; that is,

$$K_2 = \frac{[CO]^2}{[O_2]} = \left\{ \frac{[CO]}{[O_2]^{1/2}} \right\}^2 = K_1^{\ 2}$$

When the stoichiometric coefficients of a balanced equation are multiplied by some factor, the equilibrium constant for the new equation (K_{new}) is the old equilibrium constant (K_{old}) raised to the power of the multiplication factor.

In the case of the oxidation of carbon, the second equation was obtained by multiplying the first equation by two. Therefore, K_2 is the *square* of K_1 ($K_2 = K_1^{\ 2}$).

Let us consider what happens if a chemical equation is reversed. Here, we will compare the value of K for formic acid transferring an H^+ ion to water

$$HCO_2H(aq) + H_2O(\ell) \rightleftharpoons HCO_2^-(aq) + H_3O^+(aq)$$

$$K_1 = \frac{[HCO_2^-][H_3O^+]}{[HCO_2H]} = 1.8 \times 10^{-4} \text{ at } 25\ °C$$

with the opposite reaction, the gain of an H^+ ion by the formate ion, HCO_2^-.

$$HCO_2^-(aq) + H_3O^+(aq) \rightleftharpoons HCO_2H(aq) + H_2O(\ell)$$

$$K_2 = \frac{[HCO_2H]}{[HCO_2^-][H_3O^+]} = 5.6 \times 10^3 \text{ at } 25\ °C$$

Here, $K_2 = 1/K_1$.

The equilibrium constants for a reaction and its reverse are the reciprocals of one another.

It is often useful to add two equations to obtain the equation for a net process. As an example, consider the reactions that take place when silver chloride dissolves in water (to a *very* small extent) and ammonia is added to the solution. Ammonia reacts with silver ions to form a water-soluble compound, $Ag(NH_3)_2Cl$ (Figure 16.6). Adding the equation for dissolving solid AgCl to the equation for the reaction of Ag^+ ions with ammonia gives the equation for the net reaction, dissolving solid AgCl in aqueous ammonia. (All equilibrium constants are given at 25 °C.)

$AgCl(s) \rightleftharpoons Ag^+(aq) + Cl^-(aq)$ $K_1 = [Ag^+][Cl^-] = 1.8 \times 10^{-10}$

$Ag^+(aq) + 2\ NH_3(aq) \rightleftharpoons [Ag(NH_3)_2]^+(aq)$ $K_2 = \dfrac{[Ag(NH_3)_2^+]}{[Ag^+][NH_3]^2} = 1.1 \times 10^7$

Net equation:

$AgCl(s) + 2\ NH_3(aq) \rightleftharpoons [Ag(NH_3)_2]^+(aq) + Cl^-(aq)$

Balanced Equations and Equilibrium Constants

You should now know

1. how to write an equilibrium constant expression from the balanced equation, recognizing that the concentrations of solids and liquids used as solvents do not appear in the expression.

2. that when the stoichiometric coefficients in a balanced equation are changed by a factor of n, $K_{new} = (K_{old})^n$.

3. that when a balanced equation is reversed, $K_{new} = 1/K_{old}$.

4. that when several balanced equations (each with its own equilibrium constant, K_1, K_2, etc.) are added to obtain a net, balanced equation, $K_{net} = K_1 \times K_2 \times K_3 \times ...$.

AgCl(s) in water   After adding NH₃(aq)

FIGURE 16.6 Dissolving silver chloride in aqueous ammonia. *(left)* A precipitate of AgCl(s) is suspended in water. *(right)* When aqueous ammonia is added, the ammonia reacts with the trace of silver ion in solution, the equilibrium shifts, and the silver chloride dissolves.

To obtain the equilibrium constant for the net reaction, K_{net}, we *multiply* the equilibrium constants for the two reactions, K_1 by K_2.

$$K_{net} = K_1 \times K_2 = [Ag^+][Cl^-] \times \frac{[Ag(NH_3)_2^+]}{[Ag^+][NH_3]^2} = \frac{[Ag(NH_3)_2^+][Cl^-]}{[NH_3]^2}$$

$$K_{net} = K_1 \times K_2 = 2.0 \times 10^{-3}$$

When two or more chemical equations are added to produce a net equation, the equilibrium constant for the net equation is the product of the equilibrium constants for the added equations.

EXAMPLE 16.7   Balanced Equations and Equilibrium Constants

Problem A mixture of nitrogen, hydrogen, and ammonia is brought to equilibrium. When the equation is written using whole-number coefficients, as follows, the value of K is 3.5×10^8 at 25 °C.

Equation 1: $N_2(g) + 3 H_2(g) \rightleftharpoons 2 NH_3(g)$ $K_1 = 3.5 \times 10^8$

However, the equation can also be written as given in Equation 2. What is the value of K_2?

Equation 2: $\frac{1}{2} N_2(g) + \frac{3}{2} H_2(g) \rightleftharpoons NH_3(g)$ $K_2 = ?$

The decomposition of ammonia to the elements (Equation 3) is the reverse of its formation (Equation 1). What is the value of K_3?

Equation 3: $2 NH_3(g) \rightleftharpoons N_2(g) + 3 H_2(g)$ $K_3 = ?$

What Do You Know? You know the value of K for a given balanced equation. You want to know how the value of K changes as the stoichiometric coefficients change or when the equation is reversed.

Strategy Determine how the desired reaction is related to the given reaction(s). (Was a given chemical reaction multiplied by a factor? Was a reaction reversed? Were two or more reactions added?) Use the relationships discussed to determine the effect(s) of these transformations on the given K value(s). See also *Problem Solving Tip 16.2*.

Solution Equation 2 can be obtained by multiplying Equation 1 by 1/2. Thus K_2 is equal to K_1 raised to the one-half power, $K_1^{1/2}$. To confirm this relationship between K_1 and K_2, write the equilibrium constant expressions for these two balanced equations.

$$K_1 = \frac{[NH_3]^2}{[N_2][H_2]^3} \qquad K_2 = \frac{[NH_3]}{[N_2]^{1/2}[H_2]^{3/2}}$$

Writing these expressions makes it clear that K_2 is the square root of K_1.

$$K_2 = \left(K_1\right)^{1/2} = \sqrt{K_1} = \sqrt{3.5 \times 10^8} = 1.9 \times 10^4$$

Equation 3 is the reverse of Equation 1, and its equilibrium constant expression is

$$K_3 = \frac{[N_2][H_2]^3}{[NH_3]^2}$$

In this case, K_3 is the reciprocal of K_1. That is, $K_3 = 1/K_1$.

$$K_3 = \frac{1}{K_1} = \frac{1}{3.5 \times 10^8} = 2.9 \times 10^{-9}$$

Think about Your Answer

Notice that the production of ammonia from the elements has a large equilibrium constant and is product-favored (see Section 16.2). As expected, the reverse reaction, the decomposition of ammonia to its elements, has a small equilibrium constant and is reactant-favored.

Check Your Understanding

The conversion of oxygen to ozone has a very small equilibrium constant.

$$3/2\ O_2(g) \rightleftharpoons O_3(g) \qquad K = 2.5 \times 10^{-29}$$

(a) What is the value of K when the equation is written using whole-number coefficients?

$$3\ O_2(g) \rightleftharpoons 2\ O_3(g)$$

(b) What is the value of K for the conversion of ozone to oxygen?

$$2\ O_3(g) \rightleftharpoons 3\ O_2(g)$$

REVIEW & CHECK FOR SECTION 16.5

The following equilibrium constants are given at 500 K:

$H_2(g) + Br_2(g) \rightleftharpoons 2\ HBr(g)$	$K_p = 7.9 \times 10^{11}$
$H_2(g) \rightleftharpoons 2\ H(g)$	$K_p = 4.8 \times 10^{-41}$
$Br_2(g) \rightleftharpoons 2\ Br$	$K_p = 2.2 \times 10^{-15}$

Calculate K_p for the reaction $H + Br \rightarrow HBr$.

(a) $K_p = 8.3 \times 10^{-44}$ (b) $K_p = 7.5 \times 10^{66}$ (c) $K_p = 2.7 \times 10^{33}$

16.6 Disturbing a Chemical Equilibrium

The equilibrium between reactants and products may be disturbed in three ways: (1) by changing the temperature, (2) by changing the concentration of a reactant or product, or (3) by changing the volume (for systems involving gases) (Table 16.2).

Table 16.2 **Effects of Disturbances on Equilibrium Composition**

Disturbance	Change as Mixture Returns to Equilibrium	Effect on Equilibrium	Effect on K
Reactions Involving Solids, Liquids, or Gases			
Rise in temperature	Energy is consumed by system	Shift in endothermic direction	Change
Drop in temperature	Energy is generated by system	Shift in exothermic direction	Change
Addition of reactant*	Some of added reactant is consumed	Product concentration increases	No change
Addition of product*	Some of added product is consumed	Reactant concentration increases	No change
Reactions Involving Gases			
Decrease in volume, increase in pressure	Pressure decreases	Composition changes to reduce total number of gas molecules	No change
Increase in volume, decrease in pressure	Pressure increases	Composition changes to increase total number of gas molecules	No change

*Does not apply when an insoluble solid reactant or product is added. Recall that their "concentrations" do not appear in the reaction quotient.

A change in any of the factors that determine the equilibrium conditions of a system will cause the system to change in such a manner as to reduce or counteract the effect of the change. This statement is often referred to as *Le Chatelier's principle* (◄ page 627). It is a shorthand way of saying how the quantities of reactants and products are adjusted so that equilibrium is restored, that is, so that the reaction quotient is once again equal to the equilibrium constant.

Effect of the Addition or Removal of a Reactant or Product

If the concentration of a reactant or product is changed from its equilibrium value *at a given temperature*, equilibrium will be reestablished eventually. The new equilibrium concentrations of reactants and products will be different, but the value of the equilibrium constant expression will still equal K (Table 16.2). To illustrate this, let us return to the butane/isobutane equilibrium (with $K = 2.5$).

$$CH_3CH_2CH_2CH_3 \rightleftharpoons \underset{\text{isobutane}}{CH_3\overset{\overset{\displaystyle CH_3}{|}}{C}HCH_3} \qquad K = 2.5$$

$$\underset{\text{butane}}{CH_3CH_2CH_2CH_3}$$

Suppose the equilibrium mixture consists of two molecules of butane and five molecules of isobutane (Figure 16.7). The reaction quotient, Q, is 5/2 (or 2.5/1), the

$Q = 5/2 = K$

An equilibrium mixture of five isobutane molecules and two butane molecules.

Seven isobutane are added.

$Q = 12/2 > K$

Seven isobutane molecules are added, so the system is no longer at equilibrium.

The system returns to equilibrium.

$Q = 10/4 = K$

A net of two isobutane molecules has changed to butane molecules, to once again give an equilibrium mixture where the ratio of isobutane to butane is 5:2 (or 2.5:1).

FIGURE 16.7 Addition of more reactant or product to an equilibrium system.

value of the equilibrium constant for the reaction. Now we add seven more molecules of isobutane to the mixture to give a ratio of 12 isobutane molecules to two butane molecules. The reaction quotient is now 6/1. This means Q is greater than K, and the system will change to reestablish equilibrium. To do so, some molecules of isobutane must be changed into butane molecules, a process that continues until the ratio [isobutane]/[butane] is once again 2.5/1. In this particular case, if two of the 12 isobutane molecules change to butane, the ratio of isobutane to butane is again equal to K (= 10/4 = 2.5/1), and equilibrium is reestablished.

Strategy Map 16.8

PROBLEM
What are the **equilibrium concentrations** of reactant and product after adding **excess reactant**?

↓

DATA/INFORMATION KNOWN
• Balanced equation • Value of K_c • **Initial concentrations** of **reactant** and **product** and amount of **excess reactant** added

> STEP 1. Enter *concentration changes* in ICE table and derive **equilibrium concentrations** in terms of unknown quantity *x*.

Equilibrium concentrations of **reactant** and **product** are defined in terms of the unknown quantity **x**.

> STEP 2. Enter **equilibrium concentrations** in K_c expression and solve for **x**.

Value of **x**

> STEP 3. Use value of **x** to derive **equilibrium concentrations**.

Values of equilibrium concentrations

⊙WL INTERACTIVE EXAMPLE 16.8   Effect of Concentration Changes on Equilibrium

Problem Assume equilibrium has been established in a 1.00-L flask with [butane] = 0.500 mol/L and [isobutane] = 1.25 mol/L.

$$\text{Butane} \rightleftharpoons \text{Isobutane} \quad K = 2.50$$

Then 1.50 mol of butane is added. What are the concentrations of butane and isobutane when equilibrium is reestablished?

What Do You Know? Here you know the value of K, the balanced equation, the original equilibrium concentrations of reactant and product, and the amount of reactant added to the system at equilibrium.

Strategy After adding excess butane, $Q < K$. To reestablish equilibrium, the concentration of butane must decrease by an amount x and that of isobutane must increase, also by an amount x. Use an ICE table to track the changes.

Solution First organize the information in a modified ICE table.

Equation	Butane	⇌	Isobutane
Initial (M)	0.500		1.25
Concentration immediately on adding butane (M)	0.500 + 1.50		1.25
Change in concentration to reestablish equilibrium (M)	−x		+x
Equilibrium (M)	0.500 + 1.50 − x		1.25 + x

The entries in this table were arrived at as follows:

(a) The concentration of butane when equilibrium is reestablished will be the original equilibrium concentration plus what was added (1.50 mol/L) minus the concentration of butane that is converted to isobutane to reestablish equilibrium. The quantity of butane converted to isobutane is unknown and so is designated as x.

(b) The concentration of isobutane when equilibrium is reestablished is the concentration that was already present (1.25 mol/L) plus the concentration formed (x mol/L) on reestablishing equilibrium.

Having defined [butane] and [isobutane] when equilibrium is reestablished and remembering that K is a constant (= 2.50), we can write

$$K = 2.50 = \frac{[\text{isobutane}]}{[\text{butane}]}$$

We now calculate the new equilibrium composition:

$$2.50 = \frac{1.25 + x}{0.500 + 1.50 - x} = \frac{1.25 + x}{2.00 - x}$$

$$2.50\,(2.00 - x) = 1.25 + x$$

$$x = 1.07 \text{ mol/L}$$

[butane] = 0.500 + 1.50 − x = 0.93 M and [isobutane] = 1.25 + x = 2.32 M

Answer check: new ratio [isobutane]/[butane] = 2.32/0.93 = 2.5

Think about Your Answer It is useful to see a graphical solution to this problem because it emphasizes the point that, after adding excess butane, some butane is consumed on proceeding to the new equilibrium mixture and additional isobutane is formed. In the diagram here any mixture of butane and isobutane lying on the equilibrium line represents an equilibrium mixture. Mixtures in the blue portion of the diagram have $Q > K$, whereas those in the tan portion have $Q < K$. In this case, adding butane produced a mixture in the $Q < K$ region of the diagram. As predicted by Le Chatelier's principle, the added "stress" on the system is relieved by converting some butane to isobutane to achieve a new equilibrium mixture when $Q = K$.

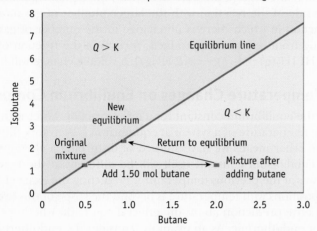

A graphical representation of the butane-isobutane problem.

Check Your Understanding

Equilibrium exists between butane and isobutane when [butane] = 0.20 M and [isobutane] = 0.50 M. An additional 2.00 mol/L of isobutane is added to the mixture. What are the concentrations of butane and isobutane after equilibrium has again been attained?

Effect of Volume Changes on Gas-Phase Equilibria

For a reaction that involves gases, what happens to equilibrium concentrations or pressures if the size of the container is changed? (Such a change occurs, for example, when fuel and air are compressed in an automobile engine.) To answer this question, recall that concentrations are in moles per liter. If the volume of a gas changes, its concentration therefore must also change, and the equilibrium composition can change. As an example, consider the following equilibrium:

$$2\ NO_2(g) \rightleftharpoons N_2O_4(g)$$
brown gas   colorless gas

$$K_c = \frac{[N_2O_4]}{[NO_2]^2} = 170 \text{ at } 298 \text{ K}$$

What happens to this equilibrium if the volume of the flask holding the gases is suddenly halved? The immediate result is that the concentrations of both gases will double. For example, assume equilibrium is established when $[N_2O_4]$ is 0.0280 mol/L and $[NO_2]$ is 0.0128 mol/L. When the volume is halved, $[N_2O_4]$ becomes 0.0560 mol/L, and $[NO_2]$ is 0.0256 mol/L. The reaction quotient, Q, under these circumstances is $(0.0560)/(0.0256)^2 = 85.4$, a value less than K. Because Q is less than K, the quantity of product must increase at the expense of the reactants to return to equilibrium, and the new equilibrium composition will have a higher concentration of N_2O_4 than immediately after the volume change.

$$2\ NO_2(g) \rightleftharpoons N_2O_4(g)$$

decrease volume of container
$$\xrightarrow{\hspace{3cm}}$$
NO_2 is converted to N_2O_4
until equilibrium is attained

The concentration of NO_2 decreases twice as much as the concentration of N_2O_4 increases because one molecule of N_2O_4 is formed by consuming two molecules of

NO_2. This occurs until the reaction quotient, $Q = [N_2O_4]/[NO_2]^2$, is once again equal to K. The net effect of the volume decrease is to decrease the number of molecules in the gas phase.

The conclusions for the NO_2/N_2O_4 equilibrium can be generalized:

- For reactions involving gases, the stress of a volume decrease (a pressure increase) will be counterbalanced by a change in the equilibrium composition to one having a smaller number of gas molecules.
- For a volume increase (a pressure decrease), the equilibrium composition will favor the side of the reaction with the larger number of gas molecules.
- For a reaction in which there is no change in the number of gas molecules in proceeding from reactants to products, such as in the reaction of H_2 and I_2 to produce HI [$H_2(g) + I_2(g) \rightleftharpoons 2\ HI(g)$], a volume change will have no effect.

Effect of Temperature Changes on Equilibrium Composition

The value of the equilibrium constant for a given reaction varies with temperature. Changing the temperature of a system at equilibrium is therefore different in some ways from the other means we have studied of disturbing a chemical equilibrium because the equilibrium constant itself will be different at the new temperature from what it was at the previous temperature. Predicting the exact changes in equilibrium compositions with temperature is beyond the scope of this text, but you can make a qualitative prediction about the effect if you know whether the reaction is exothermic or endothermic. As an example, consider the endothermic reaction of N_2 with O_2 to give NO.

$$N_2(g) + O_2(g) \rightleftharpoons 2\ NO(g) \qquad \Delta_rH° = +180.6\ \text{kJ/mol-rxn}$$

$$K = \frac{[NO]^2}{[N_2][O_2]}$$

Le Chatelier's principle allows us to predict how the value of K will vary with temperature. The formation of NO from N_2 and O_2 is endothermic; that is, energy must be provided as heat for the reaction to occur. We might imagine that heat is a "reactant." If the system is at equilibrium and the temperature then increases, the system will adjust to alleviate this "stress." The way to counteract the energy input is to use up some of the energy added as heat by consuming N_2 and O_2 and producing more NO as the system returns to equilibrium. This raises the value of the numerator ($[NO]^2$) and lowers the value of the denominator ($[N_2][O_2]$) in the reaction quotient, Q, resulting in a higher value of K.

This prediction is borne out. The following table lists the equilibrium constant for this reaction at various temperatures. As predicted, the equilibrium constant and thus the proportion of NO in the equilibrium mixture increases with temperature.

Equilibrium Constant, K	Temperature (K)
4.5×10^{-31}	298
6.7×10^{-10}	900
1.7×10^{-3}	2300

As another example, consider the combination of molecules of the brown gas NO_2 to form colorless N_2O_4. An equilibrium between these compounds is readily achieved in a closed system (Figure 16.8).

$$2\ NO_2(g) \rightleftharpoons N_2O_4(g) \qquad \Delta_rH° = -57.1\ \text{kJ/mol-rxn}$$

$$K = \frac{[N_2O_4]}{[NO_2]^2}$$

Equilibrium Constant, K	Temperature (K)
1300	273
170	298

Higher temperature   Lower temperature

© Cengage Learning/Marna C. Clarke

FIGURE 16.8 Effect of temperature on an equilibrium. The tubes in the photograph both contain gaseous NO_2 (brown) and N_2O_4 (colorless) at equilibrium. K is larger at the lower temperature because the equilibrium favors colorless N_2O_4. This is clearly seen in the tube at the right, where the gas in the ice bath at 0 °C is only slightly brown, which indicates a smaller concentration of the brown gas NO_2. At 50 °C (the tube at the left), the equilibrium is shifted toward NO_2, as indicated by the darker brown color.

Here, the reaction is exothermic, so we might imagine heat as being a reaction "product." By lowering the temperature of the system, as in Figure 16.8, some energy is removed as heat. The removal of energy can be counteracted if the reaction produces energy as heat by the combination of NO_2 molecules to give more N_2O_4. Thus, the equilibrium concentration of NO_2 decreases; the concentration of N_2O_4 increases; and the value of K is larger at lower temperatures.

In summary,

- when the temperature of a system at equilibrium increases, the equilibrium will shift in the direction that absorbs energy as heat (Table 16.2)—that is, in the endothermic direction.
- if the temperature decreases, the equilibrium will shift in the direction that releases energy as heat—that is, in the exothermic direction.
- changing the temperature changes the value of K.

REVIEW & CHECK FOR SECTION 16.6

The formation of ammonia from its elements is an important industrial process.

$$3\ H_2(g) + N_2(g) \rightleftharpoons 2\ NH_3(g)$$

1. Does the reaction shift to the right or to the left, or does it remain unchanged, when extra H_2 is added?

    (a) shift left   (c) unchanged

    (b) shift right

2. Does the reaction shift to the right or to the left, or does it remain unchanged, when the volume of the system is increased?

    (a) shift left   (c) unchanged

    (b) shift right

3. For the equilibrium $2\ SO_2(g) + O_2(g) \rightleftharpoons 2\ SO_3(g)$, K has the following values: 4.0×10^{24} at 300 K, 2.5×10^{10} at 500 K, and 3.0×10^4 at 700 K. Is this reaction exothermic or endothermic?

    (a) exothermic   (b) endothermic

CASE STUDY

Applying Equilibrium Concepts—The Haber-Bosch Ammonia Process

Nitrogen-containing substances are used around the world to stimulate the growth of field crops. Farmers from Portugal to Tibet have used animal waste for centuries as a "natural" fertilizer. In the 19th century, industrialized countries imported nitrogen-rich marine bird manure from Peru, Bolivia, and Chile, but the supply of this material was clearly limited. In 1898, William Ramsay (the discoverer of the noble gases, page 109) pointed out that the amount of "fixed nitrogen" in the world was being depleted and predicted that world food shortages would occur by the mid-20th century as a result. That Ramsay's prediction failed to materialize was due in part to the work of Fritz Haber (1868–1934). In about 1908, Haber developed a method to make ammonia directly from the elements,

$$N_2(g) + 3\ H_2(g) \rightleftharpoons 2\ NH_3(g)$$

and, a few years later, Carl Bosch (1874–1940) perfected the industrial scale synthesis. Ammonia is now made for pennies per kilogram and is consistently ranked in the top five chemicals produced in the United States, with 15–20 billion kilograms produced annually. Not only is ammonia used directly as a fertilizer, but it is also a starting material for making nitric acid and ammonium nitrate, among other things.

The manufacture of ammonia (Figure A) is a good example of the role that kinetics and chemical equilibria play in practical chemistry.

The $N_2 + H_2$ reaction is exothermic and product-favored ($K > 1$ at 25 °C).

At 25 °C, K (calc'd value) = 3.5×10^8 and $\Delta_r H° = -92.2$ kJ/mol-rxn

Unfortunately, the reaction at 25 °C is slow, so it is carried out at a higher temperature to increase the reaction rate. The problem with this, however, is that the equilibrium constant declines with temperature, as predicted by Le Chatelier's principle.

At 450 °C, K (experimental value) = 0.16 and $\Delta_r H° = -111.3$ kJ/mol-rxn

Thus, the yield declines with increasing temperature.

Figure A The Haber-Bosch process for ammonia synthesis. A mixture of H_2 and N_2 is pumped over a catalytic surface. The NH_3 is collected as a liquid (at -33 °C), and unchanged reactants are recycled in the catalytic chamber.

There are two things that can be done. The first is to raise the pressure. This does not change the value of K, but an increase in pressure can be compensated by converting 4 mol of reactants to 2 mol of product.

In an industrial ammonia plant, it is necessary to balance reaction rate (improved at higher temperature) with product yield (K is smaller at higher temperatures). Additionally, a catalyst is often used to accelerate the reaction. An effective catalyst for the Haber-Bosch process is Fe_3O_4 mixed with KOH, SiO_2, and Al_2O_3 (all inexpensive chemicals). Because the catalyst is not effective below 400 °C, the process is carried out at 450–500 °C and 250 atm pressure.

Questions:

1. Anhydrous ammonia is used directly as a fertilizer, but much of it is also converted to other fertilizers, ammonium nitrate and urea.
   (a) How is NH_3 converted to ammonium nitrate?

(b) Urea is formed in the reaction of ammonia and CO_2.

$$2\ NH_3(g) + CO_2(g) \rightleftharpoons (NH_2)_2CO(s) + H_2O(g)$$

Which would favor urea production, high temperature or high pressure? ($\Delta_f H°$ for solid urea = -333.1 kJ/mol-rxn)

2. One important aspect of the Haber-Bosch process is the source of the hydrogen. This is made from natural gas in a process called *steam reforming*.

$$CH_4(g) + H_2O(g) \rightarrow CO(g) + 3\ H_2(g)$$
$$CO(g) + H_2O(g) \rightarrow CO_2(g) + H_2(g)$$

(a) Are the two reactions above endo- or exothermic?
(b) To obtain the H_2 necessary to manufacture 15 billion kilograms of NH_3, how much CH_4 is required, and what mass of CO_2 is produced as a by-product?

Answers to these questions are available in Appendix N.

CHAPTER GOALS REVISITED

Now that you have studied this chapter, you should ask whether you have met the chapter goals. In particular, you should be able to:

Understand the nature and characteristics of chemical equilibria

a.   Chemical reactions are reversible and equilibria are dynamic (Section 16.1).

Understand the significance of the equilibrium constant, *K*, and reaction quotient, *Q*.

a. Write the reaction quotient, *Q*, for a chemical reaction (Section 16.2). When the system is at equilibrium, the reaction quotient is called the *equilibrium constant expression* and has a constant value called the *equilibrium constant,* which is symbolized by *K* (Equation 16.1). **Study Questions: 1–4.**

b. Recognize that the concentrations of solids, pure liquids, and solvents (e.g., water) are not included in the equilibrium constant expression (Section 16.2).

c. Recognize that a large value of *K* (*K* > 1) means the reaction is product-favored, and the product concentrations are greater than the reactant concentrations at equilibrium. A small value of *K* (*K* < 1) indicates a reactant-favored reaction in which the product concentrations are smaller than the reactant concentrations at equilibrium (Section 16.2). **Study Questions: 66, 68.**

d. Appreciate the fact that equilibrium concentrations may be expressed in terms of reactant and product concentrations (in moles per liter) and that *K* is then sometimes designated as K_c. Alternatively, concentrations of gases may be represented by partial pressures, and *K* for such cases is designated K_p (Section 16.2). **Study Questions: 53, 60.**

Understand how to use *K* in quantitative studies of chemical equilibria

a. Use the reaction quotient (*Q*) to decide whether a reaction is at equilibrium (*Q* = *K*), or if there will be a net conversion of reactants to products (*Q* < *K*) or products to reactants (*Q* > *K*) to attain equilibrium (Section 16.2). **Study Questions: 3–6, 35, 36.**

b. Calculate an equilibrium constant given the reactant and product concentrations at equilibrium (Section 16.3). **Study Questions: 7–11, 29, 33, 34, 44, 61a.**

c. Use equilibrium constants to calculate the concentration (or pressure) of a reactant or a product at equilibrium (Section 16.4). **Study Questions: 16, 17, 32, 36, 42, 46, 47, 50–54, 56, 59–61, and Go Chemistry Module 21.**

d. Know how *K* changes as different stoichiometric coefficients are used in a balanced equation, if the equation is reversed, or if several equations are added to give a new net equation (Section 16.5). **Study Questions: 19–24, 31, 37.**

Predict how a system at equilibrium will respond if the reaction conditions are changed.

a. Know how to predict, using Le Chatelier's principle, the effect of a disturbance on a chemical equilibrium—a change in temperature, a change in concentrations, or a change in volume or pressure for a reaction involving gases (Section 16.6 and Table 16.2). **Study Questions: 25–28, 39, 41, 54, 62.**

ⓊWL and **[go Chemistry]**

Sign in at **www.cengage.com/owl** to:
* View tutorials and simulations, develop problem-solving skills, and complete online homework assigned by your professor.
* For quick review and exam prep, download Go Chemistry mini lecture modules from OWL (or purchase them at **www.cengagebrain.com**)

❓ Access **How Do I Solve It?** tutorials on how to approach problem solving using concepts in this chapter.

Key Equations

Equation 16.1 (page 723) The equilibrium constant expression. At equilibrium, the ratio of products to reactants (each raised to the power corresponding to its stoichiometric coefficient) has a constant value, *K* (at a particular temperature). For the general reaction $aA + bB \rightleftharpoons cC + dD$,

$$\text{Equilibrium constant} = K = \frac{[C]^c[D]^d}{[A]^a[B]^b}$$

Equation 16.2 (page 727) For the general reaction $aA + bB \rightleftharpoons cC + dD$, the ratio of product to reactant concentrations at any point in the reaction is the reaction quotient, *Q*.

$$\text{Reaction quotient} = Q = \frac{[C]^c[D]^d}{[A]^a[B]^b}$$

Equation 16.3 (page 736) This approximation is used to solve for the equilibrium concentrations of *B* and *C* (= *x*) in the general reaction $A \rightleftharpoons B + C$ when the value of 100 × *K* is less than the original concentration of $A(= [A]_0)$.

$$K = \frac{[B][C]}{[A]} \approx \frac{(x)(x)}{[A]_0}$$

Study Questions

⭕WL Interactive versions of these questions are assignable in OWL.

▲ denotes challenging questions.

Blue-numbered questions have answers in Appendix R and fully worked solutions in the *Student Solutions Manual*.

Practicing Skills

Writing Equilibrium Constant Expressions
(See Section 16.2 and Example 16.1.)

1. Write equilibrium constant expressions for the following reactions. For gases, use either pressures or concentrations.
   (a) $2 H_2O_2(g) \rightleftharpoons 2 H_2O(g) + O_2(g)$
   (b) $CO(g) + \frac{1}{2} O_2(g) \rightleftharpoons CO_2(g)$
   (c) $C(s) + CO_2(g) \rightleftharpoons 2 CO(g)$
   (d) $NiO(s) + CO(g) \rightleftharpoons Ni(s) + CO_2(g)$

2. Write equilibrium constant expressions for the following reactions. For gases, use either pressures or concentrations.
   (a) $3 O_2(g) \rightleftharpoons 2 O_3(g)$
   (b) $Fe(s) + 5 CO(g) \rightleftharpoons Fe(CO)_5(g)$
   (c) $(NH_4)_2CO_3(s) \rightleftharpoons 2 NH_3(g) + CO_2(g) + H_2O(g)$
   (d) $Ag_2SO_4(s) \rightleftharpoons 2 Ag^+(aq) + SO_4^{2-}(aq)$

The Equilibrium Constant and Reaction Quotient
(See Section 16.2 and Example 16.2.)

3. $K_c = 5.6 \times 10^{-12}$ at 500 K for the dissociation of iodine molecules to iodine atoms.

$$I_2(g) \rightleftharpoons 2 I(g)$$

A mixture has $[I_2] = 0.020$ mol/L and $[I] = 2.0 \times 10^{-8}$ mol/L. Is the reaction at equilibrium (at 500 K)? If not, which way must the reaction proceed to reach equilibrium?

4. The reaction

$$2 NO_2(g) \rightleftharpoons N_2O_4(g)$$

has an equilibrium constant, K_c, of 170 at 25 °C. If 2.0×10^{-3} mol of NO_2 is present in a 10.-L flask along with 1.5×10^{-3} mol of N_2O_4, is the system at equilibrium? If it is not at equilibrium, does the concentration of NO_2 increase or decrease as the system proceeds to equilibrium?

5. A mixture of SO_2, O_2, and SO_3 at 1000 K contains the gases at the following concentrations: $[SO_2] = 5.0 \times 10^{-3}$ mol/L, $[O_2] = 1.9 \times 10^{-3}$ mol/L, and $[SO_3] = 6.9 \times 10^{-3}$ mol/L. Is the reaction at equilibrium? If not, which way will the reaction proceed to reach equilibrium?

$$2 SO_2(g) + O_2(g) \rightleftharpoons 2 SO_3(g) \quad K_c = 279$$

6. The equilibrium constant, K_c, for the reaction

$$2 NOCl(g) \rightleftharpoons 2 NO(g) + Cl_2(g)$$

is 3.9×10^{-3} at 300 °C. A mixture contains the gases at the following concentrations: $[NOCl] = 5.0 \times 10^{-3}$ mol/L, $[NO] = 2.5 \times 10^{-3}$ mol/L, and $[Cl_2] = 2.0 \times 10^{-3}$ mol/L. Is the reaction at equilibrium at 300 °C? If not, in which direction does the reaction proceed to come to equilibrium?

Calculating an Equilibrium Constant
(See Section 16.3 and Examples 16.3 and 16.4.)

7. The reaction

$$PCl_5(g) \rightleftharpoons PCl_3(g) + Cl_2(g)$$

was examined at 250 °C. At equilibrium, $[PCl_5] = 4.2 \times 10^{-5}$ mol/L, $[PCl_3] = 1.3 \times 10^{-2}$ mol/L, and $[Cl_2] = 3.9 \times 10^{-3}$ mol/L. Calculate K_c for the reaction.

8. An equilibrium mixture of SO_2, O_2, and SO_3 at a high temperature contains the gases at the following concentrations: $[SO_2] = 3.77 \times 10^{-3}$ mol/L, $[O_2] = 4.30 \times 10^{-3}$ mol/L, and $[SO_3] = 4.13 \times 10^{-3}$ mol/L. Calculate the equilibrium constant, K_c, for the reaction.

$$2 SO_2(g) + O_2(g) \rightleftharpoons 2 SO_3(g)$$

9. The reaction

$$C(s) + CO_2(g) \rightleftharpoons 2 CO(g)$$

occurs at high temperatures. At 700 °C, a 2.0-L flask contains 0.10 mol of CO, 0.20 mol of CO_2, and 0.40 mol of C at equilibrium.
   (a) Calculate K_c for the reaction at 700 °C.
   (b) Calculate K_c for the reaction, also at 700 °C, if the amounts at equilibrium in the 2.0-L flask are 0.10 mol of CO, 0.20 mol of CO_2, and 0.80 mol of C.
   (c) Compare the results of (a) and (b). Does the quantity of carbon affect the value of K_c? Explain.

10. Hydrogen and carbon dioxide react at a high temperature to give water and carbon monoxide.

$$H_2(g) + CO_2(g) \rightleftharpoons H_2O(g) + CO(g)$$

   (a) Laboratory measurements at 986 °C show that there are 0.11 mol each of CO and H_2O vapor and 0.087 mol each of H_2 and CO_2 at equilibrium in a 1.0-L container. Calculate the equilibrium constant for the reaction at 986 °C.
   (b) Suppose 0.050 mol each of H_2 and CO_2 are placed in a 2.0-L container. When equilibrium is achieved at 986 °C, what amounts of CO(g) and $H_2O(g)$, in moles, would be present? [Use the value of K_c from part (a).]

11. A mixture of CO and Cl_2 is placed in a reaction flask: $[CO] = 0.0102$ mol/L and $[Cl_2] = 0.00609$ mol/L. When the reaction

$$CO(g) + Cl_2(g) \rightleftharpoons COCl_2(g)$$

has come to equilibrium at 600 K, $[Cl_2] = 0.00301$ mol/L.

(a) Calculate the concentrations of CO and $COCl_2$ at equilibrium.

(b) Calculate K_c.

12. You place 3.00 mol of pure SO_3 in an 8.00-L flask at 1150 K. At equilibrium, 0.58 mol of O_2 has been formed. Calculate K_c for the reaction at 1150 K.

$$2\ SO_3(g) \rightleftharpoons 2\ SO_2(g) + O_2(g)$$

Using Equilibrium Constants
(See Section 16.4 and Examples 16.5 and 16.6.)

13. The value of K_c for the interconversion of butane and isobutane is 2.5 at 25 °C.

butane   isobutane

If you place 0.017 mol of butane in a 0.50-L flask at 25 °C and allow equilibrium to be established, what will be the equilibrium concentrations of the two forms of butane?

14. Cyclohexane, C_6H_{12}, a hydrocarbon, can isomerize or change into methylcyclopentane, a compound of the same formula ($C_5H_9CH_3$) but with a different molecular structure.

cyclohexane   methylcyclopentane

The equilibrium constant has been estimated to be 0.12 at 25 °C. If you had originally placed 0.045 mol of cyclohexane in a 2.8-L flask, what would be the concentrations of cyclohexane and methylcyclopentane when equilibrium is established?

15. The equilibrium constant for the dissociation of iodine molecules to iodine atoms

$$I_2(g) \rightleftharpoons 2\ I(g)$$

is 3.76×10^{-3} at 1000 K. Suppose 0.105 mol of I_2 is placed in a 12.3-L flask at 1000 K. What are the concentrations of I_2 and I when the system comes to equilibrium?

16. The equilibrium constant, K_c, for the reaction

$$N_2O_4(g) \rightleftharpoons 2\ NO_2(g)$$

at 25 °C is 170. Suppose 15.6 g of N_2O_4 is placed in a 5.000-L flask at 25 °C. Calculate the following:

(a) the amount of NO_2 (mol) present at equilibrium;

(b) the percentage of the original N_2O_4 that is dissociated.

17. Carbonyl bromide decomposes to carbon monoxide and bromine.

$$COBr_2(g) \rightleftharpoons CO(g) + Br_2(g)$$

K_c is 0.190 at 73 °C. If you place 0.500 mol of $COBr_2$ in a 2.00-L flask and heat it to 73 °C, what are the equilibrium concentrations of $COBr_2$, CO, and Br_2? What percentage of the original $COBr_2$ decomposed at this temperature?

18. Iodine dissolves in water, but its solubility in a nonpolar solvent such as CCl_4 is greater.

Nonpolar I_2
Polar H_2O
Polar H_2O
Shake the test tube
Nonpolar CCl_4
Nonpolar CCl_4 and I_2

Photos © Cengage Learning/Charles D. Winters

Extracting iodine (I_2) from water with the nonpolar solvent CCl_4. I_2 is more soluble in CCl_4 and, after shaking a mixture of water and CCl_4, the I_2 has accumulated in the more dense CCl_4 layer.

The equilibrium constant is 85.0 for the process

$$I_2(aq) \rightleftharpoons I_2(CCl_4)$$

You place 0.0340 g of I_2 in 100.0 mL of water. After shaking it with 10.0 mL of CCl_4, how much I_2 remains in the water layer?

Manipulating Equilibrium Constant Expressions
(See Section 16.5 and Example 16.7.)

19. Which of the following correctly relates the equilibrium constants for the two reactions shown?

$$A + B \rightleftharpoons 2\ C \qquad K_1$$
$$2\ A + 2\ B \rightleftharpoons 4\ C \qquad K_2$$

(a) $K_2 = 2K_1$ (c) $K_2 = 1/K_1$
(b) $K_2 = K_1^2$ (d) $K_2 = 1/K_1^2$

20. Which of the following correctly relates the equilibrium constants for the two reactions shown?

$$A + B \rightleftharpoons 2\ C \qquad K_1$$
$$C \rightleftharpoons \tfrac{1}{2}\ A + \tfrac{1}{2}\ B \qquad K_2$$

(a) $K_2 = 1/(K_1)^{1/2}$ (c) $K_2 = K_1^2$
(b) $K_2 = 1/K_1$ (d) $K_2 = -K_1^{1/2}$

21. Consider the following equilibria involving $SO_2(g)$ and their corresponding equilibrium constants.

$$SO_2(g) + \tfrac{1}{2}\ O_2(g) \rightleftharpoons SO_3(g) \qquad K_1$$
$$2\ SO_3(g) \rightleftharpoons 2\ SO_2(g) + O_2(g) \qquad K_2$$

Which of the following expressions relates K_1 to K_2?

(a) $K_2 = K_1^2$ (d) $K_2 = 1/K_1$
(b) $K_2^2 = K_1$ (e) $K_2 = 1/K_1^2$
(c) $K_2 = K_1$

22. The equilibrium constant K for the reaction

$$CO_2(g) \rightleftharpoons CO(g) + \frac{1}{2} O_2(g)$$

is 6.66×10^{-12} at 1000 K. Calculate K for the reaction

$$2\,CO(g) + O_2(g) \rightleftharpoons 2\,CO_2(g)$$

23. Calculate K for the reaction

$$SnO_2(s) + 2\,CO(g) \rightleftharpoons Sn(s) + 2\,CO_2(g)$$

given the following information:

$$SnO_2(s) + 2\,H_2(g) \rightleftharpoons Sn(s) + 2\,H_2O(g) \quad K = 8.12$$

$$H_2(g) + CO_2(g) \rightleftharpoons H_2O(g) + CO(g) \quad K = 0.771$$

24. Calculate K for the reaction

$$Fe(s) + H_2O(g) \rightleftharpoons FeO(s) + H_2(g)$$

given the following information:

$$H_2O(g) + CO(g) \rightleftharpoons H_2(g) + CO_2(g) \quad K = 1.6$$

$$FeO(s) + CO(g) \rightleftharpoons Fe(s) + CO_2(g) \quad K = 0.67$$

Disturbing a Chemical Equilibrium
(See Section 16.6 and Example 16.8.)

25. Dinitrogen trioxide decomposes to NO and NO_2 in an endothermic process ($\Delta_r H^\circ = 40.5$ kJ/mol-rxn).

$$N_2O_3(g) \rightleftharpoons NO(g) + NO_2(g)$$

Predict the effect of the following changes on the position of the equilibrium; that is, state which way the equilibrium will shift (left, right, or no change) when each of the following changes is made.
(a) adding more $N_2O_3(g)$
(b) adding more $NO_2(g)$
(c) increasing the volume of the reaction flask
(d) lowering the temperature

26. K_p for the following reaction is 0.16 at 25 °C:

$$2\,NOBr(g) \rightleftharpoons 2\,NO(g) + Br_2(g)$$

The enthalpy change for the reaction at standard conditions is +16.3 kJ/mol-rxn. Predict the effect of the following changes on the position of the equilibrium; that is, state which way the equilibrium will shift (left, right, or no change) when each of the following changes is made.
(a) adding more $Br_2(g)$
(b) removing some $NOBr(g)$
(c) decreasing the temperature
(d) increasing the container volume

27. Consider the isomerization of butane with an equilibrium constant of $K = 2.5$. (See Study Question 13.) The system is originally at equilibrium with [butane] = 1.0 M and [isobutane] = 2.5 M.
(a) If 0.50 mol/L of isobutane is suddenly added and the system shifts to a new equilibrium position, what is the equilibrium concentration of each gas?
(b) If 0.50 mol/L of butane is added to the original equilibrium mixture and the system shifts to a new equilibrium position, what is the equilibrium concentration of each gas?

28. The decomposition of NH_4HS

$$NH_4HS(s) \rightleftharpoons NH_3(g) + H_2S(g)$$

is an endothermic process. Using Le Chatelier's principle, explain how increasing the temperature would affect the equilibrium. If more NH_4HS is added to a flask in which this equilibrium exists, how is the equilibrium affected? What if some additional NH_3 is placed in the flask? What will happen to the pressure of NH_3 if some H_2S is removed from the flask?

General Questions

These questions are not designated as to type or location in the chapter. They may combine several concepts.

29. Suppose 0.086 mol of Br_2 is placed in a 1.26-L flask and heated to 1756 K, a temperature at which the halogen dissociates to atoms.

$$Br_2(g) \rightleftharpoons 2\,Br(g)$$

If Br_2 is 3.7% dissociated at this temperature, calculate K_c.

30. The equilibrium constant for the reaction

$$N_2(g) + O_2(g) \rightleftharpoons 2\,NO(g)$$

is 1.7×10^{-3} at 2300 K.
(a) What is K for the reaction when written as follows?

$$\frac{1}{2} N_2(g) + \frac{1}{2} O_2(g) \rightleftharpoons NO(g)$$

(b) What is K for the following reaction?

$$2\,NO(g) \rightleftharpoons N_2(g) + O_2(g)$$

31. K_p for the formation of phosgene, $COCl_2$, is 6.5×10^{11} at 25 °C.

$$CO(g) + Cl_2(g) \rightleftharpoons COCl_2(g)$$

What is the value of K_p for the dissociation of phosgene?

$$COCl_2(g) \rightleftharpoons CO(g) + Cl_2(g)$$

32. The equilibrium constant, K_c, for the following reaction is 1.05 at 350 K.

$$2\,CH_2Cl_2(g) \rightleftharpoons CH_4(g) + CCl_4(g)$$

If an equilibrium mixture of the three gases at 350 K contains 0.0206 M $CH_2Cl_2(g)$ and 0.0163 M CH_4, what is the equilibrium concentration of CCl_4?

33. Carbon tetrachloride can be produced by the following reaction:

$$CS_2(g) + 3\,Cl_2(g) \rightleftharpoons S_2Cl_2(g) + CCl_4(g)$$

Suppose 1.2 mol of CS_2 and 3.6 mol of Cl_2 are placed in a 1.00-L flask. After equilibrium has been achieved, the mixture contains 0.90 mol CCl_4. Calculate K_c.

34. Equal numbers of moles of H_2 gas and I_2 vapor are mixed in a flask and heated to 700 °C. The initial concentration of each gas is 0.0088 mol/L, and 78.6% of the I_2 is consumed when equilibrium is achieved according to the equation

$$H_2(g) + I_2(g) \rightleftharpoons 2\,HI(g)$$

Calculate K_c for this reaction.

35. The equilibrium constant for the butane $\rightleftharpoons$ isobutane isomerization reaction is 2.5 at 25 °C. If 1.75 mol of butane and 1.25 mol of isobutane are mixed, is the system at equilibrium? If not, when it proceeds to equilibrium, which reagent increases in concentration? Calculate the concentrations of the two compounds when the system reaches equilibrium.

36. At 2300 K the equilibrium constant for the formation of NO(g) is 1.7×10^{-3}.

$$N_2(g) + O_2(g) \rightleftharpoons 2\,NO(g)$$

(a) Analysis shows that the concentrations of N_2 and O_2 are both 0.25 M, and that of NO is 0.0042 M under certain conditions. Is the system at equilibrium?
(b) If the system is not at equilibrium, in which direction does the reaction proceed?
(c) When the system is at equilibrium, what are the equilibrium concentrations?

37. Which of the following correctly relates the two equilibrium constants for the two reactions shown?

$$NOCl(g) \rightleftharpoons NO(g) + \tfrac{1}{2}\,Cl_2(g) \qquad K_1$$

$$2\,NO(g) + Cl_2(g) \rightleftharpoons 2\,NOCl(g) \qquad K_2$$

(a) $K_2 = -K_1^2$ (c) $K_2 = 1/K_1^2$
(b) $K_2 = 1/(K_1)^{1/2}$ (d) $K_2 = 2K_1$

38. Sulfur dioxide is readily oxidized to sulfur trioxide.

$$2\,SO_2(g) + O_2(g) \rightleftharpoons 2\,SO_3(g) \qquad K_c = 279$$

If we add 3.00 g of SO_2 and 5.00 g of O_2 to a 1.0-L flask, approximately what quantity of SO_3 will be in the flask once the reactants and the product reach equilibrium?
(a) 2.21 g (c) 3.61 g
(b) 4.56 g (d) 8.00 g

(*Note:* The full solution to this problem results in a cubic equation. Do not try to solve it exactly. Decide only which of the answers is most reasonable.)

39. Heating a metal carbonate leads to decomposition.

$$BaCO_3(s) \rightleftharpoons BaO(s) + CO_2(g)$$

Predict the effect on the equilibrium of each change listed below. Answer by choosing (i) no change, (ii) shifts left, or (iii) shifts right.
(a) add $BaCO_3$ (c) add BaO
(b) add CO_2 (d) raise the temperature
(e) increase the volume of the flask containing the reaction

40. Carbonyl bromide decomposes to carbon monoxide and bromine.

$$COBr_2(g) \rightleftharpoons CO(g) + Br_2(g)$$

K_c is 0.190 at 73 °C. Suppose you place 0.500 mol of $COBr_2$ in a 2.00-L flask and heat it to 73 °C (see Study Question 17). After equilibrium has been achieved, you add an additional 2.00 mol of CO.
(a) How is the equilibrium mixture affected by adding more CO?
(b) When equilibrium is reestablished, what are the new equilibrium concentrations of $COBr_2$, CO, and Br_2?
(c) How has the addition of CO affected the percentage of $COBr_2$ that decomposed?

41. Phosphorus pentachloride decomposes at higher temperatures.

$$PCl_5(g) \rightleftharpoons PCl_3(g) + Cl_2(g)$$

An equilibrium mixture at some temperature consists of 3.120 g of PCl_5, 3.845 g of PCl_3, and 1.787 g of Cl_2 in a 1.00-L flask. If you add 1.418 g of Cl_2, how will the equilibrium be affected? What will the concentrations of PCl_5, PCl_3, and Cl_2 be when equilibrium is reestablished?

42. Ammonium hydrogen sulfide decomposes on heating.

$$NH_4HS(s) \rightleftharpoons NH_3(g) + H_2S(g)$$

If K_p for this reaction is 0.11 at 25 °C (when the partial pressures are measured in atmospheres), what is the total pressure in the flask at equilibrium?

43. Ammonium iodide dissociates reversibly to ammonia and hydrogen iodide if the salt is heated to a sufficiently high temperature.

$$NH_4I(s) \rightleftharpoons NH_3(g) + HI(g)$$

Some ammonium iodide is placed in a flask, which is then heated to 400 °C. If the total pressure in the flask when equilibrium has been achieved is 705 mm Hg, what is the value of K_p (when partial pressures are in atmospheres)?

44. When solid ammonium carbamate sublimes, it dissociates completely into ammonia and carbon dioxide according to the following equation:

$$(NH_4)(H_2NCO_2)(s) \rightleftharpoons 2\,NH_3(g) + CO_2(g)$$

At 25 °C, experiment shows that the total pressure of the gases in equilibrium with the solid is 0.116 atm. What is the equilibrium constant, K_p?

45. The equilibrium reaction $N_2O_4(g) \rightleftharpoons 2\,NO_2(g)$ has been thoroughly studied (Figure 16.8).
(a) If the total pressure in a flask containing NO_2 and N_2O_4 gas at 25 °C is 1.50 atm and the value of K_p at this temperature is 0.148, what fraction of the N_2O_4 has dissociated to NO_2?
(b) What happens to the fraction dissociated if the volume of the container is increased so that the total equilibrium pressure falls to 1.00 atm?

46. In the gas phase, acetic acid exists as an equilibrium of monomer and dimer molecules. (The dimer consists of two molecules linked through hydrogen bonds.)

The equilibrium constant, K_c, at 25 °C for the monomer–dimer equilibrium

$$2\ CH_3CO_2H \rightleftharpoons (CH_3CO_2H)_2$$

has been determined to be 3.2×10^4. Assume that acetic acid is present initially at a concentration of 5.4×10^{-4} mol/L at 25 °C and that no dimer is present initially.

(a) What percentage of the acetic acid is converted to dimer?

(b) As the temperature increases, in which direction does the equilibrium shift? (Recall that hydrogen-bond formation is an exothermic process.)

47. Assume 3.60 mol of ammonia is placed in a 2.00-L vessel and allowed to decompose to the elements.

$$2\ NH_3(g) \rightleftharpoons N_2(g) + 3\ H_2(g)$$

If the experimental value of K_c is 6.3 for this reaction at the temperature in the reactor, calculate the equilibrium concentration of each reagent. What is the total pressure in the flask?

48. The total pressure for a mixture of N_2O_4 and NO_2 is 1.5 atm. If $K_p = 7.1$ (at 25 °C), calculate the partial pressure of each gas in the mixture.

$$2\ NO_2(g) \rightleftharpoons N_2O_4(g)$$

49. K_c for the decomposition of ammonium hydrogen sulfide is 1.8×10^{-4} at 25 °C.

$$NH_4HS(s) \rightleftharpoons NH_3(g) + H_2S(g)$$

(a) When the pure salt decomposes in a flask, what are the equilibrium concentrations of NH_3 and H_2S?

(b) If NH_4HS is placed in a flask already containing 0.020 mol/L of NH_3 and then the system is allowed to come to equilibrium, what are the equilibrium concentrations of NH_3 and H_2S?

50. The equilibrium constant, K_p, is 0.14 at 25 °C for the following reaction:

$$N_2O_4(g) \rightleftharpoons 2\ NO_2(g)$$

If the total pressure of the gas mixture is 2.5 atm at equilibrium, what is the partial pressure of each gas?

51. ▲ A 15-L flask at 300 K contains 64.4 g of a mixture of NO_2 and N_2O_4 in equilibrium. What is the total pressure in the flask? (K_p for $2\ NO_2\ (g) \rightleftharpoons N_2O_4(g)$ is 7.1.)

52. ▲ Lanthanum oxalate decomposes when heated to lanthanum(III) oxide, CO, and CO_2.

$$La_2(C_2O_4)_3(s) \rightleftharpoons La_2O_3(s) + 3\ CO(g) + 3\ CO_2(g)$$

(a) If, at equilibrium, the total pressure in a 10.0-L flask is 0.200 atm, what is the value of K_p?

(b) Suppose 0.100 mol of $La_2(C_2O_4)_3$ was originally placed in the 10.0-L flask. What quantity of $La_2(C_2O_4)_3$ remains unreacted at equilibrium at 373 K?

53. ▲ The reaction of hydrogen and iodine to give hydrogen iodide has an equilibrium constant, K_c, of 56 at 435 °C.

(a) What is the value of K_p?

(b) Suppose you mix 0.45 mol of H_2 and 0.45 mol of I_2 in a 10.0-L flask at 425 °C. What is the total pressure of the mixture before and after equilibrium is achieved?

(c) What is the partial pressure of each gas at equilibrium?

54. Sulfuryl chloride, SO_2Cl_2, is used as a reagent in the synthesis of organic compounds. When heated to a sufficiently high temperature, it decomposes to SO_2 and Cl_2.

$$SO_2Cl_2(g) \rightleftharpoons SO_2(g) + Cl_2(g) \qquad K_c = 0.045 \text{ at } 375 °C$$

(a) A 1.00-L flask containing 6.70 g of SO_2Cl_2 is heated to 375 °C. What is the concentration of each of the compounds in the system when equilibrium is achieved? What fraction of SO_2Cl_2 has dissociated?

(b) What are the concentrations of SO_2Cl_2, SO_2, and Cl_2 at equilibrium in the 1.00-L flask at 375 °C if you begin with a mixture of SO_2Cl_2 (6.70 g) and Cl_2 (1.00 atm)? What fraction of SO_2Cl_2 has dissociated?

(c) Compare the fractions of SO_2Cl_2 in parts (a) and (b). Do they agree with your expectations based on Le Chatelier's principle?

55. ▲ Hemoglobin (Hb) can form a complex with both O_2 and CO. For the reaction

$$HbO_2(aq) + CO(g) \rightleftharpoons HbCO(aq) + O_2(g)$$

at body temperature, K is about 200. If the ratio $[HbCO]/[HbO_2]$ comes close to 1, death is probable. What partial pressure of CO in the air is likely to be fatal? Assume the partial pressure of O_2 is 0.20 atm.

56. ▲ Limestone decomposes at high temperatures.

$$CaCO_3(s) \rightleftharpoons CaO(s) + CO_2(g)$$

At 1000 °C, $K_p = 3.87$. If pure $CaCO_3$ is placed in a 5.00-L flask and heated to 1000 °C, what quantity of $CaCO_3$ must decompose to achieve the equilibrium pressure of CO_2?

57. At 1800 K, oxygen dissociates very slightly into its atoms.

$$O_2(g) \rightleftharpoons 2\ O(g) \qquad K_p = 1.2 \times 10^{-10}$$

If you place 1.0 mol of O_2 in a 10.-L vessel and heat it to 1800 K, how many O atoms are present in the flask?

58. ▲ Nitrosyl bromide, NOBr, dissociates readily at room temperature.

$$NOBr(g) \rightleftharpoons NO(g) + \tfrac{1}{2} Br_2(g)$$

Some NOBr is placed in a flask at 25 °C and allowed to dissociate. The total pressure at equilibrium is 190 mm Hg and the compound is found to be 34% dissociated. What is the value of K_p?

59. ▲ Boric acid and glycerin form a complex

$$B(OH)_3(aq) + glycerin(aq) \rightleftharpoons B(OH)_3 \cdot glycerin(aq)$$

with an equilibrium constant of 0.90. If the concentration of boric acid is 0.10 M, how much glycerin should be added, per liter, so that 60.% of the boric acid is in the form of the complex?

60. ▲ The dissociation of calcium carbonate has an equilibrium constant of $K_p = 1.16$ at 800 °C.

$$CaCO_3(s) \rightleftharpoons CaO(s) + CO_2(g)$$

(a) What is K_c for the reaction?
(b) If you place 22.5 g of $CaCO_3$ in a 9.56-L container at 800 °C, what is the pressure of CO_2 in the container?
(c) What percentage of the original 22.5-g sample of $CaCO_3$ remains undecomposed at equilibrium?

61. ▲ A sample of N_2O_4 gas with a pressure of 1.00 atm is placed in a flask. When equilibrium is achieved, 20.0% of the N_2O_4 has been converted to NO_2 gas.
(a) Calculate K_p.
(b) If the original pressure of N_2O_4 is 0.10 atm, what is the percent dissociation of the gas? Is the result in agreement with Le Chatelier's principle?

62. ▲ A reaction important in smog formation is

$$O_3(g) + NO(g) \rightleftharpoons O_2(g) + NO_2(g) \qquad K = 6.0 \times 10^{34}$$

(a) If the initial concentrations are $[O_3] = 1.0 \times 10^{-6}$ M, $[NO] = 1.0 \times 10^{-5}$ M, $[NO_2] = 2.5 \times 10^{-4}$ M, and $[O_2] = 8.2 \times 10^{-3}$ M, is the system at equilibrium? If not, in which direction does the reaction proceed?
(b) If the temperature is increased, as on a very warm day, will the concentrations of the products increase or decrease? (*Hint:* You may have to calculate the enthalpy change for the reaction to find out if it is exothermic or endothermic.)

In the Laboratory

63. ▲ The ammonia complex of trimethylborane, $(NH_3)B(CH_3)_3$, dissociates at 100 °C to its components with $K_p = 4.62$ (when the pressures are in atmospheres).

$(NH_3)B(CH_3)_3(g)$ ⇌ $B(CH_3)_3(g)$ + $NH_3(g)$

If NH_3 is changed to some other molecule, the equilibrium constant is different.

For $[(CH_3)_3P]B(CH_3)_3$ $K_p = 0.128$

For $[(CH_3)_3N]B(CH_3)_3$ $K_p = 0.472$

(a) If you begin an experiment by placing 0.010 mol of each complex in a flask, which would have the largest partial pressure of $B(CH_3)_3$ at 100 °C?
(b) If 0.73 g (0.010 mol) of $(NH_3)B(CH_3)_3$ is placed in a 100.-mL flask and heated to 100 °C, what is the partial pressure of each gas in the equilibrium mixture, and what is the total pressure? What is the percent dissociation of $(NH_3)B(CH_3)_3$?

64. The photographs below show what occurs when a solution of potassium chromate is treated with a few drops of concentrated hydrochloric acid. Some of the bright yellow chromate ion is converted to the orange dichromate ion.

$$2\,CrO_4^{2-}(aq) + 2\,H_3O^+(aq) \rightleftharpoons Cr_2O_7^{2-}(aq) + 3\,H_2O(\ell)$$

(a) Explain this experimental observation in terms of Le Chatelier's principle.
(b) What would you observe if you treated the orange solution with sodium hydroxide? Explain your observation.

65. The photograph below (a) shows what occurs when a solution of iron(III) nitrate is treated with a few drops of aqueous potassium thiocyanate. The nearly colorless iron(III) ion is converted to a red $[Fe(H_2O)_5SCN]^{2+}$ ion. (This is a classic test for the presence of iron(III) ions in solution.)

$$[Fe(H_2O)_6]^{3+}(aq) + SCN^-(aq) \rightleftharpoons$$
$$[Fe(H_2O)_5SCN]^{2+}(aq) + H_2O(\ell)$$

(a) Adding KSCN   **(b) Adding Ag⁺**

(a) As more KSCN is added to the solution, the color becomes even more red. Explain this observation.
(b) Silver ions form a white precipitate with SCN^- ions. What would you observe on adding a few drops of aqueous silver nitrate to a red solution of $[Fe(H_2O)_5SCN]^+$ ions? Explain your observation.

66. ▲ The photographs at the bottom of the page show what occurs when you add ammonia to aqueous nickel(II) nitrate and then add ethylenediamine ($NH_2CH_2CH_2NH_2$) to the intermediate blue-purple solution.

$[Ni(H_2O)_6]^{2+}(aq) + 6 NH_3(aq)$
green
$$\rightleftharpoons [Ni(NH_3)_6]^{2+}(aq) + 6 H_2O(\ell) \qquad K_1$$
blue-purple

$[Ni(NH_3)_6]^{2+}(aq) + 3 NH_2CH_2CH_2NH_2(aq)$
blue-purple
$$\rightleftharpoons [Ni(NH_2CH_2CH_2NH_2)_3]^{2+}(aq) + 6 NH_3(aq) \quad K_2$$
violet

(a) Write a chemical equation for the formation of $[Ni(NH_2CH_2CH_2NH_2)_3]^{2+}$ from $[Ni(H_2O)_6]^{2+}$ and ethylenediamine, and relate the value of K for this reaction to K_1 and K_2.

(b) Which species, $[Ni(NH_2CH_2CH_2NH_2)_3]^{2+}$, $[Ni(NH_3)_6]^{2+}$, or $[Ni(H_2O)_6]^{2+}$ is the most stable? Explain.

Summary and Conceptual Questions

The following questions may use concepts from this and previous chapters.

67. Decide whether each of the following statements is true or false. If false, change the wording to make it true.

(a) The magnitude of the equilibrium constant is always independent of temperature.

(b) When two chemical equations are added to give a net equation, the equilibrium constant for the net equation is the product of the equilibrium constants of the summed equations.

(c) The equilibrium constant for a reaction has the same value as K for the reverse reaction.

(d) Only the concentration of CO_2 appears in the equilibrium constant expression for the reaction $CaCO_3(s) \rightleftharpoons CaO(s) + CO_2(g)$.

(e) For the reaction $CaCO_3(s) \rightleftharpoons CaO(s) + CO_2(g)$, the value of K is numerically the same, whether the amount of CO_2 is expressed as moles/liter or as gas pressure.

68. Neither $PbCl_2$ nor PbF_2 is appreciably soluble in water. If solid $PbCl_2$ and solid PbF_2 are placed in equal amounts of water in separate beakers, in which beaker is the concentration of Pb^{2+} greater? Equilibrium constants for these solids dissolving in water are as follows:

$PbCl_2(s) \rightleftharpoons Pb^{2+}(aq) + 2 Cl^-(aq) \qquad K = 1.7 \times 10^{-5}$

$PbF_2(s) \rightleftharpoons Pb^{2+}(aq) + 2 F^-(aq) \qquad K = 3.7 \times 10^{-8}$

69. Characterize each of the following as product- or reactant-favored at equilibrium.

(a) $CO(g) + \frac{1}{2} O_2(g) \rightleftharpoons CO_2(g) \quad K_p = 1.2 \times 10^{45}$

(b) $H_2O(g) \rightleftharpoons H_2(g) + \frac{1}{2} O_2(g) \quad K_p = 9.1 \times 10^{-41}$

(c) $CO(g) + Cl_2(g) \rightleftharpoons COCl_2(g) \quad K_p = 6.5 \times 10^{11}$

70. ▲ The size of a flask containing colorless $N_2O_4(g)$ and brown $NO_2(g)$ at equilibrium is rapidly reduced to half the original volume.

$$N_2O_4(g) \rightleftharpoons 2 NO_2(g)$$

(a) What color change (if any) is observed immediately upon halving the flask size?

(b) What color change (if any) is observed during the process in which equilibrium is reestablished in the flask?

71. Describe an experiment that would allow you to prove that the system $3 H_2(g) + N_2(g) \rightleftharpoons 2 NH_3(g)$ is a dynamic equilibrium. (*Hint:* Consider using a stable isotope such as ^{15}N or ^2H.)

72. Consider the following equilibrium:

$COBr_2(g) \rightleftharpoons CO(g) + Br_2(g) \quad K_c = 0.190$ at 73 °C

(a) A 1.0 mol sample of $COBr_2$ is transferred to a 2.0-L flask and heated until equilibrium is attained. Calculate the equilibrium concentrations of each species.

(b) The volume of the container is decreased to 1.0 L and the system allowed to return to equilibrium. Calculate the new equilibrium concentrations. (*Hint:* The calculation will be easier if you view this as a new problem with the new initial concentration of $COBr_2$ of 1.0 mol/L.)

Photos © Cengage Learning/ Charles D. Winters

NH_3

$[Ni(H_2O)_6]^{2+}$

$[Ni(NH_3)_6]^{2+}$

Add ethylenediamine $NH_2CH_2CH_2NH_2$

$[Ni(NH_2CH_2CH_2NH_2)_3]^{2+}$

Applying Chemical Principles

Trivalent Carbon

The octet rule is a guiding principle in organic chemistry. As a result, when someone discovers a molecule that does not obey the octet rule, organic chemists are always interested. The synthesis of the triphenylmethyl radical, $(C_6H_5)_3C$ was one such event.

The triphenylmethyl radical (**compound 2**), the first known persistent organic free radical, was discovered over 100 years ago by Moses Gomberg, a chemist at the University of Michigan. Gomberg set out to make hexaphenylethane $[(C_6H_5)_3C–C(C_6H_5)_3]$ (**compound 3**). When he combined the reactants $(C_6H_5)_3CCl$ (**compound 1**) and Zn, he obtained a yellow solution that became more intensely yellow when heated and was reactive toward oxygen and halogens. This extreme reactivity led Gomberg to conclude that the yellow color was due to the presence of $(C_6H_5)_3C$ in solution. The existence of the stable free radical was explained by the fact that there are three large phenyl groups around a carbon atom, which prevents the radical from undergoing the expected dimerization to hexaphenylethane.

Actually, the triphenylmethyl radical does dimerize, but not the way Gomberg had expected. A diamagnetic, white solid crystalline dimer (**compound 4**) can be isolated from the solutions containing the radical. The dimerization occurs between a methyl carbon radical on one molecule and the phenyl ring on a second. When redissolved in benzene, the original yellow solution forms.

Studies determined that compounds **4** and **2** exist in solution in equilibrium. The value of K_c for the dimer-monomer equilibrium (**4** $\rightleftharpoons$ **2**) in benzene is 4.1×10^{-4} at 20 °C.

Interestingly, Gomberg finished his initial publication with the following statement: "This work will be continued and I wish to reserve the field for myself." In the United States, chemical research is competitive and Gomberg's wish was not respected.

Questions:

1. Freezing point depression is one means of determining the molar mass of a compound. The freezing point depression constant of benzene is –5.12 °C/m.
   (a) When a 0.503 g sample of the white crystalline dimer is dissolved in 10.0 g benzene, the freezing point of benzene is decreased by 0.542 °C. Verify that the molar mass of the dimer is 475 g/mol when determined by freezing point depression. Assume no dissociation of the dimer occurs.
   (b) The correct molar mass of the dimer is 487 g/mol. Explain why the dissociation equilibrium causes the freezing point depression calculation to yield a lower molar mass for the dimer.

2. What concentration of the monomer will exist at equilibrium with 0.015 mol/L of the dimer (**2**) in benzene at 20 °C?

3. A 0.64 g sample of the white crystalline dimer (**4**) is dissolved in 25.0 mL of benzene at 20 °C. Use the equilibrium constant to calculate the concentrations of monomer (**2**) and dimer (**4**) in this solution.

4. Predict whether the dissociation of the dimer to the monomer is exothermic or endothermic, based on the fact that at higher temperatures the yellow color of the solution intensifies.

5. Which of the organic species mentioned in this story is paramagnetic?
   (a) triphenylmethyl chloride
   (b) triphenylmethyl radical
   (c) the triphenylmethyl dimer

Reference:

M. Gomberg, *Journal of the American Chemical Society*, Vol. 22, pp. 757-771, 1900.

17 Principles of Chemical Reactivity: The Chemistry of Acids and Bases

© Cengage Learning/Charles D. Winters

Aspirin Is Over 100 Years Old! Aspirin is one of the most successful nonprescription drugs ever made. Americans swallow more than 50 million aspirin tablets a day, mostly for the pain-relieving (analgesic) effects of the drug. Aspirin also wards off heart disease and thrombosis (blood clots), and it has even been suggested as a possible treatment for certain cancers and for senile dementia.

Hippocrates (460–370 BC), the ancient Greek physician, recommended an infusion of willow bark to ease the pain of childbirth. It was not until the 19th century that an Italian chemist, Raffaele Piria, isolated salicylic acid, the active compound in the bark. Soon thereafter, it was found that the acid could be extracted from a wild flower, *Spiraea ulmaria*. It is from the name of this plant that the name "aspirin" (a + spiraea) is derived.

Hippocrates's willow bark extract, salicylic acid, is an analgesic, but it is also very irritating to the stomach lining. It was therefore an important advance when chemists at Bayer Chemicals in Germany found, in 1897, that a derivative of salicylic acid, acetylsalicylic acid, was also a useful drug

and had fewer side effects. This is the compound we now call "aspirin."

Acetylsalicylic acid slowly reverts to salicylic acid, and acetic acid in the presence of moisture; therefore, if you smell the characteristic odor of acetic acid in an old bottle of aspirin, the tablets are too old and should be discarded.

Aspirin (acetylsalicylic acid) is a component of various over-the-counter medicines, such as Anacin, Ecotrin, Excedrin, and Alka-Seltzer. The latter is a combination of aspirin with citric acid and sodium bicarbonate. Sodium bicarbonate is a base and reacts with the acid to produce the sodium salt of acetylsalicylic acid, a form of aspirin that is water-soluble and quicker acting.

Questions:

1. Aspirin has a pK_a of 3.49, and that of acetic acid is 4.74. Which is the stronger acid?
2. Identify the acidic H atom in aspirin.
3. Write an equation for the ionization of aspirin.

Answers to these questions are available in Appendix N.

CHAPTER GOALS

See Chapter Goals Revisited (page 796) for Study Questions keyed to these goals.

- Use the Brønsted–Lowry and Lewis theories of acids and bases.

- Apply the principles of chemical equilibrium to acids and bases in aqueous solution.

- Predict the outcome of reactions of acids and bases.

- Understand the influence of structure and bonding on acid–base properties.

Acids and bases are among the most common substances in nature. Amino acids are the building blocks of proteins. The repository of genetic information in your cells is DNA, deoxyribonucleic acid. The pH of the lakes, rivers, and oceans is affected by dissolved acids and bases, and many bodily functions depend on acids and bases. You were introduced to acids and bases and to some of their chemistry in Chapter 3, but this chapter and the next take up the chemistry of this important class of substances in more detail.

OWL

Sign in to OWL at **www.cengage.com/owl** to view tutorials and simulations, develop problem-solving skills, and complete online homework assigned by your professor.

17.1 Acids and Bases: A Review

In Chapter 3, you were introduced to two definitions of acids and bases: the Arrhenius definition and the Brønsted–Lowry definition. According to the Arrhenius definition, an acid is any substance that, when dissolved in water, increases the concentration of hydrogen ions, H^+ (◄ page 128). An Arrhenius base is any substance that increases the concentration of hydroxide ions, OH^-, when dissolved in water. Based on the Arrhenius definition, hydrochloric acid is therefore classified as an acid, and sodium hydroxide is classified as a base.

Download mini lecture videos for key concept review and exam prep from OWL or purchase them from **www.cengagebrain.com**

$$HCl(aq) \rightarrow H^+(aq) + Cl^-(aq)$$

$$NaOH(aq) \rightarrow Na^+(aq) + OH^-(aq)$$

Using this definition, reactions between acids and bases involve the combination of H^+ and OH^- ions to form water (and a salt).

$$NaOH(aq) + HCl(aq) \rightarrow H_2O(\ell) + NaCl(aq)$$

The Brønsted–Lowry definition of acids and bases is more general and views acid–base behavior in terms of proton transfer from one substance to another. *A Brønsted–Lowry acid is a proton (H^+) donor, and a Brønsted–Lowry base is a proton acceptor*, a definition that extends the list of acids and bases and the scope of acid–base reactions. In the following reaction, HCl acts as a Brønsted–Lowry acid, and water acts as a Brønsted–Lowry base because HCl transfers a H^+ ion to H_2O to form the hydronium ion, H_3O^+.

$$HCl(aq) + H_2O(\ell) \rightleftharpoons H_3O^+(aq) + Cl^-(aq)$$

We will begin this chapter by looking at Brønsted–Lowry acid–base chemistry in more detail.

REVIEW & CHECK FOR SECTION 17.1

Which of the following is a list of Brønsted–Lowry acids?

(a) CH_3CO_2H, $Al(OH)_3$, H_3PO_4

(b) NH_4^+, NH_3, HCl

(c) H_2CO_3, CH_3CO_2H, H_3PO_4

17.2 The Brønsted–Lowry Concept of Acids and Bases Extended

A wide variety of Brønsted–Lowry acids is known. These include some molecular compounds such as nitric acid,

$$HNO_3(aq) \ + \ H_2O(\ell) \rightleftharpoons NO_3^-(aq) + H_3O^+(aq)$$
acid

cations such as NH_4^+,

$$NH_4^+(aq) \ + \ H_2O(\ell) \rightleftharpoons NH_3(aq) + H_3O^+(aq)$$
acid

and anions.

$$H_2PO_4^-(aq) \ + \ H_2O(\ell) \rightleftharpoons HPO_4^{2-}(aq) \ + \ H_3O^+(aq)$$

Similarly, many different types of species can act as Brønsted–Lowry bases in their reactions with water. These include some molecular compounds,

$$NH_3(aq) \ + \ H_2O(\ell) \rightleftharpoons NH_4^+(aq) + OH^-(aq)$$
base

and anions.

$$CO_3^{2-}(aq) \ + \ H_2O(\ell) \rightleftharpoons HCO_3^-(aq) \ + \ OH^-(aq)$$

Hydrated metal cations can also function as acids and bases. Some of these ions act as Brønsted–Lowry acids:

$$[Fe(H_2O)_6]^{3+}(aq) + H_2O(\ell) \rightleftharpoons [Fe(H_2O)_5(OH)]^{2+}(aq) + H_3O^+(aq)$$

while others act as Brønsted–Lowry bases.

$$[Al(H_2O)_5(OH)]^{2+}(aq) + H_2O(\ell) \rightleftharpoons [Al(H_2O)_6]^{3+}(aq) + OH^-(aq)$$

Acids such as HF, HCl, HNO_3, and CH_3CO_2H (acetic acid) are all capable of donating one proton and so are called **monoprotic acids.** Other acids, called **polyprotic acids** (Table 17.1), are capable of donating two or more protons. Sulfuric acid is a familiar example of a polyprotic acid.

$$H_2SO_4(aq) \quad + \quad H_2O(\ell) \rightleftharpoons HSO_4^-(aq) \quad + \quad H_3O^+(aq)$$

$$HSO_4^-(aq) \quad + \quad H_2O(\ell) \rightleftharpoons SO_4^{2-}(aq) \quad + \quad H_3O^+(aq)$$

Just as there are acids that can donate more than one proton, so there are **polyprotic bases** that can accept more than one proton. The fully deprotonated anions of polyprotic acids are polyprotic bases; examples include SO_4^{2-}, PO_4^{3-}, CO_3^{2-}, and $C_2O_4^{2-}$. The carbonate ion, for example, can accept two protons.

$$CO_3^{2-}(aq) + H_2O(\ell) \rightleftharpoons HCO_3^-(aq) + OH^-(aq)$$
base

$$HCO_3^-(aq) + H_2O(\ell) \rightleftharpoons H_2CO_3(aq) + OH^-(aq)$$
base

Some molecules (such as water) and ions can behave either as Brønsted acids or bases and are referred to as being **amphiprotic** (◀ page 131). An example of an amphiprotic anion that is particularly important in biochemical systems is the dihydrogen phosphate anion (Table 17.1).

$$H_2PO_4^-(aq) + H_2O(\ell) \rightleftharpoons H_3O^+(aq) + HPO_4^{2-}(aq)$$
acid

$$H_2PO_4^-(aq) + H_2O(\ell) \rightleftharpoons H_3PO_4(aq) + OH^-(aq)$$
base

© Cengage Learning/Charles D. Winters

Carboxylic acid groups

Tartaric acid, $H_2C_4H_4O_6$, is a naturally occurring diprotic acid. Tartaric acid and its potassium salt are found in grapes and other fruits. The acidic protons are the H atoms of the $-CO_2H$ or carboxylic acid groups.

Table 17.1 Polyprotic Acids and Bases

Acid Form	Amphiprotic Form	Base Form
H_2S (hydrosulfuric acid or hydrogen sulfide)	HS^- (hydrogen sulfide ion)	S^{2-} (sulfide ion)
H_3PO_4 (phosphoric acid)	$H_2PO_4^-$ (dihydrogen phosphate ion) HPO_4^{2-} (hydrogen phosphate ion)	PO_4^{3-} (phosphate ion)
H_2CO_3 (carbonic acid)	HCO_3^- (hydrogen carbonate ion or bicarbonate ion)	CO_3^{2-} (carbonate ion)
$H_2C_2O_4$ (oxalic acid)	$HC_2O_4^-$ (hydrogen oxalate ion)	$C_2O_4^{2-}$ (oxalate ion)

Conjugate Acid–Base Pairs

The reaction of the hydrogen corbonate ion and water exemplifies a feature of Brønsted acid–base chemistry: a Brønsted acid and base produce a new acid and base.

In the forward direction, HCO_3^- is the Brønsted base because it captures H^+ from the Brønsted acid, H_2O. The products are a new Brønsted acid and base. In the reverse direction, the H_2CO_3 is the acid, and OH^- is the base.

A **conjugate acid–base pair** consists of two species that differ from each other by the presence of one hydrogen ion. Thus, H_2CO_3 and HCO_3^- comprise a conjugate acid–base pair. In this pair, HCO_3^- is the conjugate base of the acid H_2CO_3, and H_2CO_3 is the conjugate acid of the base HCO_3^-. There is a second conjugate acid–base pair in this reaction: H_2O and OH^-. In fact, *every reaction between a Brønsted acid and a Brønsted base involves two conjugate acid–base pairs* (Table 17.2).

REVIEW & CHECK FOR SECTION 17.2

1. H_3PO_4, phosphoric acid, can donate two protons to water to form the monohydrogen phosphate ion, HPO_4^{2-}. Is the monohydrogen phosphate ion an acid, a base, or amphiprotic?

   (a) acid   (b) base   (c) amphiprotic

2. The cyanide ion, CN^-, accepts a proton from water to form HCN. Is CN^- a Brønsted acid or base or is it amphiprotic?

   (a) acid   (b) base   (c) amphiprotic

3. In the following reaction, identify the acid on the left and its conjugate base on the right.

$$HNO_3(aq) + NH_3(aq) \rightleftharpoons NH_4^+(aq) + NO_3^-(aq)$$

   (a) acid = NH_3 and conjugate base = NH_4^+

   (b) acid = HNO_3 and conjugate base = NO_3^-

   Similarly, identify the base on the left and its conjugate acid on the right.

   (a) base = NH_3 and conjugate acid = NH_4^+

   (b) base = HNO_3 and conjugate acid = NO_3^-

4. Identify the conjugate acid/base pairs in the reaction of HF and acetic acid.

$$HF(aq) + CH_3CO_2^-(aq) \rightleftharpoons F^-(aq) + CH_3CO_2H(aq)$$

   (a) $HF/CH_3CO_2^-$ and F^-/CH_3CO_2H

   (b) HF/CH_3CO_2H and $F^-/CH_3CO_2^-$

   (c) HF/F^- and $CH_3CO_2H/CH_3CO_2^-$

17.3　Water and the pH Scale

Because we generally use aqueous solutions of acids and bases and because the acid–base reactions in your body occur in your aqueous interior, we want to consider the behavior of water in terms of chemical equilibria.

Table 17.2 Acid–Base Reactions and Conjugate Acid–Base Pairs*

Name	Acid 1		Base 2		Base 1		Acid 2
Hydrochloric acid	HCl	+	H_2O	⇌	Cl^-	+	H_3O^+
Nitric acid	HNO_3	+	H_2O	⇌	NO_3^-	+	H_3O^+
Carbonic acid	H_2CO_3	+	H_2O	⇌	HCO_3^-	+	H_3O^+
Acetic acid	CH_3CO_2H	+	H_2O	⇌	$CH_3CO_2^-$	+	H_3O^+
Hydrocyanic acid	HCN	+	H_2O	⇌	CN^-	+	H_3O^+
Hydrogen sulfide	H_2S	+	H_2O	⇌	HS^-	+	H_3O^+
Ammonia	H_2O	+	NH_3	⇌	OH^-	+	NH_4^+
Carbonate ion	H_2O	+	CO_3^{2-}	⇌	OH^-	+	HCO_3^-
Water	H_2O	+	H_2O	⇌	OH^-	+	H_3O^+

*Acid 1 and base 1 are a conjugate pair, as are base 2 and acid 2.

Water Autoionization and the Water Ionization Constant, K_w

An acid such as HCl does not need to be present for the hydronium ion to exist in water. In fact, two water molecules can interact with each other to produce a hydronium ion and a hydroxide ion by proton transfer from one water molecule to the other.

$$2 H_2O(\ell) \rightleftharpoons H_3O^+(aq) + OH^-(aq)$$

This **autoionization** reaction of water was demonstrated a century ago by Friedrich Kohlrausch (1840–1910). He found that, even after water is painstakingly purified, it still conducts electricity to a very small extent. We now know this is because autoionization produces very low concentrations of H_3O^+ and OH^- ions. *Water autoionization is the cornerstone of our concepts of aqueous acid–base behavior.*

The water autoionization equilibrium lies far to the left side. In fact, in pure water at 25 °C, only about two out of a billion (10^9) water molecules are ionized at any instant. To express this idea more quantitatively, we can write the equilibrium constant expression for autoionization.

$$K_w = [H_3O^+][OH^-] = 1.0 \times 10^{-14} \text{ at } 25 \text{ °C} \tag{17.1}$$

There are several important aspects of this equation.

- Based on the rules for writing equilibrium constants, we do not include the concentration of water.
- The equilibrium constant is given a special symbol, K_w, and is known as the **autoionization constant for water**.
- Because autoionization is the only source of hydronium and hydroxide ions in pure water, we know that $[H_3O^+]$ must be equal to $[OH^-]$. Electrical conductivity measurements of pure water show that $[H_3O^+] = [OH^-] = 1.0 \times 10^{-7}$ M at 25 °C, so K_w has a value of 1.0×10^{-14} at 25 °C.

In pure water, the hydronium ion and hydroxide ion concentrations are equal, and the water is said to be neutral. If some acid or base is added to pure water, however, the equilibrium

$$2 H_2O(\ell) \rightleftharpoons H_3O^+(aq) + OH^-(aq)$$

● **K_w and Temperature** The equation $K_w = [H_3O^+][OH^-]$ is valid for pure water and for any aqueous solution. The numerical value for K_w, however, is temperature dependent. Because the autoionization reaction is endothermic, K_w increases with temperature.

T (°C)	K_w
10	0.29×10^{-14}
15	0.45×10^{-14}
20	0.68×10^{-14}
25	1.01×10^{-14}
30	1.47×10^{-14}
50	5.48×10^{-14}

● **The Magnitude of $[H_3O^+]$ in Pure Water** The ionization of two water molecules out of a billion produces a H_3O^+ concentration of 1×10^{-7} M. To have a sense of this tiny amount, this would be like identifying just 14 people out of the current population of the earth, about 7 billion.

is disturbed. Adding acid raises the concentration of the H_3O^+ ions, so the solution is acidic. To oppose this increase, Le Chatelier's principle (◄ Section 16.6) predicts that a small fraction of the H_3O^+ ions will react with OH^- ions from water autoionization to form water. This lowers $[OH^-]$ until the product of $[H_3O^+]$ and $[OH^-]$ is again equal to 1.0×10^{-14} at 25 °C. Similarly, adding a base to pure water gives a basic solution because the OH^- ion concentration has increased. Le Chatelier's principle predicts that some of the added OH^- ions will react with H_3O^+ ions present in the solution from water autoionization, thereby lowering $[H_3O^+]$ until the value of the product of $[H_3O^+]$ and $[OH^-]$ equals 1.0×10^{-14} at 25 °C.

Thus, for aqueous solutions at 25 °C, we can say that

- In a neutral solution, $[H_3O^+] = [OH^-]$.
  Both are equal to 1.0×10^{-7} M.
- In an acidic solution, $[H_3O^+] > [OH^-]$.
  $[H_3O^+] > 1.0 \times 10^{-7}$ M and $[OH^-] < 1.0 \times 10^{-7}$ M.
- In a basic solution, $[H_3O^+] < [OH^-]$.
  $[H_3O^+] < 1.0 \times 10^{-7}$ M and $[OH^-] > 1.0 \times 10^{-7}$ M.

EXAMPLE 17.1   Hydronium and Hydroxide Ion Concentrations in a Solution of a Strong Base

Problem What are the hydroxide and hydronium ion concentrations in a 0.0012 M solution of NaOH at 25 °C?

What Do You Know? You know the concentration of NaOH and that it is a strong base, 100% dissociated into ions in water.

Strategy Because NaOH is a strong base we assume that the OH^- ion concentration is the same as the NaOH concentration. The H_3O^+ ion concentration can then be calculated using Equation 17.1.

Solution The initial concentration of OH^- is 0.0012 M.

$$0.0012 \text{ mol NaOH per liter} \rightarrow 0.0012 \text{ M Na}^+(aq) + 0.0012 \text{ M OH}^-(aq)$$

Substituting the OH^- concentration into Equation 17.1, we have

$$K_w = 1.0 \times 10^{-14} = [H_3O^+][OH^-] = [H_3O^+](0.0012)$$

and so

$$[H_3O^+] = \frac{1.0 \times 10^{-14}}{0.0012} = 8.3 \times 10^{-12} \text{ M}$$

Think about Your Answer Why didn't we take into account the ions produced by water autoionization when we calculated the concentration of hydroxide ions? It should add OH^- and H_3O^+ ions to the solution. If x is equal to the concentration of OH^- ions generated by the autoionization of water, then, when equilibrium is achieved,

$$[OH^-] = (0.0012 \text{ M} + OH^- \text{ from water autoionization}) = (0.0012 \text{ M} + x)$$

In pure water, the concentration of OH^- ion generated by autoionization is 1.0×10^{-7} M. Le Chatelier's principle (◄ Section 16.6) suggests that the concentration should be even smaller when OH^- ions are already present in solution from NaOH; that is, x should be much less than 1.0×10^{-7} M. This means x in the term $(0.0012 + x)$ is insignificant compared with 0.0012. (Following the rules for significant figures, the sum of 0.0012 and a number even smaller than 1.0×10^{-7} is 0.0012.) Thus, the equilibrium concentration of OH^- is equivalent to the concentration of NaOH in the solution.

Check Your Understanding

A solution of the strong acid HCl has $[HCl] = 4.0 \times 10^{-3}$ M. What are the concentrations of H_3O^+ and OH^- in this solution at 25 °C? (Recall that because HCl is a strong acid, it is 100% ionized in water.)

The pH Scale

The **pH** of a solution is defined as the negative of the base-10 logarithm (log) of the hydronium ion concentration (◄ Section 4.6, page 178).

$$pH = -\log[H_3O^+] \qquad \text{(4.3 and 17.2)}$$

In a similar way, we can define the pOH of a solution as the negative of the base-10 logarithm of the hydroxide ion concentration.

$$pOH = -\log[OH^-] \qquad \text{(17.3)}$$

In pure water, the hydronium and hydroxide ion concentrations are both 1.0×10^{-7} M. Therefore, for pure water at 25 °C

$$pH = -\log(1.0 \times 10^{-7}) = 7.00$$

In the same way, you can show that the pOH of pure water is also 7.00 at 25 °C.

If we take the negative logarithms of both sides of the expression $K_w = [H_3O^+][OH^-]$, we obtain another useful equation.

$$K_w = 1.0 \times 10^{-14} = [H_3O^+][OH^-]$$
$$-\log K_w = -\log(1.0 \times 10^{-14}) = -\log([H_3O^+][OH^-])$$
$$pK_w = 14.00 = -\log([H_3O^+]) + (-\log[OH^-])$$

$$pK_w = 14.00 = pH + pOH \qquad \text{(17.4)}$$

The sum of the pH and pOH of a solution must be equal to 14.00 at 25 °C.

As illustrated in Figures 4.11 and 17.1, solutions with pH less than 7.00 (at 25 °C) are acidic, whereas solutions with pH greater than 7.00 are basic. Solutions with pH = 7.00 at 25 °C are neutral.

Calculating pH

The calculation of pH from the hydronium ion concentration, or the concentration of hydronium ion from pH, was introduced in Chapter 4 (◄ page 178). The *Review & Check* questions below review those calculations.

REVIEW & CHECK FOR SECTION 17.3

1. What is the pH of a 0.0012 M NaOH solution at 25 °C?

   (a) 2.92   (b) 11.08   (c) 8.67

2. The pH of a diet soda is 4.32 at 25 °C. What is the hydronium ion concentration in the soda?

   (a) 4.8×10^{-5} M   (b) 2.1×10^{-10} M   (c) 2.1×10^{-4} M

3. If the pH of a solution containing the strong base Sr(OH)$_2$ is 10.46 at 25 °C, what is the concentration of Sr(OH)$_2$?

   (a) 3.5×10^{-11} M   (b) 2.9×10^{-4} M   (c) 6.9×10^{-11} M   (d) 1.4×10^{-4} M

● **Working with Logarithms** See Appendix A for more on using logarithms.

	pH	$[H_3O^+]$	$[OH^-]$	pOH
Basic	14.00	1.0×10^{-14}	1.0×10^{0}	0.00
	10.00	1.0×10^{-10}	1.0×10^{-4}	4.00
Neutral	7.00	1.0×10^{-7}	1.0×10^{-7}	7.00
Acidic	4.00	1.0×10^{-4}	1.0×10^{-10}	10.00
	0.00	1.0×10^{0}	1.0×10^{-14}	14.00

FIGURE 17.1 pH and pOH. This figure illustrates the relationship of hydronium ion and hydroxide ion concentrations and of pH and pOH.

17.4 Equilibrium Constants for Acids and Bases

In Chapter 3, it was stated that acids and bases can be divided roughly into those that are strong electrolytes (such as HCl, HNO_3, and NaOH) and those that are weak electrolytes (such as CH_3CO_2H and NH_3) (Figure 17.2) (◄ Table 3.1, Common Acids and Bases, page 129). Hydrochloric acid is a strong acid, so 100% of the acid ionizes to produce hydronium and chloride ions. In contrast, acetic acid is a weak electrolyte because it ionizes only to a very small extent in water.

$$CH_3CO_2H(aq) + H_2O(\ell) \rightleftharpoons H_3O^+(aq) + CH_3CO_2^-(aq)$$

The acid, its anion, and the hydronium ion are all present at equilibrium in solution, but the ions are present in very low concentration relative to the acid concentration. For example, in a 0.100 M solution of acetic acid, $[H_3O^+]$ and $[CH_3CO_2^-]$ are each about 0.0013 M whereas that of un-ionized acetic acid, $[CH_3CO_2H]$, is 0.099 M.

Similarly, ammonia is a weak base.

$$NH_3(aq) + H_2O(\ell) \rightleftharpoons NH_4^+(aq) + OH^-(aq)$$

Only about 1% of ammonia molecules in a 0.100 M solution react with water to produce the ammonium and hydroxide ions.

One way to define the relative strengths of a series of acids is to measure the pH of solutions of acids of equal concentration: the lower the pH, the greater the concentration of hydronium ion, the stronger the acid. Similarly, for a series of weak bases, $[OH^-]$ will increase, and the pH will increase as the bases become stronger.

- For a strong monoprotic acid, $[H_3O^+]$ in solution is equal to the original acid concentration. Similarly, for a strong monoprotic base, $[OH^-]$ will be equal to the original base concentration.
- For a weak acid, $[H_3O^+]$ will be much less than the original acid concentration. That is, $[H_3O^+]$ will be smaller than if the acid were a strong acid of the same concentration. Similarly, a weak base will give a smaller $[OH^-]$ than if the base were a strong base of the same concentration.
- For a series of weak monoprotic acids (of the type HA) of the same concentration, $[H_3O^+]$ will increase (and the pH will decline) as the acids become stronger. Similarly, for a series of weak bases, $[OH^-]$ will increase (and the pH will increase) as the bases become stronger.

Strong Acid

HCl completely ionizes in aqueous solution.

HCl

(a) Hydrochloric acid, a strong acid, is sold for household use as "muriatic acid." The acid completely ionizes in water.

Weak Acid

Acetic acid, CH_3CO_2H, ionizes only slightly in water.

CH_3CO_2H

(b) Vinegar is a solution of acetic acid, a weak acid that ionizes only to a small extent in water.

Weak Base

The weak base ammonia reacts to a small extent with water to give a weakly basic solution.

NH_3

(c) Ammonia is a weak base, ionizing to a small extent in water.

FIGURE 17.2 Strong and weak acids and bases.

Strong or Weak?

How can you tell whether an acid or a base is weak? The easiest way is to remember those few that are strong. All others are probably weak.

Common strong acids include the following:

Hydrohalic acids: HCl, HBr, and HI (but not HF)
Nitric acid: HNO_3

Sulfuric acid: H_2SO_4 (for loss of first H^+ only)
Perchloric acid: $HClO_4$

Some common strong bases include the following:

All Group 1A hydroxides: LiOH, NaOH, KOH, RbOH, CsOH

Group 2A hydroxides: $Sr(OH)_2$ and $Ba(OH)_2$. [$Mg(OH)_2$ and $Ca(OH)_2$ are not considered strong bases because they do not dissolve appreciably in water.]

The relative strength of an acid or base can also be expressed quantitatively with an equilibrium constant, often called an **ionization constant**. For the general acid HA, we can write

$$HA(aq) + H_2O(\ell) \rightleftharpoons H_3O^+(aq) + A^-(aq)$$

$$K_a = \frac{[H_3O^+][A^-]}{[HA]} \qquad (17.5)$$

where the equilibrium constant, K, has a subscript "a" to indicate that it is an equilibrium constant for an acid in water. For weak acids, the value of K_a is less than 1 because the product $[H_3O^+][A^-]$ is less than the equilibrium concentration of the weak acid $[HA]$. For a series of acids, the acid strength increases as the value of K_a increases.

Similarly, we can write the equilibrium expression for a weak base B in water. Here, we label K with a subscript "b." Its value is less than 1 for weak bases.

$$B(aq) + H_2O(\ell) \rightleftharpoons BH^+(aq) + OH^-(aq)$$

$$K_b = \frac{[BH^+][OH^-]}{[B]} \qquad (17.6)$$

Some acids and bases are listed in Table 17.3, each with its value of K_a or K_b. The following are important concepts concerning this table.

- Acids are listed in the table at the left, and their conjugate bases are listed on the right.
- A large value of K indicates that ionization products are strongly favored, whereas a small value of K indicates that reactants are favored.
- The strongest acids are at the upper left. They have the largest K_a values. K_a values become smaller on descending the chart as acid strength declines.
- The strongest bases are at the lower right. They have the largest K_b values. K_b values become larger on descending the chart as base strength increases.
- *The weaker the acid, the stronger its conjugate base.* That is, the smaller the value of K_a, the larger the value of K_b.
- Some acids or bases are listed as having K_a or K_b values that are large or very small. Aqueous acids that are stronger than H_3O^+ are completely ionized (HNO_3, for example), so their K_a values are "large." Their conjugate bases (such as NO_3^-) do not produce meaningful concentrations of OH^- ions, so their K_b values are "very small." Similar arguments follow for strong bases and their conjugate acids.

Table 17.3 Ionization Constants for Some Acids and Their Conjugate Bases at 25 °C

Acid Name	Acid	K_a	Base	K_b	Base Name
Perchloric acid	$HClO_4$	Large	ClO_4^-	Very small	Perchlorate ion
Sulfuric acid	H_2SO_4	Large	HSO_4^-	Very small	Hydrogen sulfate ion
Hydrochloric acid	HCl	Large	Cl^-	Very small	Chloride ion
Nitric acid	HNO_3	Large	NO_3^-	Very small	Nitrate ion
Hydronium ion	H_3O^+	1.0	H_2O	1.0×10^{-14}	Water
Sulfurous acid	H_2SO_3	1.2×10^{-2}	HSO_3^-	8.3×10^{-13}	Hydrogen sulfite ion
Hydrogen sulfate ion	HSO_4^-	1.2×10^{-2}	SO_4^{2-}	8.3×10^{-13}	Sulfate ion
Phosphoric acid	H_3PO_4	7.5×10^{-3}	$H_2PO_4^-$	1.3×10^{-12}	Dihydrogen phosphate ion
Hexaaquairon(III) ion	$[Fe(H_2O)_6]^{3+}$	6.3×10^{-3}	$[Fe(H_2O)_5OH]^{2+}$	1.6×10^{-12}	Pentaaquahydroxoiron(III) ion
Hydrofluoric acid	HF	7.2×10^{-4}	F^-	1.4×10^{-11}	Fluoride ion
Nitrous acid	HNO_2	4.5×10^{-4}	NO_2^-	2.2×10^{-11}	Nitrite ion
Formic acid	HCO_2H	1.8×10^{-4}	HCO_2^-	5.6×10^{-11}	Formate ion
Benzoic acid	$C_6H_5CO_2H$	6.3×10^{-5}	$C_6H_5CO_2^-$	1.6×10^{-10}	Benzoate ion
Acetic acid	CH_3CO_2H	1.8×10^{-5}	$CH_3CO_2^-$	5.6×10^{-10}	Acetate ion
Propanoic acid	$CH_3CH_2CO_2H$	1.3×10^{-5}	$CH_3CH_2CO_2^-$	7.7×10^{-10}	Propanoate ion
Hexaaquaaluminum ion	$[Al(H_2O)_6]^{3+}$	7.9×10^{-6}	$[Al(H_2O)_5OH]^{2+}$	1.3×10^{-9}	Pentaaquahydroxoaluminum ion
Carbonic acid	H_2CO_3	4.2×10^{-7}	HCO_3^-	2.4×10^{-8}	Hydrogen carbonate ion
Hexaaquacopper(II) ion	$[Cu(H_2O)_6]^{2+}$	1.6×10^{-7}	$[Cu(H_2O)_5OH]^+$	6.3×10^{-8}	Pentaaquahydroxocopper(II) ion
Hydrogen sulfide	H_2S	1×10^{-7}	HS^-	1×10^{-7}	Hydrogen sulfide ion
Dihydrogen phosphate ion	$H_2PO_4^-$	6.2×10^{-8}	HPO_4^{2-}	1.6×10^{-7}	Hydrogen phosphate ion
Hydrogen sulfite ion	HSO_3^-	6.2×10^{-8}	SO_3^{2-}	1.6×10^{-7}	Sulfite ion
Hypochlorous acid	$HClO$	3.5×10^{-8}	ClO^-	2.9×10^{-7}	Hypochlorite ion
Hexaaqualead(II) ion	$[Pb(H_2O)_6]^{2+}$	1.5×10^{-8}	$[Pb(H_2O)_5OH]^+$	6.7×10^{-7}	Pentaaquahydroxolead(II) ion
Hexaaquacobalt(II) ion	$[Co(H_2O)_6]^{2+}$	1.3×10^{-9}	$[Co(H_2O)_5OH]^+$	7.7×10^{-6}	Pentaaquahydroxocobalt(II) ion
Boric acid	$B(OH)_3(H_2O)$	7.3×10^{-10}	$B(OH)_4^-$	1.4×10^{-5}	Tetrahydroxoborate ion
Ammonium ion	NH_4^+	5.6×10^{-10}	NH_3	1.8×10^{-5}	Ammonia
Hydrocyanic acid	HCN	4.0×10^{-10}	CN^-	2.5×10^{-5}	Cyanide ion
Hexaaquairon(II) ion	$[Fe(H_2O)_6]^{2+}$	3.2×10^{-10}	$[Fe(H_2O)_5OH]^+$	3.1×10^{-5}	Pentaaquahydroxoiron(II) ion
Hydrogen carbonate ion	HCO_3^-	4.8×10^{-11}	CO_3^{2-}	2.1×10^{-4}	Carbonate ion
Hexaaquanickel(II) ion	$[Ni(H_2O)_6]^{2+}$	2.5×10^{-11}	$[Ni(H_2O)_5OH]^+$	4.0×10^{-4}	Pentaaquahydroxonickel(II) ion
Hydrogen phosphate ion	HPO_4^{2-}	3.6×10^{-13}	PO_4^{3-}	2.8×10^{-2}	Phosphate ion
Water	H_2O	1.0×10^{-14}	OH^-	1.0	Hydroxide ion
Hydrogen sulfide ion*	HS^-	1×10^{-19}	S^{2-}	1×10^5	Sulfide ion
Ethanol	C_2H_5OH	Very small	$C_2H_5O^-$	Large	Ethoxide ion
Ammonia	NH_3	Very small	NH_2^-	Large	Amide ion
Hydrogen	H_2	Very small	H^-	Large	Hydride ion

*The values of K_a for HS^- and K_b for S^{2-} are estimates.

Increasing Acid Strength →

To illustrate some of these ideas, let us compare some common acids and bases. For example, HF is a stronger acid than HClO, which is in turn stronger than HCO_3^-,

Increasing acid strength

HCO_3^-	$HClO$	HF
$K_a = 4.8 \times 10^{-11}$	$K_a = 3.5 \times 10^{-8}$	$K_a = 7.2 \times 10^{-4}$

and their conjugate bases become stronger from F^- to ClO^- to CO_3^{2-}.

Increasing base strength

CO_3^{2-}	ClO^-	F^-
$K_b = 2.1 \times 10^{-4}$	$K_b = 2.9 \times 10^{-7}$	$K_a = 1.4 \times 10^{-11}$

Nature abounds in acids and bases (Figure 17.3). Many naturally occurring acids contain the carboxyl group (–CO_2H) (see page 759), and a few are illustrated here. Notice that the organic portion of the molecule has an effect on its relative strength (as described further in Section 17.10).

K_a increases; acid strength increases

propanoic acid, $CH_3CH_2CO_2H$
$K_a = 1.3 \times 10^{-5}$

acetic acid, CH_3CO_2H
$K_a = 1.8 \times 10^{-5}$

formic acid, HCO_2H
$K_a = 1.8 \times 10^{-4}$

K_b of conjugate base increases

There are many naturally occurring weak bases as well (Figure 17.3). Ammonia and its conjugate acid, the ammonium ion, are part of the nitrogen cycle in the environment (▶ page 949). Biological systems reduce nitrate ion to NH_3 and NH_4^+ and incorporate nitrogen into amino acids and proteins. Many bases are derived from NH_3 by replacement of the H atoms with organic groups.

ammonia
$K_b = 1.8 \times 10^{-5}$

methylamine
$K_b = 5.0 \times 10^{-4}$

aniline
$K_b = 4.0 \times 10^{-10}$

Ammonia is a weaker base than methylamine (K_b for NH_3 < K_b for CH_3NH_2). This means that the conjugate acid of ammonia, NH_4^+ ($K_a = 5.6 \times 10^{-10}$), is stronger than the methylammonium ion, the conjugate acid of methylamine, $CH_3NH_3^+$ ($K_a = 2.0 \times 10^{-11}$).

K_a Values for Polyprotic Acids

Like all polyprotic acids, phosphoric acid ionizes in a series of steps, three in this case.

First ionization step: $K_{a1} = 7.5 \times 10^{-3}$

$$H_3PO_4(aq) + H_2O(\ell) \rightleftharpoons H_2PO_4^-(aq) + H_3O^+(aq)$$

Second ionization step: $K_{a2} = 6.2 \times 10^{-8}$

$$H_2PO_4^-(aq) + H_2O(\ell) \rightleftharpoons HPO_4^{2-}(aq) + H_3O^+(aq)$$

The tartness of lemons and oranges comes from the weak acid citric acid. The acid is found widely in nature and in many consumer products.

Caffeine is a well-known stimulant and a weak base.

Photos © Cengage Learning/Charles D. Winters

FIGURE 17.3 Natural acids and bases. Hundreds of acids and bases occur in nature. Our foods contain a wide variety, and biochemically important molecules are often acids and bases.

Third ionization step: $K_{a3} = 3.6 \times 10^{-13}$

$$HPO_4^{2-}(aq) + H_2O(\ell) \rightleftharpoons PO_4^{3-}(aq) + H_3O^+(aq)$$

We observe that the K_a value for each successive step becomes smaller because it is more difficult to remove H^+ from a negatively charged ion, such as $H_2PO_4^-$, than from a neutral molecule, such as H_3PO_4. Similarly, the larger the negative charge of the anionic acid, the more difficult it is to remove H^+. Finally, for many inorganic polyprotic acids, K_a values become smaller by about 10^5 for each proton removed.

Logarithmic Scale of Relative Acid Strength, pK_a

Many chemists and biochemists use a logarithmic scale to report and compare relative acid strengths.

$$pK_a = -\log K_a \tag{17.7}$$

The pK_a of an acid is the negative log of the K_a value (just as pH is the negative log of the hydronium ion concentration). For example, acetic acid has a pK_a value of 4.74.

$$pK_a = -\log (1.8 \times 10^{-5}) = 4.74$$

The pK_a value becomes smaller as the acid strength increases.

—— Acid strength increases ⟶

Propanoic acid	**Acetic acid**	**Formic acid**
$CH_3CH_2CO_2H$	CH_3CO_2H	HCO_2H
$K_a = 1.3 \times 10^{-5}$	$K_a = 1.8 \times 10^{-5}$	$K_a = 1.8 \times 10^{-4}$
$pK_a = 4.89$	$pK_a = 4.74$	$pK_a = 3.74$

—— pK_a decreases ⟶

Relating the Ionization Constants for an Acid and Its Conjugate Base

Let us look again at Table 17.3. From the top of the table to the bottom, the strengths of the acids decline (K_a becomes smaller), and the strengths of their conjugate bases increase (the values of K_b increase). Examining a few cases shows that the product of K_a for an acid and K_b for its conjugate base is equal to a constant, specifically K_w.

● **A Relation Among pK Values** A useful relationship for an acid–conjugate base pair follows from Equation 17.8.
$$pK_w = pK_a + pK_b$$

$$K_a \times K_b = K_w \tag{17.8}$$

Consider the specific case of the ionization of a weak acid, say HCN, and the interaction of its conjugate base, CN^-, with H_2O.

Weak acid:	$HCN(aq) + H_2O(\ell) \rightleftharpoons H_3O^+(aq) + CN^-(aq)$	$K_a = 4.0 \times 10^{-10}$
Conjugate base:	$CN^-(aq) + H_2O(\ell) \rightleftharpoons HCN(aq) + OH^-(aq)$	$K_b = 2.5 \times 10^{-5}$
	$2\,H_2O(\ell) \rightleftharpoons H_3O^+(aq) + OH^-(aq)$	$K_w = 1.0 \times 10^{-14}$

Adding the equations gives the chemical equation for the autoionization of water, and the numerical value is indeed 1.0×10^{-14}. That is,

$$K_a \times K_b = \left(\frac{[H_3O^+][\cancel{CN^-}]}{[\cancel{HCN}]} \right) \left(\frac{[\cancel{HCN}][OH^-]}{[\cancel{CN^-}]} \right) = [H_3O^+][OH^-] = K_w$$

Equation 17.8 is useful because K_b can be calculated from K_a. The value of K_b for the cyanide ion, for example, is

$$K_b \text{ for } CN^- = \frac{K_w}{K_a \text{ for HCN}} = \frac{1.0 \times 10^{-14}}{4.0 \times 10^{-10}} = 2.5 \times 10^{-5}$$

REVIEW & CHECK FOR SECTION 17.4

Use Table 17.3 to answer the following questions.

1. Which of the following is the strongest acid?

   (a) HF (b) H_2S (c) HOCl (d) CH_3CO_2H

2. Which acid has the strongest conjugate base?

   (a) HNO_2 (b) $C_6H_5CO_2H$ (c) HCN (d) HCl

3. Which of the following has a pK_a value of 4.20?

   (a) $C_6H_5CO_2H$ (b) CH_3CO_2H (c) HCO_2H (d) HF

4. What is the pK_a for the conjugate acid of ammonia?

   (a) 4.74 (b) 9.25 (c) 5.60 (d) 7.00

5. K_a for lactic acid, $CH_3CHOHCO_2H$, is 1.4×10^{-4}. What is pK_b for the conjugate base of this acid, $CH_3CHOHCO_2^-$?

   (a) 3.85 (b) 7.00 (c) 10.15 (d) 12.60

17.5 Acid–Base Properties of Salts

A number of the acids and bases listed in Table 17.3 are cations or anions. As described earlier, anions can act as Brønsted bases because they can accept a proton from an acid to form the conjugate acid of the ion.

$$CO_3^{2-}(aq) + H_2O(\ell) \rightleftharpoons HCO_3^-(aq) + OH^-(aq)$$
$$K_b = 2.1 \times 10^{-4}$$

You should also notice that many metal cations in water are Brønsted acids.

$$[Al(H_2O)_6]^{3+}(aq) + H_2O(\ell) \rightleftharpoons [Al(H_2O)_5(OH)]^{2+}(aq) + H_3O^+(aq)$$
$$K_a = 7.9 \times 10^{-6}$$

Table 17.4 summarizes the acid–base properties of some common cations and anions. As you look over this table, notice the following points:

- Anions that are conjugate bases of strong acids (for example, Cl^- and NO_3^-) are such weak bases that they have no effect on solution pH.
- There are numerous basic anions (such as CO_3^{2-}). All are the conjugate bases of weak acids.
- The acid–base behavior of anions of polyprotic acids depends on the extent of deprotonation. For example, a fully deprotonated anion (such as CO_3^{2-}) will be basic. A partially deprotonated anion (such as HCO_3^-) is amphiprotic. Its behavior will depend on the other species in the reaction.

● **Hydrolysis Reactions and Hydrolysis Constants** Chemists often say that, when ions interact with water to produce acidic or basic solutions, the ions "hydrolyze" in water, or they undergo "hydrolysis." Thus, some books refer to the K_a and K_b values of ions as "hydrolysis constants," K_h.

© Cengage Learning/Charles D. Winters

Many aqueous metal cations are Brønsted acids. A pH measurement of a dilute solution of copper(II) sulfate shows that the solution is clearly acidic. Among the common cations, Al^{3+} and transition metal ions form acidic solutions in water.

Table 17.4 Acid and Base Properties of Some Ions in Aqueous Solution

	Neutral		**Basic**			**Acidic**
Anions	Cl^- NO_3^- Br^- ClO_4^- I^-		$CH_3CO_2^-$ CN^- SO_4^{2-} HCO_2^- PO_4^{3-} HPO_4^{2-} CO_3^{2-} HCO_3^- SO_3^{2-} S^{2-} HS^- OCl^- F^- NO_2^-			HSO_4^- $H_2PO_4^-$ HSO_3^-
Cations	Li^+ Na^+ Ca^{2+} K^+ Ba^{2+}		$[Al(H_2O)_5(OH)]^{2+}$ (for example)			$[Al(H_2O)_6]^{3+}$ and hydrated transition metal cations (such as $[Fe(H_2O)_6]^{3+}$) NH_4^+

- Alkali metal and alkaline earth cations have no measurable effect on solution pH.
- Basic cations are conjugate bases of acidic cations such as $[Al(H_2O)_6]^{3+}$.
- Acidic cations fall into two categories: (a) metal cations with $2+$ and $3+$ charges and (b) ammonium ions (and its organic derivatives). All metal cations are hydrated in water, forming ions such as $[M(H_2O)_6]^{n+}$. However, only when M is a 2+ or 3+ ion, particularly a transition metal ion, does the ion act as an acid.

⍥WL   INTERACTIVE EXAMPLE 17.2   Acid–Base Properties of Salts

Problem Decide whether each of the following will give rise to an acidic, basic, or neutral solution in water.

(a) $NaNO_3$ (d) $NaHCO_3$

(b) K_3PO_4 (e) NH_4F

(c) $FeCl_2$

What Do You Know? You know the salt formulas and, from Tables 17.3 and 17.4, you know the effect of the constituent ions on pH.

Strategy First, identify the cation and anion in each salt. Next, use Tables 17.3 and 17.4 to describe the acid–base properties of each ion. Finally decide on the overall acid–base properties of the salt.

Solution

(a) $NaNO_3$: This salt gives a neutral, aqueous solution (pH = 7). Neither the sodium ion, Na^+, nor the nitrate ion, NO_3^- (the very weak conjugate base of a strong acid), affects the solution pH.

(b) K_3PO_4: An aqueous solution of K_3PO_4 should be basic (pH > 7) because PO_4^{3-} is the conjugate base of the weak acid HPO_4^{2-}. The K^+ ion, like the Na^+ ion, does not affect the solution pH.

(c) $FeCl_2$: An aqueous solution of $FeCl_2$ should be weakly acidic (pH < 7). The Fe^{2+} ion in water, $[Fe(H_2O)_6]^{2+}$, is a Brønsted acid. In contrast, Cl^- is the very weak conjugate base of the strong acid HCl, so it does not contribute excess OH^- ions to the solution.

(d) $NaHCO_3$: Some additional information is needed concerning salts of amphiprotic anions such as HCO_3^-. Because they have an ionizable hydrogen, they can act as acids,

$$HCO_3^-(aq) + H_2O(\ell) \rightleftharpoons CO_3^{2-}(aq) + H_3O^+(aq) \qquad K_a = 4.8 \times 10^{-11}$$

but because they are anions, they can also act as bases and accept an H^+ ion from water.

$$HCO_3^-(aq) + H_2O(\ell) \rightleftharpoons H_2CO_3(aq) + OH^-(aq) \qquad K_b = 2.4 \times 10^{-8}$$

Strategy Map 17.2

PROBLEM

Decide whether a salt is **acidic**, **basic**, or **neutral**.

↓

DATA/INFORMATION KNOWN

- The formula of the salt: K_3PO_4

STEP 1. Identify the **cation** and **anion**.

Cation = K^+, anion = PO_4^{3-}

STEP 2. Identify the nature of the **cation**.

K^+ is a **neutral** cation.

STEP 3. Identify the nature of the **anion**.

PO_4^{3-} is a *relatively strong* base.

STEP 4. Decide on the acid–base properties of the salt.

↓

K_3PO_4 is **basic**.

PROBLEM SOLVING TIP 17.2

Aqueous Solutions of Salts

Because aqueous solutions of salts are found in our bodies and throughout our economy and environment, it is important to know how to predict their acid and base properties. Information on the pH of an aqueous solution of a salt is summarized in Table 17.4. Consider also the following examples:

Cation	Anion	pH of the Solution
From strong base (Na^+)	From strong acid (Cl^-)	$= 7$ (neutral)
From strong base (K^+)	From weak acid ($CH_3CO_2^-$)	> 7 (basic)
From weak base (NH_4^+)	From strong acid (Cl^-)	< 7 (acidic)
From any weak base (BH^+)	From any weak acid (A^-)	Depends on relative acid strength of BH^+ and base strength of A^-

Whether the solution is acidic or basic will depend on the relative magnitude of K_a and K_b. In the case of the hydrogen carbonate anion, K_b is larger than K_a, so $[OH^-]$ is larger than $[H_3O^+]$, and an aqueous solution of $NaHCO_3$ will be slightly basic.

(e) NH_4F: What happens if you have a salt based on an acidic cation and a basic anion? One example is ammonium fluoride. Here, the ammonium ion would decrease the pH, and the fluoride ion would increase the pH.

$NH_4^+(aq) + H_2O(\ell) \rightleftharpoons H_3O^+(aq) + NH_3(aq)$ $\qquad K_a (NH_4^+) = 5.6 \times 10^{-10}$

$F^-(aq) + H_2O(\ell) \rightleftharpoons HF(aq) + OH^-(aq)$ $\qquad K_b (F^-) = 1.4 \times 10^{-11}$

Because $K_a (NH_4^+) > K_b (F^-)$, the ammonium ion is a stronger acid than the fluoride ion is a base. The resulting solution should be slightly acidic.

Think about Your Answer There are several important points here:

- Anions that are conjugate bases of strong acids—such as Cl^- and NO_3^-—have no effect on solution pH.

- To determine whether a salt is acidic, basic, or neutral, we must take into account both the cation and the anion. When a salt has an acidic cation and a basic anion, the pH of the solution will be determined by the ion that is the stronger acid or base.

Check Your Understanding

For each of the following salts in water, predict whether the pH will be greater than, less than, or equal to 7.

(a) KBr   (b) NH_4NO_3 (c) $AlCl_3$ (d) Na_2HPO_4

REVIEW & CHECK FOR SECTION 17.5

1. Adding NaH_2PO_4 to water will cause the pH to

 (a) increase   (b) decrease   (c) stay the same

2. Adding KCN to water will cause the pH to

 (a) increase   (b) decrease   (c) stay the same

17.6 Predicting the Direction of Acid–Base Reactions

According to the Brønsted–Lowry theory, all acid–base reactions can be written as equilibria involving the acid and base and their conjugates.

Acid + base $\rightleftharpoons$ conjugate base of the acid + conjugate acid of the base

In Sections 17.4 and 17.5, we used equilibrium constants to provide information about the relative strengths of acids and bases. Now we want to show how these constants can be used to decide whether a particular acid–base reaction is product- or reactant–favored at equilibrium.

Hydrochloric acid is a strong acid. Its equilibrium constant for reaction with water is very large, with the equilibrium lying completely to the right.

$$HCl(aq) + H_2O(\ell) \rightleftharpoons H_3O^+(aq) + Cl^-(aq)$$

Strong acid ($\approx$ 100% ionized), $K \gg 1$

$[H_3O^+] \approx$ initial concentration of the acid

Of the two acids here, HCl is stronger than H_3O^+. Of the two bases, H_2O and Cl^-, water is the stronger base and wins out in the competition for the proton. Thus, the equilibrium lies to the side of the chemical equation having the weaker acid and base.

In contrast to HCl and other strong acids, acetic acid, a *weak* acid, ionizes to only a very small extent (Table 17.3).

$$CH_3CO_2H(aq) + H_2O(\ell) \rightleftharpoons H_3O^+(aq) + CH_3CO_2^-(aq)$$

Weak acid ($<$ 100% ionized), $K = 1.8 \times 10^{-5}$

$[H_3O^+] \ll$ initial concentration of the acid

When equilibrium is achieved in a 0.1 M aqueous solution of CH_3CO_2H, the concentrations of $H_3O^+(aq)$ and $CH_3CO_2^-(aq)$ are each only about 0.001 M. Approximately 99% of the acetic acid is not ionized.

Again, the equilibrium lies toward the side of the reaction having the weaker acid and base.

These two examples of the relative extent of acid–base reactions illustrate a general principle:

> All proton transfer reactions proceed from the stronger acid and base to the weaker acid and base.

Using this principle and Table 17.3, you can predict which reactions are product-favored and which are reactant-favored at equilibrium. Consider the possible reaction of phosphoric acid and acetate ion to give acetic acid and the dihydrogen phosphate ion. Table 17.3 informs us that H_3PO_4 is a stronger acid ($K_a = 7.5 \times 10^{-3}$) than acetic acid ($K_a = 1.8 \times 10^{-5}$), and the acetate ion ($K_b = 5.6 \times 10^{-10}$) is a stronger base than the dihydrogen phosphate ion ($K_b = 1.3 \times 10^{-12}$).

● **General Principle of Reactivity**
A general principle in chemistry is that more reactive substances react to form less reactive substances. Here you see the result of this for acid–base reactions: The stronger acid and stronger base always react to form the weaker acid and weaker base.

Thus, mixing phosphoric acid with sodium acetate will produce a significant amount of dihydrogen phosphate ion and acetic acid. That is, the equilibrium is predicted to lie to the right because the reaction proceeds from the stronger acid–base combination to the weaker acid–base combination.

Reaction of vinegar and baking soda. This reaction involves the weak acid acetic acid and the weak base HCO_3^- from sodium hydrogen carbonate. Based on the values of the equilibrium constants, the reaction is predicted to proceed to the right to produce acetate ion, CO_2, and water.

EXAMPLE 17.3   Reactions of Acids and Bases

Problem Write a balanced, net ionic equation for the reaction that occurs between acetic acid and sodium bicarbonate. Decide whether the equilibrium lies predominantly to the left or to the right.

What Do You Know? You know the identity of the acid, and you know that the other reactant, $NaHCO_3$, is a water-soluble salt that forms Na^+ and HCO_3^- ions in water. You also know that the HCO_3^- ion is amphiprotic, but it must act as a base toward acetic acid in this reaction. You need to know the ionization constants for acetic acid and the HCO_3^- ion and for their conjugates.

Strategy

*   Identify the products of the acid–base reaction (which arise by H^+ transfer from acetic acid to the base, HCO_3^-). That is, identify the conjugate base of acetic acid and the conjugate acid of HCO_3^-.

*   Write a balanced chemical equation for the equilibrium between the acid and base and their conjugate base and acid.

*   Use Table 17.3 to decide which is the weaker of the two acids (or the weaker of the two bases). The equilibrium will favor the weaker acid and base.

Solution The conjugate base of acetic acid is the acetate ion, $CH_3CO_2^-$, and the conjugate acid of the base HCO_3^- is H_2CO_3. Hydrogen ion transfer from the acid to the base occurs by the following net ionic equation:

$$CH_3CO_2H(aq) \quad + \quad HCO_3^-(aq) \quad \rightleftharpoons \quad CH_3CO_2^-(aq) \quad + \quad H_2CO_3(aq)$$
$$K_a = 1.8 \times 10^{-5} \qquad K_b = 2.4 \times 10^{-8} \qquad\qquad K_b = 5.6 \times 10^{-10} \qquad K_a = 4.2 \times 10^{-7}$$

The value of K_a or K_b (from Table 17.3) is given for each reactant and product. The equilibrium constants show that H_2CO_3 is a weaker acid than CH_3CO_2H, and $CH_3CO_2^-$ is a weaker base than HCO_3^-. The reaction favors the side having the weaker acid and base—that is, the right side.

Think about Your Answer One product of the reaction of acetic acid and $NaHCO_3$ is H_2CO_3, which dissociates into CO_2 and H_2O. As you can see in the photograph in the margin, CO_2 bubbles out of the solution. The equilibrium for the dissociation of H_2CO_3 to form CO_2 and H_2O lies far to the right.

$$H_2CO_3(aq) \rightleftharpoons CO_2(g) + H_2O(\ell)$$

The loss of a product, CO_2, causes the equilibrium to shift further to the right. See the discussion of gas-forming reactions in Chapter 3 and of Le Chatelier's principle in Section 16.6.

Check Your Understanding

(a) Which is the stronger Brønsted acid, HCO_3^- or NH_4^+? Which has the stronger conjugate base?

(b) Is a reaction between HCO_3^- ions and NH_3 product- or reactant-favored at equilibrium?

$$HCO_3^-(aq) + NH_3(aq) \rightleftharpoons CO_3^{2-}(aq) + NH_4^+(aq)$$

(c) You mix solutions of sodium hydrogen phosphate and ammonia. The net ionic equation for a possible reaction is

$$HPO_4^{2-}(aq) + NH_3(aq) \rightleftharpoons PO_4^{3-}(aq) + NH_4^+(aq)$$

Does the equilibrium lie to the left or to the right for this reaction?

REVIEW & CHECK FOR SECTION 17.6

1. Is the reaction of NaCN and HCl in water product- or reactant-favored at equilibrium?

    (a) reactant-favored   (b) product-favored

2. In the following reaction, does the equilibrium lie predominantly to the left or to the right?

$$HS^-(aq) + H_3PO_4(aq) \rightleftharpoons H_2S(aq) + H_2PO_4^-(aq)$$

    (a) left   (b) right

17.7 Types of Acid–Base Reactions

The reaction of hydrochloric acid and sodium hydroxide is the classic example of a strong acid–strong base reaction, whereas the reaction of citric acid and bicarbonate ion represents the reaction of a weak acid and weak base (Figure 17.4). These are two of four general types of acid–base reactions (Table 17.5). Because acid–base reactions are among the most important classes of chemical reactions, it is useful for you to know the outcome of the various types of these reactions.

The Reaction of a Strong Acid with a Strong Base

Strong acids and bases are effectively 100% ionized in solution. Therefore, the complete ionic equation for the reaction of HCl (strong acid) and NaOH (strong base) is

$$H_3O^+(aq) + Cl^-(aq) + Na^+(aq) + OH^-(aq) \rightleftharpoons 2\,H_2O(\ell) + Na^+(aq) + Cl^-(aq)$$

which leads to the following net ionic equation

$$H_3O^+(aq) + OH^-(aq) \rightleftharpoons 2\,H_2O(\ell) \qquad K = 1/K_w = 1.0 \times 10^{14}$$

The net ionic equation for the reaction of any strong acid with any strong base is always simply the reaction of hydronium ion and hydroxide ion to give water (◀ Section 3.6). Because this reaction is the reverse of the autoionization of water, it has an equilibrium constant of $1/K_w$. This very large value of K shows that, for all practical purposes, the reactants are completely consumed to form products. Thus, if equal numbers of moles of NaOH and HCl are mixed, the result is just a solution of NaCl in water. The constituents of NaCl, Na^+ and Cl^- ions, which arise from a strong base and a strong acid, respectively, produce a neutral aqueous solution. For this reason, reactions of strong acids and bases are often called "neutralizations."

> Mixing equal amounts (moles) of a strong base and a strong acid produces a neutral solution (pH = 7.00 at 25 °C).

FIGURE 17.4 Reaction of a weak acid with a weak base. The bubbles coming from the tablet are carbon dioxide. This arises from the reaction of a weak Brønsted acid (citric acid) with a weak Brønsted base (HCO_3^-). The reaction is driven to completion by gas evolution.

● **Formic Acid + NaOH** The equilibrium constant for the reaction of formic acid and sodium hydroxide is 1.8×10^{10}. Can you confirm this? (See Study Question 17.97.)

The Reaction of a Weak Acid with a Strong Base

Consider the reaction of the naturally occurring weak acid formic acid, HCO_2H, with sodium hydroxide. The net ionic equation is

$$HCO_2H(aq) + OH^-(aq) \rightleftharpoons H_2O(\ell) + HCO_2^-(aq)$$

Table 17.5 Characteristics of Acid–Base Reactions

Type	Example	Net Ionic Equation	Species Present after Equal Amounts Are Mixed; pH
Strong acid + strong base	HCl + NaOH	$H_3O^+(aq) + OH^-(aq) \rightleftharpoons 2\,H_2O(\ell)$	Cl^-, Na^+, pH = 7
Strong acid + weak base	$HCl + NH_3$	$H_3O^+(aq) + NH_3(aq) \rightleftharpoons NH_4^+(aq) + H_2O(\ell)$	Cl^-, NH_4^+, pH < 7
Weak acid + strong base	$HCO_2H + NaOH$	$HCO_2H(aq) + OH^-(aq) \rightleftharpoons HCO_2^-(aq) + H_2O(\ell)$	HCO_2^-, Na^+, pH > 7
Weak acid + weak base	$HCO_2H + NH_3$	$HCO_2H(aq) + NH_3(aq) \rightleftharpoons HCO_2^-(aq) + NH_4^+(aq)$	HCO_2^-, NH_4^+, pH dependent on K_a and K_b of conjugate acid and base

In the reaction of formic acid with NaOH, OH^- is a much stronger base than HCO_2^- ($K_b = 5.6 \times 10^{-11}$), and the reaction is predicted to proceed to the right. If equal amounts of weak acid and base are mixed, the final solution will contain sodium formate ($NaHCO_2$), a salt that is 100% dissociated in water. The Na^+ ion is a Group IA cation and so gives a neutral solution. The formate ion, however, is the conjugate base of a weak acid (Table 17.3), so the solution is basic. This example leads to a useful general conclusion:

> Mixing equal amounts (moles) of a strong base and a weak acid produces a salt whose anion is the conjugate base of the weak acid. The solution is basic, with the pH depending on K_b for the anion.

The Reaction of a Strong Acid with a Weak Base

The net ionic equation for the reaction of the strong acid HCl and the weak base NH_3 is

$$H_3O^+(aq) + NH_3(aq) \rightleftharpoons H_2O(\ell) + NH_4^+(aq)$$

The hydronium ion, H_3O^+, is a much stronger acid than NH_4^+ ($K_a = 5.6 \times 10^{-10}$), and NH_3 is a stronger base ($K_b = 1.8 \times 10^{-5}$) than H_2O. Therefore, reaction is predicted to proceed to the right and essentially to completion. Thus, after mixing equal amounts of HCl and NH_3, the solution contains the salt ammonium chloride, NH_4Cl. The Cl^- ion has no effect on the solution pH (Tables 17.3 and 17.4). However, the NH_4^+ ion is the conjugate acid of the weak base NH_3, so the solution at the conclusion of the reaction is acidic. In general, we can conclude that

- **Ammonia + HCl** The equilibrium constant for the reaction of a strong acid with aqueous ammonia is 1.8×10^9. Can you confirm this? (See Study Question 17.96.)

> Mixing equal amounts (moles) of a strong acid and a weak base produces a salt whose cation is the conjugate acid of the weak base. The solution is acidic, with the pH depending on K_a for the cation.

The Reaction of a Weak Acid with a Weak Base

If acetic acid, a weak acid, is mixed with ammonia, a weak base, the following reaction occurs.

$$CH_3CO_2H(aq) + NH_3(aq) \rightleftharpoons NH_4^+(aq) + CH_3CO_2^-(aq)$$

You know that the reaction is product-favored because CH_3CO_2H is a stronger acid than NH_4^+ and NH_3 is a stronger base than $CH_3CO_2^-$ (Table 17.3). Thus, if equal amounts of the acid and base are mixed, the resulting solution contains ammonium acetate, $NH_4CH_3CO_2$. Is this solution acidic or basic? On page 771 you learned that this depends on the relative values of K_a for the conjugate acid (here, NH_4^+; $K_a = 5.6 \times 10^{-10}$) and K_b for the conjugate base (here, $CH_3CO_2^-$; $K_b = 5.6 \times 10^{-10}$). In this case, the values of K_a and K_b are the same, so the solution is predicted to be neutral.

- **K for Reaction of Weak Acid and Weak Base** The equilibrium constant for the reaction between a weak acid and a weak base is $K_{net} = K_w/(K_a \cdot K_b)$. Can you confirm this? (See Study Question 17.121.)

> Mixing equal amounts (moles) of a weak acid and a weak base produces a salt whose cation is the conjugate acid of the weak base and whose anion is the conjugate base of the weak acid. The solution pH depends on the relative K_a and K_b values.

REVIEW & CHECK FOR SECTION 17.7

1. Equal amounts (moles) of HCl(aq) and NaCN(aq) are mixed. The resulting solution is

   (a) acidic   (b) basic   (c) neutral

2. Equal amounts (moles) of acetic acid(aq) and sodium sulfite, Na_2SO_3(aq), are mixed. The resulting solution is

   (a) acidic   (b) basic   (c) neutral

3. Equal amounts (moles) of NaOH(aq) and NaH_2PO_4(aq) are mixed. The resulting solution is

   (a) acidic   (b) basic   (c) neutral

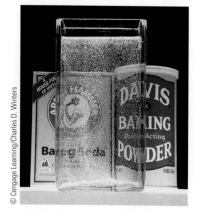

A weak acid reacting with a weak base. Baking powder contains the weak acid calcium dihydrogen phosphate, $Ca(H_2PO_4)_2$. This can react with the basic HCO_3^- ion in baking soda to give HPO_4^{2-}, CO_2 gas, and water.

17.8 Calculations with Equilibrium Constants

Determining K from Initial Concentrations and Measured pH

The K_a and K_b values found in Table 17.3 and in the more extensive tables in Appendices H and I were all determined by experiment. There are several experimental methods available, but one approach, illustrated by the following example, is to determine the pH of the solution.

Strategy Map 17.4

PROBLEM

Calculate K_a for the ionization of **lactic acid**, a weak acid.

$\downarrow$

DATA/INFORMATION KNOWN

- Acid concentration
- Solution pH

> **STEP 1.** Write **balanced equation** and K_a **expression**, and set up **ICE table**.

K_a expression and ICE table

> **STEP 2.** Enter **equilibrium concentrations** in ICE table.

At equilibrium:
$[H_3O^+] = [\text{Conjugate base}] = x$
$[\text{Lactic acid}] = \text{original conc.} - x$

> **STEP 3.** Convert **pH** to $[H_3O^+]$, and solve for x

Equilibrium concentrations of **lactic acid, hydronium ion**, and **lactate ion**

> **STEP 4.** Enter **equilibrium concentrations** into K_a **expression** and solve.

Value of K_a

⬤WL **INTERACTIVE EXAMPLE 17.4** Calculating a K_a Value from a Measured pH

Problem A 0.10 M aqueous solution of lactic acid, $CH_3CHOHCO_2H$, has a pH of 2.43. What is the value of K_a for lactic acid?

What Do You Know? To calculate K_a, you need to know the equilibrium concentration of each species. The pH of the solution allows you to calculate the equilibrium concentration of H_3O^+, and you can derive the other equilibrium concentrations from this.

Strategy

- Write the equilibrium constant expression, set up an ICE table, and convert pH to $[H_3O^+]$, the hydronium ion equilibrium concentration.

- Enter the initial concentration of $CH_3CHOHCO_2H$ on the initial (I) line of the ICE table and the equilibrium concentration of H_3O^+ on the equilibrium (E) line.

- Assign the variable x to represent changes in concentration. Based on the reaction stoichiometry the change in $[CH_3CHOHCO_2H]$ is $-x$ and the change in $[CH_3CHOHCO_2^-]$ is $+x$. Enter these values in the change (C) line of the table.

- Recognize that the hydronium ion equilibrium concentration, $[H_3O^+]$, is equal to x.

- Enter the expressions for the final equilibrium concentrations of all three species on the E line of the ICE table. Using this, determine the values of the other equilibrium concentrations.

- Use the equilibrium concentrations to solve for K_a.

Solution The equation for the reaction of lactic acid with water and its equilibrium constant expression are

$$CH_3CHOHCO_2H(aq) + H_2O(\ell) \rightleftharpoons CH_3CHOHCO_2^-(aq) + H_3O^+(aq)$$
$$\text{lactic acid} \qquad\qquad\qquad \text{lactate ion}$$

$$K_a \text{ (lactic acid)} = \frac{[H_3O^+][CH_3CHOHCO_2^-]}{[CH_3CHOHCO_2H]}$$

Begin by converting the pH to $[H_3O^+]$:

$$[H_3O^+] = 10^{-pH} = 10^{-2.43} = 3.7 \times 10^{-3} \text{ M}$$

Enter in the ICE table the concentrations before equilibrium is established, the change that occurs as the reaction proceeds to equilibrium, and the concentrations when equilibrium has been achieved. (See Examples 16.2–16.5.)

Equilibrium	$CH_3CHOHCO_2H$	+	H_2O	$\rightleftharpoons$	$CH_3CHOHCO_2^-$	+	H_3O^+
Initial (M)	0.10				0		0
Change (M)	$-x$				$+x$		$+x$
Equilibrium (M)	$(0.10 - x)$				x		x

The following points can be made concerning the ICE table.

- The quantity x represents the equilibrium concentrations of hydronium ion and lactate ion. That is, at equilibrium $x = [H_3O^+] = [CH_3CHOHCO_2^-] = 3.7 \times 10^{-3}$ M.

- By stoichiometry, x is also the concentration of acid that ionized on proceeding to equilibrium.

With these points in mind, we can calculate K_a for lactic acid.

$$K_a \text{ (lactic acid)} = \frac{[H_3O^+][CH_3CHOHCO_2^-]}{[CH_3CHOHCO_2H]}$$

$$= \frac{(3.7 \times 10^{-3})(3.7 \times 10^{-3})}{0.10 - 0.0037} = \boxed{1.4 \times 10^{-4}}$$

Comparing this value of K_a with others in Table 17.3, we see lactic acid is similar to formic acid in its strength.

Think about Your Answer Hydronium ion, H_3O^+, is present in solution from lactic acid ionization and from water autoionization. Le Chatelier's principle informs us that the H_3O^+ from lactic acid will suppress the H_3O^+ coming from the water autoionization. Because $[H_3O^+]$ from water must be less than 10^{-7} M, the pH is almost completely a reflection of H_3O^+ from lactic acid. (See Example 17.1.)

lactic acid, $CH_3CHOHCO_2H$

Lactic acid, $CH_3CHOHCO_2H$. Lactic acid is a weak monoprotic acid that occurs naturally in sour milk and arises from metabolism in the human body.

Check Your Understanding

A solution prepared from 0.055 mol of butanoic acid dissolved in sufficient water to give 1.0 L of solution has a pH of 2.72. Determine K_a for butanoic acid. The acid ionizes according to the balanced equation

$$CH_3CH_2CH_2CO_2H(aq) + H_2O(\ell) \rightleftharpoons H_3O^+(aq) + CH_3CH_2CH_2CO_2^-(aq)$$

Module 22: Equilibrium: pH of a Weak Acid covers concepts in this section.

There is an important point to notice in Example 17.4. The lactic acid concentration at equilibrium was given by $(0.10 - x)$ where x was found from the solution pH to be 3.7×10^{-3} M. By the usual rules governing significant figures $(0.10 - 0.0037)$ is equal to 0.10. The acid is weak, so very little of it ionizes (approximately 4%), and the equilibrium concentration of lactic acid is essentially equal to the initial acid concentration. Neglecting to subtract 0.0037 from 0.10 has no effect on the answer, which is known only to two significant figures.

Like lactic acid, most weak acids (HA) are so weak that the equilibrium concentration of the acid, [HA], is effectively its initial concentration ($= [HA]_0$). This leads to the useful conclusion that the denominator in the equilibrium constant expression for dilute solutions of most weak acids is simply $[HA]_0$, the original or initial concentration of the weak acid.

$$HA(aq) + H_2O(\ell) \rightleftharpoons H_3O^+(aq) + A^-(aq)$$

$$K_a = \frac{[H_3O^+][A^-]}{[HA]_0 - [H_3O^+]} \approx \frac{[H_3O^+][A^-]}{[HA]_0}$$

Analysis shows that

> The approximation that
>
> $$[HA]_{\text{equilibrium}} = [HA]_0 - [H_3O^+] \approx [HA]_0$$
>
> is valid whenever $[HA]_0$ is greater than or equal to $100 \times K_a$.

This is the same approximation we used in Chapter 16 when deciding whether we needed to solve quadratic equations exactly (◀ Problem Solving Tip 16.1).

What Is the pH of an Aqueous Solution of a Weak Acid or Base?

Knowing values of the equilibrium constants for weak acids and bases enables us to calculate the pH of a solution of a weak acid or base.

Strategy Map 17.5

PROBLEM

Calculate the **pH** for a weak acid solution knowing the value of K_a.

↓

DATA/INFORMATION KNOWN

- Acid concentration
- Value of K_a

↓

STEP 1. Write **balanced equation** and K_a **expression**, and set up **ICE table**.

↓

K_a expression and ICE table

↓

STEP 2. Enter **equilibrium concentrations** in ICE table.

↓

At equilibrium:
$[H_3O^+] = $ [conjugate base] $= x$
[acid] $=$ original conc. $- x$

↓

STEP 3. Enter **equilibrium concentrations** in K_a.

↓

K_a **expression** with equilibrium concentrations in terms of x

↓

STEP 4. Solve K_a **expression** for x.

↓

$x =$ value of $[H_3O^+]$

↓

STEP 5. Convert $[H_3O^+]$ to **pH**.

↓

pH of solution

ⓊWL **INTERACTIVE EXAMPLE 17.5** Calculating Equilibrium Concentrations and pH from K_a

Problem Calculate the pH of a 0.020 M solution of benzoic acid ($C_6H_5CO_2H$) given that $K_a = 6.3 \times 10^{-5}$ for the acid.

$$C_6H_5CO_2H(aq) + H_2O(\ell) \rightleftharpoons H_3O^+(aq) + C_6H_5CO_2^-(aq)$$

What Do You Know? You know the value of K_a for the acid and its initial concentration. You need to find the equilibrium concentration of H_3O^+ in order to calculate the pH.

Strategy This is similar to Examples 16.5 and 16.6, where you wanted to find the concentration of a reaction product. The strategy is the same:

- Write the equilibrium constant expression and set up an ICE table.

- Enter the initial concentration of $C_6H_5CO_2H$ on the initial (I) line of the ICE table.

- The variable x represents changes in concentration, so the change in $[C_6H_5CO_2H]$ is $-x$ and the change in product concentrations is $+x$. Enter these values in the change (C) line of the table.

- Enter the expressions for the final equilibrium concentrations of all three species on the E line of the ICE table, and then transfer these expressions to the equilibrium constant expression and solve for x.

- Convert $[H_3O^+] (= x)$ to pH.

Solution Organize the information in an ICE table.

Equilibrium	$C_6H_5CO_2H$	+	H_2O	$\rightleftharpoons$	$C_6H_5CO_2^-$	+	H_3O^+
Initial (M)	0.020				0		0
Change (M)	$-x$				$+x$		$+x$
Equilibrium (M)	$(0.020 - x)$				x		x

According to reaction stoichiometry,

$$[H_3O^+] = [C_6H_5CO_2^-] = x \text{ at equilibrium}$$

the concentration of acid ionized is x. Thus, the benzoic acid concentration at equilibrium is

$$[C_6H_5CO_2H] = \text{initial acid concentration} - \text{concentration of acid that ionized}$$

$$[C_6H_5CO_2H] = 0.020 - x$$

Substituting these equilibrium concentrations into the K_a expression, we have

$$K_a = \frac{[H_3O^+][C_6H_5CO_2^-]}{[C_6H_5CO_2H]}$$

$$6.3 \times 10^{-5} = \frac{(x)(x)}{0.020 - x}$$

The value of x is small compared with 0.020 (because $[HA]_0 > 100 \times K_a$; 0.020 M $> 6.3 \times 10^{-3}$). Therefore, you can use the approximate expression.

$$K_a = 6.3 \times 10^{-5} = \frac{x^2}{0.020}$$

Solving for x, we have

$$x = \sqrt{K_a \times (0.020)} = 0.0011 \text{ M}$$

and we find that

$$[H_3O^+] = [C_6H_5CO_2^-] = 0.0011 \text{ M}$$

and

$$[C_6H_5CO_2H] = (0.020 - x) = 0.019 \text{ M}$$

Finally, the pH of the solution is found to be

$$pH = -\log(1.1 \times 10^{-3}) = \boxed{2.96}$$

Think about Your Answer We made the approximation that $(0.020 - x) \approx 0.020$. If we do not make the approximation and instead solve the exact expression, $x = [H_3O^+] = 0.0011$ M. This is the same answer to two significant figures that we obtained from the "approximate" expression. Finally, notice that we again ignored any H_3O^+ that arises from water ionization.

Check Your Understanding

What are the equilibrium concentrations of acetic acid, the acetate ion, and H_3O^+ for a 0.10 M solution of acetic acid ($K_a = 1.8 \times 10^{-5}$)? What is the pH of the solution?

EXAMPLE 17.6   Calculating Equilibrium Concentrations and pH from K_a and Using the Method of Successive Approximations

Problem What is the pH of a 0.0010 M solution of formic acid? What is the concentration of formic acid at equilibrium? The acid is moderately weak, with $K_a = 1.8 \times 10^{-4}$.

$$HCO_2H(aq) + H_2O(\ell) \rightleftharpoons HCO_2^-(aq) + H_3O^+(aq)$$

What Do You Know? You know the value of K_a for the acid and its initial concentration. You need to find the equilibrium concentration of H_3O^+ in order to calculate the pH.

Strategy This is similar to Example 17.5, where you wanted to find the concentration of a reaction product, except that an approximate solution will not be possible. The strategy is the same:

- Write the equilibrium constant expression and set up an ICE table.

- Enter the initial concentration of HCO_2H on the initial (I) line of the ICE table.

- The variable x represents changes in concentration, so the change in $[HCO_2H]$ is $-x$ and the change in product concentrations is $+x$. Enter these values in the change (C) line of the table.

- Enter the expressions for the final equilibrium concentrations of all three species on the E line of the ICE table, and then transfer these expressions to the equilibrium constant expression and solve for x.

- Convert $[H_3O^+]$ ($= x$) to pH.

Solution The ICE table is as follows.

Equilibrium	$HCO_2H + H_2O$	$\rightleftharpoons$	HCO_2^-	$+$	H_3O^+
Initial (M)	0.0010		0		0
Change (M)	$-x$		$+x$		$+x$
Equilibrium (M)	$(0.0010 - x)$		x		x

Substituting the values in the table into the K_a expression we have

$$K_a = \frac{[H_3O^+][HCO_2^-]}{[HCO_2H]} = 1.8 \times 10^{-4} = \frac{(x)(x)}{0.0010 - x}$$

In this example, $[HA]_0$ ($= 0.0010$ M) is *not* greater than $100 \times K_a$ ($= 1.8 \times 10^{-2}$), so the usual approximation is not reasonable. Thus, we have to find the equilibrium concentrations by solving the "exact" expression. This can be solved with the quadratic formula or by successive approximations (Appendix A). Let us use the successive approximation method here.

To use the **successive approximations approach**, begin by solving the approximate expression for x.

$$1.8 \times 10^{-4} = \frac{(x)(x)}{0.0010}$$

Solving this, we find $x = 4.2 \times 10^{-4}$. Put this value into the expression for x in the denominator of the exact expression.

$$1.8 \times 10^{-4} = \frac{(x)(x)}{0.0010 - x} = \frac{(x)(x)}{0.0010 - 4.2 \times 10^{-4}}$$

Solving this equation for x, we now find $x = 3.2 \times 10^{-4}$. Again, put this value into the denominator, and solve for x.

$$1.8 \times 10^{-4} = \frac{(x)(x)}{0.0010 - x} = \frac{(x)(x)}{0.0010 - 3.2 \times 10^{-4}}$$

Continue this procedure until the value of x does not change from one cycle to the next. In this case, two more cycles give us the result that

$$x = [H_3O^+] = [HCO_2^-] = 3.4 \times 10^{-4} \text{ M}$$

Thus,

$$[HCO_2H] = 0.0010 - x \approx 0.0007 \text{ M}$$

and the pH of the formic acid solution is

$$pH = -\log (3.4 \times 10^{-4}) = 3.47$$

Think about Your Answer If we had used the approximate expression to find the H_3O^+ concentration, we would have obtained a value of $[H_3O^+] = 4.2 \times 10^{-4}$ M. The simplifying assumption led to a large error, about 24%. The approximate solution fails in this case because (a) the acid concentration is small and (b) the acid is not all that weak.

Check Your Understanding

What are the equilibrium concentrations of HF, F^- ion, and H_3O^+ ion in a 0.00150 M solution of HF? What is the pH of the solution?

Just as acids can be molecular species or ions, so too can bases be ionic or molecular (Figures 17.3–17.5). Many molecular bases are based on nitrogen, with ammonia being the simplest. Many other nitrogen-containing bases occur naturally; caffeine and nicotine are two that are well known. The anionic conjugate bases of weak acids make up another group of bases. The following example describes the calculation of the pH for a solution of sodium acetate.

© Cengage Learning/Charles D. Winters

Ammonia, NH_3
$K_b = 1.8 \times 10^{-5}$

Caffeine, $C_8H_{10}N_4O_2$
$K_b = 2.5 \times 10^{-4}$

Benzoate ion, $C_6H_5CO_2^-$
$K_b = 1.6 \times 10^{-10}$

Phosphate ion, PO_4^{3-}
$K_b = 2.8 \times 10^{-2}$

FIGURE 17.5 Examples of weak bases. Weak bases in water include molecules having one or more N atoms capable of accepting an H^+ ion and anions of weak acids such as benzoate and phosphate.

◉WL INTERACTIVE EXAMPLE 17.7 The pH of a Solution of a Weakly Basic Salt, Sodium Acetate

Problem What is the pH of a 0.015 M solution of sodium acetate, $NaCH_3CO_2$?

What Do You Know? You know sodium acetate is basic in water because the acetate ion, the conjugate base of a weak acid, acetic acid, reacts with water to form OH^- (Tables 17.3 and 17.4). (You also know that the sodium ion of sodium acetate does not affect the solution pH.) Finally, you know the value of K_b for the acetate ion (Table 17.3) and its initial concentration. You need to find the equilibrium concentration of H_3O^+ in order to calculate the pH.

Strategy This is similar to Examples 17.5 and 17.6, where you wanted to find the concentration of a reaction product.

- Write the balanced equation and the equilibrium constant expression, and set up an ICE table.

- Enter the initial concentration of $CH_3CO_2^-$ on the initial (I) line of the ICE table.

- The variable x represents changes in concentration, so the change in $[CH_3CO_2^-]$ is $-x$ and the change in product concentrations is $+x$. Enter these values in the change (C) line of the table.

- Enter the expressions for the equilibrium concentrations of all three species on the E line of the ICE table, and then transfer these to the equilibrium constant expression and solve for x.

- The value of $x = [OH^-]$. Determine $[H_3O^+]$ from this value using the expression $K_w = [H_3O^+][OH^-]$, then calculate pH from $[H_3O^+]$.

Solution The value of K_b for the acetate ion is 5.6×10^{-10} (Table 17.3).

$$CH_3CO_2^-(aq) + H_2O(\ell) \rightleftharpoons CH_3CO_2H(aq) + OH^-(aq)$$

Set up an ICE table to summarize the initial and equilibrium concentrations of the species in solution.

Equilibrium	$CH_3CO_2^-$	+	H_2O	$\rightleftharpoons$	CH_3CO_2H	+	OH^-
Initial (M)	0.015				0		0
Change (M)	$-x$				$+x$		$+x$
Equilibrium (M)	$(0.015 - x)$				x		x

Next, substitute the values in the table into the K_b expression.

$$K_b = 5.6 \times 10^{-10} = \frac{[CH_3CO_2H][OH^-]}{[CH_3CO_2^-]} = \frac{x^2}{0.015 - x}$$

The acetate ion, a weak base, has a very small value of K_b. Therefore, we assume that x, the concentration of hydroxide ion generated by reaction of acetate ion with water, is very small, and we use the approximate expression to solve for x.

$$K_b = 5.6 \times 10^{-10} = \frac{x^2}{0.015}$$

$$x = [OH^-] = [CH_3CO_2H] = \sqrt{(5.6 \times 10^{-10})(0.015)} = 2.9 \times 10^{-6} \text{ M}$$

To calculate the pH of the solution, we need the hydronium ion concentration. In aqueous solutions, it is always true that, at 25 °C,

$$K_w = 1.0 \times 10^{-14} = [H_3O^+][OH^-]$$

Therefore,

$$[H_3O^+] = \frac{K_w}{[OH^-]} = \frac{1.0 \times 10^{-14}}{2.9 \times 10^{-6}} = 3.5 \times 10^{-9} \text{ M}$$

$$pH = -\log(3.5 \times 10^{-9}) = 8.46$$

The acetate ion gives rise to a weakly basic solution as expected for the conjugate base of a weak acid.

Strategy Map 17.7

PROBLEM

Calculate the **pH** for a weak base knowing the value of K_b.

↓

DATA/INFORMATION KNOWN

- Base concentration
- Value of K_b

STEP 1. Write **balanced equation** and K_b **expression**, and set up **ICE table**.

K_b expression and ICE table

STEP 2. Enter **equilibrium concentrations** in ICE table.

At equilibrium:
$[OH^-]$ = [conjugate acid] = x
[base] = original conc. $- x$

STEP 3. Enter **equilibrium concentrations** in K_b.

K_b **expression** with equilibrium concentrations in terms of x

STEP 4. Solve K_b **expression** for x.

x = value of $[OH^-]$

STEP 5. Using $[OH^-]$ and K_w, calculate $[H_3O^+]$ and then **pH**.

↓

pH of solution

Think about Your Answer The hydroxide ion concentration (x) is indeed quite small relative to the initial acetate ion concentration so the approximate expression is appropriate. (Note that $100 \times K_b$ is less than the initial base concentration.)

Check Your Understanding

The weak base, ClO^- (hypochlorite ion), is used in the form of $NaClO$ as a disinfectant in swimming pools and water treatment plants. What are the concentrations of $HClO$ and OH^- and the pH of a 0.015 M solution of $NaClO$?

Strategy Map 17.8

PROBLEM

Calculate **pH** of solution after the reaction of a **weak base** and a **strong acid**.

↓

DATA/INFORMATION KNOWN

- Reactant concentrations
- Reactant volumes

> **STEP 1.** Write **balanced equation** and solve **stoichiometry problem**.

Know **amounts of reactants** and derive **amount of product**.

> **STEP 2.** Decide if product is **weak acid** or **weak base**.

Product is a **weak acid** (NH_4^+)

> **STEP 3.** Calculate concentration of NH_4^+.

Concentration of weak acid whose K_a is known.

> **STEP 4.** Solve for $[H_3O^+]$ as in Examples 17.5 - 17.7.

Value of $[H_3O^+]$

> **STEP 5.** Convert $[H_3O^+]$ to **pH**.

pH of solution

Ⓦ WL **INTERACTIVE EXAMPLE 17.8**　Calculating the pH after the Reaction of a Weak Base with a Strong Acid

Problem What is the pH of the solution that results from mixing 25 mL of 0.016 M NH_3 and 25 mL of 0.016 M HCl?

What Do You Know? You know this is an acid–base reaction (HCl + NH_3), and you know the amount of each reactant (calculated from the volume and concentration of each). Because equal volumes and concentrations are involved, neither the acid nor the base is in excess, and none will remain after the reaction. To find the pH of the solution after reaction, you need to know the amount of product, whether it is a weak acid or weak base, and its concentration. The final step then involves a weak acid or weak base equilibrium calculation (Examples 17.5–17.7).

Strategy This question involves three problems in one:

(a) *Writing a balanced equation:* First write a balanced equation for the reaction that occurs and then decide whether the reaction products are acids or bases. Here, the weak acid NH_4^+ is the product of interest.

(b) *Stoichiometry problem:* Finding the "initial" NH_4^+ concentration is a stoichiometry problem: What amount of NH_4^+ (in moles) is produced in the HCl + NH_3 reaction, and in what volume of solution is the NH_4^+ ion found?

(c) *Equilibrium problem:* Calculating the pH involves first solving an equilibrium problem. The crucial piece of information needed for this calculation is the "initial" concentration of NH_4^+ from part (b).

Solution If equal amounts (moles) of base (NH_3) and acid (HCl) are mixed, the result should be an acidic solution because the significant species remaining in solution upon completion of the reaction is NH_4^+, the conjugate acid of the weak base ammonia (see Tables 17.3 and 17.5).

(a) *Writing balanced equations*

The equation for the product-favored reaction of HCl (the supplier of hydronium ion) with NH_3 to give NH_4^+:

$$NH_3(aq) + H_3O^+(aq) \rightarrow NH_4^+(aq) + H_2O(\ell)$$

The equation for the reactant-favored reaction of NH_4^+, the product, with water:

$$NH_4^+(aq) + H_2O(\ell) \rightleftharpoons H_3O^+(aq) + NH_3(aq)$$

(b) *Stoichiometry problem*

Amount of HCl and NH_3 consumed:

$$(0.025 \text{ L HCl})(0.016 \text{ mol/L}) = 4.0 \times 10^{-4} \text{ mol HCl}$$

$$(0.025 \text{ L } NH_3)(0.016 \text{ mol/L}) = 4.0 \times 10^{-4} \text{ mol } NH_3$$

Amount of NH_4^+ produced upon completion of the reaction:

$$4.0 \times 10^{-4} \text{ mol } NH_3 \left(\frac{1 \text{ mol } NH_4^+}{1 \text{ mol } NH_3} \right) = 4.0 \times 10^{-4} \text{ mol } NH_4^+$$

PROBLEM SOLVING TIP 17.3

Table 17.5 summarizes the outcome of mixing various types of acids and bases. But how do you calculate a numerical value for the pH, particularly in the case of mixing a weak acid with a strong base or a weak base with a strong acid? The strategy (Example 17.8) is to recognize that this involves two calculations: a stoichiometry calculation and an equilibrium calculation. The key to this is that you need to know the concentration of the weak acid or weak base produced when the acid

What is the pH After Mixing Equal Numbers of Moles of an Acid and a Base

and base are mixed. Answering the following questions will guide you to an answer:

(a) What amounts of acid and base are used (in moles)? (This is a stoichiometry problem.)

(b) What is the total volume of the solution after mixing the acid and base solutions?

(c) What is the concentration of the weak acid or base produced on mixing the acid and base solutions?

(d) Using the concentration found in Step (c), what is the hydronium ion concentration in the solution? (This is an equilibrium problem.)

(e) Calculate the pH of the solution from $[H_3O^+]$.

Concentration of NH_4^+: Combining 25 mL each of HCl and NH_3 gives a total solution volume of 50. mL. Therefore, the concentration of NH_4^+ is

$$[NH_4^+] = \frac{4.0 \times 10^{-4} \text{ mol}}{0.050 \text{ L}} = 8.0 \times 10^{-3} \text{ M}$$

(c) *Acid–base equilibrium problem*

With the initial concentration of ammonium ion known, set up an ICE table to find the equilibrium concentration of hydronium ion.

Equilibrium	NH_4^+	+	H_2O	$\rightleftharpoons$	NH_3	+	H_3O^+
Initial (M)	0.0080				0		0
Change (M)	−x				+x		+x
Equilibrium (M)	(0.0080 − x)				x		x

Next, substitute the values in the table into the K_a expression for the ammonium ion. Thus, we have

$$K_a = 5.6 \times 10^{-10} = \frac{[H_3O^+][NH_3]}{[NH_4^+]} = \frac{(x)(x)}{0.0080 - x}$$

The ammonium ion is a very weak acid, as reflected by the very small value of K_a. Therefore, x, the concentration of hydronium ion generated by reaction of ammonium ion with water, is assumed to be very small, and the approximate expression is used to solve for x. (Here $100 \times K_a$ is much less than the original acid concentration.)

$$K_a = 5.6 \times 10^{-10} \approx \frac{x^2}{0.0080}$$

$$x = \sqrt{(5.6 \times 10^{-10})(0.0080)}$$

$$= [H_3O^+] = [NH_3] = 2.1 \times 10^{-6} \text{ M}$$

$$pH = -\log(2.1 \times 10^{-6}) = 5.67$$

Think about Your Answer As predicted (Table 17.5), the solution after mixing equal amounts of a strong acid and weak base is weakly acidic.

Check Your Understanding

Calculate the pH after mixing 15 mL of 0.12 M acetic acid with 15 mL of 0.12 M NaOH. What are the major species in solution at equilibrium (besides water), and what are their concentrations?

CASE STUDY

Would You Like Some Belladonna Juice in Your Drink?

The belladonna plant produces black, cherry-sized berries that look good enough to eat. But you should think twice because the plant is also called *deadly nightshade*. The berries contain atropine, a base, which is toxic and has been used by women and men for centuries to eliminate old lovers and political enemies.

The name for the plant, *belladonna*, comes from the Italian meaning "beautiful woman." Courtesans and actresses in Venice in the 16th century would put a drop or two of the juice in their eyes. It would dilate the pupils and give them a "fashionable, doe-like" appearance that could last several days.

Atropine was used for some years by physicians to dilate the eye, and it is used to treat such conditions as bradycardia, an extremely low heart rate. It is also an antidote for sarin, a nerve gas. In fact, victims of a sarin gas attack in Japan in the 1990s were treated with atropine, and soldiers in the first Gulf War in 1990–1991 carried atropine as an antidote in the event of a nerve gas attack.

Berries of the belladonna plant, a source of atropine

© WILDLIFE GmbH/Alamy

But atropine is mostly remembered in history as a poison. A fatal dose is around 100 mg. One legend is that Cleopatra at first wanted to commit suicide by taking atropine. She had a slave try it first, but the slave's death was not pleasant, so she opted for the bite of an asp, a deadly snake.

At the height of the Roman Empire, poisoning with atropine and other agents was so often used that a law was passed in 82 BC to "suppress domestic poisoning." It apparently had little effect.

The symptoms of atropine poisoning are well known. Physicians say the patient is "red as a beet" because the blood vessels dilate. Or you can be "blind as a bat" because the pupils are so dilated that vision is blurred. "Dry as a bone" is another symptom arising from the suppression of the salivary glands. In addition, you can be "hot as a hare" because your body temperature goes up and stays up for some hours. Finally, you can be "mad as a hatter" (like the hatter in *Alice in Wonderland*) because you act like a drunk person.

Atropine is not very soluble in water. However, because atropine is a base—like so many other naturally occurring substances such as caffeine, nicotine, morphine, heroin, and amphetamine—it reacts with acids. For example, reaction with sulfuric acid forms the sulfate salt. This salt is so soluble that 1 mL of a saturated solution of this compound contains many times the amount needed for a fatal dose.

If you are interested in the history of atropine as a murder weapon be sure to read about the attempted murder of Alexandra Agutter by her husband in Scotland in the 1990s. Just like an episode of CSI!

Atropine, $C_{17}H_{23}NO_3$.

Questions:

1. If a fatal dose of atropine is 100. mg, what amount of compound (moles) is this?
2. When atropine is added to sulfuric acid, a proton attaches to the molecule. What is the site of attachment?
3. The pK_a of the conjugate acid of atropine is 4.35. How does this compare with the pK_a values for the conjugate acids of ammonia, methylamine, and aniline (page 767)?
4. Atropine is chiral. (See Chapter 10.) Which C atom is the site of chirality? (Of the two enantiomers, only one is physiologically active.)

Answers to these questions are available in Appendix N.

Reference:

J. Emsley, *Molecules of Murder*, Royal Society of Chemistry, London, 2008.

REVIEW & CHECK FOR SECTION 17.8

1. What is $[H_3O^+]$ in a 0.10 M solution of HCN at 25 °C? (K_a for HCN = 4.0×10^{-10})

   (a) 1.6×10^{-9} M   (c) 2.0×10^{-5} M

   (b) 6.3×10^{-6} M   (d) 4.0×10^{-11} M

2. A 0.040 M solution of an acid, HA, has a pH of 3.02 at 25 °C. What is K_a for this acid?

   (a) 2.3×10^{-5} (c) 2.4×10^{-2}

   (b) 5.7×10^{-4} (d) 4.3×10^{-10}

3. What are the pH and ion concentrations in a solution of 0.10 M sodium formate, $NaCHO_2$? K_b for the formate ion, HCO_2^- is 5.6×10^{-11}.

	pH	$[Na^+]$	$[CHO_2^-]$	$[OH^-]$
(a)	5.63	0.10	0.10	2.4×10^{-6}
(b)	8.37	0.10	0.10	2.4×10^{-6}
(c)	8.22	0.050	0.050	1.7×10^{-6}
(d)	5.63	0.10	0.10	4.2×10^{-9}

4. You mix 0.40 g of NaOH with 100 mL of 0.10 M acetic acid. What is the pH of the resulting solution?

(a) less than 7   (b) equal to 7   (c) greater than 7

17.9 Polyprotic Acids and Bases

Because polyprotic acids are capable of donating more than one proton (Table 17.1), they present us with additional challenges when predicting the pH of their solutions. For many inorganic polyprotic acids, such as phosphoric acid, carbonic acid, and hydrosulfuric acid (H_2S), the ionization constant for each successive loss of a proton is about 10^4 to 10^6 smaller than the previous ionization step. This means that the first ionization step of a polyprotic acid produces up to about a million times more H_3O^+ ions than the second step. For this reason, *the pH of many inorganic polyprotic acids depends primarily on the hydronium ion generated in the first ionization step; the hydronium ion produced in the second step can be neglected.* The same principle applies to the fully deprotonated conjugate bases of polyprotic acids. This is illustrated by the calculation of the pH of a solution of carbonate ion, an important base in our environment (Example 17.9).

EXAMPLE 17.9   Calculating the pH of the Solution of a Polyprotic Base

Problem The carbonate ion, CO_3^{2-}, is a base in water, forming the hydrogen carbonate ion, which in turn can form carbonic acid.

$$CO_3^{2-}(aq) + H_2O(\ell) \rightleftharpoons HCO_3^-(aq) + OH^-(aq) \qquad K_{b1} = 2.1 \times 10^{-4}$$

$$HCO_3^-(aq) + H_2O(\ell) \rightleftharpoons H_2CO_3(aq) + OH^-(aq) \qquad K_{b2} = 2.4 \times 10^{-8}$$

What is the pH of a 0.10 M solution of Na_2CO_3?

What Do You Know? You know the balanced equations and the values of K_b for the ions as well as the concentration of the carbonate ion.

Strategy The first ionization constant, K_{b1}, is much larger than the second, K_{b2}, so the hydroxide ion concentration in the solution results almost entirely from the first step. Therefore, you can calculate the OH^- concentration produced in the first ionization step, but we will test the conclusion that OH^- produced in the second step is negligible.

Solution Set up an ICE table for the reaction of the carbonate ion (Equilibrium Table 1).

Equilibrium Table 1—Reaction of CO_3^{2-} Ion

Equilibrium	CO_3^{2-}	$+$	H_2O	$\rightleftharpoons$	HCO_3^-	$+$	OH^-
Initial (M)	0.10				0		0
Change	$-x$				$+x$		$+x$
Equilibrium (M)	$(0.10 - x)$				x		x

Based on this table, the equilibrium concentration of OH^- $(= x)$ can then be calculated.

$$K_{b1} = 2.1 \times 10^{-4} = \frac{[HCO_3^-][OH^-]}{[CO_3^{2-}]} = \frac{x^2}{0.10 - x}$$

© Cengage Learning/Charles D. Winters

A polyprotic acid. Malic acid $C_4H_4O_4$ is a diprotic acid occurring in apples. It is also classified as an alpha-hydroxy acid because it has an OH group on the C atom next to the CO_2H (in the alpha position). It is one of a large group of natural alpha-hydroxy acids such as lactic acid, citric acid, and ascorbic acid. Alpha-hydroxy acids have been touted as an ingredient in "anti-aging" skin creams. They work by accelerating the natural process by which skin replaces the outer layer of cells with new cells.

© Cengage Learning/Charles D. Winters

Sodium carbonate, a polyprotic base. This common substance is a base in aqueous solution. Its primary use is in the glass industry. Although it used to be manufactured, it is now mined as the mineral trona, $Na_2CO_3 \cdot NaHCO_3 \cdot 2 H_2O$.

Because K_{b1} is relatively small, it is reasonable to make the approximation that $(0.10 - x) \approx 0.10$. Therefore,

$$x = [HCO_3^-] = [OH^-] = \sqrt{(2.1 \times 10^{-4})(0.10)} = 4.6 \times 10^{-3} \text{ M}$$

Using this value of $[OH^-]$, you can calculate the pOH of the solution,

$$pOH = -\log(4.6 \times 10^{-3}) = 2.34$$

and then use the relationship $pH + pOH = 14$ to calculate the pH.

$$pH = 14 - pOH = 11.66$$

Finally, you can conclude that the concentration of the carbonate ion is, to a good approximation, 0.10 M.

$$[CO_3^{2-}] = 0.10 - 0.0046 \approx 0.10 \text{ M}$$

The HCO_3^- ion produced in the first step could acquire another proton to give H_2CO_3 and this could affect the pH. But does this occur to a meaningful extent? To test this, set up a second ICE Table.

Equilibrium Table 2—Reaction of HCO_3^- Ion

Equilibrium	HCO_3^-	$+$	H_2O	$\rightleftharpoons$	H_2CO_3	$+$	OH^-
Initial (M)	4.6×10^{-3}				0		4.6×10^{-3}
Change (M)	$-y$				$+y$		$+y$
Equilibrium (M)	$(4.6 \times 10^{-3} - y)$				y		$(4.6 \times 10^{-3} + y)$

Because K_{b2} is so small, the second step occurs to a much smaller extent than the first step. This means the amount of H_2CO_3 and OH^- produced in the second step $(= y)$ is much smaller than 10^{-3} M. Therefore, it is reasonable that both $[HCO_3^-]$ and $[OH^-]$ are very close to 4.6×10^{-3} M.

$$K_{b2} = 2.4 \times 10^{-8} = \frac{[H_2CO_3][OH^-]}{[HCO_3^-]} = \frac{(y)(4.6 \times 10^{-3})}{4.6 \times 10^{-3}}$$

Because $[HCO_3^-]$ and $[OH^-]$ have nearly identical values, they cancel from the expression, and we find that $[H_2CO_3]$ is simply equal to K_{b2}.

$$y = [H_2CO_3] = K_{b2} = 2.4 \times 10^{-8} \text{ M}$$

The amount of OH^- produced in this reaction is negligible. The hydroxide ion is essentially all produced in the first equilibrium process.

Think about Your Answer It is almost always the case that the pH of a solution of an inorganic polyprotic acid is due to the hydronium ion generated in the first ionization step. Similarly, the pH of a polyprotic base is due to the OH^- ion produced in the first ionization step.

Check Your Understanding

What is the pH of a 0.10 M solution of oxalic acid, $H_2C_2O_4$? What are the concentrations of H_3O^+, $HC_2O_4^-$, and the oxalate ion, $C_2O_4^{2-}$? (See Appendix H for K_a values.)

REVIEW & CHECK FOR SECTION 17.9

Hydrazine (N_2H_4) is like CO_3^{2-} in that it is a polyprotic base ($K_{b1} = 8.5 \times 10^{-7}$ and $K_{b2} = 8.9 \times 10^{-16}$). The two conjugate acids are $N_2H_5^+$ and $N_2H_6^{2+}$. What is the expected pH of a 0.025 M solution of N_2H_4?

(a) 3.83   (b) 8.32   (c) 10.16

17.10 Molecular Structure, Bonding, and Acid–Base Behavior

One of the most interesting aspects of chemistry is the correlation between a molecule's structure and bonding and its chemical properties. Because so many acids and bases play such a key role in chemistry, it is especially useful to see if there are some general principles governing acid–base behavior.

Acid Strength of the Hydrogen Halides, HX

Aqueous HF is a weak Brønsted acid in water, whereas the other hydrohalic acids— aqueous HCl, HBr, and HI—are all strong acids. Experiments show that the acid strength increases in the order HF << HCl < HBr < HI. A detailed analysis of the factors that lead to these differences in acid strength in this group is interesting (see *A Closer Look, Acid Strengths and Molecular Structure,* page 788), and predictions about relative acid strength can be made based on the sum of two energy quantities, the energy required to break the H—X bond (the bond dissociation enthalpy, page 383) and the electron attachment enthalpy of the halogen (page 320). That is, when a hydrohalic acid HX ionizes in water,

$$HX(aq) + H_2O(\ell) \rightarrow H_3O^+(aq) + X^-(aq)$$

the sum of the two energy terms

Change in energy $\propto$ HX bond dissociation enthalpy + electron attachment enthalpy of X

should correlate with acid strength. Stronger acids should result when the H—X bond is more easily broken (as signaled by a smaller, positive value of ΔH for bond dissociation) and a more negative value for the electron attachment enthalpy of X.

The bond dissociation enthalpy and electron attachment enthalpy effects can work together (a weak H—X bond and a large, negative electron attachment enthalpy of the X group) to produce a strong acid, but they can also work in opposite directions. The balance of the two effects is important. Let us examine some data for the Group 7A binary acids, HX.

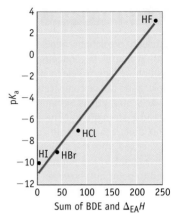

FIGURE 17.6 The effect of H—X bond enthalpy and X electron attachment enthalpy on acid strength. Stronger acids have weaker H—X bonds and X atoms with more negative electron attachment enthalpies. (BDE is the bond dissociation enthalpy of the H—X bond, and $\Delta_{EA}H$ is the electron attachment enthalpy of the halogen atom, see page 321.) See M. Moran, *Journal of Chemical Education,* Vol. 83, pp. 800–803, 2006.

————— Increasing acid strength ————→

	HF	HCl	HBr	HI
pK_a	+3.14	−7	−9	−10
H—X bond strength (kJ/mol)	565	432	366	299
Electron attachment enthalpy of X (kJ/mol)	−328	−349	−325	−295
Sum (kJ/mol)	237	83	41	4

In this series of acids, the bond enthalpy factor dominates: the weakest acid, HF, has the strongest H—X bond, and the strongest acid, HI, has the weakest H—X bond. However, the electron attachment enthalpy of X is most negative with Cl, less so with F and Br, and much less so with I. A less negative electron attachment enthalpy should lead to a weaker acid, but it is the *sum* of the two effects that leads to the observation that HI is the strongest acid. In Figure 17.6 you see there is a good correlation between an acid's pK$_a$ and the *sum* of the enthalpies for bond dissociation and electron attachment enthalpy.

Comparing Oxoacids: HNO₂ and HNO₃

Nitrous acid (HNO_2) and nitric acid (HNO_3) are representative of several series of **oxoacids**. Oxoacids contain an atom (usually a nonmetal atom) bonded to one or more oxygen atoms, some with hydrogen atoms attached. Besides those based on N, you are familiar with the sulfur- and chlorine-based oxoacids (Table 17.6). In all these series of related compounds, the acid strength increases as the number of oxy-

Table 17.6 Oxoacids

Acid	pK$_a$
Cl-Based Oxoacids	
HOCl	7.46
HOClO ($HClO_2$)	~ 2
HOClO$_2$ ($HClO_3$)	~ −3
HOClO$_3$ ($HClO_4$)	~ −8
S-Based Oxoacids	
(HO)$_2$SO [H_2SO_3]	1.92, 7.21
(HO)$_2$SO$_2$ [H_2SO_4]	~ −3, 1.92

Linus Pauling stated the general relationship that, for oxoacids with the general formula (HO)$_n$E(O)$_m$, the value of pK$_a$ is about 8–5m. When $n > 1$, the pK$_a$ increases by about 5 for each successive loss of a proton.

A CLOSER LOOK

Acid Strengths and Molecular Structure

Although predictions about acid strength in aqueous solution are fairly simple to make, a complete explanation can be complicated.

Acid strength is sometimes correlated with the strength and the polarity of the H—X bond, readily identifiable characteristics derived from the structure of the acid, the reactant in the ionization process. We need to point out, however, that when one is assessing any chemical reaction, it is necessary to consider both reactants and products. Looking only at the reactant when dealing with acid ionization only takes you halfway.

When evaluating the strength of an acid HX(aq), we are looking at the following reaction:

$$HX(aq) + H_2O(\ell) \rightleftharpoons H_3O^+(aq) + X^-(aq)$$

To fully explain the extent of ionization, we must consider characteristics of both the acid and the anion. The ability of the anion to spread out the negative charge across the ion, for example, and the solvation of the anion by the solvent are among the issues that must have some relevance in an explanation of the strength of the acid.

How enthalpy changes contribute to acid strength can be assessed using a thermochemical cycle (such as the one used to evaluate a lattice enthalpy, page 599). Consider the relative acid strengths of the hydrogen halides. The enthalpy change for the ionization of an acid in water can be related to other enthalpy changes as shown in the diagram. The solvation of H⁺ (Step 5) and the ionization energy of H(g) (Step 3) are common to all of the hydrogen halides and do not contribute to the differences among hydrogen halides, but the four remaining terms are different. For the hydrogen halides, the bond dissociation

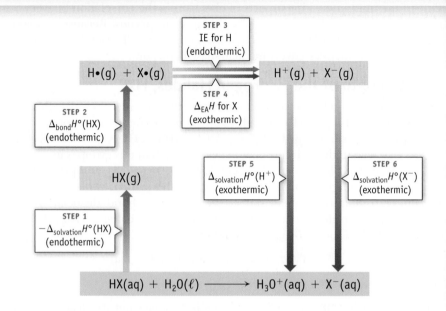

enthalpy (Step 2) of HF is much larger than the dissociation enthalpies of the other hydrogen halides. However, it is compensated for significantly by the enthalpy of solvation of the anion (Step 6), which for the fluoride ion is much more exothermic than the solvation energies of the other halide ions. The electron attachment enthalpy is also a contributor to the differences in overall enthalpy changes. Electron attachment enthalpy values vary among the halogens, but to a smaller extent than the variation in bond energy and the enthalpy of solvation of the halide ion. Differences in solvation energy for the molecular species (Step 1) are minimal.

A complete analysis of strengths of acids in aqueous solution will include consideration of both enthalpies and entropies. Entropy has yet to be discussed in this text

in detail (▶ Chapter 19) but we noted earlier (◀ page 622) that entropy plays an important role in solution chemistry, specifically in determining solubilities. It is not surprising that entropy has a role in determining acid strength, too. Indeed, differences in entropy changes are significant in accounting for the differences in acid strength of the hydrogen halides.

Although all of these terms contribute to acid strength, acid strength can often be correlated with a subset of this information, as can be seen by the examples presented in this section. We point out, however, that correlations, while highly useful to a chemist because they can be used to make important predictions, are at best only partial explanations.

gen atoms bonded to the central element increases. Thus, nitric acid (HNO_3) is a stronger acid than nitrous acid (HNO_2).

HNO₃, strong acid,
$pK_a = -1.4$

HNO₂, weak acid,
$pK_a = +3.35$

Let's apply the bond enthalpy/electron affinity analysis to HNO_3 and HNO_2.

	Increasing acid strength ⟶	
	HNO₂	**HNO₃**
pK_a	+3.35	−1.4
H—O bond strength (kJ/mol)	328	423
Electron attachment enthalpy of X (kJ/mol)	−219	−377
Sum (kJ/mol)	109	46

nitrous acid, HNO₂   nitric acid, HNO₃

FIGURE 17.7 Electrostatic potential surfaces for the nitrogen oxoacids. Both surfaces show the O—H bond is quite polar. More importantly, calculations show that the OH bond becomes more polar as more O atoms are added to N.

Partial Charges

Molecule	H Atom	O Atom of OH	N Atom
HNO₂	+0.39	−0.35	+0.14
HNO₃	+0.41	−0.47	+0.76

As in the case of the Group 7A acids, we again see that acid strength correlates with the sum of the enthalpies for bond breaking and X group (NO₂ or NO₃) electron attachment enthalpy.

Our previous analysis of the Group 7A acids showed that, in that series, the H—X bond strength was the more important factor; as the H—X bond became stronger, the acid became weaker. However, the data for HNO₃ and HNO₂ show this is not true here. The O—H bond is stronger in the stronger acid HNO₃. Instead, the electron attachment term is the more important term in this correlation. These same effects are observed for other oxyacids such as the chlorine-based oxoacids HOCl < HOClO < HOClO₂ < HOClO₃ and the S-based oxoacids (Table 17.6). How is this to be interpreted?

In HNO₃, there are two other oxygen atoms bonded to the central nitrogen atom, whereas in HNO₂ only one other oxygen is bonded to the nitrogen atom. By attaching more electronegative O atoms to nitrogen, we are increasing the electron affinity of the group attached to hydrogen, and anything that increases the affinity of the X group for an electron should also make HX a stronger acid and X⁻ a weaker conjugate base. This is another way of saying that if X⁻ has a way to accommodate and stabilize a negative charge, it will be a weaker conjugate base. In the case of oxoacids, additional oxygen atoms have the effect of stabilizing the anion because the negative charge on the anion can be dispersed over more atoms. In the nitrate ion, for example, the negative charge is shared equally over the three oxygen atoms. This is represented symbolically by the three resonance structures for this ion.

$$\left[\begin{array}{c} :\!\ddot{O}: \\ \| \\ \overset{\displaystyle\cdot\cdot}{N} \\ :\!\ddot{O} \quad \ddot{O}: \end{array}\right]^{-} \longleftrightarrow \left[\begin{array}{c} :\!\ddot{O}: \\ \cdot\cdot \\ N \\ \ddot{O} \quad \ddot{O}: \end{array}\right]^{-} \longleftrightarrow \left[\begin{array}{c} :\!\ddot{O}: \\ \cdot\cdot \\ N \\ :\!\ddot{O} \quad \ddot{O} \end{array}\right]^{-}$$

In nitrite ion, only two atoms share the negative charge. Therefore, NO₂⁻ is a stronger conjugate base than NO₃⁻. In general, greater stabilization of the products formed by ionizing the acid contributes to increased acidity.

Table 17.7 and Figure 17.7 show that another empirical correlation can be made between the structure of an acid and its acidity: In a series of related acids, the larger the formal charge on the central atom, the stronger the acid (Table 17.7). For example, the N atom formal charge in the weak acid HNO₂ is 0, whereas it is +1 in the strong acid HNO₃, and these are reflected by the results of theoretical calculations cited in Figure 17.7.

In summary, molecules such as the oxoacids can behave as stronger Brønsted acids when the anion created by loss of H⁺ is stable and able to accommodate the negative charge. These conditions are promoted by

- the presence of electronegative atoms attached to the central atom.
- the possibility of resonance structures for the anion, which lead to delocalization of the negative charge over the anion and thus to a more stable ion.
- greater positive formal charge of the central atom.

Why Are Carboxylic Acids Brønsted Acids?

There is a large class of organic acids, typified by acetic acid (CH₃CO₂H) (Figure 17.8), called *carboxylic acids* because all have the carboxylic acid group, —CO₂H (◄ page 467). The arguments used to explain the acidity of oxoacids can

Table 17.7 Correlation of Atom Formal Charge and pK_a

	Central Atom Formal Charge	pK_a
:Ö—H | :Ö—S—Ö: | :Ö—H	+2	−3
H :Ö—H | | :Ö—S—Ö:	+1	1.92
:Ö—Cl—Ö—H	+1	2
:Cl—Ö—H	0	7.46

also be applied to carboxylic acids. The O—H bond in these compounds is polar, a prerequisite for ionization.

FIGURE 17.8 Electrostatic potential surface and partial charges for acetic acid. The H atoms of the molecule are all positively charged, but the H atom of the OH is much more highly charged. As expected, both of the electronegative O atoms have a partial negative charge. The table below gives some of the computer-calculated partial charges on the acid.

Atom or Group	Calc'd Partial Charge
H of OH	+0.43
O of OH	−0.62
H of CH₃	+0.23

polar O—H bond broken by interaction of positively charged H atom with hydrogen-bonded H₂O

In addition, carboxylate anions are stabilized by delocalizing the negative charge over the two oxygen atoms.

The simple carboxylic acids, RCO_2H in which R is a hydrocarbon group (◄ Section 10.4), do not differ markedly in acid strength (compare acetic acid, $pK_a = 4.74$, and propanoic acid, $pK_a = 4.89$, Table 17.3). The acidity of carboxylic acids is enhanced, however, if electronegative substituents replace the hydrogens in the alkyl ($-CH_3$ or $-C_2H_5$) group. Compare, for example, the pK_a values of a series of acetic acids in which hydrogen is replaced sequentially by the more electronegative element chlorine.

Acid		pK_a Value	
CH_3CO_2H	Acetic acid	4.74	
$ClCH_2CO_2H$	Chloroacetic acid	2.85	Increasing acid
Cl_2CHCO_2H	Dichloroacetic acid	1.49	strength
Cl_3CCO_2H	Trichloroacetic acid	0.7	

As in the nitrogen oxoacids, increasingly electronegative substituents lead to an increase in acid strength. One argument is that electronegative substituents stabilize the negative charge of the anion. That is, the $Cl_3CCO_2^-$ anion is more stable than the $H_3CCO_2^-$ anion, so the formation of $Cl_3CCO_2^-$ is more favored than the formation of $CH_3CO_2^-$. Thus, the $Cl_3CCO_2^-$ anion is a weaker base than the $CH_3CO_2^-$ anion.

Finally, why are the C—H hydrogens of carboxylic acids not dissociated as H^+ instead of (or in addition to) the O—H hydrogen atom? The calculated partial positive charges listed in Figure 17.8 show that the H atoms of the CH_3 group have a much smaller positive partial charge than the O—H hydrogen atom. Furthermore, in carboxylic acids, the C atom of the CH_3 group is not sufficiently electronegative to accommodate the negative charge left if the bond breaks as $C—H \rightarrow C:^- + H^+$, and the product anion is not well stabilized.

Why Are Hydrated Metal Cations Brønsted Acids?

When a coordinate covalent bond is formed between a metal cation and a water molecule, the positive charge of the metal ion and its small size means that the electrons of the $H_2O \rightarrow M^{n+}$ bond are very strongly attracted to the metal (Section 17.11). As a result, the O—H bonds of the bound water molecules are polarized, just as in oxoacids and carboxylic acids. The net effect is that a H atom of a coordinated water molecule is removed as H^+ more readily than in an uncoordinated water molecule. Thus, a hydrated metal cation functions as a Brønsted acid or proton donor.

$$[Cu(H_2O)_6]^{2+} + H_2O(\ell) \rightleftharpoons [Cu(H_2O)_5(OH)]^+(aq) + H_3O^+(aq)$$

The acidity of the hydrated metal ion increases with increasing charge. Consulting Table 17.3, you see that the K_a of +3 ions (for example Al^{3+} and Fe^{3+}) is greater than for +2 cations (Cu^{2+}, Pb^{2+}, Co^{2+}, Fe^{2+}, Ni^{2+}). Ions with a single positive charge such as Na^+ and K^+ are not acidic. (This is similar to the effect of central atom formal charge in a series of related acids. See Table 17.7.)

Why Are Anions Brønsted Bases?

Anions, particularly oxoanions such as PO_4^{3-}, are Brønsted bases. The negatively charged anion interacts with the positively charged H atom of a polar water molecule, and an H^+ ion is transferred to the anion.

The data in Table 17.8 show that, in a series of related anions, the basicity of an anionic base increases as the negative charge of the anion increases.

- **Polarization of O—H Bonds** Water molecules attached to a metal cation have strongly polarized O—H bonds.

$$(H_2O)_5M^{n+} \longleftarrow \overset{H^{\delta+}}{\underset{\delta-}{:O-H^{\delta+}}}$$

REVIEW & CHECK FOR SECTION 17.10

1. Which of the following is the stronger acid?

   (a) H_2SeO_4 (b) H_2SeO_3

2. Which of the following should be the stronger acid?

   (a) $[Fe(H_2O)_6]^{2+}$ (b) $[Fe(H_2O)_6]^{3+}$

3. Which of the following should be the stronger acid?

   (a) HOCl   (b) HOBr

Table 17.8 **Basic Oxoanions**

Anion	pK$_b$
PO_4^{3-}	1.55
HPO_4^{2-}	6.80
$H_2PO_4^-$	11.89
CO_3^{2-}	3.68
HCO_3^-	7.62
SO_3^{2-}	6.80
HSO_3^-	12.08

17.11   The Lewis Concept of Acids and Bases

The concept of acid–base behavior advanced by Brønsted and Lowry in the 1920s works well for reactions involving proton transfer. However, a more general acid–base concept was developed by Gilbert N. Lewis in the 1930s (◄ page 342). This concept is based on the sharing of electrons pairs between an acid and a base.

> A **Lewis acid** is a substance that can accept a pair of electrons from another atom to form a new bond, and a **Lewis base** is a substance that can donate a pair of electrons to another atom to form a new bond.

This means that an acid–base reaction in the Lewis sense occurs when a molecule (or ion) donates a pair of electrons to another molecule (or ion).

$$\begin{array}{cccc} A & + & B: & \rightarrow & B{\rightarrow}A \\ \text{acid} & & \text{base} & & \text{adduct} \end{array}$$

The product is often called an **acid–base adduct.** In Section 8.5, this type of chemical bond was called a *coordinate covalent bond.*

Formation of a hydronium ion from H^+ and water, and the formation of the ammonium ion from H^+ and ammonia, are good examples of a Lewis acid–base reaction (Figure 17.9). The H^+ ion has no electrons in its valence (1s) shell, and the

FIGURE 17.9 Protonation of water and ammonia are examples of Lewis acid–base reactions.

FIGURE 17.10 The Lewis acid–base complex ion $[Cu(NH_3)_4]^{2+}$. Here, aqueous ammonia was added to aqueous $CuSO_4$ (the light blue solution at the bottom of the beaker). The small concentration of OH^- in $NH_3(aq)$ first led to the formation of insoluble blue-white $Cu(OH)_2$ (the solid in the middle of the beaker). With additional NH_3, however, the deep blue, soluble complex ion formed (the solution at the top of the beaker). The model in the text shows the copper(II)–ammonia complex ion.

water molecule has two unshared pairs of electrons (located in sp^3 hybrid orbitals). One of the lone pairs of a water molecule oxygen atom can be shared with an H^+ ion, thus forming an O—H bond in an H_3O^+ ion. A similar interaction occurs between H^+ and the nitrogen lone pair on ammonia to form the ammonium ion.

Lewis acid–base reactions are very common. In general, they involve Lewis acids that are cations or neutral molecules with an available, empty valence orbital and bases that are anions or neutral molecules with a lone electron pair.

Cationic Lewis Acids

Just as H^+ and water form a Lewis acid–base adduct, metal cations interact with water molecules to form hydrated cations (Figure 17.10 and page 551). In these species, coordinate covalent bonds form between the metal cation and a lone pair of electrons on the O atom of each water. For example, an iron(II) ion, Fe^{2+}, forms six coordinate covalent bonds to water.

$$Fe^{2+}(aq) + 6\ H_2O(\ell) \rightarrow [Fe(H_2O)_6]^{2+}(aq)$$

Solutions of transition metal cations are generally very colorful (Figures 17.10 and 17.11 and Section 22.3). Chemists call the species formed by coordination of water to a metal ion **complex ions** or, because of the presence of coordinate covalent bonds, **coordination complexes**. Several are listed in Table 17.3 as acids, and their behavior is described further in Chapter 22.

Ammonia is an excellent Lewis base and, like water, it also combines with metal cations to give adducts (complex ions), which are often very colorful. For example, copper(II) ions, light blue in aqueous solution (Figure 17.10), react with ammonia to give a deep blue adduct with four ammonia molecules surrounding each Cu^{2+} ion.

$$Cu^{2+}(aq) + 4\ NH_3(aq) \longrightarrow [Cu(NH_3)_4]^{2+}(aq)$$
$$\text{light blue} \hspace{5cm} \text{deep blue}$$

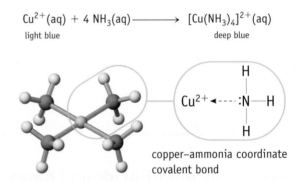

copper–ammonia coordinate covalent bond

Hydroxide ion, OH^-, is an excellent Lewis base and binds readily to metal cations to give metal hydroxides. An important feature of the chemistry of some metal

$[Fe(H_2O)_6]^{3+}$ $[Ni(H_2O)_6]^{2+}$
$[Co(H_2O)_6]^{2+}$ $[Cu(H_2O)_6]^{2+}$

(a) Solutions of the nitrate salts of iron(III), cobalt(II), nickel(II), and copper(II) all have characteristic colors.

octahedral
$[M(H_2O)_6]^{n+}$

tetrahedral
$Be^{2+}(aq) + 4\ H_2O(\ell) \longrightarrow [Be(H_2O)_4]^{2+}(aq)$

water–metal ion coordinate covalent bond

(b) Models of complex ions (Lewis acid–base adducts) formed between a metal cation and water molecules. Such complexes often have six or four water molecules arranged octahedrally or tetrahedrally around the metal cation.

FIGURE 17.11 Metal cations in water.

Table 17.9 Some Common Amphoteric Metal Hydroxides*

Hydroxide	Reaction as a Base	Reaction as an Acid
$Al(OH)_3$	$Al(OH)_3(s) + 3 H_3O^+(aq) \rightleftharpoons Al^{3+}(aq) + 6 H_2O(\ell)$	$Al(OH)_3(s) + OH^-(aq) \rightleftharpoons [Al(OH)_4]^-(aq)$
$Zn(OH)_2$	$Zn(OH)_2(s) + 2 H_3O^+(aq) \rightleftharpoons Zn^{2+}(aq) + 4 H_2O(\ell)$	$Zn(OH)_2(s) + 2 OH^-(aq) \rightleftharpoons [Zn(OH)_4]^{2-}(aq)$
$Sn(OH)_4$	$Sn(OH)_4(s) + 4 H_3O^+(aq) \rightleftharpoons Sn^{4+}(aq) + 8 H_2O(\ell)$	$Sn(OH)_4(s) + 2 OH^-(aq) \rightleftharpoons [Sn(OH)_6]^{2-}(aq)$
$Cr(OH)_3$	$Cr(OH)_3(s) + 3 H_3O^+(aq) \rightleftharpoons Cr^{3+}(aq) + 6 H_2O(\ell)$	$Cr(OH)_3(s) + OH^-(aq) \rightleftharpoons [Cr(OH)_4]^-(aq)$

* The aqueous metal cations are best described as $[M(H_2O)_6]^{n+}$.

hydroxides is that they are **amphoteric**. An amphoteric metal hydroxide can behave as an acid or a base (Table 17.9). The chemistry of aluminum hydroxide, $Al(OH)_3$, is one of the best examples of this behavior (Figure 17.12). Adding OH^- to a precipitate of $Al(OH)_3$ produces the water-soluble complex ion $[Al(OH)_4]^-$. In this reaction, $Al(OH)_3$ is acting as a Lewis acid.

$$Al(OH)_3(s) + OH^-(aq) \rightarrow [Al(OH)_4]^-(aq)$$
$$\text{acid} \qquad\quad \text{base}$$

If acid is added to the $Al(OH)_3$ precipitate, it again dissolves. This time, however, aluminum hydroxide is acting as a base.

$$Al(OH)_3(s) + 3 H_3O^+(aq) \rightarrow Al^{3+}(aq) + 6 H_2O(\ell)$$
$$\text{base} \qquad\qquad \text{acid}$$

Adding aqueous ammonia to a soluble salt of Al^{3+} leads to a precipitate of $Al(OH)_3$.

(a) Add $NH_3(aq)$

(b) Add $NaOH(aq)$

Adding a strong base (NaOH) to $Al(OH)_3$ dissolves the precipitate. Here, aluminum hydroxide acts as a Lewis acid toward the Lewis base OH^- and forms the soluble sodium salt of the complex ion $[Al(OH)_4]^-$.

(c) Add $HCl(aq)$

$Al(OH)_3$ dissolves when a strong acid (HCl) is added. In this case, $Al(OH)_3$ acts as a Brønsted base and forms a soluble aluminum salt and water.

Photos © Cengage Learning/Charles D. Winters

FIGURE 17.12 The amphoteric nature of $Al(OH)_3$. Aluminum hydroxide is formed by the reaction of aqueous Al^{3+} and ammonia.

$$Al^{3+}(aq) + 3 NH_3(aq) + 3 H_2O(\ell) \rightleftharpoons Al(OH)_3(s) + 3 NH_4^+(aq)$$

Reactions of solid $Al(OH)_3$ with aqueous NaOH and HCl demonstrate that aluminum hydroxide is amphoteric.

Molecular Lewis Acids

Lewis's acid–base concept also accounts for the fact that oxides of nonmetals such as CO_2 and SO_2 behave as acids (◀ Section 3.6). Because oxygen is more electronegative than C, the C—O bonding electrons in CO_2 are polarized away from carbon and toward oxygen. This causes the carbon atom to be slightly positive, and it is this atom that the negatively charged Lewis base OH^- can attack to give, ultimately, the bicarbonate ion.

● **CO_2 in Basic Solution** This reaction of CO_2 with OH^- is the first step in the precipitation of $CaCO_3$ when CO_2 is bubbled into a solution of $Ca(OH)_2$ (Figure 3.5, page 117).

Similarly, SO_2 reacts with aqueous OH^- to form the HSO_3^- ion.

Compounds based on the Group 3A elements boron and aluminum are among the most-studied Lewis acids. One example is a reaction in organic chemistry that is catalyzed by the Lewis acid $AlCl_3$. The mechanism of this important reaction—called the *Friedel-Crafts reaction*—is illustrated here. In the first step, a Lewis base, the Cl^- ion, transfers from the reactant, here CH_3COCl, to the Lewis acid to give $[AlCl_4]^-$ and an organic cation. The organic cation attacks a benzene molecule to give a cationic intermediate, and this then interacts with $[AlCl_4]^-$ to produce HCl and the final organic product.

Molecular Lewis Bases

Ammonia is the parent compound of an enormous number of compounds that behave as Lewis and Brønsted bases (Figure 17.13). These molecules all have an electronegative N atom with a partial negative charge surrounded by three bonds and a lone pair of electrons. Owing to this partially negative N atom, they can extract a proton from water.

Hydrogen bond with water.
H^+ ion moves to N atom.

trimethylamine   pyridine   nicotine   glycine, an amino acid

FIGURE 17.13 Nitrogen-based Lewis and Brønsted bases. All have an N atom surrounded by three bonds and a lone pair of electrons.

In addition, the lone pair can be used to form a coordinate covalent bond to Lewis acids such as a metal cation (◀ page 792).

Ammonia is widely distributed in nature and is involved as a Lewis base in numerous reactions. One example where this is important is in the conversion of ammonia to urea (NH_2CONH_2) in natural systems. The process begins with the reaction of bicarbonate ion with ATP (adenosine triphosphate), and a subsequent step in the mechanism is the following:

intermediate

Here, the Lewis base ammonia attacks a carbon atom with a partial positive charge. The dihydrogen phosphate ion is then released, yielding the $NH_2CO_2^-$ ion, which eventually forms urea in another step in this reaction mechanism.

Electrostatic potential surfaces for NH_3 and H_2O. The red or negative region of these surfaces corresponds to the lone pair of electrons on N or the two pairs on O. The N atom of NH_3 has a calculated partial charge of -1.0, and the H atoms have a charge of $+0.33$. The N atom lone pair of NH_3 is involved in forming a hydrogen bond with the polar O—H bond of water. The NH_3 is both a Lewis and a Brønsted base and can remove the proton from water to form NH_4^+ and OH^-.

REVIEW & CHECK FOR SECTION 17.11

1. Which of the following can act as a Lewis acid? (*Hint:* In each case, draw the Lewis electron dot structure of the molecule or ion. Are there lone pairs of electrons on the central atom? If so, it can be a Lewis base. Does the central atom lack an electron pair? If so, it can behave as a Lewis acid.)

    (a) PH_3 (c) H_2S

    (b) BCl_3 (d) HS^-

2. The molecule whose structure is illustrated here is amphetamine, a stimulant. Which description best fits this molecule? (*Note:* There may be more than one answer.)

    (a) Brønsted acid   (b) Lewis acid   (c) Brønsted base   (d) Lewis base

and

Sign in at **www.cengage.com/owl** to:
- View tutorials and simulations, develop problem-solving skills, and complete online homework assigned by your professor.
- For quick review and exam prep, download Go Chemistry mini lecture modules from OWL (or purchase them at **www.cengagebrain.com**)

❓ Access **How Do I Solve It?** tutorials on how to approach problem solving using concepts in this chapter.

CHAPTER GOALS REVISITED

Now that you have studied this chapter, you should ask whether you have met the chapter goals. In particular, you should be able to:

Use the Brønsted–Lowry and Lewis theories of acids and bases

a. Define and use the Brønsted concept of acids and bases (Sections 17.1 and 17.2).

b. Recognize common monoprotic and polyprotic acids and bases, and write balanced equations for their ionization in water (Section 17.2).

c. Appreciate when a substance can be amphiprotic (Section 17.2). **Study Questions: 5, 6.**

d. Recognize the Brønsted acid and base in a reaction, and identify the conjugate partner of each (Section 17.2). **Study Questions: 1–4, 7, 8.**

e. Use the water ionization constant, K_w (Section 17.3).

f. Use the pH concept (Section 17.3). **Study Questions: 9–14.**

g. Identify common strong acids and bases (Tables 3.1 and 17.3).

h. Recognize some common weak acids and understand that they can be neutral molecules (such as acetic acid), cations (NH_4^+ or hydrated metal ions such as $[Fe(H_2O)_6]^{2+}$, or anions (such as HCO_3^-) (Table 17.3).

Apply the principles of chemical equilibrium to acids and bases in aqueous solution

a. Write equilibrium constant expressions for weak acids and bases (Section 17.4).

b. Calculate pK_a from K_a (or K_a from pK_a), and understand how pK_a is correlated with acid strength (Section 17.4). **Study Questions: 15, 16, 23–28, 104, 106.**

c. Understand the relationship between K_a for a weak acid and K_b for its conjugate base (Section 17.4). **Study Questions: 17, 18, 29–32.**

d. Write equations for acid–base reactions, and decide whether they are product- or reactant-favored at equilibrium (Section 17.6 and Table 17.5). **Study Questions: 33–40.**

e. Calculate the equilibrium constant for a weak acid (K_a) or a weak base (K_b) from experimental information (such as pH, $[H_3O^+]$, or $[OH^-]$) (Section 17.8 and Example 17.4). **Study Questions: 41–44, 85, 107.**

f. Use the equilibrium constant and other information to calculate the pH of a solution of a weak acid or weak base (Section 17.8 and Examples 17.5 and 17.6). **Study Questions: 47–56, 65, 66, 89, 91, 99, and Go Chemistry Module 22.**

g. Describe the acid–base properties of salts, and calculate the pH of a solution of a salt of a weak acid or of a weak base (Section 17.5 and Example 17.7). **Study Questions: 57–60, 84, 92, 93, 103, 121.**

Predict the outcome of reactions of acids and bases

a. Recognize the type of acid–base reaction, and describe its result (Section 17.7).

b. Calculate the pH after an acid–base reaction (Section 17.7 and Example 17.8). **Study Questions: 61–64, 98, 102.**

Understand the influence of structure and bonding on acid–base properties

a. Appreciate the connection between the structure of a compound and its acidity or basicity (Section 17.10). **Study Questions: 69–72, 74, 114.**

b. Characterize a compound as a Lewis base (an electron-pair donor) or a Lewis acid (an electron-pair acceptor) (Section 17.11). **Study Questions: 73–76, 108.**

Key Equations

Equation 17.1 (page 761) Water ionization constant.

$$K_w = [H_3O^+][OH^-] = 1.0 \times 10^{-14} \text{ at 25 °C}$$

Equation 17.2 (page 763) Definition of pH (see also Equation 4.3).

$$pH = -\log[H_3O^+]$$

Equation 17.3 (page 763) Definition of pOH.

$$pOH = -\log[OH^-]$$

Equation 17.4 (page 763) Definition of $pK_w = pH + pOH$ (= 14.00 at 25 °C).

$$pK_w = 14.00 = pH + pOH$$

Equation 17.5 (page 765) Equilibrium expression for a general acid, HA, in water.

$$K_a = \frac{[H_3O^+][A^-]}{[HA]}$$

Equation 17.6 (page 765) Equilibrium expression for a general base, B, in water.

$$K_b = \frac{[BH^+][OH^-]}{[B]}$$

Equation 17.7 (page 768) Definition of pK_a.

$$pK_a = -\log K_a$$

Equation 17.8 (page 768) Relationship of K_a, K_b, and K_w, where K_a and K_b are for a conjugate acid–base pair.

$$K_a \times K_b = K_w$$

Study Questions

⏻WL Interactive versions of these questions are assignable in OWL.

▲ denotes challenging questions.

Blue-numbered questions have answers in Appendix R and fully worked solutions in the *Student Solutions Manual*.

Practicing Skills

The Brønsted Concept
(See Sections 17.1 and 17.2.)

1. Write the formula and give the name of the conjugate base of each of the following acids.
   (a) HCN   (b) HSO_4^- (c) HF

2. Write the formula and give the name of the conjugate acid of each of the following bases.
   (a) NH_3 (b) HCO_3^- (c) Br^-

3. What are the products of each of the following acid–base reactions? Indicate the acid and its conjugate base and the base and its conjugate acid.
   (a) $HNO_3 + H_2O \rightarrow$
   (b) $HSO_4^- + H_2O \rightarrow$
   (c) $H_3O^+ + F^- \rightarrow$

4. What are the products of each of the following acid–base reactions? Indicate the acid and its conjugate base and the base and its conjugate acid.
   (a) $HClO_4 + H_2O \rightarrow$
   (b) $NH_4^+ + H_2O \rightarrow$
   (c) $HCO_3^- + OH^- \rightarrow$

5. Write balanced equations showing how the hydrogen oxalate ion, $HC_2O_4^-$, can be both a Brønsted acid and a Brønsted base.

6. Write balanced equations showing how the HPO_4^{2-} ion of sodium hydrogen phosphate, Na_2HPO_4, can be a Brønsted acid or a Brønsted base.

7. In each of the following acid–base reactions, identify the Brønsted acid and base on the left and their conjugate partners on the right.
   (a) $HCO_2H(aq) + H_2O(\ell) \rightleftharpoons HCO_2^-(aq) + H_3O^+(aq)$
   (b) $NH_3(aq) + H_2S(aq) \rightleftharpoons NH_4^+(aq) + HS^-(aq)$
   (c) $HSO_4^-(aq) + OH^-(aq) \rightleftharpoons SO_4^{2-}(aq) + H_2O(\ell)$

8. In each of the following acid–base reactions, identify the Brønsted acid and base on the left and their conjugate partners on the right.
   (a) $C_5H_5N(aq) + CH_3CO_2H(aq) \rightleftharpoons$
       $C_5H_5NH^+(aq) + CH_3CO_2^-(aq)$
   (b) $N_2H_4(aq) + HSO_4^-(aq) \rightleftharpoons$
       $N_2H_5^+(aq) + SO_4^{2-}(aq)$
   (c) $[Al(H_2O)_6]^{3+}(aq) + OH^-(aq) \rightleftharpoons$
       $[Al(H_2O)_5OH]^{2+}(aq) + H_2O(\ell)$

pH Calculations
(See Section 17.3 and Examples 4.8 and 17.1.)

9. An aqueous solution has a pH of 3.75. What is the hydronium ion concentration of the solution? Is it acidic or basic?

10. A saturated solution of milk of magnesia, $Mg(OH)_2$, has a pH of 10.52. What is the hydronium ion concentration of the solution? What is the hydroxide ion concentration? Is the solution acidic or basic?

11. What is the pH of a 0.0075 M solution of HCl? What is the hydroxide ion concentration of the solution?

12. What is the pH of a 1.2×10^{-4} M solution of KOH? What is the hydronium ion concentration of the solution?

13. What is the pH of a 0.0015 M solution of $Ba(OH)_2$?

14. The pH of a solution of $Ba(OH)_2$ is 10.66 at 25 °C. What is the hydroxide ion concentration in the solution? If the solution volume is 125 mL, what mass of $Ba(OH)_2$ must have been dissolved?

Equilibrium Constants for Acids and Bases
(See Sections 17.4 and 17.5 and Example 17.2.)

15. Several acids are listed here with their respective equilibrium constants:

$$C_6H_5OH(aq) + H_2O(\ell) \rightleftharpoons H_3O^+(aq) + C_6H_5O^-(aq)$$
$$K_a = 1.3 \times 10^{-10}$$

$$HCO_2H(aq) + H_2O(\ell) \rightleftharpoons H_3O^+(aq) + HCO_2^-(aq)$$
$$K_a = 1.8 \times 10^{-4}$$

$$HC_2O_4^-(aq) + H_2O(\ell) \rightleftharpoons H_3O^+(aq) + C_2O_4^{2-}(aq)$$
$$K_a = 6.4 \times 10^{-5}$$

(a) Which is the strongest acid? Which is the weakest acid?
(b) Which acid has the weakest conjugate base?
(c) Which acid has the strongest conjugate base?

16. Several acids are listed here with their respective equilibrium constants.

$$HF(aq) + H_2O(\ell) \rightleftharpoons H_3O^+(aq) + F^-(aq)$$
$$K_a = 7.2 \times 10^{-4}$$

$$HPO_4^{2-}(aq) + H_2O(\ell) \rightleftharpoons H_3O^+(aq) + PO_4^{3-}(aq)$$
$$K_a = 3.6 \times 10^{-13}$$

$$CH_3CO_2H(aq) + H_2O(\ell) \rightleftharpoons H_3O^+(aq) + CH_3CO_2^-(aq)$$
$$K_a = 1.8 \times 10^{-5}$$

(a) Which is the strongest acid? Which is the weakest acid?
(b) What is the conjugate base of the acid HF?
(c) Which acid has the weakest conjugate base?
(d) Which acid has the strongest conjugate base?

17. Which of the following ions or compounds has the strongest conjugate base? Briefly explain your choice.
(a) HSO_4^- (b) CH_3CO_2H (c) $HOCl$

18. Which of the following compounds or ions has the strongest conjugate acid? Briefly explain your choice.
(a) CN^- (b) NH_3 (c) SO_4^{2-}

19. Dissolving K_2CO_3 in water gives a basic solution. Write a balanced equation showing how this salt can produce a basic solution.

20. Dissolving ammonium bromide in water gives an acidic solution. Write a balanced equation showing how this can occur.

21. If each of the salts listed here were dissolved in water to give a 0.10 M solution, which solution would have the highest pH? Which would have the lowest pH?
(a) Na_2S (d) NaF
(b) Na_3PO_4 (e) $NaCH_3CO_2$
(c) NaH_2PO_4 (f) $AlCl_3$

22. Which of the following common food additives would give a basic solution when dissolved in water?
(a) $NaNO_3$ (used as a meat preservative)
(b) $NaC_6H_5CO_2$ (sodium benzoate; used as a soft-drink preservative)
(c) Na_2HPO_4 (used as an emulsifier in the manufacture of pasteurized cheese)

pK_a: A Logarithmic Scale of Acid Strength
(See Section 17.4.)

23. A weak acid has a K_a of 6.5×10^{-5}. What is the value of pK_a for the acid?

24. If K_a for a weak acid is 2.4×10^{-11}, what is the value of pK_a?

25. Epinephrine hydrochloride has a pK_a value of 9.53. What is the value of K_a? Where does the acid fit in Table 17.3?

26. An organic acid has p$K_a = 8.95$. What is its K_a value? Where does the acid fit in Table 17.3?

27. Which is the stronger of the following two acids?
(a) benzoic acid, $C_6H_5CO_2H$, p$K_a = 4.20$
(b) 2-chlorobenzoic acid, $ClC_6H_4CO_2H$, p$K_a = 2.90$

28. Which is the stronger of the following two acids?
(a) acetic acid, CH_3CO_2H, $K_a = 1.8 \times 10^{-5}$
(b) chloroacetic acid, $ClCH_2CO_2H$, p$K_a = 2.85$

Ionization Constants for Weak Acids and Their Conjugate Bases
(See Section 17.4.)

29. Chloroacetic acid ($ClCH_2CO_2H$) has $K_a = 1.41 \times 10^{-3}$. What is the value of K_b for the chloroacetate ion ($ClCH_2CO_2^-$)?

30. A weak base has $K_b = 1.5 \times 10^{-9}$. What is the value of K_a for the conjugate acid?

31. The trimethylammonium ion, $(CH_3)_3NH^+$, is the conjugate acid of the weak base trimethylamine, $(CH_3)_3N$. A chemical handbook gives 9.80 as the pK_a value for $(CH_3)_3NH^+$. What is the value of K_b for $(CH_3)_3N$?

32. The chromium(III) ion in water, $[Cr(H_2O)_6]^{3+}$, is a weak acid with p$K_a = 3.95$. What is the value of K_b for its conjugate base, $[Cr(H_2O)_5OH]^{2+}$?

Predicting the Direction of Acid–Base Reactions
(See Section 17.6 and Example 17.3.)

33. Acetic acid and sodium hydrogen carbonate, $NaHCO_3$, are mixed in water. Write a balanced equation for the acid–base reaction that could, in principle, occur. Using Table 17.3, decide whether the equilibrium lies predominantly to the right or to the left.

34. Ammonium chloride and sodium dihydrogen phosphate, NaH_2PO_4, are mixed in water. Write a balanced equation for the acid–base reaction that could, in principle, occur. Using Table 17.3, decide whether the equilibrium lies predominantly to the right or to the left.

35. For each of the following reactions, predict whether the equilibrium lies predominantly to the left or to the right. Explain your predictions briefly.
(a) $NH_4^+(aq) + Br^-(aq) \rightleftharpoons NH_3(aq) + HBr(aq)$
(b) $HPO_4^{2-}(aq) + CH_3CO_2^-(aq) \rightleftharpoons$
$$PO_4^{3-}(aq) + CH_3CO_2H(aq)$$
(c) $[Fe(H_2O)_6]^{3+}(aq) + HCO_3^-(aq) \rightleftharpoons$
$$[Fe(H_2O)_5(OH)]^{2+}(aq) + H_2CO_3(aq)$$

36. For each of the following reactions, predict whether the equilibrium lies predominantly to the left or to the right. Explain your predictions briefly.
(a) $H_2S(aq) + CO_3^{2-}(aq) \rightleftharpoons HS^-(aq) + HCO_3^-(aq)$
(b) $HCN(aq) + SO_4^{2-}(aq) \rightleftharpoons CN^-(aq) + HSO_4^-(aq)$
(c) $SO_4^{2-}(aq) + CH_3CO_2H(aq) \rightleftharpoons$
$$HSO_4^-(aq) + CH_3CO_2^-(aq)$$

Types of Acid–Base Reactions
(See Section 17.7.)

37. Equal molar quantities of sodium hydroxide and sodium hydrogen phosphate (Na_2HPO_4) are mixed.
(a) Write the balanced, net ionic equation for the acid–base reaction that can, in principle, occur.
(b) Does the equilibrium lie to the right or left?

38. Equal molar quantities of hydrochloric acid and sodium hypochlorite (NaClO) are mixed.
(a) Write the balanced, net ionic equation for the acid–base reaction that can, in principle, occur.
(b) Does the equilibrium lie to the right or left?

39. Equal molar quantities of acetic acid and sodium hydrogen phosphate (Na_2HPO_4) are mixed.
(a) Write a balanced, net ionic equation for the acid–base reaction that can, in principle, occur.
(b) Does the equilibrium lie to the right or left?

40. Equal molar quantities of ammonia and sodium dihydrogen phosphate (NaH_2PO_4) are mixed.
(a) Write a balanced, net ionic equation for the acid–base reaction that can, in principle, occur.
(b) Does the equilibrium lie to the right or left?

Using pH to Calculate Ionization Constants
(See Section 17.8 and Example 17.4.)

41. A 0.015 M solution of hydrogen cyanate, HOCN, has a pH of 2.67.
(a) What is the hydronium ion concentration in the solution?
(b) What is the ionization constant, K_a, for the acid?

42. A 0.10 M solution of chloroacetic acid, $ClCH_2CO_2H$, has a pH of 1.95. Calculate K_a for the acid.

43. A 0.025 M solution of hydroxylamine has a pH of 9.11. What is the value of K_b for this weak base?

$$H_2NOH(aq) + H_2O(\ell) \rightleftharpoons H_3NOH^+(aq) + OH^-(aq)$$

44. Methylamine, CH_3NH_2, is a weak base.

$$CH_3NH_2(aq) + H_2O(\ell) \rightleftharpoons CH_3NH_3^+(aq) + OH^-(aq)$$

If the pH of a 0.065 M solution of the amine is 11.70, what is the value of K_b?

45. A 2.5×10^{-3} M solution of an unknown acid has a pH of 3.80 at 25 °C.
(a) What is the hydronium ion concentration of the solution?
(b) Is the acid a strong acid, a moderately weak acid (K_a of about 10^{-5}), or a very weak acid (K_a of about 10^{-10})?

46. A 0.015 M solution of a base has a pH of 10.09.
(a) What are the hydronium and hydroxide ion concentrations of this solution?
(b) Is the base a strong base, a moderately weak base (K_b of about 10^{-5}), or a very weak base (K_b of about 10^{-10})?

Using Ionization Constants
(See Section 17.8 and Examples 17.5–17.6.)

47. What are the equilibrium concentrations of hydronium ion, acetate ion, and acetic acid in a 0.20 M aqueous solution of acetic acid?

48. The ionization constant of a very weak acid, HA, is 4.0×10^{-9}. Calculate the equilibrium concentrations of H_3O^+, A^-, and HA in a 0.040 M solution of the acid.

49. What are the equilibrium concentrations of H_3O^+, CN^-, and HCN in a 0.025 M solution of HCN? What is the pH of the solution?

50. Phenol (C_6H_5OH), commonly called *carbolic acid*, is a weak organic acid.

$$C_6H_5OH(aq) + H_2O(\ell) \rightleftharpoons C_6H_5O^-(aq) + H_3O^+(aq)$$
$$K_a = 1.3 \times 10^{-10}$$

If you dissolve 0.195 g of the acid in enough water to make 125 mL of solution, what is the equilibrium hydronium ion concentration? What is the pH of the solution?

51. What are the equilibrium concentrations of NH_3, NH_4^+, and OH^- in a 0.15 M solution of ammonia? What is the pH of the solution?

52. A hypothetical weak base has $K_b = 5.0 \times 10^{-4}$. Calculate the equilibrium concentrations of the base, its conjugate acid, and OH^- in a 0.15 M solution of the base.

53. The weak base methylamine, CH_3NH_2, has $K_b = 4.2 \times 10^{-4}$. It reacts with water according to the equation

$$CH_3NH_2(aq) + H_2O(\ell) \rightleftharpoons CH_3NH_3^+(aq) + OH^-(aq)$$

Calculate the equilibrium hydroxide ion concentration in a 0.25 M solution of the base. What are the pH and pOH of the solution?

54. Calculate the pH of a 0.12 M aqueous solution of the base aniline, $C_6H_5NH_2$ ($K_b = 4.0 \times 10^{-10}$).

$$C_6H_5NH_2(aq) + H_2O(\ell) \rightleftharpoons C_6H_5NH_3^+(aq) + OH^-(aq)$$

55. Calculate the pH of a 0.0010 M aqueous solution of HF.

56. A solution of hydrofluoric acid, HF, has a pH of 2.30. Calculate the equilibrium concentrations of HF, F^-, and H_3O^+, and calculate the amount of HF originally dissolved per liter.

Acid–Base Properties of Salts
(See Sections 17.5 and 17.8 and Example 17.7.)

57. Calculate the hydronium ion concentration and pH in a 0.20 M solution of ammonium chloride, NH_4Cl.

58. ▲ Calculate the hydronium ion concentration and pH for a 0.015 M solution of sodium formate, $NaHCO_2$.

59. Sodium cyanide is the salt of the weak acid HCN. Calculate the concentrations of H_3O^+, OH^-, HCN, and Na^+ in a solution prepared by dissolving 10.8 g of NaCN in enough water to make 5.00×10^2 mL of solution at 25 °C.

60. The sodium salt of propanoic acid, $NaCH_3CH_2CO_2$, is used as an antifungal agent by veterinarians. Calculate the equilibrium concentrations of H_3O^+ and OH^-, and the pH, for a solution of 0.10 M $NaCH_3CH_2CO_2$.

pH after an Acid–Base Reaction
(See Example 17.8.)

61. Calculate the hydronium ion concentration and pH of the solution that results when 22.0 mL of 0.15 M acetic acid, CH_3CO_2H, is mixed with 22.0 mL of 0.15 M NaOH.

62. Calculate the hydronium ion concentration and the pH when 50.0 mL of 0.40 M NH_3 is mixed with 50.0 mL of 0.40 M HCl.

63. For each of the following cases, decide whether the pH is less than 7, equal to 7, or greater than 7.
    (a) Equal volumes of 0.10 M acetic acid, CH_3CO_2H, and 0.10 M KOH are mixed.
    (b) 25 mL of 0.015 M NH_3 is mixed with 25 mL of 0.015 M HCl.
    (c) 150 mL of 0.20 M HNO_3 is mixed with 75 mL of 0.40 M NaOH.

64. For each of the following cases, decide whether the pH is less than 7, equal to 7, or greater than 7.
    (a) 25 mL of 0.45 M H_2SO_4 is mixed with 25 mL of 0.90 M NaOH.
    (b) 15 mL of 0.050 M formic acid, HCO_2H, is mixed with 15 mL of 0.050 M NaOH.
    (c) 25 mL of 0.15 M $H_2C_2O_4$ (oxalic acid) is mixed with 25 mL of 0.30 M NaOH. (Both H^+ ions of oxalic acid are removed with NaOH.)

Polyprotic Acids and Bases
(See Section 17.9 and Example 17.9.)

65. Sulfurous acid, H_2SO_3, is a weak acid capable of providing two H^+ ions.
    (a) What is the pH of a 0.45 M solution of H_2SO_3?
    (b) What is the equilibrium concentration of the sulfite ion, SO_3^{2-}, in the 0.45 M solution of H_2SO_3?

66. Ascorbic acid (vitamin C, $C_6H_8O_6$) is a diprotic acid ($K_{a1} = 6.8 \times 10^{-5}$ and $K_{a2} = 2.7 \times 10^{-12}$). What is the pH of a solution that contains 5.0 mg of acid per milliliter of solution?

ascorbic acid

67. Hydrazine, N_2H_4, can interact with water in two steps.

$$N_2H_4(aq) + H_2O(\ell) \rightleftharpoons N_2H_5^+(aq) + OH^-(aq)$$
$$K_{b1} = 8.5 \times 10^{-7}$$

$$N_2H_5^+(aq) + H_2O(\ell) \rightleftharpoons N_2H_6^{2+}(aq) + OH^-(aq)$$
$$K_{b2} = 8.9 \times 10^{-16}$$

    (a) What is the concentration of OH^-, $N_2H_5^+$, and $N_2H_6^{2+}$ in a 0.010 M aqueous solution of hydrazine?
    (b) What is the pH of the 0.010 M solution of hydrazine?

68. Ethylenediamine, $H_2NCH_2CH_2NH_2$, can interact with water in two steps, forming OH^- in each step (▶ Appendix I). If you have a 0.15 M aqueous solution of the amine, calculate the concentrations of $[H_3NCH_2CH_2NH_3]^{2+}$ and OH^-.

ethylenediamine

Molecular Structure, Bonding, and Acid–Base Behavior
(See Section 17.10.)

69. Which should be the stronger acid, HOCN or HCN? Explain briefly. (In HOCN, the H^+ ion is attached to the O atom of the OCN^- ion.)

70. Which should be the stronger Brønsted acid, $[V(H_2O)_6]^{2+}$ or $[V(H_2O)_6]^{3+}$?

71. Explain why benzenesulfonic acid is a Brønsted acid.

benzenesulfonic acid

72. The structure of ethylenediamine is illustrated in Study Question 68. Is this compound a Brønsted acid, a Brønsted base, a Lewis acid, or a Lewis base, or some combination of these?

Lewis Acids and Bases
(See Section 17.11.)

73. Decide whether each of the following substances should be classified as a Lewis acid or a Lewis base.
    (a) H_2NOH in the reaction

    $$H_2NOH(aq) + HCl(aq) \longrightarrow [H_3NOH]Cl(aq)$$

    (b) Fe^{2+}
    (c) CH_3NH_2 (*Hint:* Draw the electron dot structure.)

74. Decide whether each of the following substances should be classified as a Lewis acid or a Lewis base.
    (a) BCl_3 (*Hint:* Draw the electron dot structure.)
    (b) H_2NNH_2, hydrazine (*Hint:* Draw the electron dot structure.)
    (c) the reactants in the reaction

    $$Ag^+(aq) + 2 NH_3(aq) \rightleftharpoons [Ag(NH_3)_2]^+(aq)$$

75. Carbon monoxide forms complexes with low-valent metals. For example, $Ni(CO)_4$ and $Fe(CO)_5$ are well known. CO also forms complexes with the iron(II) ion in hemoglobin, which prevents the hemoglobin from acting in its normal way. Is CO a Lewis acid or a Lewis base?

76. Trimethylamine, $(CH_3)_3N$, is a common reagent. It interacts readily with diborane gas, B_2H_6. The latter dissociates to BH_3, and this forms a complex with the amine, $(CH_3)_3N \rightarrow BH_3$. Is the BH_3 fragment a Lewis acid or a Lewis base?

General Questions

These questions are not designated as to type or location in the chapter. They may combine several concepts.

77. About this time, you may be wishing you had an aspirin. Aspirin is an organic acid (page 756) with a K_a of 3.27 $\times 10^{-4}$ for the reaction

$$HC_9H_7O_4(aq) + H_2O(\ell) \rightleftharpoons C_9H_7O_4^-(aq) + H_3O^+(aq)$$

If you have two tablets, each containing 0.325 g of aspirin (mixed with a neutral "binder" to hold the tablet together), and you dissolve them in a glass of water to give 225 mL of solution, what is the pH of the solution?

78. Consider the following ions: NH_4^+, CO_3^{2-}, Br^-, S^{2-}, and ClO_4^-.
   (a) Which of these ions in water gives an acidic solution and which gives a basic solution?
   (b) Which of these anions will have no effect on the pH of an aqueous solution?
   (c) Which ion is the strongest base?
   (d) Write a chemical equation for the reaction of each basic anion with water.

79. A 2.50-g sample of a solid that could be $Ba(OH)_2$ or $Sr(OH)_2$ was dissolved in enough water to make 1.00 L of solution. If the pH of the solution is 12.61, what is the identity of the solid?

80. ▲ In a particular solution, acetic acid is 11% ionized at 25 °C. Calculate the pH of the solution and the mass of acetic acid dissolved to yield 1.00 L of solution.

81. Hydrogen sulfide, H_2S, and sodium acetate, $NaCH_3CO_2$, are mixed in water. Using Table 17.3, write a balanced equation for the acid–base reaction that could, in principle, occur. Does the equilibrium lie toward the products or the reactants?

82. For each of the following reactions, predict whether the equilibrium lies predominantly to the left or to the right. Explain your prediction briefly.
   (a) $HCO_3^-(aq) + SO_4^{2-}(aq) \rightleftharpoons$
   $$CO_3^{2-}(aq) + HSO_4^-(aq)$$
   (b) $HSO_4^-(aq) + CH_3CO_2^-(aq) \rightleftharpoons$
   $$SO_4^{2-}(aq) + CH_3CO_2H(aq)$$
   (c) $[Co(H_2O)_6]^{2+}(aq) + CH_3CO_2^-(aq) \rightleftharpoons$
   $$[Co(H_2O)_5(OH)]^+(aq) + CH_3CO_2H(aq)$$

83. A monoprotic acid HX has $K_a = 1.3 \times 10^{-3}$. Calculate the equilibrium concentrations of HX and H_3O^+ and the pH for a 0.010 M solution of the acid.

84. Arrange the following 0.10 M solutions in order of increasing pH.
   (a) NaCl   (d) $NaCH_3CO_2$
   (b) NH_4Cl (e) KOH
   (c) HCl

85. *m*-Nitrophenol, a weak acid, can be used as a pH indicator because it is yellow at a pH above 8.6 and colorless at a pH below 6.8. If the pH of a 0.010 M solution of the compound is 3.44, calculate its pK_a.

HO

—NO₂

m-nitrophenol

86. The butylammonium ion, $C_4H_9NH_3^+$, has a K_a of 2.3×10^{-11}.

$$C_4H_9NH_3^+(aq) + H_2O(\ell) \rightleftharpoons H_3O^+(aq) + C_4H_9NH_2(aq)$$

   (a) Calculate K_b for the conjugate base, $C_4H_9NH_2$ (butylamine).
   (b) Place the butylammonium ion and its conjugate base in Table 17.3. Name an acid weaker than $C_4H_9NH_3^+$ and a base stronger than $C_4H_9NH_2$.
   (c) What is the pH of a 0.015 M solution of butylammonium chloride?

87. The local anesthetic novocaine is the hydrogen chloride salt of an organic base, procaine.

$$\underset{\text{procaine}}{C_{13}H_{20}N_2O_2(aq)} + HCl(aq) \longrightarrow \underset{\text{novocaine}}{[HC_{13}H_{20}N_2O_2]^+Cl^-(aq)}$$

The pK_a for novocaine is 8.85. What is the pH of a 0.0015 M solution of novocaine?

88. Pyridine is a weak organic base and readily forms a salt with hydrochloric acid.

$$\underset{\text{pyridine}}{C_5H_5N(aq)} + HCl(aq) \longrightarrow \underset{\text{pyridinium ion}}{C_5H_5NH^+(aq)} + Cl^-(aq)$$

What is the pH of a 0.025 M solution of pyridinium hydrochloride, $[C_5H_5NH^+]Cl^-$?

89. The base ethylamine ($CH_3CH_2NH_2$) has a K_b of 4.3×10^{-4}. A closely related base, ethanolamine ($HOCH_2CH_2NH_2$), has a K_b of 3.2×10^{-5}.
   (a) Which of the two bases is stronger?
   (b) Calculate the pH of a 0.10 M solution of the stronger base.

90. Chloroacetic acid, $ClCH_2CO_2H$, is a moderately weak acid ($K_a = 1.40 \times 10^{-3}$). If you dissolve 94.5 mg of the acid in water to give 125 mL of solution, what is the pH of the solution?

91. Saccharin ($HC_7H_4NO_3S$) is a weak acid with $pK_a = 2.32$ at 25 °C. It is used in the form of sodium saccharide, $NaC_7H_4NO_3S$. What is the pH of a 0.10 M solution of sodium saccharide at 25 °C?

saccharin

92. Given the following solutions:
   (a) 0.1 M NH_3 (e) 0.1 M NH_4Cl
   (b) 0.1 M Na_2CO_3 (f) 0.1 M $NaCH_3CO_2$
   (c) 0.1 M NaCl   (g) 0.1 M $NH_4CH_3CO_2$
   (d) 0.1 M CH_3CO_2H

   (i)   Which of the solutions are acidic?
   (ii) Which of the solutions are basic?
   (iii) Which of the solutions is most acidic?

93. For each of the following salts, predict whether a 0.10 M solution has a pH less than, equal to, or greater than 7.
    (a) $NaHSO_4$
    (f) $NaNO_3$
    (b) NH_4Br
    (g) Na_2HPO_4
    (c) $KClO_4$
    (h) $LiBr$
    (d) Na_2CO_3
    (i) $FeCl_3$
    (e) $(NH_4)_2S$
    Which solution has the highest pH? The lowest pH?

94. Nicotine, $C_{10}H_{14}N_2$, has two basic nitrogen atoms (page 795), and both can react with water.

$$Nic(aq) + H_2O(\ell) \rightleftharpoons NicH^+(aq) + OH^-(aq)$$

$$NicH^+(aq) + H_2O(\ell) \rightleftharpoons NicH_2^{2+}(aq) + OH^-(aq)$$

K_{b1} is 7.0×10^{-7} and K_{b2} is 1.1×10^{-10}. Calculate the approximate pH of a 0.020 M solution.

95. Oxalic acid is a relatively weak diprotic acid. Calculate the equilibrium constant for the reaction shown below from K_{a1} and K_{a2}. (See Appendix H for the required K_a values.)

$$H_2C_2O_4(aq) + 2 H_2O(\ell) \rightleftharpoons C_2O_4^{2-}(aq) + 2 H_3O^+(aq)$$

96. ▲ The equilibrium constant for the reaction of hydrochloric acid and ammonia is 1.8×10^9 (page 775). Confirm this value.

97. ▲ The equilibrium constant for the reaction of formic acid and sodium hydroxide is 1.8×10^{10} (page 774). Confirm this value.

98. ▲ Calculate the pH of the solution that results from mixing 25.0 mL of 0.14 M formic acid and 50.0 mL of 0.070 M sodium hydroxide.

99. ▲ To what volume should 1.00×10^2 mL of any weak acid, HA, with a concentration 0.20 M be diluted to double the percentage ionization?

100. ▲ The hydrogen phthalate ion, $C_8H_5O_4^-$, is a weak acid with $K_a = 3.91 \times 10^{-6}$.

$$C_8H_5O_4^-(aq) + H_2O(\ell) \rightleftharpoons C_8H_4O_4^{2-}(aq) + H_3O^+(aq)$$

What is the pH of a 0.050 M solution of potassium hydrogen phthalate, $KC_8H_5O_4$? *Note:* To find the pH for a solution of the anion, we must take into account that the ion is amphiprotic. It can be shown that, for most cases of amphiprotic ions, the H_3O^+ concentration is

$$[H_3O^+] = \sqrt{K_1 \times K_2}$$

For phthalic acid, $C_8H_6O_4$, K_1 is 1.12×10^{-3}, and K_2 is 3.91×10^{-6}.

101. ▲ You prepare a 0.10 M solution of oxalic acid, $H_2C_2O_4$. What molecules and ions exist in this solution? List them in order of decreasing concentration.

102. ▲ You mix 30.0 mL of 0.15 M NaOH with 30.0 mL of 0.15 M acetic acid. What molecules and ions exist in this solution? List them in order of decreasing concentration.

In the Laboratory

103. Describe an experiment that will allow you to place the following three bases in order of increasing base strength: NaCN, CH_3NH_2, Na_2CO_3.

104. The data below compare the strength of acetic acid with a related series of acids, where the H atoms of the CH_3 group in acetic acid are successively replaced by Br.

Acid	pK_a
CH_3CO_2H	4.74
$BrCH_2CO_2H$	2.90
Br_2CHCO_2H	1.39
Br_3CCO_2H	−0.147

(a) What trend in acid strength do you observe as H is successively replaced by Br? Can you suggest a reason for this trend?
(b) Suppose each of the acids above was present as a 0.10 M aqueous solution. Which would have the highest pH? The lowest pH?

105. ▲ You have three solutions labeled A, B, and C. You know only that each contains a different cation—Na^+, NH_4^+, or H_3O^+. Each has an anion that does not contribute to the solution pH (e.g., Cl^-). You also have two other solutions, Y and Z, each containing a different anion, Cl^- or OH^-, with a cation that does not influence solution pH (e.g., K^+). If equal amounts of B and Y are mixed, the result is an acidic solution. Mixing A and Z gives a neutral solution, whereas B and Z give a basic solution. Identify the five unknown solutions. (Adapted from D. H. Barouch: *Voyages in Conceptual Chemistry*, Boston, Jones and Bartlett, 1997.)

	Y	Z
A		neutral
B	acidic	basic
C		

106. A hydrogen atom in the organic base pyridine, C_5H_5N, can be substituted by various atoms or groups to give XC_5H_4N, where X is an atom such as Cl or a group such as CH_3. The following table gives K_a values for the conjugate acids of a variety of substituted pyridines.

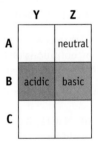

substituted pyridine (aq) + HCl(aq) ⟶ conjugate acid (aq) + Cl⁻(aq)

Atom or Group X	K_a of Conjugate Acid
NO_2	5.9×10^{-2}
Cl	1.5×10^{-4}
H	6.8×10^{-6}
CH_3	1.0×10^{-6}

(a) Suppose each conjugate acid is dissolved in sufficient water to give a 0.050 M solution. Which solution would have the highest pH? The lowest pH?

(b) Which of the substituted pyridines is the strongest Brønsted base? Which is the weakest Brønsted base?

107. Nicotinic acid, $C_6H_5NO_2$, is found in minute amounts in all living cells, but appreciable amounts occur in liver, yeast, milk, adrenal glands, white meat, and corn. Whole-wheat flour contains about 60. μg per gram of flour. One gram (1.00 g) of the acid dissolves in water to give 60. mL of solution having a pH of 2.70. What is the approximate value of K_a for the acid?

nicotinic acid

108. ▲ Equilibrium constants can be measured for the dissociation of Lewis acid–base complexes such as the dimethyl ether complex of BF_3, $(CH_3)_2O{\rightarrow}BF_3$. The value of K (here K_p) for the reaction is 0.17 at 125 °C.

$$(CH_3)_2O{\rightarrow}BF_3(g) \rightleftharpoons BF_3(g) + (CH_3)_2O(g)$$

(a) Describe each product as a Lewis acid or a Lewis base.

(b) If you place 1.00 g of the complex in a 565-mL flask at 125 °C, what is the total pressure in the flask? What are the partial pressures of the Lewis acid, the Lewis base, and the complex?

109. ▲ Sulfanilic acid, which is used in making dyes, is made by reacting aniline with sulfuric acid.

$H_2SO_4(aq) +$ [aniline structure] $\longrightarrow$ [sulfanilic acid structure, SO_3H] $+ H_2O(\ell)$

aniline   sulfanilic acid

(a) Is aniline a Brønsted base, a Lewis base, or both? Explain, using its possible reactions with HCl, BF_3, or other acid.

(b) Sulfanilic acid has a pK_a value of 3.23. The sodium salt of the acid, $Na(H_2NC_6H_4SO_3)$, is quite soluble in water. If you dissolve 1.25 g of the salt in water to give 125 mL of solution, what is the pH of the solution?

110. Amino acids are an important group of compounds (◀ page 492). At low pH, both the carboxylic acid group (—CO_2H) and the amine group (—NHR) are protonated. However, as the pH of the solution increases (say by adding base), the carboxylic acid proton is removed, usually at a pH between 2 and 3. In a middle range of pHs, therefore, the amine group is protonated, but the carboxylic acid group has lost the proton. (This is called a *zwitterion*.) At more basic pH values, the amine proton is dissociated.

[alanine cationic form] $\xrightarrow{pK_a = 2.4}$ [zwitterionic form]

alanine cationic form   zwitterionic form

$\xrightarrow{pK_a = 9.7}$ [anionic form]

anionic form

What is the pH of a 0.20 M solution of alanine hydrochloride, $[NH_3CHCH_3CO_2H]Cl$?

Summary and Conceptual Questions

The following questions may use concepts from this and previous chapters.

111. How can water be both a Brønsted base and a Lewis base? Can water be a Brønsted acid? A Lewis acid?

112. The nickel(II) ion exists as $[Ni(H_2O)_6]^{2+}$ in aqueous solution. Why is this solution acidic? As part of your answer, include a balanced equation depicting what happens when $[Ni(H_2O)_6]^{2+}$ interacts with water.

113. The halogens form three stable, weak acids, HOX.

Acid	pK_a
HOCl	7.46
HOBr	8.7
HOI	10.6

(a) Which is the strongest of these acids?

(b) Explain why the acid strength changes as the halogen atom is changed.

114. The acidity of the oxoacids was described on page 789, and a larger number of acids are listed in the table below.

$E(OH)_m$	pK_a	$EO(OH)_m$	pK_a	$EO_2(OH)_m$	pK_a	$EO_3(OH)_m$	pK_a
Very weak		**Weak**		**Strong**		**Very strong**	
Cl(OH)	7.5	ClO(OH)	2	$ClO_2(OH)$	−3	$ClO_3(OH)$	−10
Br(OH)	8.7	NO(OH)	3.4	$NO_2(OH)$	−1.4		
I(OH)	10.6	IO(OH)	1.6	$IO_2(OH)$	0.8		
$Si(OH)_4$	9.7	$SO(OH)_2$	1.8	$SO_2(OH)_2$	−3		
$Sb(OH)_3$	11.0	$SeO(OH)_2$	2.5	$SeO_2(OH)_2$	−3		
$As(OH)_3$	9.2	$AsO(OH)_3$	2.3				
		$PO(OH)_3$	2.1				
		$HPO(OH)_2$	1.8				
		$H_2PO(OH)$	2.0				

(a) What general trends do you see in these data?

(b) What has a greater effect on acidity, the number of O atoms bonded directly to the central atom E or the number of OH groups?

(c) Look at the acids based on Cl, N, and S. Is there a correlation of acidity with the formal charge on the central atom, E?

(d) The acid H_3PO_3 has a pK_a of 1.8, and this led to some insight into its structure. If the structure of the acid were $P(OH)_3$, what would be its predicted pK_a value? Given that this is a diprotic acid, which H atoms are lost as H^+ ions?

The acid H_3PO_3.

115. Perchloric acid behaves as an acid, even when it is dissolved in sulfuric acid.

(a) Write a balanced equation showing how perchloric acid can transfer a proton to sulfuric acid.

(b) Draw a Lewis electron dot structure for sulfuric acid. How can sulfuric acid function as a base?

116. You purchase a bottle of water. On checking its pH, you find that it is not neutral, as you might have expected. Instead, it is slightly acidic. Why?

117. Iodine, I_2, is much more soluble in an aqueous solution of potassium iodide, KI, than it is in pure water. The anion found in solution is I_3^-.

(a) Draw an electron dot structure for I_3^-.

(b) Write an equation for this reaction, indicating the Lewis acid and the Lewis base.

118. ▲ Uracil is a base found in RNA (◀ page 497). Indicate sites in the molecule where hydrogen bonding is possible or that are sites of Lewis basicity.

uracil

119. Chemists often refer to the *degree of ionization* of a weak acid or base and give it the symbol α. The equilibrium constant in terms of α and C_o, the initial acid or base concentration, is given by the useful equation

$$K = \frac{\alpha^2 C_o}{(1 - \alpha)}$$

As an example, the degree of ionization for 0.010 M acetic acid is 0.013.

(a) Show how we can arrive at the general equation given above.

(b) Calculate the degree of ionization for the ammonium ion in 0.10 M NH_4Cl.

120. ▲ Exploring the degree of ionization equation in Study Question 119:

(a) Calculate the degree of ionization, α, for formic acid at the following concentrations: 0.0100 M, 0.0200 M, 0.0400 M, 0.100 M, 0.200 M, 0.400 M, 1.00 M, 2.00 M, and 4.00 M.

(b) Plot the results of the calculation as α versus formic acid concentration. Is there a linear relationship? If not, try plotting the logarithm of C_o versus α.

(c) What can you conclude about the relationship of the degree of ionization and the initial acid or base concentration?

121. ▲ Consider a salt of a weak base and a weak acid such as ammonium cyanide. Both the NH_4^+ and CN^- ions interact with water in aqueous solution, but the net reaction can be considered as a proton transfer from NH_4^+ to CN^-.

$$NH_4^+(aq) + CN^-(aq) \rightleftharpoons NH_3(aq) + HCN(aq)$$

(a) Show that the equilibrium constant for this reaction, K_{net}, is

$$K_{net} = \frac{K_w}{K_a K_b}$$

where K_a is the ionization constant for the weak acid HCN and K_b is the constant for the weak base NH_3.

(b) Calculate K_{net} values for each of the following: NH_4CN, $NH_4CH_3CO_2$, and NH_4F. Which salt has the largest value of K_{net} and why?

(c) Predict whether a solution of each of the compounds in (b) is acidic or basic. Explain how you made this prediction. (You do not need a calculation to make this prediction.)

Applying Chemical Principles

The Leveling Effect, Nonaqueous Solvents, and Superacids

What is the strongest Brønsted acid that can exist in water? The answer is the hydronium ion. Although the common strong acids (HCl, HBr, HI, HNO_3, $HClO_4$, and H_2SO_4) are all stronger acids than H_3O^+, these acids ionize completely in water. The result is that all Brønsted acids with acidities above a certain value are equally acidic in water and, thus, their acid strength is indistinguishable. This is referred to as the *leveling effect* of water.

Similarly, the strongest base that can exist in water is OH^-. Any base that is stronger than OH^- will react completely with water to give OH^-. The amide ion, NH_2^-, and the oxide ion, O^{2-}, both stronger bases than OH^-, react completely with water, giving OH^-.

Although strong acids behave identically in water, they are not equally strong. One means of differentiating the strengths of these acids is to measure the degree of their ionization in solvents other than water. These solvents, like water, must be Brønsted bases. Additionally, the solvents must be weaker bases than water so that they are not fully protonated by a strong acid. One such solvent is acetic acid. Pure acetic acid—known as *glacial acetic acid*—is similar to water in that it can both donate or accept protons. Dissolution of hydrochloric acid in acetic acid, for example, yields the following chemical reaction:

$$HCl + CH_3CO_2H \rightleftharpoons CH_3CO_2H_2^+ + Cl^-$$

Unlike the ionization of HCl in water, this reaction does not go to completion. The pK value of this reaction is 8.8. Two other important acids, $HClO_4$ and H_2SO_4 (first proton only), have pK values of 5.3 and 6.8, respectively.

Other acids are even stronger, and are often called *superacids*. One superacid is fluorosulfonic acid (HSO_3F), which is about 1000 times stronger than sulfuric acid. Even this acid pales in comparison to a mixture of HSO_3F and SbF_5, which, depending on the concentrations, may be over 10^{16} times stronger than 100% sulfuric acid. It is sold under a suitable name, "Magic Acid."

Questions:

1. Convert the pK values to K values for the ionization of HCl, $HClO_4$, and H_2SO_4 in glacial acetic acid. Rank these acids in order from strongest to weakest.

George Olah (1927-present). Much of the early research on superacids was done by Olah, and he received the Nobel Prize in chemistry for this work in 1994.

2. Other solvents also undergo autoionization.
   (a) Write a chemical equation for the autoionization of glacial acetic acid.
   (b) The equilibrium constant for the autoionization of glacial acetic acid is 3.2×10^{-15} at 25°C. Determine the concentration of $[CH_3CO_2H_2]^+$ in acetic acid at 25°C.

3. Write an equation for the reaction of the amide ion (a stronger base than OH^-) and water. Does the equilibrium favor products or reactants?

4. Will a solution of $HClO_4$ in glacial acetic acid be a strong conductor of electricity, a weak conductor, or a nonconductor?

5. To measure the relative strengths of bases stronger than OH^-, it is necessary to choose a solvent that is a weaker acid than water. One such solvent is liquid ammonia.
   (a) Write a chemical equation for the autoionization of ammonia.
   (b) What is the strongest acid and base that can exist in liquid ammonia?
   (c) Will a solution of HCl in liquid ammonia be a strong electrical conductor, a weak conductor, or a nonconductor?
   (d) Oxide ion (O^{2-}) is a stronger base than the amide ion (NH_2^-). Write an equation for the reaction of O^{2-} with NH_3 in liquid ammonia. Will the equilibrium favor products or reactants?

18 Principles of Chemical Reactivity: Other Aspects of Aqueous Equilibria

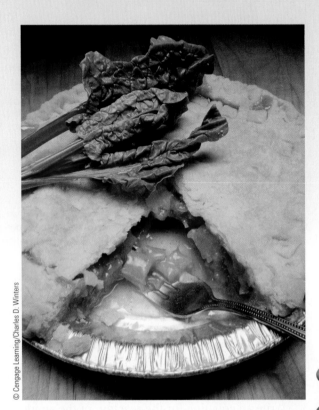

© Cengage Learning/Charles D. Winters

Nature's Acids Many people grow rhubarb in gardens because the stalks of the plant, when stewed with sugar, make a wonderful dessert or filling for a pie or tart. But the leaves can make you sick! Why?

Rhubarb leaves are a source of at least seven organic acids, among them acetic and citric acids. But the most abundant is oxalic acid, $H_2C_2O_4$.

$$H_2O(\ell) + H_2C_2O_4(aq) \rightleftharpoons H_3O^+(aq) + HC_2O_4^-(aq)$$

$$H_2O(\ell) + HC_2O_4^-(aq) \rightleftharpoons H_3O^+(aq) + C_2O_4^{2-}(aq)$$

Rhubarb leaves contain between 0.1% and 1.4% by weight oxalic acid, while other leafy vegetables such as cabbage, spinach, and beet tops have lesser amounts.

While oxalic acid and other acids give the tart taste many of us enjoy with rhubarb, there is a problem with ingesting it: Oxalic acid interferes with essential elements in the body such as iron, magnesium, and, especially, calcium. The Ca^{2+} ion and oxalic acid react to form insoluble calcium oxalate, CaC_2O_4.

$$Ca^{2+}(aq) + H_2C_2O_4(aq) + 2\ H_2O(\ell) \rightarrow CaC_2O_4(s) + 2\ H_3O^+(aq)$$

Not only does this effectively remove calcium ions from the body, but calcium oxalate crystals can also grow into painful kidney and bladder stones. Because of this, people susceptible to kidney stones are put on a low-oxalic acid diet. Such people also have to be careful of taking too much vitamin C, a compound that can be turned into oxalic acid in the body. People have died from accidentally drinking antifreeze because the ethylene glycol in the antifreeze is converted to oxalic acid in the body. Symptoms of oxalic acid poisoning include nausea, vomiting, abdominal pain, and hemorrhages.

Because oxalic acid also occurs in other edible substances, including cocoa, peanuts, and tea, the average person consumes about 150 mg of oxalic acid a day. But will it kill you? For a person weighing about 145 pounds (65.7 kg), the lethal dose is around 24 grams of pure oxalic acid. You would have to eat a field of rhubarb leaves or drink an ocean of tea to come close to a fatal dose of oxalic acid. What would happen first, however, is that you may have severe diarrhea. Your gut recognizes oxalic acid as something to be eliminated and is stimulated to get rid of it.

In spite of the minor health risk from eating too much rhubarb, this plant and others have been cultivated for thousands of years for their healthful properties. The Chinese particularly have used rhubarb in traditional medicine for centuries. Indeed, it was so important that emperors of China in the 18th and 19th centuries forbade its export. Rhubarb was also cultivated in Russia and later in England. It made first its appearance in the United States in about 1800.

When you enjoy a slice of rhubarb pie, think about the topics in this chapter: the chemistry of acids and bases and of insoluble substances.

Questions:

1. Suppose you eat 28 grams of rhubarb leaves with an oxalic acid content of 1.2% by weight.
   (a) What volume of 0.25 M NaOH is required to titrate completely the oxalic acid in the leaves?
   (b) What mass of calcium oxalate could be formed from the oxalic acid in these leaves?
2. The solubility product constant of calcium oxalate is estimated to be 4×10^{-9}. What is its solubility in grams per liter?

Answers to these questions are available in Appendix N.

CHAPTER GOALS

See Chapter Goals Revisited (page 846) for Study Questions keyed to these goals.

- Understand the common ion effect.

- Understand the control of pH in aqueous solutions with buffers.

- Evaluate the pH in the course of acid–base titrations.

- Apply chemical equilibrium concepts to the solubility of ionic compounds.

I n Chapter 3, we described four fundamental types of chemical reactions: acid–base reactions, precipitation reactions, gas-forming reactions, and oxidation-reduction reactions. In the present chapter, we want to apply the principles of chemical equilibria to a further understanding the first two kinds of reactions.

With regard to acid–base reactions, we are looking for answers to the following questions:

- How can we control the pH in a solution?
- What happens when an acid and base are mixed in any amount?

Precipitation reactions can also be understood in terms of chemical equilibria. The following questions are discussed in this chapter:

- If aqueous solutions of two ionic compounds are mixed, will precipitation occur?
- To what extent does an "insoluble" substance actually dissolve?
- What chemical reactions can be used to dissolve a precipitate?

18.1 The Common Ion Effect

In the previous chapter, we looked at the behavior of weak acids and bases in aqueous solution. But what happens to the pH of an acetic acid solution to which you added a significant concentration of its conjugate base, the acetate ion? The answer is that the pH of such a solution—weak acid/conjugate base or weak base/conjugate acid—is different than the pH of a solution of the weak acid or base by itself. The effect on the pH that is produced by having a significant concentration of acetate ion in an acetic acid solution, for example, is called the **common ion effect**. The name comes from the fact that the added acetate ion is "common" to the ionization equilibrium reaction of acetic acid.

$$CH_3CO_2H(aq) + H_2O(\ell) \rightleftharpoons H_3O^+(aq) + CH_3CO_2^-(aq)$$

We want to explore this aspect of acid–base chemistry here because it will be important in understanding *buffer solutions*, as you shall see in Section 18.2.

How does the common ion effect work (Figure 18.1)? If 1.0 L of a 0.25 M acetic acid solution has a pH of 2.67, what is the pH after adding 0.10 mol of sodium acetate? Sodium acetate, $NaCH_3CO_2$, is 100% dissociated into its ions, Na^+ and

FIGURE 18.1 The common ion effect. Approximately equal amounts of acetic acid (left flask, pH about 2.7) and sodium acetate, a base (right flask, pH about 9), were mixed in the beaker. The pH meter shows that the resulting solution in the beaker has a lower hydronium ion concentration (a pH of about 5) than the acetic acid solution, owing to the presence of acetate ion, the conjugate base of the acid and an ion common to the ionization reaction of the acid. (The acid and base solutions each had about the same concentration. Each solution contains universal indicator. This dye is red in low pH, yellow in slightly acidic media, and green in neutral to weakly basic media.)

Aqueous acetic acid pH 2.7

Aqueous sodium acetate pH 9

Mixture of acetic acid and sodium acetate

$CH_3CO_2^-$, in water. Sodium ion has no effect on the pH of a solution (◀ Table 17.4 and Example 17.2). Thus, the important components of the solution are the weak acid (CH_3CO_2H) and its conjugate base ($CH_3CO_2^-$). Assume the acid ionizes to give H_3O^+ and $CH_3CO_2^-$, both in the amount x. This means that, relative to their initial concentrations, CH_3CO_2H decreases in concentration slightly (by an amount x) and $CH_3CO_2^-$ increases slightly (by an amount x).

● **The Common Ion Effect** In this ICE table, the first row (Initial) reflects the assumption that no ionization of the acid (or hydrolysis of the conjugate base) has yet occurred. Ionization of the acid in the presence of the conjugate base then produces x mol/L of hydronium ion and x mol/L more of the conjugate base.

Equation	CH_3CO_2H	+	H_2O	⇌	H_3O^+	+	$CH_3CO_2^-$
Initial (M)	0.25				0		0.10
Change (M)	$-x$				$+x$		$+x$
Equilibrium (M)	$(0.25 - x)$				x		$0.10 + x$

Because we have been able to define the equilibrium concentrations of acid and conjugate base and we know K_a, the hydronium ion concentration ($= x$) can be calculated from the usual equilibrium constant expression.

$$K_a = 1.8 \times 10^{-5} = \frac{[H_3O^+][CH_3CO_2^-]}{[CH_3CO_2H]} = \frac{(x)(0.10 + x)}{0.25 - x}$$

Now, because acetic acid is a weak acid and because it is ionizing in the presence of a significant concentration of its conjugate base, let us assume x is quite small. That is, it is reasonable to assume that $(0.10 + x)M \approx 0.10$ M and that $(0.25 - x)M \approx 0.25$ M. This leads to the "approximate" expression.

$$K_a = 1.8 \times 10^{-5} = \frac{[H_3O^+][CH_3CO_2^-]}{[CH_3CO_2H]} = \frac{(x)(0.10)}{0.25}$$

Solving this, we find that $x = [H_3O^+] = 4.5 \times 10^{-5}$ M and the pH is 4.35.

● **Equilibrium Constants and Temperature** Unless specified otherwise, all equilibrium constants and all calculations in this chapter are at 25 °C.

Without added $NaCH_3CO_2$, which provides the "common ion" $CH_3CO_2^-$, you can calculate that ionization of 0.25 M acetic acid will produce H_3O^+ and $CH_3CO_2^-$ ions in a concentration of 0.0021 M (to give a pH of 2.67). Le Chatelier's principle, however, predicts that the added common ion causes the reaction to proceed less far to the right. Hence, as we have found, $x = [H_3O^+]$ is less than 0.0021 M in the presence of added acetate ion. (Finally, note that the simplifying assumptions were valid.)

⬤WL   INTERACTIVE EXAMPLE 18.1   Reaction of Lactic Acid with a
Deficiency of Sodium Hydroxide

Problem What is the pH of the solution that results from adding 25.0 mL of 0.0500 M NaOH to 25.0 mL of 0.100 M lactic acid? (K_a for lactic acid $= 1.4 \times 10^{-4}$)

$$H_3C-\overset{\overset{\displaystyle H}{|}}{\underset{\underset{\displaystyle OH}{|}}{C}}-\overset{\overset{\displaystyle O}{\|}}{C}-O-H(aq) + OH^-(aq) \rightleftharpoons H_2O(\ell) + H_3C-\overset{\overset{\displaystyle H}{|}}{\underset{\underset{\displaystyle OH}{|}}{C}}-\overset{\overset{\displaystyle O}{\|}}{C}-O^-(aq)$$

lactic acid ($HC_3H_5O_3$)
$K_a = 1.4 \times 10^{-4}$

lactate ion ($C_3H_5O_3^-$)

What Do You Know? You know the amounts of the acid and base (from the volume and concentration of each), and you know the ionization constant for the weak acid.

Strategy There are two parts to this problem: a stoichiometry problem followed by an equilibrium problem.

Part 1: *Stoichiometry Problem*

(a) Work a limiting reactant problem (in moles) to determine the amounts of lactic acid and lactate remaining after the reaction between lactic acid and sodium hydroxide.

(b) Calculate the concentrations of lactic acid and lactate ion that are present following the reaction of lactic acid with NaOH.

Part 2: *Equilibrium Problem*

(a) Set up an ICE table where the initial acid and conjugate base concentrations are known and the changes in the amount of acid consumed and amount of conjugate base produced are defined as x.

(b) Insert the equilibrium concentrations in the K_a expression for lactic acid and solve for x.

(c) Calculate the pH from the equilibrium hydronium ion concentration ($= x$).

Solution

Part 1: *Stoichiometry Problem*

(a) Amounts of NaOH and lactic acid used in the reaction

$$(0.0250 \text{ L NaOH})(0.0500 \text{ mol/L}) = 1.25 \times 10^{-3} \text{ mol NaOH}$$

$$(0.0250 \text{ L lactic acid})(0.100 \text{ mol/L}) = 2.50 \times 10^{-3} \text{ mol lactic acid}$$

(b) Amount of lactate ion produced by the acid–base reaction

Recognizing that NaOH is the limiting reactant, we have

$$(1.25 \times 10^{-3} \text{ mol NaOH})\left(\frac{1 \text{ mol lactate ion}}{1 \text{ mol NaOH}}\right) = 1.25 \times 10^{-3} \text{ mol lactate ion produced}$$

(c) Amount of lactic acid consumed

$$(1.25 \times 10^{-3} \text{ mol NaOH})\left(\frac{1 \text{ mol lactic acid}}{1 \text{ mol NaOH}}\right) = 1.25 \times 10^{-3} \text{ mol lactic acid consumed}$$

(d) Amount of lactic acid remaining when reaction is complete.

$$2.50 \times 10^{-3} \text{ mol lactic acid available} - 1.25 \times 10^{-3} \text{ mol lactic acid consumed}$$

$$= 1.25 \times 10^{-3} \text{ mol lactic acid remaining}$$

(e) Concentrations of lactic acid and lactate ion after reaction. Note that the total solution volume after reaction is 50.0 mL or 0.0500 L.

$$[\text{Lactic acid}] = \frac{1.25 \times 10^{-3} \text{ mol lactic acid}}{0.0500 \text{ L}} = 2.50 \times 10^{-2} \text{ M}$$

Strategy Map 18.1

PROBLEM

Calculate **pH** after combining solutions of **NaOH** and **lactic acid.**

↓

DATA/INFORMATION KNOWN

• Solution concentrations
• Solution volumes
• Value of acid K_a

STEP 1. Stoichiometry problem.

Concentrations of **lactic acid** and **lactate ion** after acid-base reaction

STEP 2. Enter **equilibrium concentrations** in ICE table.

At equilibrium:
$[H_3O^+] = x$
$[\text{Lactic acid}] = $ original conc. $- x$
$[\text{Lactate ion}] = $ original conc. $+ x$

STEP 3. Enter **equilibrium concentrations** in K_a.

K_a **expression** with equilibrium concentrations in terms of **x**

STEP 4. Solve K_a **expression** for **x**.

Value of $[H_3O^+]$

STEP 5. Convert $[H_3O^+]$ to **pH.**

pH of solution

Because the amount of lactic acid remaining is the same as the amount of lactate ion produced, we have

$$[\text{Lactic acid}] = [\text{lactate ion}] = 2.50 \times 10^{-2}\ M$$

Part 2: *Equilibrium Problem*

The concentrations just determined are used as the initial concentrations in an ICE table.

Equilibrium	$HC_3H_5O_3 + H_2O$	$\rightleftharpoons$	H_3O^+	+	$C_3H_5O_3^-$
Initial (M)	0.0250		0		0.0250
Change (M)	$-x$		$+x$		$+x$
Equilibrium (M)	$(0.0250 - x)$		x		$(0.0250 + x)$

Substituting the concentrations into the equilibrium expression, we have

$$K_a\ (\text{lactic acid}) = 1.4 \times 10^{-4} = \frac{[H_3O^+][C_3H_5O_2^-]}{[HC_3H_5O_2]} = \frac{(x)(0.0250 + x)}{0.0250 - x}$$

Making the assumption that x is small with respect to 0.0250 M, we see that

$$K_a = 1.4 \times 10^{-4}\ M = x = [H_3O^+], \text{ which gives a pH of } 3.85.$$

Think about Your Answer There are several final points to be made:

- Our assumption that $x \ll 0.0250$ is valid.

- By a separate calculation, we can show that a 0.025 M lactic acid solution has a pH of 2.73. The presence of 0.025 M lactate ion (a Brønsted base) in this solution has resulted in an increase of the pH to 3.85

- Here a base was added to the acidic solution. A useful observation is that *adding base to any solution will always result in an increase in pH.*

Check Your Understanding

You have a 0.30 M solution of formic acid (HCO_2H) and have added enough sodium formate ($NaHCO_2$) to make the solution 0.10 M in the salt. Calculate the pH of the formic acid solution before and after adding solid sodium formate.

> **REVIEW & CHECK FOR SECTION 18.1**
>
> What is the pH of the solution that results from adding 30.0 mL of 0.100 M NaOH to 45.0 mL of 0.100 M acetic acid?
>
> (a) 2.87 (b) 5.05 (c) 7.00

Module 23: Understanding Acid–Base Buffers covers concepts in this section.

18.2 Controlling pH: Buffer Solutions

The addition of a small quantity of strong acid or base, say 0.010 mol, to a liter of human blood leads to a change in pH of only about 0.1 pH units from the normal pH of about 7.4. In comparison, if you add 0.010 mol of HCl to 1.0 L of pure water, the pH drops from 7 to 2. Addition of 0.010 mol of NaOH to pure water increases the pH from 7 to 12. Blood, and many other body fluids, are said to be buffered. A **buffer** causes solutions to be resistant to a change in pH when a strong acid or base is added (Figure 18.2).

There are two requirements for a buffer:

- Two substances are needed: an acid capable of reacting with added OH^- ions and a base that can consume added H_3O^+ ions.
- The acid and base must not react with each another.

FIGURE 18.2 Buffer solutions.

Before	After adding 0.10 M HCl

(a) The pH electrode is indicating the pH of water that contains a trace of acid (and bromphenol blue acid–base indicator). The solution at the left is a buffer solution with a pH of about 7. (It also contains bromphenol blue dye.)

(b) When 5 mL of 0.10 M HCl is added to each solution, the pH of the water drops several units, whereas the pH of the buffer stays essentially constant, as implied by the fact that the indicator color does not change.

These requirements mean a buffer is usually prepared from a conjugate acid–base pair: (1) a weak acid and its conjugate base (acetic acid and acetate ion, for example), or (2) a weak base and its conjugate acid (ammonia and ammonium ion, for example). Some buffers commonly used in the laboratory are given in Table 18.1.

To see how a buffer works, consider an acetic acid/acetate ion buffer. Acetic acid, a weak acid, is needed to consume any added hydroxide ions.

$$CH_3CO_2H(aq) + OH^-(aq) \rightleftharpoons CH_3CO_2^-(aq) + H_2O(\ell) \qquad K = 1.8 \times 10^9$$

The equilibrium constant for the reaction is very large because OH^- is a much stronger base than acetate ion, $CH_3CO_2^-$ (◄ Section 17.6 and Table 17.3). This means that any OH^- entering the solution from an outside source is consumed completely. In a similar way, any hydronium ion added to the solution reacts with the acetate ion present in the buffer.

$$H_3O^+(aq) + CH_3CO_2^-(aq) \rightleftharpoons H_2O(\ell) + CH_3CO_2H(aq) \qquad K = 5.6 \times 10^4$$

The equilibrium constant for this reaction is also quite large because H_3O^+ is a much stronger acid than CH_3CO_2H.

The next several examples illustrate how to calculate the pH of a buffer solution, how to prepare a buffer, and how a buffer can control the pH of a solution.

● **Buffers and the Common Ion Effect** The common ion effect is observed for an acid (or base) ionizing in the presence of its conjugate base (or acid). A buffer is a solution of an acid, for example, and its conjugate base.

Table 18.1 **Some Commonly Used Buffer Systems**

Weak Acid	Conjugate Base	Acid K_a (pK_a)	Useful pH Range
Phthalic acid, $C_6H_4(CO_2H)_2$	Hydrogen phthalate ion, $C_6H_4(CO_2H)(CO_2)^-$	1.3×10^{-3} (2.89)	1.9–3.9
Acetic acid, CH_3CO_2H	Acetate ion, $CH_3CO_2^-$	1.8×10^{-5} (4.74)	3.7–5.8
Dihydrogen phosphate ion, $H_2PO_4^-$	Hydrogen phosphate ion, HPO_4^{2-}	6.2×10^{-8} (7.21)	6.2–8.2
Hydrogen phosphate ion, HPO_4^{2-}	Phosphate ion, PO_4^{3-}	3.6×10^{-13} (12.44)	11.4–13.4

Strategy Map 18.2

PROBLEM

Calculate **pH** of a **buffer solution.**

DATA/INFORMATION KNOWN

- Concentration of **weak acid**
- Concentration of **conjugate base**
- Value of acid K_a

STEP 1. Write **balanced equation** and K_a **expression**, and set up **ICE table.**

K_a expression and ICE table

STEP 2. Enter **equilibrium concentrations** in ICE table.

At equilibrium:
$[H_3O^+] = x$
$[\text{Weak acid}]$ = original conc. $- x$
$[\text{Conjugate base}]$ = original conc. $+ x$

STEP 3. Enter **equilibrium concentrations** in K_a.

K_a **expression** with equilibrium concentrations in terms of x

STEP 4. Solve K_a **expression** for x.

Value of $[H_3O^+]$

STEP 5. Convert $[H_3O^+]$ to **pH.**

pH of solution

◉WL INTERACTIVE EXAMPLE 18.2 pH of a Buffer Solution

Problem What is the pH of an acetic acid/sodium acetate buffer with $[CH_3CO_2H] = 0.700$ M and $[CH_3CO_2^-] = 0.600$ M?

What Do You Know? The hydronium ion concentration (and so the pH) of a buffer can be calculated if you know concentrations of the weak acid, its conjugate base, and K_a, as is the case here.

Strategy

- Write the balanced equation and the equilibrium constant expression.

- Set up an ICE table where the initial concentrations of acid and conjugate base are known, and the change in their concentrations is designated by x.

- Use the K_a expression to solve for the hydronium ion concentration (as in Example 17.5).

Solution

Equilibrium	CH_3CO_2H + H_2O	$\rightleftharpoons$	H_3O^+	+	$CH_3CO_2^-$
Initial (M)	0.700		0		0.600
Change (M)	$-x$		$+x$		$+x$
Equilibrium (M)	$0.700 - x$		x		$0.600 + x$

The appropriate equilibrium constant expression is

$$K_a = 1.8 \times 10^{-5} = \frac{[H_3O^+][CH_3CO_2^-]}{[CH_3CO_2H]} = \frac{(x)(0.600 + x)}{0.700 - x}$$

As explained on page 808, the value of x will be very small with respect to 0.700 or 0.600, so we can use the "approximate expression" to find x, the hydronium ion concentration.

$$K_a = 1.8 \times 10^{-5} = \frac{[H_3O^+][CH_3CO_2^-]}{[CH_3CO_2H]} = \frac{(x)(0.600)}{0.700}$$

$$x = 2.1 \times 10^{-5} \text{ M}$$

$$pH = -\log (2.1 \times 10^{-5}) = 4.68$$

Think about Your Answer The pH of the buffer has a value between the pH of 0.700 M acetic acid (2.45) and 0.600 M sodium acetate (9.26).

Check Your Understanding

What is the pH of a buffer solution composed of 0.50 M formic acid (HCO_2H) and 0.70 M sodium formate ($NaHCO_2$)?

General Expressions for Buffer Solutions

In Example 18.2, we found the hydronium ion concentration of the acetic acid/acetate ion buffer solution by solving for x in the equation

$$K_a = 1.8 \times 10^{-5} = \frac{[H_3O^+][CH_3CO_2^-]}{[CH_3CO_2H]} = \frac{(x)(0.600)}{0.700}$$

If this equation is rearranged, we have a useful equation that can help you better understand how a buffer works.

$$[H_3O^+] = \frac{[CH_3CO_2H]}{[CH_3CO_2^-]} \times K_a$$

That is, the hydronium ion concentration in the acetic acid/acetate ion buffer is given by the ratio of the acid and conjugate base concentrations times the acid ionization constant. Indeed, this is true for all solutions of *a weak acid and its conjugate base.*

$$[H_3O^+] = \frac{[\text{acid}]}{[\text{conjugate base}]} \times K_a \tag{18.1}$$

It is often convenient to use Equation 18.1 in a different form. If we take the negative logarithm of each side of the equation, we have

$$-\log[H_3O^+] = \left\{-\log\frac{[acid]}{[conjugate\ base]}\right\} + \left(-\log K_a\right)$$

You know that $-\log[H_3O^+]$ is defined as pH, and $-\log K_a$ is defined as pK_a (◀ Sections 17.3 and 17.4). Furthermore, because

$$-\log\frac{[acid]}{[conjugate\ base]} = +\log\frac{[conjugate\ base]}{[acid]}$$

the preceding equation can be rewritten as

$$pH = pK_a + \log\frac{[conjugate\ base]}{[acid]} \qquad (18.2)$$

This equation is known as the **Henderson–Hasselbalch equation.**

Both Equations 18.1 and 18.2 show that *the pH of a buffer solution is controlled by two factors:*

* the strength of the acid (as expressed by K_a or pK_a)
* and the relative amounts of acid and conjugate base

The solution pH is established primarily by the value of K_a or pK_a, and the pH is fine-tuned by adjusting the acid-to-conjugate base ratio.

When the concentrations of conjugate base and acid are the same in a solution, the ratio [conjugate base]/[acid] is 1. The log of 1 is zero, so pH = pK_a under these circumstances. If there is more of the conjugate base in the solution than acid, for example, then pH > pK_a. Conversely, if there is more acid than conjugate base in solution, then pH < pK_a.

● **Buffer Solutions** You will find it generally useful to consider all buffer solutions as composed of a weak acid and its conjugate base. Suppose, for example, a buffer is composed of the weak base ammonia and its conjugate acid ammonium ion. The hydronium ion concentration can be found from Equation 18.1 or 18.2 by assuming the buffer is composed of the weak acid NH_4^+ and its conjugate base, NH_3.

● **pK_a and Using The Henderson–Hasselbalch Equation** Many handbooks of chemistry list acid ionization constants in terms of pK_a values, so the approximate pH values of possible buffer solutions are readily apparent.

EXAMPLE 18.3   Using the Henderson–Hasselbalch Equation

Problem Benzoic acid ($C_6H_5CO_2H$, 2.00 g) and sodium benzoate ($NaC_6H_5CO_2$, 2.00 g) are dissolved in enough water to make 1.00 L of solution. Calculate the pH of the solution using the Henderson–Hasselbalch equation.

What Do You Know? You know the masses of weak acid and conjugate base and the volume of solution. (From these you can calculate the concentrations of these reagents, which you need for the Henderson–Hasselbalch equation.) You also know the K_a for the weak acid (Table 17.3 or Appendix H), from which you can calculate the required pK_a for the acid.

Strategy Calculate the acid and conjugate base concentrations and substitute these into the Henderson–Hasselbalch equation along with the value of pK_a for the acid.

Solution

K_a for benzoic acid is 6.3×10^{-5}. Therefore, p$K_a = -\log(6.3 \times 10^{-5}) = 4.20$

Next, you need the concentrations of the acid (benzoic acid) and its conjugate base (benzoate ion).

$$2.00\ g\ benzoic\ acid \left(\frac{1\ mol}{122.1\ g}\right) = 0.0164\ mol\ benzoic\ acid$$

$$2.00\ g\ sodium\ benzoate \left(\frac{1\ mol}{144.1\ g}\right) = 0.0139\ mol\ sodium\ benzoate$$

Because the solution volume is 1.00 L, the concentrations are [benzoic acid] = 0.0164 M and [sodium benzoate] = 0.0139 M. Therefore, using Equation 18.2, you have

$$pH = 4.20 + \log\frac{0.0139}{0.0164} = 4.20 + \log(0.848) = 4.13$$

Think about Your Answer Notice that the pH is less than the pK_a because the concentration of acid is greater than the concentration of the conjugate base (and so the ratio of conjugate base to acid concentration is less than 1).

Check Your Understanding

Use the Henderson–Hasselbalch equation to calculate the pH of 1.00 L of a buffer solution containing 15.0 g of $NaHCO_3$ and 18.0 g of Na_2CO_3. (Consider this buffer as a solution of the weak acid HCO_3^- with CO_3^{2-} as its conjugate base.)

Preparing Buffer Solutions

To be useful, a buffer solution must have two characteristics:

- *pH Control:* It should control the pH at the desired value. The Henderson–Hasselbalch equation shows us how this can be done.

$$pH = pK_a + \log \frac{[\text{conjugate base}]}{[\text{acid}]}$$

  First, an acid is chosen whose pK_a (or K_a) is near the intended value of pH (or $[H_3O^+]$). Second, the exact value of pH (or $[H_3O^+]$) is then achieved by adjusting the acid-to-conjugate base ratio. (Example 18.4 illustrates this approach.)

- *Buffer capacity:* The buffer should have the ability to keep the pH approximately constant after the addition of reasonable amounts of acid and base. For example, the concentration of acetic acid in an acetic acid/acetate ion buffer must be sufficient to consume all the hydroxide ion that may be added and still control the pH (see Example 18.4). Buffers are usually prepared as 0.10 M to 1.0 M solutions of reagents. However, any buffer will lose its ability to moderate changes if too much strong acid or base is added.

EXAMPLE 18.4   Preparing a Buffer Solution

Problem You wish to prepare 1.0 L of a buffer solution with a pH of 4.30. A list of possible acids (and their conjugate bases) follows:

Acid	Conjugate Base	K_a	pK_a
HSO_4^-	SO_4^{2-}	1.2×10^{-2}	1.92
CH_3CO_2H	$CH_3CO_2^-$	1.8×10^{-5}	4.74
HCO_3^-	CO_3^{2-}	4.8×10^{-11}	10.32

Which combination should be selected, and what should be the ratio of acid to conjugate base?

What Do You Know? You know the desired pH of the buffer, and you have a list of possible acid/conjugate base combinations.

Strategy Use either the general equation for a buffer (Equation 18.1) or the Henderson–Hasselbalch equation (Equation 18.2). Equation 18.1 informs you that $[H_3O^+]$ should be close to the acid K_a value, and Equation 18.2 tells you that pH should be close to the acid pK_a value. Either will establish which acid you will use. Having decided which acid to use, convert pH to $[H_3O^+]$ to use Equation 18.1. If you use Equation 18.2, use the pK_a value in the table. Finally, calculate the ratio of acid to conjugate base.

Solution The hydronium ion concentration for the buffer is found from the targeted pH.

$$pH = 4.30, \text{ so } [H_3O^+] = 10^{-pH} = 10^{-4.30} = 5.0 \times 10^{-5} \text{ M}$$

Of the acids given, only acetic acid (CH_3CO_2H) has a K_a value close to that of the desired $[H_3O^+]$ (or a pK_a close to a pH of 4.30). Now you need only to adjust the ratio $[CH_3CO_2H]/[CH_3CO_2^-]$ to achieve the desired hydronium ion concentration.

$$[H_3O^+] = 5.0 \times 10^{-5} \text{ M} = \frac{[CH_3CO_2H]}{[CH_3CO_2^-]}(1.8 \times 10^{-5})$$

Rearrange this equation to find the ratio $[CH_3CO_2H]/[CH_3CO_2^-]$.

$$\frac{[CH_3CO_2H]}{[CH_3CO_2^-]} = \frac{[H_3O^+]}{K_a} = \frac{5.0 \times 10^{-5}}{1.8 \times 10^{-5}} = \frac{2.8 \text{ mol/L}}{1.0 \text{ mol/L}}$$

Therefore, if you add 0.28 mol of acetic acid and 0.10 mol of sodium acetate (or any other pair of molar quantities in the ratio 2.8/1) to enough water to prepare 1.0 L of solution, the buffer solution will have a pH of 4.30.

Think about Your Answer If you prefer to use the Henderson–Hasselbalch equation, you would have

$$pH = 4.30 = 4.74 + \log\frac{[CH_3CO_2^-]}{[CH_3CO_2H]}$$

$$\log\frac{[CH_3CO_2^-]}{[CH_3CO_2H]} = 4.30 - 4.74 = -0.44$$

$$\frac{[CH_3CO_2^-]}{[CH_3CO_2H]} = 10^{-0.44} = 0.36$$

The ratio of conjugate base to acid, $[CH_3CO_2^-]/[CH_3CO_2H]$, is 0.36. The reciprocal of this ratio {$= [CH_3CO_2H]/[CH_3CO_2^-] = 1/0.36$} is 2.8/1. This is the same result obtained previously using Equation 18.1.

Check Your Understanding

Using an acetic acid/sodium acetate buffer solution, what ratio of acid to conjugate base will you need to maintain the pH at 5.00? Describe how you would prepare such a solution.

Example 18.4 illustrates several important points concerning buffer solutions. The hydronium ion concentration depends not only on the K_a value of the acid but also on the ratio of acid and conjugate base concentrations. However, even though we write these ratios in terms of reagent concentrations, it is *the relative number of moles of acid and conjugate base that is important in determining the pH of a buffer solution.* Because both reagents are dissolved in the same solution, their concentrations depend on the same solution volume. In Example 18.4, the ratio 2.8/1 for acetic acid and sodium acetate implies that 2.8 times as many moles of acid were dissolved per liter as moles of sodium acetate.

$$\frac{[CH_3CO_2H]}{[CH_3CO_2^-]} = \frac{2.8 \text{ mol } CH_3CO_2H/L}{1.0 \text{ mol } CH_3CO_2^-/L} = \frac{2.8 \text{ mol } CH_3CO_2H}{1.0 \text{ mol } CH_3CO_2^-}$$

Notice that on dividing one concentration by the other, the volumes "cancel." This means that we only need to ensure that the ratio of moles of acid to moles of conjugate base is 2.8 to 1 in this example. The acid and its conjugate base could have been dissolved in any reasonable amount of water. This also means that *diluting a buffer solution will not change its pH.* Commercially available buffer solutions are often sold as premixed, dry reagents. To use them, you only need to mix the reagents in some volume of pure water (Figure 18.3).

© Cengage Learning/Charles D. Winters

FIGURE 18.3 A commercial buffer solution. The solid acid and conjugate base in the packet are mixed with water to give a solution with the indicated pH. The quantity of water used does not matter because the ratio [acid]/[conjugate base] does not depend on the solution volume. (However, if too much water is added, the acid and conjugate base concentrations will be too low, and the buffer capacity could be exceeded. Again, buffer solutions usually have solute concentrations around 0.1 M to 1.0 M.)

PROBLEM SOLVING TIP 18.1

Buffer Solutions

The following is a summary of important aspects of buffer solutions.

- A buffer resists changes in pH on adding small quantities of acid or base.
- A buffer consists of a weak acid and its conjugate base.
- The hydronium ion concentration of a buffer solution can be calculated from Equation 18.1,

$$[H_3O^+] = \frac{[acid]}{[conjugate\ base]} \times K_a$$

or the pH can be calculated from the Henderson–Hasselbalch equation (Equation 18.2).

$$pH = pK_a + \log\frac{[conjugate\ base]}{[acid]}$$

- The pH depends primarily on the K_a of the weak acid and secondarily on the relative amounts of acid and conjugate base.
- The function of the weak acid of a buffer is to consume added base, and the

function of the conjugate base is to consume added acid. Such reactions affect the relative quantities of weak acid and its conjugate base. Because this ratio of acid to its conjugate base has only a secondary effect on the pH, the pH can be maintained relatively constant.

- The buffer must have sufficient capacity to react with reasonable quantities of added acid or base.

How Does a Buffer Maintain pH?

Now let us explore quantitatively how a given buffer solution can maintain the pH of a solution on adding a small amount of strong acid.

EXAMPLE 18.5   How Does a Buffer Maintain a Constant pH?

Problem What is the change in pH when 1.00 mL of 1.00 M HCl is added to (1) 1.000 L of pure water and to (2) 1.000 L of acetic acid/sodium acetate buffer with $[CH_3CO_2H] = 0.700$ M and $[CH_3CO_2^-] = 0.600$ M? (The pH of this acetic acid/acetate ion buffer is 4.68. See Example 18.2.)

What Do You Know? You know HCl is a strong acid and ionizes completely to supply H_3O^+ ions. In the first problem, when HCl is added to pure water, the concentration of HCl in the solution determines the pH. In the second problem, the conjugate base of the weak acid will react with the added HCl. Therefore, you need to perform a stoichiometry calculation to determine the new weak acid/conjugate base concentrations before you can calculate the pH.

Strategy

Part 1: *involves two steps:*

- Find the H_3O^+ concentration when adding 1.00 mL of acid to 1.000 L of pure water.

- Convert the value of $[H_3O^+]$ for the dilute solution to pH.

Part 2: *involves three steps:*

- A stoichiometry calculation to find how the concentrations of acid and conjugate base change on adding H_3O^+

- An equilibrium calculation to find $[H_3O^+]$ for a buffer solution where the concentrations of CH_3CO_2H and $CH_3CO_2^-$ are slightly altered owing to the reaction of $CH_3CO_2^-$ with added H_3O^+

- Conversion of $[H_3O^+]$ to pH

Solution

Part 1: *Adding Acid to Pure Water*

1.00 mL of 1.00 M HCl represents 0.00100 mol of acid. If this is added to 1.000 L of pure water, the H_3O^+ concentration of the water changes from 10^{-7} to almost 10^{-3},

$$c_1 \times V_1 = c_2 \times V_2$$

$$(1.00\ M)(0.00100\ L) = c_2 \times (1.001\ L)$$

$$c_2 = [H_3O^+]\ in\ diluted\ solution = 9.99 \times 10^{-4}\ M$$

and so the pH falls from 7.00 to 3.00.

Part 2: *Adding Acid to an Acetic Acid/Acetate Buffer Solution*

HCl is a strong acid that is 100% ionized in water and supplies H_3O^+, which reacts completely with the base (acetate ion) in the buffer solution according to the following equation:

$$H_3O^+(aq) + CH_3CO_2^-(aq) \rightleftharpoons H_2O(\ell) + CH_3CO_2H(aq)$$

	H_3O^+ from Added HCl	$CH_3CO_2^-$ from Buffer	CH_3CO_2H from Buffer
Initial amount of acid or base (mol = $c \times V$)	0.00100	0.600	0.700
Change (mol)	−0.00100	−0.00100	+0.00100
After reaction (mol)	0	0.599	0.701
Concentrations after reaction (c = mol/V)	0	0.598	0.700

Because the added HCl reacts completely with acetate ion to produce acetic acid, the solution after this reaction (with $V = 1.001$ L) is once again a buffer containing only the weak acid and its salt. Now you only need to use Equation 18.1 (or the Henderson–Hasselbalch equation) to find $[H_3O^+]$ and the pH in the buffer solution as in Examples 18.2 and 18.3.

Equilibrium	CH_3CO_2H	+	H_2O	$\rightleftharpoons$	H_3O^+	+	$CH_3CO_2^-$
Initial (M)	0.700				0		0.598
Change (M)	−x				+x		+x
Equilibrium (M)	0.700 − x				x		0.598 +x

As usual, you can make the approximation that x, the concentration of H_3O^+ formed by ionizing acetic acid in the presence of acetate ion, is very small compared with 0.700 M or 0.598 M. Using Equation 18.1, you should get a pH of 4.68.

$$[H_3O^+] = x = \frac{[CH_3CO_2H]}{[CH_3CO_2^-]} \times K_a = \left(\frac{0.700 \text{ mol}}{0.598 \text{ mol}}\right)(1.8 \times 10^{-5}) = 2.1 \times 10^{-5} \text{ M}$$

$$pH = 4.68$$

Think about Your Answer Within the number of significant figures allowed, the pH of the buffer solution does not change after adding this amount of HCl. The buffer solution contains the conjugate base of the weak acid, and the base consumed the added HCl. In contrast, the pH changed by 4 units when the same amount of HCl was added to 1.0 L of pure water.

Check Your Understanding

Calculate the pH of 0.500 L of a buffer solution composed of 0.50 M formic acid (HCO_2H) and 0.70 M sodium formate ($NaHCO_2$) before and after adding 10.0 mL of 1.0 M HCl.

REVIEW & CHECK FOR SECTION 18.2

1. Which choice would be a good buffer solution?

   (a) 0.20 M HCN and 0.10 M KCN   (c) 0.20 M CH_3CO_2H and 0.10 M HCO_2H

   (b) 0.20 M HCl and 0.10 M KOH   (d) 0.10 HCl and 0.010 M KCl

2. If an acetic acid/sodium acetate buffer solution is prepared from 100. mL of 0.10 M acetic acid, what volume of 0.10 M sodium acetate must be added to have a pH of 4.00.

   (a) 100. mL   (b) 50. mL   (c) 36 mL   (d) 18 mL

3. What is the pH of a buffer composed of 100. mL of 0.20 M NH_4Cl and 200. mL of 0.10 M NH_3?

   (a) 4.85   (c) 7.00   (e) 10.05

   (b) 9.25   (d) 5.65

4. To prepare a buffer containing CH_3CO_2H and $NaCH_3CO_2$ and having a pH of 5, the ratio of the concentration of CH_3CO_2H to that of $NaCH_3CO_2$ should be about

(a) 1/1   (b) 1.8/1   (c) 1/1.8   (d) 5.0/1

18.3 Acid–Base Titrations

A titration is one of the most useful ways of determining accurately the quantity of an acid, a base, or some other substance in a mixture or of ascertaining the purity of a substance. You learned how to perform the stoichiometry calculations involved in titrations in Chapter 4 (◄ Section 4.7). In Chapter 17, we described the following points regarding acid–base reactions (◄ Section 17.7):

- The pH at the equivalence point of a strong acid–strong base titration is 7. The solution at the equivalence point is truly "neutral" *only* when a strong acid is titrated with a strong base and vice versa.

- ● **Equivalence Point** The equivalence point for a reaction is the point at which one reactant has been completely consumed by addition of another reactant. See page 183.

- If the substance being titrated is a weak acid or base, then the pH at the equivalence point is not 7 (◄ Table 17.5).
  (a) A weak acid titrated with strong base leads to pH > 7 at the equivalence point due to the conjugate base of the weak acid.
  (b) A weak base titrated with strong acid leads to pH < 7 at the equivalence point due to the conjugate acid of the weak base.

A knowledge of buffer solutions and how they work will now allow us to understand more fully how the pH changes in the course of an acid–base reaction.

● **Weak Acid–Weak Base Titrations** Titrations combining a weak acid and weak base are generally not done because the equivalence point often cannot be accurately judged.

Titration of a Strong Acid with a Strong Base

Figure 18.4 illustrates what happens to the pH as 0.100 M NaOH is slowly added to 50.0 mL of 0.100 M HCl.

$$HCl(aq) + NaOH(aq) \rightarrow NaCl(aq) + H_2O(\ell)$$

Net ionic equation: $H_3O^+(aq) + OH^-(aq) \rightarrow 2\ H_2O(\ell)$

Let us focus on four regions on this plot.

- pH of the initial solution
- pH as NaOH is added to the HCl solution before the equivalence point
- pH at the equivalence point
- pH after the equivalence point

Before beginning the titration, the 0.100 M solution of HCl has a pH of 1.00. As NaOH is added to the acid solution, the amount of HCl declines, and the acid remaining is dissolved in an ever-increasing volume of solution. Thus, $[H_3O^+]$ decreases,

FIGURE 18.4 The change in pH as a strong acid is titrated with a strong base. In this case, 50.0 mL of 0.100 M HCl is titrated with 0.100 M NaOH. The pH at the equivalence point is 7.0 for the reaction of a strong acid with a strong base.

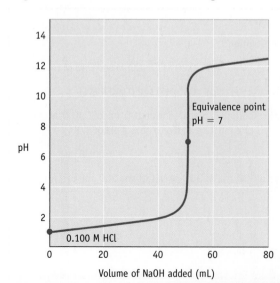

50.0 mL of 0.100 M HCl titrated with 0.100 M NaOH	
Volume of base added	pH
0.0	1.00
10.0	1.18
20.0	1.37
40.0	1.95
45.0	2.28
48.0	2.69
49.0	3.00
50.0	7.00
51.0	11.00
55.0	11.68
60.0	11.96
80.0	12.36
100.0	12.52
very large amount	13.00 (maximum)

CASE STUDY

Take a Deep Breath

Maintenance of pH is vital to the cells of all living organisms because enzyme activity is influenced by pH. The primary protection against harmful pH changes in cells is provided by buffer systems, which maintain the intracellular pH of most cells between 6.9 and 7.4. Two important biological buffer systems control pH in this range: the bicarbonate/carbonic acid system (HCO_3^-/H_2CO_3) and the phosphate system ($HPO_4^{2-}/H_2PO_4^-$).

The bicarbonate/carbonic acid buffer is important in blood plasma, where three equilibria are important.

$$CO_2(g) \rightleftharpoons CO_2(\text{dissolved})$$

$$CO_2(\text{dissolved}) + H_2O(\ell) \rightleftharpoons H_2CO_3(aq)$$

$$H_2CO_3(aq) + H_2O(\ell) \rightleftharpoons$$
$$H_3O^+(aq) + HCO_3^-(aq)$$

The overall equilibrium for the second and third steps has $pK_{\text{overall}} = 6.3$ at 37 °C, the temperature of the human body. Thus,

$$7.4 = 6.3 + \log\frac{[HCO_3^-]}{[CO_2(\text{dissolved})]}$$

Although the value of pK_{overall} is about 1 pH unit away from the blood pH, the natural partial pressure of CO_2 in the alveoli of the lungs (about 40 mm Hg) is sufficient to keep [CO_2(dissolved)] at about 1.2×10^{-3} M and [HCO_3^-] at about 1.5×10^{-2} M as required to maintain this pH.

If blood pH rises above about 7.45, you can suffer from a condition called *alkalosis*. *Respiratory alkalosis* can arise from hyperventilation when a person breathes quickly to expel CO_2 from the lungs. This has the effect of lowering the CO_2 concentration, which in turn leads to a lower H_3O^+ concentration and a higher pH. This same condition can also arise from severe anxiety or from an oxygen deficiency at high altitude. It can

© Cengage Learning/Charles D. Winters

ultimately lead to overexcitability of the central nervous system, muscle spasms, convulsions, and death. One way to treat acute respiratory alkalosis is to breathe into a paper bag. The CO_2 you exhale is recycled. This raises the blood CO_2 level and causes the equilibria above to shift to the right, thus raising the hydronium ion concentration and lowering the pH.

Metabolic alkalosis can occur if you take large amounts of sodium bicarbonate to treat stomach acid (which is mostly HCl at a pH of about 1 to 2). It also commonly occurs when a person vomits profusely. This depletes the body of hydrogen ions, which leads to an increase in bicarbonate ion concentration.

Athletes can use the H_2CO_3/HCO_3^- equilibrium to enhance their performance. Strenuous activity produces high levels of lactic acid, and this can lower blood pH and cause muscle cramps. To counteract this, athletes will prepare before a race by hyperventilating for some seconds to raise blood

pH, thereby helping to neutralize the acidity from the lactic acid.

Acidosis is the opposite of alkalosis. There was a case of a toddler who came to the hospital with viral gastroenteritis and *metabolic acidosis*. He had severe diarrhea, was dehydrated, and had a high rate of respiration. One function of the bicarbonate ion is to neutralize stomach acid in the intestines. However, because of his diarrhea, the toddler was losing bicarbonate ions in his stool, and his blood pH was too low. To compensate, the toddler was breathing rapidly and blowing off CO_2 through the lungs (the effect of which is to lower [H_3O^+] and raise the pH).

Respiratory acidosis results from a buildup of CO_2 in the body. This can be caused by pulmonary problems, by head injuries, or by drugs such as anesthetics and sedatives. It can be reversed by breathing rapidly and deeply. Doubling the breathing rate increases the blood pH by about 0.23 units.

Questions:
Phosphate ions are abundant in cells, both as the ions themselves and as important substituents on organic molecules. Most importantly, the pK_a for the $H_2PO_4^-$ ion is 7.20, which is very close to the high end of the normal pH range in the body.

$$H_2PO_4^-(aq) + H_2O(\ell) \rightleftharpoons$$
$$H_3O^+(aq) + HPO_4^{2-}(aq)$$

1. What should the ratio [HPO_4^{2-}]/[$H_2PO_4^-$] be to control the pH at 7.4?
2. A typical total phosphate concentration in a cell, [HPO_4^{2-}] + [$H_2PO_4^-$], is 2.0×10^{-2} M. What are the concentrations of HPO_4^{2-} and $H_2PO_4^-$ at pH 7.4?

Answers to these questions are available in Appendix N.

---

and the pH slowly increases. As an example, let us find the pH of the solution after 10.0 mL of 0.100 M NaOH has been added to 50.0 mL of 0.100 M HCl. Here, we set up a table to list the amounts of acid and base before reaction, the changes in those amounts, and the amounts remaining after reaction. Be sure to notice that the volume of the solution after reaction is the sum of the combined volumes of NaOH and HCl (60.0 mL or 0.0600 L in this case).

	$H_3O^+(aq)$	$+$	$OH^-(aq)$	$\rightarrow$	$2\ H_2O(\ell)$
Initial amount (mol = $c \times V$)	0.00500		0.00100		
Change (mol)	−0.00100		−0.00100		
After reaction (mol)	0.00400		0		
After reaction (c = mol/V)	0.00400 mol/0.0600 L		0		
	= 0.0667 M				

• **Titrations, Stoichiometry, and Limiting Reactants** In the titration of an acid with a base (as in Figure 18.4) the limiting reactant is the base before the equivalence point. After the equivalence point it will be the acid.

After addition of 10.0 mL of NaOH, the final solution has a hydronium ion concentration of 0.0667 M, and so the pH is

$$pH = -\log[H_3O^+] = -\log(0.0667) = 1.176$$

After 49.5 mL of base has been added—that is, just before the equivalence point—we can use the same approach to show that the pH is 3.3. The solution being titrated is still quite acidic, even very close to the equivalence point.

The pH of the equivalence point in an acid–base titration is the value at the steepest point in the vertical portion of the pH versus volume of titrant curve. (The **titrant** is the substance being added during the titration.) In the HCl/NaOH titration illustrated in Figure 18.4, you see that the pH increases very rapidly near the equivalence point. In fact, in this case the pH rises 7 units (the H_3O^+ concentration decreases by a factor of 10 million!) when only a drop or two of the NaOH solution is added, and the steepest point of the vertical portion of the curve is at a pH of 7.00.

> The pH of the solution at the equivalence point in a monoprotic strong acid–strong base reaction is always 7.00 (at 25 °C) because the solution contains a neutral salt.

After all of the HCl has been consumed and the slightest excess of NaOH has been added, the solution will be basic, and the pH will continue to increase as more NaOH is added (and the solution volume increases). For example, if we calculate the pH of the solution after 55.0 mL of 0.100 M NaOH has been added to 50.0 mL of 0.100 M HCl, we find

	$H_3O^+(aq)$	+	$OH^-(aq)$	→	$2 H_2O(\ell)$
Initial amount (mol = $c \times V$)	0.00500		0.00550		
Change (mol)	−0.00500		−0.00500		
After reaction (mol)	0		0.00050		
After reaction (c = mol/V)	0		0.00050 mol/0.1050 L = 0.0048 M		

At this point, the solution has a hydroxide ion concentration of 0.0048 M. Calculate the pOH from this value, then use this to calculate pH.

$$pOH = -\log[OH^-] = -\log(0.0048) = 2.32$$

$$pH = 14.00 - pOH = 11.68$$

Titration of a Weak Acid with a Strong Base

The titration of a weak acid with a strong base is somewhat different from the strong acid–strong base titration. Look carefully at the curve for the titration of 100.0 mL of 0.100 M acetic acid with 0.100 M NaOH (Figure 18.5),

$$CH_3CO_2H(aq) + NaOH(aq) \rightarrow NaCH_3CO_2(aq) + H_2O(\ell)$$

and focus on three points on this curve:

- *The pH before titration begins.* The pH before any base is added can be calculated from the weak acid K_a value and the acid concentration (◀ Example 17.5).
- *The pH at the equivalence point.* At the equivalence point, the solution contains only sodium acetate, the CH_3CO_2H and NaOH having been consumed. The pH is controlled by the acetate ion, the conjugate base of acetic acid.
- *The pH at the halfway point (half-equivalence point) of the titration.* Here, the pH is equal to the pK_a of the weak acid, a conclusion discussed in more detail in following paragraphs.

As NaOH is added to acetic acid, the base is consumed and sodium acetate is produced. Thus, at every point between the beginning of the titration (when only acetic acid is present) and the equivalence point (when only sodium acetate is present), the solution contains both acetic acid and its salt, sodium acetate. These are

FIGURE 18.5 **The change in pH during the titration of a weak acid with a strong base.** Here, 100.0 mL of 0.100 M acetic acid is titrated with 0.100 M NaOH. Note especially the following: **(a) Before titration.** A 0.100 M solution of acetic acid has a pH of 2.87. **(b) Halfway point.** The pH at the point at which half the acid has reacted with base is equal to the pK_a for the acid (pH = pK_a = 4.74). **(c) Equivalence point.** The solution contains the acetate ion, a weak base. Therefore, the solution is basic, with a pH of 8.72.

the components of a *buffer solution*, and the hydronium ion concentration can be calculated from Equation 18.3 or 18.4.

$$[H_3O^+] = \frac{[\text{weak acid remaining}]}{[\text{conjugate base produced}]} \times K_a \tag{18.3}$$

or

$$pH = pK_a + \log\frac{[\text{conjugate base produced}]}{[\text{weak acid remaining}]} \tag{18.4}$$

The fact that a buffer is present for most of the region between the beginning of the titration and the equivalence point is the reason that the pH of the solution only rises slowly after a few milliliters of titrant has been added.

What happens to the pH when *exactly* half of the acid has been consumed by base? Half of the acid (CH_3CO_2H) has been converted to the conjugate base ($CH_3CO_2^-$), and half remains. Therefore, the concentration of weak acid remaining is equal to the concentration of conjugate base produced ($[CH_3CO_2H] = [CH_3CO_2^-]$). Using Equations 18.3 or 18.4, we see that

$$[H_3O^+] = (1) \times K_a \qquad \text{or} \qquad pH = pK_a + \log(1)$$

Because $\log(1) = 0$, we come to the following general conclusion:

> At the halfway point in the titration of a weak acid with a strong base
> $$[H_3O^+] = K_a \text{ and } pH = pK_a$$
> (18.5)

In the particular case of the titration of acetic acid with a strong base, $[H_3O^+] = 1.8 \times 10^{-5}$ M at the halfway point, and so the pH is 4.74. This is equal to the pK_a of acetic acid.

● **Acid–Base Titrations** See Problem
Solving Tip 18.2 on page 826:
Calculating the pH at Various Stages
in an Acid–Base Titration.

☑WL   **INTERACTIVE EXAMPLE 18.6**   Titration of Acetic Acid with
Sodium Hydroxide

Problem Consider the titration of 100.0 mL of 0.100 M acetic acid with 0.100 M NaOH (see Figure 18.5).

$$CH_3CO_2H(aq) + OH^-(aq) \rightarrow CH_3CO_2^-(aq) + H_2O(\ell)$$

(a)   What is the pH of the solution when 90.0 mL of 0.100 M NaOH has been added to 100.0 mL of 0.100 M acetic acid?

(b)   What is the pH at the equivalence point?

(c)   What is the pH after 110.0 mL of NaOH has been added?

What Do You Know? You know the concentrations and volumes of the acid and base and the balanced equation for the reaction. For part (a) you know K_a of acetic acid and for part (b) you know K_b for the acetate ion (◀ Table 17.3). You might also recognize that part (a) is like Example 18.1.

Strategy Each part of the problem has at least two steps:

(1)   The first step in each part involves a limiting-reactant stoichiometry calculation to determine the amounts of acetic acid, sodium hydroxide, and acetate ion present after the acid–base reaction has gone to completion.

(2)   **Part (a):** Before the equivalence point, do an equilibrium calculation to find $[H_3O^+]$ for a buffer solution where the amounts of CH_3CO_2H and $CH_3CO_2^-$ are known from the stoichiometry calculation. (See Example 18.1.)

Part (b): Only the acetate ion remains at the equivalence point. (See Example 17.7.) Determine the concentration of this ion after the acid–base reaction goes to completion. Using the balanced equation for the reaction of the acetate ion with water and its corresponding K_b, determine the equilibrium hydroxide ion concentration. Convert this to the equilibrium hydronium ion concentration and calculate the pH.

Part (c): After the equivalence point, the solution contains both the acetate ion and excess NaOH, but the latter controls the pH. Determine the concentration of excess NaOH (and $[OH^-]$), and then convert $[OH^-]$ to pH.

Solution

Part (a): *pH before the Equivalence Point*

First calculate the amounts of reactants before reaction (= concentration × volume) and then use the principles of stoichiometry to calculate the amounts of reactants and products after reaction. The limiting reactant is NaOH, so some CH_3CO_2H remains along with the product, $CH_3CO_2^-$.

Equation	CH_3CO_2H	+	OH^-	⇌	$CH_3CO_2^-$	+	H_2O
Initial (mol)	0.0100		0.00900		0		
Change (mol)	−0.00900		−0.00900		+0.00900		
After reaction (mol)	0.0010		0		0.00900		

The ratio of amounts (moles) of acid to conjugate base is the same as the ratio of their concentrations. Therefore, we can use the amounts of weak acid remaining and conjugate base formed to find the pH from Equation 18.3.

$$[H_3O^+] = \frac{\text{mol } CH_3CO_2H}{\text{mol } CH_3CO_2^-} \times K_a = \left(\frac{0.0010 \text{ mol}}{0.0090 \text{ mol}}\right)(1.8 \times 10^{-5}) = 2.0 \times 10^{-6} \text{ M}$$

$$pH = -\log(2.0 \times 10^{-6}) = \boxed{5.70}$$

The pH is 5.70, in agreement with Figure 18.5. Notice that this pH is appropriate for a point after the halfway point (4.74) but before the equivalence point (8.72).

Part (b): *pH at the Equivalence Point*

To reach the equivalence point, 0.0100 mol of NaOH has been added to 0.0100 mol of CH_3CO_2H and 0.0100 mol of $CH_3CO_2^-$ has been formed.

Equation	CH_3CO_2H	+	OH^-	$\rightleftharpoons$	$CH_3CO_2^-$	+	H_2O
Initial (mol)	0.0100		0.0100		0		
Change (mol)	−0.0100		−0.0100		+0.0100		
After reaction (mol)	0		0		0.0100		

Because two solutions, each with a volume of 100.0 mL, have been combined, the concentration of $CH_3CO_2^-$ at the equivalence point is (0.0100 mol/0.200 L) = 0.0500 M. Next, set up an ICE table for the reaction of this weak base with water,

Equation	$CH_3CO_2^-$	+	H_2O	$\rightleftharpoons$	CH_3CO_2H	+	OH^-
Initial (M)	0.0500				0		0
Change (M)	−x				+x		+x
After reaction (M)	0.0500 − x				x		x

and calculate the concentration of OH^- ion using K_b for the weak base.

$$K_b \text{ for } CH_3CO_2^- = 5.6 \times 10^{-10} = \frac{[CH_3CO_2H][OH^-]}{[CH_3CO_2^-]} = \frac{(x)(x)}{0.0500 - x}$$

Making the usual assumption that x is small with respect to 0.0500 M,

$$x = [OH^-] = 5.3 \times 10^{-6} \text{ M and so the pOH} = 5.28$$

$$pH = 14.00 - 5.28 = 8.72$$

Part (c): *pH after the Equivalence Point*

Now the limiting reactant is CH_3CO_2H, and the solution contains excess OH^- ion from the unused NaOH as well as from the hydrolysis of $CH_3CO_2^-$.

Equation	CH_3CO_2H	+	OH^-	$\rightleftharpoons$	$CH_3CO_2^-$	+	H_2O
Initial (mol)	0.0100		0.0110		0		
Change (mol)	−0.0100		−0.0100		+0.0100		
After reaction (mol)	0		0.0010		0.0100		

The amount of OH^- produced by $CH_3CO_2^-$ hydrolysis is very small [see part (b)], so the pH of the solution after the equivalence point is determined by the excess NaOH (in 210 mL of solution).

$$[OH^-] = 0.0010 \text{ mol}/0.210 \text{ L} = 4.8 \times 10^{-3} \text{ M (pOH} = 2.32)$$

$$pH = 14.00 - 2.32 = 11.68$$

Think about Your Answer The pH at the equivalence point (8.72) indicates the solution is mildly basic, as expected for a solution of the conjugate base of a weak acid. As more NaOH is added past the equivalence point the solution becomes substantially more basic (pH = 11.68).

Check Your Understanding

The titration of 0.100 M acetic acid with 0.100 M NaOH is described in the text. What is the pH of the solution when 35.0 mL of the base has been added to 100.0 mL of 0.100 M acetic acid?

Strategy Map 18.6

PROBLEM — *Part (b)*
Calculate **pH** at the *equivalence point* for a titration of **acetic acid** with **NaOH**.

↓

DATA/INFORMATION KNOWN
- Solution concentrations
- Solution volumes
- Value of conjugate base K_b

> **STEP 1.** Stoichiometry problem

Concentration of **acetate ion** at *equivalence point* of acid-base titration

> **STEP 2.** Enter **equilibrium concentrations** in ICE table.

At equilibrium:
$[OH^-] = [\text{Acetic acid}] = x$
$[\text{Acetate ion}] = \text{original conc.} - x$

> **STEP 3.** Enter **equilibrium concentrations** in K_b.

K_b **expression** with equilibrium concentrations in terms of **x**

> **STEP 4.** Solve K_b **expression** for **x**.

Value of $[OH^-]$

> **STEP 5.** Convert $[OH^-]$ to **pH**.

pH of solution

FIGURE 18.6 Titration curve for a diprotic acid. The curve for the titration of 100.0 mL of 0.100 M oxalic acid ($H_2C_2O_4$, a weak diprotic acid) with 0.100 M NaOH. The first equivalence point (at 100 mL) occurs when the first hydrogen ion of $H_2C_2O_4$ is titrated, and the second (at 200 mL) occurs at the completion of the reaction. The curve for pH versus volume of NaOH added shows an initial rise at the first equivalence point and then another rise at the second equivalence point.

Titration of Weak Polyprotic Acids

The titrations illustrated thus far have been for the reaction of a monoprotic acid (HA) with a base such as NaOH. It is possible to extend the discussion of titrations to polyprotic acids such as oxalic acid, $H_2C_2O_4$.

$$H_2C_2O_4(aq) + H_2O(\ell) \rightleftharpoons HC_2O_4^-(aq) + H_3O^+(aq) \qquad K_{a1} = 5.9 \times 10^{-2}$$

$$HC_2O_4^-(aq) + H_2O(\ell) \rightleftharpoons C_2O_4^-(aq) + H_3O^+(aq) \qquad K_{a2} = 6.4 \times 10^{-5}$$

Figure 18.6 illustrates the curve for the titration of 100 mL of 0.100 M oxalic acid with 0.100 M NaOH. The first significant rise in pH is experienced when 100 mL of base has been added, indicating that the first proton of the acid has been titrated.

$$H_2C_2O_4(aq) + OH^-(aq) \rightleftharpoons HC_2O_4^-(aq) + H_2O(aq)$$

When the second proton of oxalic acid is titrated, the pH again rises significantly.

$$HC_2O_4^-(aq) + OH^-(aq) \rightleftharpoons C_2O_4^{2-}(aq) + H_2O(\ell)$$

The pH at this second equivalence point is controlled by the oxalate ion, $C_2O_4^{2-}$.

$$C_2O_4^{2-}(aq) + H_2O(\ell) \rightleftharpoons HC_2O_4^-(aq) + OH^-(aq)$$

$$K_b = K_w/K_{a2} = 1.6 \times 10^{-10}$$

Calculation of the pH at the equivalence point indicates that it should be about 8.4, as observed.

Titration of a Weak Base with a Strong Acid

Finally, it is useful to consider the titration of a weak base with a strong acid. Figure 18.7 illustrates the pH curve for the titration of 100.0 mL of 0.100 M NH_3 with 0.100 M HCl.

$$NH_3(aq) + H_3O^+(aq) \rightleftharpoons NH_4^+(aq) + H_2O(\ell)$$

The initial pH for a 0.100 M NH_3 solution is 11.13. As the titration progresses, the important species in solution are the weak acid NH_4^+ and its conjugate base, NH_3.

$$NH_4^+(aq) + H_2O(\ell) \rightleftharpoons NH_3(aq) + H_3O^+(aq) \qquad K_a = 5.6 \times 10^{-10}$$

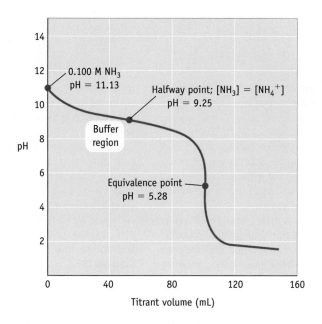

FIGURE 18.7 Titration of a weak base with a strong acid. The change in pH during the titration of a weak base (100.0 mL of 0.100 M NH$_3$) with a strong acid (0.100 M HCl). The pH at the half-neutralization point is equal to the pK_a for the conjugate acid (NH$_4^+$) of the weak base (NH$_3$) (pH = pK_a = 9.25). At the equivalence point, the solution contains the NH$_4^+$ ion, a weak acid, so the pH is about 5.

At the halfway point, the concentrations of NH$_4^+$ and NH$_3$ are the same, so

$$[H_3O^+] = \frac{[NH_4^+]}{[NH_3]} \times K_a = 5.6 \times 10^{-10}$$

$$[H_3O^+] = K_a$$

$$pH = pK_a = -\log(5.6 \times 10^{-10}) = 9.25$$

As the addition of HCl to NH$_3$ continues, the pH declines slowly because of the buffering action of the NH$_3$/NH$_4^+$ combination. Near the equivalence point, however, the pH drops rapidly. At the equivalence point, the solution contains only ammonium chloride, a weak Brønsted acid, and the solution is weakly acidic.

EXAMPLE 18.7   Titration of Ammonia with HCl

Problem What is the pH of the solution at the equivalence point in the titration of 100.0 mL of 0.100 M ammonia with 0.100 M HCl (see Figure 18.7)?

What Do You Know? This problem resembles part (b) of Example 18.6, although here you are titrating a weak base with a strong acid. In both examples you know the quantities of reagents and want to know the pH at the equivalence point. Here you need to know the K_a value for NH$_4^+$, the conjugate acid of the weak base, NH$_3$.

Strategy As in Example 18.6, this problem has two steps: (a) a stoichiometry calculation to find the concentration of NH$_4^+$ at the equivalence point, and (b) an equilibrium calculation to find [H$_3$O$^+$] for a solution of the weak acid NH$_4^+$.

Solution

Part 1: *Stoichiometry Problem*

Here, we are titrating 0.0100 mol of NH$_3$ (= $c \times V$), so 0.0100 mol of HCl is required. Thus, 100.0 mL of 0.100 M HCl (= 0.0100 mol HCl) must be used in the titration.

Equation	NH$_3$	+	H$_3$O$^+$	⇌	NH$_4^+$	+	H$_2$O
Initial (mol = $c \times V$)	0.0100		0.0100		0		
Change on reaction (mol)	−0.0100		−0.0100		+0.0100		
After reaction (mol)	0		0		0.0100		
Concentration (M)	0		0		0.0100 mol (in 0.200L) = 0.0500 M		

PROBLEM SOLVING TIP 18.2

Calculating the pH at Various Stages in an Acid–Base Titration

Finding the pH at or before the equivalence point for an acid–base reaction always involves several calculation steps. There are no shortcuts. Consider the *titration of a weak base, B, with a strong acid* as in Example 18.7. (The same principles apply to other acid–base reactions.)

$$H_3O^+(aq) + B(aq) \rightleftharpoons BH^+(aq) + H_2O(\ell)$$

A: Determining the pH before the equivalence point.
Step 1. *Solve the stoichiometry problem.* Up to the equivalence point, acid is consumed completely to leave a solution containing some base (B) and its conjugate acid (BH$^+$).

Use the principles of stoichiometry to calculate (a) the amount of acid added, (b) the amount of base remaining, and (c) the amount of conjugate acid (BH$^+$) formed.
Step 2. Calculate the concentrations of B and BH$^+$. Recognize that the volume of the solution at any point is the sum of the original volume of base solution plus the volume of acid solution added.
Step 3. *Calculate the pH.* At any point before the equivalence point, the solution is a buffer solution because both B and BH$^+$ are present. Calculate [H$_3$O$^+$] using the concentra-

tions of Step 2 and the value of K_a for the conjugate acid of the weak base.
B: Determining the pH at the equivalence point.
Calculate the concentration of the conjugate acid using the procedure of Part A. Use the value of K_a for the conjugate acid of the weak base and the procedure outlined in Example 18.7. (For a titration of a weak acid with a strong base, use the value of K_b for the conjugate base of the acid and follow the procedure outlined in Example 18.6.)

Part 2: Equilibrium Problem

When the equivalence point is reached, the solution consists of 0.0500 M NH$_4$$^+$. The pH is determined by the hydrolysis of this weak acid.

Equation	NH$_4$$^+$	+	H$_2$O	$\rightleftharpoons$	NH$_3$	+	H$_3$O$^+$
Initial (M)	0.0500				0		0
Change (M)	$-x$				$+x$		$+x$
Equilibrium (M)	$0.0500 - x$				x		x

Using K_a for the weak acid NH$_4$$^+$, we have

$$K_a = 5.6 \times 10^{-10} = \frac{[NH_3][H_3O^+]}{[NH_4^+]} = \frac{x^2}{0.0500 - x}$$

Simplifying, $x = [H_3O^+] = \sqrt{(5.6 \times 10^{-10})(0.0500)} = 5.3 \times 10^{-6}$ M

pH = 5.28

Think about Your Answer The pH at the equivalence point (5.28) indicates the solution is mildly acidic, as expected for a solution of the conjugate acid of a weak base.

Check Your Understanding

Calculate the pH after 75.0 mL of 0.100 M HCl has been added to 100.0 mL of 0.100 M NH$_3$. See Figure 18.7.

Roses are a natural indicator.
(a) The pigment in red rose petals was extracted with ethanol; the extract was a faint red. **(b)** After adding one drop of 6 M HCl, the color changed to a vivid red. **(c)** Adding two drops of 6 M NH$_3$ produced a green color, and **(d)** adding 1 drop each of HCl and NH$_3$ (to give a buffer solution) gave a blue solution. **(e)** Finally, adding a few milligrams of Al(NO$_3$)$_3$ turned the solution deep purple. (The deep purple color with aluminum ions was so intense that the solution had to be diluted significantly to take the photo.)

(a)   (b)   (c)   (d)   (e)

pH Indicators

Many organic compounds, both natural and synthetic, have a color that changes with pH (Figure 18.8). Not only does this add beauty and variety to our world, but it is also a useful property in chemistry.

   You may have done an acid–base titration in the laboratory, and, before starting the titration, you added an **indicator**. The acid–base indicator is usually an organic compound that is itself a weak acid or weak base (as are many compounds that give flowers their colors). In aqueous solution, the acid form is in equilibrium with its conjugate base. Abbreviating the indicator's acid formula as HInd and the formula of its conjugate base as Ind$^-$, we can write the equilibrium equation

$$HInd(aq) + H_2O(\ell) \rightleftharpoons H_3O^+(aq) + Ind^-(aq)$$

Phenolphthalein, Brønsted acid, colorless

$(aq) + 2\,H_2O(\ell) \rightleftharpoons 2\,H_3O^+(aq) +$

Conjugate base of phenolphthalein, Brønsted base, pink

$CO_2^-(aq)$

FIGURE 18.8 Phenolphthalein, a common acid–base indicator. Phenolphthalein, a weak acid, is colorless. As the pH increases, the pink conjugate base form predominates, and the color of the solution changes. The change in color is most noticeable around pH 9. The dye is commonly used for strong acid + strong base or weak acid + strong base titrations because the pH changes from about 3 to about 10 in these cases. For other suitable indicator dyes, see Figure 18.10.

The important characteristic of acid–base indicators is that the acid form of the compound (HInd) has one color and the conjugate base (Ind⁻) has another. To see how such compounds can be used as equivalence point indicators, let us write the usual equilibrium constant expressions for the dependence of hydronium ion concentration or pH on the indicator's ionization constant (K_a) and on the relative quantities of the acid and conjugate base.

$$[H_3O^+] = \frac{[HInd]}{[Ind^-]} \times K_a \quad or \quad pH = pK_a + \log\frac{[Ind^-]}{[HInd]}$$

These equations inform us that

- when the hydronium ion concentration is equivalent to the value of K_a (or when pH = pK_a), then [HInd] = [Ind⁻]
- when [H₃O⁺] > K_a (or pH < pK_a), then [HInd] > [Ind⁻]
- when [H₃O⁺] < K_a (or pH > pK_a), then [HInd] < [Ind⁻]

Now let us apply these conclusions to, for example, the titration of an acid with a base using an indicator whose pK_a value is nearly the same as the pH at the equivalence point (Figure 18.9). At the beginning of the titration, the pH is low and [H₃O⁺] is high; the acid form of the indicator (HInd) predominates, so its color is the one observed. As the titration progresses and the pH increases ([H₃O⁺] decreases), less of the acid HInd and more of its conjugate base exist in solution. Finally, just after we reach the equivalence point, [Ind⁻] is much larger than [HInd], and the color of [Ind⁻] is observed.

Several obvious questions remain to be answered. If you are trying to analyze for an acid and add an indicator that is a weak acid, won't this affect the analysis? Recall that you use only a tiny amount of an indicator in a titration. Although the acidic indicator molecules also react with the base as the titration progresses, so little indicator is present that any error is not significant.

Another question is whether you could accurately determine the pH by observing the color change of an indicator. In practice, your eyes are not quite that good. Usually, you see the color of HInd when [HInd]/[Ind⁻] is about 10/1, and the

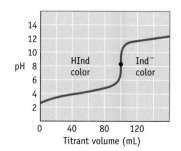

FIGURE 18.9 Indicator color changes in the course of a titration when the pK_a of the indicator HInd is about 8.

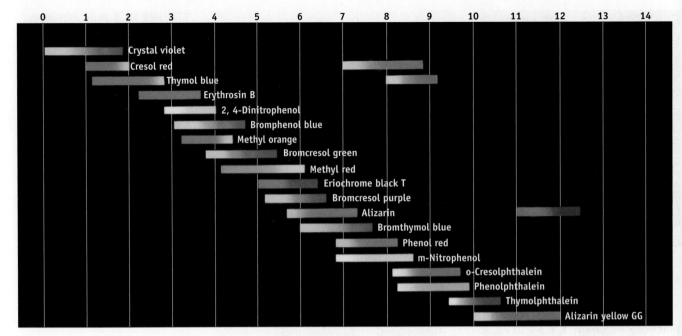

FIGURE 18.10 Common acid–base indicators. The color changes occur over a range of pH values. Notice that a few indicators have color changes over two different pH ranges.

color of Ind^- when $[HInd]/[Ind^-]$ is about 1/10. This means the color change is observed over a hydronium ion concentration interval of about 2 pH units. However, as you can see in Figures 18.4–18.7, on passing through the equivalence point of these titrations, the pH changes by as many as 7 units.

As Figure 18.10 shows, a variety of indicators is available, each changing color in a different pH range. If you are analyzing a weak acid or base by titration, you must choose an indicator that changes color in a range that includes the pH to be observed at the equivalence point. This means that an indicator that changes color in the pH range 7 ± 1 should be used for a strong acid–strong base titration. On the other hand, the pH at the equivalence point in the titration of a weak acid with a strong base is greater than 7, and you should choose an indicator that changes color at a pH near the anticipated equivalence point.

REVIEW & CHECK FOR SECTION 18.3

1. What is the pH after 25.0 mL of 0.100 M NaOH has been added to 50.0 mL of 0.100 M HCl?

   (a) 1.00   (b) 1.48   (c) 7.00   (d) 13.00

2. What is the pH at the equivalence point in the titration of 25.0 mL of 0.090 M phenol ($K_a = 1.3 \times 10^{-10}$) with 0.108 M NaOH?

   (a) 7.00   (b) 5.65   (c) 8.98   (d) 11.29

3. Use Figure 18.10 to decide which indicator is best to use in the titration of NH_3 with HCl shown in Figure 18.7.

   (a) crystal violet   (b) thymol blue   (c) methyl red   (d) phenolphthalein

---

18.4 Solubility of Salts

Precipitation reactions (◄ Section 3.5) are exchange reactions in which one of the products is a water-insoluble compound such as $CaCO_3$,

$$CaCl_2(aq) + Na_2CO_3(aq) \rightarrow CaCO_3(s) + 2\ NaCl(aq)$$

that is, a compound having a water solubility of less than about 0.01 mol of dissolved material per liter of solution (Figure 18.11).

Crocoite, lead(II) chromate, PbCrO$_4$

Rhodochrosite, manganese(II) carbonate, MnCO$_3$

Copper(II) minerals: green malachite, CuCO$_3 \cdot$ Cu(OH)$_2$, and blue azurite, 2 CuCO$_3 \cdot$ Cu(OH)$_2$

FIGURE 18.11 Some insoluble substances.

How do you know when to predict an insoluble compound as the product of a reaction? In Chapter 3, we listed some guidelines for predicting solubility (◄ Figure 3.10) and mentioned a few important minerals that are insoluble in water. Now we want to make our estimates of solubility more quantitative and to explore conditions under which some compounds precipitate and others do not.

The Solubility Product Constant, K_{sp}

Silver bromide, AgBr, is used in photographic film. If some AgBr is placed in pure water, a tiny amount of the compound dissolves, and an equilibrium is established.

$$\text{AgBr(s)} \rightleftharpoons \text{Ag}^+(\text{aq, } 7.35 \times 10^{-7} \text{ M}) + \text{Br}^-(\text{aq, } 7.35 \times 10^{-7} \text{ M})$$

When sufficient AgBr has dissolved and equilibrium is attained, the solution is said to be **saturated** (◄ Section 14.2), and experiments show that the concentrations of the silver and bromide ions in the solution are each about 7.35×10^{-7} M at 25 °C. The extent to which an insoluble salt dissolves can be expressed in terms of the equilibrium constant for the dissolving process. In this case, the appropriate expression is

$$K_{sp} = [\text{Ag}^+][\text{Br}^-]$$

The equilibrium constant that reflects the solubility of a compound is often referred to as its **solubility product constant**. Chemists frequently use the notation K_{sp} for such constants, the subscript "sp" denoting a "solubility product."

The water solubility of a compound, and thus its K_{sp} value, can be estimated by determining the concentration of the cation or anion when the compound dissolves. For example, if we find that AgBr dissolves to give a silver ion concentration of 7.35×10^{-7} mol/L, we know that 7.35×10^{-7} mol of AgBr must have dissolved per liter of solution (and that the bromide ion concentration also equals 7.35×10^{-7} M). Therefore, the calculated value of the equilibrium constant for AgBr is

$$K_{sp} = [\text{Ag}^+][\text{Br}^-] = (7.35 \times 10^{-7})(7.35 \times 10^{-7}) = 5.40 \times 10^{-13} \text{ (at 25 °C)}$$

Equilibrium constants for dissolving other insoluble salts can be calculated in the same manner.

The solubility product constant, K_{sp}, for any salt always has the form

$$\text{A}_x\text{B}_y(\text{s}) \rightleftharpoons x \text{ A}^{y+}(\text{aq}) + y \text{ B}^{x-}(\text{aq}) \qquad K_{sp} = [\text{A}^{y+}]^x[\text{B}^{x-}]^y \qquad \textbf{(18.6)}$$

For example,

$$\text{CaF}_2(\text{s}) \rightleftharpoons \text{Ca}^{2+}(\text{aq}) + 2 \text{ F}^-(\text{aq}) \qquad K_{sp} = [\text{Ca}^{2+}][\text{F}^-]^2 = 5.3 \times 10^{-11}$$

$$\text{Ag}_2\text{SO}_4(\text{s}) \rightleftharpoons 2 \text{ Ag}^+(\text{aq}) + \text{SO}_4{}^{2-}(\text{aq}) \qquad K_{sp} = [\text{Ag}^+]^2[\text{SO}_4{}^{2-}] = 1.2 \times 10^{-5}$$

The numerical values of K_{sp} for a few salts are given in Table 18.2, and more values are collected in Appendix J.

● **Writing Equilibrium Constant Expressions** Solids are not included in these equations. See page 724.

Table 18.2 Some Common Insoluble Compounds and Their K_{sp} Values*

Formula	Name	K_{sp} (25 °C)	Common Names/Uses
$CaCO_3$	Calcium carbonate	3.4×10^{-9}	Calcite, iceland spar
$MnCO_3$	Manganese(II) carbonate	2.3×10^{-11}	Rhodochrosite (forms rose-colored crystals)
$FeCO_3$	Iron(II) carbonate	3.1×10^{-11}	Siderite
CaF_2	Calcium fluoride	5.3×10^{-11}	Fluorite (source of HF and other inorganic fluorides)
$AgCl$	Silver chloride	1.8×10^{-10}	Chlorargyrite
$AgBr$	Silver bromide	5.4×10^{-13}	Used in photographic film
$CaSO_4$	Calcium sulfate	4.9×10^{-5}	Hydrated form is commonly called *gypsum*
$BaSO_4$	Barium sulfate	1.1×10^{-10}	Barite (used in "drilling mud" and as a component of paints)
$SrSO_4$	Strontium sulfate	3.4×10^{-7}	Celestite
$Ca(OH)_2$	Calcium hydroxide	5.5×10^{-5}	Slaked lime

* The values in this table were taken from *Lange's Handbook of Chemistry*, 15th edition, McGraw-Hill Publishers, New York, NY (1999). Additional K_{sp} values are given in Appendix J.

Do not confuse the *solubility* of a compound with its *solubility product constant.* The *solubility* of a salt is the quantity present in some volume of a saturated solution, expressed in moles per liter, grams per 100 mL, or other units. The *solubility product constant* is an equilibrium constant. Nonetheless, there is a connection between them: If one is known, the other can, in principle, be calculated.

Relating Solubility and K_{sp}

Solubility product constants are determined by careful laboratory measurements of the concentrations of ions in solution.

Strategy Map 18.8

PROBLEM

Calculate K_{sp} of **CaF$_2$** from its **solubility**.

↓

DATA/INFORMATION KNOWN

- Concentration of Ca^{2+}
- Form of K_{sp}
- Balanced equation

STEP 1. Calculate **F⁻ concentration**.

↓

$[F^-] = 2 \times [Ca^{2+}]$

STEP 2. Enter **equilibrium concentrations** in K_{sp} expression and calculate K_{sp}.

Value of K_{sp}

⏻WL INTERACTIVE EXAMPLE 18.8 K_{sp} from Solubility Measurements

Problem Calcium fluoride, the main component of the mineral fluorite, dissolves to a slight extent in water.

$$CaF_2(s) \rightleftharpoons Ca^{2+}(aq) + 2\ F^-(aq) \qquad K_{sp} = [Ca^{2+}][F^-]^2$$

Calculate the K_{sp} value for CaF_2 if the calcium ion concentration has been found to be 2.3×10^{-4} mol/L.

What Do You Know? You know the balanced equation for the process, Ca^{2+} concentration, and the K_{sp} expression.

Strategy

- Calculate the fluoride ion concentration from [Ca^{2+}] and stoichiometry.

- Insert the values for [F⁻] and [Ca^{2+}] into the K_{sp} expression and calculate the value of K_{sp}.

Solution When CaF_2 dissolves in water, the balanced equation shows that the concentration of F⁻ ion must be twice the Ca^{2+} ion concentration.

If [Ca^{2+}] = 2.3×10^{-4} M, then [F⁻] = $2 \times$ [Ca^{2+}] = 4.6×10^{-4} M

This means the solubility product constant is

$$K_{sp} = [Ca^{2+}][F^-]^2 = (2.3 \times 10^{-4})(4.6 \times 10^{-4})^2 = 4.9 \times 10^{-11}$$

Think about Your Answer A common student error is to forget the reaction stoichiometry. Be sure to notice that for every Ca^{2+} ion in solution there are two F⁻ ions.

Check Your Understanding

The barium ion concentration, [Ba^{2+}], in a saturated solution of barium fluoride is 3.6×10^{-3} M. Calculate the value of the K_{sp} for BaF$_2$.

$$BaF_2(s) \rightleftharpoons Ba^{2+}(aq) + 2\ F^-(aq)$$

Minerals and Gems—The Importance of Solubility

Minerals and gems are among nature's most beautiful creations. Many, such as rubies, are metal oxides, and the various types of quartz are based on silicon dioxide. Another large class of gemstones consists largely of metal silicates. These include emerald, topaz, aquamarine, and tourmaline.

Yet another large class of minerals and of a few gemstones is carbonates. Rhodochrosite, one of the most beautiful red stones, is manganese(II) carbonate. And one of the most abundant minerals on earth is limestone, calcium carbonate, which is also a major component of sea shells and corals.

Hydroxides are represented by azurite, which is a mixed carbonate/hydroxide with the formula $Cu_3(OH)_2(CO_3)_2$. Turquoise is a mixed hydroxide/phosphate based on copper(II), the source of the blue color of turquoise.

Among the most common minerals are sulfides such as golden iron pyrite (FeS_2), black stibnite (Sb_2S_3), red cinnabar (HgS), and yellow orpiment (As_2S_3).

Other smaller classes of minerals exist; one of the smallest is the class based on the halides, and the best example is fluorite. Fluorite, CaF_2, exhibits a wide range of colors from purple to green to yellow.

What do all of these minerals and gems have in common? They are all insoluble or poorly soluble in water. If they were more soluble, they would be dissolved in the world's lakes and oceans.

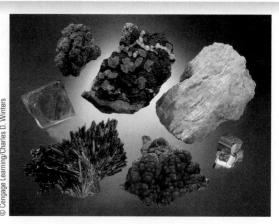

© Cengage Learning/Charles D. Winters

Mineral samples (clockwise from the top center): red rhodochrosite, yellow orpiment, golden iron pyrite, green-blue turquoise, black stibnite, purple fluorite, and blue azurite. Formulas are in the text. See also Figure 18.11.

K_{sp} values for insoluble salts can be used to estimate the solubility of a solid salt or to determine whether a solid will precipitate when solutions of its anion and cation are mixed. Let us first look at an example of the estimation of the solubility of a salt from its K_{sp} value.

OWL   INTERACTIVE EXAMPLE 18.9   Solubility from K_{sp}

Problem The K_{sp} for the mineral barite ($BaSO_4$, Figure 18.12) is 1.1×10^{-10} at 25 °C. Calculate the solubility of barium sulfate in pure water in (a) moles per liter and (b) grams per liter.

What Do You Know? You know the formula for the mineral and its K_{sp} value.

Strategy When $BaSO_4$ dissolves, equimolar amounts of Ba^{2+} ions and SO_4^{2-} ions are produced. Thus, the solubility of $BaSO_4$ can be estimated by calculating the equilibrium concentration of either Ba^{2+} or SO_4^{2-} from the solubility product constant.

- Write the balanced equation and the K_{sp} expression.

- Set up an ICE table, designating the unknown concentrations of Ba^{2+} and SO_4^{2-} in solution as x.

- Using x for $[Ba^{2+}]$ and $[SO_4^{2-}]$ in the K_{sp} expression, solve for x.

Solution The equation for the solubility of $BaSO_4$ and its K_{sp} expression are

$$BaSO_4(s) \rightleftharpoons Ba^{2+}(aq) + SO_4^{2-}(aq) \qquad K_{sp} = [Ba^{2+}][SO_4^{2-}] = 1.1 \times 10^{-10}$$

Denote the solubility of $BaSO_4$ (in mol/L) by x; that is, x moles of $BaSO_4$ dissolve per liter. Therefore, both $[Ba^{2+}]$ and $[SO_4^{2-}]$ must also equal x at equilibrium.

Equation	$BaSO_4(s)$	$\rightleftharpoons$	$Ba^{2+}(aq)$	+	$SO_4^{2-}(aq)$
Initial (M)			0		0
Change (M)			$+x$		$+x$
Equilibrium (M)			x		x

Because K_{sp} is the product of the barium ion and sulfate ion concentrations, K_{sp} is the square of the solubility, x,

$$K_{sp} = [Ba^{2+}][SO_4^{2-}] = 1.1 \times 10^{-10} = (x)(x) = x^2$$

Strategy Map 18.9

PROBLEM

Calculate **solubility** of $BaSO_4$ from K_{sp}.

↓

DATA/INFORMATION KNOWN

- K_{sp} for $BaSO_4$
- Balanced equation

STEP 1. Write the **balanced equation** and K_{sp} **expression**, and set up **ICE table**.

At equilibrium:
$[Ba^{2+}] = [SO_4^{2-}] = x$

STEP 2. Enter **equilibrium concentrations** in K_{sp} expression.

K_{sp} **expression** with equilibrium concentrations in terms of x

STEP 3. Solve K_{sp} **expression** for x.

$x = $ Solubility $= [Ba^{2+}] = [SO_4^{2-}]$

(a) A sample of the mineral barite, which is mostly barium sulfate. "Drilling mud," used in drilling oil wells, consists of clay, barite, and calcium carbonate.

(b) Barium sulfate is opaque to x-rays, so it is used by physicians to examine the digestive tract. A patient drinks a "cocktail" containing $BaSO_4$, and the progress of the $BaSO_4$ through the digestive organs can be followed by x-ray analysis. This photo is an x ray of the gastrointestinal tract after a person ingested barium sulfate.

FIGURE 18.12 Barium sulfate. Barium sulfate, a white solid, is quite insoluble in water ($K_{sp} = 1.1 \times 10^{-10}$) (see Example 18.9).

and so the value of x is

$$x = [Ba^{2+}] = [SO_4^{2-}] = \sqrt{K_{sp}} = \sqrt{1.1 \times 10^{-10}} = 1.0 \times 10^{-5} \text{ M}$$

The solubility of $BaSO_4$ in pure water is 1.0×10^{-5} mol/L. To find its solubility in g/L, we only need to multiply by the molar mass of $BaSO_4$.

$$\text{Solubility in g/L} = (1.0 \times 10^{-5} \text{ mol/L})(233 \text{ g/mol}) = 0.0024 \text{ g/L}$$

Think about Your Answer As noted in Figure 18.12, $BaSO_4$ is used to investigate the digestive track. It is fortunate the compound is so insoluble, because water- and acid-soluble barium salts are toxic.

Check Your Understanding

Calculate the solubility of AgCN in moles per liter and grams per liter. K_{sp} for AgCN is 6.0×10^{-17}.

EXAMPLE 18.10 Solubility from K_{sp}

Problem Knowing that the K_{sp} value for MgF_2 is 5.2×10^{-11}, calculate the solubility of the salt in (a) moles per liter and (b) grams per liter.

What Do You Know? You know the formula for magnesium fluoride and its K_{sp} value.

Strategy The solubility must be defined in terms that will allow you to solve the K_{sp} expression for this value. From stoichiometry, we can say that if x mol of MgF_2 dissolves, then x mol of Mg^{2+} and $2x$ mol of F^- appear in solution. This means the MgF_2 solubility (in moles dissolved per liter) is equivalent to the concentration of Mg^{2+} ions in the solution.

- Write the balanced equation and the K_{sp} expression.

- Set up an ICE table, designating the unknown concentrations of Mg^{2+} and F^- in solution as x and $2x$, respectively.

- Using x for $[Mg^{2+}]$ and $2x$ for $[F^-]$ in the K_{sp} expression, solve for x.

Solution

$$MgF_2(s) \rightleftharpoons Mg^{2+}(aq) + 2 F^-(aq) \qquad K_{sp} = [Mg^{2+}][F^-]^2 = 5.2 \times 10^{-11}$$

Equation	$MgF_2(s)$	$\rightleftharpoons$	$Mg^{2+}(aq)$	+	$2 F^-(aq)$
Initial (M)			0		0
Change (M)			$+x$		$+2x$
Equilibrium (M)			x		$2x$

A CLOSER LOOK

Solubility Calculations

The K_{sp} value reported for lead(II) chloride, $PbCl_2$, is 1.7×10^{-5}. If we assume the appropriate equilibrium in solution is

$$PbCl_2(s) \rightleftharpoons Pb^{2+}(aq) + 2\ Cl^-(aq)$$

the calculated solubility of $PbCl_2$ is 0.016 M. The experimental value for the solubility of the salt, however, is 0.036 M, more than twice the calculated value! What is the problem? One is that the chemical behavior is sometimes much more complicated than the equation defining K_{sp}, as illustrated below.

The main problem in the lead(II) chloride case, and in many others, is that the compound dissolves but is not 100% dissociated into its constituent ions. Instead, it dissolves as the undissociated salt or forms ion pairs.

Other problems that lead to discrepancies between calculated and experimental solubilities are the reactions of ions (particularly anions) with water and complex ion formation. An example of the former effect is the product-favored reaction of sulfide ion with water, that is, *hydrolysis*.

$$S^{2-}(aq) + H_2O(\ell) \rightleftharpoons HS^-(aq) + OH^-(aq)$$

This means that the solubility of a metal sulfide is better described by a chemical equation such as

$$NiS(s) + H_2O(\ell) \rightleftharpoons Ni^{2+}(aq) + HS^-(aq) + OH^-(aq)$$

Complex ion formation is illustrated by the fact that lead chloride is more soluble in the presence of excess chloride ion, owing to the formation of the complex ion $PbCl_4^{2-}$.

$$PbCl_2(s) + 2\ Cl^-(aq) \rightleftharpoons PbCl_4^{2-}(aq)$$

Hydrolysis and complex ion formation are discussed further on pages 837–838 and 843–846, respectively.

References:
- L. Meites, J. S. F. Pode, and H. C. Thomas: *Journal of Chemical Education,* Vol. 43, pp. 667–672, 1966.
- S. J. Hawkes: *Journal of Chemical Education,* Vol. 75, pp. 1179–1181, 1998.
- R. W. Clark and J. M. Bonicamp: *Journal of Chemical Education,* Vol. 75, pp. 1182–1185, 1998.
- R. J. Myers: *Journal of Chemical Education,* Vol. 63, pp. 687–690, 1986.

Substituting the equilibrium concentrations for $[Mg^{2+}]$ and $[F^-]$ into the K_{sp} expression, you find

$$K_{sp} = [Mg^{2+}][F^-]^2 = (x)(2x)^2 = 4x^3$$

Solving the equation for x,

$$x = \sqrt[3]{\frac{K_{sp}}{4}} = \sqrt[3]{\frac{5.2 \times 10^{-11}}{4}} = 2.4 \times 10^{-4}$$

you find that 2.4×10^{-4} moles of MgF_2 dissolve per liter. The solubility of MgF_2 in grams per liter is

$$(2.4 \times 10^{-4}\ mol/L)(62.3\ g/mol) = 0.015\ g\ MgF_2/L$$

Think about Your Answer Problems like this one might provoke our students to ask the question, "Aren't you counting things twice when you multiply x by 2 and then square it as well?" in the expression $K_{sp} = (x)(2x)^2$. The answer is no. The 2 in the $2x$ term is based on the stoichiometry of the compound. The exponent of 2 on the F^- ion concentration arises from the rules for writing equilibrium expressions.

Check Your Understanding

Calculate the solubility of $Ca(OH)_2$ in moles per liter and grams per liter using the value of K_{sp} in Appendix J.

The *relative* solubilities of salts can often be deduced by comparing values of solubility product constants, but you must be careful! For example, the K_{sp} for silver chloride is

$$AgCl(s) \rightleftharpoons Ag^+(aq) + Cl^-(aq) \qquad K_{sp} = 1.8 \times 10^{-10}$$

whereas that for silver chromate is

$$Ag_2CrO_4(s) \rightleftharpoons 2\ Ag^+(aq) + CrO_4^{2-}(aq) \qquad K_{sp} = 9.0 \times 10^{-12}$$

In spite of the fact that Ag_2CrO_4 has a smaller numerical K_{sp} value than AgCl, the chromate salt is about 10 times *more* soluble than the chloride salt. If you determine solubilities from K_{sp} values as in the examples above, you would find the solubility of AgCl is 1.3×10^{-5} mol/L, whereas that of Ag_2CrO_4 is 1.3×10^{-4} mol/L. From this example and countless others, we conclude that

> Direct comparisons of the solubility of two salts on the basis of their K_{sp} values can be made only for salts having the same cation-to-anion ratio.

This means, for example, that you can directly compare solubilities of 1:1 salts such as the silver halides by comparing their K_{sp} values.

$$AgI\ (K_{sp} = 8.5 \times 10^{-17}) < AgBr\ (K_{sp} = 5.4 \times 10^{-13}) < AgCl\ (K_{sp} = 1.8 \times 10^{-10})$$
$$\xrightarrow{\text{increasing } K_{sp} \text{ and increasing solubility}}$$

Similarly, you could compare 1:2 salts such as the lead halides,

$$PbI_2\ (K_{sp} = 9.8 \times 10^{-9}) < PbBr_2\ (K_{sp} = 6.6 \times 10^{-6}) < PbCl_2\ (K_{sp} = 1.7 \times 10^{-5})$$
$$\xrightarrow{\text{increasing } K_{sp} \text{ and increasing solubility}}$$

but you cannot directly compare a 1:1 salt (AgCl) with a 2:1 salt (Ag_2CrO_4).

Solubility and the Common Ion Effect

The test tube on the left in Figure 18.13 contains a precipitate of silver acetate, $AgCH_3CO_2$, in water. The solution is saturated, and the silver ions and acetate ions in the solution are in equilibrium with solid silver acetate.

$$AgCH_3CO_2(s) \rightleftharpoons Ag^+(aq) + CH_3CO_2^-(aq)$$

But what would happen if the silver ion concentration is increased, say by adding silver nitrate? Le Chatelier's principle (◄ Section 16.6) suggests—and we observe—that more silver acetate precipitate should form because a product ion has been added, causing the equilibrium to shift to form more silver acetate.

The ionization of weak acids and bases is affected by the presence of an ion common to the equilibrium process (Section 18.1), and the effect of adding silver ions to a saturated silver acetate solution is another example of the common ion effect. Adding a common ion to a saturated solution of a salt will lower the salt solubility (unless a complex ion can form; see *A Closer Look*, page 833).

FIGURE 18.13 The common ion effect. The tube at the *left* contains a saturated solution of silver acetate, $AgCH_3CO_2$. When 1.0 M $AgNO_3$ is added to the tube *(right)*, more solid silver acetate forms.

EXAMPLE 18.11 The Common Ion Effect and Salt Solubility

Problem If solid AgCl is placed in 1.00 L of 0.55 M NaCl, what mass of AgCl will dissolve?

What Do You Know? You know the formula of the insoluble compound, its K_{sp} (Table 18.2 and Appendix J), and its molar mass. You also know that the presence of an ion common to the equilibrium (Cl^-) suppresses the solubility of AgCl.

Strategy To determine the solubility of AgCl in the presence of excess Cl^-, calculate the concentration of the Ag^+ ion.

- Write the balanced equation and the K_{sp} expression for AgCl.

- Set up an ICE table, and enter 0.55 M as the initial concentration of the common ion, Cl^-.

- Define the solubility of AgCl as x. This is the increase in the concentration of Ag^+ and Cl^- in solution as AgCl dissolves. Enter this information on the change (C) line in the ICE table.

- Fill in the last line (E) of the ICE table with x for $[Ag^+]$ and $(0.55 + x)$ for $[Cl^-]$. Solve the K_{sp} expression for x.

Solution Set up an ICE table to show the concentrations of Ag^+ and Cl^- when equilibrium is attained.

Equation	AgCl(s)	$\rightleftharpoons$	$Ag^+(aq)$	+	$Cl^-(aq)$
Initial (M)			0		0.55
Change (M)			$+x$		$+x$
Equilibrium (M)			x		$0.55 + x$

The equilibrium concentrations from the table are substituted into the K_{sp} expression,

$$K_{sp} = 1.8 \times 10^{-10} = [Ag^+][Cl^-] = (x)(0.55 + x)$$

This is a quadratic equation and can be solved by the methods in Appendix A. An easier approach, however, is to make the approximation that x is very small with respect to 0.55 [and so $(0.55 + x) \approx 0.55$]. This is a reasonable assumption because we know that the solubility is very small without the common ion Cl^- and that it will be even smaller in the presence of added Cl^-. Therefore,

$$K_{sp} = 1.8 \times 10^{-10} = (x)(0.55)$$

$$x = [Ag^+] = 3.3 \times 10^{-10} \text{ M}$$

The solubility in grams per liter is then

$$(3.3 \times 10^{-10} \text{ mol/L})(143 \text{ g/mol}) = 4.7 \times 10^{-8} \text{ g/L}$$

As predicted by Le Chatelier's principle, the solubility of AgCl in the presence of added Cl^- is less (3.3×10^{-10} M) than in pure water (1.3×10^{-5} M).

Think about Your Answer The approximation we made here is similar to the approximations we make in acid–base equilibrium problems. However, as a final step, we should check its validity by substituting the calculated value of x into the exact expression $K_{sp} = (x)(0.55 + x)$. If the product $(x)(0.55 + x)$ is the same as the given value of K_{sp}, the approximation is valid.

$$K_{sp} = (x)(0.55 + x) = (3.3 \times 10^{-10})(0.55 + 3.3 \times 10^{-10}) = 1.8 \times 10^{-10}$$

Check Your Understanding

Calculate the solubility of $BaSO_4$ (a) in pure water and (b) in the presence of 0.010 M $Ba(NO_3)_2$. K_{sp} for $BaSO_4$ is 1.1×10^{-10}.

EXAMPLE 18.12   The Common Ion Effect and Salt Solubility

Problem Calculate the solubility of silver chromate, Ag_2CrO_4, at 25 °C in the presence of 0.0050 M K_2CrO_4 solution.

$$Ag_2CrO_4(s) \rightleftharpoons 2 Ag^+(aq) + CrO_4^{2-}(aq)$$

$$K_{sp} = [Ag^+]^2[CrO_4^{2-}] = 9.0 \times 10^{-12}$$

For comparison, the solubility of Ag_2CrO_4 in pure water is 1.3×10^{-4} mol/L.

What Do You Know? You know the formula and K_{sp} value for Ag_2CrO_4.

Strategy In the presence of chromate ion from the water-soluble salt K_2CrO_4, the concentration of Ag^+ ions produced by Ag_2CrO_4 will be less than in pure water. Assume the solubility of Ag_2CrO_4 is x mol/L. This means the concentration of Ag^+ ions will be $2x$ mol/L, whereas the concentration of CrO_4^{2-} ions will be x mol/L plus the concentration of CrO_4^{2-} already in the solution.

- Write the balanced equation and the K_{sp} expression for Ag_2CrO_4.

- Set up an ICE table, and enter 0.0050 M as the initial concentration of the common ion, CrO_4^{2-}.

- Designate the increase in the concentration of the CrO_4^{2-} ion in solution as x and the increase in $[Ag^+]$ as $2x$.

- Using $2x$ for $[Ag^+]$ and $(0.0050 + x)$ for $[CrO_4^{2-}]$ in the K_{sp} expression, solve for x.

Solution

Equation	$Ag_2CrO_4(s)$	$\rightleftharpoons$	$2 Ag^+(aq)$	$+$	$CrO_4^{2-}(aq)$
Initial (M)			0		0.0050
Change (M)			$+2x$		$+x$
Equilibrium (M)			$2x$		$0.0050 + x$

Substituting the equilibrium concentrations into the K_{sp} expression, we have

$$K_{sp} = 9.0 \times 10^{-12} = [Ag^+]^2[CrO_4^{2-}]$$

$$K_{sp} = (2x)^2(0.0050 + x)$$

As in Example 18.11, you can make the approximation that x is very small with respect to 0.0050, and so $(0.0050 + x) \approx 0.0050$. Therefore, the approximate expression is

$$K_{sp} = 9.0 \times 10^{-12} = [Ag^+]^2[CrO_4^{2-}] \approx (2x)^2(0.0050)$$

Solving, we find x, the solubility of silver chromate in the presence of excess chromate ion, is

$$x = \text{Solubility of } Ag_2CrO_4 = 2.1 \times 10^{-5} \text{ M}$$

Think about Your Answer The silver ion concentration in the presence of the common ion is

$$[Ag^+] = 2x = 4.2 \times 10^{-5} \text{ M}$$

This silver ion concentration is indeed less than its value in pure water (2.6×10^{-4} M), owing to the presence of an ion "common" to the equilibrium.

Check Your Understanding

Calculate the solubility of $Zn(CN)_2$ at 25 °C (a) in pure water and (b) in the presence of 0.10 M $Zn(NO_3)_2$. K_{sp} for $Zn(CN)_2$ is 8.0×10^{-12}.

There are two important general ideas from Examples 18.11 and 18.12:

- The solubility of a salt will be reduced by the presence of a common ion, in accordance with Le Chatelier's principle.
- We made the approximation that the amount of common ion added to the solution was very large in comparison with the amount of that ion coming from the insoluble salt, and this allowed us to simplify our calculations. This is almost always the case, but you should check to be sure.

The Effect of Basic Anions on Salt Solubility

The next time you are tempted to wash a supposedly insoluble salt down the kitchen or laboratory drain, stop and consider the consequences. Many metal ions such as lead, chromium, and mercury are toxic in the environment. Even if a so-called insoluble salt of one of these cations does not appear to dissolve, its solubility in water may be greater than you think, in part owing to the possibility that the anion of the salt is a weak base or the cation is a weak acid.

Lead(II) sulfide, PbS, which is found in nature as the mineral galena (Figure 18.14), provides an example of the effect of the acid–base properties of an ion on salt solubility. When placed in water, a trace amount dissolves,

$$PbS(s) \rightleftharpoons Pb^{2+}(aq) + S^{2-}(aq)$$

and one product of the reaction is the sulfide ion, which is itself a strong base.

$$S^{2-}(aq) + H_2O(\ell) \rightleftharpoons HS^-(aq) + OH^-(aq) \qquad K_b = 1 \times 10^5$$

This ion undergoes extensive hydrolysis (reaction with water) (◄ Table 17.3), which decreases its concentration, and the equilibrium process for dissolving PbS shifts to the right. Thus, the lead ion concentration in solution is greater than expected from the simple dissociation of the salt.

The lead(II) sulfide example leads to the following general observation:

> Any salt containing an anion that is the conjugate base of a weak acid will dissolve in water to a greater extent than given by K_{sp}.

This means that salts of phosphate, acetate, carbonate, and cyanide, as well as sulfide, can be affected, because all of these anions undergo the general hydrolysis reaction

$$X^-(aq) + H_2O(\ell) \rightleftharpoons HX(aq) + OH^-(aq)$$

The observation that ions from insoluble salts can undergo hydrolysis is related to another useful, general conclusion:

> Insoluble salts in which the anion is the conjugate base of a weak acid dissolve in strong acids.

Insoluble salts containing anions such as acetate, carbonate, hydroxide, phosphate, and sulfide dissolve in strong acids. For example, you know that if a strong acid is added to a water-insoluble metal carbonate such as $CaCO_3$, the salt dissolves (◄ Section 3.7).

$$CaCO_3(s) + 2\,H_3O^+(aq) \rightarrow Ca^{2+}(aq) + 3\,H_2O(\ell) + CO_2(g)$$

You can think of this as the result of a series of reactions.

$CaCO_3(s) \rightleftharpoons Ca^{2+}(aq) + CO_3{}^{2-}(aq)$	$K_{sp} = 3.4 \times 10^{-9}$
$CO_3{}^{2-}(aq) + H_3O^+(aq) \rightleftharpoons HCO_3{}^-(aq) + H_2O(\ell)$	$1/K_{a2} = 1/4.8 \times 10^{-11} = 2.1 \times 10^{10}$
$HCO_3{}^-(aq) + H_3O^+(aq) \rightleftharpoons H_2CO_3(aq) + H_2O(\ell)$	$1/K_{a1} = 1/4.2 \times 10^{-7} = 2.4 \times 10^6$
Overall: $CaCO_3(s) + 2\,H_3O^+(aq) \rightleftharpoons Ca^{2+}(aq) + 2\,H_2O(\ell) + H_2CO_3(aq)$	

$$K_{net} = (K_{sp})(1/K_{a2})(1/K_{a1}) = 1.7 \times 10^8$$

Carbonic acid, a product of this reaction, is not stable,

$$H_2CO_3(aq) \rightleftharpoons CO_2(g) + H_2O(\ell) \qquad K \approx 10^5$$

and you see CO_2 bubbling out of the solution, a process that moves the $CaCO_3 + H_3O^+$ equilibrium even further to the right. Calcium carbonate dissolves completely in strong acid!

Many metal sulfides are also soluble in strong acids

$$FeS(s) + 2\,H_3O^+(aq) \rightleftharpoons Fe^{2+}(aq) + H_2S(aq) + 2\,H_2O(\ell)$$

FIGURE 18.14 Lead(II) sulfide (galena). This and other metal sulfides dissolve in water to a greater extent than expected because the sulfide ion reacts with water to form the very stable species HS⁻ and OH⁻.

$$PbS(s) + H_2O(\ell) \rightleftharpoons$$
$$Pb^{2+}(aq) + HS^-(aq) + OH^-(aq)$$

The model of PbS shows that the unit cell is cubic, a feature reflected by the cubic crystals of the mineral galena.

● **Metal Sulfide Solubility** The true solubility of a metal sulfide is better represented by a modified solubility product constant, K_{spa}, which is defined as follows:

$$MS(s) \rightleftharpoons M^{2+}(aq) + S^{2-}(aq)$$
$$K_{sp} = [M^{2+}][S^{2-}]$$

$$S^{2-}(aq) + H_2O(\ell) \rightleftharpoons$$
$$HS^-(aq) + OH^-(aq)$$
$$K_b = [HS^-][OH^-]/[S^{2-}]$$

Net reaction:

$$MS(s) + H_2O(\ell) \rightleftharpoons$$
$$HS^-(aq) + M^{2+}(aq) + OH^-(aq)$$
$$K_{spa} = [M^{2+}][HS^-][OH^-] = K_{sp} \times K_b$$

Values for K_{spa} for several metal sulfides are included in Appendix J.

FIGURE 18.15 The effect of the anion on salt solubility in acid.
(left) A precipitate of AgCl (white) and Ag$_3$PO$_4$ (yellow). *(right)* Adding a strong acid (HNO$_3$) dissolves Ag$_3$PO$_4$ (and leaves insoluble AgCl). The basic anion PO$_4^{3-}$ reacts with acid to give H$_3$PO$_4$, whereas Cl$^-$ is too weakly basic to form HCl.

Add strong acid.

precipitate of
AgCl and Ag$_3$PO$_4$

precipitate of
AgCl

as are metal phosphates (Figure 18.15),

$$Ag_3PO_4(s) + 3\ H_3O^+(aq) \rightleftharpoons 3\ Ag^+(aq) + H_3PO_4(aq) + 3\ H_2O(\ell)$$

and metal hydroxides.

$$Mg(OH)_2(s) + 2\ H_3O^+(aq) \rightleftharpoons Mg^{2+}(aq) + 4\ H_2O(\ell)$$

In general, the solubility of a salt containing the conjugate base of a weak acid is increased by addition of a stronger acid to the solution. In contrast, salts are not soluble in strong acid if the anion is the conjugate base of a strong acid. For example, AgCl is not soluble in strong acid

$$AgCl(s) \rightleftharpoons Ag^+(aq) + Cl^-(aq) \qquad\qquad K_{sp} = 1.8 \times 10^{-10}$$

$$H_3O^+(aq) + Cl^-(aq) \rightleftharpoons HCl(aq) + H_2O(\ell) \qquad K \ll 1$$

because Cl$^-$ is a very weak base (◄ Table 17.3), and so its concentration is not lowered by a reaction with the strong acid H$_3$O$^+$ (Figure 18.15). This same conclusion would also apply to insoluble salts of Br$^-$ and I$^-$.

REVIEW & CHECK FOR SECTION 18.4

1. What is the K_{sp} expression for silver carbonate?

    (a) $K_{sp} = [Ag^+][CO_3^{2-}]$ (c) $K_{sp} = [Ag^+][CO_3^{2-}]^2$

    (b) $K_{sp} = [Ag^+]^2[CO_3^{2-}]$

2. Using K_{sp} values, predict which salt in each pair is more soluble in water.

    (a)   AgCl ($K_{sp} = 1.8 \times 10^{-10}$) or AgCN ($K_{sp} = 6.0 \times 10^{-17}$)

    (b)   Mg(OH)$_2$ ($K_{sp} = 5.6 \times 10^{-12}$) or Ca(OH)$_2$ ($K_{sp} = 5.5 \times 10^{-5}$)

    (c)   Ca(OH)$_2$ ($K_{sp} = 5.5 \times 10^{-5}$) or CaSO$_4$ ($K_{sp} = 4.9 \times 10^{-5}$)

3. What is the solubility of PbSO$_4$ in water at 25 °C? (K_{sp} for PbSO$_4$ = 2.5 × 10^{-8})

    (a)   2.5 × 10^{-8} M   (b)   1.6 × 10^{-4} M   (c)   6.3 × 10^{-16} M

4. What is the solubility of PbSO$_4$ in water at 25 °C if the solution already contains 0.25 M Na$_2$SO$_4$? (K_{sp} for PbSO$_4$ = 2.5 × 10^{-8})

    (a)   1.0 × 10^{-7} M   (b)   1.6 × 10^{-4} M   (c)   6.3 × 10^{-9} M

5. Which compound should be more soluble in 0.1 M HCl?

    (a)   FeCO$_3$ ($K_{sp} = 3.1 \times 10^{-11}$)   (b)   AgCl ($K_{sp} = 1.8 \times 10^{-10}$)

18.5 Precipitation Reactions

Metal-bearing ores contain the metal in the form of an insoluble salt (Figure 18.16), and, to complicate matters, ores often contain several such metal salts. Many industrial methods for separating metals from their ores involve dissolving metal salts to obtain the metal ion or ions in solution. The solution is then concentrated in some manner, and a precipitating agent is added to precipitate selectively only one type of metal ion as an insoluble salt. In the case of nickel, for example, the Ni^{2+} ion can be precipitated as insoluble nickel(II) sulfide or nickel(II) carbonate.

$$Ni^{2+}(aq) + HS^-(aq) + H_2O(\ell) \rightleftharpoons NiS(s) + H_3O^+(aq) \qquad K = 1.7 \times 10^{18}$$

$$Ni^{2+}(aq) + CO_3^{2-}(aq) \rightleftharpoons NiCO_3(s) \qquad\qquad\qquad\quad K = 7.1 \times 10^6$$

After separating the insoluble salt, the final step in obtaining the metal itself is to reduce the metal cation to the metal either chemically or electrochemically (▶ Chapter 20).

Our immediate goal is to work out methods to determine whether a precipitate will form under a given set of conditions. For example, if Ag^+ and Cl^- are present at some given concentrations, will AgCl precipitate from the solution?

FIGURE 18.16 Minerals. Minerals are insoluble salts. The minerals shown here are light purple fluorite (calcium fluoride), black hematite [iron(III) oxide], and rust brown goethite, a mixture of iron(III) oxide and iron(III) hydroxide.

© Cengage Learning/Charles D. Winters

K_{sp} and the Reaction Quotient, Q

Silver chloride, like silver bromide, is used in photographic films. It dissolves to a very small extent in water and has a correspondingly small value of K_{sp}.

$$AgCl(s) \rightleftharpoons Ag^+(aq) + Cl^-(aq) \qquad K_{sp} = [Ag^+][Cl^-] = 1.8 \times 10^{-10}$$

But look at the problem from the other direction: If a solution contains Ag^+ and Cl^- ions at some concentration, will AgCl precipitate from solution? This is the same question we asked in Section 16.2 when we wanted to know if a given mixture of reactants and products was an equilibrium mixture, if the reactants continued to form products, or if products would revert to reactants. The procedure there was to calculate the reaction quotient, Q.

For silver chloride, the expression for the reaction quotient, Q, is

$$Q = [Ag^+][Cl^-]$$

Recall that *the difference between Q and K is that the concentrations in the reaction quotient expression, Q, may or may not be those at equilibrium.* For the case of a slightly soluble salt such as AgCl, we can reach the following conclusions (◀ Section 16.2).

1. If $Q = K_{sp}$, the solution is saturated.

When $Q = K_{sp}$ the ion concentrations have reached their maximum value.

2. If $Q < K_{sp}$, the solution is not saturated.

This can mean either of two things: (i) If solid AgCl is present, more will dissolve until equilibrium is achieved (when $Q = K_{sp}$). (ii) If solid AgCl is not already present, more $Ag^+(aq)$ or more $Cl^-(aq)$ (or both) could be added to the solution until precipitation of solid AgCl begins (when $Q > K_{sp}$).

3. If $Q > K_{sp}$, the solution is oversaturated and precipitation will occur.

The concentrations of Ag^+ and Cl^- in solution are too high, and AgCl will precipitate until $Q = K_{sp}$.

CASE STUDY

Chemical Equilibria in the Oceans

Although there is continuing debate about the issue of global warming, the matter of the amount of CO_2 in Earth's atmosphere seems settled: There has been a significant increase since the beginning of the Industrial Revolution in the 18th century. Along with this increase in atmospheric CO_2, there has also been a documented increase in the amount of CO_2 absorbed by the world's oceans. Indeed, over the last 200 years the oceans have absorbed about 550 billion tons of CO_2 (currently about 22 million tons per day). The author of a recent paper in *Nature* stated that "If you took all of the man-made carbon in the ocean and released it into the air, atmospheric levels of CO_2 would be 20% higher." If the oceans had not absorbed that much CO_2, earth's temperature is predicted to be 2 °C warmer, a point at which significant climate change would occur. The absorption of CO_2 by the oceans has prevented much of this gas from entering the atmosphere, but there is evidence that the oceans are becoming a less efficient sink. And that is not the only problem.

When CO_2 dissolves in the ocean, it forms carbonic acid, a weak acid in equilibrium with hydronium ions and bicarbonate ions (as well as a small concentration of carbonate ions).

$$CO_2(g) + H_2O(\ell) \rightleftharpoons H_2CO_3(aq)$$

$$H_2CO_3(aq) + H_2O(\ell) \rightleftharpoons H_3O^+(aq) + HCO_3^-(aq)$$

$$HCO_3^-(aq) + H_2O(\ell) \rightleftharpoons H_3O^+(aq) + CO_3^{2-}(aq)$$

Aragonite, a form of $CaCO_3$.

Carbonate ions are required by many marine organisms such as plankton, shellfish, and fish to produce shells, made of $CaCO_3$, and skeletons. There are two naturally occurring forms of calcium carbonate: calcite and aragonite. Most mollusk shells are made of aragonite, and, as the K_{sp} values show, aragonite ($K_{sp} = 6.0 \times 10^{-9}$) is slightly more soluble than calcite ($K_{sp} = 3.4 \times 10^{-9}$).

Because carbonate ions are central to the life of marine organisms, any change in the calcium carbonate equilibrium

$$CaCO_3(s) \rightleftharpoons Ca^{2+}(aq) + CO_3^{2-}(aq)$$

can lead to significant changes in marine life. If, for example, the carbonate ion concentration in the oceans drops below the saturation level, calcium carbonate will dissolve. A paper published in the journal *Science* in 2009 reports that that is indeed happening, espe-

cially in the Arctic Ocean. (The pH of ocean surface water is now about 8.1, a drop from 8.2 in the 18th century.) Hydronium ions from dissolved CO_2 react with carbonate ions to produce bicarbonate ions, thus disrupting the calcium carbonate equilibrium and affecting the shells of marine creatures (page 128). This trend is exacerbated by the fact that northern rivers and melting sea ice are introducing increasing amounts of fresh water into the Arctic Ocean, which lowers the CO_3^{2-} concentration and allows aragonite to dissolve.

The chemistry of the oceans is a delicate equilibrium, and anthropogenic and natural effects can cause serious disruption in the chemistry. In fact a marine geochemist said in 2009 that "High-latitude oceans may already be at a tipping point for carbonate shell builders."

Question:

How much more soluble is aragonite than calcite? Compare the solubility of $CaCO_3$ from these two sources on a gram per liter basis.

The answer to this question is available in Appendix N.

References:

1. S. Khatiwala, *Nature*, 2009, *462*, 346.
2. M. Yamamoto-Kawai, F. A. McLaughlin, E. C. Carmack, S. Nishino, and K. Shimada, *Science*, 2009, *326*, 1098–1100, and references therein.
3. R. Petkewich, *Chemical & Engineering News*, February 23, 2009, pp. 56–58.

⏺WL **INTERACTIVE EXAMPLE 18.13** **Solubility and the Reaction Quotient**

Problem Solid AgCl has been placed in a beaker of water. After some time, the concentrations of Ag^+ and Cl^- are each 1.2×10^{-5} mol/L. Has the system reached equilibrium? If not, will more AgCl dissolve?

What Do You Know? You know the balanced equation for dissolving the AgCl, its value of K_{sp}, and the Ag^+ and Cl^- concentrations.

Strategy

• Write the balanced equation for dissolving the salt and then write the expression for the reaction quotient, Q.

• Use the experimental ion concentrations to calculate the reaction quotient Q. Compare Q and K_{sp} to decide if the system is at equilibrium (if $Q = K_{sp}$).

Solution

$$AgCl(s) \rightleftharpoons Ag^+(aq) + Cl^-(aq) \qquad K_{sp} = [Ag^+][Cl^-] = 1.8 \times 10^{-10}$$

$$Q = [Ag^+][Cl^-] = (1.2 \times 10^{-5})(1.2 \times 10^{-5}) = 1.4 \times 10^{-10}$$

Here, Q is less than K_{sp} (1.8×10^{-10}). The solution is not yet saturated, and AgCl will continue to dissolve until $Q = K_{sp}$, at which point $[Ag^+] = [Cl^-] = 1.3 \times 10^{-5}$ M. That is, an additional 0.1×10^{-5} mol of AgCl will dissolve per liter.

Think about Your Answer Dissolving is often a fairly slow process. If you measure the ion concentrations at a particular time, they may not have yet reached an equilibrium value, as is the case here. In contrast, acid–base reactions generally proceed rapidly to equilibrium.

Check Your Understanding

Solid PbI_2 ($K_{sp} = 9.8 \times 10^{-9}$) is placed in a beaker of water. After a period of time, the lead(II) concentration is measured and found to be 1.1×10^{-3} M. Has the system reached equilibrium? That is, is the solution saturated? If not, will more PbI_2 dissolve?

K_{sp}, the Reaction Quotient, and Precipitation Reactions

Using the reaction quotient and the solubility product constant, we can decide (1) if a precipitate will form when the ion concentrations are known or (2) what concentrations of ions are required to begin the precipitation of an insoluble salt.

Suppose the concentration of magnesium ion in an aqueous solution is 1.5×10^{-6} M. If enough NaOH is added to make the solution 1.0×10^{-4} M in hydroxide ion, OH^-, will precipitation of $Mg(OH)_2$ occur ($K_{sp} = 5.6 \times 10^{-12}$)? If not, will it occur if the concentration of OH^- is increased to 1.0×10^{-2} M?

Our strategy is similar to that in Example 18.13. That is, use the ion concentrations to calculate the value of Q and then compare Q with K_{sp} to decide if the system is at equilibrium. We begin with the equation for the dissolution of $Mg(OH)_2$.

$$Mg(OH)_2(s) \rightleftharpoons Mg^{2+}(aq) + 2\ OH^-(aq)$$

When the concentrations of magnesium and hydroxide ions are the first ones stated above, we find that Q is less than K_{sp}.

$$Q = [Mg^{2+}][OH^-]^2 = (1.5 \times 10^{-6})(1.0 \times 10^{-4})^2 = 1.5 \times 10^{-14}$$

$$Q\ (1.5 \times 10^{-14}) < K_{sp}\ (5.6 \times 10^{-12})$$

This means the solution is not yet saturated, and precipitation does not occur. When $[OH^-]$ is increased to 1.0×10^{-2} M, the reaction quotient is 1.5×10^{-10},

$$Q = (1.5 \times 10^{-6})(1.0 \times 10^{-2})^2$$

$$Q = 1.5 \times 10^{-10} > K_{sp}\ (5.6 \times 10^{-12})$$

and the reaction quotient is now *larger* than K_{sp}. Precipitation of $Mg(OH)_2$ occurs and will continue until the Mg^{2+} and OH^- ion concentrations have decreased to the point where their product is equal to K_{sp}.

Now let us turn to a similar problem: deciding how much of the precipitating agent is required to begin the precipitation of an ion at a given concentration level.

◉WL **INTERACTIVE EXAMPLE 18.14** **Ion Concentrations Required to Begin Precipitation**

Problem The concentration of barium ion, Ba^{2+}, in a solution is 0.010 M.

(a) What concentration of sulfate ion, SO_4^{2-}, is required to begin the precipitation of $BaSO_4$?

(b) When the concentration of sulfate ion in the solution reaches 0.015 M, what concentration of barium ion will remain in solution?

What Do You Know? There are three terms in the K_{sp} expression: K_{sp} and the anion and cation concentrations. Here, you know K_{sp} (1.1×10^{-10}) and one of the ion concentrations. You can then calculate the other ion concentration.

Strategy Map 18.13

PROBLEM

Does **AgCl** precipitate at specified values of **[Ag⁺]** and **[Cl⁻]**?

↓

DATA/INFORMATION KNOWN

- K_{sp} value for AgCl
- Ag^+ concentration
- Cl^- concentration

STEP 1. Write expression for Q, the reaction quotient.

$$Q = [Ag^+][Cl^-]$$

STEP 2. Enter concentrations in Q expression and solve.

$Q < K_{sp}$, so more AgCl will dissolve.

Strategy Map 18.14

PROBLEM

What concentration of SO_4^{2-} is required to begin precipitation of $BaSO_4$?

↓

DATA/INFORMATION KNOWN

- K_{sp} value for $BaSO_4$
- Initial $[Ba^{2+}]$

> **STEP 1.** Write **expression** for K_{sp}.

$K_{sp} = [Ba^{2+}][SO_4^{2-}]$

> **STEP 2.** Enter Ba^{2+} **concentration** and solve for $[SO_4^{2-}]$.

↓

$BaSO_4$ begins to precipitate when $[SO_4^{2-}]$ exceeds calculated value.

Strategy

- Write the balanced equation for dissolving $BaSO_4$ and the K_{sp} expression.

- **Part (a):** Use the K_{sp} expression to calculate $[SO_4^{2-}]$ when $[Ba^{2+}] = 0.010$ M.

- **Part (b):** Use the K_{sp} expression to calculate $[Ba^{2+}]$ when $[SO_4^{2-}] = 0.015$ M.

Solution

$$BaSO_4(s) \rightleftharpoons Ba^{2+}(aq) + SO_4^{2-}(aq) \qquad K_{sp} = [Ba^{2+}][SO_4^{2-}] = 1.1 \times 10^{-10}$$

(a) When the product of the ion concentrations exceeds the K_{sp} ($= 1.1 \times 10^{-10}$)—that is, when $Q > K_{sp}$—precipitation will occur. The Ba^{2+} ion concentration is known (0.010 M), so the SO_4^{2-} ion concentration necessary for precipitation can be calculated.

$$[SO_4^{2-}] = \frac{K_{sp}}{[Ba^{2+}]} = \frac{1.1 \times 10^{-10}}{0.010} = 1.1 \times 10^{-8} \text{ M}$$

The result tells us that if the sulfate ion concentration is just slightly greater than 1.1×10^{-8} M, $BaSO_4$ will begin to precipitate.

(b) If the sulfate ion concentration is increased to 0.015 M, the maximum concentration of Ba^{2+} ion that can exist in solution (in equilibrium with $BaSO_4$) is

$$[Ba^{2+}] = \frac{K_{sp}}{[SO_4^{2-}]} = \frac{1.1 \times 10^{-10}}{0.015} = 7.3 \times 10^{-9} \text{ M}$$

Think about Your Answer The fact that the barium ion concentration is so small when $[SO_4^{2-}] = 0.015$ M means that the Ba^{2+} ion has been essentially removed from solution. (It began at 0.010 M and has decreased by a factor of about 1 million.)

Check Your Understanding

What is the minimum concentration of I^- that can cause precipitation of PbI_2 from a 0.050 M solution of $Pb(NO_3)_2$? K_{sp} for PbI_2 is 9.8×10^{-9}. What concentration of Pb^{2+} ions remains in solution when the concentration of I^- is 0.0015 M?

EXAMPLE 18.15 K_{sp} and Precipitations

Problem Suppose you mix 100.0 mL of 0.0200 M $BaCl_2$ with 50.0 mL of 0.0300 M Na_2SO_4. Will $BaSO_4$ ($K_{sp} = 1.1 \times 10^{-10}$) precipitate?

What Do You Know? You know the concentration of two different compounds in solutions of differing volumes and so you can calculate the amount (moles) of each substance. You also know that $BaCl_2$ and Na_2SO_4 will combine to give a precipitate, $BaSO_4$, if they are mixed in sufficient concentration. You also know the K_{sp} value for $BaSO_4$.

Strategy Here, you mix two solutions, one containing Ba^{2+} ions and the other SO_4^{2-} ions, both with known concentration and volume, and insoluble $BaSO_4$ may be formed.

- Find the concentration of each of these ions after mixing.

- Knowing the ion concentrations in the combined solution, calculate Q and compare it with the K_{sp} value for $BaSO_4$ to decide if $BaSO_4$ will precipitate under these circumstances.

Solution First, use the equation $c_1V_1 = c_2V_2$ (◄ Section 4.5) to calculate c_2, the concentration of the Ba^{2+} and SO_4^{2-} ions after mixing, to give a new solution with a volume of 150.0 mL ($= V_2$).

$$[Ba^{2+}] \text{ after mixing} = \frac{(0.0200 \text{ mol/L})(0.1000 \text{ L})}{0.1500 \text{ L}} = 0.0133 \text{ M}$$

$$[SO_4^{2-}] \text{ after mixing} = \frac{(0.0300 \text{ mol/L})(0.0500 \text{ L})}{0.1500 \text{ L}} = 0.0100 \text{ M}$$

The equilibrium governing the reaction that can occur is

$$BaSO_4(s) \rightleftharpoons Ba^{2+}(aq) + SO_4{}^{2-}(aq) \qquad K_{sp} = [Ba^{2+}][SO_4{}^{2-}] = 1.1 \times 10^{-10}$$

Now the reaction quotient can be calculated.

$$Q = [Ba^{2+}][SO_4{}^{2-}] = (0.0133)(0.0100) = 1.33 \times 10^{-4}$$

Q is much larger than K_{sp}, so $BaSO_4$ precipitates.

Think about Your Answer The K_{sp} value for $BaSO_4$ is very small, so mixing solutions with Ba^{2+} and $SO_4{}^{2-}$ ions, even in very low concentration, can lead to the precipitation of $BaSO_4$.

Check Your Understanding

You have 100.0 mL of 0.0010 M silver nitrate. Will AgCl precipitate if you add 5.0 mL of 0.025 M HCl?

REVIEW & CHECK FOR SECTION 18.5

Will $SrSO_4$ precipitate from a solution containing 2.5×10^{-4} M strontium ion, Sr^{2+}, if enough of the soluble salt Na_2SO_4 is added to make the solution 2.5×10^{-4} M in $SO_4{}^{2-}$? K_{sp} for $SrSO_4$ is 3.4×10^{-7}.

(a) yes   (b) no   (c) can't decide

18.6 Equilibria Involving Complex Ions

Metal ions exist in aqueous solution as complex ions (◄ Section 17.11) (Figure 18.17). Complex ions consist of the metal ion and other molecules or ions bound into a single entity. In water, metal ions are always surrounded by water molecules, with the negative end of the polar water molecule, the oxygen atom, attracted to the positive metal ion. In the case of Ni^{2+}, the ion exists as $[Ni(H_2O)_6]^{2+}$ in water. On adding ammonia, water molecules are displaced successively, and in the presence of a high enough concentration of ammonia, the complex ion $[Ni(NH_3)_6]^{2+}$ exists. Many organic molecules also form complex ions with metal ions, one example being the complex with the dimethylglyoximate ion in Figure 18.17.

The molecules or ions that bind to metal ions are called **ligands** (► Chapter 22). In aqueous solution, metal ions and ligands exist in equilibrium, and the equilibrium constants for these reactions are referred to as **formation constants**, K_f (Appendix K). For example,

$$Cu^{2+}(aq) + NH_3(aq) \rightleftharpoons [Cu(NH_3)]^{2+}(aq) \qquad K_{f1} = 2.0 \times 10^4$$

$$[Cu(NH_3)]^{2+}(aq) + NH_3(aq) \rightleftharpoons [Cu(NH_3)_2]^{2+}(aq) \qquad K_{f2} = 4.7 \times 10^3$$

$$[Cu(NH_3)_2]^{2+}(aq) + NH_3(aq) \rightleftharpoons [Cu(NH_3)_3]^{2+}(aq) \qquad K_{f3} = 1.1 \times 10^3$$

$$[Cu(NH_3)_3]^{2+}(aq) + NH_3(aq) \rightleftharpoons [Cu(NH_3)_4]^{2+}(aq) \qquad K_{f4} = 2.0 \times 10^2$$

In these reactions, Cu^{2+} begins as $[Cu(H_2O)_4]^{2+}$, but ammonia successively displaces the water molecules. Overall, the formation of the tetraammine copper(II) complex ion has an equilibrium constant of 2.1×10^{13} ($= K_{f1} \times K_{f2} \times K_{f3} \times K_{f4}$).

$$Cu^{2+}(aq) + 4\, NH_3(aq) \rightleftharpoons [Cu(NH_3)_4]^{2+}(aq) \qquad K_f = 2.1 \times 10^{13}$$

Dimethylglyoximate complex of Ni^{2+} ion

© Cengage Learning/Charles D. Winters

— $[Ni(NH_3)_6]^{2+}$

— $[Ni(H_2O)_6]^{2+}$

FIGURE 18.17 Complex ions. The green solution contains soluble $Ni(H_2O)_6{}^{2+}$ ions in which water molecules are bound to Ni^{2+} ions by ion–dipole forces. This complex ion gives the solution its green color. The Ni^{2+}-ammonia complex ion is purple. The red, insoluble solid is the dimethylglyoximate complex of the Ni^{2+} ion $[Ni(C_4H_7O_2N_2)_2]$ (model at top). Formation of this beautiful red insoluble compound is the classical test for the presence of the aqueous Ni^{2+} ion.

EXAMPLE 18.16 Complex Ion Equilibria

Problem What is the concentration of Cu^{2+} ions in a solution prepared by adding 0.00100 mol of $Cu(NO_3)_2$ to 1.00 L of 1.50 M NH_3? K_f for the copper-ammonia complex ion $[Cu(NH_3)_4]^{2+}$ is 2.1×10^{13}.

What Do You Know? Here you know the concentration of the species that form the complex ion (Cu^{2+} and NH_3), and you know the formation constant for the ion.

Strategy The formation constant for the complex ion is very large, so you start with the assumption that all of the Cu^{2+} ions react with NH_3 to form $[Cu(NH_3)_4]^{2+}$. That is, the initial concentration of the complex ion, $[Cu(NH_3)_4]^{2+}$ is 0.00100 M. This cation then dissociates to produce Cu^{2+} ions and additional NH_3 in solution. The equilibrium constant for the dissociation of $[Cu(NH_3)_4]^{2+}$ is the reciprocal of K_f because the dissociation of the ion is the reverse of its formation.

- Write a balanced equation for the dissociation of the complex ion that formed in solution and set up an ICE table.

- Assume that all of the Cu^{2+} ions in the solution are in the form of $[Cu(NH_3)_4]^{2+}$ (0.00100 M). This means that $[NH_3]$ = original concentration $- 4 \times 0.00100$ M.

- Assume the concentration of complex ion dissociated at equilibrium is x, so x mol/L of Cu^{2+} are released to solution as are $4x$ mol/L of NH_3.

- Use the equilibrium concentrations of the ions in the expression for $K_{dissociation}$ ($= 1/K_f$) and solve for x (which is the concentration of Cu^{2+} at equilibrium).

Solution Set up an ICE table for the dissociation of $[Cu(NH_3)_4]^{2+}$.

Equation	$[Cu(NH_3)_4]^{2+}(aq)$	$\rightleftharpoons$ $Cu^{2+}(aq)$	+ $4NH_3(aq)$
Initial (M)	0.00100	0	1.50 − 0.00400 M
Change (M)	−x	+x	+4x
Equilibrium (M)	0.00100 − x ≈ 0.00100	x	1.50 − 0.00400 + 4x ≈ 1.50

Here we assume that x is so small that the concentration of the complex ion is very nearly 0.00100 M and that the NH_3 concentration at equilibrium is essentially what was there originally.

$$K_{dissociation} = \frac{1}{K_f} = \frac{1}{2.1 \times 10^{13}} = \frac{[Cu^{2+}][NH_3]^4}{\{[Cu(NH_3)_4]^{2+}\}} = \frac{(x)(1.50)^4}{0.00100}$$

$$x = [Cu^{2+}] = 9.4 \times 10^{-18} \text{ M}$$

Think about Your Answer Make sure to test your assumption that x is so small it can neglected in determining the equilibrium concentrations of $[Cu(NH_3)_4]^{2+}$ and NH_3. It certainly is in this case.

Check Your Understanding

Silver nitrate (0.0050 mol) is added to 1.00 L of 1.00 M NH_3. What is the concentration of Ag^+ ions at equilibrium?

$$Ag^+(aq) + 2NH_3(aq) \rightleftharpoons [Ag(NH_3)_2]^+(aq) \qquad K_f = 1.1 \times 10^7$$

REVIEW & CHECK FOR SECTION 18.6

Iron(II) chloride (0.0025 mol) is added to 1.00 L of 0.500 M NaCN. What is the concentration of Fe^{2+} ions at equilibrium? K_f for $[Fe(CN)_6]^{4-}$ is 1.0×10^{35}.

(a) 1.0×10^{-35} M   (b) 1.9×10^{-36} M   (c) 5.2×10^{-38} M

18.7 Solubility and Complex Ions

Silver chloride does not dissolve either in water or in strong acid, but it does dissolve in ammonia because it forms a water-soluble complex ion, $[Ag(NH_3)_2]^+$ (Figure 18.18).

$$AgCl(s) + 2NH_3(aq) \rightleftharpoons [Ag(NH_3)_2]^+(aq) + Cl^-(aq)$$

We can view dissolving AgCl(s) as a two-step process. First, AgCl dissolves minimally in water, giving $Ag^+(aq)$ and $Cl^-(aq)$ ion. Then, the $Ag^+(aq)$ ion combines with NH_3 to give the ammonia complex. Lowering the $Ag^+(aq)$ concentration through complexation with NH_3 shifts the solubility equilibrium to the right, and more solid AgCl dissolves.

$$AgCl(s) \rightleftharpoons Ag^+(aq) + Cl^-(aq) \qquad K_{sp} = 1.8 \times 10^{-10}$$

$$Ag^+(aq) + 2\,NH_3(aq) \rightleftharpoons [Ag(NH_3)_2]^+(aq) \qquad K_f = 1.1 \times 10^7$$

This is an example of combining or "coupling" two (or more) equilibria where one is a product-favored reaction and the other is reactant-favored.

The large value of the formation constant for $[Ag(NH_3)_2]^+$ means that the equilibrium lies well to the right, and AgCl can dissolve in the presence of NH_3. If you combine K_f with K_{sp}, you obtain the net equilibrium constant for the interaction of AgCl and aqueous ammonia.

$$K_{net} = K_{sp} \times K_f = (1.8 \times 10^{-10})(1.1 \times 10^7) = 2.0 \times 10^{-3}$$

$$K_{net} = 2.0 \times 10^{-3} = \frac{\{[Ag(NH_3)_2]^+\}[Cl^-]}{[NH_3]^2}$$

Even though the value of K_{net} seems small, if you use a large concentration of NH_3, the concentration of $[Ag(NH_3)_2]^+$ in solution can be appreciable. Silver chloride is thus much more soluble in the presence of ammonia than in pure water.

The stabilities of various complex ions involving silver(I) can be compared by comparing values of their formation constants.

Formation Equilibrium	K_f
$Ag^+(aq) + 2\,Cl^-(aq) \rightleftharpoons [AgCl_2]^-(aq)$	1.1×10^5
$Ag^+(aq) + 2\,S_2O_3{}^{2-}(aq) \rightleftharpoons [Ag(S_2O_3)_2]^{3-}(aq)$	2.9×10^{13}
$Ag^+(aq) + 2\,CN^-(aq) \rightleftharpoons [Ag(CN)_2]^-(aq)$	1.3×10^{21}

The formation of all three silver complexes is strongly product-favored. The cyanide complex ion $[Ag(CN)_2]^-$ is the most stable of the three.

Figure 18.18 shows what happens as complex ions are formed. Beginning with a precipitate of AgCl, adding aqueous ammonia dissolves the precipitate to give the

• **Complex Ions** Complex ions are prevalent in chemistry and are the basis of such biologically important substances as hemoglobin and vitamin B_{12}. They are described in more detail in Chapter 22.

AgCl(s),
$K_{sp} = 1.8 \times 10^{-10}$

(a) AgCl precipitates on adding NaCl(aq) to $AgNO_3(aq)$.

$[Ag(NH_3)_2]^+(aq)$

(b) The precipitate of AgCl dissolves on adding aqueous NH_3 to give water-soluble $[Ag(NH_3)_2]^+$.

AgBr(s),
$K_{sp} = 5.4 \times 10^{-13}$

(c) The silver-ammonia complex ion is changed to insoluble AgBr on adding NaBr(aq).

$[Ag(S_2O_3)_2]^{3-}(aq)$

(d) Solid AgBr is dissolved on adding $Na_2S_2O_3(aq)$. The product is the water-soluble complex ion $[Ag(S_2O_3)_2]^{3-}$.

$NH_3(aq)$ → $NaBr(aq)$ → $Na_2S_2O_3(aq)$ →

Photos © Cengage Learning/Charles D. Winters

FIGURE 18.18 Forming and dissolving precipitates. Insoluble compounds often dissolve upon addition of a complexing agent.

soluble complex ion $[Ag(NH_3)_2]^+$. Silver bromide is even more stable than $[Ag(NH_3)_2]^+$, so AgBr ($K_{sp} = 5.4 \times 10^{-13}$) forms in preference to the complex ion on adding bromide ion. If thiosulfate ion, $S_2O_3^{2-}$, is then added, AgBr dissolves due to the formation of $[Ag(S_2O_3)_2]^{3-}$, a complex ion with a large formation constant (2.9×10^{13}).

EXAMPLE 18.17   Complex Ions and Solubility

Problem What is the value of the equilibrium constant, K_{net}, for dissolving AgBr in a solution containing the thiosulfate ion, $S_2O_3^{2-}$ (Figure 18.18)? Does AgBr dissolve readily on adding aqueous sodium thiosulfate to the solid?

What Do You Know? There are two equilibria here. One is for dissolving AgBr in water to give Ag^+ and Br^- ions, and its equilibrium constant is K_{sp}. The other is the formation of $[Ag(S_2O_3)_2]^{3-}$ ions from Ag^+ and $S_2O_3^{2-}$ ions; its equilibrium constant is K_f.

Strategy Summing several equilibrium processes gives the net chemical equation. K_{net} is the product of the values of K of the summed chemical equations (◀ Section 16.5).

Solution The overall reaction for dissolving AgBr in the presence of the thiosulfate anion is the sum of two equilibrium processes.

$$AgBr(s) \rightleftharpoons Ag^+(aq) + Br^-(aq) \qquad\qquad K_{sp} = 5.0 \times 10^{-13}$$

$$Ag^+(aq) + 2\ S_2O_3^{2-}(aq) \rightleftharpoons [Ag(S_2O_3)_2]^{3-}(aq) \qquad\qquad K_f = 2.9 \times 10^{13}$$

Net chemical equation:

$$AgBr(aq) + 2\ S_2O_3^{2-}(aq) \rightleftharpoons [Ag(S_2O_3)_2]^{3-}(aq) + Br^-(aq) \qquad K_{net} = K_{sp} \times K_f = 15$$

AgBr is predicted to dissolve readily in aqueous $Na_2S_2O_3$, as observed (Figure 18.18).

Think about Your Answer The value of K_{net} is greater than 1, indicating a product-favored reaction at equilibrium.

Check Your Understanding

Calculate the value of the equilibrium constant, K_{net}, for dissolving $Cu(OH)_2$ in aqueous ammonia (to form the complex ion $[Cu(NH_3)_4]^{2+}$) (◀ Figure 17.10).

> **REVIEW & CHECK FOR SECTION 18.7**
>
> What is the equilibrium constant for the process of dissolving AgI by the addition of aqueous NaCN? K_{sp} for AgI is 8.5×10^{-17}, and K_f for $[Ag(CN)_2]^-$ is 1.3×10^{21}.
>
> (a) 6.5×10^{-4} (b) 8.7×10^4 (c) 1.1×10^5

CHAPTER GOALS REVISITED

Now that you have studied this chapter, you should ask whether you have met the chapter goals. In particular, you should be able to:

Understand the common ion effect

a.   Predict the effect of the addition of a "common ion" on the pH of the solution of a weak acid or base (Section 18.1). Study Questions: 1–4, 109.

Understand the control of pH in aqueous solutions with buffers

a.   Describe the functioning of buffer solutions. (Section 18.2). Go Chemistry Module 23.

b.   Use the Henderson–Hasselbalch equation (Equation 18.2) to calculate the pH of a buffer solution of given composition. Study Questions: 5–8, 11–14.

c.   Describe how a buffer solution of a given pH can be prepared. Study Questions: 9, 10, 15–18, 83, 90, 101, 102, 109.

d.   Calculate the pH of a buffer solution before and after adding acid or base. Study Questions: 19–22.

Evaluate the pH in the course of acid–base titrations

a. Predict the pH of an acid–base reaction at its equivalence point (Section 18.3; see also Sections 17.6 and 17.7). **Study Questions: 24–30, 74, 76, 98, 108.**

Acid	Base	pH at Equivalence Point
Strong	Strong	= 7 (neutral)
Strong	Weak	< 7 (acidic)
Weak	Strong	> 7 (basic)

b. Understand the differences between the titration curves for a strong acid–strong base titration and titrations in which one of the substances is weak.
c. Describe how an indicator functions in an acid–base titration. **Study Questions: 31, 97–99.**

Apply chemical equilibrium concepts to the solubility of ionic compounds

a. Write the equilibrium constant expression—relating concentrations of ions in solutions to K_{sp}—for any insoluble salt (Section 18.4). **Study Questions: 37, 38.**
b. Calculate K_{sp} values from experimental data (Section 18.4). **Study Questions: 39–44.**
c. Estimate the solubility of a salt from the value of K_{sp} (Section 18.4). **Study Questions: 45–48, 96, 105.**
d. Calculate the solubility of a salt in the presence of a common ion (Section 18.4). **Study Questions: 53–56.**
e. Understand how hydrolysis of basic anions affects the solubility of a salt (Section 18.4). **Study Questions: 57, 58, 112.**
f. Decide if a precipitate will form when the ion concentrations are known Section 18.5). **Study Questions: 59–62, 73, 80, 88, 89.**
g. Calculate the ion concentrations that are required to begin the precipitation of an insoluble salt (Section 18.5). **Study Questions: 63, 78, 87–89.**
h. Understand that the formation of a complex ion can increase the solubility of an insoluble salt (Sections 18.6 and 18.7). **Study Questions: 65–70, 86, 92.**

Key Equations

Equation 18.1 (page 812) Hydronium ion concentration in a buffer solution composed of a weak acid and its conjugate base.

$$[H_3O^+] = \frac{[\text{acid}]}{[\text{conjugate base}]} \times K_a$$

Equation 18.2 (page 813) Henderson–Hasselbalch equation. To calculate the pH of a buffer solution composed of a weak acid and its conjugate base.

$$pH = pK_a + \log\frac{[\text{conjugate base}]}{[\text{acid}]}$$

Equation 18.3 (page 821) Equation to calculate the hydronium ion concentration before the equivalence point in the titration of a weak acid with a strong base. See also Equation 18.4 for the version of the equation based on the Henderson–Hasselbalch equation.

$$[H_3O^+] = \frac{[\text{weak acid remaining}]}{[\text{conjugate base produced}]} \times K_a$$

Equation 18.5 (page 821) The relationship between the pH of the solution and the pK_a of the weak acid (or $[H_3O^+]$ and K_a) at the halfway or half-neutralization point in the titration of a weak acid with a strong base (or of a weak base with a strong acid).

$$[H_3O^+] = K_a \text{ and } pH = pK_a$$

Equation 18.6 (page 829) The general equilibrium constant expression, K_{sp} (solubility constant) for dissolving a poorly soluble salt, A_xB_y.

$$A_xB_y(s) \rightleftharpoons x\ A^{y+}(aq) + y\ B^{x-}(aq) \qquad K_{sp} = [A^{y+}]^x[B^{x-}]^y$$

Study Questions

⭕WL Interactive versions of these questions are assignable in OWL.

▲ denotes challenging questions.

Blue-numbered questions have answers in Appendix R and fully worked solutions in the *Student Solutions Manual*.

Practicing Skills

The Common Ion Effect and Buffer Solutions
(See Section 18.1 and 18.2 and Examples 18.1 and 18.2.)

1. Does the pH of the solution increase, decrease, or stay the same when you
   (a) add solid ammonium chloride to a dilute aqueous solution of NH_3?
   (b) add solid sodium acetate to a dilute aqueous solution of acetic acid?
   (c) add solid NaCl to a dilute aqueous solution of NaOH?

2. Does the pH of the solution increase, decrease, or stay the same when you
   (a) add solid sodium oxalate, $Na_2C_2O_4$, to 50.0 mL of 0.015 M oxalic acid, $H_2C_2O_4$?
   (b) add solid ammonium chloride to 75 mL of 0.016 M HCl?
   (c) add 20.0 g of NaCl to 1.0 L of 0.10 M sodium acetate, $NaCH_3CO_2$?

3. What is the pH of a solution that consists of 0.20 M ammonia, NH_3, and 0.20 M ammonium chloride, NH_4Cl?

4. What is the pH of 0.15 M acetic acid to which 1.56 g of sodium acetate, $NaCH_3CO_2$, has been added?

5. What is the pH of the solution that results from adding 30.0 mL of 0.015 M KOH to 50.0 mL of 0.015 M benzoic acid?

6. What is the pH of the solution that results from adding 25.0 mL of 0.12 M HCl to 25.0 mL of 0.43 M NH_3?

7. What is the pH of the buffer solution that contains 2.2 g of NH_4Cl in 250 mL of 0.12 M NH_3? Is the final pH lower or higher than the pH of the 0.12 M ammonia solution?

8. Lactic acid ($CH_3CHOHCO_2H$) is found in sour milk, in sauerkraut, and in muscles after activity. (K_a for lactic acid = 1.4×10^{-4}.)
   (a) If 2.75 g of $NaCH_3CHOHCO_2$, sodium lactate, is added to 5.00×10^2 mL of 0.100 M lactic acid, what is the pH of the resulting buffer solution?
   (b) Is the pH of the buffered solution lower or higher than the pH of the lactic acid solution?

9. What mass of sodium acetate, $NaCH_3CO_2$, must be added to 1.00 L of 0.10 M acetic acid to give a solution with a pH of 4.50?

10. What mass of ammonium chloride, NH_4Cl, must be added to exactly 5.00×10^2 mL of 0.10 M NH_3 solution to give a solution with a pH of 9.00?

Using the Henderson–Hasselbalch Equation
(See Section 18.2 and Example 18.3.)

11. Calculate the pH of a solution that has an acetic acid concentration of 0.050 M and a sodium acetate concentration of 0.075 M.

12. Calculate the pH of a solution that has an ammonium chloride concentration of 0.050 M and an ammonia concentration of 0.045 M.

13. A buffer is composed of formic acid and its conjugate base, the formate ion.
    (a) What is the pH of a solution that has a formic acid concentration of 0.050 M and a sodium formate concentration of 0.035 M?
    (b) What must the ratio of acid to conjugate base be to have a pH value 0.50 units higher than the value calculated in part (a)?

14. A buffer solution is composed of 1.360 g of KH_2PO_4 and 5.677 g of Na_2HPO_4.
    (a) What is the pH of the buffer solution?
    (b) What mass of KH_2PO_4 must be added to decrease the buffer solution pH by 0.50 unit from the value calculated in part (a)?

Preparing a Buffer Solution
(See Section 18.2 and Example 18.4.)

15. Which of the following combinations would be the best to buffer the pH of a solution at approximately 9?
    (a) HCl and NaCl
    (b) NH_3 and NH_4Cl
    (c) CH_3CO_2H and $NaCH_3CO_2$

16. Which of the following combinations would be the best to buffer the pH of a solution at approximately 7?
    (a) H_3PO_4 and NaH_2PO_4
    (b) NaH_2PO_4 and Na_2HPO_4
    (c) Na_2HPO_4 and Na_3PO_4

17. Describe how to prepare a buffer solution from NaH_2PO_4 and Na_2HPO_4 to have a pH of 7.5.

18. Describe how to prepare a buffer solution from NH_3 and NH_4Cl to have a pH of 9.5.

Adding an Acid or a Base to a Buffer Solution
(See Section 18.2 and Example 18.5.)

19. A buffer solution was prepared by adding 4.95 g of sodium acetate, $NaCH_3CO_2$, to 2.50×10^2 mL of 0.150 M acetic acid, CH_3CO_2H.
    (a) What is the pH of the buffer?
    (b) What is the pH of 1.00×10^2 mL of the buffer solution if you add 82 mg of NaOH to the solution?

20. You dissolve 0.425 g of NaOH in 2.00 L of a buffer solution that has $[H_2PO_4^-] = [HPO_4^{2-}] = 0.132$ M. What is the pH of the solution before adding NaOH? After adding NaOH?

21. A buffer solution is prepared by adding 0.125 mol of ammonium chloride to 5.00×10^2 mL of 0.500 M solution of ammonia.
    (a) What is the pH of the buffer?
    (b) If 0.0100 mol of HCl gas is bubbled into 5.00×10^2 mL of the buffer, what is the new pH of the solution?

22. What is the pH change when 20.0 mL of 0.100 M NaOH is added to 80.0 mL of a buffer solution consisting of 0.169 M NH_3 and 0.183 M NH_4Cl?

More about Acid–Base Reactions: Titrations
(See Section 18.3 and Examples 18.6 and 18.7.)

23. Phenol, C_6H_5OH, is a weak organic acid. Suppose 0.515 g of the compound is dissolved in enough water to make 125 mL of solution. The resulting solution is titrated with 0.123 M NaOH.

    $$C_6H_5OH(aq) + OH^-(aq) \rightleftharpoons C_6H_5O^-(aq) + H_2O(\ell)$$

    (a) What is the pH of the original solution of phenol?
    (b) What are the concentrations of all of the following ions at the equivalence point: Na^+, H_3O^+, OH^-, and $C_6H_5O^-$?
    (c) What is the pH of the solution at the equivalence point?

24. Assume you dissolve 0.235 g of the weak acid benzoic acid, $C_6H_5CO_2H$, in enough water to make 1.00×10^2 mL of solution and then titrate the solution with 0.108 M NaOH.

    $$C_6H_5CO_2H(aq) + OH^-(aq) \rightleftharpoons C_6H_5CO_2^-(aq) + H_2O(\ell)$$

    (a) What was the pH of the original benzoic acid solution?
    (b) What are the concentrations of all of the following ions at the equivalence point: Na^+, H_3O^+, OH^-, and $C_6H_5CO_2^-$?
    (c) What is the pH of the solution at the equivalence point?

25. You require 36.78 mL of 0.0105 M HCl to reach the equivalence point in the titration of 25.0 mL of aqueous ammonia.
    (a) What was the concentration of NH_3 in the original ammonia solution?
    (b) What are the concentrations of H_3O^+, OH^-, and NH_4^+ at the equivalence point?
    (c) What is the pH of the solution at the equivalence point?

26. A titration of 25.0 mL of a solution of the weak base aniline, $C_6H_5NH_2$, requires 25.67 mL of 0.175 M HCl to reach the equivalence point.

    $$C_6H_5NH_2(aq) + H_3O^+(aq) \rightleftharpoons C_6H_5NH_3^+(aq) + H_2O(\ell)$$

    (a) What was the concentration of aniline in the original solution?
    (b) What are the concentrations of H_3O^+, OH^-, and $C_6H_5NH_3^+$ at the equivalence point?
    (c) What is the pH of the solution at the equivalence point?

Titration Curves and Indicators
(See Section 18.3 and Figures 18.4–18.10.)

27. Without doing detailed calculations, sketch the curve for the titration of 30.0 mL of 0.10 M NaOH with 0.10 M HCl. Indicate the approximate pH at the beginning of the titration and at the equivalence point. What is the total solution volume at the equivalence point?

28. Without doing detailed calculations, sketch the curve for the titration of 50 mL of 0.050 M pyridine, C_5H_5N (a weak base), with 0.10 M HCl. Indicate the approximate pH at the beginning of the titration and at the equivalence point. What is the total solution volume at the equivalence point?

29. You titrate 25.0 mL of 0.10 M NH_3 with 0.10 M HCl.
    (a) What is the pH of the NH_3 solution before the titration begins?
    (b) What is the pH at the equivalence point?
    (c) What is the pH at the halfway point of the titration?
    (d) What indicator in Figure 18.10 could be used to detect the equivalence point?
    (e) Calculate the pH of the solution after adding 5.00, 15.0, 20.0, 22.0, and 30.0 mL of the acid. Combine this information with that in parts (a)–(c) and plot the titration curve.

30. Construct a rough plot of pH versus volume of base for the titration of 25.0 mL of 0.050 M HCN with 0.075 M NaOH.
    (a) What is the pH before any NaOH is added?
    (b) What is the pH at the halfway point of the titration?
    (c) What is the pH when 95% of the required NaOH has been added?
    (d) What volume of base, in milliliters, is required to reach the equivalence point?
    (e) What is the pH at the equivalence point?
    (f) What indicator would be most suitable for this titration? (See Figure 18.10.)
    (g) What is the pH when 105% of the required base has been added?

31. Using Figure 18.10, suggest an indicator to use in each of the following titrations:
    (a) The weak base pyridine is titrated with HCl.
    (b) Formic acid is titrated with NaOH.
    (c) Ethylenediamine, a weak diprotic base, is titrated with HCl.

32. Using Figure 18.10, suggest an indicator to use in each of the following titrations.
    (a) $NaHCO_3$ is titrated to CO_3^{2-} with NaOH.
    (b) Hypochlorous acid is titrated with NaOH.
    (c) Trimethylamine is titrated with HCl.

Solubility Guidelines
(See Sections 3.4 and 3.5, Figure 3.10, and Example 3.2.)

33. Name two insoluble salts of each of the following ions.
    (a) Cl^-
    (b) Zn^{2+}
    (c) Fe^{2+}

34. Name two insoluble salts of each of the following ions.
    (a) SO_4^{2-}
    (b) Ni^{2+}
    (c) Br^-

35. Using the solubility guidelines (◀ Figure 3.10), predict whether each of the following is insoluble or soluble in water.
(a) $(NH_4)_2CO_3$
(b) $ZnSO_4$
(c) NiS
(d) $BaSO_4$

36. Predict whether each of the following is insoluble or soluble in water.
(a) $Pb(NO_3)_2$
(b) $Fe(OH)_3$
(c) $ZnCl_2$
(d) CuS

Writing Solubility Product Constant Expressions
(See Section 18.4.)

37. For each of the following insoluble salts, (1) write a balanced equation showing the equilibrium occurring when the salt is added to water, and (2) write the K_{sp} expression.
(a) $AgCN$
(b) $NiCO_3$
(c) $AuBr_3$

38. For each of the following insoluble salts, (1) write a balanced equation showing the equilibrium occurring when the salt is added to water, and (2) write the K_{sp} expression.
(a) $PbSO_4$
(b) BaF_2
(c) Ag_3PO_4

Calculating K_{sp}
(See Section 18.4 and Example 18.8.)

39. When 1.55 g of solid thallium(I) bromide is added to 1.00 L of water, the salt dissolves to a small extent.

$$TlBr(s) \rightleftharpoons Tl^+(aq) + Br^-(aq)$$

The thallium(I) and bromide ions in equilibrium with TlBr each have a concentration of 1.9×10^{-3} M. What is the value of K_{sp} for TlBr?

40. At 20 °C, a saturated aqueous solution of silver acetate, $AgCH_3CO_2$, contains 1.0 g of the silver compound dissolved in 100.0 mL of solution. Calculate K_{sp} for silver acetate.

$$AgCH_3CO_2(s) \rightleftharpoons Ag^+(aq) + CH_3CO_2^-(aq)$$

41. When 250 mg of SrF_2, strontium fluoride, is added to 1.00 L of water, the salt dissolves to a very small extent.

$$SrF_2(s) \rightleftharpoons Sr^{2+}(aq) + 2 F^-(aq)$$

At equilibrium, the concentration of Sr^{2+} is found to be 1.03×10^{-3} M. What is the value of K_{sp} for SrF_2?

42. Calcium hydroxide, $Ca(OH)_2$, dissolves in water to the extent of 1.78 g per liter. What is the value of K_{sp} for $Ca(OH)_2$?

$$Ca(OH)_2(s) \rightleftharpoons Ca^{2+}(aq) + 2 OH^-(aq)$$

43. You add 0.979 g of $Pb(OH)_2$ to 1.00 L of pure water at 25 °C. The pH is 9.15. Estimate the value of K_{sp} for $Pb(OH)_2$.

44. You place 1.234 g of solid $Ca(OH)_2$ in 1.00 L of pure water at 25 °C. The pH of the solution is found to be 12.68. Estimate the value of K_{sp} for $Ca(OH)_2$.

Estimating Salt Solubility from K_{sp}
(See Section 18.4 and Examples 18.9 and 18.10.)

45. Estimate the solubility of silver iodide in pure water at 25 °C (a) in moles per liter and (b) in grams per liter.

$$AgI(s) \rightleftharpoons Ag^+(aq) + I^-(aq)$$

46. What is the molar concentration of $Au^+(aq)$ in a saturated solution of AuCl in pure water at 25 °C?

$$AuCl(s) \rightleftharpoons Au^+(aq) + Cl^-(aq)$$

47. Estimate the solubility of calcium fluoride, CaF_2, (a) in moles per liter and (b) in grams per liter of pure water.

$$CaF_2(s) \rightleftharpoons Ca^{2+}(aq) + 2 F^-(aq)$$

48. Estimate the solubility of lead(II) bromide (a) in moles per liter and (b) in grams per liter of pure water.

49. The K_{sp} value for radium sulfate, $RaSO_4$, is 4.2×10^{-11}. If 25 mg of radium sulfate is placed in 1.00×10^2 mL of water, does all of it dissolve? If not, how much dissolves?

50. If 55 mg of lead(II) sulfate is placed in 250 mL of pure water, does all of it dissolve? If not, how much dissolves?

51. Use K_{sp} values to decide which compound in each of the following pairs is more soluble. (▶ Appendix J.)
(a) $PbCl_2$ or $PbBr_2$
(b) HgS or FeS
(c) $Fe(OH)_2$ or $Zn(OH)_2$

52. Use K_{sp} values to decide which compound in each of the following pairs is more soluble. (▶ Appendix J.)
(a) $AgBr$ or $AgSCN$
(b) $SrCO_3$ or $SrSO_4$
(c) AgI or PbI_2
(d) MgF_2 or CaF_2

The Common Ion Effect and Salt Solubility
(See Section 18.4 and Examples 18.11 and 18.12.)

53. Calculate the molar solubility of silver thiocyanate, AgSCN, in pure water and in water containing 0.010 M NaSCN.

54. Calculate the solubility of silver bromide, AgBr, in moles per liter, in pure water. Compare this value with the molar solubility of AgBr in 225 mL of water to which 0.15 g of NaBr has been added.

55. Compare the solubility, in milligrams per milliliter, of silver iodide, AgI, (a) in pure water and (b) in water that is 0.020 M in $AgNO_3$.

56. What is the solubility, in milligrams per milliliter, of BaF_2, (a) in pure water and (b) in water containing 5.0 mg/mL KF?

The Effect of Basic Anions on Salt Solubility
(See pages 837–838.)

57. Which insoluble compound in each pair should be more soluble in nitric acid than in pure water?
    (a) $PbCl_2$ or PbS
    (b) Ag_2CO_3 or AgI
    (c) $Al(OH)_3$ or $AgCl$

58. Which compound in each pair is more soluble in water than is predicted by a calculation from K_{sp}?
    (a) AgI or Ag_2CO_3
    (b) $PbCO_3$ or $PbCl_2$
    (c) $AgCl$ or $AgCN$

Precipitation Reactions
(See Section 18.5 and Examples 18.13–18.15.)

59. You have a solution that has a lead(II) ion concentration of 0.0012 M. If enough soluble chloride-containing salt is added so that the Cl^- concentration is 0.010 M, will $PbCl_2$ precipitate?

60. Sodium carbonate is added to a solution in which the concentration of Ni^{2+} ion is 0.0024 M. Will precipitation of $NiCO_3$ occur (a) when the concentration of the carbonate ion is 1.0×10^{-6} M or (b) when it is 100 times greater (1.0×10^{-4} M)?

61. If the concentration of Zn^{2+} in 10.0 mL of water is 1.63×10^{-4} M, will zinc hydroxide, $Zn(OH)_2$, precipitate when 4.0 mg of NaOH is added?

62. You have 95 mL of a solution that has a lead(II) concentration of 0.0012 M. Will $PbCl_2$ precipitate when 1.20 g of solid NaCl is added?

63. If the concentration of Mg^{2+} ion in seawater is 1350 mg/L, what OH^- concentration is required to precipitate $Mg(OH)_2$?

64. Will a precipitate of $Mg(OH)_2$ form when 25.0 mL of 0.010 M NaOH is combined with 75.0 mL of a 0.10 M solution of magnesium chloride?

Equilibria Involving Complex Ions
(See Sections 18.6 and 18.7 and Examples 18.16 and 18.17.)

65. Zinc hydroxide is amphoteric (◄ page 793). Use equilibrium constants to show that, given sufficient OH^-, $Zn(OH)_2$ can dissolve in NaOH.

66. Solid silver iodide, AgI, can be dissolved by adding aqueous sodium cyanide. Calculate K_{net} for the following reaction.

$$AgI(s) + 2\ CN^-(aq) \rightleftharpoons [Ag(CN)_2]^-(aq) + I^-(aq)$$

67. ▲ What amount of ammonia (moles) must be added to dissolve 0.050 mol of AgCl suspended in 1.0 L of water?

68. Can you dissolve 15.0 mg of AuCl in 100.0 mL of water if you add 15.0 mL of 6.00 M NaCN?

69. What is the solubility of AgCl (a) in pure water and (b) in 1.0 M NH_3?

70. The chemistry of silver(I) cyanide:
    (a) Calculate the solubility of AgCN(s) in water from the K_{sp} value.
    (b) Calculate the value of the equilibrium constant for the reaction

$$AgCN(s) + CN^-(aq) \rightleftharpoons [Ag(CN)_2]^-(aq)$$

from K_{sp} and K_f values and predict from this value whether AgCN(s) would dissolve in KCN(aq).
    (c) Determine the equilibrium constant for the reaction

$$AgCN(s) + 2\ S_2O_3^{2-}(aq)$$
$$\rightleftharpoons [Ag(S_2O_3)_2]^{3-}(aq) + CN^-(aq)$$

Calculate the solubility of AgCN in a solution containing 0.10 M $S_2O_3^{2-}$ and compare the value to the solubility in water [part (a)].

General Questions

These questions are not designated as to type or location in the chapter. They may combine several concepts.

71. In each of the following cases, decide whether a precipitate will form when mixing the indicated reagents, and write a balanced equation for the reaction.
    (a) $NaBr(aq) + AgNO_3(aq)$
    (b) $KCl(aq) + Pb(NO_3)_2(aq)$

72. In each of the following cases, decide whether a precipitate will form when mixing the indicated reagents, and write a balanced equation for the reaction.
    (a) $Na_2SO_4(aq) + Mg(NO_3)_2(aq)$
    (b) $K_3PO_4(aq) + FeCl_3(aq)$

73. If you mix 48 mL of 0.0012 M $BaCl_2$ with 24 mL of 1.0×10^{-6} M Na_2SO_4, will a precipitate of $BaSO_4$ form?

74. Calculate the hydronium ion concentration and the pH of the solution that results when 20.0 mL of 0.15 M acetic acid, CH_3CO_2H, is mixed with 5.0 mL of 0.17 M NaOH.

75. Calculate the hydronium ion concentration and the pH of the solution that results when 50.0 mL of 0.40 M NH_3 is mixed with 25.0 mL of 0.20 M HCl.

76. For each of the following cases, decide whether the pH is less than 7, equal to 7, or greater than 7.
    (a) Equal volumes of 0.10 M acetic acid, CH_3CO_2H, and 0.10 M KOH are mixed.
    (b) 25 mL of 0.015 M NH_3 is mixed with 12 mL of 0.015 M HCl.
    (c) 150 mL of 0.20 M HNO_3 is mixed with 75 mL of 0.40 M NaOH.
    (d) 25 mL of 0.45 M H_2SO_4 is mixed with 25 mL of 0.90 M NaOH.

77. Rank the following compounds in order of increasing solubility in water: Na_2CO_3, $BaCO_3$, Ag_2CO_3.

78. A sample of hard water contains about 2.0×10^{-3} M Ca^{2+}. A soluble fluoride-containing salt such as NaF is added to "fluoridate" the water (to aid in the prevention of dental cavities). What is the maximum concentration of F^- that can be present without precipitating CaF_2?

Dietary sources of fluoride ion. Adding fluoride ion to drinking water (or toothpaste) prevents the formation of dental cavities.

79. What is the pH of a buffer solution prepared from 5.15 g of NH_4NO_3 and 0.10 L of 0.15 M NH_3? What is the new pH if the solution is diluted with pure water to a volume of 5.00×10^2 mL?

80. If you place 5.0 mg of $SrSO_4$ in 1.0 L of pure water, will all of the salt dissolve before equilibrium is established, or will some salt remain undissolved?

SO_4^{2-}

Celestite, $SrSO_4$
Strontium sulfate

81. Describe the effect on the pH of the following actions and explain why there is not an effect:
  (a) Adding sodium acetate, $NaCH_3CO_2$, to 0.100 M CH_3CO_2H
  (b) Adding $NaNO_3$ to 0.100 M HNO_3

82. What volume of 0.120 M NaOH must be added to 100. mL of 0.100 M $NaHC_2O_4$ to reach a pH of 4.70?

83. ▲ A buffer solution is prepared by dissolving 1.50 g each of benzoic acid, $C_6H_5CO_2H$, and sodium benzoate, $NaC_6H_5CO_2$, in 150.0 mL of solution.
  (a) What is the pH of this buffer solution?
  (b) Which buffer component must be added, and in what quantity, to change the pH to 4.00?
  (c) What quantity of 2.0 M NaOH or 2.0 M HCl must be added to the buffer to change the pH to 4.00?

84. What volume of 0.200 M HCl must be added to 500.0 mL of 0.250 M NH_3 to have a buffer with a pH of 9.00?

85. What is the equilibrium constant for the following reaction?

$$AgCl(s) + I^-(aq) \rightleftharpoons AgI(s) + Cl^-(aq)$$

Does the equilibrium lie predominantly to the left or to the right? Will AgI form if iodide ion, I^-, is added to a saturated solution of AgCl?

86. Calculate the equilibrium constant for the following reaction.

$$Zn(OH)_2(s) + 2\ CN^-(aq) \rightleftharpoons$$
$$Zn(CN)_2(s) + 2\ OH^-(aq)$$

Does the equilibrium lie predominantly to the left or to the right?

87. ▲ In principle, the ions Ba^{2+} and Ca^{2+} can be separated by the difference in solubility of their fluorides, BaF_2 and CaF_2. If you have a solution that is 0.10 M in both Ba^{2+} and Ca^{2+}, CaF_2 will begin to precipitate first as fluoride ion is added slowly to the solution.
  (a) What concentration of fluoride ion will precipitate the maximum amount of Ca^{2+} ion without precipitating BaF_2?
  (b) What concentration of Ca^{2+} remains in solution when BaF_2 just begins to precipitate?

88. ▲ A solution contains 0.10 M iodide ion, I^-, and 0.10 M carbonate ion, CO_3^{2-}.
  (a) If solid $Pb(NO_3)_2$ is slowly added to the solution, which salt will precipitate first, PbI_2 or $PbCO_3$?
  (b) What will be the concentration of the first ion that precipitates (CO_3^{2-} or I^-) when the second, more soluble salt begins to precipitate?

Lead(II) iodide ($K_{sp} = 9.8 \times 10^{-9}$) is a bright yellow solid.

89. ▲ A solution contains Ca^{2+} and Pb^{2+} ions, both at a concentration of 0.010 M. You wish to separate the two ions from each other as completely as possible by precipitating one but not the other using aqueous Na_2SO_4 as the precipitating agent.
    (a) Which will precipitate first as sodium sulfate is added, $CaSO_4$ or $PbSO_4$?
    (b) What will be the concentration of the first ion that precipitates (Ca^{2+} or Pb^{2+}) when the second, more soluble salt begins to precipitate?

90. Buffer capacity is defined as the number of moles of a strong acid or strong base that is required to change the pH of 1 L of the buffer solution by one unit. What is the buffer capacity of a solution that is 0.10 M in acetic acid and 0.10 M in sodium acetate?

91. The Ca^{2+} ion in hard water can be precipitated as $CaCO_3$ by adding soda ash, Na_2CO_3. If the calcium ion concentration in hard water is 0.010 M and if the Na_2CO_3 is added until the carbonate ion concentration is 0.050 M, what percentage of the calcium ions has been removed from the water? (You may neglect carbonate ion hydrolysis.)

© Cengage Learning/Charles D. Winters

This sample of calcium carbonate ($K_{sp} = 3.4 \times 10^{-9}$) was deposited in a cave formation.

92. Some photographic film is coated with crystals of AgBr suspended in gelatin. Some of the silver ions are reduced to silver metal on exposure to light. Unexposed AgBr is then dissolved with sodium thiosulfate in the "fixing" step.

    $AgBr(s) + 2\,S_2O_3{}^{2-}(aq) \rightleftharpoons$
    $$[Ag(S_2O_3)_2]^{3-}(aq) + Br^-(aq)$$

    (a) What is the equilibrium constant for this reaction?
    (b) What mass of $Na_2S_2O_3$ must be added to dissolve 1.00 g of AgBr suspended in 1.00 L of water?

In the Laboratory

93. Each pair of ions below is found together in aqueous solution. Using the table of solubility product constants in Appendix J, devise a way to separate these ions by adding a reagent to precipitate one of the ions as an insoluble salt and leaving the other in solution.
    (a) Ba^{2+} and Na^+
    (b) Ni^{2+} and Pb^{2+}

94. Each pair of ions below is found together in aqueous solution. Using the table of solubility product constants in Appendix J, devise a way to separate these ions by adding a reagent to precipitate one of the ions as an insoluble salt and leave the other in solution.
    (a) Cu^{2+} and Ag^+
    (b) Al^{3+} and Fe^{3+}

95. ▲ The cations Ba^{2+} and Sr^{2+} can be precipitated as very insoluble sulfates.
    (a) If you add sodium sulfate to a solution containing these metal cations, each with a concentration of 0.10 M, which is precipitated first, $BaSO_4$ or $SrSO_4$?
    (b) What will be the concentration of the first ion that precipitates (Ba^{2+} or Sr^{2+}) when the second, more soluble salt begins to precipitate?

96. ▲ You will often work with salts of Fe^{3+}, Pb^{2+}, and Al^{3+} in the laboratory. (All are found in nature, and all are important economically.) If you have a solution containing these three ions, each at a concentration of 0.10 M, what is the order in which their hydroxides precipitate as aqueous NaOH is slowly added to the solution?

97. Aniline hydrochloride, $(C_6H_5NH_3)Cl$, is a weak acid. (Its conjugate base is the weak base aniline, $C_6H_5NH_2$.) The acid can be titrated with a strong base such as NaOH.

    $C_6H_5NH_3{}^+(aq) + OH^-(aq) \rightleftharpoons$
    $$C_6H_5NH_2(aq) + H_2O(\ell)$$

    Assume 50.0 mL of 0.100 M aniline hydrochloride is titrated with 0.185 M NaOH. (K_a for aniline hydrochloride is 2.4×10^{-5}.)
    (a) What is the pH of the $(C_6H_5NH_3)Cl$ solution before the titration begins?
    (b) What is the pH at the equivalence point?
    (c) What is the pH at the halfway point of the titration?
    (d) Which indicator in Figure 18.10 could be used to detect the equivalence point?
    (e) Calculate the pH of the solution after adding 10.0, 20.0, and 30.0 mL of base.
    (f) Combine the information in parts (a), (b), (c), and (e), and plot an approximate titration curve.

98. The weak base ethanolamine, $HOCH_2CH_2NH_2$, can be titrated with HCl.

$$HOCH_2CH_2NH_2(aq) + H_3O^+(aq) \rightleftharpoons$$
$$HOCH_2CH_2NH_3^+(aq) + H_2O(\ell)$$

Assume you have 25.0 mL of a 0.010 M solution of ethanolamine and titrate it with 0.0095 M HCl. (K_b for ethanolamine is 3.2×10^{-5}.)

(a) What is the pH of the ethanolamine solution before the titration begins?

(b) What is the pH at the equivalence point?

(c) What is the pH at the halfway point of the titration?

(d) Which indicator in Figure 18.10 would be the best choice to detect the equivalence point?

(e) Calculate the pH of the solution after adding 5.00, 10.0, 20.0, and 30.0 mL of the acid.

(f) Combine the information in parts (a), (b), (c), and (e), and plot an approximate titration curve.

99. For the titration of 50.0 mL of 0.150 M ethylamine, $C_2H_5NH_2$, with 0.100 M HCl, find the pH at each of the following points, and then use that information to sketch the titration curve and decide on an appropriate indicator.

(a) At the beginning, before HCl is added

(b) At the halfway point in the titration

(c) When 75% of the required acid has been added

(d) At the equivalence point

(e) When 10.0 mL more HCl has been added than is required

(f) Sketch the titration curve.

(g) Suggest an appropriate indicator for this titration.

100. A buffer solution with a pH of 12.00 consists of Na_3PO_4 and Na_2HPO_4. The volume of solution is 200.0 mL.

(a) Which component of the buffer is present in a larger amount?

(b) If the concentration of Na_3PO_4 is 0.400 M, what mass of Na_2HPO_4 is present?

(c) Which component of the buffer must be added to change the pH to 12.25? What mass of that component is required?

101. To have a buffer with a pH of 2.50, what volume of 0.150 M NaOH must be added to 100. mL of 0.230 M H_3PO_4?

102. ▲ What mass of Na_3PO_4 must be added to 80.0 mL of 0.200 M HCl to obtain a buffer with a pH of 7.75?

103. You have a solution that contains $AgNO_3$, $Pb(NO_3)_2$, and $Cu(NO_3)_2$. Devise a separation method that results in having Ag^+ in one test tube, Pb^{2+} in another, and Cu^{2+} in a third test tube. Use solubility guidelines and K_{sp} and K_f values.

104. Once you have separated the three salts in Study Question 103 into three test tubes, you now need to confirm their presence.

(a) For Pb^{2+} ion, one way to do this is to treat a precipitate of $PbCl_2$ with K_2CrO_4 to produce the bright yellow insoluble solid, $PbCrO_4$. Using K_{sp} values, confirm that the chloride salt should be converted to the chromate salt.

PbCl₂
precipitate

White $PbCl_2$ is converted to yellow $PbCrO_4$ on adding K_2CrO_4.

(b) Suggest a method for confirming the presence of Ag^+ and Cu^{2+} ions using complex ions.

Summary and Conceptual Questions

The following questions may use concepts from this and previous chapters.

105. Suggest a method for separating a precipitate consisting of a mixture of solid CuS and solid $Cu(OH)_2$.

106. Which of the following barium salts should dissolve in a strong acid such as HCl: $Ba(OH)_2$, $BaSO_4$, or $BaCO_3$?

107. Explain why the solubility of Ag_3PO_4 can be greater in water than is calculated from the K_{sp} value of the salt.

108. Two acids, each approximately 0.01 M in concentration, are titrated separately with a strong base. The acids show the following pH values at the equivalence point: HA, pH = 9.5, and HB, pH = 8.5.

(a) Which is the stronger acid, HA or HB?

(b) Which of the conjugate bases, A^- or B^-, is the stronger base?

109. Composition diagrams, commonly known as "alpha plots," are often used to visualize the species in a solution of an acid or base as the pH is varied. The diagram for 0.100 M acetic acid is shown here.

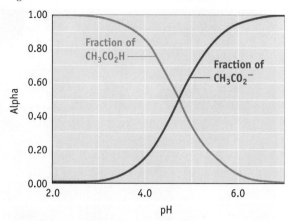

The plot shows how the fraction [alpha (α)] of acetic acid in solution,

$$\alpha = \frac{[CH_3CO_2H]}{[CH_3CO_2H] + [CH_3CO_2^-]}$$

changes as the pH increases (blue curve). (The red curve shows how the fraction of acetate ion, $CH_3CO_2^-$, changes as the pH increases.) Alpha plots are another way of viewing the relative concentrations of acetic acid and acetate ion as a strong base is added to a solution of acetic acid in the course of a titration.

(a) Explain why the fraction of acetic acid declines and that of acetate ion increases as the pH increases.

(b) Which species predominates at a pH of 4, acetic acid or acetate ion? What is the situation at a pH of 6?

(c) Consider the point where the two lines cross. The fraction of acetic acid in the solution is 0.5, and so is that of acetate ion. That is, the solution is half acid and half conjugate base; their concentrations are equal. At this point, the graph shows the pH is 4.74. Explain why the pH at this point is 4.74.

110. The composition diagram, or alpha plot, for the important acid–base system of carbonic acid, H_2CO_3, is illustrated below. (See Study Question 109 for more information on such diagrams.)

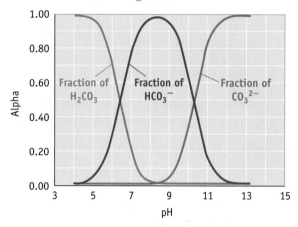

(a) Explain why the fraction of bicarbonate ion, HCO_3^-, rises and then falls as the pH increases.

(b) What is the composition of the solution when the pH is 6.0? When the pH is 10.0?

(c) If you wanted to buffer a solution at a pH of 11.0, what should be the ratio of HCO_3^- to CO_3^{2-}?

111. The chemical name for aspirin is acetylsalicylic acid. It is believed that the analgesic and other desirable properties of aspirin are due not to the aspirin itself but rather to the simpler compound salicylic acid, $C_6H_4(OH)CO_2H$, which results from the breakdown of aspirin in the stomach.

salicylic acid

(a) Give approximate values for the following bond angles in the acid: (i) C—C—C in the ring; (ii) O—C=O; (iii) either of the C—O—H angles; and (iv) C—C—H.

(b) What is the hybridization of the C atoms of the ring? Of the C atom in the —CO_2H group?

(c) Experiment shows that 1.00 g of the acid will dissolve in 460 mL of water. If the pH of this solution is 2.4, what is K_a for the acid?

(d) If you have salicylic acid in your stomach and if the pH of gastric juice is 2.0, calculate the percentage of salicylic acid that will be present in the stomach in the form of the salicylate ion, $C_6H_4(OH)CO_2^-$.

(e) Assume you have 25.0 mL of a 0.014 M solution of salicylic acid and titrate it with 0.010 M NaOH. What is the pH at the halfway point of the titration? What is the pH at the equivalence point?

112. Aluminum hydroxide reacts with phosphoric acid to give $AlPO_4$. The substance is used industrially in adhesives, binders, and cements.
    (a) Write the balanced equation for the preparation of $AlPO_4$ from aluminum hydroxide and phosphoric acid.
    (b) If you begin with 152 g of aluminum hydroxide and 3.00 L of 0.750 M phosphoric acid, what is the theoretical yield of $AlPO_4$?
    (c) If you place 25.0 g of $AlPO_4$ in 1.00 L of water, what are the concentrations of Al^{3+} and PO_4^{3-} at equilibrium? (Neglect hydrolysis of aqueous Al^{3+} and PO_4^{3-} ions.) K_{sp} for $AlPO_4$ is 1.3×10^{-20}.
    (d) Does the solubility of $AlPO_4$ increase or decrease on adding HCl? Explain.

© Cengage Learning/Charles D. Winters

This is a sample of hydrated aluminum phosphate, a mineral known as augelite.

Applying Chemical Principles

Everything That Glitters . . .

For thousands of years gold has been used in jewelry and for currency. Gold does not tarnish, and it can be drawn into wires or hammered into sheets. In modern society, the most important application of this element may be in electronics, where its high conductivity and resistance to corrosion make it invaluable for wires and connectors.

Gold mining evokes images of miners panning for gold in mountain streams or chopping rocks with pick axes. However, the percentage of gold in most deposits is too low for these extraction methods to be feasible. Today's miners blast and crush enormous quantities of gold-bearing ore and then dissolve gold from the ore using a chemical process involving cyanide ion and oxygen.

$$4\ Au(s) + 8\ NaCN(aq) + O_2(g) + 2\ H_2O(\ell) \rightarrow$$
$$4\ NaAu(CN)_2(aq) + 4\ NaOH(aq)$$

The solution containing the soluble $[Au(CN)_2]^-$ ion is filtered to separate it from the solids. Metallic gold is then recovered by reacting the cyanide complex with zinc. The zinc reduces the gold(I) complex to elemental gold and then joins with the cyanide to form $[Zn(CN)_4]^{2-}$.

Large volumes of 0.035% aqueous sodium cyanide are used for gold extraction. Unfortunately, unsafe disposal and accidental discharges have resulted in environmental disasters. In 2000, the collapse of dams in Baia Mare, Romania, resulted in millions of liters of cyanide waste entering the Tisza and Danube river. All aquatic life for miles downstream was killed. Although research into safer extraction methods is ongoing, extraction by cyanide ion is still the primary means of obtaining gold.

Using gold. *(left)* Much of current gold use today is in electronic devices. The microprocessor connector pins are coated with a thin film of gold. *(right)* The dome of St. Isaac's Cathedral in St. Petersburg, Russia, is covered with 100 kg of pure gold. (It was completed in 1858.)

Questions:

1. Approximately 0.10 g of sodium cyanide is fatal to humans. What volume (in mL) of 0.035 mass percent NaCN solution contains a fatal dose of sodium cyanide? Assume the density of the solution is 1.0 g/mL.
2. What is the minimum volume of 0.0071 M NaCN(aq) necessary to dissolve the gold from 1.0 metric ton (1000 kg) of ore if the ore contains 0.012% gold?
3. Use the formation constant of $[Au(CN)_2]^-$ in Appendix K to determine the equilibrium concentration of $Au^+(aq)$ in a solution that is 0.0071 M CN^- and 1.1×10^{-4} M $[Au(CN)_2]^-$. Is it reasonable to conclude that 100% of the gold in solution is present as the $[Au(CN)_2]^-$ complex ion? Explain.

4. Silver undergoes similar reactions as those shown for gold. Both metals react with cyanide ion in the presence of oxygen to form soluble complexes, and both are reduced by zinc. The reaction of Ag^+ with cyanide ion may be viewed as two sequential steps:

    (1) $Ag^+(aq) + CN^-(aq) \rightleftharpoons AgCN(s)$
    (2) $AgCN(s) + CN^-(aq) \rightleftharpoons [Ag(CN)_2]^-(aq)$

    $Ag^+(aq) + 2\ CN^-(aq) \rightleftharpoons [Ag(CN)_2]^-(aq)$
    $K_f = 1.3 \times 10^{21}$

    (a) Use the solubility product equilibrium constant (Appendix J) of AgCN(s) to determine the equilibrium constant for step 1.
    (b) Use the equilibrium constants from Step 1 and the overall reaction to determine the equilibrium constant for Step 2.
    (c) Excess AgCN(s) is combined with 1.0 L of 0.0071 M $CN^-(aq)$ and allowed to equilibrate. Calculate the equilibrium concentrations of CN^- and $[Ag(CN)_2]^-$ using the equilibrium constant for step 2. Assume no change in volume occurs.
5. Write a balanced chemical equation for the reaction of $NaAu(CN)_2(aq)$ and $Zn(s)$.

19 Principles of Chemical Reactivity: Entropy and Free Energy

© Cengage Learning/Charles D. Winters

The Combustion of Hydrogen Gas. The exothermic reaction of hydrogen with oxygen to form water. (A hydrogen-filled balloon was ignited with a candle.)

Hydrogen for the Future?

In Chapter 5, you learned that the first law of thermodynamics states that energy is conserved in the universe. In this chapter, you will learn about the second law of thermodynamics. Two of the key concepts involved in the second law are (1) energy goes from being more concentrated to being more dispersed in the universe and (2) it is not possible to have 100% of the energy in a process be transferred as work. Energy is at the forefront of discussions of public policy today, and these fundamental laws of thermodynamics are key to understanding these issues.

One of the best energy sources for the future could be hydrogen. One could imagine a cycle in which water is decomposed by running an electric current through it to produce hydrogen and oxygen, and then the hydrogen and oxygen are recombined in a very exothermic process to yield water. Based on the first law of thermodynamics, however,

the best that we could hope for is to get the same exact amount of energy back from the process as we had to put in to decompose the water. The second law of thermodynamics makes things even worse. Because we cannot transform 100% of the energy released into useful work, the energy that we could use from the combustion step would be less than what would be needed to generate the hydrogen in the first place.

Is there a way around this problem? One widely used way to produce hydrogen is the reaction of carbon or methane with steam, for which there is a net release of energy when we account for both the energy needed to obtain the hydrogen and the energy released when the hydrogen is burned. Another potential solution is to use a renewable energy source such as solar or wind energy to decompose water. The laws of thermodynamics still apply but it is not as important in such a case that less energy is obtained than was needed because the input of energy came from an abundant and renewable energy resource.

Scientists are actively seeking ways to make hydrogen a useful, economical, and safe fuel for the future. Underlying this search, chemistry and the laws of thermodynamics play essential roles.

Questions:

1. Calculate $\Delta_r H°$, $\Delta_r S°$, and $\Delta_r G°$ for the reaction (at 298.15 K)
   $$2\ H_2O(\ell) \rightarrow 2\ H_2(g) + O_2(g)$$
2. Calculate $\Delta_r H°$, $\Delta_r S°$ and $\Delta_r G°$ for the reaction (at 298.15 K)
   $$CH_4(g) + H_2O(g) \rightarrow 3\ H_2(g) + CO(g)$$

Answers to these questions are available in Appendix N.

CHAPTER GOALS

See Chapter Goals Revisited (page 884) for Study Questions keyed to these goals.

- Understand the concept of entropy and its relationship to reaction spontaneity.

- Calculate the change in entropy for a system, its surroundings, and the universe to determine whether a process is spontaneous under standard conditions.

- Understand and use the Gibbs free energy.

Change is central to chemistry, so it is important to understand the factors that determine whether a change will occur. In chemistry, we encounter many examples of chemical change (chemical reactions) and physical change (the formation of mixtures, expansion of gases, and changes of state, to name a few). Chemists use the term **spontaneous** to represent a change that occurs without outside intervention. *Spontaneous changes occur only in the direction that leads to equilibrium.* Whether or not the process is spontaneous does not tell us anything about the rate of the change or the extent to which a process will occur before equilibrium is reached. It says only that the change will occur in a specific direction (toward equilibrium) and will occur naturally and unaided.

If a piece of hot metal is placed in a beaker of cold water, energy is transferred as heat spontaneously from the hot metal to the cooler water (Figure 19.1), and energy transfer will continue until the two objects are at the same temperature and thermal equilibrium is attained. Similarly, chemical reactions proceed spontaneously until equilibrium is reached, regardless of whether the position of the equilibrium favors products or reactants. We readily recognize that, starting with pure reactants, all product-favored reactions must be spontaneous, such as the formation of water from gaseous hydrogen and oxygen and the neutralization of H_3O^+(aq) and OH^-(aq). Be aware, though, that reactant-favored reactions are also spontaneous until equilibrium is achieved. Even though the dissolution of $CaCO_3$ is reactant-favored at equilibrium, if you place a handful of $CaCO_3$ in water, the process of dissolving will proceed spontaneously until equilibrium is reached.

Systems never change spontaneously in a direction that takes them farther from equilibrium. Given two objects at the same temperature, in contact but thermally isolated from their surroundings, it will never happen that one will heat up while the other becomes colder. Gas molecules will never spontaneously congregate at one end of a flask. Similarly, once equilibrium is established, the small amount of dissolved $CaCO_3$ in equilibrium with solid $CaCO_3$ will not spontaneously precipitate from solution, nor will a greater amount of $CaCO_3$ spontaneously dissolve.

The factors that determine the directionality and extent of change are among the topics of this chapter.

19.1 Spontaneity and Energy Transfer as Heat

We can readily recognize many chemical reactions that are spontaneous, such as hydrogen and oxygen combining to form water, methane burning to give CO_2 and H_2O, Na and Cl_2 reacting to form NaCl, and HCl(aq) and NaOH(aq) reacting to

OWL

Sign in to OWL at **www.cengage.com/owl** to view tutorials and simulations, develop problem-solving skills, and complete online homework assigned by your professor.

go Chemistry

Download mini lecture videos for key concept review and exam prep from OWL or purchase them from **www.cengagebrain.com**

FIGURE 19.1 A spontaneous process. The heated metal cylinder is placed in water. Energy transfers as heat spontaneously from the metal to water, that is, from the hotter object to the cooler object.

PROBLEM SOLVING TIP 19.1

To understand the thermodynamic concepts introduced in this chapter, be sure to review the ideas of Chapter 5.

System: The part of the universe under study.

Surroundings: The rest of the universe exclusive of the system, capable of exchanging energy and/or matter with the system.

Exothermic: Energy transfers as heat from the system to the surroundings.

Endothermic: Energy transfers as heat from the surroundings to the system.

A Review of Concepts of Thermodynamics

First law of thermodynamics: The law of conservation of energy; energy cannot be created or destroyed. The change in internal energy of a system is the sum of energy transferred into or out of the system as heat and/or as work, $\Delta U = q + w$.

Enthalpy change: The energy transferred as heat under conditions of constant pressure.

State function: A quantity whose value depends only on the state of the system;

changes in a state function can be calculated by taking into account the initial and final states of a system.

Standard conditions: Pressure of 1 bar (1 bar = 0.98692 atm) and solution concentration of 1 m.

Standard enthalpy of formation, $\Delta_f H°$: The enthalpy change occurring when 1 mol of a compound is formed from its elements in their standard states.

● **Spontaneous Processes** A spontaneous physical or chemical change proceeds to equilibrium without outside intervention. Such a process may or may not be product-favored at equilibrium.

form H_2O and $NaCl(aq)$. A common feature of these reactions is that they are exothermic, so it would be tempting to conclude that evolution of energy as heat is the criterion that determines whether a reaction or process is spontaneous. Further inspection, however, reveals significant flaws in this reasoning. This is especially evident with the inclusion of some common spontaneous changes that are endothermic or energy neutral:

- *Dissolving NH_4NO_3.* The ionic compound NH_4NO_3 dissolves spontaneously in water. The process is endothermic ($\Delta_r H° = +25.7$ kJ/mol).
- *Expansion of a gas into a vacuum.* A system is set up with two flasks connected by a valve (Figure 19.2). One flask is filled with a gas, and the other is evacuated. When the valve is opened, the gas will flow spontaneously from one flask to the other until the pressure is the same throughout. The expansion of an ideal gas is energy neutral (although expansion of most real gases is endothermic).
- *Phase changes.* Melting of ice is an endothermic process. Above 0 °C, the melting of ice is spontaneous. Below 0 °C, melting of ice is not spontaneous. At 0 °C, no net change will occur; liquid water and ice coexist at equilibrium. This example illustrates that temperature can have a role in determining spontaneity and that equilibrium is somehow an important aspect of the problem.
- *Energy transfer as heat.* The temperature of a cold soft drink sitting in a warm environment will rise until the beverage reaches the ambient temperature. The energy required for this process comes from the surroundings. Energy transfer as heat from a hotter object (the surroundings) to a cooler object (the soft drink) is spontaneous.
- The reaction of H_2 and I_2 to form HI is endothermic, and the reverse reaction, the decomposition of HI to form H_2 and I_2, is exothermic. If $H_2(g)$ and $I_2(g)$ are mixed, a reaction forming HI will occur [$H_2(g) + I_2(g) \rightleftharpoons 2\,HI(g)$] until equilibrium is reached. Furthermore, if $HI(g)$ is placed in a container, there will also be a reaction, but in the reverse direction, until equilibrium is achieved. Notice that approach to equilibrium occurs spontaneously from either direction.

On further reflection, it is logical to conclude that evolution of heat cannot be a sufficient criterion in determining spontaneity. The first law of thermodynamics tells us that in any process energy must be conserved. If energy is transferred out of a system, then the same amount of energy must be transferred to the surroundings. Exothermicity of the system is always accompanied by an endothermic change in the surroundings. If energy evolution were the only factor determining whether a change is spontaneous, then for every spontaneous process there would be a corresponding nonspontaneous change in the surroundings. We must search further than the first law of thermodynamics to determine whether a change is spontaneous.

gas-filled flask   evacuated flask

open valve

When the valve is opened the gas expands irreversibly to fill both flasks.

FIGURE 19.2 Spontaneous expansion of a gas.

19.2 Dispersal of Energy: Entropy

We have shown that we cannot use energy itself as an indicator of spontaneity because energy is conserved in any process; we always end up with the same amount of energy as we had at the beginning. Imagine dropping this book on the floor. (But don't actually drop it!) It would fall spontaneously. The initial potential energy it has from being a certain distance above the floor is converted to kinetic energy. When the book hits the floor, the kinetic energy of the book is converted into other forms of kinetic energy: acoustic energy and thermal energy of the book, floor, and air, since these are all heated up somewhat. This example leads to two important points. First, the total energy is conserved. Second, there is a directionality to this process. The book will spontaneously fall to the ground, but we will not observe a book on its own jump spontaneously from the floor up to a desk. Is there a way to predict this directionality?

Let us consider the initial and final states for this process. Initially, the energy is concentrated in the book—the book has a certain potential energy as it is held above the floor. At the end of the process, this energy has been dispersed to the air, floor, and book. The energy has gone from being concentrated to being more dispersed. This is the indicator for which we have been searching. *In a spontaneous process, energy goes from being more concentrated to being more dispersed.*

There is a state function (◄ Section 5.4) called **entropy (S)** that allows us to quantify this. The **second law of thermodynamics** states that *a spontaneous process is one that results in an increase of the entropy of the universe.* In a spontaneous process ΔS(universe) is greater than zero; this corresponds to energy being dispersed in the process.

Because thermal energy is caused by the random motion of particles, potential energy is dispersed when it is converted to thermal energy. This conversion occurs when energy is transferred as heat, q. It is therefore not surprising that q is a part of the mathematical definition of ΔS. In addition, the effect of a given quantity of energy transferred as heat on energy dispersal is different at different temperatures. It turns out that a given q has a greater effect on ΔS at a lower temperature than at a higher temperature; that is, the extent of energy dispersal is inversely proportional to the temperature.

Our proposed definition for ΔS is thus q/T, but this is still not quite correct. We must be a little more specific about q. The value of q used in the calculation of an entropy change must be the energy transferred as heat under what are called *reversible conditions*, which we symbolize as q_{rev} (see *A Closer Look: Reversible and Irreversible Processes*, page 862). Our mathematical definition of ΔS is therefore q_{rev} divided by the absolute (Kelvin) temperature:

$$\Delta S = \frac{q_{rev}}{T} \qquad\qquad (19.1)$$

As expected from this equation, the units for entropy are J/K.

● **Entropy** For a more complete discussion of entropy, see the papers by F. L. Lambert, such as "Entropy Is Simple, Qualitatively," *Journal of Chemical Education*, Vol. 79, pp. 1241–1246, 2002, and references therein. See also Lambert's site: **entropysite.oxy.edu**

● **Second Law of Thermodynamics** For a spontaneous process, ΔS (universe) > 0.

A CLOSER LOOK

Reversible and Irreversible Processes

To determine entropy changes experimentally, the energy transferred by heating and cooling must be measured for a reversible process. But what is a reversible process?

The test for reversibility is that after carrying out a change along a given path (for example, energy added as heat), it must be possible to return to the starting point by the same path (energy taken away as heat) without altering the surroundings. Melting of ice and freezing of water at 0 °C are examples of reversible processes. Given a mixture of ice and water at equilibrium, adding energy as heat in small increments will convert ice to water; removing energy as heat in small increments will convert water back to ice.

Reversibility is closely associated with equilibrium. Assume that we have a system at equilibrium. Reversible changes can be made by very slightly perturbing the equilibrium and letting the system readjust.

Spontaneous processes are often not reversible. Suppose a gas is allowed to expand into a vacuum. No work is done in this process because there is no force to resist expansion. To return the system to its original state, it is necessary to compress the gas. Doing so means doing work on the system, however, because the system will not return to its original state on its own. In this process, the energy content of the surroundings decreases by the amount of work

expended by the surroundings. The system can be restored to its original state, but the surroundings will be altered in the process.

In summary, there are two important points concerning reversibility:

- At every step along a reversible pathway between two states, the system remains at equilibrium.
- Spontaneous processes often follow irreversible pathways and involve nonequilibrium conditions.

To determine the entropy change for a process, it is necessary to identify a reversible pathway. Only then can an entropy change for the process be calculated from q_{rev} and the Kelvin temperature.

REVIEW & CHECK FOR SECTION 19.2

1. In a spontaneous process, ΔS(universe) is

   (a) < 0 (b) $= 0$ (c) > 0

2. Which of the following is true for a spontaneous process but not for a nonspontaneous process? Energy in the universe is

   (a) concentrated   (b) conserved   (c) dispersed   (d) not conserved

3. For a particular system, q_{rev} at 25 °C is equal to + 950. J. What is its value of ΔS?

   (a) 38 J/K   (b) 3.19 J/K   (c) −3.19 J/K   (d) −38 J/K

19.3 Entropy: A Microscopic Understanding

Entropy is a measure of the extent of energy dispersal. In all spontaneous physical and chemical processes, energy changes from being localized or concentrated to being more dispersed or spread out. In a spontaneous process, the change in entropy, ΔS, of the universe indicates the extent to which energy is dispersed in a process carried out at a temperature T. So far, however, we have not explained why dispersal of energy occurs, nor have we given an equation for entropy itself. In order to do this, we will need to consider energy in its quantized form and matter on the atomic level.

Dispersal of Energy

We can explore the dispersal of energy using a simple example: energy being transferred as heat between hot and cold gaseous atoms. Consider an experiment involving two containers, one holding hot atoms and the other with cold atoms. Because they have translational energy, the atoms move randomly in each container and collide with the walls. When the containers are in contact, energy is transferred through the container walls. Eventually, both containers will be at the same temperature; the energy originally localized in the hotter atoms is distributed over a greater number of atoms; and the atoms in each container will have the same distribution of energies.

For further insight, we shall use a statistical explanation to show why energy is dispersed in a system. With statistical arguments, systems must include large

Possible distribution of energy packets

1,1   1,2   1,3   1,4   2,2

2,4   2,3   4,4   3,4   3,3

FIGURE 19.3 Energy dispersal.
Possible ways of distributing two packets of energy among four atoms. To keep our analysis simple, we assume that initially there is one atom with two quanta of energy (1) and three atoms (2, 3 and 4) with no energy. There are 10 different ways to distribute the two quanta of energy among the four atoms.

numbers of particles for the arguments to be accurate. It will be easiest, however, if we look first at simple examples to understand the underlying concept and then extrapolate our conclusions to larger systems.

Consider a simple system in which, initially, there is one atom (1) with two discrete packets, or quanta, of energy and three other atoms (2, 3, and 4) with no energy (Figure 19.3). When these four atoms are brought together, the total energy in the system is 2 quanta. Collisions among the atoms allow energy to be transferred so that, over time, all distributions of the two packets of energy over the four atoms are seen. There are 10 different ways to distribute these 2 quanta of energy over the four atoms. Each of these 10 different ways to distribute the energy is called a **microstate**. In only one of these microstates do the 2 quanta remain on atom 1. In fact, only in 4 of the 10 microstates [1,1; 2,2; 3,3; and 4,4] is the energy concentrated on a single atom. In the majority of cases, 6 out of 10, the energy is distributed to two different atoms. Even in this small sample (four atoms) with only two packets of energy, it is more likely that at any given time the energy will be distributed to two atoms rather than concentrated on a single atom. There is a distinct preference that the energy will be dispersed over a greater number of atoms.

Let us now add more atoms to our system. We again begin with one atom (1) having 2 quanta of energy but now have five other atoms (2, 3, 4, 5, and 6) with no energy. Collisions let the energy be transferred between the atoms, and we now find there are 21 possible microstates (Figure 19.4). There are six microstates in which the energy is concentrated on one atom, including one in which the energy is still on atom 1, but there are now 15 out of 21 microstates (or 71.4%) in which the energy is present on two different atoms. As the number of particles increases, therefore, the number of microstates available increases dramatically, and the fraction of microstates in which the energy is concentrated rather than dispersed goes down dramatically. It is much more likely that the energy will be dispersed rather than concentrated.

Number of Microstates	Distribution of 2 Quanta of Energy Among Six Atoms					
6	1:1	2:2	3:3	4:4	5:5	6:6
5	1:2	2:3	3:4	4:5	5:6	
4	1:3	2:4	3:5	4:6		
3	1:4	2:5	3:6			
2	1:5	2:6				
1	1:6					

FIGURE 19.4 Distributing 2 quanta of energy among six atoms. (Atoms are labeled 1 to 6.) There are 21 ways—21 microstates—of distributing 2 quanta of energy among six atoms.

Now let us return to an example using a total of four atoms but increase the quantity of energy from 2 quanta to 6 quanta. Assume that we start with two atoms having 3 quanta of energy each. The other two atoms initially have zero energy (Figure 19.5). Through collisions, energy can be transferred to achieve different distributions of energy among the four atoms. In all, there are 84 microstates, falling into nine basic patterns. For example, one possible arrangement has one atom with 3 quanta of energy, and three atoms with 1 quantum each. There are four

FIGURE 19.5 Energy dispersal. Possible ways of distributing 6 quanta of energy among four atoms. A total of 84 microstates is possible.

Number of different ways to achieve this arrangement

(a) Initially, four particles are separated from each other. Two particles each have 3 quanta of energy, and the other two have none. A total of 6 quanta of energy will be distributed once the four particles interact.

(b) Once the particles begin to interact, there are nine ways to distribute the 6 available quanta. Each of these arrangements will have multiple ways of distributing the energy among the four atoms. Part (c) shows how the arrangement on the right can be achieved four ways.

(c) There are four different ways to have four particles (a, b, c, and d) such that one particle has 3 quanta of energy and the other three each have 1 quantum of energy.

Ludwig Boltzmann (1844–1906). Engraved on his tombstone in Vienna, Austria, is his equation defining entropy. The constant k is now known as Boltzmann's constant.

● **How Many Microstates?** To give you a sense of the number of microstates available to a substance, consider a mole of ice at 273 K, where $S° = 41.3$ J/K · mol. Using Boltzmann's equation, we find that $W = 10^{1,299,000,000,000,000,000,000,000}$. That is, there are many, many more microstates for 1 mol of ice than there are atoms in the universe (about 10^{80}).

microstates in which this is true (Figure 19.5c). Increasing the number of quanta from 2 to 6 with the same number of atoms increased the number of possible microstates from 10 to 84. In this case, increasing the amount of energy that is dispersed resulted in an increase in the number of microstates.

Statistical analyses for larger aggregates of atoms and energy quanta become increasingly complex, but the conclusions are even more compelling. As the number of particles and/or quanta increases, the number of energy microstates grows rapidly. A larger number of microstates allows the extent to which the energy is dispersed and/or the amount of the energy dispersed to increase. Ludwig Boltzmann proposed that the entropy of a system (the dispersal of energy at a given temperature) results from the number of microstates available. *As the number of microstates increases, so does the entropy of the system.* He expressed this idea in the equation

$$S = k \ln W \qquad (19.2)$$

which states that the entropy of a system, S, is proportional to the natural logarithm of the number of accessible microstates, W, that belong to a given energy of a system or substance. (The proportionality constant, k, is now known as **Boltzmann's constant** and has a value of 1.381×10^{-23} J/K.) Within these microstates, it turns out that those states that disperse energy over the largest number of atoms are vastly more probable than the others.

Dispersal of Matter: Dispersal of Energy Revisited

In many processes, it appears that the dispersal of matter also contributes to spontaneity. We shall see, however, that these effects can also be explained in terms of energy dispersal. Let us examine a specific case. Matter dispersal was illustrated in Figure 19.2 by the expansion of a gas into a vacuum. How is this spontaneous expansion of a gas related to energy dispersal and entropy?

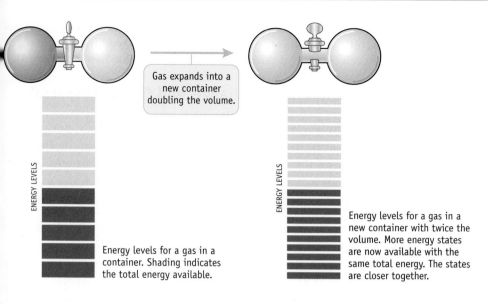

FIGURE 19.6 Energy (and matter) dispersal. As the size of the container for the chemical or physical change increases, the number of microstates accessible to the atoms or molecules of the system increases, and the density of states increases. A consequence of the distribution of molecules over a greater number of microstates is an increase in entropy.

Note that for a gas in a container of the size likely to be found in a laboratory, the energy levels are so closely spaced that we do not usually think in terms of quantization of energy levels. For most purposes, the system can be regarded as having a continuum of energy levels.

Gas expands into a new container doubling the volume.

ENERGY LEVELS

Energy levels for a gas in a container. Shading indicates the total energy available.

ENERGY LEVELS

Energy levels for a gas in a new container with twice the volume. More energy states are now available with the same total energy. The states are closer together.

We begin with the premise that all energy is quantized and that this applies to any system, including gas molecules in a room or in a reaction flask. You know from the previous discussion of kinetic-molecular theory that the molecules in a gas sample have a distribution of energies (◄ Figure 11.14) (often referred to as a *Boltzmann distribution*). The molecules are assigned to (or "occupy") quantized microstates, most of them in states near the average energy of the system, but fewer of them in states of high or low energy. (For a gas in a laboratory-sized container, the energy levels are so closely spaced that, for most purposes, there is a continuum of energy states.)

When the gas expands to fill a larger container, the average energy of the sample and the energy for the particles in a given energy range are constant. However, quantum mechanics shows (for now, you will have to take our word for it) that as a consequence of having a larger volume in which the molecules can move in the expanded state, there is an increase in the number of microstates and that those microstates are even more closely spaced than before (Figure 19.6). The result of this greater density of microstates is that the number of microstates available to the gas particles increases when the gas expands. Gas expansion, a dispersal of matter, leads to the dispersal of energy over a larger number of microstates and thus to an increase in entropy.

The logic applied to the expansion of a gas into a vacuum can be used to rationalize the mixing of two gases, the mixing of two liquids, or the dissolution of a solid in a liquid (Figure 19.7). For example, if flasks containing O_2 and N_2 are connected (in an experimental setup like that in Figure 19.6), the two gases diffuse together, eventually leading to a mixture in which O_2 and N_2 molecules are evenly distributed throughout the total volume. A mixture of O_2 and N_2 will never separate into samples of each component of its own accord. The gases spontaneously move toward a situation in which each gas and its energy are maximally dispersed. The energy of the system is dispersed over a larger number of microstates, and the entropy of the

● **Statistical Thermodynamics** The arguments presented here come from a branch of chemistry called *statistical thermodynamics*. See H. Jungermann, *Journal of Chemical Education*, Vol. 83, pp. 1686–1694, 2006.

Photos © Cengage Learning/Charles D. Winters

Time

FIGURE 19.7 Dissolving KMnO₄ in water. A small quantity of solid, purple $KMnO_4$ is added to water *(left)*. With time, the solid dissolves, and the highly colored MnO_4^- ions (and the K^+ ions) become dispersed throughout the solution. Entropy makes a large contribution to the mixing of liquids and solutions (page 621).

system increases. Indeed, this is a large part of the explanation for the fact that similar liquids (such as oil and gasoline or water and ethanol) will readily form homogeneous solutions. Recall the rule of thumb that "like dissolves like" (◄ Chapter 14).

A Summary: Entropy, Entropy Change, and Energy Dispersal

● **Entropy Change on Gas Expansion** The entropy change for a gas expansion can be calculated from

$$\Delta S = nR\ln(V_{final}/V_{initial})$$

At a given temperature, V is proportional to the number of microstates, so the equation is related to $k \ln(W_{final}/W_{initial})$.

According to Boltzmann's equation (Equation 19.2), entropy is proportional to the number of ways that energy can be dispersed in a substance, that is, to the number of microstates available to the system (W). Thus, there will be a change in entropy, ΔS, if there is a change in the number of microstates over which energy can be dispersed.

$$\Delta S = S_{final} - S_{initial} = k \, (\ln W_{final} - \ln W_{initial}) = k \ln(W_{final}/W_{initial})$$

Our focus as chemists is on ΔS, and we shall be mainly concerned with the dispersion of energy in systems and surroundings during a physical or chemical change.

REVIEW & CHECK FOR SECTION 19.3

1. As the number of microstates over which energy can be distributed in a system increases, its entropy

   (a) decreases   (b) increases   (c) remains constant

2. Calculate the change in entropy for a system in going from a condition with 5 accessible microstates to 30 accessible microstates.

   (a) -2.5×10^{-23} J/K (b) 9.4×10^{-24} J/K (c) 2.5×10^{-23} J/K (d) 8.3×10^{-23} J/K

19.4 Entropy Measurement and Values

For any substance under a given set of conditions, a numerical value for entropy can be determined. The greater the dispersal of energy, the greater the entropy and the larger the value of S. The point of reference for entropy values is established by the **third law of thermodynamics**. Defined by Ludwig Boltzmann, the third law states that *a perfect crystal at 0 K has zero entropy; that is, $S = 0$.* The entropy of an element or compound under any other set of conditions is the entropy gained by converting the substance from 0 K to those conditions. To determine the value of S, it is necessary to measure the energy transferred as heat under reversible conditions for the conversion from 0 K to the defined conditions and then to use Equation 19.1 ($\Delta S = q_{rev}/T$). Because it is necessary to add energy as heat to raise the temperature, *all substances have positive entropy values at temperatures above 0 K.* Negative values of entropy cannot occur. Recognizing that entropy is directly related to energy added as heat allows us to predict several general features of entropy values:

● Raising the temperature of a substance corresponds to adding energy as heat. Thus, the entropy of a substance will increase with an increase in temperature.

● Conversions from solid to liquid and from liquid to gas typically require large inputs of energy as heat. Consequently, there is a large increase in entropy in conversions involving changes of state (Figure 19.8).

Standard Entropy Values, $S°$

● **Negative Entropy Values** A glance at thermodynamic tables indicates that ions in aqueous solution can and do have negative entropy values listed. However, these are not absolute entropies. For ions, the entropy of H⁺(aq) is arbitrarily assigned a standard entropy of zero.

We introduced the concept of standard states into the earlier discussion of enthalpy (◄ Chapter 5), and we can similarly define the entropy of any substance in its standard state. The **standard molar entropy**, $S°$, of a substance is the entropy gained by converting 1 mol of it from a perfect crystal at 0 K to standard state conditions (1 bar, 1 molal for a solution) at the specified temperature. The units for standard molar entropy values are J/K · mol. Generally, values of $S°$ found in tables of data refer to a temperature of 298 K. Appendix L lists many standard molar entropies at 298 K. More extensive lists of $S°$ values can be found in standard reference sources such as the NIST tables (**webbook.nist.gov**).

(a)

(b)

The entropy of liquid bromine, $Br_2(\ell)$, is 152.2 J/K · mol, and that for bromine vapor is 245.47 J/K · mol.

The entropy of ice, which has a highly ordered molecular arrangement, is smaller than the entropy of liquid water.

FIGURE 19.8 Entropy and states of matter.

Scanning a list of standard entropies (such as those in Appendix L) will show that *large molecules generally have larger entropies than small molecules.* With a larger molecule, there are more ways for the molecule to rotate and vibrate, which provides a larger number of energy microstates over which energy can be distributed. As an example, consider the standard entropies for methane (CH_4), ethane (C_2H_6), and propane (C_3H_8), whose values are 186.3, 229.2, and 270.3 J/K · mol, respectively. Also, *molecules with more complex structures have larger entropies than molecules with simpler structures.* The effect of molecular structure can also be seen when comparing atoms or molecules of similar molar mass: Gaseous argon, CO_2, and C_3H_8 have entropies of 154.9, 213.7, and 270.3 J/K · mol, respectively.

Tables of entropy values also show that *entropies of gases are larger than those for liquids, and entropies of liquids are larger than those for solids.* In a solid, the particles have fixed positions in the solid lattice. When a solid melts, these particles have more freedom to assume different positions, resulting in an increase in the number of microstates available and an increase in entropy. When a liquid evaporates, constraints due to forces between the particles nearly disappear, the volume increases greatly, and a large entropy increase occurs. For example, the standard entropies of $I_2(s)$, $Br_2(\ell)$, and $Cl_2(g)$ are 116.1, 152.2, and 223.1 J/K · mol, respectively.

Finally, as illustrated in Figure 19.8, *for a given substance, a large increase in entropy accompanies changes of state,* reflecting the relatively large energy transfer as heat required to carry out these processes (as well as the dispersion of energy over a larger number of available microstates). For example, the entropies of liquid and gaseous water are 65.95 and 188.84 J/K · mol.

Entropy Values at 25 °C for some Hydrocarbons

	$S°$ (J/K · mol)
methane	186.3
ethane	229.2
propane	270.3

EXAMPLE 19.1   Entropy Comparisons

Problem Which substance has the higher entropy under standard conditions at 25 °C? Explain your reasoning. Check your answer against data in Appendix L.

(a) $NO_2(g)$ or $N_2O_4(g)$

(b) $I_2(g)$ or $I_2(s)$

What Do You Know? Entropy decreases in the order gas > liquid > solid, and larger molecules of related substances have greater entropies than smaller molecules.

Strategy For each part, identify the difference between the two substances and relate this to the general rules for entropy given above.

Solution

(a) Both NO_2 and N_2O_4 are gases. N_2O_4 is a larger molecule than NO_2 and so is expected to have the higher standard entropy.

(b) For a given substance, gases have higher entropies than solids, so $I_2(g)$ is expected to have the greater standard entropy.

Think about Your Answer $S°$ values in Appendix L confirm these predictions. At 25 °C, $S°$ for $NO_2(g)$ is 240.04 J/K · mol, and $S°$ for $N_2O_4(g)$ is 304.38 J/K · mol. $S°$ for $I_2(g)$ is 260.69 J/K · mol; $S°$ for $I_2(s)$ is 116.135 J/K · mol.

Check Your Understanding

Predict which substance in each par has the higher entropy and explain your reasoning.

(a) $O_2(g)$ or $O_3(g)$

(b) $SnCl_4(\ell)$ or $SnCl_4(g)$

Determining Entropy Changes in Physical and Chemical Processes

It is possible to use standard molar entropy values quantitatively to calculate the change in entropy that occurs in various processes under standard conditions. The standard entropy change for a reaction ($\Delta_r S°$) is the sum of the standard molar entropies of the products, each multiplied by its stoichiometric coefficient, minus the sum of the standard molar entropies of the reactants, each multiplied by its stoichiometric coefficient.

$$\Delta_r S° = \Sigma n S°(\text{products}) - \Sigma n S°(\text{reactants}) \tag{19.3}$$

This equation allows us to calculate entropy changes for a *system* in which reactants are completely converted to products, under standard conditions. To illustrate, let us calculate $\Delta_r S°$ for the oxidation of NO with O_2.

$$2\ NO(g) + O_2(g) \rightarrow 2\ NO_2(g)$$

$$\Delta_r S° = (2\ \text{mol}\ NO_2/\text{mol-rxn})\ S°[NO_2(g)] -$$
$$\{(2\ \text{mol}\ NO(g)/\text{mol-rxn})\ S°[NO(g)] + (1\ \text{mol}\ O_2/\text{mol-rxn})\ S°[O_2(g)]\}$$

$$= (2\ \text{mol}\ NO_2/\text{mol-rxn})(240.0\ \text{J/K} \cdot \text{mol}) -$$
$$[(2\ \text{mol}\ NO(g)/\text{mol-rxn})(210.8\ \text{J/K} \cdot \text{mol}) + (1\ \text{mol}\ O_2/\text{mol-rxn})(205.1\ \text{J/K} \cdot \text{mol})]$$

$$= -146.7\ \text{J/K} \cdot \text{mol-rxn}$$

The entropy of the system decreases, as is generally observed when some number of gaseous reactants has been converted to fewer molecules of gaseous products.

The reaction of NO with O_2. The entropy of the system decreases when two molecules of gas are produced from three molecules of gaseous reactants.

Strategy Map 19.2

PROBLEM

Calculate $\Delta_r S°$ for a reaction.

↓

DATA/INFORMATION

• Balanced chemical equation
• $S°$ values (Appendix L)

STEP 1. Calculate $\Delta_r S°$ using Equation 19.3.

↓

$\Delta_r S°$ for the reaction

⬤WL INTERACTIVE EXAMPLE 19.2 Predicting and Calculating $\Delta_r S°$ for a Reaction

Problem Calculate the standard entropy changes for the following processes.

(a) Evaporation of 1.00 mol of liquid ethanol to ethanol vapor:

$$C_2H_5OH(\ell) \rightarrow C_2H_5OH(g)$$

(b) Formation of ammonia from hydrogen and nitrogen based on the following equation:

$$N_2(g) + 3\ H_2(g) \rightarrow 2\ NH_3(g)$$

What Do You Know? For each part, you are given a balanced chemical equation and asked to determine the standard entropy change for the reaction ($\Delta_r S°$). Values of standard molar entropies for the substances can be found in Appendix L.

Strategy Entropy changes for each system can be calculated from values of standard entropies (Appendix L) using Equation 19.3.

Solution

(a) Evaporation of ethanol

$\Delta_r S° = \Sigma n S°(\text{products}) - \Sigma n S°(\text{reactants})$

$= (1 \text{ mol } C_2H_5OH(g)/\text{mol-rxn}) \, S°[C_2H_5OH(g)] - (1 \text{ mol } C_2H_5OH(\ell)/\text{mol-rxn}) \, S°[C_2H_5OH(\ell)]$

$= (1 \text{ mol } C_2H_5OH(g)/\text{mol-rxn})(282.70 \text{ J/K} \cdot \text{mol}) - (1 \text{ mol } C_2H_5OH(\ell)/\text{ mol-rxn})(160.7 \text{ J/K} \cdot \text{mol})$

$= +122.0 \text{ J/K} \cdot \text{mol-rxn}$

(b) Formation of ammonia

$\Delta_r S° = \Sigma n S°(\text{products}) - \Sigma n S°(\text{reactants})$

$= (2 \text{ mol } NH_3(g)/\text{mol-rxn}) \, S°[NH_3(g)] -$
$\qquad\qquad \{(1 \text{ mol } N_2(g)/\text{mol-rxn}) \, S°[N_2(g)] + (3 \text{ mol } H_2(g)/\text{mol-rxn}) \, S°[H_2(g)]\}$

$= (2 \text{ mol } NH_3(g)/\text{mol-rxn})(192.77 \text{ J/K} \cdot \text{mol}) -$
$\qquad [(1 \text{ mol } N_2(g)/\text{mol-rxn})(191.56 \text{ J/K} \cdot \text{mol}) + (3 \text{ mol } H_2(g)/\text{mol-rxn})(130.7 \text{ J/K} \cdot \text{mol})]$

$= -198.12 \text{ J/K} \cdot \text{mol-rxn}$

Think about Your Answer Predictions for the signs of these entropy changes can be made using the guidelines given in the text. In part (a), a large positive value for the entropy change is expected because the process converts ethanol from a liquid to a vapor. In part (b), a decrease in entropy is predicted because the number of moles of gases decreases from four to two.

Check Your Understanding

Calculate the standard entropy changes for the following processes using the entropy values in Appendix L. Are the signs of the calculated values of $\Delta_r S°$ in accord with predictions?

(a) Dissolving 1 mol of $NH_4Cl(s)$ in water: $NH_4Cl(s) \rightarrow NH_4Cl(aq)$

(b) Oxidation of ethanol: $C_2H_5OH(g) + 3 O_2(g) \rightarrow 2 CO_2(g) + 3 H_2O(g)$

• **Amount of Substance and Thermodynamic Calculations** In the calculation here and in all others in this chapter, when we write, for example,

$\qquad 282.70 \text{ J/K} \cdot \text{mol}$

for the standard entropy of ethanol at 298 K, we mean

$\qquad 282.70 \text{ J/K} \cdot \text{mol } C_2H_5OH(\ell)$

The identifying formula has been left off for the sake of simplicity.

REVIEW & CHECK FOR SECTION 19.4

1. Without doing any calculations, identify which of the following lists the materials in order of increasing entropy.

(a) $H_2O(\ell) < NaCl(s) < NH_3(g)$ (c) $NaCl(s) < H_2O(\ell) < NH_3(g)$

(b) $H_2O(\ell) < NH_3(g) < NaCl(s)$ (d) $NH_3(g) < H_2O(\ell) < NaCl(s)$

2. Without doing any calculations, predict the sign of $\Delta_r S°$ for the following reaction:

$$Zn(s) + 2 HCl(aq) \rightarrow ZnCl_2(aq) + H_2(g)$$

(a) $\Delta_r S° < 0$ (b) $\Delta_r S° = 0$ (c) $\Delta_r S° > 0$

3. Calculate $\Delta_r S°$ for the following reaction at 25 °C.

$$2 H_2(g) + O_2(g) \rightarrow 2 H_2O(\ell)$$

(a) $-326.6 \text{ J/K} \cdot \text{mol-rxn}$ (c) $139.9 \text{ J/K} \cdot \text{mol-rxn}$

(b) $-139.9 \text{ J/K} \cdot \text{mol-rxn}$ (d) $326.6 \text{ J/K} \cdot \text{mol-rxn}$

19.5 Entropy Changes and Spontaneity

As illustrated by Example 19.2, the standard entropy change *for the system* in a physical or chemical change can be either positive (evaporation of ethanol) or negative (synthesis of ammonia from nitrogen and hydrogen). How does this information contribute to determining the spontaneity of the process?

A List of Common Entropy-Favored Processes

must be added to a system to increase its temperature (that is, $q > 0$), so q_{rev}/T is necessarily positive.

- The entropy of a gas increases with an increase in volume. A larger volume pro-

vides a larger number of energy states over which to disperse energy.

- Reactions that increase the number of moles of gases in a system are accompanied by an increase in entropy.

As discussed previously (page 861), spontaneity is determined by the *second law of thermodynamics*, which states that *a spontaneous process is one that results in an increase of entropy in the universe*. The universe has two parts: the system and its surroundings (◄ Section 5.1), and so it makes sense that the entropy change for the universe is the sum of the entropy changes for the system and the surroundings. Under standard conditions, the entropy change for the universe, $\Delta S°$(universe) is

$$\Delta S°(universe) = \Delta S°(system) + \Delta S°(surroundings) \tag{19.4}$$

The calculation in Example 19.2 gave us the entropy change under standard conditions for a system, only half of the information needed. Now we will have to determine how the change being studied affects the entropy of the surroundings so that we can then find the entropy change for the universe.

The value of $\Delta S°$(universe) calculated from Equation 19.4 is the entropy change when reactants are converted *completely* to products, with all species at standard conditions. *A process is spontaneous under standard conditions if $\Delta S°$(universe) is greater than zero.* As an example of the determination of reaction spontaneity, let us calculate $\Delta S°$(universe) for the reaction currently used to manufacture methanol, CH_3OH.

$$CO(g) + 2 H_2(g) \rightarrow CH_3OH(\ell)$$

● **Using ΔS°(universe)** For a process that is spontaneous under standard conditions:

$$\Delta S°(universe) > 0$$

For a process at equilibrium under standard conditions:

$$\Delta S°(universe) = 0$$

For a process that is not spontaneous under standard conditions:

$$\Delta S°(universe) < 0$$

Note that these conclusions refer to the *complete* conversion of reactants to products.

If $\Delta S°$(universe) is positive, the conversion of 1 mol of $CO(g)$ and 2 mol of $H_2(g)$ to 1 mol of $CH_3OH(\ell)$ will be spontaneous under standard conditions.

Calculating ΔS°(system) To calculate $\Delta S°$(system), we start by defining the system to include the reactants and products. This means that $\Delta S°$(system) corresponds to the entropy change for the reaction, $\Delta_r S°$. Calculation of this entropy change follows the procedure given in Example 19.2.

$$\Delta S°(system) = \Delta_r S° = \Sigma n S°(products) - \Sigma n S°(reactants)$$

$$= (1 \text{ mol } CH_3OH(\ell)/mol\text{-rxn}) \, S°[CH_3OH(\ell)] - \{(1 \text{ mol } CO(g)/mol\text{-rxn}) \, S°[CO(g)] + (2 \text{ mol } H_2(g)/mol\text{-rxn}) \, S°[H_2(g)]\}$$

$$= (1 \text{ mol } CH_3OH(\ell)/mol\text{-rxn})(127.2 \text{ J/K} \cdot mol) - [(1 \text{ mol } CO(g)/mol\text{-rxn})(197.7 \text{ J/K} \cdot mol) + (2 \text{ mol } H_2(g)/mol\text{-rxn})(130.7 \text{ J/K} \cdot mol)]$$

$$= -331.9 \text{ J/K} \cdot mol\text{-rxn}$$

A decrease in entropy for the system is expected because three moles of gaseous reactants are converted to one mole of a liquid product.

Calculating ΔS°(surroundings) We now need to calculate the entropy change for the surroundings. Recall from Equation 19.1 that for a reversible change, ΔS is equal to q_{rev}/T. Under constant pressure conditions and assuming a reversible process, the entropy change in the surroundings results from the fact that the enthalpy change for the reaction ($q_{rev} = \Delta_r H$) affects the surroundings. That is, the energy associated with an exothermic chemical reaction is dispersed into the surroundings. Recognizing that $\Delta H°$(surroundings) $= -\Delta_r H°$(system), the entropy change for the surroundings can be calculated by the equation

$$\Delta S°(surroundings) = \Delta H°(surroundings)/T = -\Delta_r H°(system)/T$$

For the synthesis of methanol by the reaction given, the enthalpy change can be cal-culated from enthalpy of formation data using Equation 5.6 (page 234).

$\Delta H°$(system) $= \Sigma n\Delta_f H°$(products) $- \Sigma n\Delta_f H°$(reactants)

$\quad$ = (1 mol $CH_3OH(\ell)$/mol-rxn) $\Delta_f H°[CH_3OH(\ell)]$ −
$\qquad$ {(1 mol $CO(g)$/mol-rxn) $\Delta_f H°[CO(g)]$ +
$\qquad\qquad$ (2 mol $H_2(g)$/mol-rxn) $\Delta_f H°[H_2(g)]$}

$\quad$ = (1 mol $CH_3OH(\ell)$/mol-rxn)(−238.4 kJ/mol) −
$\qquad$ [(1 mol $CO(g)$/mol-rxn)(−110.5 kJ/mol) +
$\qquad\qquad$ (2 mol $H_2(g)$/mol-rxn)(0 kJ/ mol)]

$\quad$ = −127.9 kJ/mol-rxn

Assuming that the process is reversible and occurs at a constant temperature and pressure, the entropy change for the surroundings in the methanol synthesis is +429.2 J/K · mol-rxn, calculated as follows.

$\Delta S°$(surroundings) $= -\Delta_r H°$(system)$/T$

$\quad$ = −[(−127.9 kJ/mol-rxn)/298 K)](1000 J/kJ)

$\quad$ = +429.2 J/K · mol-rxn

Calculating $\Delta S°$(universe), the Entropy Change for the System and Surroundings

The pieces are now in place to calculate the entropy change in the universe. For the formation of $CH_3OH(\ell)$ from $CO(g)$ and $H_2(g)$, $\Delta S°$(universe) is

$\Delta S°$(universe) $= \Delta S°$(system) $+ \Delta S°$(surroundings)

$\quad$ = −331.9 J/K · mol-rxn + 429.2 J/K · mol-rxn

$\quad$ = +97.3 J/K · mol-rxn

The positive value indicates an increase in the entropy of the universe. It follows from the second law of thermodynamics that this reaction is spontaneous.

⬚WL INTERACTIVE EXAMPLE 19.3 Determining Whether a Process Is Spontaneous

Problem Calculate $\Delta S°$(universe) for the process of dissolving NaCl in water at 298 K.

What Do You Know? The process occurring is NaCl(s) → NaCl(aq). $\Delta S°$(universe) is equal to the sum of $\Delta S°$(system) and $\Delta S°$(surroundings). Values of $S°$ and $\Delta_f H°$ for NaCl(s) and NaCl(aq) are given in Appendix L.

Strategy The entropy change for the system, $\Delta S°$(system), can be calculated from values of $S°$ for the two species using Equation 19.3. $\Delta_r H°$ can be calculated from values of $\Delta_f H°$ for the two species using Equation 5.6 (page 234). $\Delta S°$(surroundings) is determined by dividing $-\Delta_r H°$ for the process by the Kelvin temperature. The sum of $\Delta S°$(system) and $\Delta S°$(surroundings) is $\Delta S°$(universe). If this value is positive, then the process is spontaneous under standard conditions.

Solution

Calculate $\Delta S°$(system)

$\Delta S°$(system) $= \Sigma n S°$(products) $- \Sigma n S°$(reactants)

$\quad$ = (1 mol NaCl(aq)/mol-rxn) $S°$[NaCl(aq)] − (1 mol NaCl(s)/mol-rxn) $S°$[NaCl(s)]

$\quad$ = (1 mol NaCl(aq)/mol-rxn)(115.5 J/K · mol) − (1 mol NaCl(s)/mol-rxn)(72.11 J/K · mol)

$\quad$ = +43.4 J/K · mol-rxn

Calculate $\Delta S°$(surroundings)

$\Delta_r H°$(system) $= \Sigma n\Delta_f H°$(products) $- \Sigma n\Delta_f H°$(reactants)

$\quad$ = (1 mol NaCl(aq)/mol-rxn) $\Delta_f H°$[NaCl(aq)] − (1 mol NaCl(s)/mol-rxn) $\Delta_f H°$[NaCl(s)]

$\quad$ = (1 mol NaCl(aq)/mol-rxn)(−407.27 kJ/mol) − (1 mol NaCl(s)/mol-rxn)(−411.12 kJ/mol)

$\quad$ = +3.85 kJ/mol-rxn

Strategy Map 19.3

PROBLEM

Determine the value of $\Delta S°$(universe) for a chemical reaction.

↓

KNOWN DATA/INFORMATION

- Balanced chemical equation
- Temperature
- Values of $S°$, $\Delta_f H°$(Appendix L)

STEP 1. Calculate $\Delta_r S°$ using Equation 19.3.

$\Delta S°$(system)

STEP 2. Calculate $\Delta_r H°$ using Equation 5.6.
Change the sign of $\Delta_r H°$ and divide this by T (in K).

$\Delta S°$(surroundings)

STEP 3. Add $\Delta S°$(system) and $\Delta S°$(surroundings).

$\Delta S°$(universe)

The entropy change of the surroundings is determined by dividing $-\Delta_r H°$(system) by the Kelvin temperature.

$$\Delta S°(\text{surroundings}) = -\Delta_r H°(\text{system})/T$$

$$= [(-3.85 \text{ kJ/mol-rxn}/298 \text{ K})](1000 \text{ J/1 kJ})$$

$$= -12.9 \text{ J/K} \cdot \text{mol-rxn}$$

Calculate $\Delta S°$(universe)

The overall entropy change—the change of entropy in the universe—is the sum of the values for the system and the surroundings.

$$\Delta S°(\text{universe}) = \Delta S°(\text{system}) + \Delta S°(\text{surroundings})$$

$$= (+43.4 \text{ J/K} \cdot \text{mol-rxn}) + (-12.9 \text{ J/K} \cdot \text{mol-rxn})$$

$$= +30.5 \text{ J/K} \cdot \text{mol-rxn}$$

Think about Your Answer The sum of the two entropy quantities is positive, indicating that the entropy in the universe increases; thus, the process is spontaneous under standard conditions. Notice that the spontaneity of the process results from $\Delta S°$(system) and not from $\Delta S°$(surroundings).

Check Your Understanding

Is the reaction of hydrogen and chlorine to give hydrogen chloride gas predicted to be spontaneous under standard conditions (at 298 K)?

$$H_2(g) + Cl_2(g) \rightarrow 2 \text{ HCl}(g)$$

Predict the spontaneity of the reaction based on $\Delta_r H°$ and $\Delta_r S°$, and then calculate $\Delta S°$(universe) to verify your prediction.

• **$\Delta S°$(universe), Spontaneity, and Standard Conditions** It is important to reiterate that $\Delta H°$ and $\Delta S°$ values for a reaction are for the *complete* conversion of reactants to products under standard conditions. If $\Delta S°$(universe) is > 0, the reaction as written is spontaneous *under standard conditions*. However, one can calculate values for ΔS(universe) (without the superscript zero) for *nonstandard* conditions. If ΔS(universe) is > 0, the reaction is spontaneous under those conditions. However, it is possible that this same reaction under standard conditions is not spontaneous [$\Delta S°$(universe) < 0]. We will return to this point on pages 875–877.

In Summary: Spontaneous or Not?

In the preceding examples, predictions about the spontaneity of a process under standard conditions were made using values of $\Delta S°$(system) and $\Delta H°$(system) calculated from tables of thermodynamic data. It will be useful to look at all possibilities that result from the interplay of these two quantities. There are four possible outcomes when these two quantities are paired (Table 19.1). In two, $\Delta H°$(system) and $\Delta S°$(system) work in concert (Types 1 and 4 in Table 19.1). In the other two, the two quantities are opposed (Types 2 and 3).

Processes in which both the standard enthalpy and entropy changes favor energy dispersal (Type 1) are always spontaneous under standard conditions. Processes disfavored by both their standard enthalpy and entropy changes in the system (Type 4) can *never* be spontaneous under standard conditions. Let us consider examples that illustrate each situation.

Table 19.1 Predicting Whether a Reaction Will Be Spontaneous Under Standard Conditions

Reaction Type	$\Delta H°$(system)	$\Delta S°$(system)	Spontaneous Process? (Standard Conditions)
1	Exothermic, < 0	Positive, > 0	Spontaneous at all temperatures. $\Delta S°$(universe) > 0.
2	Exothermic, < 0	Negative, < 0	Depends on relative magnitudes of $\Delta H°$ and $\Delta S°$. Spontaneous at lower temperatures.
3	Endothermic, > 0	Positive, > 0	Depends on relative magnitudes of $\Delta H°$ and $\Delta S°$. Spontaneous at higher temperatures.
4	Endothermic, > 0	Negative, < 0	Not spontaneous at any temperature. $\Delta S°$(universe) < 0.

Combustion reactions are always exothermic and often produce a larger number of gaseous product molecules from a few reactant molecules. They are Type 1 reactions. The equation for the combustion of butane is an example.

$$2\ C_4H_{10}(g) + 13\ O_2(g) \rightarrow 8\ CO_2(g) + 10\ H_2O(g)$$

For this reaction, $\Delta_rH° = -5315.1$ kJ/mol · rxn, and $\Delta_rS° = 312.4$ J/K · mol-rxn. Both contribute to this reaction being spontaneous under standard conditions.

Hydrazine, N_2H_4, is used as a high-energy rocket fuel. Synthesis of N_2H_4 from gaseous N_2 and H_2 would be attractive because these reactants are inexpensive.

$$N_2(g) + 2\ H_2(g) \rightarrow N_2H_4(\ell)$$

However, this reaction fits into the Type 4 category. The reaction is endothermic ($\Delta_rH° = +50.63$ kJ/mol-rxn), and the entropy change is negative ($\Delta_rS° = -331.4$ J/K·mol-rxn) (1 mol of liquid is produced from 3 mol of gases), so the reaction is not spontaneous under standard conditions, and complete conversion of reactants to products will not occur without outside intervention.

In the two other possible outcomes, entropy and enthalpy changes oppose each other. A process could be favored by the enthalpy change but disfavored by the entropy change (Type 2), or vice versa (Type 3). In either instance, whether a process is spontaneous depends on which factor is more important.

Temperature also influences the value of $\Delta S°$(universe). Because the enthalpy change for the surroundings is divided by the temperature to obtain $\Delta S°$(surroundings), the numerical value of $\Delta S°$(surroundings) will be smaller (either less positive or less negative) at higher temperatures. In contrast, $\Delta S°$(system) and $\Delta H°$(system) do not vary much with temperature. Thus, the effect of $\Delta S°$(surroundings) relative to $\Delta S°$(system) is diminished at higher temperature. Stated another way, at higher temperature, the enthalpy change becomes a less important factor in determining the overall entropy change. Consider the two cases where $\Delta H°$(system) and $\Delta S°$(system) are in opposition (Table 19.1):

- Type 2: Exothermic processes with $\Delta S°$(system) < 0. Such processes become less favorable with an increase in temperature.
- Type 3: Endothermic processes with $\Delta S°$(system) > 0. These processes become more favorable as the temperature increases.

The effect of temperature is illustrated by two examples. The first is the reaction of N_2 and H_2 to form NH_3. The reaction is exothermic, and thus it is favored by energy dispersal to the surroundings. The entropy change for the system is unfavorable, however, because the reaction, $N_2(g) + 3\ H_2(g) \rightarrow 2\ NH_3(g)$, converts four moles of gaseous reactants to two moles of gaseous products. The favorable enthalpy effect [$\Delta_rS°$(surroundings) = $-\Delta_rH°$(system)/T] becomes less important at higher temperatures. It is therefore reasonable to expect that the reaction will not be spontaneous if the temperature is high enough.

The second example considers the thermal decomposition of NH_4Cl (Figure 19.9). At room temperature, NH_4Cl is a stable, white, crystalline salt. When heated strongly, it decomposes to $NH_3(g)$ and $HCl(g)$. The reaction is endothermic (enthalpy-disfavored) but entropy-favored because of the formation of two moles of gas from one mole of a solid reactant. The reaction is increasingly favored at higher temperatures.

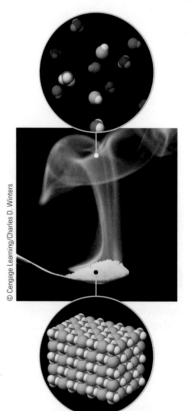

FIGURE 19.9 Thermal decomposition of NH₄Cl(s). White, solid ammonium chloride, NH_4Cl(s), is heated in a spoon. At high temperatures, decomposition to form $NH_3(g)$ and $HCl(g)$ is spontaneous. At lower temperatures, the reverse reaction, forming NH_4Cl(s), is spontaneous. As gaseous $HCl(g)$ and $NH_3(g)$ cool, they recombine to form solid NH_4Cl, the white "smoke" seen in this photo.

© Cengage Learning/Charles D. Winters

REVIEW & CHECK FOR SECTION 19.5

1. Calculate $\Delta_rS°$ for the following reaction at 25 °C:

$$N_2(g) + 2\ O_2(g) \rightarrow 2\ NO_2(g)$$

(a) −480.1 J/K · mol-rxn

(b) −121.6 J/K · mol-rxn

(c) 121.6 J/K · mol-rxn

(d) 480.1 J/K · mol-rxn

2. Calculate $\Delta S°$(universe) for the following reaction at 25.0 °C:

    $$C(graphite) + O_2(g) \rightarrow CO_2(g)$$

    (a) -1317 J/K · mol-rxn   (c) 4.4 J/K · mol-rxn

    (b) 3.1 J/K · mol-rxn   (d) 1320 J/K · mol-rxn

3. If $\Delta_r H° = +467.9$ kJ/mol-rxn and $\Delta_r S° = +560.7$ J/K · mol-rxn for the following reaction

    $$2\ Fe_2O_3(s) + 3\ C(graphite) \rightarrow 4\ Fe(s) + 3\ CO_2(g)$$

    then, under standard conditions, this reaction will be spontaneous

    (a) at all temperatures   (c) at lower temperatures

    (b) at higher temperatures   (d) at no temperature

19.6 Gibbs Free Energy

The method used so far to determine whether a process is spontaneous required evaluation of two quantities, $\Delta S°$(system) and $\Delta S°$(surroundings). Wouldn't it be convenient to have a single thermodynamic function that serves the same purpose? A function associated with the system only—one that does not require assessment of the surroundings—would be even better. Such a function exists. It is called the **Gibbs free energy**, with the name honoring J. Willard Gibbs (1839–1903). Gibbs free energy, G, often referred to simply as "free energy," is defined mathematically as

$$G = H - TS$$

where H is enthalpy, T is the Kelvin temperature, and S is entropy. In this equation, G, H, and S all refer to the system. Because enthalpy and entropy are state functions (◄ Section 5.4), free energy is also a state function.

Every substance possesses free energy, but the actual quantity is seldom known. Instead, just as with enthalpy (H) and internal energy (U), we are concerned with *changes* in free energy, ΔG, that occur in chemical and physical processes.

Let us first see how to use free energy as a way to determine whether a reaction is spontaneous. We can then ask further questions about the meaning of the term "free energy" and its use in deciding whether a reaction is product- or reactant-favored.

The Change in the Gibbs Free Energy, ΔG

Recall the equation defining the entropy change for the universe:

$$\Delta S(universe) = \Delta S(surroundings) + \Delta S(system)$$

The entropy change of the surroundings equals the negative of the change in enthalpy of the system divided by T. Thus,

$$\Delta S(universe) = -\Delta H(system)/T + \Delta S(system)$$

Multiplying through this equation by $-T$, gives the equation

$$-T\Delta S(universe) = \Delta H(system) - T\Delta S(system)$$

Gibbs defined the free energy function so that $\Delta G(system) = -T\Delta S(universe)$. Thus, the general expression relating changes in free energy to the enthalpy and entropy changes in the system is the following.

$$\Delta G = \Delta H - T\Delta S$$

Under standard conditions, we can rewrite this, the Gibbs free energy equation, as

$$\Delta G° = \Delta H° - T\Delta S° \tag{19.5}$$

● **J. Willard Gibbs (1839–1903)**
Gibbs received a Ph.D. from Yale University in 1863. His was the first Ph.D. in science awarded from an American university.

Gibbs Free Energy, Spontaneity, and Chemical Equilibrium

Because $\Delta_r G^\circ$ is related directly to ΔS°(universe), the Gibbs free energy can be used as a criterion of spontaneity for physical and chemical changes. As shown earlier, the signs of $\Delta_r G^\circ$ and ΔS°(universe) will be opposites $[\Delta_r G^\circ (\text{system}) = -T\Delta S^\circ (\text{universe})]$. Therefore, we find the following relationships:

$\Delta_r G^\circ < 0$	The process is spontaneous in the direction written under standard conditions.
$\Delta_r G^\circ = 0$	The process is at equilibrium under standard conditions.
$\Delta_r G^\circ > 0$	The process is not spontaneous in the direction written under standard conditions.

To better understand the Gibbs function, let us examine the diagrams in Figure 19.10. The free energy of pure reactants is plotted on the left, and the free energy of the pure products on the right. The extent of reaction, plotted on the x-axis, goes from zero (pure reactants) to one (pure products). In both cases in Figure 19.10, the free energy initially declines as reactants begin to form products; it reaches a minimum at equilibrium and then increases again as we move from the equilibrium position to pure products. *The free energy at equilibrium, where there is a mixture of reactants and products, is always lower than the free energy of the pure reactants and of the pure products. A reaction proceeds spontaneously toward the minimum in free energy, which corresponds to equilibrium.*

$\Delta_r G^\circ$ *is the change in free energy accompanying the chemical reaction in which the reactants are converted completely to the products under standard conditions.* Mathematically, it is the difference in free energy between the products and the reactants under standard conditions. If the free energy of the products is less than that of the reactants, then $\Delta_r G^\circ < 0$, and the reaction is spontaneous under standard conditions (Figure 19.10a). Conversely, if the free energy of the products is greater than that of the reactants, then $\Delta_r G^\circ$ is positive ($\Delta_r G^\circ > 0$), and the reaction is not spontaneous under standard conditions (Figure 19.10b).

Notice that in Figure 19.10a, the equilibrium position occurs closer to the product side than to the reactant side. This is a product-favored reaction at equilibrium. In Figure 19.10b, we find the opposite. The reaction is reactant-favored at equilibrium. It is no accident that the reaction with a negative $\Delta_r G^\circ$ is product-favored, whereas the one with the positive $\Delta_r G^\circ$ is reactant-favored at equilibrium. It turns out that this is always true as the discussion below will show.

FIGURE 19.10 Free energy changes in the course of a reaction. The difference in free energy between the pure reactants in their standard states and the pure products in their standard states is $\Delta_r G^\circ$. Here, Q is the reaction quotient, and K is the equilibrium constant.

Now let us consider what happens to the instantaneous slope of the curve in Figure 19.10 as the reaction proceeds. Initially, this slope is negative, corresponding to a negative ΔG in moving from point to point. Eventually, however, the free energy reaches a minimum. At this point, the instantaneous slope of the graph is zero ($\Delta G = 0$) and the reaction has reached equilibrium. If we move past the equilibrium point, the instantaneous slope is positive ($\Delta G > 0$); proceeding further to products is not spontaneous. In fact, the reverse reaction will occur spontaneously; the reaction will once again proceed toward equilibrium.

The relationship of $\Delta_r G°$ (the value of $\Delta_r G$ under standard conditions) and the value of $\Delta_r G$ under nonstandard conditions is given by Equation 19.6:

$$\Delta_r G = \Delta_r G° + RT \ln Q \tag{19.6}$$

where R is the universal gas constant, T is the temperature in kelvins, and Q is the reaction quotient (◄ Section 16.2).

$$Q = \frac{[C]^c[D]^d}{[A]^a[B]^b} \text{ for } aA + bB \rightarrow cC + dD$$

Equation 19.6 informs us that, at a given temperature, $\Delta_r G$ is determined by the values of $\Delta_r G°$ and Q. When the system reaches equilibrium, no further net change in concentration of reactants and products will occur, and $\Delta_r G = 0$ and $Q = K$. Substituting these values into Equation 19.6 gives

$$0 = \Delta_r G° + RT \ln K \text{ (at equilibrium)}$$

Rearranging this equation leads to a useful relationship between the standard free energy change for a reaction and the equilibrium constant, K, Equation 19.7:

$$\Delta_r G° = -RT \ln K \tag{19.7}$$

From this equation, we learn that, when $\Delta_r G°$ is negative, K is greater than 1, and we say the reaction is *product-favored at equilibrium*. The more negative the value of $\Delta_r G°$, the larger the equilibrium constant. This makes sense because, as described in Chapter 16, large equilibrium constants are associated with product-favored reactions. The converse is also true: For *reactant-favored* reactions, $\Delta_r G°$ is positive, and K is less than 1. Finally, if $K = 1$ (a special set of conditions), then $\Delta_r G° = 0$.

Let us now see that Equation 19.6 can yield the relationsips between Q and K that we have been using since Chapter 16.

$$\Delta_r G = \Delta_r G° + RT \ln Q$$

Substituting $-RT \ln K$ for $\Delta_r G°$ (Equation 19.7) gives

$$\Delta_r G = -RT \ln K + RT \ln Q$$

This equation can be rearranged as follows:

$$\Delta_r G = RT (\ln Q - \ln K)$$

$$\Delta_r G/RT = \ln Q - \ln K$$

Furthermore, as long as the reaction is "descending" from the free energy of the pure reactants to the equilibrium position, $\Delta_r G$ is negative, implying that the reaction is spontaneous in the forward direction. Because $\Delta_r G$ is negative, we can write:

When $\Delta_r G < 0$, then $\ln Q - \ln K < 0$

Therefore, $\ln Q < \ln K$

and $Q < K$

This means that for a reaction to be spontaneous, $\Delta_r G$ must be negative (a spontaneous reaction), and Q must be less than K ($Q < K$), just as has been stated earlier. A similar analysis shows that if $\Delta_r G$ is positive, then $Q > K$.

A reactant-favored process. If a sample of yellow lead(II) iodide is placed in pure water, a small amount of the compound will dissolve spontaneously ($\Delta_r G < 0$ and $Q < K$) until equilibrium is reached. Because PbI_2 is quite insoluble ($K_{sp} = 9.8 \times 10^{-9}$), however, the process of dissolving the compound is reactant-favored at equilibrium. We may conclude, therefore, that the value of $\Delta_r G°$ is positive.

A Summary: Gibbs Free Energy (Δ_rG and $\Delta_rG°$), the Reaction Quotient (Q) and Equilibrium Constant (K), and Reaction Favorability

Let us summarize the relationships among $\Delta_rG°$, Δ_rG, Q, and K.

- In Figure 19.10, you see that free energy decreases to a minimum as a system approaches equilibrium. The free energy of the mixture of reactants and products at equilibrium is always lower than the free energy of the pure reactants or of the pure products.
- When $\Delta_rG < 0$, the reaction is proceeding spontaneously toward equilibrium and $Q < K$.
- When $\Delta_rG > 0$, the reaction is beyond the equilibrium point and is not spontaneous in the forward direction. It will be spontaneous in the reverse direction; $Q > K$.
- When $\Delta_rG = 0$, the reaction is at equilibrium; $Q = K$.
- When $\Delta_rG° < 0$, the reaction is *spontaneous under standard conditions*. The system will proceed to an equilibrium position at which point the products will dominate in the reaction mixture because $K > 1$. That is, the reaction is *product-favored* at equilibrium.
- When $\Delta_rG° > 0$, the reaction is *not spontaneous under standard conditions*. The system will proceed to the equilibrium position at which point the reactants will dominate in the equilibrium mixture because $K < 1$. That is, the reaction is *reactant-favored* at equilibrium.
- For the special condition where $\Delta_rG° = 0$, the reaction is at equilibrium at standard conditions, with $K = 1$.

What Is "Free" Energy?

The term *free energy* was not arbitrarily chosen. In any given process, the free energy represents the maximum energy available to do useful work (mathematically, $\Delta G = w_{max}$). In this context, the word *free* means "available."

To illustrate the reasoning behind this relationship, consider a reaction carried out under standard conditions and in which energy is evolved as heat ($\Delta_rH° < 0$) and entropy decreases ($\Delta_rS° < 0$).

$$2\ H_2(g) + O_2(g) \rightarrow 2\ H_2O(g)$$

$$\Delta_rH° = -483.6\ \text{kJ/mol-rxn and } \Delta_rS° = -88.8\ \text{J/K} \cdot \text{mol-rxn}$$

$$\Delta_rG° = -483.6\ \text{kJ/mol-rxn} - (298\ K)(-0.0888\ \text{kJ/mol-rxn}) = -457.2\ \text{kJ/mol-rxn}$$

At first glance, it might seem reasonable that all the energy released as heat (-483.6 kJ/mol-rxn) would be available. This energy could be transferred to the surroundings and would thus be available to do work. This is not the case, however. A negative entropy change in this reaction means that energy is less dispersed in the products than in the reactants. A portion of the energy released from the reaction must be used to reverse energy dispersal in the system; that is, to concentrate energy in the product. The energy left over is "free," or available to perform work. Here, the free energy change amounts to -457.2 kJ/mol-rxn.

REVIEW & CHECK FOR SECTION 19.6

1. For a reaction to be spontaneous, ΔG will be _____ than zero and Q will be _____ than K.

   (a) greater, greater   (b) greater, less   (c) less, greater   (d) less, less

2. A reaction that is spontaneous under standard conditions is also

   (a) product-favored at equilibrium   (b) reactant-favored at equilibrium

3. A process that has $\Delta G° < 0$ can never be spontaneous in the forward direction. This statement is

   (a) true   (b) false

19.7 Calculating and Using Free Energy

Standard Free Energy of Formation

The standard free energy of formation of a compound, $\Delta_f G°$, is the free energy change that occurs to form one mole of the compound from the component elements, with products and reactants in their standard states. By defining $\Delta_f G°$ in this way, *the free energy of formation of an element in its standard state is zero.*

Just as the standard enthalpy or entropy change for a reaction can be calculated using values of $\Delta_f H°$ (Equation 5.6) or $S°$ (Equation 19.3), the standard free energy change for a reaction can be calculated from values of $\Delta_f G°$ using a similar equation, where n represents the stoichiometric coefficient of the material in the balanced chemical equation under consideration:

$$\Delta_r G° = \Sigma n \Delta_f G°(\text{products}) - \Sigma n \Delta_f G°(\text{reactants}) \tag{19.8}$$

Calculating $\Delta_r G°$, the Free Energy Change for a Reaction Under Standard Conditions

The free energy change for a reaction under standard conditions can be calculated from thermodynamic data in two ways, either from standard enthalpy and entropy changes using values of $\Delta_f H°$ and $S°$ (as we did on the previous page for the formation of H_2O) or directly from values of $\Delta_f G°$ found in tables. These calculations are illustrated in the following two examples.

EXAMPLE 19.4   Calculating $\Delta_r G°$ from $\Delta_r H°$ and $\Delta_r S°$

Problem Calculate the standard free energy change, $\Delta_r G°$, for the formation of methane from carbon and hydrogen at 298 K, using tabulated values of $\Delta_f H°$ and $S°$. Is the reaction spontaneous under standard conditions? Is it product-favored or reactant-favored at equilibrium?

$$C(\text{graphite}) + 2\,H_2(g) \rightarrow CH_4(g)$$

What Do You Know? You are given a balanced chemical equation and asked to determine the standard free energy change for the reaction ($\Delta_r G°$). Values of standard molar enthalpies of formation and standard molar entropies for the substances can be found in Appendix L.

Strategy The values of $\Delta_f H°$ and $S°$ are first combined to find $\Delta_r H°$ and $\Delta_r S°$. With these values known, $\Delta_r G°$ can be calculated using Equation 19.5. When doing the calculation, remember that $S°$ values are given in units of J/K · mol, whereas $\Delta_f H°$ values are given in units of kJ/mol.

Solution

	C(graphite)	+	2 H₂(g)	→	CH₄(g)
$\Delta_f H°$ (kJ/mol)	0		0		−74.9
$S°$ (J/K·mol)	+5.6		+130.7		+186.3

From these values, we can find both $\Delta_r H°$ and $\Delta_r S°$ for the reaction:

$\Delta_r H° = \Sigma n \Delta_f H°(\text{products}) - \Sigma n \Delta_f H°(\text{reactants})$

   $= (1 \text{ mol } CH_4(g)/\text{mol-rxn}) \, \Delta_f H°[CH_4(g)] - \{(1 \text{ mol } C(\text{graphite})/\text{mol-rxn}) \, \Delta_f H°[C(\text{graphite})] +$
   $(2 \text{ mol } H_2(g)/\text{mol-rxn}) \, \Delta_f H°[H_2(g)]\}$

   $= (1 \text{ mol } CH_4(g)/\text{mol-rxn})(-74.9 \text{ kJ/mol}) -$
   $[(1 \text{ mol } C(\text{graphite})/\text{mol-rxn})(0 \text{ kJ/mol}) + (2 \text{ mol } H_2(g)/\text{mol-rxn})(0 \text{ kJ/mol})]$

   $= -74.9 \text{ kJ/mol-rxn}$

$\Delta_r S° = \Sigma n S°(\text{products}) - \Sigma n S°(\text{reactants})$

   $= (1 \text{ mol } CH_4(g)/\text{mol-rxn}) \, S°[CH_4(g)] -$
   $\{(1 \text{ mol } C(\text{graphite})/\text{mol-rxn}) \, S°[C(\text{graphite})] + (2 \text{ mol } H_2(g)/\text{mol-rxn}) \, S°[H_2(g)]\}$

   $= (1 \text{ mol } CH_4(g)/\text{mol-rxn})(186.3 \text{ J/K} \cdot \text{mol}) -$
   $[1 \text{ mol } C(\text{graphite})/\text{mol-rxn}](5.6 \text{ J/K} \cdot \text{mol}) + (2 \text{ mol } H_2(g)/\text{mol-rxn})(130.7 \text{ J/K} \cdot \text{mol})]$

   $= -80.7 \text{ J/K} \cdot \text{mol-rxn}$

Combining the values of $\Delta_r H°$ and $\Delta_r S°$ using Equation 19.5 gives $\Delta_r G°$.

$$\Delta_r G° = \Delta_r H° - T\Delta_r S°$$

$$= -74.9 \text{ kJ/mol-rxn} - [(298 \text{ K})(-80.7 \text{ J/K} \cdot \text{mol-rxn})](1 \text{ kJ/1000 J})$$

$$= -50.9 \text{ kJ/mol-rxn}$$

$\Delta_r G°$ is negative at 298 K, so the reaction is predicted to be spontaneous under standard conditions at this temperature. It is also predicted to be product-favored at equilibrium.

Think about Your Answer One of the most common mistakes students make is to forget to make sure that $\Delta_r H$ and $\Delta_r S$ are both in terms of the same energy unit (in this case, kJ). In this example, the product $T\Delta_r S°$ is negative (-24.0 J/mol-rxn) and disfavors the reaction. However, the entropy change is relatively small, and $\Delta_r H° = -74.9$ kJ/mol-rxn is the dominant term. Chemists call this an *enthalpy-driven reaction*.

Check Your Understanding

Using values of $\Delta_f H°$ and $S°$ to find $\Delta_r H°$ and $\Delta_r S°$, calculate the free energy change, $\Delta_r G°$, for the formation of 2 mol of $NH_3(g)$ from the elements at standard conditions and 25 °C.

$$N_2(g) + 3 H_2(g) \rightarrow 2 NH_3(g)$$

⦿WL **INTERACTIVE EXAMPLE 19.5** Calculating $\Delta_r G°$ Using Free Energies of Formation

Problem Calculate the standard free energy change for the combustion of one mole of methane using values for standard free energies of formation of the products and reactants. Is the reaction spontaneous under standard conditions? Is it product-favored or reactant-favored at equilibrium?

What Do You Know? You are asked to determine the standard free energy change for a reaction ($\Delta_r G°$). Values of standard molar free energies of formation for the substances involved in the reaction can be found in Appendix L.

Strategy Write a balanced equation for the reaction. Then, use Equation 19.8 with values of $\Delta_f G°$ obtained from Appendix L.

Solution The balanced equation and values of $\Delta_f G°$ for each reactant and product are

$$CH_4(g) + 2 O_2(g) \rightarrow 2 H_2O(g) + CO_2(g)$$

| $\Delta_f G°$ (kJ/mol) | -50.8 | 0 | -228.6 | -394.4 |

These values can then be substituted into Equation 19.8.

$$\Delta_r G° = \Sigma n\Delta_f G°(\text{products}) - \Sigma n\Delta_f G°(\text{reactants})$$

$$= \{(2 \text{ mol } H_2O(g)/\text{mol-rxn}) \Delta_f G°[H_2O(g)] + (1 \text{ mol } CO_2(g)/\text{mol-rxn}) \Delta_f G°[CO_2(g)]\}$$
$$- \{(1 \text{ mol } CH_4(g)/\text{mol-rxn}) \Delta_f G°[CH_4(g)] + (2 \text{ mol } O_2(g)/\text{mol-rxn}) \Delta_f G°[O_2(g)]\}$$

$$= [(2 \text{ mol } H_2O(g)/\text{mol-rxn})(-228.6 \text{ kJ/mol}) + (1 \text{ mol } CO_2(g)/\text{mol-rxn})(-394.4 \text{ kJ/mol})]$$
$$- [(1 \text{ mol } CH_4(g)/\text{mol-rxn})(-50.8 \text{ kJ/mol}) + (2 \text{ mol } O_2(g)/\text{mol-rxn})(0 \text{ kJ/mol})]$$

$$= -800.8 \text{ kJ/mol-rxn}$$

The large negative value of $\Delta_r G°$ indicates that the reaction is spontaneous under standard conditions and that it is product-favored at equilibrium.

Think about Your Answer Common errors made by students in this calculation are (1) overlooking the stoichiometric coefficients in the equation and (2) confusing the signs for the terms when using Equation 19.8.

Check Your Understanding

Calculate the standard free energy change for the oxidation of 1.00 mol of $SO_2(g)$ to form $SO_3(g)$ using values of $\Delta_f G°$.

Strategy Map 19.5

PROBLEM

Calculate $\Delta_r G°$ for a reaction.

KNOWN DATA/INFORMATION
- Description of chemical reaction
- $\Delta_f G°$ values (Appendix L)

STEP 1. Write a **balanced chemical equation.**

Balanced chemical equation

STEP 2. Calculate $\Delta_r G°$ using Equation 19.8.

$\Delta_r G°$

Free Energy and Temperature

The definition of free energy, $G = H - TS$, informs us that free energy is a function of temperature, so $\Delta_r G°$ will change as the temperature changes (Figure 19.11). A consequence of this dependence on temperature is that, in certain instances, reactions can be product-favored at equilibrium at one temperature and reactant-favored at another. Those instances arise when the $\Delta_r H°$ and $T\Delta_r S°$ terms work in opposite directions:

- Processes that are entropy-favored ($\Delta_r S° > 0$) and enthalpy-disfavored ($\Delta_r H° > 0$)
- Processes that are enthalpy-favored ($\Delta_r H° < 0$) and entropy-disfavored ($\Delta_r S° < 0$)

Let us explore the relationship of $\Delta G°$ and T further and illustrate how it can be used to advantage.

Calcium carbonate is the primary component of limestone, marble, and seashells. Heating $CaCO_3$ produces lime, CaO, an important chemical, along with gaseous CO_2. The data below from Appendix L are at 298 K (25 °C).

	CaCO₃(s)	→	CaO(s)	+	CO₂(g)
$\Delta_f G°$ (kJ/mol)	−1129.16		−603.42		−394.36
$\Delta_f H°$ (kJ/mol)	−1207.6		−635.09		−393.51
$S°$ (J/K · mol)	91.7		38.2		213.74

For the conversion of 1 mol of $CaCO_3(s)$ to 1 mol of $CaO(s)$ under standard conditions, $\Delta_r G° = +131.38$ kJ, $\Delta_r H° = +179.0$ kJ, and $\Delta_r S° = +160.2$ J/K. Although the reaction is entropy-favored, the large positive and unfavorable enthalpy change dominates at 298 K. Thus, the standard free energy change is positive at 298 K and 1 bar, indicating that the reaction is not spontaneous under standard conditions and is therefore reactant-favored at equilibrium.

The temperature dependence of $\Delta_r G°$ provides a means to turn the $CaCO_3$ decomposition into a product-favored reaction. Notice that the entropy change in the

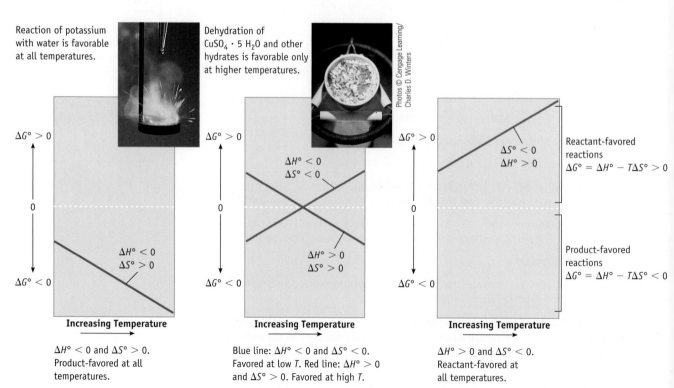

Reaction of potassium with water is favorable at all temperatures.

Dehydration of $CuSO_4 \cdot 5\ H_2O$ and other hydrates is favorable only at higher temperatures.

Photos © Cengage Learning/ Charles D. Winters

$\Delta G° > 0$

$\Delta H° < 0$
$\Delta S° > 0$

$\Delta G° < 0$

$\Delta H° < 0$ and $\Delta S° > 0$.
Product-favored at all temperatures.

$\Delta G° > 0$

$\Delta H° < 0$
$\Delta S° < 0$

$\Delta H° > 0$
$\Delta S° > 0$

$\Delta G° < 0$

Blue line: $\Delta H° < 0$ and $\Delta S° < 0$.
Favored at low T. Red line: $\Delta H° > 0$ and $\Delta S° > 0$. Favored at high T.

$\Delta G° > 0$

$\Delta S° < 0$
$\Delta H° > 0$

$\Delta G° < 0$

Reactant-favored reactions
$\Delta G° = \Delta H° − T\Delta S° > 0$

Product-favored reactions
$\Delta G° = \Delta H° − T\Delta S° < 0$

$\Delta H° > 0$ and $\Delta S° < 0$.
Reactant-favored at all temperatures.

Increasing Temperature

FIGURE 19.11 The variation in $\Delta_r G°$ with temperature.

CASE STUDY

Thermodynamics and Living Things

The laws of thermodynamics apply to all chemical reactions. It should come as no surprise, therefore, that issues of spontaneity and calculations involving ΔG also arise in studies of biochemical reactions. For biochemical processes, however, a different standard state is often used. Most of the usual definition is retained: 1 bar pressure for gases and 1 m concentration for aqueous solutes with the exception of one very important solute. Rather than using a standard state of 1 molal for hydronium ions (corresponding to a pH of about 0), biochemists use a hydronium concentration of 1×10^{-7} M, corresponding to a pH of 7. This pH is much more useful for biochemical reactions. When biochemists use this as the standard state, they write the symbol $'$ next to the thermodynamic function. For example, they would write $\Delta G°'$ (pronounced *delta G zero prime*).

Living things require energy to perform their many functions. One of the main reactions involved in providing this energy is that of adenosine triphosphate (ATP) with water, a reaction for which $\Delta_r G°' = -30.5$ kJ/mol–rxn (◄ *The Chemistry of Life: Biochemistry*).

ATP, adenosine triphosphate

One of the key functions of the process of respiration is to produce molecules of ATP for our bodies to use. ATP is produced in the reaction of adenosine diphosphate (ADP) with hydrogen phosphate ($HP_i = HPO_4^{2-}$),

$$ADP + HP_i + H^+ \rightarrow ATP + H_2O$$
$$\Delta_r G°' = +30.5 \text{ kJ/mol-rxn}$$

a reaction that is not spontaneous under standard conditions and thus reactant-favored at equilibrium. How then do our bodies get this reaction to occur? The answer is to couple the production of ATP with another reaction that is even more product-favored than ATP production is reactant-favored. For example, organisms carry out the oxidation of carbohydrates in a multistep process, producing energy. One of the compounds produced in the process called *glycolysis* is phosphoenolpyruvate (PEP).

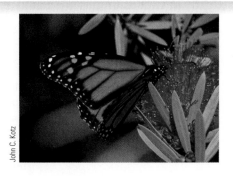

John C. Kotz

PEP, phosphoenolpyruvate

Its reaction with water is product-favored at equilibrium

$$PEP + H_2O \rightarrow Pyruvate + HP_i$$
$$\Delta_r G°' = -61.9 \text{ kJ/mol-rxn}$$

This reaction and ATP formation are linked through the HP_i that is produced in the PEP reaction. If both reactions are carried out, we obtain the following:

$$PEP + H_2O \rightarrow Pyruvate + HP_i$$
$$\Delta_r G°' = -61.9 \text{ kJ/mol-rxn}$$

$$ADP + HP_i + H^+ \rightarrow ATP + H_2O$$
$$\Delta_r G°' = +30.5 \text{ kJ/mol-rxn}$$

$$\overline{PEP + ADP + H^+ \rightarrow Pyruvate + ATP}$$
$$\Delta_r G°' = -31.4 \text{ kJ/mol-rxn}$$

The overall reaction has a negative value for $\Delta_r G°'$ and thus is product-favored at equilibrium. ATP is formed in this process.

The coupling of reactions to produce a system that is product-favored is used in a multitude of reactions that occur in our bodies.

Questions:

1. Consider the hydrolysis reactions of creatine phosphate and adenosine-5'-monophosphate.

   Creatine Phosphate + H_2O
   $\rightarrow$ Creatine + HP_i

   $\Delta_r G°' = -43.3$ kJ/mol-rxn

   Adenosine-5'-Monophosphate + H_2O
   $\rightarrow$ Adenosine + HP_i

   $\Delta_r G°' = -9.2$ kJ/mol-rxn

   Which of the following combinations produces a reaction that is product-favored at equilibrium: for creatine phosphate to transfer phosphate to adenosine or for adenosine-5'-monophosphate to transfer phosphate to creatine?

2. Assume the reaction A(aq) + B(aq) $\rightarrow$ C(aq) + H_3O^+(aq) produces one hydronium ion. What is the mathematical relationship between $\Delta G°'$ and $\Delta G°$ at 25 °C? (*Hint:* Use the equation $\Delta G = \Delta G° + RT \ln Q$ and substitute $\Delta G°'$ for ΔG.)

Answers to these questions are available in Appendix N.

reaction is positive as a result of the formation of CO_2 gas in the reaction. Thus, raising the temperature results in the value of $T\Delta_r S°$ becoming increasingly large. At a high enough temperature, $T\Delta_r S°$ will outweigh the enthalpy effect, and the process will become product-favored at equilibrium.

How high must the temperature be for this reaction to become product-favored? An estimate of the temperature can be obtained using Equation 19.5, by calculating the temperature at which $\Delta_r G° = 0$. Above that temperature, $\Delta_r G°$ will have a negative value.

$$\Delta_r G° = \Delta_r H° - T\Delta_r S°$$

$$0 = (179.0 \text{ kJ/mol-rxn})(1000 \text{ J/kJ}) - T(160.2 \text{ J/K} \cdot \text{mol-rxn})$$

$$T = 1117 \text{ K (or 844 °C)}$$

• **CaCO₃ Decomposition** Experiments show that the pressure of CO_2 in an equilibrium system [$CaCO_3(s) \rightleftharpoons$ $CaO(s) + CO_2(g)$] is 1 bar at about 900 °C ($K = 1$ and $\Delta G° = 0$), close to our estimated temperature.

How accurate is this result? As noted earlier, this answer is only an estimate of the temperature needed. One source of error is the assumption that $\Delta_r H°$ and $\Delta S°$ do not vary with temperature, an assumption that is not strictly true. There is always a small variation in these values when the temperature changes—not large enough to be important if the temperature range is narrow, but potentially a problem over wider temperature ranges such as seen in this example. As an estimate, however, a temperature in the range of 850 °C for this reaction is reasonable.

Strategy Map 19.6

PROBLEM

Determine the **temperature** above which a chemical reaction is **product-favored** at **equilibrium**.

↓

KNOWN DATA/INFORMATION

• Balanced chemical equation
• Temperature
• Values of $\Delta_f H°$ and $S°$

STEP 1. Calculate $\Delta_r H°$ using Equation 5.6.

$\Delta_r H°$

STEP 2. Calculate $\Delta_r S°$ using Equation 19.3.

$\Delta_r S°$

STEP 3. Use the equation $\Delta_r G° = \Delta_r H° - T\Delta_r S°$ to determine the temperature at which $\Delta_r G° = 0$.

Temperature above which the reaction is **product-favored** at **equilibrium**.

 INTERACTIVE EXAMPLE 19.6   Effect of Temperature on $\Delta_r G°$

Problem The decomposition of liquid $Ni(CO)_4$ to produce nickel metal and carbon monoxide has a $\Delta_r G°$ value of 40 kJ/mol-rxn at 25 °C.

$$Ni(CO)_4(\ell) \rightarrow Ni(s) + 4 \, CO(g)$$

Use values of $\Delta_f H°$ and $S°$ for the reactant and products to estimate the temperature at which the reaction becomes product-favored at equilibrium.

What Do You Know? You are given a balanced chemical equation. Values of standard molar enthalpies of formation and standard molar entropies for the substances can be found in the chemical literature. You also know that the key temperature to determine is that at which $\Delta_r G°$ is zero.

Strategy The reaction is reactant-favored at equilibrium at 298 K. However, if the entropy change is positive for the reaction and the reaction is endothermic (with a positive value of $\Delta_r H°$), then a higher temperature may allow the reaction to become product-favored at equilibrium. Therefore, we first find $\Delta_r H°$ and $\Delta_r S°$ to see if their values meet our criteria for spontaneity at a higher temperature, and then we calculate the temperature at which the following condition is met: $0 = \Delta_r H° - T\Delta_r S°$.

Solution Values for $\Delta_f H°$ and $S°$ are obtained from the chemical literature for the substances involved.

	$Ni(CO)_4(\ell)$	→	$Ni(s)$	+	$4 \, CO(g)$
$\Delta_f H°$(kJ/mol)	−632.0		0		−110.525
$S°$(J/K · mol)	320.1		29.87		197.67

For a process in which 1 mol of liquid $Ni(CO)_4$ is converted to 1 mol of $Ni(s)$ and 4 mol of $CO(g)$, we find

$$\Delta_r H° = +189.9 \text{ kJ/mol-rxn}$$

$$\Delta_r S° = +500.5 \text{ J/K mol-rxn}$$

We use these values of $\Delta_r H°$ and $\Delta_r S°$ to find the temperature at which $\Delta_r G° = 0$.

$$\Delta_r G° = \Delta_r H° - T\Delta_r S°$$

$$0 = (189.9 \text{ kJ/mol-rxn})(1000 \text{ J/kJ}) - T(500.5 \text{ J/K} \cdot \text{mol-rxn})$$

$$T = 379.4 \text{ K (or 106.2 °C)}$$

Think about Your Answer At 298 K, the reaction is reactant-favored at equilibrium largely because it is quite endothermic. However, the positive entropy change allows the reaction to be product-favored at equilibrium at a higher temperature.

Check Your Understanding

Oxygen was first prepared by Joseph Priestley (1733–1804) by heating HgO. Use data in Appendix L to estimate the temperature required to decompose $HgO(s)$ into $Hg(\ell)$ and $O_2(g)$.

Using the Relationship between $\Delta_r G°$ and K

Equation 19.7 provides a direct route to determine the standard free energy change from experimentally determined equilibrium constants. Alternatively, it allows calculation of an equilibrium constant from thermochemical data contained in tables or obtained from an experiment.

⊌WL   INTERACTIVE EXAMPLE 19.7   Calculating K_p from $\Delta_r G°$

Problem Determine the standard free energy change, $\Delta_r G°$, for the formation of 1.00 mol of $NH_3(g)$ from nitrogen and hydrogen, and use this value to calculate the equilibrium constant for this reaction at 25 °C.

What Do You Know? You are given enough information so you can write a balanced chemical equation for the desired chemical reaction. Values of $\Delta_f G°$ are given in Appendix L.

Strategy The free energy of formation of ammonia represents the free energy change to form 1.00 mol of $NH_3(g)$ from the elements. The equilibrium constant for this reaction is calculated from $\Delta_r G°$ using Equation 19.7. Because the reactants and products are gases, the calculated value will be K_p.

Solution Begin by specifying a balanced equation for the chemical reaction under investigation.

$$\tfrac{1}{2}\ N_2(g) + \tfrac{3}{2}\ H_2(g) \rightleftharpoons NH_3(g)$$

The free energy change for this reaction is -16.37 kJ/mol-rxn ($\Delta_r G° = \Delta_f G°$ for $NH_3(g)$; Appendix L). In a calculation of K_p using Equation 19.7, we will need consistent units. If we use the gas constant, R, in units of 8.3145 J/K · mol, then the value of $\Delta_r G°$ must be in J/mol-rxn (and not kJ/mol-rxn). The temperature is 25 °C (298.15 K).

$$\Delta_r G° = -RT \ln K$$

$$-16{,}370 \text{ J/mol-rxn} = (-8.3145 \text{ J/K · mol-rxn})(298.15 \text{ K}) \ln K_p$$

$$\ln K_p = 6.604$$

$$K_p = 738$$

Think about Your Answer The value of $\Delta_r G°$ is less than zero, indicating that this reaction is spontaneous under standard conditions and therefore product-favored at equilibrium. The value of K_p calculated is greater than 1 as it should be for such a process. This example illustrates how to calculate equilibrium constants from thermodynamic data. In fact, many equilibrium constants you find in the chemical literature are not experimentally determined but are instead calculated from thermodynamic data in this way.

Check Your Understanding

Determine the value of the equilibrium constant, K_p, for the decomposition of calcium carbonate to calcium oxide and carbon dioxide gas at 298.15 K.

Strategy Map 19.7

PROBLEM

Determine the **equilibrium constant** for a reaction using **thermodynamic data**.

↓

KNOWN DATA/INFORMATION

- Information to write a balanced chemical equation
- The values of $\Delta_f G°$
- Temperature

STEP 1. Write the **balanced chemical equation**.

Balanced chemical equation

STEP 2. Calculate $\Delta_r G°$ using values of $\Delta_f G°$ in Equation 19.8.

$\Delta_r G°$

STEP 3. Use the equation $\Delta_r G° = -RT \ln K$ to determine the value of **K**.

Equilibrium constant, **K**

EXAMPLE 19.8   Calculating $\Delta_r G°$ from K_{sp} for an Insoluble Solid

Problem The value of K_{sp} for $AgCl(s)$ at 25 °C is 1.8×10^{-10}. Determine $\Delta_r G°$ for the process $Ag^+(aq) + Cl^-(aq) \rightleftharpoons AgCl(s)$ at 298.15 K.

What Do You Know You are given the value of K_{sp}. The process of interest is the reverse of the chemical equation for K_{sp}. You also know the temperature.

Strategy The chemical equation given is the opposite of the equation used to define K_{sp}; therefore, the equilibrium constant for this reaction is $1/K_{sp}$. This value is used in Equation 19.7 to calculate $\Delta_r G°$.

Solution

For $Ag^+(aq) + Cl^-(aq) \rightleftharpoons AgCl(s)$,

$$K = 1/K_{sp} = 1/\ 1.8 \times 10^{-10} = 5.6 \times 10^9$$

$$\Delta_r G° = -RT \ln K = -(8.3145 \text{ J/K · mol-rxn})(298.15 \text{ K}) \ln(5.6 \times 10^9)$$

$$= -56 \text{ kJ/mol-rxn}$$

Think about Your Answer The negative value of $\Delta_r G°$ indicates that the precipitation of AgCl from $Ag^+(aq)$ and $Cl^-(aq)$ is product-favored at equilibrium.

Check Your Understanding

Determine the value of $\Delta_r G°$ for the reaction $C(s) + CO_2(g) \rightleftharpoons 2\ CO(g)$ from data in Appendix L. Use this result to calculate the equilibrium constant.

REVIEW & CHECK FOR SECTION 19.7

1. Given that $\Delta_r H° = -2219$ kJ/mol-rxn and that $\Delta_r S° = -216$ J/K · mol-rxn at 25 °C, determine the value of $\Delta_r G°$ at 25 °C for the reaction

    $$C_3H_8(g) + 5\ O_2(g) \rightarrow 3\ CO_2(g) + 4\ H_2O(\ell)$$

    (a)   −2283 kJ/mol-rxn   (c)   −2155 kJ/mol-rxn

    (b)   −2214 kJ/mol-rxn   (d) 6.218×10^4 kJ/mol-rxn

2. Using values of $\Delta_f G°$, determine the value of $\Delta_r G°$ at 25 °C for the reaction

    $$2\ KClO_3(s) \rightarrow 2\ KCl(s) + 3\ O_2(g)$$

    (a)   −225 kJ/mol-rxn   (c)   112 kJ/mol-rxn

    (b)   −112 kJ/mol-rxn   (d)   225 kJ/mol-rxn

3. The value of K_p for the following reaction at 425 °C is 0.018. What is the value of $\Delta_r G°$ at this temperature?

    $$2\ HI(g) \rightleftharpoons H_2(g) + I_2(g)$$

    (a) 1.0×10^1 kJ/mol-rxn   (c)   23 kJ/mol-rxn

    (b)   −14 kJ/mol-rxn   (d)   240 kJ/mol-rxn

---

 and

OWL and **go Chemistry**

Sign in at **www.cengage.com/owl** to:
- View tutorials and simulations, develop problem-solving skills, and complete online homework assigned by your professor.
- For quick review and exam prep, download Go Chemistry mini lecture modules from OWL (or purchase them at **www.cengagebrain.com**)

? Access **How Do I Solve It?** tutorials on how to approach problem solving using concepts in this chapter.

CHAPTER GOALS REVISITED

Now that you have studied this chapter, you should ask whether you have met the chapter goals. In particular, you should be able to:

Understand the concept of entropy and its relationship to reaction spontaneity

a.   Understand that entropy is a measure of energy dispersal (Section 19.2). Study Questions: 1, 2.

b.   Recognize that an entropy change is the energy transferred as heat for a reversible process divided by the Kelvin temperature. (*A Closer Look*, Section 19.2 and Equation 19.1) Study Questions: 40–42.

c.   Identify common processes that are entropy-favored (Section 19.4). Study Question: 3.

Calculate the change in entropy for a system, its surroundings, and the universe to determine whether a process is spontaneous under standard conditions

a.   Calculate entropy changes from tables of standard entropy values (Section 19.4). Study Questions: 4–8.

b.   Use standard entropy and enthalpy changes to predict whether a reaction will be spontaneous under standard conditions (Section 19.5 and Table 19.1). Study Questions: 9–12.

c.   Recognize how temperature influences whether a reaction is spontaneous (Section 19.5). Study Questions: 13, 14, 23–26.

Understand and use the Gibbs free energy

a. Understand the connection between enthalpy and entropy changes and the Gibbs free energy change for a process (Section 19.6). **Study Questions: 15, 16.**

b. Understand the relationship of $\Delta_r G$, $\Delta_r G°$, Q, K, reaction spontaneity, and product- or reactant-favorability (Section 19.6).

Q	ΔG	Spontaneous?
$Q < K$	$\Delta G < 0$	Spontaneous to the right as the equation is written
$Q = K$	$\Delta G = 0$	Reaction is at equilibrium
$Q > K$	$\Delta G > 0$	Not spontaneous to the right; spontaneous to the left

K	$\Delta G°$	Reactant-Favored or Product-Favored at Equilibrium?	Spontaneous Under Standard Conditions?
$K \gg 1$	$\Delta G° < 0$	Product-favored	Spontaneous under standard conditions
$K = 1$	$\Delta G° = 0$	$[C]^c[D]^d = [A]^a[B]^b$ at equilibrium	At equilibrium under standard conditions
$K \ll 1$	$\Delta G° > 0$	Reactant-favored	Not spontaneous under standard conditions

c. Describe and use the relationship between the free energy change under standard conditions and equilibrium constants, and calculate K from $\Delta_r G°$ (Sections 19.6 and 19.7). **Study Questions: 27–30, 44, 48, 50, 61, and Go Chemistry Module 24.**

d. Calculate the change in free energy at standard conditions for a reaction from the enthalpy and entropy changes under standard conditions or from the standard free energy of formation of reactants and products ($\Delta_f G°$) (Section 19.7). **Study Questions: 15–20, 46, 55, 56, 75, 79.**

e. Know how free energy changes with temperature (Section 19.7). **Study Questions: 23–26, 57, 59, 70.**

Key Equations

Equation 19.1 (page 861) Calculate the entropy change from the energy transferred as heat for a reversible process and the temperature at which it occurs.

$$\Delta S = \frac{q_{rev}}{T}$$

Equation 19.2 (page 864) The Boltzmann equation: The entropy of a system, S, is proportional to the number of accessible microstates, W, belonging to a given energy of a system or substance.

$$S = k \ln W$$

Equation 19.3 (page 868) Calculate the standard entropy change under standard conditions for a process from the tabulated entropies of the products and reactants and the stoichiometric coefficients (n) of the substances in the balanced chemical equation for the reaction.

$$\Delta_r S° = \Sigma n S°(\text{products}) - \Sigma n S°(\text{reactants})$$

Equation 19.4 (page 870) Calculate the total entropy change for a system and its surroundings, to determine whether a process is spontaneous under standard conditions.

$$\Delta S°(\text{universe}) = \Delta S°(\text{system}) + \Delta S°(\text{surroundings})$$

Equation 19.5 (page 874) Calculate the free energy change for a process from enthalpy and entropy changes.

$$\Delta G° = \Delta H° - T\Delta S°$$

Equation 19.6 (page 876) Relates the free energy change under nonstandard conditions ($\Delta_r G$) to the standard free energy change ($\Delta_r G°$) and the reaction quotient Q.

$$\Delta_r G = \Delta_r G° + RT \ln Q$$

Equation 19.7 (page 876): Relates the standard free energy change for a reaction and its equilibrium constant.

$$\Delta_r G° = -RT \ln K$$

Equation 19.8 (page 878): Calculate the standard free energy change for a reaction using tabulated values of $\Delta_f G°$ and the stoichiometric coefficients (n) of the substances in the balanced chemical equation for the reaction.

$$\Delta_r G° = \Sigma n\Delta_f G°(\text{products}) - \Sigma n\Delta_f G°(\text{reactants})$$

Study Questions

OWL Interactive versions of these questions are assignable in OWL.

▲ denotes challenging questions.

Blue-numbered questions have answers in Appendix R and fully worked solutions in the *Student Solutions Manual*.

Practicing Skills

Entropy
(See Sections 19.2–19.4 and Examples 19.1 and 19.2.)

1. Which substance has the higher entropy?
   (a) dry ice (solid CO_2) at -78 °C or $CO_2(g)$ at 0 °C
   (b) liquid water at 25 °C or liquid water at 50 °C
   (c) pure alumina, $Al_2O_3(s)$, or ruby (ruby is Al_2O_3 in which some Al^{3+} ions in the crystalline lattice are replaced with Cr^{3+} ions)
   (d) one mole of $N_2(g)$ at 1 bar pressure or one mole of $N_2(g)$ at 10 bar pressure (both at 298 K)

2. Which substance has the higher entropy?
   (a) a sample of pure silicon (to be used in a computer chip) or a piece of silicon containing a trace of another element such as boron or phosphorus
   (b) $O_2(g)$ at 0 °C or $O_2(g)$ at -50 °C
   (c) $I_2(s)$ or $I_2(g)$, both at room temperature
   (d) one mole of $O_2(g)$ at 1 bar pressure or one mole of $O_2(g)$ at 0.01 bar pressure (both at 298 K)

3. Use $S°$ values to calculate the standard entropy change, $\Delta_r S°$, for each of the following processes and comment on the sign of the change.
   (a) $KOH(s) \rightarrow KOH(aq)$
   (b) $Na(g) \rightarrow Na(s)$
   (c) $Br_2(\ell) \rightarrow Br_2(g)$
   (d) $HCl(g) \rightarrow HCl(aq)$

4. Use $S°$ values to calculate the standard entropy change, $\Delta_r S°$, for each of the following processes, and comment on the sign of the change.
   (a) $NH_4Cl(s) \rightarrow NH_4Cl(aq)$
   (b) $CH_3OH(\ell) \rightarrow CH_3OH(g)$
   (c) $CCl_4(g) \rightarrow CCl_4(\ell)$
   (d) $NaCl(s) \rightarrow NaCl(g)$

5. Calculate the standard entropy change for the formation of 1.0 mol of the following compounds from the elements at 25 °C.
   (a) $HCl(g)$ (b) $Ca(OH)_2(s)$

6. Calculate the standard entropy change for the formation of 1.0 mol of the following compounds from the elements at 25 °C.
   (a) $H_2S(g)$ (b) $MgCO_3(s)$

7. Calculate the standard entropy change for the following reactions at 25 °C. Comment on the sign of $\Delta_r S°$.
   (a) $2 Al(s) + 3 Cl_2(g) \rightarrow 2 AlCl_3(s)$
   (b) $2 CH_3OH(\ell) + 3 O_2(g) \rightarrow 2 CO_2(g) + 4 H_2O(g)$

8. Calculate the standard entropy change for the following reactions at 25 °C. Comment on the sign of $\Delta_r S°$.
   (a) $2 Na(s) + 2 H_2O(\ell) \rightarrow 2 NaOH(aq) + H_2(g)$
   (b) $Na_2CO_3(s) + 2 HCl(aq) \rightarrow 2 NaCl(aq) + H_2O(\ell) + CO_2(g)$

$\Delta_r S°$(universe) and Spontaneity
(See Sections 19.2–19.5 and Example 19.3.)

9. Is the reaction $Si(s) + 2 Cl_2(g) \rightarrow SiCl_4(g)$ spontaneous under standard conditions at 298 K? Answer this question by calculating $\Delta S°$(system), $\Delta S°$(surroundings), and $\Delta S°$(universe). (Define reactants and products as the system.)

10. Is the reaction $Si(s) + 2 H_2(g) \rightarrow SiH_4(g)$ spontaneous under standard conditions at 298 K? Answer this question by calculating calculating $\Delta S°$(system), $\Delta S°$(surroundings), and $\Delta S°$(universe). (Define reactants and products as the system.)

11. Calculate $\Delta S°$(universe) for the decomposition of 1 mol of liquid water to form gaseous hydrogen and oxygen. Is this reaction spontaneous under these conditions at 25 °C? Explain your answer briefly.

12. Calculate $\Delta S°$(universe) for the formation of 1 mol $HCl(g)$ from gaseous hydrogen and chlorine. Is this reaction spontaneous under these conditions at 25 °C? Explain your answer briefly.

13. Classify each of the reactions according to one of the four reaction types summarized in Table 19.1.
    (a) $Fe_2O_3(s) + 2 Al(s) \rightarrow 2 Fe(s) + Al_2O_3(s)$

    $\Delta_r H° = -851.5$ kJ/mol-rxn
    $\Delta_r S° = -375.2$ J/K · mol-rxn

    (b) $N_2(g) + 2 O_2(g) \rightarrow 2 NO_2(g)$

    $\Delta_r H° = 66.2$ kJ/mol-rxn
    $\Delta_r S° = -121.6$ J/K · mol-rxn

14. Classify each of the reactions according to one of the four reaction types summarized in Table 19.1.
    (a) $C_6H_{12}O_6(s) + 6\ O_2(g) \rightarrow 6\ CO_2(g) + 6\ H_2O(\ell)$

    $\Delta_r H^\circ = -673\ kJ/mol\text{-rxn}$
    $\Delta_r S^\circ = 60.4\ J/K \cdot mol\text{-rxn}$

    (b) $MgO(s) + C(graphite) \rightarrow Mg(s) + CO(g)$

    $\Delta_r H^\circ = 490.7\ kJ/mol\text{-rxn}$
    $\Delta_r S^\circ = 197.9\ J/K \cdot mol\text{-rxn}$

Gibbs Free Energy
(See Section 19.6 and 19.7 and Example 19.4.)

15. Using values of $\Delta_f H^\circ$ and S°, calculate $\Delta_r G^\circ$ for each of the following reactions at 25 °C.
    (a) $2\ Pb(s) + O_2(g) \rightarrow 2\ PbO(s)$
    (b) $NH_3(g) + HNO_3(aq) \rightarrow NH_4NO_3(aq)$

    Which of these reactions is (are) predicted to be product-favored at equilibrium? Are the reactions enthalpy- or entropy-driven?

16. Using values of $\Delta_f H^\circ$ and S°, calculate $\Delta_r G^\circ$ for each of the following reactions at 25 °C.
    (a) $2\ Na(s) + 2\ H_2O(\ell) \rightarrow 2\ NaOH(aq) + H_2(g)$
    (b) $6\ C(graphite) + 3\ H_2(g) \rightarrow C_6H_6(\ell)$

    Which of these reactions is (are) predicted to be product-favored at equilibrium? Are the reactions enthalpy- or entropy-driven?

17. Using values of $\Delta_f H^\circ$ and S°, calculate the standard molar free energy of formation, $\Delta_f G^\circ$, for each of the following compounds:
    (a) $CS_2(g)$
    (b) $NaOH(s)$
    (c) $ICl(g)$

    Compare your calculated values of $\Delta_f G^\circ$ with those listed in Appendix L. Which of these formation reactions are predicted to be spontaneous under standard conditions at 25 °C?

18. Using values of $\Delta_f H^\circ$ and S°, calculate the standard molar free energy of formation, $\Delta_f G^\circ$, for each of the following:
    (a) $Ca(OH)_2(s)$
    (b) $Cl(g)$
    (c) $Na_2CO_3(s)$

    Compare your calculated values of $\Delta_f G^\circ$ with those listed in Appendix L. Which of these formation reactions are predicted to be spontaneous under standard conditions at 25 °C?

Free Energy of Formation
(See Sections 19.6 and 19.7 and Example 19.5.)

19. Using values of $\Delta_f G^\circ$, calculate $\Delta_r G^\circ$ for each of the following reactions at 25 °C. Which are product-favored at equilibrium?
    (a) $2\ K(s) + Cl_2(g) \rightarrow 2\ KCl(s)$
    (b) $2\ CuO(s) \rightarrow 2\ Cu(s) + O_2(g)$
    (c) $4\ NH_3(g) + 7\ O_2(g) \rightarrow 4\ NO_2(g) + 6\ H_2O(g)$

20. Using values of $\Delta_f G^\circ$, calculate $\Delta_r G^\circ$ for each of the following reactions at 25 °C. Which are product-favored at equilibrium?
    (a) $HgS(s) + O_2(g) \rightarrow Hg(\ell) + SO_2(g)$
    (b) $2\ H_2S(g) + 3\ O_2(g) \rightarrow 2\ H_2O(g) + 2\ SO_2(g)$
    (c) $SiCl_4(g) + 2\ Mg(s) \rightarrow 2\ MgCl_2(s) + Si(s)$

21. For the reaction $BaCO_3(s) \rightarrow BaO(s) + CO_2(g)$, $\Delta_r G^\circ = +219.7\ kJ$. Using this value and other data available in Appendix L, calculate the value of $\Delta_f G^\circ$ for $BaCO_3(s)$.

22. For the reaction $TiCl_2(s) + Cl_2(g) \rightarrow TiCl_4(\ell)$, $\Delta_r G^\circ = -272.8\ kJ$. Using this value and other data available in Appendix L, calculate the value of $\Delta_f G^\circ$ for $TiCl_2(s)$.

Effect of Temperature on ΔG
(See Section 19.7 and Example 19.6.)

23. Determine whether the reactions listed below are entropy-favored or disfavored under standard conditions. Predict how an increase in temperature will affect the value of $\Delta_r G^\circ$.
    (a) $N_2(g) + 2\ O_2(g) \rightarrow 2\ NO_2(g)$
    (b) $2\ C(s) + O_2(g) \rightarrow 2\ CO(g)$
    (c) $CaO(s) + CO_2(g) \rightarrow CaCO_3(s)$
    (d) $2\ NaCl(s) \rightarrow 2\ Na(s) + Cl_2(g)$

24. Determine whether the reactions listed below are entropy-favored or disfavored under standard conditions. Predict how an increase in temperature will affect the value of $\Delta_r G^\circ$.
    (a) $I_2(g) \rightarrow 2\ I(g)$
    (b) $2\ SO_2(g) + O_2(g) \rightarrow 2\ SO_3(g)$
    (c) $SiCl_4(g) + 2\ H_2O(\ell) \rightarrow SiO_2(s) + 4\ HCl(g)$
    (d) $P_4(s,\ white) + 6\ H_2(g) \rightarrow 4\ PH_3(g)$

25. Heating some metal carbonates, among them magnesium carbonate, leads to their decomposition.

    $$MgCO_3(s) \rightarrow MgO(s) + CO_2(g)$$

    (a) Calculate $\Delta_r G^\circ$ and $\Delta_r S^\circ$ for the reaction.
    (b) Is the reaction spontaneous under standard conditions at 298 K?
    (c) Is the reaction predicted to be spontaneous at higher temperatures?

26. Calculate $\Delta_r H^\circ$ and $\Delta_r S^\circ$ for the reaction of tin(IV) oxide with carbon.

    $$SnO_2(s) + C(s) \rightarrow Sn(s) + CO_2(g)$$

    (a) Is the reaction spontaneous under standard conditions at 298 K?
    (b) Is the reaction predicted to be spontaneous at higher temperatures?

Free Energy and Equilibrium Constants
(See Section 19.7 and Example 19.7.)

27. The standard free energy change, $\Delta_r G^\circ$, for the formation of $NO(g)$ from its elements is $+86.58\ kJ/mol$ at 25 °C. Calculate K_p at this temperature for the equilibrium

    $$\tfrac{1}{2}\ N_2(g) + \tfrac{1}{2}\ O_2(g) \rightleftharpoons NO(g)$$

    Comment on the sign of ΔG° and the magnitude of K_p.

28. The standard free energy change, $\Delta_r G^\circ$, for the formation of $O_3(g)$ from $O_2(g)$ is $+163.2\ kJ/mol$ at 25 °C. Calculate K_p at this temperature for the equilibrium

    $$3\ O_2(g) \rightleftharpoons 2\ O_3(g)$$

    Comment on the sign of ΔG° and the magnitude of K_p.

29. Calculate $\Delta_r G°$ at 25 °C for the formation of 1.00 mol of $C_2H_6(g)$ from $C_2H_4(g)$ and $H_2(g)$. Use this value to calculate K_p for the equilibrium.

$$C_2H_4(g) + H_2(g) \rightleftharpoons C_2H_6(g)$$

Comment on the sign of $\Delta_r G°$ and the magnitude of K_p.

30. Calculate $\Delta_r G°$ at 25 °C for the formation of 1.00 mol of $C_2H_5OH(g)$ from $C_2H_4(g)$ and $H_2O(g)$. Use this value to calculate K_p for the equilibrium.

$$C_2H_4(g) + H_2O(g) \rightleftharpoons C_2H_5OH(g)$$

Comment on the sign of $\Delta_r G°$ and the magnitude of K_p.

General Questions

These questions are not designated as to type or location in the chapter. They may combine several concepts.

31. Compare the compounds in each set below and decide which is expected to have the higher entropy. Assume all are at the same temperature. Check your answers using data in Appendix L.
    (a) $HF(g)$, $HCl(g)$, or $HBr(g)$
    (b) $NH_4Cl(s)$ or $NH_4Cl(aq)$
    (c) $C_2H_4(g)$ or $N_2(g)$ (two substances with the same molar mass)
    (d) $NaCl(s)$ or $NaCl(g)$

32. Using standard entropy values, calculate $\Delta_r S°$ for the formation of 1.0 mol of $NH_3(g)$ from $N_2(g)$ and $H_2(g)$ at 25 °C.

33. About 5 billion kilograms of benzene, C_6H_6, is made each year. Benzene is used as a starting material for many other compounds and as a solvent (although it is also a carcinogen, and its use is restricted). One compound that can be made from benzene is cyclohexane, C_6H_{12}.

$$C_6H_6(\ell) + 3 H_2(g) \rightarrow C_6H_{12}(\ell)$$

$$\Delta_r H° = -206.7 \text{ kJ}; \quad \Delta_r S° = -361.5 \text{ J/K}$$

Is this reaction predicted to be product-favored at equilibrium at 25 °C? Is the reaction enthalpy- or entropy-driven?

34. Hydrogenation, the addition of hydrogen to an organic compound, is an industrially important reaction. Calculate $\Delta_r H°$, $\Delta_r S°$, and $\Delta_r G°$ for the hydrogenation of octene, C_8H_{16}, to give octane, C_8H_{18}, at 25 °C. Is the reaction product- or reactant-favored at equilibrium?

$$C_8H_{16}(g) + H_2(g) \rightarrow C_8H_{18}(g)$$

Along with data in Appendix L, the following information is needed for this calculation.

Compound	$\Delta_f H°$ (kJ/mol)	S° (J/K · mol)
Octene	−82.93	462.8
Octane	−208.45	463.639

35. Is the combustion of ethane, C_2H_6, product-favored at equilibrium at 25 °C?

$$C_2H_6(g) + \frac{7}{2} O_2(g) \rightarrow 2 CO_2(g) + 3 H_2O(g)$$

Answer the question by calculating the value of $\Delta S°$ (universe) at 298 K, using values of $\Delta_f H°$ and S° in Appendix L. Does the answer agree with your preconceived idea of this reaction?

36. Write a balanced equation that depicts the formation of 1 mol of $Fe_2O_3(s)$ from its elements. What is the standard free energy of formation of 1.00 mol of $Fe_2O_3(s)$? What is the value of $\Delta G°$ when 454 g (1 lb) of $Fe_2O_3(s)$ is formed from the elements?

37. When vapors from hydrochloric acid and aqueous ammonia come in contact, they react, producing a white "cloud" of solid NH_4Cl (Figure 19.9).

$$HCl(g) + NH_3(g) \rightleftharpoons NH_4Cl(s)$$

Defining the reactants and products as the system under study:
    (a) Predict whether $\Delta S°$(system), $\Delta S°$(surroundings), $\Delta S°$(universe), $\Delta_r H°$, and $\Delta_r G°$ (at 298 K) are greater than zero, equal to zero, or less than zero; and explain your prediction. Verify your predictions by calculating values for each of these quantities.
    (b) Calculate the value of K_p for this reaction at 298 K.

38. Calculate $\Delta S°$(system), $\Delta S°$(surroundings), and $\Delta S°$(universe) for each of the following processes at 298 K, and comment on how these systems differ.
    (a) $HNO_3(g) \rightarrow HNO_3(aq)$
    (b) $NaOH(s) \rightarrow NaOH(aq)$

39. Methanol is now widely used as a fuel in race cars. Consider the following reaction as a possible synthetic route to methanol.

$$C(\text{graphite}) + \frac{1}{2} O_2(g) + 2 H_2(g) \rightleftharpoons CH_3OH(\ell)$$

Calculate K_p for the formation of methanol at 298 K using this reaction. Would this reaction be more product-favored at a different temperature?

40. The enthalpy of vaporization of liquid diethyl ether, $(C_2H_5)_2O$, is 26.0 kJ/mol at the boiling point of 35.0 °C. Calculate $\Delta S°$ for a vapor-to-liquid transformation at 35.0 °C.

41. Calculate the entropy change, $\Delta S°$, for the vaporization of ethanol, C_2H_5OH, at its normal boiling point, 78.0 °C. The enthalpy of vaporization of ethanol is 39.3 kJ/mol.

42. Using thermodynamic data, estimate the normal boiling point of ethanol. (Recall that liquid and vapor are in equilibrium at 1.0 atm pressure at the normal boiling point.) The actual normal boiling point is 78 °C. How well does your calculated result agree with the actual value?

43. The following reaction is reactant-favored at equilibrium at room temperature.

$$COCl_2(g) \rightarrow CO(g) + Cl_2(g)$$

Will raising or lowering the temperature make it product-favored?

44. When calcium carbonate is heated strongly, CO_2 gas is evolved. The equilibrium pressure of CO_2 is 1.00 bar at 897 °C, and $\Delta_r H°$ at 298 K is 179.0 kJ.

$$CaCO_3(s) \rightarrow CaO(s) + CO_2(g)$$

Estimate the value of $\Delta_r S°$ at 897 °C for the reaction.

45. Sodium reacts violently with water according to the equation

$$Na(s) + H_2O(\ell) \rightarrow NaOH(aq) + \frac{1}{2} H_2(g)$$

Without doing calculations, predict the signs of $\Delta_r H°$ and $\Delta_r S°$ for the reaction. Verify your prediction with a calculation.

46. Yeast can produce ethanol by the fermentation of glucose ($C_6H_{12}O_6$), which is the basis for the production of most alcoholic beverages.

$$C_6H_{12}O_6(aq) \rightarrow 2\ C_2H_5OH(\ell) + 2\ CO_2(g)$$

Calculate $\Delta_r H°$, $\Delta_r S°$, and $\Delta_r G°$ for the reaction at 25 °C. Is the reaction product- or reactant-favored? In addition to the thermodynamic values in Appendix L, you will need the following data for $C_6H_{12}O_6(aq)$:

$\Delta_f H° = -1260.0$ kJ/mol; $S° = 289$ J/K · mol; and $\Delta_f G° = -918.8$ kJ/mol.

47. Elemental boron, in the form of thin fibers, can be made by reducing a boron halide with H_2.

$$BCl_3(g) + \tfrac{3}{2} H_2(g) \rightarrow B(s) + 3\ HCl(g)$$

Calculate $\Delta_r H°$, $\Delta_r S°$, and $\Delta_r G°$ at 25 °C for this reaction. Is the reaction predicted to be product-favored at equilibrium at 25 °C? If so, is it enthalpy- or entropy-driven? [$S°$ for B(s) is 5.86 J/K · mol.]

48. ▲ Estimate the vapor pressure of ethanol at 37 °C using thermodynamic data. Express the result in millimeters of mercury.

49. The equilibrium constant, K_p, for $N_2O_4(g) \rightleftharpoons$ 2 $NO_2(g)$ is 0.14 at 25 °C. Calculate $\Delta_r G°$ for the conversion of $N_2O_4(g)$ to $NO_2(g)$ from this constant, and compare this value with that determined from the $\Delta_f G°$ values in Appendix L.

50. ▲ Estimate the boiling point of water in Denver, Colorado (where the altitude is 1.60 km and the atmospheric pressure is 630 mm Hg or 0.840 bar).

51. The equilibrium constant for the butane $\rightleftharpoons$ isobutane equilibrium at 25 °C is 2.50. Calculate $\Delta_r G°$ at this temperature in units of kJ/mol.

butane $\rightleftharpoons$ isobutane

$$CH_3CH_2CH_2CH_3 \quad \rightleftharpoons \quad CH_3\overset{\displaystyle CH_3}{\underset{\displaystyle |}{CH}}CH_3$$

$$K_c = \frac{[\text{isobutane}]}{[\text{butane}]} = 2.50 \text{ at } 298 \text{ K}$$

52. A crucial reaction for the production of synthetic fuels is the production of H_2 by the reaction of coal with steam. The chemical reaction is

$$C(s) + H_2O(g) \rightarrow CO(g) + H_2(g)$$

(a) Calculate $\Delta_r G°$ for this reaction at 25 °C, assuming C(s) is graphite.
(b) Calculate K_p for the reaction at 25 °C.
(c) Is the reaction predicted to be product-favored at equilibrium at 25 °C? If not, at what temperature will it become so?

53. Calculate $\Delta_r G°$ for the decomposition of sulfur trioxide to sulfur dioxide and oxygen.

$$2\ SO_3(g) \rightleftharpoons 2\ SO_2(g) + O_2(g)$$

(a) Is the reaction product-favored at equilibrium at 25 °C?
(b) If the reaction is not product-favored at 25 °C, is there a temperature at which it will become so? Estimate this temperature.
(c) Estimate the equilibrium constant for the reaction at 1500 °C.

54. Methanol can be made by partial oxidation of methane by $O_2(g)$.

$$CH_4(g) + \tfrac{1}{2} O_2(g) \rightleftharpoons CH_3OH(\ell)$$

(a) Determine $\Delta S°$(system), $\Delta S°$ (surroundings), and $\Delta S°$ (universe) for this process.
(b) Is this reaction product-favored at equilibrium at 25 °C?

55. A cave in Mexico was recently discovered to have some interesting chemistry. Hydrogen sulfide, H_2S, reacts with oxygen in the cave to give sulfuric acid, which drips from the ceiling in droplets with a pH less than 1. The reaction occurring is

$$H_2S(g) + 2\ O_2(g) \rightarrow H_2SO_4(\ell)$$

Calculate $\Delta_r H°$, $\Delta_r S°$, and $\Delta_r G°$. Is the reaction product-favored at equilibrium at 25 °C? Is it enthalpy- or entropy-driven?

56. Wet limestone is used to scrub SO_2 gas from the exhaust gases of power plants. One possible reaction gives hydrated calcium sulfite:

$$CaCO_3(s) + SO_2(g) + \tfrac{1}{2} H_2O(\ell) \rightleftharpoons\\ CaSO_3 \cdot \tfrac{1}{2} H_2O(s) + CO_2(g)$$

Another reaction gives hydrated calcium sulfate:

$$CaCO_3(s) + SO_2(g) + \tfrac{1}{2} H_2O(\ell) + \tfrac{1}{2} O_2(g) \rightleftharpoons\\ CaSO_4 \cdot \tfrac{1}{2} H_2O(s) + CO_2(g)$$

(a) Which is the more product-favored reaction? Use the data in the table below and any other information needed in Appendix L to calculate $\Delta_r G°$ for each reaction at 25 °C.

	$CaSO_3 \cdot \tfrac{1}{2} H_2O(s)$	$CaSO_4 \cdot \tfrac{1}{2} H_2O(s)$
$\Delta_f H°$ (kJ/mol)	−1311.7	−1574.65
$S°$ (J/K · mol)	121.3	134.8

(b) Calculate $\Delta_r G°$ for the reaction

$$CaSO_3 \cdot \tfrac{1}{2} H_2O(s) + \tfrac{1}{2} O_2(g) \rightleftharpoons CaSO_4 \cdot \tfrac{1}{2} H_2O(s)$$

Is this reaction product- or reactant-favored at equilibrium?

57. Sulfur undergoes a phase transition between 80 and 100 °C.

$$S_8(\text{rhombic}) \rightarrow S_8(\text{monoclinic})$$

$\Delta_r H° = 3.213$ kJ/mol-rxn $\Delta_r S° = 8.7$ J/K · mol-rxn

(a) Estimate $\Delta_r G°$ for the transition at 80.0 °C and 110.0 °C. What do these results tell you about the stability of the two forms of sulfur at each of these temperatures?
(b) Calculate the temperature at which $\Delta_r G° = 0$. What is the significance of this temperature?

58. Calculate the entropy change for dissolving HCl gas in water at 25 °C. Is the sign of $\Delta S°$ what you expected? Why or why not?

In the Laboratory

59. Some metal oxides can be decomposed to the metal and oxygen under reasonable conditions. Is the decomposition of silver(I) oxide product-favored at 25 °C?

$$2\ Ag_2O(s) \rightarrow 4\ Ag(s) + O_2(g)$$

If not, can it become so if the temperature is raised? At what temperature does the reaction become product-favored?

60. Copper(II) oxide, CuO, can be reduced to copper metal with hydrogen at higher temperatures.

$$CuO(s) + H_2(g) \rightarrow Cu(s) + H_2O(g)$$

Is this reaction product- or reactant-favored at equilibrium at 298 K?

If copper metal is heated in air, a black film of CuO forms on the surface. In this photo, the heated bar, covered with a black CuO film, has been bathed in hydrogen gas. Black, solid CuO is reduced rapidly to copper at higher temperatures.

61. Calculate $\Delta_f G°$ for HI(g) at 350 °C, given the following equilibrium partial pressures: $P(H_2)$ = 0.132 bar, $P(I_2)$ = 0.295 bar, and $P(HI)$ = 1.61 bar. At 350 °C and 1 bar, I_2 is a gas.

$$\tfrac{1}{2}\ H_2(g) + \tfrac{1}{2}\ I_2(g) \rightleftharpoons HI(g)$$

62. Calculate the equilibrium constant for the formation of NiO at 1627 °C. Can the reaction proceed in the forward direction if the initial pressure of O_2 is below 1.00 mm Hg? {$\Delta_f G°$ [NiO(s)] = −72.1 kJ/mol at 1627 °C}

$$Ni(s) + \tfrac{1}{2}\ O_2(g) \rightleftharpoons NiO(s)$$

63. Titanium(IV) oxide is converted to titanium carbide with carbon at a high temperature.

$$TiO_2(s) + 3\ C(s) \rightarrow 2\ CO(g) + TiC(s)$$

Compound	Free Energies of Formation at 727 °C, kJ/mol
TiO₂(s)	−757.8
TiC(s)	−162.6
CO(g)	−200.2

(a) Calculate $\Delta_r G°$ and K at 727 °C
(b) Is the reaction product-favored at equilibrium at this temperature?
(c) How can the reactant or product concentrations be adjusted for the reaction to be spontaneous at 727 °C?

64. Cisplatin [*cis*-diamminedichloroplatinum(II)] is a potent treatment for certain types of cancers, but the *trans* isomer is not effective. What is the equilibrium constant at 298 K for the transformation of the *cis* to the *trans* isomer? Which is the favored isomer at 298 K, the *cis* or the *trans* isomer?

Compound	$\Delta_f H°$ (kJ/mol, 298 K)	$\Delta_f G°$ (kJ/mol, 298 K)
Cis-Pt(NH₃)₂Cl₂	−467.4	−228.7
Trans-Pt(NH₃)₂Cl₂	−480.3	−222.8

cis isomer   *trans* isomer

Summary and Conceptual Questions

The following questions may use concepts from this and previous chapters.

65. ▲ Mercury vapor is dangerous because breathing it brings this toxic element into the lungs. We wish to estimate the vapor pressure of mercury at two different temperatures from the following data:

	$\Delta_f H°$ (kJ/mol)	$S°$ (J/K · mol)	$\Delta_f G°$ (kJ/mol)
Hg(ℓ)	0	76.02	0
Hg(g)	61.38	174.97	31.88

Estimate the temperature at which K_p for the process Hg(ℓ) $\rightleftharpoons$ Hg(g) is equal to 1.00 (and the vapor pressure of Hg is 1.00 bar). Next, estimate the temperature at whch the vapor pressure is (1/760) bar. (Experimental vapor pressures are 1.00 mm Hg at 126.2 °C and 1.00 bar at 356.6 °C.) (*Note:* The temperature at which P = 1.00 bar can be calculated from thermodynamic data. To find the other temperature, you will need to use the temperature for P = 1.00 bar and the Clausius–Clapeyron equation on page 570.)

66. Explain why each of the following statements is incorrect.
(a) Entropy increases in all spontaneous reactions.
(b) Reactions with a negative free energy change ($\Delta_r G°$ < 0) are product-favored and occur with rapid transformation of reactants to products.
(c) All spontaneous processes are exothermic.
(d) Endothermic processes are never spontaneous.

67. Decide whether each of the following statements is true or false. If false, rewrite it to make it true.
(a) The entropy of a substance increases on going from the liquid to the vapor state at any temperature.
(b) An exothermic reaction will always be spontaneous.
(c) Reactions with a positive $\Delta_r H°$ and a positive $\Delta_r S°$ can never be product-favored.
(d) If $\Delta_r G°$ for a reaction is negative, the reaction will have an equilibrium constant greater than 1.

68. Under what conditions is the entropy of a pure substance 0 J/K · mol? Could a substance at standard conditions have a value of 0 J/K · mol? A negative entropy value? Are there any conditions under which a substance will have negative entropy? Explain your answer.

69. In Chapter 14, you learned that entropy, as well as enthalpy, plays a role in the solution process. If $\Delta H°$ for the solution process is zero, explain how the process can be driven by entropy.

70. ▲ Consider the formation of NO(g) from its elements.

$$N_2(g) + O_2(g) \rightleftharpoons 2\,NO(g)$$

   (a) Calculate K_p at 25 °C. Is the reaction product-favored at this temperature?
   (b) Assuming $\Delta_r H°$ and $\Delta_r S°$ are nearly constant with temperature, calculate $\Delta_r G°$ at 700 °C. Estimate K_p from the new value of $\Delta_r G°$ at 700 °C. Is the reaction product-favored at 700 °C?
   (c) Using K_p at 700 °C, calculate the equilibrium partial pressures of the three gases if you mix 1.00 bar each of N_2 and O_2.

71. Write a chemical equation for the oxidation of $C_2H_6(g)$ by $O_2(g)$ to form $CO_2(g)$ and $H_2O(g)$. Defining this as the system:
   (a) Predict whether the signs of $\Delta S°$ (system), $\Delta S°$ (surroundings), and $\Delta S°$ (universe) will be greater than zero, equal to zero, or less than zero. Explain your prediction.
   (b) Predict the signs of $\Delta_r H°$ and $\Delta_r G°$. Explain how you made this prediction.
   (c) Will the value of K_p be very large, very small, or near 1? Will the equilibrium constant, K_p, for this system be larger or smaller at temperatures greater than 298 K? Explain how you made this prediction.

72. The normal melting point of benzene, C_6H_6, is 5.5 °C. For the process of melting, what is the sign of each of the following?
   (a) $\Delta H°$ (c) $\Delta G°$ at 5.5 °C   (e) $\Delta G°$ at 25.0 °C
   (b) $\Delta S°$ (d) $\Delta G°$ at 0.0 °C

73. Calculate the standard molar entropy change, $\Delta_r S°$, for each of the following reactions at 25 °C:
   1. $C(s) + 2\,H_2(g) \rightarrow CH_4(g)$
   2. $CH_4(g) + \frac{1}{2}\,O_2(g) \rightarrow CH_3OH(\ell)$
   3. $C(s) + 2\,H_2(g) + \frac{1}{2}\,O_2(g) \rightarrow CH_3OH(\ell)$

   Verify that these values are related by the equation $\Delta_r S°(1) + \Delta_r S°(2) = \Delta_r S°(3)$. What general principle is illustrated here?

74. For each of the following processes, predict the algebraic sign of $\Delta_r H°$, $\Delta_r S°$, and $\Delta_r G°$. No calculations are necessary; use your common sense.
   (a) The decomposition of liquid water to give gaseous oxygen and hydrogen, a process that requires a considerable amount of energy.
   (b) Dynamite is a mixture of nitroglycerin, $C_3H_5N_3O_9$, and diatomaceous earth. The explosive decomposition of nitroglycerin gives gaseous products such as water, CO_2, and others; much heat is evolved.
   (c) The combustion of gasoline in the engine of your car, as exemplified by the combustion of octane.

$$2\,C_8H_{18}(g) + 25\,O_2(g) \rightarrow 16\,CO_2(g) + 18\,H_2O(g)$$

75. "Heater Meals" are food packages that contain their own heat source. Just pour water into the heater unit, wait a few minutes, and voilà! You have a hot meal.

$$Mg(s) + 2\,H_2O(\ell) \rightarrow Mg(OH)_2(s) + H_2(g)$$

The heat for the heater unit is produced by the reaction of magnesium with water.

   (a) Confirm that this is a spontaneous reaction under standard conditions.
   (b) What mass of magnesium is required to produce sufficient energy to heat 225 mL of water (density = 0.995 g/mL) from 25 °C to the boiling point?

76. Use values of $\Delta_f G°$ for solid and gaseous iodine at 25 °C (Appendix L) to calculate the equilibrium vapor pressure of iodine at this temperature.

Iodine, I_2, readily sublimes at room temperature.

77. Oxygen dissolved in water can cause corrosion in hot-water heating systems. To remove oxygen, hydrazine (N_2H_4) is often added. Hydrazine reacts with dissolved O_2 to form water and N_2.
   (a) Write a balanced chemical equation for the reaction of hydrazine and oxygen. Identify the oxidizing and reducing agents in this redox reaction.
   (b) Calculate $\Delta_r H°$, $\Delta_r S°$, and $\Delta_r G°$ for this reaction involving 1 mol of N_2H_4 at 25 °C.
   (c) Because this is an exothermic reaction, energy is evolved as heat. What temperature change is expected in a heating system containing 5.5×10^4 L of water? (Assume no energy is lost to the surroundings.)
   (d) The mass of a hot-water heating system is 5.5×10^4 kg. What amount of O_2 (in moles) would be present in this system if it is filled with water saturated with O_2? (The solubility of O_2 in water at 25 °C is 0.000434 g per 100 g of water.)
   (e) Assume hydrazine is available as a 5.0% solution in water. What mass of this solution should be added to totally consume the dissolved O_2 [described in part (d)]?
   (f) Assuming the N_2 escapes as a gas, calculate the volume of $N_2(g)$ (measured at 273 K and 1.00 atm) that will be produced.

78. The formation of diamond from graphite is a process of considerable importance.

graphite   diamond

(a) Using data in Appendix L, calculate $\Delta_r S°$, $\Delta_r H°$, and $\Delta_r G°$ for this process at 25 °C.

(b) The calculations will suggest that this process is not possible at any temperature. However, the synthesis of diamonds by this reaction is a commercial process. How can this contradiction be rationalized? (*Note:* In the industrial synthesis, high pressure and high temperatures are used.)

79. Iodine, I_2, dissolves readily in carbon tetrachloride. For this process, $\Delta H° = 0$ kJ/mol.

$$I_2(s) \rightarrow I_2 \text{ (in } CCl_4 \text{ solution)}$$

What is the sign of $\Delta_r G°$? Is the dissolving process entropy-driven or enthalpy-driven? Explain briefly.

80. Write an equation for the reaction of $Fe_2O_3(s)$ and $C(s)$ to give $Fe(s)$ and $CO(g)$ (one of the reactions occurring in a blast furnace). How does $\Delta_r G°$ vary with temperature? Is there a temperature at which the reaction is spontaneous?

81. Write an equation for the decomposition of 1.0 mol of gaseous methanol to the elements in their standard states.

(a) Does the spontaneity of the decomposition of CH_3OH change as the temperature increases?

(b) Is there a temperature between 400 K and 1000 K at which the decomposition is spontaneous?

82. Consider the reaction of NO and Cl_2 to produce NOCl.

(a) What is $\Delta S°$ (system) for this reaction?

(b) Does $\Delta S°$ (system) change with temperature?

(c) Does $\Delta S°$ (surroundings) change with temperature?

(d) Does $\Delta S°$ (universe) always change with an increase in temperature?

(e) Do exothermic reactions always lead to positive values of $\Delta S°$ (universe)?

(f) Is the NO + Cl_2 reaction spontaneous at 298 K? At 700 K?

83. ▲ The Haber–Bosch process for the production of ammonia is one of the key industrial processes in developed countries.

$$N_2(g) + 3 H_2(g) \rightleftharpoons 2 NH_3(g)$$

(a) Calculate $\Delta_r G°$ for the reaction at 298 K, 800 K, and 1300 K. Data at 298 K are given in Appendix L. Data for the other temperatures are as follows:

Temperature	$\Delta_r H°$ (kJ/mol)	$\Delta_r S°$ (J/K · mol)
800 K	−107.4	−225.4
1300 K	−112.4	−228.0

How does the free energy change for the reaction change with temperature?

(b) Calculate the equilibrium constant for the reaction at 298 K, 800 K, and 1300 K.

(c) Calculate the mole fraction of ammonia in the equilibrium mixture at each of the temperatures. At what temperature is the mole fraction of NH_3 the largest?

84. ▲ Muscle cells need energy to contract. One biochemical pathway for energy transfer is the breakdown of glucose to pyruvate in a process called *glycolysis*. In the presence of sufficient oxygen in the cell, pyruvate is oxidized to CO_2 and H_2O to make further energy available. However, under extreme conditions not enough oxygen can be supplied to the cells, so muscle cells produce lactate ion according to the reaction

$$\underset{\text{pyruvate}}{H_3C-\overset{\overset{O}{\|}}{C}-\overset{\overset{O}{\|}}{C}-O^-} + NADH + H^+$$

$$\xrightarrow[\text{dehydrogenase}]{\text{lactate}} \underset{\text{lactate}}{H_3C-\overset{\overset{OH}{|}}{\underset{H}{C}}-\overset{\overset{O}{\|}}{C}-O^-} + NAD^+$$

where $\Delta_r G°' = -25.1$ kJ/mol. In living cells, the pH value is about 7. The hydronium ion concentration is constant and is included in $\Delta G°$, which is then called $\Delta_r G°'$ (as explained on page 881). (*This problem is taken from the problems for the 36th International Chemistry Olympiad for high school students held in Kiel, Germany, in 2004.*)

(a) Calculate $\Delta_r G°$ for the reaction at 25 °C.

(b) Calculate the equilibrium constant K'. (The hydronium ion concentration is included in the constant. That is, $K' = K \cdot [H_3O^+]$ for the reaction at 25 °C and pH = 7.0.)

(c) $\Delta_r G°'$ is the free energy change under standard conditions; that is, the concentrations of all reactants (except H_3O^+) are 1.00 mol/L. Calculate $\Delta_r G'$ at 25 °C, assuming the following concentrations in the cell: pyruvate, 380 μmol/L; NADH, 50 μmol/L; lactate ion, 3700 μmol/L; and NAD^+ ion, 540 μmol/L.

Applying Chemical Principles

Are Diamonds Forever?

Natural diamonds are created over 150 kilometers beneath the Earth's surface. At these depths, enormous pressures and high temperatures convert graphite, the more stable allotrope of carbon at lower pressure, into diamond. It is believed that volcanic eruptions push diamonds to the Earth's surface. If a diamond is pushed to the surface quickly, it will cool before it has a chance to revert to graphite. Although diamonds are thermodynamically unstable at room temperature, the activation barrier for conversion is too high for the process to occur.

Diamonds have been synthesized in laboratories since the 1950s by duplicating the conditions that exist deep underground. To produce a synthetic diamond, a seed crystal of diamond is combined with graphite and nickel (or chromium), then subjected to pressures greater than 50,000 atmospheres and temperatures around 1500 °C. The nickel, now molten, simultaneously acts as a solvent for carbon and a catalyst for the formation of diamond. If conditions are maintained near the equilibrium line between diamond and graphite (Figure 1), single crystals of synthetic diamonds may be grown to sizes larger than one carat in approximately three days. Synthetic diamonds may be produced in a variety of colors. One of the most common colors is yellow, which results from a small amount of nitrogen replacing carbon in diamond's lattice. Is this a problem? Probably not. Natural yellow diamonds are extremely rare and sell for high prices.

Currently, a technique known as *chemical vapor deposition* (CVD) is being used to grow diamonds in a vacuum and at lower temperatures (800 °C). In CVD, methane and hydrogen gases are atomized above a diamond seed crystal. Hydrogen atoms bond with carbon atoms on the diamond's surface, preventing the carbon atoms from forming double bonds with its neighbors. Carbon radicals, from the decomposed methane, slowly replace the

FIGURE 2 Diamond wafers. The chemical vapor deposition (CVD) technique allows the synthesis of diamond in the shape of extended disks or wafers. Under optimized growth conditions the properties of these disks approach those of perfect diamond single crystals.

hydrogen atoms on the diamond's surface, building a larger diamond, one atom layer at a time. In addition to gemstones, the CVD method may be used to create diamond windows or thin diamond films over a variety of substrates (Figure 2).

Questions:

1. The decomposition of diamond to graphite [C(diamond) → C(graphite)] is thermodynamically favored, but occurs slowly at room temperature.
   (a) Use $\Delta_f G°$ values from Appendix L to calculate $\Delta_r G°$ and K_{eq} for the reaction under standard conditions and 298.15 K.
   (b) Use $\Delta_f H°$ and $S°$ values from Appendix L to calculate $\Delta_r G°$ and K_{eq} for the reaction at 1000 K. Assume that enthalpy and entropy values are valid at these temperatures. Does heating shift the equilibrium toward the formation of diamond or graphite?
   (c) Why is the formation of diamond favored at high pressures?
   (d) The phase diagram shows that diamond is thermodynamically favored over graphite at 20,000 atmospheres pressure at room temperature. Why is this conversion actually done at much higher temperatures and pressures?

2. It has been demonstrated that buckminsterfullerene (C_{60}), another allotrope of carbon (page 63), may be converted into diamond at room temperature and 20,000 atmospheres pressure (about 2 GPa). The standard enthalpy of formation, $\Delta_f H°$, for buckminsterfullerene is 2320 kJ/mol at 298.2 K.
   (a) Calculate $\Delta_r H°$ for the conversion of C_{60} to diamond at standard state conditions and 298.2 K.
   (b) Assuming that the standard entropy per mole of carbon in both C_{60} and diamond is comparable (both about 2.3 J/K mol), is the conversion of C_{60} to diamond product-favored at room temperature?

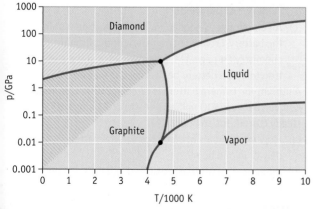

FIGURE 1 Phase diagram for carbon. The hatched areas are regions where the two phases can coexist. Pressures are in gigapascals (where 1 GPa is about 9900 atm).

20 Principles of Chemical Reactivity: Electron Transfer Reactions

Courtesy General Motors/Orlando Sentinel/MCT

Battery Power

The 20th century was the century of the use and abuse of petroleum. The 21st century has to be the century of the discovery and use of alternative energy sources. Many of these will involve electrochemistry, the use of chemical reactions to produce electricity (batteries), or the use of electricity to produce chemical change (electrolysis).

The lithium-ion battery in your laptop computer or your phone, or the nickel-metal hydride battery in your hybrid car, works because redox reactions release chemical energy. (When you recharge the battery, you use electric energy to rejuvenate the chemicals in the battery.) But don't for a moment think that everything is understood about batteries or how to make them smaller, cheaper, or more efficient. One of the most important areas of research today is in battery technology, especially lithium-based batteries. Companies and universities around the world are searching for new battery designs that are lightweight, inexpensive, safe, environmentally kind, and that produce sufficient energy.

Electric vehicles. The forthcoming Chevrolet Volt will use lithium-ion batteries for propulsion. (For more on lithium-ion batteries see page 582.)

Questions:

1. The simplest way to write the reaction for discharge in a lithium-ion battery is

    $$Li(on\ carbon)(s) + CoO_2(s) \rightarrow 6\ C(s) + LiCoO_2(s)$$

    (a) What are the oxidation numbers for cobalt in the two substances in the battery?
    (b) In such a battery, what reaction occurs at the cathode? At the anode?
    (c) An electrolyte is needed for ion conduction within the battery. From what you know about lithium chemistry (◀ page 324, for example), can the electrolyte in the battery be dissolved in water?
2. A lithium-ion camera battery is rated at 7500 mAh. That is, it can deliver 7500 milliamps (mA) or 7.5 amps of steady current for an hour.
    (a) How many moles of electrons can the battery deliver in one hour?
    (b) What mass of lithium is oxidized under these conditions in 1 hour?

Answers to these questions are available in Appendix N.

CHAPTER GOALS

*See Chapter Goals Revisited (page 935) for
Study Questions keyed to these goals.*

- Balance equations for oxidation–
reduction reactions in acidic or basic
solutions using the half-reaction
approach.

- Understand the principles underlying
voltaic cells.

- Understand how to use
electrochemical potentials.

- Explore electrolysis, the use of
electrical energy to produce chemical
change.

Let us introduce you to electrochemistry and electron transfer reactions with
a simple experiment. Place a piece of copper in an aqueous solution of silver
nitrate. After a short time, metallic silver deposits on the copper, and the solution takes on the blue color typical of aqueous Cu^{2+} ions (Figure 20.1). The following oxidation–reduction (redox) reaction has occurred:

$$Cu(s) + 2\ Ag^+(aq) \rightarrow Cu^{2+}(aq) + 2\ Ag(s)$$

At the particulate level, Ag^+ ions in solution come into direct contact with the copper surface where the transfer of electrons occurs. Two electrons are transferred
from a Cu atom to two Ag^+ ions. Copper ions, Cu^{2+}, enter the solution, and silver

OWL

Sign in to OWL at **www.cengage.com/
owl** to view tutorials and simulations,
develop problem-solving skills, and
complete online homework assigned
by your professor.

Download mini lecture videos for
key concept review and exam prep
from OWL or purchase them from
www.cengagebrain.com

A clean piece of copper wire will be placed
in a solution of silver nitrate, $AgNO_3$.

With time, the copper reduces Ag^+ ions
to silver metal crystals, and the copper
metal is oxidized to copper ions, Cu^{2+}.

The blue color of the solution is due to
the presence of aqueous copper(II) ions.

Add $AgNO_3(aq)$

After
several days

Silver ions in solution

Surface of copper wire

Cu^{2+}

FIGURE 20.1 The oxidation of copper by silver ions. Note that water molecules are not
shown for clarity.

atoms are deposited on the copper surface. This product-favored reaction continues until one or both of the reactants is consumed.

Can we use the reaction between copper metal and silver ions to generate an electric current? When the reactants, $Cu(s)$ and $Ag^+(aq)$, are in direct contact, electrons are transferred directly from copper atoms to silver ions, and an increase in temperature (heating) rather than electrical work results. Instead, we can run the reaction in an apparatus that allows electrons to be transferred from one reactant to the other through an electrical circuit. The movement of electrons through the circuit constitutes an electric current that can be used to light a light bulb or to run a motor.

Devices that use chemical reactions to produce an electric current are called **voltaic cells** or **galvanic cells**, names honoring Count Alessandro Volta (1745–1827) and Luigi Galvani (1737–1798). All voltaic cells work in the same general way: They use product-favored redox reactions, and the electrons produced by the reducing agent are transferred through an electric circuit to the oxidizing agent.

A voltaic cell converts chemical energy to electrical energy. The opposite process, the use of electric energy to effect a chemical change, occurs in **electrolysis**. An example is the electrolysis of water (◄ Figure 1.10), in which electrical energy is used to split water into its component elements, hydrogen and oxygen. Electrolysis is also used to electroplate one metal onto another, to obtain aluminum from its common ore (bauxite, mostly Al_2O_3), and to prepare important chemicals such as chlorine.

Electrochemistry is the field of chemistry that considers chemical reactions that produce or are caused by electrical energy. Because all electrochemical reactions are oxidation–reduction (redox) reactions, we begin our exploration of this subject by first describing electron transfer reactions in more detail.

• **Two Types of Electrochemical Processes**
• Chemical change can produce an electric current in a voltaic cell.
• Electric energy can cause chemical change in the process of electrolysis.

• **Oxidation Numbers** Oxidation numbers (page 139) can be used to determine whether a substance is oxidized or reduced. An element is oxidized if its oxidation number increases. The oxidation number decreases in a reduction.

20.1 Oxidation–Reduction Reactions

In an oxidation–reduction reaction, electron transfer occurs between a reducing agent and an oxidizing agent (◄ Section 3.8). The essential features of all electron transfer reactions are as follows:

- One reactant is oxidized, and one is reduced.
- The extent of oxidation and reduction must balance.
- The oxidizing agent (the chemical species causing oxidation) is reduced.
- The reducing agent (the chemical species causing reduction) is oxidized.

These aspects of oxidation–reduction or redox reactions are illustrated for the reaction of copper metal and silver ion (Figure 20.1).

Cu oxidized, oxidation number increases;
Cu is the reducing agent.

$$Cu(s) + 2\ Ag^+(aq) \longrightarrow Cu^{2+}(aq) + 2\ Ag(s)$$

Ag^+ reduced, oxidation number decreases;
Ag^+ is the oxidizing agent.

go Chemistry

Module 25: Oxidation–Reduction Reactions covers concepts in this section.

Balancing Oxidation–Reduction Equations

All equations for oxidation–reduction reactions must be balanced for both mass and charge. The same number of atoms appear in the products and reactants of an equation, and the sum of electric charges of all the species on each side of the equation arrow must be the same. Charge balance guarantees that the number of electrons produced in oxidation equals the number of electrons consumed in reduction.

Balancing some redox equations can be complicated, but fortunately some systematic procedures can be used in these cases. Here, we describe the **half-reaction method**, a procedure that involves writing separate, balanced equations for the oxidation and reduction processes. One half-reaction describes the oxidation part of the reaction, and a second half-reaction describes the reduction part.

When a reaction has been determined to involve oxidation and reduction (by noting, for example, that oxidation state changes have occurred), the equation is separated into two half-reactions, which are then balanced for mass and charge. The equation for the overall reaction is then the sum of these two balanced half-reactions, after adjustments have been made (if necessary) in one or both half-reaction equations so that the numbers of electrons transferred from reducing agent to oxidizing agent balance. For example, the half-reactions for the reaction of copper metal with silver ions are

Reduction half-reaction: $Ag^+(aq) + e^- \rightarrow Ag(s)$

Oxidation half-reaction: $Cu(s) \rightarrow Cu^{2+}(aq) + 2\ e^-$

Notice that the equations for the half-reactions are themselves balanced for mass and charge. In the copper half-reaction, there is one Cu atom on each side of the equation (mass balance). The electric charge on the right side of the equation is 0 (the sum of +2 for the ion and −2 for two electrons), as it is on the left side (charge balance).

To produce the net chemical equation, we will add the two half-reactions. First, however, we must multiply the silver half-reaction by 2.

$$2\ Ag^+(aq) + 2\ e^- \rightarrow 2\ Ag(s)$$

Each mole of copper atoms produces two moles of electrons, and two moles of Ag^+ ions are required to consume those electrons.

Finally, adding the two half-reactions and canceling electrons from both sides leads to the net ionic equation for the reaction.

Reduction half-reaction: $2\ [Ag^+(aq) + e^- \rightarrow Ag(s)]$

Oxidation half-reaction: $Cu(s) \rightarrow Cu^{2+}(aq) + 2\ e^-$

Net ionic equation $\overline{Cu(s) + 2\ Ag^+(aq) \rightarrow Cu^{2+}(aq) + 2\ Ag(s)}$

The resulting net ionic equation is balanced for mass and charge.

⬤WL   INTERACTIVE EXAMPLE 20.1   Balancing Oxidation–Reduction Equations

Problem Balance the following net ionic equation

$$Al(s) + Cu^{2+}(aq) \rightarrow Al^{3+}(aq) + Cu(s)$$

Identify the oxidizing agent, the reducing agent, the substance oxidized, and the substance reduced. Write balanced half-reactions and the balanced net ionic equation. See Figure 20.2 for photographs of this reaction.

(a) A ball of aluminum foil is added to a solution of $Cu(NO_3)_2$ and NaCl.

(b) A coating of copper is soon seen on the surface of the aluminum, and the reaction generates a significant amount of energy as heat.

FIGURE 20.2 Reduction of Cu^{2+} by Al. Aluminum always has a thin coating of Al_2O_3 on the surface, which protects the metal from further reaction. However, in the presence of Cl^- ion, the coating is breached, and reaction occurs. See Example 20.1.

Strategy Map 20.1

PROBLEM

Balance the equation for the reaction of **Al** and **Cu²⁺**.

↓

KNOWN DATA/INFORMATION

- Products
- Reactants

STEP 1. Identify reaction as **redox**.

↓

Oxidation numbers change, so this is a redox reaction.

STEP 2. Write half-reactions.

Reduction half-reaction
Oxidation half-reaction

STEP 3. Balance each half-reaction for **mass**.

Half-reactions balanced for mass

STEP 4. Use electrons for **charge balance**.

Half-reactions balanced for charge.

STEP 5. Multiply each half-reaction by a factor so **red. agent** supplies as many electrons as **ox. agent** acquires.

Half-reactions balanced for **mass** and **charge**

STEP 6. Add half-reactions.

↓

Overall **balanced equation**

STEP 7. Simplify, and **check for balance**.

Final balanced equation checked for correctness.

What Do You Know? You know that Al is producing Al^{3+} ions, and copper(II) ions are producing copper metal.

Strategy

- Make sure the reaction is an oxidation–reduction reaction by checking each element to see whether the oxidation numbers change.

- Separate the equation into half-reactions, identifying what has been reduced (oxidizing agent) and what has been oxidized (reducing agent). (You may wish to review oxidation numbers and oxidation–reduction reactions in Section 3.8.)

- Balance the half-reactions, first for mass and then for charge.

- Add the two half-reactions, after ensuring that the reducing agent half-reaction involves the same number of moles of electrons as the oxidizing agent half-reaction.

Solution

Step 1. *Recognize the Reaction as an Oxidation–Reduction Reaction.*

Here, the oxidation number for aluminum changes from 0 to +3, and the oxidation number of copper changes from +2 to 0. Aluminum is oxidized and serves as the reducing agent. Copper(II) ions are reduced, and Cu^{2+} is the oxidizing agent.

Step 2. *Separate the Process into Half-Reactions.*

Reduction: $\quad\quad\quad\quad Cu^{2+}(aq) \rightarrow Cu(s)$
(Oxidation number of Cu decreases.)

Oxidation: $\quad\quad\quad\quad Al(s) \rightarrow Al^{3+}(aq)$
(Oxidation number of Al increases.)

Step 3. *Balance Each Half-Reaction for Mass.*

Both half-reactions are already balanced for mass.

Step 4. *Balance Each Half-Reaction for Charge.*

To balance the equations for charge, add electrons to the more positive side of each half-reaction to bring the charge on that side of the equation down to the same value as is present on the other side.

Reduction: $\quad\quad\quad 2\ e^- + Cu^{2+}(aq) \rightarrow Cu(s)$
(Each Cu^{2+} ion requires two electrons.)

Oxidation: $\quad\quad\quad Al(s) \rightarrow Al^{3+}(aq) + 3\ e^-$
(Each Al atom releases three electrons.)

Step 5. *Multiply Each Half-Reaction by an Appropriate Factor.*

The reducing agent must donate as many electrons as the oxidizing agent acquires. Three Cu^{2+} ions are required to take on the six electrons produced by two Al atoms. Thus, we multiply the Cu^{2+}/Cu half-reaction by 3 and the Al/Al^{3+} half-reaction by 2.

Reduction: $\quad\quad\quad 3[2\ e^- + Cu^{2+}(aq) \rightarrow Cu(s)]$

Oxidation: $\quad\quad\quad 2[Al(s) \rightarrow Al^{3+}(aq) + 3\ e^-]$

Step 6. *Add the Half-Reactions to Produce the Overall Balanced Equation.*

Reduction: $\quad\quad\quad 6\ e^- + 3\ Cu^{2+}(aq) \rightarrow 3\ Cu(s)$

Oxidation: $\quad\quad\quad 2\ Al(s) \rightarrow 2\ Al^{3+}(aq) + 6\ e^-$

Net ionic equation: $\quad 3\ Cu^{2+}(aq) + 2\ Al(s) \rightarrow 3\ Cu(s) + 2\ Al^{3+}(aq)$

Step 7. *Simplify by Eliminating Reactants and Products That Appear on Both Sides.*

This step is not required here.

Think about Your Answer You should always check the overall equation to ensure there is mass and charge balance. In this case, three Cu atoms and two Al atoms appear on each side. The net electric charge on each side is $+6$. The equation is balanced.

Check Your Understanding

Aluminum reacts with nonoxidizing acids to give $Al^{3+}(aq)$ and $H_2(g)$. The (unbalanced) equation is

$$Al(s) + H^+(aq) \rightarrow Al^{3+}(aq) + H_2(g)$$

Write balanced equations for the half-reactions and the balanced net ionic equation. Identify the oxidizing agent, the reducing agent, the substance oxidized, and the substance reduced.

Balancing Equations in Acid Solution

When balancing equations for redox reactions in aqueous solution, it is sometimes necessary to add water molecules (H_2O) and either $H^+(aq)$ in acidic solution or $OH^-(aq)$ in basic solution to the equation. Equations that include oxoanions such as SO_4^{2-}, NO_3^-, ClO^-, CrO_4^{2-}, and MnO_4^- and organic compounds fall into this category. The process is outlined in Example 20.2 for the reduction of an oxocation in acid solution and in Example 20.3 for a reaction in basic solution.

● **Balancing Equations in Acid Solution** To simplify equations, we shall use H^+ instead of H_3O^+ when balancing equations in acid solution.

⬤WL **INTERACTIVE EXAMPLE 20.2** Balancing Equations for Oxidation–Reduction Reactions in Acid Solution

Problem Balance the net ionic equation for the reaction of the dioxovanadium(V) ion, VO_2^+, with zinc in acid solution to form VO^{2+} (Figure 20.3).

$$VO_2^+(aq) + Zn(s) \rightarrow VO^{2+}(aq) + Zn^{2+}(aq)$$

What Do You Know? You know that the VO_2^+ ions produce VO^{2+} ions, and Zn metal produces Zn^{2+} ions. You need to know how H^+ ions and water are used to balanced the O atoms involved in the reaction.

Strategy Follow the strategy outlined in the text and Example 20.1. Note that water and H^+ ions will appear as product and reactant, respectively, in the half-reaction for the reduction of VO_2^+ ion.

The VO_2^+ ion is yellow in acid solution.

Zn added. With time, the yellow VO_2^+ ion is reduced to blue VO^{2+} ion.

With time, the blue VO^{2+} ion is further reduced to green V^{3+} ion.

Finally, green V^{3+} ion is reduced to violet V^{2+} ion.

VO_2^+

Add Zn

VO^{2+}

V^{3+}

V^{2+}

FIGURE 20.3 Reduction of vanadium(V) with zinc. See Example 20.2 for the balanced equation for the first stage of the reaction.

Strategy Map 20.2

PROBLEM

Balance the equation for the reaction of **Zn** and **VO₂⁺** in acid solution.

↓

KNOWN DATA/INFORMATION

- Products
- Reactants

↓

STEP 1. Identify reaction as **redox**.

Oxidation numbers change, so this is a redox reaction.

↓

STEP 2. Write half-reactions.

Reduction half-reaction
Oxidation half-reaction

↓

STEP 3. Balance each half-reaction for **mass**. Use **H⁺** and **H₂O** as reactants or products if necessary for mass balance.

Half-reactions **balanced for mass**. May include H⁺ and H₂O in addition to original reactants and products.

↓

STEP 4. Use electrons for **charge balance**.

Half-reactions balanced for charge.

↓

STEP 5. Multiply each half-reaction by a factor so **red. agent** supplies as many electrons as **ox. agent** acquires.

Half-reactions balanced for **mass** and **charge**.

↓

STEP 6. Add half-reactions.

Overall **balanced equation**

↓

STEP 7. Simplify and **check for balance**.

Final equation checked for correctness.

Solution

Step 1. *Recognize the Reaction as an Oxidation–Reduction Reaction.*

The oxidation number of V changes from +5 in VO_2^+ to +4 in VO^{2+}. The oxidation number of Zn changes from 0 in the metal to +2 in Zn^{2+}.

Step 2. *Separate the Process into Half-Reactions.*

Oxidation: $Zn(s) \rightarrow Zn^{2+}(aq)$
(Zn(s) is oxidized and is the reducing agent.)

Reduction: $VO_2^+(aq) \rightarrow VO^{2+}(aq)$
(VO_2^+(aq) is reduced and is the oxidizing agent.)

Step 3. *Balance the Half-Reactions for Mass.*

Begin by balancing all atoms except H and O. (These atoms are always the last to be balanced because they often appear in more than one reactant or product.)

Zinc half-reaction: $Zn(s) \rightarrow Zn^{2+}(aq)$

This half-reaction is already balanced for mass.

Vanadium half-reaction: $VO_2^+(aq) \rightarrow VO^{2+}(aq)$

The V atoms in this half-reaction are already balanced. An oxygen-containing species must be added to the right side of the equation to achieve an O atom balance, however.

$$VO_2^+(aq) \rightarrow VO^{2+}(aq) + (\text{need 1 O atom})$$

In acid solution, add H_2O to the side requiring O atoms, one H_2O molecule for each O atom required.

$$VO_2^+(aq) \rightarrow VO^{2+}(aq) + H_2O(\ell)$$

There are now two unbalanced H atoms on the right. Because the reaction occurs in an acidic solution, H⁺ ions are present. Therefore, a mass balance for H can be achieved by adding H⁺ to the side of the equation deficient in H atoms. Here, two H⁺ ions are added to the left side of the equation.

$$2\,H^+(aq) + VO_2^+(aq) \rightarrow VO^{2+}(aq) + H_2O(\ell)$$

Step 4. *Balance the Half-Reactions for Charge by Adding Electrons to the More Positive Side to Make the Charges Equal on Both Sides.*

Two electrons are added to the right side of the zinc half-reaction to bring its charge down to the same value as is present on the left side (in this case, zero).

Zinc half-reaction: $Zn(s) \rightarrow Zn^{2+}(aq) + 2\,e^-$.

The mass-balanced VO_2^+ equation has a net charge of 3+ on the left side and 2+ on the right. Therefore, 1 e^- is added to the more positive left side.

Vanadium half-reaction: $e^- + 2\,H^+(aq) + VO_2^+(aq) \rightarrow VO^{2+}(aq) + H_2O(\ell)$

As a check on your work, notice that the vanadium atom changes in oxidation number from +5 to +4 and so needs to acquire one electron for each vanadium atom reduced.

Step 5. *Multiply the Half-Reactions by Appropriate Factors so That the Reducing Agent Donates as Many Electrons as the Oxidizing Agent Consumes.*

Here, the oxidation half-reaction supplies 2 mol of electrons per mol of Zn, and the reduction half-reaction consumes 1 mol of electrons per mol of VO_2^+. Therefore, the reduction half-reaction must be multiplied by 2. Now 2 mol of the oxidizing agent (VO_2^+) consumes the 2 mol of electrons provided per mol of the reducing agent (Zn).

$$Zn(s) \rightarrow Zn^{2+}(aq) + 2\,e^-$$

$$2[e^- + 2\,H^+(aq) + VO_2^+(aq) \rightarrow VO^{2+}(aq) + H_2O(\ell)]$$

Step 6. *Add the Half-Reactions to Give the Balanced, Overall Equation.*

Oxidation half-reaction: $Zn(s) \rightarrow Zn^{2+}(aq) + 2\ e^-$

Reduction half-reaction: $2\ e^- + 4\ H^+(aq) + 2\ VO_2^+(aq) \rightarrow 2\ VO^{2+}(aq) + 2\ H_2O(\ell)$

Net ionic equation: $\overline{Zn(s) + 4\ H^+(aq) + 2\ VO_2^+(aq) \rightarrow Zn^{2+}(aq) + 2\ VO^{2+}(aq) + 2\ H_2O(\ell)}$

Step 7. *Simplify by Eliminating Reactants and Products That Appear on Both Sides.*

This step is not required here.

Think about Your Answer Check the overall equation to ensure that there is a mass and charge balance.

Mass balance:	1 Zn, 2 V, 4 H, and 4 O
Charge balance:	Each side has a net charge of $+6$.

FIGURE 20.4 **The reaction of purple permanganate ion (MnO_4^-) with iron(II) ions in acid solution.** The products are the nearly colorless Mn^{2+} and Fe^{3+} ions.

Check Your Understanding

1. The yellow dioxovanadium(V) ion, $VO_2^+(aq)$, is reduced by zinc metal in three steps. The first step reduces it to blue $VO^{2+}(aq)$. This ion is further reduced to green $V^{3+}(aq)$ in the second step, and V^{3+} can be reduced to violet $V^{2+}(aq)$ in a third step. In each step, zinc is oxidized to $Zn^{2+}(aq)$. Write balanced net ionic equations for Steps 2 and 3. (This reduction sequence is shown in Figure 20.3.)

2. A common laboratory analysis for iron is to titrate aqueous iron(II) ion with a solution of potassium permanganate of precisely known concentration. Use the half-reaction method to write the balanced net ionic equation for the reaction in acid solution.

$$MnO_4^-(aq) + Fe^{2+}(aq) \rightarrow Mn^{2+}(aq) + Fe^{3+}(aq)$$

Identify the oxidizing agent, the reducing agent, the substance oxidized, and the substance reduced. See Figure 20.4.

Balancing Equations in Basic Solution

Example 20.2 illustrates the technique of balancing equations for redox reactions involving oxocations and oxoanions that occur in acid solution. Under these conditions, H^+ ion or the H^+/H_2O pair can be used to achieve a balanced equation if required. Conversely, in basic solution, only OH^- ion or the OH^-/H_2O pair can be used.

EXAMPLE 20.3 Balancing Equations for Oxidation–Reduction Reactions in Basic Solution

Problem Aluminum metal is oxidized in aqueous base, with water serving as the oxidizing agent. The products of the reaction are $[Al(OH)_4]^-(aq)$ and $H_2(g)$. Write a balanced net ionic equation for this reaction.

What Do You Know? You know the reactants and products. Here the reaction is in basic solution, so OH^- ions may be involved and perhaps water as well.

Strategy The strategy is basically that of Examples 20.1 and 20.2 with the exception that you will need to decide if OH^- ions are involved and if H_2O is also included in the half-reactions.

Solution

Step 1. *Recognize the Reaction as an Oxidation–Reduction Reaction.*

The unbalanced equation is

$$Al(s) + H_2O(\ell) \rightarrow [Al(OH)_4]^-(aq) + H_2(g)$$

Here, aluminum is oxidized, with its oxidation number changing from 0 to $+3$. Hydrogen is reduced, with its oxidation number decreasing from $+1$ to zero.

Step 2. *Separate the Process into Half-Reactions.*

Oxidation half-reaction: $Al(s) \rightarrow [Al(OH)_4]^-(aq)$
(Al oxidation number increased from 0 to +3.)

Reduction half-reaction: $H_2O(\ell) \rightarrow H_2(g)$
(H oxidation number decreased from +1 to 0.)

Step 3. *Balance the Half-Reactions for Mass.*

Addition of OH^- or OH^- and H_2O is required for mass balance in both half-reactions. In the case of the aluminum half-reaction, we simply add OH^- ions to the left side.

Oxidation half-reaction: $Al(s) + 4\ OH^-(aq) \rightarrow [Al(OH)_4]^-(aq)$

To balance the half-reaction for water reduction, notice that an oxygen-containing species must appear on the right side of the equation. Because H_2O is a reactant, we use OH^-, which is present in this basic solution, as the other product.

Reduction half-reaction: $2\ H_2O(\ell) \rightarrow H_2(g) + 2\ OH^-(aq)$

Step 4. *Balance the Half-Reactions for Charge.*

Electrons are added to balance charge.

Oxidation half-reaction: $Al(s) + 4\ OH^-(aq) \rightarrow [Al(OH)_4]^-(aq) + 3\ e^-$

Reduction half-reaction: $2\ H_2O(\ell) + 2\ e^- \rightarrow H_2(g) + 2\ OH^-(aq)$

Step 5. *Multiply the Half-Reactions by Appropriate Factors so That the Reducing Agent Donates as Many Electrons as the Oxidizing Agent Consumes.*

Here, electron balance is achieved by using 2 mol of Al to provide 6 mol of e^-, which are then acquired by 6 mol of H_2O.

Oxidation half-reaction: $2[Al(s) + 4\ OH^-(aq) \rightarrow [Al(OH)_4]^-(aq) + 3\ e^-]$

Reduction half-reaction: $3[2\ H_2O(\ell) + 2\ e^- \rightarrow H_2(g) + 2\ OH^-(aq)]$

Step 6. *Add the Half-Reactions.*

$$2\ Al(s) + 8\ OH^-(aq) \rightarrow 2\ [Al(OH)_4]^-(aq) + 6\ e^-$$

$$6\ H_2O(\ell) + 6\ e^- \rightarrow 3\ H_2(g) + 6\ OH^-(aq)$$

Net equation: $2\ Al(s) + 8\ OH^-(aq) + 6\ H_2O(\ell) \rightarrow 2\ [Al(OH)_4]^-(aq) + 3\ H_2(g) + 6\ OH^-(aq)$

Step 7. *Simplify by Eliminating Reactants and Products That Appear on Both Sides.*

Six OH^- ions can be canceled from the two sides of the equation:

$$2\ Al(s) + 2\ OH^-(aq) + 6\ H_2O(\ell) \rightarrow 2\ [Al(OH)_4]^-(aq) + 3\ H_2(g)$$

Think about Your Answer   The final equation is balanced for mass and charge.

Mass balance: 2 Al, 14 H, and 8 O

Charge balance: There is a net −2 charge on each side.

Check Your Understanding

Voltaic cells based on the reduction of sulfur are under development. One such cell involves the reaction of sulfur with aluminum under basic conditions.

$$Al(s) + S(s) \rightarrow Al(OH)_3(s) + HS^-(aq)$$

(a)   Balance this equation, showing each balanced half-reaction.

(b)   Identify the oxidizing and reducing agents, the substance oxidized, and the substance reduced.

Balancing Oxidation–Reduction Equations—A Summary

- The number of electrons in a half-reaction reflects the change in oxidation number of the element being oxidized or reduced.
- Electrons are always a component of half-reactions but should never appear in the overall equation.

- Include charges in the formulas for ions. Omitting the charge, or writing the charge incorrectly, is one of the most common errors seen on student papers.
- The best way to become competent in balancing redox equations is to practice, practice, practice.

REVIEW & CHECK FOR SECTION 20.1

1. Copper(II) sulfide reacts with nitric acid according to the balanced equation:

   $$3\ CuS(s) + 8\ H^+(aq) + 2\ NO_3^-(aq) \rightarrow 3\ Cu^{2+}(aq) + 3\ S(s) + 4\ H_2O(\ell) + 2\ NO(g)$$

   The substance oxidized is

   (a) CuS   (b) H^+ (c) NO_3^-

2. The balanced half-reaction for $NO_3^- \rightarrow NO$ in acid solution is

   (a) $NO_3^- \rightarrow NO + e^-$

   (b) $2\ H^+ + e^- + NO_3^- \rightarrow NO + 2\ H_2O$

   (c) $NO_3^- \rightarrow NO + O^{2-} + e^-$

   (d) $4\ H^+ + 3\ e^- + NO_3^- \rightarrow NO + 2\ H_2O$

3. The balanced half-reaction for $Br_2 \rightarrow BrO_3^-$ in basic solution is

   (a) $3\ OH^- + Br_2 \rightarrow 2\ BrO_3^- + H_2O + e^-$

   (b) $12\ OH^- + Br_2 \rightarrow 2\ BrO_3^- + 6\ H_2O + 10\ e^-$

   (c) $e^- + OH^- + Br_2 \rightarrow 2\ BrO_3^- + H_2O$

   (d) $10\ e^- + Br_2 + 6\ H_2O \rightarrow 2\ BrO_3^- + 6\ OH^-$

20.2 Simple Voltaic Cells

Let us use the reaction of copper metal and silver ions (Figure 20.1) as the basis of a voltaic cell. To do so, we place the components of the two half-reactions in separate compartments (Figure 20.5). This prevents the copper metal from transferring electrons directly to silver ions. Instead, electrons will be transferred through an external circuit, and useful work can potentially be done.

An Alternative Method of Balancing Equations in Basic Solution

(a) Balance the equation as if the reaction were carried out in acid by following Steps 1–7 in Example 20.2:

$$3\ ClO^-(aq) + H_2O(\ell) + 2\ MnO_2(s) \rightarrow$$
$$3\ Cl^-(aq) + 2\ MnO_4^-(aq) + 2\ H^+(aq)$$

(b) To adjust for the fact that this reaction is carried out in base rather than in acid, we will add the same number of hydroxide ions to both sides of the equation as there are $H^+(aq)$ ions. On the side that

had the $H^+(aq)$ ions, the $H^+(aq)$ ions and $OH^-(aq)$ ions will form $H_2O(\ell)$.

$$3\ ClO^-(aq) + H_2O(\ell) + 2\ MnO_2(s) + 2\ OH^-(aq) \rightarrow$$
$$3\ Cl^-(aq) + 2\ MnO_4^-(aq) + 2\ H^+(aq) + 2\ OH^-(aq)$$

$$3\ ClO^-(aq) + H_2O(\ell) + 2\ MnO_2(s) + 2\ OH^-(aq) \rightarrow$$
$$3\ Cl^-(aq) + 2\ MnO_4^-(aq) + 2\ H_2O(\ell)$$

(c) Simplify

$$3\ ClO^-(aq) + 2\ MnO_2(s) + 2\ OH^-(aq) \rightarrow$$
$$3\ Cl^-(aq) + 2\ MnO_4^-(aq) + H_2O(\ell)$$

The copper half-cell (on the left in Figure 20.5) consists of copper metal that serves as one electrode and a solution containing copper(II) ions. The half-cell on the right uses a silver electrode and a solution containing silver(I) ions. Important features of this simple cell are as follows:

- *The two half-cells are connected with a **salt bridge** that allows cations and anions to move between the two half-cells.* The electrolyte chosen for the salt bridge should contain ions that will not react with chemical reagents in both half-cells. In the example in Figure 20.5, $NaNO_3$ is used.
- *In all electrochemical cells, the **anode** is the electrode at which oxidation occurs. The electrode at which reduction occurs is always the **cathode**.* (In Figure 20.5, the copper electrode is the anode, and the silver electrode is the cathode.)
- *A negative sign can be assigned to the anode in a voltaic cell, and the cathode is marked with a positive sign.* The chemical oxidation occurring at the anode, which produces electrons, gives it a negative charge.
- *In all electrochemical cells, electrons flow in the external circuit from the anode to the cathode.* Electric current in the external circuit of a voltaic cell consists of electrons moving from the negative to the positive electrode.

The chemistry occurring in the cell pictured in Figure 20.5 is summarized by the following half-reactions and net ionic equation:

Cathode, reduction:	$2\ Ag^+(aq) + 2\ e^- \rightarrow 2\ Ag(s)$
Anode, oxidation:	$Cu(s) \rightarrow Cu^{2+}(aq) + 2\ e^-$
Net ionic equation:	$Cu(s) + 2\ Ag^+(aq) \rightarrow Cu^{2+}(aq) + 2\ Ag(s)$

The salt bridge is required in a voltaic cell for the reaction to proceed. In the Cu/Ag^+ voltaic cell, anions move in the salt bridge toward the copper half-cell, and cations move toward the silver half-cell (Figure 20.5). As $Cu^{2+}(aq)$ ions are formed in the copper half-cell by oxidation of copper metal, negative ions enter that cell from the salt bridge (and positive ions leave the cell), so that the numbers of positive and negative charges in the half-cell compartment remain in balance. The silver half-cell originally contained $AgNO_3$, so, as $Ag^+(aq)$ ions are

● **Salt Bridges** A simple salt bridge can be made by adding gelatin to a solution of an electrolyte. Gelatin makes the contents semi-rigid so that the salt bridge is easier to handle. Porous glass disks and ion-permeable membranes are alternatives to a salt bridge. These devices allow ions to traverse from one half-cell to the other while keeping the two solutions from mixing.

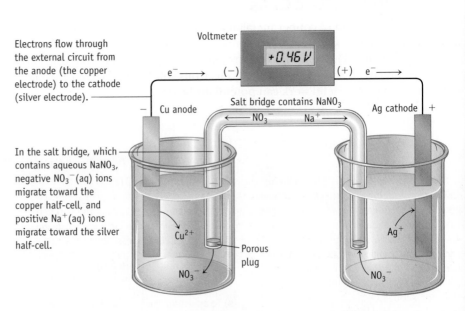

Net reaction: $Cu(s) + 2\ Ag^+(aq) \longrightarrow Cu^{2+}(aq) + 2\ Ag(s)$

FIGURE 20.5 A voltaic cell using $Cu(s)\,|\,Cu^{2+}(aq)$ and $Ag(s)\,|\,Ag^+(aq)$ half-cells. The cell is set up using 1.0 M $Cu(NO_3)_2(aq)$ and 1.0 M $AgNO_3(aq)$ solutions. Under these conditions, the cell will generate 0.46 volts at 25 °C.

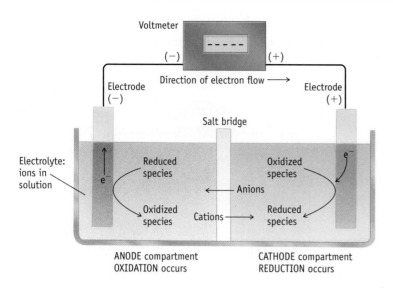

Voltmeter

Direction of electron flow ⟶

Electrode (−)   Electrode (+)

Salt bridge

Electrolyte: ions in solution

Reduced species

Oxidized species

⟵ Anions

Oxidized species

Cations ⟶

Reduced species

ANODE compartment
OXIDATION occurs

CATHODE compartment
REDUCTION occurs

FIGURE 20.6 Summary of terms used in a voltaic cell. Electrons move from the anode, the site of oxidation, through the external circuit to the cathode, the site of reduction. Charge balance in each half-cell is achieved by migration of ions through the salt bridge. Negative ions move from the reduction half-cell to the oxidation half-cell and positive ions move in the opposite direction.

reduced to silver metal, negative ions (NO_3^-) move out of the half-cell into the salt bridge, and positive ions move into the cell. A complete circuit is required for current to flow. If the salt bridge is removed, reactions at the electrodes will cease.

In Figure 20.5, the electrodes are connected by wires to a voltmeter. In an alternative setup, the connections might be to a light bulb or other device that uses electricity. Electrons are produced by oxidation of copper, and $Cu^{2+}(aq)$ ions enter the solution. The electrons traverse the external circuit to the silver electrode, where they reduce $Ag^+(aq)$ ions to silver metal. To balance the extent of oxidation and reduction, two $Ag^+(aq)$ ions are reduced for every $Cu^{2+}(aq)$ ion formed. The main features of this and of all other voltaic cells are summarized in Figure 20.6.

EXAMPLE 20.4   Electrochemical Cells

Problem Describe how to set up a voltaic cell to generate an electric current using the reaction

$$Fe(s) + Cu^{2+}(aq) \rightarrow Cu(s) + Fe^{2+}(aq)$$

Which electrode is the anode, and which is the cathode? In which direction do electrons flow in the external circuit? In which direction do the positive and negative ions flow in the salt bridge? Write equations for the half-reactions that occur at each electrode.

What Do You Know? You are told the reaction proceeds in the direction written. You also know that the half-reaction occurring in one half-cell will involve an iron electrode and a solution of an iron(II) salt such as $Fe(NO_3)_2$. The other half-cell contains a copper electrode and a soluble copper(II) salt such as $Cu(NO_3)_2$.

Strategy First, identify the two different half-cells that make up the cell. These two half-cells are linked together with a salt bridge and an external circuit, as diagrammed in Figure 20.5. The description of the cell (anode, cathode), its chemistry (oxidizing and reducing agents, substances oxidized and reduced), and the movement of electrons in the external circuit and ions through the salt bridge will be similar to the features of the Cu/Cu^{2+} and Ag^+/Ag voltaic cell discussed in the text.

Solution This voltaic cell is similar to the one diagrammed in Figure 20.5. Here we assume the two half-cells are linked with a salt bridge containing KNO_3 as the electrolyte.

Iron is oxidized, so the iron electrode is the anode:

Oxidation, anode: $Fe(s) \rightarrow Fe^{2+}(aq) + 2\ e^-$

Because copper(II) ions are reduced, the copper electrode is the cathode. The cathodic half-reaction is

Reduction, cathode: $Cu^{2+}(aq) + 2\ e^- \rightarrow Cu(s)$

In the external circuit, electrons flow from the iron electrode (anode) to the copper electrode (cathode). In the salt bridge, negative ions flow toward the iron/iron(II) half-cell, and positive ions flow in the opposite direction.

Think about Your Answer A good strategy is to focus on the movement of the negative species in the cell (electron flow in the external circuit and anion flow in the salt bridge). These species always move in a circular fashion: electrons from anode to cathode, and anions in the salt bridge in the opposite direction. If you establish which reactant is oxidized (provides electrons), you then know which electrode is the anode, in which direction electrons move in the external circuit, and in which direction anions flow in the salt bridge. (That said, don't ignore the fact that cations flow in the opposite direction to the anions in the salt bridge.)

Check Your Understanding

Describe how to set up a voltaic cell using the following half-reactions:

Reduction half-reaction: $Ag^+(aq) + e^- \rightarrow Ag(s)$

Oxidation half-reaction: $Ni(s) \rightarrow Ni^{2+}(aq) + 2\ e^-$

Which is the anode, and which is the cathode? What is the overall cell reaction? What is the direction of electron flow in an external wire connecting the two electrodes? Describe the ion flow in a salt bridge (with $NaNO_3$) connecting the cell compartments.

Voltaic Cells with Inert Electrodes

In the half-cells described so far, the metal used as an electrode is also a reactant or a product in the redox reaction. Not all half-reactions involve a metal as a reactant or product, however. With the exception of carbon in the form of graphite, most nonmetals are unsuitable as electrode materials because they do not conduct electricity. It is not possible to make an electrode from a gas, a liquid (except mercury), or a solution. Ionic solids do not make satisfactory electrodes because the ions are locked tightly in a crystal lattice, and these materials do not conduct electricity.

In situations where reactants and products cannot serve as the electrode material, an inert or chemically unreactive electrode must be used. Such electrodes are made of materials that conduct an electric current but that are neither oxidized nor reduced in the cell.

Consider constructing a voltaic cell to accommodate the following product-favored reaction:

$$2\ Fe^{3+}(aq) + H_2(g) \rightarrow 2\ Fe^{2+}(aq) + 2\ H^+(aq)$$

Reduction half-reaction: $Fe^{3+}(aq) + e^- \rightarrow Fe^{2+}(aq)$

Oxidation half-reaction: $H_2(g) \rightarrow 2\ H^+(aq) + 2\ e^-$

Neither the reactants nor the products can be used as an electrode material. Therefore, the two half-cells are set up so that the reactants and products come in contact with an electrode where they can accept or give up electrons. Graphite is a commonly used electrode material: It is a conductor of electricity, and it is inexpensive (essential in commercial cells) and not readily oxidized under the conditions encountered in most cells. Mercury is used in certain types of cells. Platinum and gold are also commonly used because both are chemically inert under most circumstances, but they are generally too costly for commercial cells.

The *hydrogen electrode* is particularly important in the field of electrochemistry because it is used as a reference in assigning cell voltages (see Section 20.4) (Figure 20.7). The electrode material is platinum, chosen because hydrogen adsorbs on the metal's surface. In this half-cell's operation, hydrogen is bubbled over the electrode, and a large surface area maximizes the contact of the gas and the electrode. The aqueous solution contains $H^+(aq)$. The half-reactions involving $H^+(aq)$ and $H_2(g)$

$$2\ H^+(aq) + 2\ e^- \rightarrow H_2(g) \quad \text{or} \quad H_2(g) \rightarrow 2\ H^+(aq) + 2\ e^-$$

take place at the electrode surface, and the electrons involved in the reaction are conducted to or from the reaction site by the metal electrode.

A half-cell using the reduction of $Fe^{3+}(aq)$ to $Fe^{2+}(aq)$ can also be set up with a platinum electrode. In this case, the solution surrounding the electrode contains iron ions in two different oxidation states. Transfer of electrons to or from the reactant occurs at the electrode surface.

A voltaic cell involving the reduction of $Fe^{3+}(aq, 1.0\ M)$ to $Fe^{2+}(aq, 1.0\ M)$ with H_2 gas is illustrated in Figure 20.8. In this cell, the hydrogen electrode is the anode (H_2 is oxidized to H^+), and the iron-containing compartment is the cathode (Fe^{3+} is reduced to Fe^{2+}). The cell produces 0.77 V.

Electrochemical Cell Notations

Chemists often use a shorthand notation to simplify cell descriptions. For example, the cell involving the reduction of silver ion with copper metal is written as

$$Cu(s)\,|\,Cu^{2+}(aq,\ 1.0\ M)\,||\,Ag^+(aq,\ 1.0\ M)\,|\,Ag(s)$$

$$\underbrace{\qquad\qquad}_{\text{Anode information}} \qquad \underbrace{\qquad\qquad}_{\text{Cathode information}}$$

© Cengage Learning/Charles D. Winters

FIGURE 20.7 Hydrogen electrode. Hydrogen gas is bubbled over a platinum electrode in a solution containing H^+ ions. Such electrodes function best if they have a large surface area. Often, platinum wires are woven into a gauze, or the metal surface is roughened either by abrasion or by chemical treatment to increase the surface area.

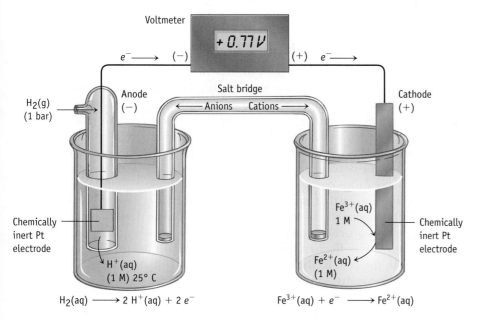

FIGURE 20.8 A voltaic cell with a hydrogen electrode. This cell has $Fe^{2+}(aq, 1.0\ M)$ and $Fe^{3+}(aq, 1.0\ M)$ in the cathode compartment and $H_2(g)$ and $H^+(aq, 1.0\ M)$ in the anode compartment. At 25 °C, the cell generates 0.77 V. (The hydrogen electrode in the anode compartment in this illustration is a simplified schematic. See Figure 20.7 for a photograph of a commercial hydrogen electrode.)

The cell using H_2 gas to reduce Fe^{3+} ions is written as

$$Pt \,|\, H_2(P = 1 \text{ bar}) \,|\, H^+(aq, 1.0 \text{ M}) \,||\, Fe^{3+}(aq, 1.0 \text{ M}), Fe^{2+}(aq, 1.0 \text{ M}) \,|\, Pt$$

Anode information   Cathode information

By convention, on the left we write the anode and information with respect to the solution with which it is in contact. A single vertical line (|) indicates a phase boundary, and double vertical lines (||) indicate a salt bridge.

REVIEW & CHECK FOR SECTION 20.2

Answer the questions based on the cell below in which the following reaction occurs:

$$Ni^{2+}(aq) + Cd(s) \rightarrow Ni(s) + Cd^{2+}(aq)$$

1. Electron transfer:

   (a) Electrons transfer from Ni to Cd   (b) Electrons transfer from Cd to Ni

2. Electrodes:

   (a) Cd is the anode and is negative   (c) Cd is the cathode and is negative

   (b) Cd is the anode and is positive   (d) Cd is the cathode and is positive

3. Salt bridge (which contains K^+ and NO_3^- ions):

   (a) NO_3^- ions move from the Cd half-cell to the Ni half-cell and K^+ ions move from the Ni half-cell to the Cd half-cell.

   (b) NO_3^- ions move from the Ni half-cell to the Cd half-cell and K^+ ions move from the Cd half-cell to the Ni half-cell.

20.3 Commercial Voltaic Cells

The cells described so far are unlikely to have practical use. They are neither compact nor robust, high priorities for most applications. In most situations, it is also important that the cell produce a constant voltage, but a problem with the cells described so far is that the voltage produced varies as the concentrations of ions in solution change (see Section 20.5). Also, the current production is low. Attempting to draw a large current results in a drop in voltage because the ion concentrations near the cathode become depleted if current is drawn too quickly. Furthermore, the negative anode charge drops owing to a build up of cations, the oxidation product.

The electrical work that can be drawn from a voltaic cell depends on the quantity of reagents consumed. A voltaic cell must have a large mass of reactants to produce current over a prolonged period. In addition, a voltaic cell that can be recharged is attractive. Recharging a cell means returning the reagents to their original sites in the cell. In the cells described so far, the movement of ions in the cell mixes the reagents, and they cannot be "unmixed" after the cell has been running.

Batteries can be classified as primary and secondary. **Primary batteries** cannot be returned to their original state by recharging, so when the reactants are

FIGURE 20.9 Some commercial voltaic cells. Commercial voltaic cells provide energy for a wide range of devices, come in a myriad of sizes and shapes, and produce different voltages. Some are rechargeable; others are discarded after use. One might think that there is nothing further to learn about batteries, but this is not true. Research on these devices is actively pursued in the chemical community.

consumed, the battery is "dead" and must be discarded. **Secondary batteries** are often called **storage batteries** or **rechargeable batteries**. The reactions in these batteries can be reversed, so the batteries can be recharged.

Years of development have led to many different commercial voltaic cells to meet specific needs (Figure 20.9), and several common ones are described below. All adhere to the principles that have been developed in earlier discussions.

Primary Batteries: Dry Cells and Alkaline Batteries

If you buy an inexpensive flashlight battery or dry cell battery, it might be a modern version of a voltaic cell invented by George LeClanché in 1866 (Figure 20.10). Zinc serves as the anode, and the cathode is a graphite rod placed down the center of the device. These cells are often called "dry cells" because there is no visible liquid phase. However, the cell contains a moist paste of NH_4Cl, $ZnCl_2$, and MnO_2, so water is present. The moisture is necessary because the ions present must be able to migrate from one electrode to the other. The cell generates a potential of 1.5 V using the following half-reactions:

Cathode, reduction: $2\ NH_4^+(aq) + 2\ e^- \rightarrow 2\ NH_3(g) + H_2(g)$

Anode, oxidation: $Zn(s) \rightarrow Zn^{2+}(aq) + 2\ e^-$

The products at the cathode are gases, which could build up pressure in the cell and cause it to rupture. The problem is avoided, however, by two other reactions that take place in the cell. Ammonia molecules bind to Zn^{2+} ions, and hydrogen gas is oxidized by MnO_2 to water.

$$Zn^{2+}(aq) + 2\ NH_3(g) + 2\ Cl^-(aq) \rightarrow Zn(NH_3)_2Cl_2(s)$$

$$2\ MnO_2(s) + H_2(g) \rightarrow Mn_2O_3(s) + H_2O(\ell)$$

Zinc-carbon dry cells were widely used because of their low cost, but they have several disadvantages. If current is drawn from the battery rapidly, the gaseous products cannot be consumed rapidly enough, so the cell resistance rises, and the voltage drops. In addition, the zinc electrode and ammonium ions are in contact in the cell, and these chemicals react slowly. Recall that zinc reacts with acid to form hydrogen. The ammonium ion, $NH_4^+(aq)$, is a weak Brønsted acid and reacts slowly with zinc. Because of this reaction, these voltaic cells cannot be stored indefinitely, a fact you may have learned from experience. When the zinc outer shell deteriorates, the battery can leak acid and perhaps damage the appliance in which it is contained.

At the present time, you are more likely to use **alkaline batteries** in your camera or flashlight because they generate current up to 50% longer than a dry cell of the

● **Batteries** The word *battery* has become part of our common language, designating any self-contained device that generates an electric current. The term battery has a more precise scientific meaning, however. It refers to a collection of two or more voltaic cells. For example, the 12-volt battery used in automobiles is made up of six voltaic cells. Each voltaic cell develops a voltage of 2 volts. Six cells connected in series produce 12 volts.

FIGURE 20.10 The common dry cell battery. Sometimes called the *zinc-carbon battery.*

same size. The chemistry of alkaline cells is quite similar to that in a zinc-carbon dry cell, except that the material inside the cell is basic (alkaline). Alkaline cells use the oxidation of zinc and the reduction of MnO_2 to generate a current, but NaOH or KOH is used in the cell instead of the acidic salt NH_4Cl.

Cathode, reduction:	$2\ MnO_2(s) + H_2O(\ell) + 2\ e^- \rightarrow Mn_2O_3(s) + 2\ OH^-(aq)$
Anode, oxidation:	$Zn(s) + 2\ OH^-(aq) \rightarrow ZnO(s) + H_2O(\ell) + 2\ e^-$

Alkaline cells, which produce 1.54 V (approximately the same voltage as the zinc-carbon dry cell), have the further advantage that the cell potential does not decline under high current loads because no gases are formed.

Prior to 2000, mercury-containing batteries were widely used in calculators, cameras, watches, heart pacemakers, and other devices. However, these small batteries were banned in the United States in the 1990s because of environmental problems. They have been replaced by several other types of batteries, such as silver oxide batteries and zinc-oxygen batteries. Both operate under alkaline conditions, and both have zinc anodes. In the silver oxide battery, which produces a voltage of about 1.5 V, the cell reactions are

Cathode, reduction:	$Ag_2O(s) + H_2O(\ell) + 2\ e^- \rightarrow 2\ Ag(s) + 2\ OH^-(aq)$
Anode, oxidation:	$Zn(s) + 2\ OH^-(aq) \rightarrow ZnO(s) + H_2O(\ell) + 2\ e^-$

The zinc-oxygen battery, which produces about 1.15–1.35 V, is unique in that atmospheric oxygen and not a metal oxide is the oxidizing agent.

Cathode, reduction:	$O_2(g) + 2\ H_2O(\ell) + 4\ e^- \rightarrow 4\ OH^-(aq)$
Anode, oxidation:	$Zn(s) + 2\ OH^-(aq) \rightarrow ZnO(s) + H_2O(\ell) + 2\ e^-$

These batteries are used in hearing aids, pagers, and medical devices.

Secondary or Rechargeable Batteries

When a zinc-carbon dry cell or an alkaline cell ceases to produce a usable electric current, it is discarded. In contrast, some types of cells can be recharged, often hundreds of times. Recharging requires applying an electric current from an external source to restore the cell to its original state. There are a number of well known types of secondary batteries in common use.

Lead Storage Battery

An automobile battery—the lead storage battery—is probably the best-known rechargeable battery (Figure 20.11). The 12-V version of this battery contains six voltaic cells, each generating about 2 V. The lead storage battery can produce a large initial current, an essential feature when starting an automobile engine.

The anode of a lead storage battery is metallic lead. The cathode is also made of lead, but it is covered with a layer of compressed, insoluble lead(IV) oxide, PbO_2. The electrodes, arranged alternately in a stack and separated by thin fiberglass sheets, are immersed in aqueous sulfuric acid. When the cell supplies electrical energy, the lead anode is oxidized to lead(II) sulfate, an insoluble substance that adheres to the electrode surface. The two electrons produced per lead atom move through the external circuit to the cathode, where PbO_2 is reduced to Pb^{2+} ions that, in the presence of H_2SO_4, also form lead(II) sulfate.

Anode

Cathode

Positive plates: lead grids filled with PbO_2

Negative plates: lead grids filled with spongy lead

FIGURE 20.11 Lead storage battery, a secondary or rechargeable battery. Each cell of the battery generates 2 V.

Cathode, reduction:	$PbO_2(s) + 4\ H^+(aq) + SO_4^{2-}(aq) + 2\ e^- \rightarrow PbSO_4(s) + 2\ H_2O(\ell)$
Anode, oxidation:	$Pb(s) + SO_4^{2-}(aq) \rightarrow PbSO_4(s) + 2\ e^-$
Net ionic equation:	$Pb(s) + PbO_2(s) + 2\ H_2SO_4(aq) \rightarrow 2\ PbSO_4(s) + 2\ H_2O(\ell)$

When current is generated, sulfuric acid is consumed and water is formed. Because water is less dense than sulfuric acid, the density of the solution decreases during this process. Therefore, one way to determine whether a lead storage battery needs to be recharged is to measure the density of the solution.

A lead storage battery is recharged by supplying electrical energy. The $PbSO_4$ coating the surfaces of the electrodes is converted back to metallic lead and PbO_2, and sulfuric acid is regenerated. Recharging this battery is possible because the reactants and products remain attached to the electrode surface. The lifetime of a lead storage battery is limited, however, because, with time, the coatings of PbO_2 and $PbSO_4$ flake off of the surface and fall to the bottom of the battery case.

Scientists and engineers would like to find an alternative to lead storage batteries, especially for use in cars. Lead storage batteries have the disadvantage of being large and heavy. In addition, lead and its compounds are toxic and their disposal adds a further complication. Nevertheless, at this time, the advantages of lead storage batteries often outweigh their disadvantages.

Tesla Motors Roadster, an all-electric car. This limited edition sports car (cost is over $100,000) is powered by a rechargeable nickel-metal hydride battery that will last for over 200 miles of driving.

Nickel-Cadmium Battries

Nickel-cadmium ("Ni-cad") batteries, used in a variety of cordless appliances such as telephones, video camcorders, and cordless power tools, are lightweight and rechargeable. The chemistry of the cell is based on the oxidation of cadmium and the reduction of nickel(III) oxide under basic conditions. As with the lead storage battery, the reactants and products formed when producing a current are solids that adhere to the electrodes.

Cathode, reduction: $NiO(OH)(s) + H_2O(\ell) + e^- \rightarrow Ni(OH)_2(s) + OH^-(aq)$

Anode, oxidation: $Cd(s) + 2\ OH^-(aq) \rightarrow Cd(OH)_2(s) + 2\ e^-$

Ni-cad batteries produce a nearly constant voltage. However, their cost is relatively high, and there are restrictions on their disposal because cadmium compounds are toxic and present an environmental hazard.

Nickel-Metal Hydride

Rechargeable nickel-metal hydride batteries (NiMH) are now in common use. You may have them in your camera or portable music player. Their most important use, however, is in electric or hybrid cars.

In the nickel-metal hydride battery, electrons are generated when H atoms interact with OH^- ions at the metal alloy anode.

$$Alloy(H) + OH^- \rightarrow Alloy + H_2O + e^-$$

The reaction at the cathode is the same as in Ni-cad batteries.

$$NiO(OH) + H_2O + e^- \rightarrow Ni(OH)_2 + OH^-$$

The "alloy" in NiMH batteries is generally a mixture of a rare earth metal such as lanthanum, cerium, or neodymium and another metal such as nickel, cobalt, manganese or aluminum.

Lithium Batteries

As we introduced on page 894 (and in Chapter 13, page 582), much of the battery research now focuses on lithium batteries, and there are two types in common use: lithium-ion and a variant, lithium-ion polymer batteries. The chemistry of both is the same.

Cathode, reduction: $Li_{1-x}CoO_2(s) + x\ Li^+ + x\ e^- \rightarrow LiCoO_2(s)$

Anode, oxidation: $Li_xC_6(s) \rightarrow x\ Li^+ + x\ e^- + 6\ C(s)$

Lithium-ion polymer batteries are popular because they can be made in any shape and so fit into products such as Amazon's Kindle and Apple's portable

● **Be Alert: Children Can Ingest Lithium Batteries!** Very small lithium batteries are used in many devices such as toys, musical greeting cards, and appliances. Unfortunately, because they are small and shiny, children put them in their mouths and can swallow them. In 2010 the *New York Times* (June 1, 2010, page D5) reported that an increasing number of children have died from reactions induced by the battery's current when the battery was swallowed.

devices. They also deliver a higher current density than lithium-ion batteries and can be charged and discharged through many cycles.

Finally, an important reason for the development of lithium-based batteries is their light weight. Lithium has a much lower density (0.53 g/cm^3) than cadmium (8.69 g/cm^3), nickel (8.91 g/cm^3), or lead (11.34 g/cm^3). This is important not only in portable devices where people do not want to carry around heavy objects but also in the automobile industry. A lighter weight for a battery in a car results in more of the energy going into moving the rest of the car and less being used simply to transport the battery.

The importance of lithium-based batteries in our 21st-century economy cannot be overstated. Most of the current development and manufacture is being done in Japan, South Korea, and China, but much of the basic technology of lithium batteries was developed in the United States, and investment is increasing.

Fuel Cells

• **Energy for Automobiles** Energy available from systems that can be used to power an automobile.

Chemical System	W · h/kg* (1 W · h = 3600 J)
Lead-acid battery	18–56
Nickel-cadmium battery	33–70
Sodium-sulfur battery	80–140
Lithium polymer battery	150
Gasoline-air combustion engine	12,200

* watt-hour/kilogram

An advantage of voltaic cells is that they are small and portable, but their size is also a limitation. The amount of electric current produced is limited by the quantity of reagents contained in the cell. When one of the reactants is completely consumed, the cell will no longer generate a current. Fuel cells avoid this limitation because the reactants (fuel and oxidant) can be supplied continuously to the cell from an external reservoir.

Although the first fuel cells were first constructed more than 150 years ago, little was done to develop this technology until the space program rekindled interest in these devices. Hydrogen-oxygen fuel cells have been used in NASA's Gemini, Apollo, and Space Shuttle programs. Not only are they lightweight and efficient, but they also have the added benefit that they generate drinking water for the ship's crew.

In a hydrogen-oxygen fuel cell (Figure 20.12), hydrogen is pumped onto the anode of the cell, and O$_2$ (or air) is directed to the cathode where the following reactions occur:

Cathode, reduction: $\quad O_2(g) + 2 H_2O(\ell) + 4 e^- \rightarrow 4 OH^-(aq)$

Anode, oxidation: $\quad H_2(g) \rightarrow 2 H^+(aq) + 2 e^-$

The two halves of the cell are separated by a special material called a proton exchange membrane (PEM). Protons, H$^+$(aq), formed at the anode traverse the PEM and react with the hydroxide ions produced at the cathode, forming water. The net reaction in the cell is thus the formation of water from H$_2$ and O$_2$. Cells currently in use run at temperatures of 70–140 °C and produce about 0.9 V.

Hydrogen-oxygen fuel cells operate at 40–60% efficiency and meet most of the requirements for use in automobiles: They operate at room temperature or slightly

FIGURE 20.12 Fuel cell design. Hydrogen gas is oxidized to H$^+$(aq) at the anode surface. On the other side of the proton exchange membrane (PEM), oxygen gas is reduced to OH$^-$(aq). The H$^+$(aq) ions travel through the PEM and combine with OH$^-$(aq), forming water.

above, start rapidly, and develop a high current density. However, cost is a serious problem as is the absence of a carbon-free way of making hydrogen. These faults, and the cost and difficulty of building a nationwide infrastructure for distributing hydrogen, remain major stumbling blocks that would need to be overcome before hydrogen fuel cells could be adopted for widespread use in automobiles.

REVIEW & CHECK FOR SECTION 20.3

1. The following half-reaction occurs in an automobile lead-acid battery:

$$PbO_2(s) + 4\ H^+(aq) + SO_4^{2-}(aq) + 2\ e^- \rightarrow PbSO_4(s) + 2\ H_2O(\ell)$$

    (a) Lead(IV) oxide is oxidized.   (c) Hydrogen ions are oxidized.

    (b) Lead(IV) oxide is reduced.   (d) Hydrogen ions are reduced.

2. You can determine if a lead-based battery is no longer working by checking the density of the solution in the battery. If the density is low, then the battery is "dead." This works because

    (a) PbO_2 is consumed.   (c) Water evaporates.

    (b) Sulfuric acid is consumed.   (d) Lead is consumed.

20.4 Standard Electrochemical Potentials

Different electrochemical cells produce different potentials: 1.5 V for alkaline cells, about 3.7 V for a lithium-ion battery, and about 2.0 V for the individual cells in a lead storage battery. In this section, we want to identify some of the factors affecting cell voltages and develop ways to calculate the expected potential of a cell based on the chemistry in the cell and the conditions used.

Electromotive Force

Electrons generated at the anode of an electrochemical cell move through the external circuit toward the cathode, and the force needed to move the electrons arises from a difference in the potential energy of electrons at the two electrodes. This difference in potential energy per electrical charge is called the **electromotive force** or **emf**, for which the literal meaning is "force causing electrons to move." Emf has units of volts (V); 1 volt is the potential difference needed to impart one joule of energy to an electric charge of one coulomb ($1\ J = 1\ V \times 1\ C$). *One coulomb is the quantity of charge that passes a point in an electric circuit when a current of 1 ampere flows for 1 second ($1\ C = 1\ A \times 1\ s$).*

- **Electrochemical Units**
- The coulomb (abbreviated C) is the standard (SI) unit of electrical charge (Appendix C, Table 6).
- 1 joule = 1 volt × 1 coulomb.
- 1 coulomb = 1 ampere × 1 second.

Measuring Standard Potentials

Imagine you planned to study cell voltages in a laboratory with two objectives: (1) to understand the factors that affect these values and (2) to be able to predict the potential of a voltaic cell. You might construct a number of different half-cells, link them together in various combinations to form voltaic cells (as in Figure 20.13), and measure the cell potentials. After a few experiments, it would become apparent that cell potentials depend on a number of factors: the half-cells used (i.e., the reaction in each half-cell and the overall or net reaction in the cell), the concentrations of reactants and products in solution, the pressure of gaseous reactants, and the temperature.

To simplify matters for now, let us consider only cell potentials measured under **standard conditions**:

- Reactants and products are present in their standard states.
- Solutes in aqueous solution have a concentration of 1.0 M.
- Gaseous reactants or products have a pressure of 1.0 bar.

A cell potential measured under these conditions is called the **standard potential** and is denoted by E°_{cell}. Unless otherwise specified, all values of E°_{cell} refer to measurements at 298 K (25 °C).

FIGURE 20.13 A voltaic cell using Zn | Zn²⁺(aq, 1.0 M) and H₂ | H⁺(aq, 1.0 M) half-cells.

- When zinc and acid are combined in an electrochemical cell, the cell generates a potential of 0.76 V under standard conditions.
- The electrode in the H₂ | H⁺(aq, 1.0 M) half-cell is the cathode, and the Zn electrode is the anode.
- Electrons flow in the external circuit to the hydrogen half-cell from the zinc half-cell.
- The positive sign of the measured voltage indicates that the hydrogen electrode is the cathode or positive electrode.

© Cengage Learning/Charles D. Winters

$$Zn(s) \longrightarrow Zn^{2+}(aq) + 2\ e^-$$

$$2\ H^+(aq) + 2\ e^- \longrightarrow H_2(g)$$

Net reaction: $Zn(s) + 2\ H^+(aq) \longrightarrow H_2(g) + Zn^{2+}(aq)$

(a) The product-favored reaction of aqueous hydrogen ions with zinc produces H₂(g) and Zn²⁺ ions.

(b) A voltaic cell that makes use of the product-favored reduction of aqueous hydrogen ions by zinc.

Suppose you set up a number of standard half-cells and connect each in turn to a **standard hydrogen electrode (SHE)**. Your apparatus would look like the voltaic cell in Figure 20.13b. For now, we will concentrate on three aspects of this cell:

1. *The reaction that occurs.* The reaction occurring in the cell pictured in Figure 20.13 could be *either* the reduction of Zn²⁺ ions with H₂ gas

$$Zn^{2+}(aq) + H_2(g) \rightarrow Zn(s) + 2\ H^+(aq)$$

   Zn²⁺(aq) is the oxidizing agent, and H₂ is the reducing agent.
   Standard hydrogen electrode would be the anode (negative electrode).

   or the reduction of H⁺(aq) ions by Zn(s).

$$Zn(s) + 2\ H^+(aq) \rightarrow Zn^{2+}(aq) + H_2(g)$$

   Zn is the reducing agent, and H⁺(aq) is the oxidizing agent.
   Standard hydrogen electrode would be the cathode (positive electrode).

   The reaction that actually occurs is the one that is product-favored at equilibrium and thus is spontaneous under standard conditions. In this case we know the product-favored reaction is the reduction of H⁺ ions by zinc metal (Figure 20.13a).

2. *Direction of electron flow in the external circuit.* In a voltaic cell, electrons always flow from the anode (negative electrode) to the cathode (positive electrode). We can tell the direction of electron movement—and therefore which is the anode and which is the cathode—by placing a voltmeter in the circuit. A positive potential is observed if the voltmeter terminal with a plus sign (+) is connected to the positive electrode or cathode [and the terminal with the minus sign (−) is connected to the negative electrode or anode]. Connected in the opposite way (plus to minus and minus to plus), the voltmeter will indicate a negative potential.

3. *Cell potential.* In Figure 20.13, the voltmeter is hooked up with its positive terminal connected to the hydrogen half-cell, and a reading of +0.76 V is observed. The hydrogen electrode is thus the positive electrode or cathode, and the reactions occurring in this cell must be

Reduction, cathode:	$2\ H^+(aq) + 2\ e^- \rightarrow H_2(g)$
Oxidation, anode:	$Zn(s) \rightarrow Zn^{2+}(aq) + 2\ e^-$
Net cell reaction:	$Zn(s) + 2\ H^+(aq) \rightarrow Zn^{2+}(aq) + H_2(g)$

EMF, Cell Potential, and Voltage

Electromotive force (emf) and cell potential (E_{cell}) are often used synonymously, but the two are subtly different. E_{cell} is a measured quantity, so its value is affected by how the measurement is made. To understand this point, consider as an analogy water in a pipe under pressure. Water pressure can be viewed as analogous to emf; it represents a force that will cause water in the pipe to move. If we open a faucet, water will flow. Opening the faucet will, however, decrease the pressure in the system.

Emf is the potential difference when no current flows. To measure E_{cell}, a voltmeter is placed in the external circuit. Although voltmeters have high internal resistance to minimize current flow, a small current flows nonetheless. As a result, the value of E_{cell} will be slightly different than the emf.

Finally, there is a difference between a *potential* and a *voltage*. The voltage of a cell has a magnitude but no sign. In contrast, the potential of a half-reaction or a cell has a sign (+ or −) and a magnitude.

This is an important result. All of the species are present in the cell at standard conditions, so the reaction can, in principle, proceed in either direction. The product-favored reaction, however, proceeds from left to right as written. This shows us that, of the two reducing agents present, zinc is better than H_2, and H^+ ions are a better oxidizing agent than zinc ions.

The potential of +0.76 V measured for the oxidation of zinc with hydrogen ions also reflects the difference in potential energy of an electron at each electrode. From the direction of flow of electrons in the external circuit (Zn electrode → H_2 electrode), we conclude that the potential energy of an electron at the zinc electrode is higher than the potential energy of the electron at the hydrogen electrode.

Hundreds of electrochemical cells like that shown in Figure 20.13 can be set up, allowing us to determine the relative oxidizing or reducing ability of various chemical species and to determine the electrical potential generated by the reaction under standard conditions. A few results are given in Figure 20.14, where half-reactions are listed as reductions. That is, the chemical species on the left are oxidizing agents and are listed in descending oxidizing ability.

● **$E°$ Values** An extensive listing of $E°$ values is found in Appendix M, and still larger tables of data can be found in chemistry reference books. A common convention, used in Appendix M, lists standard reduction potentials in two groups, one for acid and neutral solutions and the other for basic solutions.

FIGURE 20.14 A potential ladder for reduction half-reactions.

- The position of a half-reaction on this potential ladder reflects the relative ability of the species at the left to act as an oxidizing agent.
- The higher the compound or ion is in the list, the better it is as an oxidizing agent. Conversely, the atoms or ions on the right are reducing agents. The lower they are in the list, the better they are as a reducing agent.
- The potential for each half-reaction is given with its standard reduction potential, $E°_{reduction}$.
- For more information see J. R. Runo and D. G. Peters, *Journal of Chemical Education*, Vol 70, p. 708, 1993.

Standard Reduction Potentials

By doing experiments such as that illustrated by Figure 20.13, we not only have a notion of the relative oxidizing and reducing abilities of various chemical species, but we can also rank them quantitatively.

If $E°_{cell}$ is a measure of the standard potential for the cell, then $E°_{cathode}$ and $E°_{anode}$ can be taken as measures of electrode potential. Because $E°_{cell}$ reflects the difference in electrode potentials, $E°_{cell}$ must be the difference between $E°_{cathode}$ and $E°_{anode}$.

● **Equation 20.1** Equation 20.1 is another example of calculating a change from $X_{final} - X_{initial}$. Electrons move to the cathode (the "final" state) from the anode (the "initial" state). Thus, Equation 20.1 resembles equations you have seen previously in this book (such as Equations 5.6 and 6.5).

$$E°_{cell} = E°_{cathode} - E°_{anode} \qquad (20.1)$$

Here, $E°_{cathode}$ and $E°_{anode}$ are the standard *reduction* potentials for the half-cell reactions that occur at the cathode and anode, respectively. Equation 20.1 is important for three reasons:

- If you have values for $E°_{cathode}$ and $E°_{anode}$, you can calculate the standard potential, $E°_{cell}$, for a voltaic cell.
- *When the calculated value of $E°_{cell}$ is positive, the reaction as written is predicted to be product-favored at equilibrium.* Conversely, if the calculated value of $E°_{cell}$ is negative, the reaction is predicted to be reactant-favored at equilibrium. Such a reaction will be product-favored at equilibrium in a direction opposite to the way it is written.
- If you measure $E°_{cell}$ and know either $E°_{cathode}$ or $E°_{anode}$, you can calculate the other value. This value would tell you how one half-cell reaction compares with others in terms of relative oxidizing or reducing ability.

But here is a dilemma. You cannot measure individual half-cell potentials. Just as values for $\Delta_f H°$ and $\Delta_f G°$ were established by choosing a reference point (the elements in their standard states), scientists have selected a reference point for half-reactions. We assign a potential of exactly 0 V to the half-reaction that occurs at a standard hydrogen electrode (SHE).

$$2\ H^+(aq,\ 1\ M) + 2\ e^- \rightarrow H_2(g,\ 1\ bar)\ E° = 0.00\ V$$

With this standard, we can now determine $E°$ values for half-cells by measuring $E°_{cell}$ in experiments such as those described in Figures 20.8 and 20.13, where one of the electrodes is the standard hydrogen electrode. We can then quantify the information with reduction potential tables such as Figure 20.14 and use these values to make predictions about $E°_{cell}$ for new voltaic cells.

Tables of Standard Reduction Potentials

The experimental approach just described leads to lists of $E°$ values such as seen in Figure 20.14, Table 20.1, and Appendix M. Let us list some important points concerning these tables and then illustrate them in the discussion and examples that follow.

1. The half-reactions are written as "oxidized form + electrons → reduced form." The species on the left side of the reaction arrow is an oxidizing agent, and the species on the right side of the reaction arrow is a reducing agent. Therefore, *all potentials are for reduction reactions*, and the potentials (in volts vs. SHE) are called *standard reduction potentials*.
2. The more positive the value of $E°$ for the reactions in Figure 20.14, Table 20.1, and similar tables, the better the oxidizing ability of the ion or compound on the left side of the reaction. This means $F_2(g)$ is the best oxidizing agent in the table. Lithium ion at the lower-left corner of Table 20.1 is the poorest oxidizing agent because its $E°$ value is the most negative.
3. The more negative the value of the reduction potential, $E°$, the less likely the half-reaction will occur as a reduction, and the more likely the reverse

half-reaction will occur (as an oxidation). Thus, Li(s) is the strongest reducing agent in the table, and F^- is the weakest reducing agent. The reducing agents in the table (the ions, elements, and compounds at the right) increase in strength from the top to the bottom.

4. The reaction between any substance on the left in this table (an oxidizing agent) with any substance *lower* than it on the right (a reducing agent) is product-favored at equilibrium. This has been called the *northwest–southeast rule*.

Table 20.1 Standard Reduction Potentials in Aqueous Solution at 25 °C*

Reduction Half-Reaction		$E°$ (V)
$F_2(g) + 2 e^-$	$\rightarrow 2 F^-(aq)$	+2.87
$H_2O_2(aq) + 2 H^+(aq) + 2 e^-$	$\rightarrow 2 H_2O(\ell)$	+1.77
$PbO_2(s) + SO_4^{2-}(aq) + 4 H^+(aq) + 2 e^-$	$\rightarrow PbSO_4(s) + 2 H_2O(\ell)$	+1.685
$MnO_4^-(aq) + 8 H^+(aq) + 5 e^-$	$\rightarrow Mn^{2+}(aq) + 4 H_2O(\ell)$	+1.51
$Au^{3+}(aq) + 3 e^-$	$\rightarrow Au(s)$	+1.50
$Cl_2(g) + 2 e^-$	$\rightarrow 2 Cl^-(aq)$	+1.36
$Cr_2O_7^{2-}(aq) + 14 H^+(aq) + 6 e^-$	$\rightarrow 2 Cr^{3+}(aq) + 7 H_2O(\ell)$	+1.33
$O_2(g) + 4 H^+(aq) + 4 e^-$	$\rightarrow 2 H_2O(\ell)$	+1.229
$Br_2(\ell) + 2 e^-$	$\rightarrow 2 Br^-(aq)$	+1.08
$NO_3^-(aq) + 4 H^+(aq) + 3 e^-$	$\rightarrow NO(g) + 2 H_2O(\ell)$	+0.96
$OCl^-(aq) + H_2O(\ell) + 2 e^-$	$\rightarrow Cl^-(aq) + 2 OH^-(aq)$	+0.89
$Hg^{2+}(aq) + 2 e^-$	$\rightarrow Hg(\ell)$	+0.855
$Ag^+(aq) + e^-$	$\rightarrow Ag(s)$	+0.799
$Hg_2^{2+}(aq) + 2 e^-$	$\rightarrow 2 Hg(\ell)$	+0.789
$Fe^{3+}(aq) + e^-$	$\rightarrow Fe^{2+}(aq)$	+0.771
$I_2(s) + 2 e^-$	$\rightarrow 2 I^-(aq)$	+0.535
$O_2(g) + 2 H_2O(\ell) + 4 e^-$	$\rightarrow 4 OH^-(aq)$	+0.40
$Cu^{2+}(aq) + 2 e^-$	$\rightarrow Cu(s)$	+0.337
$Sn^{4+}(aq) + 2 e^-$	$\rightarrow Sn^{2+}(aq)$	+0.15
$2 H^+(aq) + 2 e^-$	$\rightarrow H_2(g)$	0.00
$Sn^{2+}(aq) + 2 e^-$	$\rightarrow Sn(s)$	−0.14
$Ni^{2+}(aq) + 2 e^-$	$\rightarrow Ni(s)$	−0.25
$V^{3+}(aq) + e^-$	$\rightarrow V^{2+}(aq)$	−0.255
$PbSO_4(s) + 2 e^-$	$\rightarrow Pb(s) + SO_4^{2-}(aq)$	−0.356
$Cd^{2+}(aq) + 2 e^-$	$\rightarrow Cd(s)$	−0.40
$Fe^{2+}(aq) + 2 e^-$	$\rightarrow Fe(s)$	−0.44
$Zn^{2+}(aq) + 2 e^-$	$\rightarrow Zn(s)$	−0.763
$2 H_2O(\ell) + 2 e^-$	$\rightarrow H_2(g) + 2 OH^-(aq)$	−0.8277
$Al^{3+}(aq) + 3 e^-$	$\rightarrow Al(s)$	−1.66
$Mg^{2+}(aq) + 2 e^-$	$\rightarrow Mg(s)$	−2.37
$Na^+(aq) + e^-$	$\rightarrow Na(s)$	−2.714
$K^+(aq) + e^-$	$\rightarrow K(s)$	−2.925
$Li^+(aq) + e^-$	$\rightarrow Li(s)$	−3.045

Increasing strength of reducing agents (arrow indicating direction down the table)

* In volts (V) versus the standard hydrogen electrode.

Product-favored reactions will always involve a reducing agent that is "southeast" of the proposed oxidizing agent.

Reduction Half-Reaction

$$I_2(s) + 2\ e^- \longrightarrow 2\ I^-(aq)$$
$$Cu^{2+}(aq) + 2\ e^- \longrightarrow Cu(s)$$
$$2\ H^+(aq) + 2\ e^- \longrightarrow H_2(g)$$
$$Fe^{2+}(aq) + 2\ e^- \longrightarrow Fe(s)$$
$$Zn^{2+}(aq) + 2\ e^- \longrightarrow Zn(s)$$

The northwest–southeast rule: The reducing agent always lies to the southeast of the oxidizing agent in a product-favored reaction.

● **Northwest–Southeast Rule** This guideline is a reflection of the idea of moving down a potential energy "ladder" in a product-favored reaction.

For example, Zn can reduce Fe^{2+}, H^+, Cu^{2+}, and I_2, but, of the species on this list, Cu can reduce only I_2.

5. The algebraic sign of the half-reaction reduction potential is the sign of the electrode when it is attached to the H_2/H^+ standard cell (see Figures 20.8 and 20.13).

6. Electrochemical potentials depend on the nature of the reactants and products and their concentrations, not on the quantities of material used. Therefore, changing the stoichiometric coefficients for a half-reaction does not change the value of $E°$. For example, the reduction of Fe^{3+} has an $E°$ of $+0.771$ V, whether the reaction is written as

● **Changing Stoichiometric Coefficients** The volt is defined as "energy/charge" (V = J/C). Multiplying a reaction by some number causes both the energy and the charge to be multiplied by that number. Thus, the ratio "energy/charge = volt" does not change.

$$Fe^{3+}(aq, 1\ M) + e^- \rightarrow Fe^{2+}(aq, 1\ M) \qquad E° = +0.771\ V$$

or as

$$2\ Fe^{3+}(aq, 1\ M) + 2\ e^- \rightarrow 2\ Fe^{2+}(aq, 1\ M) \qquad E° = +0.771\ V$$

Using Tables of Standard Reduction Potentials

Tables or "ladders" of standard reduction potentials are very useful. They allow you to predict the potential of a new voltaic cell, provide information that can be used to balance redox equations, and help predict which redox reactions are product-favored.

Calculating Standard Cell Potentials, $E°_{cell}$

The standard reduction potentials for half-reactions were obtained by measuring cell potentials. It makes sense, therefore, that these values can be combined to give the potential of some new cell.

The net reaction occurring in a voltaic cell using silver and copper half-cells is

$$2\ Ag^+(aq) + Cu(s) \rightarrow 2\ Ag(s) + Cu^{2+}(aq)$$

The silver electrode is the cathode, and the copper electrode is the anode. We know this because silver ion is reduced (to silver metal) and copper metal is oxidized (to Cu^{2+} ions). (Recall that oxidations always occur at the anode and reductions at the cathode.) Also notice that the $Cu^{2+}|Cu$ half-reaction is "southeast" of the $Ag^+|Ag$ half-reaction in the potential ladder (Figure 20.14 and Table 20.1).

$$E°_{cathode} = +0.799\ V \qquad Ag^+(aq) + e^- \longrightarrow Ag(s)$$

"Distance" from $E°_{cathode}$ to $E°_{anode}$ is 0.799 V − 0.337 V = 0.462 V.

Cu is "southeast" of Ag^+

$$E°_{anode} = +0.337\ V \qquad Cu^{2+}(aq) + 2\ e^- \longrightarrow Cu(s)$$

The potential for the voltaic cell is the difference between the standard reduction potentials for the two half-reactions.

$$E°_{cell} = E°_{cathode} - E°_{anode}$$

$$E°_{cell} = (+0.799\ V) - (+0.337\ V)$$

$$E°_{cell} = +0.462\ V$$

Notice that the value of $E°_{cell}$ is related to the "distance" between the cathode and anode reactions on the potential ladder. The products have a lower potential energy than the reactants, and the cell potential, $E°_{cell}$, has a positive value.

A positive potential calculated for the $Ag^+|Ag$ and $Cu^{2+}|Cu$ cell ($E°_{cell} = +0.462$ V) confirms that the reduction of silver ions in water with copper metal is product-favored at equilibrium (Figure 20.1). We might ask, however, about the value of $E°_{cell}$ if a reactant-favored equation had been selected. For example, what is $E°_{cell}$ for the reduction of copper(II) ions with silver metal?

Cathode, reduction:	$Cu^{2+}(aq) + 2\ e^- \rightarrow Cu(s)$
Anode, oxidation:	$2\ Ag(s) \rightarrow 2\ Ag^+(aq) + 2\ e^-$
Net ionic equation:	$2\ Ag(s) + Cu^{2+}(aq) \rightarrow 2\ Ag^+(aq) + Cu(s)$

Cell Voltage Calculation

$$E°_{cathode} = +0.337 \text{ V and } E°_{anode} = +0.799 \text{ V}$$

$$E°_{cell} = E°_{cathode} - E°_{anode} = (+0.337 \text{ V}) - (0.799 \text{ V})$$

$$E°_{cell} = -0.462 \text{ V}$$

The negative sign for $E°_{cell}$ indicates that the reaction as written is reactant-favored at equilibrium. The products of the reaction (Ag^+ and Cu) have a higher potential energy than the reactants (Ag and Cu^{2+}). For the indicated reaction to occur, a potential of at least 0.462 V would have to be imposed on the system by an external source of electricity (see Section 20.7).

Relative Strengths of Oxidizing and Reducing Agents

Five half-reactions, selected from Appendix M, are arranged from the half-reaction with the highest (most positive) $E°$ value to the one with the lowest (most negative) value.

$E°$, V		Reduction Half-Reaction
+1.36		$Cl_2(g) + 2\ e^- \longrightarrow 2\ Cl^-(aq)$
+0.80		$Ag^+(aq) + e^- \longrightarrow Ag(s)$
+0.00		$2\ H^+(aq) + 2\ e^- \longrightarrow H_2(g)$
−0.25		$Ni^{2+}(aq) + 2\ e^- \longrightarrow Ni(s)$
−0.76		$Zn^{2+}(aq) + 2\ e^- \longrightarrow Zn(s)$

(increasing strength as oxidizing agents ↑)

- The list on the left is headed by Cl_2, an element that is a strong oxidizing agent and thus is easily reduced. At the bottom of the list is $Zn^{2+}(aq)$, an ion not easily reduced and thus a poor oxidizing agent.
- On the right, the list is headed by $Cl^-(aq)$, an ion that can be oxidized to Cl_2 only with difficulty. It is a very poor reducing agent. At the bottom of the list is zinc metal, which is readily oxidized and is a good reducing agent.

By arranging these half-reactions based on $E°$ values, we have also arranged the chemical species on the two sides of the equation in order of their strengths as oxidizing or reducing agents. In this list, from strongest to weakest, the order is

$$\text{Oxidizing agents: } Cl_2 > Ag^+ > H^+ > Ni^{2+} > Zn^{2+}$$
strong ⟶ weak

$$\text{Reducing agents: } Zn > Ni > H_2 > Ag > Cl^-$$
strong ⟶ weak

Finally, notice that the value of $E°_{cell}$ is greater the farther apart the oxidizing and reducing agents are on the potential ladder. For example,

$$Zn(s) + Cl_2(g) \rightarrow Zn^{2+}(aq) + 2\ Cl^-(aq) \qquad E° = +2.12 \text{ V}$$

is more strongly product-favored than the reduction of hydrogen ions with nickel metal

$$Ni(s) + 2 H^+(aq) \rightarrow Ni^{2+}(aq) + H_2(g) \qquad E^\circ = +0.25 \text{ V}$$

EXAMPLE 20.5   Ranking Oxidizing and Reducing Agents

Problem Use the table of standard reduction potentials (Table 20.1) to do the following:

(a) Rank the halogens in order of their strength as oxidizing agents.

(b) Decide whether hydrogen peroxide (H_2O_2) in acid solution is a stronger oxidizing agent than Cl_2.

(c) Decide which of the halogens is capable of oxidizing gold metal to Au^{3+}(aq).

What Do You Know? A table of electrode potentials, such as Table 20.1 or Appendix M, contains the information needed to answer these questions.

Strategy The ability of a species on the left side of a reduction potential table to function as an oxidizing agent declines on descending the list (see points 2 and 3, pages 916–917).

Solution

(a) Ranking halogens according to oxidizing ability: The halogens (F_2, Cl_2, Br_2, and I_2) appear in the upper-left portion Table 20.1, with F_2 being highest, followed in order by the other three species. Their strengths as oxidizing agents are $F_2 > Cl_2 > Br_2 > I_2$. (The ability of bromine to oxidize iodide ions to molecular iodine is illustrated in Figure 20.15.)

(b) Comparing hydrogen peroxide and chlorine: H_2O_2 lies just below F_2 but well above Cl_2 in the potential ladder (Table 20.1). Thus, H_2O_2 is a weaker oxidizing agent than F_2 but a stronger one than Cl_2. (Note that the E° value for H_2O_2 refers to an acidic solution and standard conditions.)

(c) Which halogen will oxidize gold metal to gold(III) ions? The $Au^{3+} | Au$ half-reaction is listed below the $F_2 | F^-$ half-reaction and just above the $Cl_2 | Cl^-$ half-reaction. This tells us that, among the halogens, only F_2 is capable of oxidizing Au to Au^{3+} under standard conditions. That is, for the reaction of Au and F_2,

Oxidation, anode:	$2[Au(s) \rightarrow Au^{3+}(aq) + 3 \ e^-]$
Reduction, cathode:	$3[F_2(g) + 2 \ e^- \rightarrow 2 \ F^-(aq)]$
Net ionic equation:	$3 \ F_2(g) + 2 \ Au(s) \rightarrow 6 \ F^-(aq) + 2 \ Au^{3+}(aq)$

$$E^\circ{}_{cell} = E^\circ{}_{cathode} - E^\circ{}_{anode} = +2.87 \text{ V} - (+1.50 \text{ V}) = +1.37 \text{ V}$$

F_2 is a stronger oxidizing agent than Au^{3+}, so the reaction proceeds from left to right as written. (This is confirmed by a positive value of $E^\circ{}_{cell}$.) For the reaction of Cl_2 and Au, Table 20.1 shows us that Cl_2 is a weaker oxidizing agent than Au^{3+}, so the reaction would be expected to proceed in the opposite direction under standard conditions.

Oxidation, anode:	$2[Au(s) \rightarrow Au^{3+}(aq) + 3 \ e^-]$
Reduction, cathode:	$3[Cl_2(aq) + 2 \ e^- \rightarrow 2 \ Cl^-(aq)]$
Net ionic equation:	$3 \ Cl_2(aq) + 2 \ Au(s) \rightarrow 6 \ Cl^-(aq) + 2 \ Au^{3+}(aq)$

$$E^\circ{}_{cell} = E^\circ{}_{cathode} - E^\circ{}_{anode} = +1.36 \text{ V} - (+1.50 \text{ V}) = -0.14 \text{ V}$$

This is confirmed by the negative value for $E^\circ{}_{cell}$.

Think about Your Answer In part (c), we calculated $E^\circ{}_{cell}$ for two reactions. To achieve a balanced net ionic equation, we added the half-reactions, but only after multiplying the gold half-reaction by 2 and the halogen half-reaction by 3. (This means 6 mol of electrons were transferred from 2 mol Au to 3 mol Cl_2.) Notice that this multiplication does not change the value of E° for the half-reactions because cell potentials do not depend on the quantity of material.

Check Your Understanding

(a) Rank the following metals in their ability to function as reducing agents: Hg, Sn, and Pb.

(b) Which halogens will oxidize mercury to mercury(II)?

The test tube contains an aqueous solution of KI (top layer) and immiscible CCl_4 (bottom layer).

Add Br_2 to solution of KI, and shake.

After adding a few drops of Br_2 in water, the I_2 produced collects in the bottom CCl_4 layer and gives it a purple color. (The top layer contains excess Br_2 in water.)

The presence of I_2 in the bottom layer indicates that the added Br_2 was able to oxidize the iodide ions originally present to molecular iodine (I_2).

© Cengage Learning/Charles D. Winters

FIGURE 20.15 The reaction of bromine and iodide ion. This experiment proves that Br_2 is a better oxidizing agent than I_2.

A CLOSER LOOK

An Electrochemical Toothache

It was reported a few years ago that a 66-year-old woman had intense pain that was traced to her dental work (*New England Journal of Medicine*, Vol. 342, p. 2000, 2003). A root canal procedure had moved a mercury amalgam filling on one tooth slightly closer to a gold alloy crown on an adjacent tooth. Eating acidic foods caused her intense pain. When dental amalgams of dissimilar metals come in contact with saliva, a voltaic cell is formed that generates potentials up to several hundred millivolts—and you feel it! You can do it, too, if you chew an aluminum foil gum wrapper with teeth that have been filled with a dental amalgam. Ouch!

REVIEW & CHECK FOR SECTION 20.4

1. The net reaction that occurs in a voltaic cell is $Zn(s) + 2\,Ag^+(aq) \rightarrow Zn^{2+}(aq) + 2\,Ag(s)$.

   Calculate a potential for the cell assuming standard conditions.

   (a) 1.562 V   (b) 0.0360 V   (c) 2.361 V

2. Which metal in the following list is easiest to oxidize: Fe, Ag, Zn, Mg, Au?

   (a) Fe   (c) Zn   (e) Au

   (b) Ag   (d) Mg

3. Determine which of the following redox equations are product-favored at equilibrium.

   (i) $Ni^{2+}(aq) + H_2(g) \rightarrow Ni(s) + 2\,H^+(aq)$

   (ii) $2\,Fe^{3+}(aq) + 2\,I^-(aq) \rightarrow 2\,Fe^{2+}(aq) + I_2(s)$

   (iii) $Br_2(\ell) + 2\,Cl^-(aq) \rightarrow 2\,Br^-(aq) + Cl_2(g)$

   (iv) $Cr_2O_7^{2-}(aq) + 6\,Fe^{2+}(aq) + 14\,H^+(aq) \rightarrow 2\,Cr^{3+}(aq) + 6\,Fe^{3+}(aq) + 7\,H_2O(\ell)$

   (a) ii and iv   (b) i and iii   (c) iv only   (d) all

20.5 Electrochemical Cells under Nonstandard Conditions

Electrochemical cells seldom operate under standard conditions in the real world. Even if the cell is constructed with all dissolved species at 1 M, reactant concentrations decrease and product concentrations increase in the course of the reaction. Changing concentrations of reactants and products, as well as the temperature, will affect the cell voltage. Thus, we need to ask what happens to cell potentials under nonstandard conditions.

The Nernst Equation

Based on both theory and experimental results, it has been determined that cell potentials are related to concentrations of reactants and products and to temperature, as follows:

$$E = E° - (RT/nF)\ln Q \qquad (20.2)$$

In this equation, which is known as the **Nernst equation**, R is the gas constant (8.314472 J/K · mol); T is the temperature (K); and n is the number of moles of electrons transferred between oxidizing and reducing agents (as determined by the balanced equation for the reaction). The symbol F represents the **Faraday constant** (9.6485338×10^4 C/mol). *One Faraday is the quantity of electric charge carried by one mole of electrons.* The term Q is the reaction quotient (◀ Equation 16.2, Section 16.2).

CASE STUDY

Manganese in the Oceans

Manganese is a key component of some oxidation–reduction cycles in the oceans. According to an article in the journal *Science*, it "can perform this role because it exists in multiple oxidation states and is recycled rapidly between these states by bacterial processes."

Figure A shows how this cycle is thought to work. Manganese(II) ions in subsurface water are oxidized to form manganese(IV) oxide, MnO_2. Particles of this insoluble solid sink toward the ocean floor. However, some encounter hydrogen sulfide, which is produced in the ocean depths, rising toward the surface. Another redox reaction occurs, producing sulfur and manganese(II) ions. The newly formed Mn^{2+} ions diffuse upward, where they are again oxidized.

The manganese cycle had been thought to involve only the +2 and +4 oxidation states of manganese, and analyses of water samples assumed the dissolved manganese existed only as Mn^{2+} ions. One reason for this is that the intermediate oxidation state, Mn^{3+}, is not predicted to be stable in water. It should disproportionate to the +2 and +4 states.

$$2\ Mn^{3+}(aq) + 2\ H_2O(\ell) \longrightarrow$$
$$Mn^{2+}(aq) + MnO_2(s) + 4\ H^+(aq)$$

It is known, however, that Mn^{3+} can exist when complexed with species such as pyrophosphate ions, $P_2O_7^{4-}$.

Several years ago, geochemists suggested that Mn^{3+} ions could exist in natural water. They could be produced by bacterial action and stabilized by phosphate from ATP or ADP. They speculated that the Mn^{3+} ion could play an important part in the natural manganese cycle.

Now, other researchers have indeed discovered that, in oxygen-poor waters, the manganese(III) ion, Mn^{3+}, can persist. These ions were found in anoxic zones (zones without dissolved oxygen) below 100 m in the Black Sea and below about 15 m in the Chesapeake Bay. It is now clear that Mn^{3+} ions, which had previously been known only in the laboratory, can exist in natural waters under the right circumstances and that the manganese cycle may have to be revised.

Questions:
1. Given the following reduction potentials, show that Mn^{3+} should disproportionate to Mn^{2+} and MnO_2 at standard conditions.

$$4\ H^+(aq) + MnO_2(s) + e^- \longrightarrow$$
$$Mn^{3+}(aq) + 2\ H_2O(\ell)$$

$E^\circ = 0.95\ V$

$$Mn^{3+}(aq) + e^- \longrightarrow Mn^{2+}(aq)$$

$E^\circ = 1.50\ V$

2. Balance the following equations in acid solution.
   (a) Reduction of MnO_2 with HS^- to Mn^{2+} and S
   (b) Oxidation of Mn^{2+} with O_2 to MnO_2
3. Calculate E° for the oxidation of Mn^{2+} with O_2 to MnO_2.

Answers to these questions are available in Appendix N.

FIGURE A Manganese chemistry in the oceans. Relative concentrations of important species as a function of depth in the oceans. See K. S. Johnson, *Science*, Vol. 313, p. 1896, 2006 and R. E. Trouwborst, B. G. Clement, B. M. Tebor, B. T. Glazer, and G. W. Luther, III, *Science*, Vol. 313, pp. 1955–1957, 2006.

Substituting values for the constants in Equation 20.2, and using 298 K as the temperature, gives

$$E = E^\circ - \frac{0.0257}{n}\ln Q \quad \text{at 25 °C} \tag{20.3}$$

or, in a commonly used form using base-10 logarithms,

$$E = E^\circ - \frac{0.0592}{n}\log Q$$

In essence, the term $(RT/nF)\ln Q$ "corrects" the standard potential E° for nonstandard conditions or concentrations.

⊘WL   INTERACTIVE EXAMPLE 20.6   Using the Nernst Equation

Problem A voltaic cell is set up at 25 °C with the half-cells: $Al^{3+}(0.0010\ M)\,|\,Al$ and $Ni^{2+}(0.50\ M)\,|\,Ni$. Write an equation for the reaction that occurs when the cell generates an electric current, and determine the cell potential.

What Do You Know? You know the temperature and the identity and concentrations of the reactants and products.

Strategy

- Determine which substance is oxidized (Al or Ni) by looking at the appropriate half-reactions in Table 20.1 and deciding which is the better reducing agent (Example 20.5).

- Add the half-reactions to determine the net ionic equation, and calculate $E°_{cell}$.

- Use the Nernst equation to calculate E, the potential under nonstandard conditions.

Solution Aluminum metal is a stronger reducing agent than Ni metal. (Conversely, Ni^{2+} is a better oxidizing agent than Al^{3+}.) Therefore, Al is oxidized, and the $Al^{3+}|Al$ compartment is the anode.

Cathode, reduction:	$3\ [Ni^{2+}(aq) + 2\ e^- \rightarrow Ni(s)]$
Anode, oxidation:	$2\ [Al(s) \rightarrow Al^{3+}(aq) + 3\ e^-]$
Net ionic equation:	$2\ Al(s) + 3\ Ni^{2+}(aq) \rightarrow 2\ Al^{3+}(aq) + 3\ Ni(s)$

$$E°_{cell} = E°_{cathode} - E°_{anode}$$

$$E°_{cell} = (-0.25\ V) - (-1.66\ V) = 1.41\ V$$

The expression for Q is written based on the cell reaction. In the net reaction, $Al^{3+}(aq)$ has a coefficient of 2, so this concentration is squared. Similarly, $[Ni^{2+}(aq)]$ is cubed. Solids are not included in the expression for Q (◀ Section 16.2).

$$Q = \frac{[Al^{3+}]^2}{[Ni^{2+}]^3}$$

The net equation requires transfer of six electrons from two Al atoms to three Ni^{2+} ions, so $n = 6$, and the Nernst equation gives

$$E_{cell} = E°_{cell} - \frac{0.0257}{n}\ln\frac{[Al^{3+}]^2}{[Ni^{2+}]^3}$$

$$= +1.41\ V - \frac{0.0257}{6}\ln\frac{[0.0010]^2}{[0.50]^3}$$

$$= +1.41\ V - 0.00428\ \ln(8.0 \times 10^{-6})$$

$$= +1.41\ V - 0.00428\ (-11.74)$$

$$= 1.46\ V$$

Think about Your Answer The concentrations of Al^{3+} and Ni^{2+} both affect the cell potential. Analysis of the $\ln Q$ term in the Nernst equation shows that if $[Ni^{2+}] = 1\ M$ but $[Al^{3+}] < 1\ M$, then $E_{cell} > E°_{cell}$. The reaction is more product-favored in this situation. The reverse situation (with $[Ni^{2+}] < 1\ M$ and $[Al^{3+}] = 1\ M$) would lead to $E_{cell} < E°_{cell}$. In this example, the very low value of $[Al^{3+}]$ has the greater effect, and E_{cell} is greater than $E°_{cell}$.

Check Your Understanding

A voltaic cell is set up with an aluminum electrode in a 0.025 M $Al(NO_3)_3$(aq) solution and an iron electrode in a 0.50 M $Fe(NO_3)_2$(aq) solution. Determine the cell potential, E_{cell}, at 298 K.

Example 20.6 demonstrates the calculation of a cell potential if concentrations are known. It is also useful to apply the Nernst equation in the opposite sense, using a measured cell potential to determine an unknown concentration. A device that does just this is the pH meter (Figure 20.16). In an electrochemical cell in which H^+(aq) is a reactant or product, the cell voltage will vary predictably with the hydrogen ion concentration. The cell voltage is measured and the value used to calculate pH. Example 20.7 illustrates how E_{cell} varies with the hydrogen ion concentration in a simple cell.

Strategy Map 20.6

PROBLEM

Write an equation for the reaction involving **Al** and **Al³⁺** with **Ni** and **Ni²⁺**. Calculate E_{cell}.

↓

KNOWN DATA/INFORMATION

- Concentrations of **Al³⁺** and **Ni²⁺**
- Look up **E° values** for the half-reactions.

STEP 1. Decide which half-reactions occur at the **anode** and **cathode** based on $E°$ values.

Cathode reaction (reduction of Ni²⁺) and **anode reaction** (oxidation of Al)

STEP 2. Add half-reactions to obtain **net cell reaction**.

Net cell reaction

STEP 3. Calculate $E°_{cell}$.

$E°_{cell} = E°_{cathode} - E°_{anode}$

STEP 4. Use **Nernst equation** with known ion concentrations, calculated $E°_{cell}$, and n value to calculate E_{cell}.

E_{cell} under nonstandard conditions

FIGURE 20.16 Measuring pH.

Measuring pH with a portable pH meter that can be used in the field.

A schematic diagram of a glass electrode.

EXAMPLE 20.7 Variation of E_{cell} with Concentration

Problem A voltaic cell is set up with copper and hydrogen half-cells. Standard conditions are employed in the copper half-cell, $Cu^{2+}(aq, 1.00 M)\,|\,Cu(s)$. The hydrogen gas pressure is 1.00 bar, and $[H^+(aq)]$ in the hydrogen half-cell is the unknown. A value of 0.490 V is recorded for E_{cell} at 298 K. Determine the pH of the solution.

What Do You Know? You know the temperature, the identity of the reactants and products, the concentration of the Cu^{2+} ion, the partial pressure of H_2, and E_{cell}.

Strategy

- Determine which is the better oxidizing and reducing agent in order to decide what net reaction is occurring in the cell. Write a balanced equation for the reaction.

- Calculate $E°_{cell}$.

- Use the Nernst equation with the given Cu^{2+} ion concentration to calculate the hydrogen ion concentration.

- Calculate the pH.

Solution Based on their positions in a table of standard reduction potentials, hydrogen is a better reducing agent than copper metal, so $Cu(s)\,|\,Cu^{2+}(aq, 1.00 M)$ is the cathode, and $H_2(g, 1.00 bar)\,|\,H^+(aq, ? M)$ is the anode.

Cathode, reduction:	$Cu^{2+}(aq) + 2\,e^- \rightarrow Cu(s)$
Anode, oxidation:	$H_2(g) \rightarrow 2\,H^+(aq) + 2\,e^-$
Net ionic equation:	$H_2(g) + Cu^{2+}(aq) \rightarrow Cu(s) + 2\,H^+(aq)$

$$E°_{cell} = E°_{cathode} - E°_{anode}$$

$$E°_{cell} = (+0.337\ V) - (0.00\ V) = +0.337\ V$$

The reaction quotient, Q, is derived from the balanced net ionic equation.

$$Q = \frac{[H^+]^2}{[Cu^{2+}]P_{H_2}}$$

The net equation requires the transfer of two electrons, so $n = 2$. The value of $[Cu^{2+}]$ is 1.00 M, but $[H^+]$ is unknown. Substitute this information into the Nernst equation (and don't overlook the fact that $[H^+]$ is squared in the expression for Q).

$$E = E° - \frac{0.0257}{n} \ln \frac{[H^+]^2}{[Cu^{2+}]P_{H_2}}$$

$$0.490 \text{ V} = 0.337 \text{ V} - \frac{0.0257}{2} \ln \frac{[H^+]^2}{(1.00)(1.00)}$$

$$-11.9 = \ln[H^+]^2$$

$$[H^+] = 3 \times 10^{-3} \text{ M}$$

$$\boxed{pH = 2.6}$$

Think about Your Answer Be sure to write the balanced equation. Without it you may not have the correct exponents in the term for Q in the Nernst equation.

Check Your Understanding

The half-cells $Fe^{2+}(aq, 0.024 \text{ M}) | Fe(s)$ and $H^+(aq, 0.056 \text{ M}) | H_2(1.0 \text{ bar})$ are linked by a salt bridge to create a voltaic cell. Determine the cell potential, E_{cell}, at 298 K.

In the real world, using a hydrogen electrode in a pH meter is not practical. The apparatus is clumsy; it is anything but robust; and platinum (for the electrode) is costly. Common pH meters use a glass electrode, so called because it contains a thin glass membrane separating the cell from the solution whose pH is to be measured (Figure 20.16). Inside the glass electrode is a silver wire coated with AgCl and a solution of HCl; outside is the solution of unknown pH to be evaluated. A Ag/AgCl or calomel electrode—the latter a common reference electrode using a mercury(I)–mercury redox couple ($Hg_2Cl_2 | Hg$)—serves as the second electrode of the cell. The potential across the glass membrane depends on $[H^+]$. Common pH meters give a direct readout of pH.

REVIEW & CHECK FOR SECTION 20.5

Calculate E_{cell} at 298 K for a cell involving Sn and Cu and their ions:

$$Sn(s) | Sn^{2+}(aq, 0.25 \text{ M}) \| Cu^{2+}(aq, 0.10 \text{ M}) | Cu(s)$$

(a) 0.47 V   (b) 0.49 V   (c) 0.50 V

20.6 Electrochemistry and Thermodynamics
Work and Free Energy

The first law of thermodynamics states that the internal energy change in a system (ΔU) is related to two quantities, heat (q) and work (w): $\Delta U = q + w$ [Section 5.4]. This equation also applies to chemical changes that occur in a voltaic cell. As current flows, energy is transferred from the system (the voltaic cell) to the surroundings.

In a voltaic cell, the decrease in internal energy in the system will manifest itself ideally as electrical work done on the surroundings by the system. In practice, however, some energy is usually evolved as heat by the voltaic cell. The maximum work done by an electrochemical system (ideally, assuming no heat is generated) is proportional to the potential difference (volts) and the quantity of charge (coulombs):

$$w_{max} = nFE \qquad \qquad (20.4)$$

In this equation, E is the cell voltage, and nF is the quantity of electric charge transferred from anode to cathode.

The free energy change for a process is, by definition, the maximum amount of work that can be obtained [Section 19.6]. Because the maximum work and the cell potential are related, $E°$ and $\Delta_r G°$ can be related mathematically (taking care to assign signs correctly). The maximum work done on the surroundings when electricity is produced by a voltaic cell is $+nFE$, with the positive sign denoting an increase in energy in the surroundings. The energy content of the cell decreases by this amount. Thus, $\Delta_r G$ for the voltaic cell has the opposite sign.

$$\Delta_r G = -nFE \tag{20.5}$$

● **Units in Equation 20.6** n has units of mol e^-, and F has units of (C/mol e^-). Therefore, nF has units of coulombs (C). Because 1 J = 1 C · V, the product nFE will have units of energy (J).

Under standard conditions, the appropriate equation is

$$\Delta_r G° = -nFE° \tag{20.6}$$

This expression shows that, the more positive the value of $E°$, the more negative the value of $\Delta_r G°$ for the reaction. Also, because of the relationship between $\Delta_r G°$ and K, the farther apart the half-reactions are on the potential ladder, the more strongly product-favored the reaction is at equilibrium.

EXAMPLE 20.8   Relating $E°$ and $\Delta_r G°$

Problem The standard cell potential, $E°_{cell}$, for the reduction of silver ions with copper metal (Figure 20.5) is +0.462 V at 25 °C. Calculate $\Delta_r G°$ for this reaction.

What Do You Know? You know the cell potential under standard conditions and therefore know to use Equation 20.6 to calculate the change in free energy. In this equation F is a known constant, but n has to be determined. However, you can write the balanced equation for the cell reaction, and so obtain n from that.

Strategy Use Equation 20.6 where $E°_{cell}$ and F are known. The value of n, the number of moles of electrons transferred between copper metal and silver ions, comes from the balanced equation.

Solution In this cell, copper is the anode, and silver is the cathode. The overall cell reaction is

$$Cu(s) + 2\ Ag^+(aq) \rightarrow Cu^{2+}(aq) + 2\ Ag(s)$$

which means that each mole of copper transfers 2 mol of electrons to 2 mol of Ag^+ ions. That is, $n = 2$. Now use Equation 20.6.

$$\Delta_r G° = -nFE° = -(2\ \text{mol}\ e^-)(96,485\ \text{C/mol}\ e^-)(0.462\ \text{V}) = -89,200\ \text{C} \cdot \text{V}$$

Because 1 C · V = 1 J, we have

$$\Delta_r G° = -89,200\ \text{J or} -89.2\ \text{kJ}$$

Think about Your Answer This example demonstrates an effective method of obtaining thermodynamic values from electrochemical experiments. Keep in mind that a positive $E°$ implies a negative $\Delta_r G°$.

Check Your Understanding

The following reaction has an $E°$ value of −0.76 V:

$$H_2(g) + Zn^{2+}(aq) \rightarrow Zn(s) + 2\ H^+(aq)$$

Calculate $\Delta_r G°$ for this reaction. Is the reaction product- or reactant-favored at equilibrium?

$E°$ and the Equilibrium Constant

When a voltaic cell produces an electric current, the reactant concentrations decrease, and the product concentrations increase. The cell voltage also changes. As reactants are converted to products, the value of E_{cell} decreases and the cell potential eventually reaches zero; no further net reaction occurs, and equilibrium is achieved.

This situation can be analyzed using the Nernst equation. When $E_{cell} = 0$, the reactants and products are at equilibrium, and the reaction quotient, Q, is equal to the equilibrium constant, K. Substituting the appropriate symbols and values into the Nernst equation,

$$E = 0 = E° - \frac{0.0257}{n}\ln K$$

and collecting terms gives an equation that relates the cell potential and equilibrium constant:

$$\ln K = \frac{nE°}{0.0257} \quad \text{at 25 °C (298 K)} \quad (20.7)$$

Equation 20.7 can be used to determine values for equilibrium constants, as illustrated in Example 20.9.

ⓌWL   INTERACTIVE EXAMPLE 20.9 $E°$ and Equilibrium Constants

Problem Calculate the equilibrium constant for the reaction at 298 K:

$$Fe(s) + Cd^{2+}(aq) \rightleftharpoons Fe^{2+}(aq) + Cd(s)$$

What Do You Know? You have the balanced chemical equation and know that Equation 20.7 is required. You need to know $E°$ and n, the number of electrons transferred.

Strategy First, determine $E°_{cell}$ from $E°$ values for the two half-reactions (see Example 20.5) and from those the value of n, the other parameter required in Equation 20.7.

Solution The half-reactions and $E°$ values are

Cathode, reduction:	$Cd^{2+}(aq) + 2\ e^- \rightarrow Cd(s)$
Anode, oxidation:	$Fe(s) \rightarrow Fe^{2+}(aq) + 2\ e^-$
Net ionic equation:	$Fe(s) + Cd^{2+}(aq) \rightleftharpoons Fe^{2+}(aq) + Cd(s)$

$$E°_{cell} = E°_{cathode} - E°_{anode}$$

$$E°_{cell} = (-0.40\ V) - (-0.44\ V) = +0.04\ V$$

Now substitute $n = 2$ and $E°_{cell}$ into Equation 20.7.

$$\ln K = \frac{nE°}{0.0257} = \frac{(2)(0.04\ V)}{0.0257} = 3.1$$

$$K = 20$$

Think about Your Answer The relatively small positive voltage (0.04 V) for the cell indicates that the cell reaction is only mildly product-favored. A value of 20 for the equilibrium constant is in accord with this observation.

Check Your Understanding

Calculate the equilibrium constant at 25 °C for the reaction

$$2\ Ag^+(aq) + Hg(\ell) \rightleftharpoons 2\ Ag(s) + Hg^{2+}(aq)$$

Strategy Map 20.9

PROBLEM

Calculate an **equilibrium constant** using **electrochemical data**.

KNOWN DATA/INFORMATION

- Balanced equation

STEP 1. Decide which half-reactions occur at **anode** and **cathode** based on $E°$ values and calculate $E°_{cell}$.

$$E°_{cell} = E°_{cathode} - E°_{anode}$$

STEP 2. Use Equation 20.7 with calculated $E°_{cell}$, and n **value** to calculate $\ln K$.

Calculated $\ln K$

STEP 3. Convert $\ln K$ to K.

Equilibrium constant, K

The relationships between $E°$, K, and $\Delta_r G°$, which are summarized in Table 20.2. Values of $E°$ can be used to obtain equilibrium constants for many different chemical systems. One example is the determination of solubility product constants, K_{sp}. Let us begin with an electrode in which an insoluble ionic compound, AgCl, is a component of a half-cell. Figure 20.17 illustrates how the potential for the reduction of AgCl in the presence of Cl^- ion (1.00 M) can be determined.

$$AgCl(s) + e^- \rightarrow Ag(s) + Cl^-(aq) \quad E° = +0.222\ V$$

Table 20.2 Summary of the Relationship of K, $\Delta_rG°$, and $E°$

K	$\Delta_rG°$	$E°$	Reactant-Favored or Product-Favored at Equilibrium?	Spontaneous under Standard Conditions?
$K \gg 1$	$\Delta_rG° < 0$	$E° > 0$	Product-favored	Spontaneous under standard conditions
$K = 1$	$\Delta_rG° = 0$	$E° = 0$	$[C]^c[D]^d = [A]^a[B]^b$ at equilibrium	At equilibrium under standard conditions
$K \ll 1$	$\Delta_rG° > 0$	$E° < 0$	Reactant-favored	Not spontaneous under standard conditions

When paired with the standard hydrogen electrode, the standard reduction potential for the AgCl|Ag half-cell is +0.222 V. If this half-reaction is then paired with that for a standard silver electrode in a hypothetical voltaic cell, the cell reactions could be written as

Cathode, reduction: $AgCl(s) + e^- \rightarrow Ag(s) + Cl^-(aq)$

Anode, oxidation: $Ag(s) \rightarrow Ag^+(aq) + e^-$

Net ionic equation: $AgCl(s) \rightarrow Ag^+(aq) + Cl^-(aq)$

The equation for the net reaction represents the equilibrium of solid AgCl and its ions. The cell potential is negative,

$$E°_{cell} = E°_{cathode} - E°_{anode} = (+0.222 \text{ V}) - (+0.799 \text{ V}) = -0.577 \text{ V}$$

indicating a reactant-favored process, as would be expected based on the low solubility of AgCl. Using Equation 20.7, the value of K_{sp} can then be obtained from $E°_{cell}$.

$$\ln K = \frac{nE°}{0.0257} = \frac{(1)(-0.577 \text{ V})}{0.0257} = -22.5$$

$$K_{sp} = e^{-22.5} = 2 \times 10^{-10}$$

FIGURE 20.17 Measurement of the standard electrode potential for the Ag|AgCl electrode.

REVIEW & CHECK FOR SECTION 20.6

In Appendix M, the following standard reduction potential is reported:

$$[Zn(CN)_4]^{2-}(aq) + 2\ e^- \rightarrow Zn(s) + 4\ CN^-(aq) \qquad E° = -1.26\ V$$

Use this information, along with the data on the $Zn^{2+}(aq)\,|\,Zn$ half-cell, to calculate the equilibrium constant for the reaction

$$Zn^{2+}(aq) + 4\ CN^-(aq) \rightarrow [Zn(CN)_4]^{2-}(aq)$$

What is the value for the formation constant for this complex ion at 25 °C?

(a) 2.8×10^8 (b) 6.3×10^{16} (c) 1.9×10^{68}

20.7 Electrolysis: Chemical Change Using Electrical Energy

Thus far, we have described electrochemical cells that use product-favored redox reactions to generate an electric current. Equally important, however, is the opposite process, **electrolysis**, the use of electrical energy to bring about chemical change.

Electrolysis of water is a classic chemistry experiment, and the electroplating of metals is another example of electrolysis (Figure 20.18). In electroplating, an electric current is passed through a solution containing a salt of the metal to be plated. The object to be plated is the cathode. When metal ions in solution are reduced, the metal deposits on the object's surface.

Electrolysis is also important because it is widely used in the refining of metals such as aluminum and in the production of chemicals such as chlorine.

Electrolysis of Molten Salts

All electrolysis experiments are set up in a similar manner. The material to be electrolyzed, either a molten salt or a solution, is contained in an electrolysis cell. As was the case with voltaic cells, ions must be present in the liquid or solution for a current

Oxygen—gas   Hydrogen—gas

Water—liquid

Greenshoots Communications/Alamy

Battery
$(+)$ $(-)$
e^- e^-
$(+)$ Aqueous solution with free copper ions
$(-)$
$Cu^{2+} \rightarrow$ Cu^{2+}
$Cu^{2+} \rightarrow$
$Cu^{2+} \rightarrow$
$Cu^{2+} \rightarrow$ $Cu^{2+} \rightarrow$
$Cu^{2+} \rightarrow$
Anode   Cathode, object to be plated

(a) Electrolysis of water produces hydrogen (at the cathode) and oxygen gas (at the anode).

(b) Electroplating adds a layer of metal to the surface of an object *(left)*, either to protect the object from corrosion or to improve its physical appearance. The procedure uses an electrolysis cell, set up with the object to be plated as the cathode and a solution containing a salt of the metal to be plated *(right)*.

FIGURE 20.18 Electrolysis.

FIGURE 20.19 The preparation of sodium and chlorine by the electrolysis of molten NaCl. In the molten state, sodium ions migrate to the negative cathode, where they are reduced to sodium metal. Chloride ions migrate to the positive anode, where they are oxidized to elemental chlorine.

© Cengage Learning/Charles D. Winters

Sodium ion migrates to cathode.

Reduced to sodium metal

Chloride migrates to anode.

Oxidized to chlorine

to flow as it is the movement of ions within the cell that constitutes the electric current. The cell has two electrodes that are connected to a source of DC (direct-current) voltage. If the applied voltage is high enough, chemical reactions occur at the two electrodes. Reduction occurs at the negatively charged cathode, with electrons being transferred from that electrode to a chemical species in the cell. Oxidation occurs at the positive anode, with electrons from a chemical species being transferred to that electrode.

Let us focus our attention first on the chemical reactions that occur at each electrode in the electrolysis of a molten salt. Sodium chloride melts at about 800 °C, and in the molten state sodium ions (Na^+) and chloride ions (Cl^-) are freed from their rigid arrangement in the crystalline lattice. Therefore, if a potential is applied to the electrodes, sodium ions are attracted to the negative electrode, and chloride ions are attracted to the positive electrode (Figure 20.19). If the potential is high enough, chemical reactions occur at each electrode. At the negative cathode, Na^+ ions accept electrons and are reduced to sodium metal (a liquid at this temperature). Simultaneously, at the positive anode, chloride ions give up electrons and form elemental chlorine.

Cathode ($-$), reduction:	$2\ Na^+ + 2\ e^- \rightarrow 2\ Na(\ell)$
Anode ($+$), oxidation:	$2\ Cl^- \rightarrow Cl_2(g) + 2\ e^-$
Net ionic equation:	$2\ Na^+ + 2\ Cl^- \rightarrow 2\ Na(\ell) + Cl_2(g)$

Electrons move through the external circuit under the force exerted by the applied potential, and the movement of positive and negative ions in the molten salt

---

PROBLEM SOLVING TIP 20.3

Whether you are describing a voltaic cell or an electrolysis cell, the terms *anode* and *cathode* always refer to the electrodes at which oxidation and reduction occur, respectively. The polarity of the electrodes is reversed, however.

Electrochemical Conventions: Voltaic Cells and Electrolysis Cells

Type of Cell	Electrode	Function	Polarity
Voltaic	Anode	Oxidation	$-$
	Cathode	Reduction	$+$
Electrolysis	Anode	Oxidation	$+$
	Cathode	Reduction	$-$

constitutes the current within the cell. Finally, it is important to recognize that the reaction is not spontaneous. The energy required for this reaction to occur has been provided by the electric current.

Electrolysis of Aqueous Solutions

Sodium ions (Na^+) and chloride ions (Cl^-) are the primary species present in molten NaCl. Only chloride ions can be oxidized, and only sodium ions can be reduced. Electrolysis of a substance in aqueous solution is more complicated than the electrolysis of a molten salt, however, because water is now present. Water is an *electroactive* substance; that is, it can be oxidized or reduced in an electrochemical process.

Consider the electrolysis of aqueous sodium iodide (Figure 20.20). In this experiment, the electrolysis cell contains $Na^+(aq)$, $I^-(aq)$, and H_2O molecules. Possible *reduction reactions* at the *negative cathode* include

$$Na^+(aq) + e^- \rightarrow Na(s)$$

$$2 H_2O(\ell) + 2 e^- \rightarrow H_2(g) + 2 OH^-(aq)$$

Possible *oxidation reactions* at the *positive anode* are

$$2 I^-(aq) \rightarrow I_2(aq) + 2 e^-$$

$$2 H_2O(\ell) \rightarrow O_2(g) + 4 H^+(aq) + 4 e^-$$

In the electrolysis of aqueous NaI, $H_2(g)$ and $OH^-(aq)$ are formed by water reduction at the cathode, and iodine is formed at the anode. Thus, the overall cell process can be summarized by the following equations:

Cathode (−), reduction: $2 H_2O(\ell) + 2 e^- \rightarrow H_2(g) + 2 OH^-(aq)$

Anode (+), oxidation: $2 I^-(aq) \rightarrow I_2(aq) + 2 e^-$

Net ionic equation: $2 H_2O(\ell) + 2 I^-(aq) \rightarrow H_2(g) + 2 OH^-(aq) + I_2(aq)$

where E°_{cell} has a negative value.

$$E^\circ_{cell} = E^\circ_{cathode} - E^\circ_{anode} = (-0.8277 \text{ V}) - (+0.621 \text{ V}) = -1.449 \text{ V}$$

This process is not spontaneous under standard conditions, and a potential of *at least* 1.45 V must be *applied* to the cell for these reactions to occur. If the process had involved the oxidation of water instead of iodide ion at the anode, the required

A drop of phenolphthalein has been added to the solution in this experiment so that the formation of $OH^-(aq)$ can be detected (by the pink color of the indicator in basic solution).

Cathode (−): $2 e^- + 2 H_2O(\ell) \longrightarrow H_2(g) + 2 OH^-(aq)$

Cathode

A solution of NaI(aq) is electrolyzed, a potential applied using an external source of electricity.

Iodine forms at the anode, and H_2 and OH^- form at the cathode.

Anode (+): $2 I^-(aq) \longrightarrow I_2(aq) + 2 e^-$

FIGURE 20.20 Electrolysis of aqueous NaI.

potential would be -2.057 V $[E°_{cathode} - E°_{anode} = (-0.8277\,\text{V}) - (+1.229\,\text{V})]$, and if the reaction involving the reduction of Na^+ and the oxidation of I^- had occurred, the required potential would be -3.335 V $[E°_{cathode} - E°_{anode} = (-2.714\,\text{V}) - (+0.621\,\text{V})]$. The reaction occurring is the one requiring the smaller applied potential, so the net cell reaction in the electrolysis of $NaI(aq)$ is the oxidation of iodide and reduction of water.

What happens if an aqueous solution of some other metal halide such as $SnCl_2$ is electrolyzed? Consult Appendix M, and consider all possible half-reactions. In this case, aqueous Sn^{2+} ion is much more easily reduced ($E° = -0.14$ V) than water ($E° = -0.83$ V) at the cathode, so tin metal is produced. At the anode, two oxidations are possible: $Cl^-(aq)$ to $Cl_2(g)$ or H_2O to $O_2(g)$. Experiments show that chloride ion is oxidized in preference to water, so the reactions occurring on electrolysis of aqueous tin(II) chloride are (Figure 20.21)

Cathode (−), reduction: $\quad Sn^{2+}(aq) + 2\,e^- \rightarrow Sn(s)$

Anode (+), oxidation: $\quad \underline{2\,Cl^-(aq) \rightarrow Cl_2(g) + 2\,e^-}$

Net ionic equation: $\quad Sn^{2+}(aq) + 2\,Cl^-(aq) \rightarrow Sn(s) + Cl_2(g)$

$$E°_{cell} = E°_{cathode} - E°_{anode} = (-0.14\,\text{V}) - (+1.36\,\text{V}) = -1.50\,\text{V}$$

Formation of Cl_2 at the anode in the electrolysis of $SnCl_2(aq)$ is contrary to a prediction based on $E°$ values. If the electrode reactions were

Cathode (−), reduction: $\quad Sn^{2+}(aq) + 2\,e^- \rightarrow Sn(s)$

Anode (+), oxidation: $\quad 2\,H_2O(\ell) \rightarrow O_2(g) + 4\,H^+(aq) + 4\,e^-$

$$E°_{cell} = (-0.14\,\text{V}) - (+1.23\,\text{V}) = -1.37\,\text{V}$$

a smaller applied potential would seemingly be required. To explain the formation of chlorine instead of oxygen, we must take into account rates of reaction. The oxidation of $Cl^-(aq)$ is much more rapid than the oxidation of H_2O.

This "problem" is used to advantage in the commercially important electrolysis of aqueous $NaCl$, where a voltage high enough to oxidize both Cl^- and H_2O is used. However, because chloride ion is oxidized much faster than H_2O, Cl_2 is the major product in this electrolysis. This is the predominant means by which chlorine is produced for commercial use.

Another instance in which rates are important concerns electrode materials. Graphite, commonly used to make inert electrodes, can be oxidized. For the half-reaction $CO_2(g) + 4\,H^+(aq) + 4\,e^- \rightarrow C(s) + 2\,H_2O(\ell)$, $E°$ is $+0.20$ V, indicating that carbon is slightly easier to oxidize than copper ($E° = +0.34$ V). Based on this value, oxidation of a graphite electrode might reasonably be expected to occur during an electrolysis. And indeed it does, albeit slowly; graphite electrodes used in electrolysis cells slowly deteriorate and eventually have to be replaced.

● **Overvoltage** Voltages higher than the minimum are typically used to speed up reactions that would otherwise be slow. The term *overvoltage* is often used and refers to the voltage needed to make a reaction occur at a reasonable rate.

FIGURE 20.21 Electrolysis of aqueous tin(II) chloride. Tin metal collects at the negative cathode. Chlorine gas is formed at the positive anode. Elemental chlorine is formed in the cell, in spite of the fact that the potential for the oxidation of Cl^- is more negative than that for oxidation of water. (That is, chlorine should be less easily oxidized than water.) This is the result of chemical kinetics and illustrates the complexity of some aqueous electrochemistry.

© Cengage Learning/Charles D. Winters

One other factor—the concentration of electroactive species in solution—must be taken into account when discussing electrolyses. As shown in Section 20.6, the potential at which a species in solution is oxidized or reduced depends on concentration. Unless standard conditions are used, predictions based on $E°$ values are merely qualitative. In addition, the rate of a half-reaction depends on the concentration of the electroactive substance at the electrode surface. At a very low concentration, the rate of the redox reaction may depend on the rate at which an ion diffuses from the solution to the electrode surface.

EXAMPLE 20.10 Electrolysis of Aqueous Solutions

Problem Predict how products of the electrolysis of aqueous solutions of NaF, NaCl, NaBr, and NaI are likely to be different and predict $E°_{cell}$ for each electrolysis. (The electrolysis of NaI is illustrated in Figure 20.20.)

What Do You Know? You know the identity of the compounds to be electrolyzed, but you will need to know the $E°$ values for their half-reactions and for water electrolysis.

Strategy The main criterion used to predict the chemistry in an electrolytic cell should be the ease of oxidation and reduction, an assessment based on $E°$ values.

Solution The cathode reaction presents no problem: Water is reduced to hydroxide ion and H_2 gas in preference to reduction of $Na^+(aq)$ (as in the electrolysis of aqueous NaI). Thus, the primary cathode reaction in all cases is

$$2\ H_2O(\ell) + 2\ e^- \rightarrow H_2(g) + 2\ OH^-(aq)$$

$$E°_{cathode} = -0.83\ V$$

At the anode, you need to assess the ease of oxidation of the halide ions relative to water. Based on $E°$ values, this should be $I^-(aq) > Br^-(aq) > Cl^-(aq) >> F^-(aq)$. Fluoride ion is much more difficult to oxidize than water, and electrolysis of an aqueous solution containing this ion results exclusively in O_2 formation. That is, the primary anode reaction for NaF(aq) is

$$2\ H_2O(\ell) \rightarrow O_2(g) + 4\ H^+(aq) + 4\ e^-$$

$$E°_{anode} = +1.23\ V$$

Therefore, in this case,

$$E°_{cell} = (-0.83\ V) - (+1.23\ V) = -2.06\ V$$

Recall that chlorine is the primary product at the anode in the electrolysis of aqueous solutions of chloride salts (as in Figure 20.20). Therefore, the primary anode reaction in NaCl(aq) is

$$2\ Cl^-(aq) \rightarrow Cl_2(g) + 2\ e^-$$

$$E°_{cell} = (-0.83\ V) - (+1.36\ V) = -2.19\ V$$

Bromide ions are considerably easier to oxidize than chloride ions, so Br_2 may be expected as the primary product in the electrolysis of aqueous NaBr. For NaBr(aq), the primary anode reaction is

$$2\ Br^-(aq) \rightarrow Br_2(\ell) + 2\ e^-$$

so $E°_{cell}$ is

$$E°_{cell} = (-0.83\ V) - (+1.08\ V) = -1.91\ V$$

Thus, the electrolysis of NaBr resembles that of NaI (Figure 20.19) in producing the halogen, hydrogen gas, and hydroxide ion. The half-reactions and the cell potential for aqueous NaI were given on page 931.

Think about Your Answer As described above, you would predict from $E°$ values the ease of oxidation of halide ions is $I^-(aq) > Br^-(aq) > Cl^-(aq) >> F^-(aq)$. This is confirmed by the results.

Check Your Understanding

Predict the chemical reactions that will occur at the two electrodes in the electrolysis of an aqueous sodium hydroxide solution. What is the minimum voltage needed to cause this reaction to occur?

Electrochemistry and Michael Faraday

The terms *anion, cation, electrode,* and *electrolyte* originated with Michael Faraday (1791–1867), one of the most influential people in the history of chemistry. Faraday was apprenticed to a bookbinder in London when he was 13. This situation suited him perfectly, as he enjoyed reading the books sent to the shop for binding. By chance, one of these volumes was a small book on chemistry, which whetted his appetite for science, and he began performing experiments on electricity. In 1812, a patron of the shop invited Faraday to accompany him to the Royal Institute to attend a lecture by one of the most famous chemists of the day, Sir Humphry Davy. Faraday was intrigued by Davy's lecture and wrote to ask Davy for a position as an assistant. He was

accepted and began work in 1813. Faraday was so talented that his work proved extraordinarily fruitful, and only 12 years later he was made the director of the laboratory of the Royal Institute.

It has been said that Faraday's contributions were so enormous that, had there been Nobel Prizes when he was alive, he would have received at least six. These could have been awarded for discoveries such as the following:

- Electromagnetic induction, which led to the first transformer and electric motor
- The laws of electrolysis (the effect of electric current on chemicals)
- The magnetic properties of matter

- Benzene and other organic chemicals (which led to important chemical industries)
- The "Faraday effect" (the rotation of the plane of polarized light by a magnetic field)
- The introduction of the concept of electric and magnetic fields

Michael Fa (1791–1867

In addition to making discoveries that had profound effects on science, Faraday was an educator. He wrote and spoke about his work in memorable ways, especially in lectures to the general public that helped to popularize science.

REVIEW & CHECK FOR SECTION 20.7

You have a solution containing several metal ions, K^+, Fe^{2+}, Al^{3+}, Ag^+. Which ion will require the lowest potential to plate out on the cathode?

(a) K^+ (b) Fe^{2+} (c) Al^{3+} (d) Ag^+

20.8 Counting Electrons

Metallic silver is produced at the cathode in the electrolysis of aqueous $AgNO_3$ in which one mole of electrons is required to produce one mole of silver. In contrast, two moles of electrons are required to produce one mole of tin (Figure 20.21):

$$Sn^{2+}(aq) + 2\ e^- \rightarrow Sn(s)$$

It follows that if the number of moles of electrons flowing through the electrolysis cell could be measured, the number of moles of silver or tin produced could be calculated. Conversely, if the amount of silver or tin produced is known, then the number of moles of electrons moving through the circuit could be calculated.

The number of moles of electrons consumed or produced in an electron transfer reaction is obtained by measuring the current flowing in the external electric circuit in a given time. The **current** flowing in an electrical circuit is the amount of charge (in units of coulombs, C) per unit time, and the usual unit for current is the ampere (A). One ampere equals the passage of one coulomb of charge per second.

$$\text{Current (amperes, A)} = \frac{\text{electric charge (coulombs, C)}}{\text{time, } t \text{ (seconds, s)}} \quad (20.8)$$

● **Faraday Constant** The Faraday constant is the charge carried by 1 mol of electrons: 9.6485338×10^4 C/mol e^-.

The current passing through an electrochemical cell and the time for which the current flows are easily measured quantities. Therefore, the charge (in coulombs) that passes through a cell can be obtained by multiplying the current (in amperes) by the time (in seconds). Knowing the charge and using the Faraday constant as a conversion factor, we can calculate the number of moles of electrons that passed through an electrochemical cell. In turn, we can use this quantity to calculate the quantities of reactants and products. The following example illustrates this type of calculation.

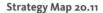

INTERACTIVE EXAMPLE 20.11 Using the Faraday Constant

Problem A current of 2.40 A is passed through a solution containing $Cu^{2+}(aq)$ for 30.0 minutes, with copper metal being deposited at the cathode. What mass of copper, in grams, is deposited?

What Do You Know? You know the current passed through the cell and the time over which it was passed.

Strategy The current and time can be used to calculate the amount of charge that passed through the cell. The Faraday constant can then be used to relate this to the amount (moles) of electrons that were used. This in turn can be related to the amount of copper metal deposited and finally to the mass of copper.

Solution

1. Calculate the charge (number of coulombs) passing through the cell in 30.0 minutes.

$$\text{Charge (C)} = \text{current (A)} \times \text{time (s)}$$

$$= (2.40\ \text{A})(30.0\ \text{min})(60.0\ \text{s/min})$$

$$= 4.32 \times 10^3\ \text{C}$$

2. Calculate the number of moles of electrons (i.e., the number of Faradays of electricity).

$$(4.32 \times 10^3\ \text{C})\left(\frac{1\ \text{mol } e^-}{96{,}485\ \text{C}}\right) = 4.48 \times 10^{-2}\ \text{mol } e^-$$

3. Calculate the amount of copper and, from this, the mass of copper.

$$\text{mass of copper} = (4.48 \times 10^{-2}\ \text{mol } e^-)\left(\frac{1\ \text{mol Cu}}{2\ \text{mol } e^-}\right)\left(\frac{63.55\ \text{g Cu}}{1\ \text{mol Cu}}\right) = 1.42\ \text{g}$$

Think about Your Answer The key relation in this calculation is "current = charge/time." Most situations will involve knowing two of these three quantities from experiment and calculating the third.

Check Your Understanding

1. Calculate the mass of O_2 produced in the electrolysis of water, using a current of 0.445 A for a period of 45 minutes.

2. In the commercial production of sodium by electrolysis, the cell operates at 7.0 V and a current of 25×10^3 A. What mass of sodium can be produced in 1 hour?

Strategy Map 20.11

PROBLEM
Calculate the **mass of copper** deposited in electrolysis cell.

↓

KNOWN DATA/INFORMATION
- Current in cell
- Time

STEP 1. Use **current × time** to calculate **charge**.

Charge passing through cell (in **coulombs**)

STEP 2. Use **Faraday constant** to calculate **moles of electrons** passed.

Moles of electrons passed in **given time**

STEP 3. Relate moles of **electrons** to moles of **metal**.

Amount of metal **(mol)** produced

STEP 4. Convert **amount** to **mass**.

Mass of metal **(g)** produced

REVIEW & CHECK FOR SECTION 20.8

If you wish to convert 0.0100 mol of $Au^{3+}(aq)$ ions into $Au(s)$ in a "gold-plating" process, how long must you electrolyze a solution if the current passing through the circuit is 2.00 amps?

(a) 483 seconds

(b) 4.83×10^4 seconds

(c) 965 seconds

(d) 1450 seconds

CHAPTER GOALS REVISITED

Now that you have studied this chapter, you should ask whether you have met the chapter goals. In particular, you should be able to:

Balance equations for oxidation–reduction reactions in acidic or basic solutions using the half-reaction approach Study Questions: 1–6, 15, 16, 49, 50, 84, 85, and Go Chemistry Module 25.

Understand the principles underlying voltaic cells

a. In a voltaic cell, identify the half-reactions occurring at the anode and the cathode, the polarity of the electrodes, the direction of electron flow in the external circuit, and the direction of ion flow in the salt bridge (Section 20.2). **Study Questions: 7–10, 51.**

Sign in at **www.cengage.com/owl** to:
- View tutorials and simulations, develop problem-solving skills, and complete online homework assigned by your professor.
- For quick review and exam prep, download Go Chemistry mini lecture modules from OWL (or purchase them at **www.cengagebrain.com**)

❓ Access **How Do I Solve It?** tutorials on how to approach problem solving using concepts in this chapter.

b. Appreciate the chemistry and advantages and disadvantages of dry cells, alkaline batteries, lead storage batteries, lithium batteries, and Ni-cad batteries (Section 20.3). **Study Questions: 11, 12.**

c. Understand how fuel cells work, and recognize the difference between batteries and fuel cells (Section 20.3). **Study Question: 101.**

Understand how to use electrochemical potentials

a. Understand the process by which standard reduction potentials are determined, and identify standard conditions as applied to electrochemistry (Section 20.4).

b. Describe the standard hydrogen electrode ($E° = 0.00$ V), and explain how it is used as the standard to determine the standard potentials of half-reactions (Section 20.4).

c. Know how to use standard reduction potentials to determine cell voltages for cells under standard conditions (Equation 20.1). **Study Questions: 13–16.**

d. Know how to use a table of standard reduction potentials (Table 20.1 and Appendix M) to rank the strengths of oxidizing and reducing agents, to predict which substances can reduce or oxidize another species, and to predict whether redox reactions will be product-favored or reactant-favored (Section 20.4). **Study Questions: 17–24, 55, 56.**

e. Use the Nernst equation (Equations 20.2 and 20.3) to calculate the cell potential under nonstandard conditions (Section 20.5). **Study Questions: 25–28, 75–79.**

f. Explain how cell voltage allows the determination of pH (Section 20.5) and other ion concentrations. **Study Questions: 29, 30, 77.**

g. Use the relationships between cell voltage ($E°_{cell}$) and free energy ($\Delta_r G°$) (Equations 20.5 and 20.6) and between $E°_{cell}$ and an equilibrium constant for the cell reaction (Equation 20.7) (Section 20.6 and Table 20.2). **Study Questions: 31–36, 60, 61, 63, 78, 82.**

Explore electrolysis, the use of electrical energy to produce chemical change

a. Describe the chemical processes occurring in an electrolysis. Recognize the factors that determine which substances are oxidized and reduced at the electrodes (Section 20.7). **Study Questions: 37–42, 74.**

b. Relate the amount of a substance oxidized or reduced to the amount of current and the time the current flows (Section 20.8). **Study Questions: 43–48, 59, 64–66.**

Key Equations

Equation 20.1 (page 915) Calculating a standard cell potential, $E°_{cell}$, from standard half-cell potentials.

$$E°_{cell} = E°_{cathode} - E°_{anode}$$

Equation 20.2 (page 921) The Nernst equation, the relationship of the cell potential under nonstandard conditions (E) to that under standard conditions ($E°$). R is the gas constant (8.314472 J/K · mol); T is the temperature (K); and n is the number of moles of electrons transferred between oxidizing and reducing agents. F is the **Faraday constant** (9.6485338×10^4 C/mol of e$^-$), and Q is the reaction quotient.

$$E = E° - (RT/nF) \ln Q$$

Equation 20.3 (page 922) Nernst equation (at 298 K).

$$E = E° - \frac{0.0257}{n} \ln Q$$

Equation 20.4 (page 925) The amount of work done (w) by an electrochemical system.

$$w_{max} = nFE$$

Equations 20.5 and 20.6 (page 926) Relationship between free energy change and the cell potential under nonstandard or standard conditions, respectively.

$$\Delta G = -nFE \text{ or } \Delta G° = -nFE°$$

Equation 20.7 (page 927) Relationship between the equilibrium constant and the standard cell potential for a reaction (at 298 K).

$$\ln K = \frac{nE°}{0.0257}$$

Equation 20.8 (page 934) Relationship between current, electric charge, and time.

$$\text{Current (amperes, A)} = \frac{\text{electric charge (coulombs, C)}}{\text{time, } t \text{ (seconds, s)}}$$

Study Questions

◉WL Interactive versions of these questions are assignable in OWL.

▲ denotes challenging questions.

Blue-numbered questions have answers in Appendix R and fully worked solutions in the *Student Solutions Manual*.

Practicing Skills

Balancing Equations for Oxidation–Reduction Reactions
(See Section 20.1 and Examples 20.1–20.3.)

When balancing the following redox equations, it may be necessary to add $H^+(aq)$ or $H^+(aq)$ plus H_2O for reactions in acid, and OH^- (aq) or $OH^-(aq)$ plus H_2O for reactions in base.

1. Write balanced equations for the following half-reactions. Specify whether each is an oxidation or reduction.
   (a) $Cr(s) \rightarrow Cr^{3+}(aq)$ (in acid)
   (b) $AsH_3(g) \rightarrow As(s)$ (in acid)
   (c) $VO_3^-(aq) \rightarrow V^{2+}(aq)$ (in acid)
   (d) $Ag(s) \rightarrow Ag_2O(s)$ (in base)

2. Write balanced equations for the following half-reactions. Specify whether each is an oxidation or reduction.
   (a) $H_2O_2(aq) \rightarrow O_2(g)$ (in acid)
   (b) $H_2C_2O_4(aq) \rightarrow CO_2(g)$ (in acid)
   (c) $NO_3^-(aq) \rightarrow NO(g)$ (in acid)
   (d) $MnO_4^-(aq) \rightarrow MnO_2(s)$ (in base)

3. Balance the following redox equations. All occur in acid solution.
   (a) $Ag(s) + NO_3^-(aq) \rightarrow NO_2(g) + Ag^+(aq)$
   (b) $MnO_4^-(aq) + HSO_3^-(aq) \rightarrow$
   $$Mn^{2+}(aq) + SO_4^{2-}(aq)$$
   (c) $Zn(s) + NO_3^-(aq) \rightarrow Zn^{2+}(aq) + N_2O(g)$
   (d) $Cr(s) + NO_3^-(aq) \rightarrow Cr^{3+}(aq) + NO(g)$

4. Balance the following redox equations. All occur in acid solution.
   (a) $Sn(s) + H^+(aq) \rightarrow Sn^{2+}(aq) + H_2(g)$
   (b) $Cr_2O_7^{2-}(aq) + Fe^{2+}(aq) \rightarrow Cr^{3+}(aq) + Fe^{3+}(aq)$
   (c) $MnO_2(s) + Cl^-(aq) \rightarrow Mn^{2+}(aq) + Cl_2(g)$
   (d) $CH_2O(aq) + Ag^+(aq) \rightarrow HCO_2H(aq) + Ag(s)$

5. Balance the following redox equations. All occur in basic solution.
   (a) $Al(s) + H_2O(\ell) \rightarrow Al(OH)_4^-(aq) + H_2(g)$
   (b) $CrO_4^{2-}(aq) + SO_3^{2-}(aq) \rightarrow Cr(OH)_3(s) + SO_4^{2-}(aq)$
   (c) $Zn(s) + Cu(OH)_2(s) \rightarrow [Zn(OH)_4]^{2-}(aq) + Cu(s)$
   (d) $HS^-(aq) + ClO_3^-(aq) \rightarrow S(s) + Cl^-(aq)$

6. Balance the following redox equations. All occur in basic solution.
   (a) $Fe(OH)_3(s) + Cr(s) \rightarrow Cr(OH)_3(s) + Fe(OH)_2(s)$
   (b) $NiO_2(s) + Zn(s) \rightarrow Ni(OH)_2(s) + Zn(OH)_2(s)$
   (c) $Fe(OH)_2(s) + CrO_4^{2-}(aq) \rightarrow$
   $$Fe(OH)_3(s) + [Cr(OH)_4]^-(aq)$$
   (d) $N_2H_4(aq) + Ag_2O(s) \rightarrow N_2(g) + Ag(s)$

Constructing Voltaic Cells
(See Section 20.2 and Example 20.4.)

7. A voltaic cell is constructed using the reaction of chromium metal and iron(II) ions.

$$2 \; Cr(s) + 3 \; Fe^{2+}(aq) \rightarrow 2 \; Cr^{3+}(aq) + 3 \; Fe(s)$$

   Complete the following sentences: Electrons in the external circuit flow from the ___ electrode to the ___ electrode. Negative ions move in the salt bridge from the ___ half-cell to the ___ half-cell. The half-reaction at the anode is ___, and that at the cathode is ___.

8. A voltaic cell is constructed using the reaction

$$Mg(s) + 2 \; H^+(aq) \rightarrow Mg^{2+}(aq) + H_2(g)$$

   (a) Write equations for the oxidation and reduction half-reactions.
   (b) Which half-reaction occurs in the anode compartment, and which occurs in the cathode compartment?
   (c) Complete the following sentences: Electrons in the external circuit flow from the ___ electrode to the ___ electrode. Negative ions move in the salt bridge from the ___ half-cell to the ___ half-cell. The half-reaction at the anode is ___, and that at the cathode is ___.

9. The half-cells $Fe^{2+}(aq)|Fe(s)$ and $O_2(g)|H_2O$ (in acid solution) are linked to create a voltaic cell.
   (a) Write equations for the oxidation and reduction half-reactions and for the overall (cell) reaction.
   (b) Which half-reaction occurs in the anode compartment, and which occurs in the cathode compartment?
   (c) Complete the following sentences: Electrons in the external circuit flow from the ___ electrode to the ___ electrode. Negative ions move in the salt bridge from the ___ half-cell to the ___ half-cell.

10. The half-cells $Sn^{2+}(aq)|Sn(s)$ and $Cl_2(g)|Cl^-(aq)$ are linked to create a voltaic cell.
    (a) Write equations for the oxidation and reduction half-reactions and for the overall (cell) reaction.
    (b) Which half-reaction occurs in the anode compartment, and which occurs in the cathode compartment?
    (c) Complete the following sentences: Electrons in the external circuit flow from the ___ electrode to the ___ electrode. Negative ions move in the salt bridge from the ___ half-cell to the ___ half-cell.

Commercial Electrochemical Cells
(See Section 20.3.)

11. What are the similarities and differences between dry cells, alkaline batteries, and Ni-cad batteries?

12. What reactions occur when a lead storage battery is recharged?

Standard Electrochemical Potentials
(See Section 20.4 and Example 20.5.)

13. Calculate the value of $E°$ for each of the following reactions. Decide whether each is product-favored in the direction written.
    (a) $2\ I^-(aq) + Zn^{2+}(aq) \rightarrow I_2(s) + Zn(s)$
    (b) $Zn^{2+}(aq) + Ni(s) \rightarrow Zn(s) + Ni^{2+}(aq)$
    (c) $2\ Cl^-(aq) + Cu^{2+}(aq) \rightarrow Cu(s) + Cl_2(g)$
    (d) $Fe^{2+}(aq) + Ag^+(aq) \rightarrow Fe^{3+}(aq) + Ag(s)$

14. Calculate the value of $E°$ for each of the following reactions. Decide whether each is product-favored in the direction written. [Reaction (d) is carried out in basic solution.]
    (a) $Br_2(\ell) + Mg(s) \rightarrow Mg^{2+}(aq) + 2\ Br^-(aq)$
    (b) $Zn^{2+}(aq) + Mg(s) \rightarrow Zn(s) + Mg^{2+}(aq)$
    (c) $Sn^{2+}(aq) + 2\ Ag^+(aq) \rightarrow Sn^{4+}(aq) + 2\ Ag(s)$
    (d) $2\ Zn(s) + O_2(g) + 2\ H_2O(\ell) + 4\ OH^-(aq) \rightarrow$
    $2\ [Zn(OH)_4]^{2-}(aq)$

15. Balance each of the following unbalanced equations; then calculate the standard potential, $E°$, and decide whether each is product-favored as written. (All reactions are carried out in acid solution.)
    (a) $Sn^{2+}(aq) + Ag(s) \rightarrow Sn(s) + Ag^+(aq)$
    (b) $Al(s) + Sn^{4+}(aq) \rightarrow Sn^{2+}(aq) + Al^{3+}(aq)$
    (c) $ClO_3^-(aq) + Ce^{3+}(aq) \rightarrow Cl_2(g) + Ce^{4+}(aq)$
    (d) $Cu(s) + NO_3^-(aq) \rightarrow Cu^{2+}(aq) + NO(g)$

16. Balance each of the following unbalanced equations; then calculate the standard potential, $E°$, and decide whether each is product-favored as written. (All reactions are carried out in acid solution.)
    (a) $I_2(s) + Br^-(aq) \rightarrow I^-(aq) + Br_2(\ell)$
    (b) $Fe^{2+}(aq) + Cu^{2+}(aq) \rightarrow Cu(s) + Fe^{3+}(aq)$
    (c) $Fe^{2+}(aq) + Cr_2O_7^{2-}(aq) \rightarrow Fe^{3+}(aq) + Cr^{3+}(aq)$
    (d) $MnO_4^-(aq) + HNO_2(aq) \rightarrow Mn^{2+}(aq) + NO_3^-(aq)$

Ranking Oxidizing and Reducing Agents
(See Section 20.4 and Example 20.5. Use a table of standard reduction potentials [Table 20.1 or Appendix M] to answer Study Questions 17–24.)

17. Consider the following half-reactions:

Half-Reaction	$E°(V)$
$Cu^{2+}(aq) + 2\ e^- \rightarrow Cu(s)$	+0.34
$Sn^{2+}(aq) + 2\ e^- \rightarrow Sn(s)$	−0.14
$Fe^{2+}(aq) + 2\ e^- \rightarrow Fe(s)$	−0.44
$Zn^{2+}(aq) + 2\ e^- \rightarrow Zn(s)$	−0.76
$Al^{3+}(aq) + 3\ e^- \rightarrow Al(s)$	−1.66

   (a) Based on $E°$ values, which metal is the most easily oxidized?
   (b) Which metals on this list are capable of reducing $Fe^{2+}(aq)$ to $Fe(s)$?
   (c) Write a balanced chemical equation for the reaction of $Fe^{2+}(aq)$ with $Sn(s)$. Is this reaction product-favored or reactant-favored?
   (d) Write a balanced chemical equation for the reaction of $Zn^{2+}(aq)$ with $Sn(s)$. Is this reaction product-favored or reactant-favored?

18. Consider the following half-reactions:

Half-Reaction	$E°(V)$
$MnO_4^-(aq) + 8\ H^+(aq) + 5\ e^- \rightarrow Mn^{2+}(aq) + 4\ H_2O(\ell)$	+1.51
$BrO_3^-(aq) + 6\ H^+(aq) + 6\ e^- \rightarrow Br^-(aq) + 3\ H_2O(\ell)$	+1.47
$Cr_2O_7^{2-}(aq) + 14\ H^+(aq) + 6\ e^- \rightarrow 2\ Cr^{3+}(aq) + 7\ H_2O(\ell)$	+1.33
$NO_3^-(aq) + 4\ H^+(aq) + 3\ e^- \rightarrow NO(g) + 2\ H_2O(\ell)$	+0.96
$SO_4^{2-}(aq) + 4\ H^+(aq) + 2\ e^- \rightarrow SO_2(g) + 2\ H_2O(\ell)$	+0.20

   (a) Choosing from among the reactants in these half-reactions, identify the strongest and weakest oxidizing agents.
   (b) Which of the oxidizing agents listed is (are) capable of oxidizing $Br^-(aq)$ to $BrO_3^-(aq)$ (in acid solution)?
   (c) Write a balanced chemical equation for the reaction of $Cr_2O_7^{2-}(aq)$ with $SO_2(g)$ in acid solution. Is this reaction product-favored or reactant-favored?
   (d) Write a balanced chemical equation for the reaction of $Cr_2O_7^{2-}(aq)$ with $Mn^{2+}(aq)$. Is this reaction product-favored or reactant-favored?

19. Which of the following elements is the best reducing agent under standard conditions?
   (a) Cu   (d) Ag
   (b) Zn   (e) Cr
   (c) Fe

20. From the following list, identify those elements that are easier to oxidize than $H_2(g)$.
(a) Cu   (d) Ag
(b) Zn   (e) Cr
(c) Fe

21. Which of the following ions is most easily reduced?
(a) $Cu^{2+}(aq)$ (d) $Ag^+(aq)$
(b) $Zn^{2+}(aq)$ (e) $Al^{3+}(aq)$
(c) $Fe^{2+}(aq)$

22. From the following list, identify the ions that are more easily reduced than $H^+(aq)$.
(a) $Cu^{2+}(aq)$ (d) $Ag^+(aq)$
(b) $Zn^{2+}(aq)$ (e) $Al^{3+}(aq)$
(c) $Fe^{2+}(aq)$

23. (a) Which halogen is most easily reduced in acidic solution: F_2, Cl_2, Br_2, or I_2?
(b) Identify the halogens that are better oxidizing agents in acidic solution than $MnO_2(s)$.

24. (a) Which ion is most easily oxidized to the elemental halogen in acidic solution: F^-, Cl^-, Br^-, or I^-?
(b) Identify the halide ions that are more easily oxidized in acidic solution than $H_2O(\ell)$.

Electrochemical Cells under Nonstandard Conditions
(See Section 20.5 and Examples 20.6 and 20.7.)

25. Calculate the potential delivered by a voltaic cell using the following reaction if all dissolved species are 2.5×10^{-2} M and the pressure of H_2 is 1.0 bar.

$$Zn(s) + 2 H_2O(\ell) + 2 OH^-(aq) \rightarrow$$
$$[Zn(OH)_4]^{2-}(aq) + H_2(g)$$

26. Calculate the potential developed by a voltaic cell using the following reaction if all dissolved species are 0.015 M.

$$2 Fe^{2+}(aq) + H_2O_2(aq) + 2 H^+(aq) \rightarrow$$
$$2 Fe^{3+}(aq) + 2 H_2O(\ell)$$

27. One half-cell in a voltaic cell is constructed from a silver wire electrode in a 0.25 M solution of $AgNO_3$. The other half-cell consists of a zinc electrode in a 0.010 M solution of $Zn(NO_3)_2$. Calculate the cell potential.

28. One half-cell in a voltaic cell is constructed from a copper wire electrode in a 4.8×10^{-3} M solution of $Cu(NO_3)_2$. The other half-cell consists of a zinc electrode in a 0.40 M solution of $Zn(NO_3)_2$. Calculate the cell potential.

29. One half-cell in a voltaic cell is constructed from a silver wire electrode in a $AgNO_3$ solution of unknown concentration. The other half-cell consists of a zinc electrode in a 1.0 M solution of $Zn(NO_3)_2$. A potential of 1.48 V is measured for this cell. Use this information to calculate the concentration of $Ag^+(aq)$.

30. One half-cell in a voltaic cell is constructed from an iron electrode in an $Fe(NO_3)_2$ solution of unknown concentration. The other half-cell is a standard hydrogen electrode. A potential of 0.49 V is measured for this cell. Use this information to calculate the concentration of $Fe^{2+}(aq)$.

Electrochemistry, Thermodynamics, and Equilibrium
(See Section 20.6 and Examples 20.8 and 20.9.)

31. Calculate $\Delta_r G°$ and the equilibrium constant for the following reactions.
(a) $2 Fe^{3+}(aq) + 2 I^-(aq) \rightleftharpoons 2 Fe^{2+}(aq) + I_2(aq)$
(b) $I_2(aq) + 2 Br^-(aq) \rightleftharpoons 2 I^-(aq) + Br_2(\ell)$

32. Calculate $\Delta_r G°$ and the equilibrium constant for the following reactions.
(a) $Zn^{2+}(aq) + Ni(s) \rightleftharpoons Zn(s) + Ni^{2+}(aq)$
(b) $Cu(s) + 2 Ag^+(aq) \rightleftharpoons Cu^{2+}(aq) + 2 Ag(s)$

33. Use standard reduction potentials (Appendix M) for the half-reactions $AgBr(s) + e^- \rightarrow Ag(s) + Br^-(aq)$ and $Ag^+(aq) + e^- \rightarrow Ag(s)$ to calculate the value of K_{sp} for AgBr.

34. Use the standard reduction potentials (Appendix M) for the half-reactions $Hg_2Cl_2(s) + 2 e^- \rightarrow 2 Hg(\ell) + 2 Cl^-(aq)$ and $Hg_2^{2+}(aq) + 2 e^- \rightarrow 2 Hg(\ell)$ to calculate the value of K_{sp} for Hg_2Cl_2.

35. Use the standard reduction potentials (Appendix M) for the half-reactions $[AuCl_4]^-(aq) + 3 e^- \rightarrow Au(s) + 4 Cl^-(aq)$ and $Au^{3+}(aq) + 3 e^- \rightarrow Au(s)$ to calculate the value of $K_{formation}$ for the complex ion $[AuCl_4]^-(aq)$.

36. Use the standard reduction potentials (Appendix M) for the half-reactions $[Zn(OH)_4]^{2-}(aq) + 2 e^- \rightarrow Zn(s) + 4 OH^-(aq)$ and $Zn^{2+}(aq) + 2 e^- \rightarrow Zn(s)$ to calculate the value of $K_{formation}$ for the complex ion $[Zn(OH)_4]^{2-}$.

Electrolysis
(See Section 20.7 and Example 20.10.)

37. Diagram the apparatus used to electrolyze molten NaCl. Identify the anode and the cathode. Trace the movement of electrons through the external circuit and the movement of ions in the electrolysis cell.

38. Diagram the apparatus used to electrolyze aqueous $CuCl_2$. Identify the reaction products, the anode, and the cathode. Trace the movement of electrons through the external circuit and the movement of ions in the electrolysis cell.

39. Which product, O_2 or F_2, is more likely to form at the anode in the electrolysis of an aqueous solution of KF? Explain your reasoning.

40. Which product, Ca or H_2, is more likely to form at the cathode in the electrolysis of $CaCl_2$? Explain your reasoning.

41. An aqueous solution of KBr is placed in a beaker with two inert platinum electrodes. When the cell is attached to an external source of electrical energy, electrolysis occurs.
(a) Hydrogen gas and hydroxide ion form at the cathode. Write an equation for the half-reaction that occurs at this electrode.
(b) Bromine is the primary product at the anode. Write an equation for its formation.

42. An aqueous solution of Na_2S is placed in a beaker with two inert platinum electrodes. When the cell is attached to an external battery, electrolysis occurs.
    (a) Hydrogen gas and hydroxide ion form at the cathode. Write an equation for the half-reaction that occurs at this electrode.
    (b) Sulfur is the primary product at the anode. Write an equation for its formation.

Counting Electrons
(See Section 20.8 and Example 20.11.)

43. In the electrolysis of a solution containing $Ni^{2+}(aq)$, metallic $Ni(s)$ deposits on the cathode. Using a current of 0.150 A for 12.2 minutes, what mass of nickel will form?

44. In the electrolysis of a solution containing $Ag^+(aq)$, metallic $Ag(s)$ deposits on the cathode. Using a current of 1.12 A for 2.40 hours, what mass of silver forms?

45. Electrolysis of a solution of $CuSO_4(aq)$ to give copper metal is carried out using a current of 0.66 A. How long should electrolysis continue to produce 0.50 g of copper?

46. Electrolysis of a solution of $Zn(NO_3)_2(aq)$ to give zinc metal is carried out using a current of 2.12 A. How long should electrolysis continue in order to prepare 2.5 g of zinc?

47. A voltaic cell can be built using the reaction between Al metal and O_2 from the air. If the Al anode of this cell consists of 84 g of aluminum, how many hours can the cell produce 1.0 A of electricity, assuming an unlimited supply of O_2?

48. Assume the specifications of a Ni-Cd voltaic cell include delivery of 0.25 A of current for 1.00 hour. What is the minimum mass of the cadmium that must be used to make the anode in this cell?

General Questions

These questions are not designated as to type or location in the chapter. They may combine several concepts.

49. Write balanced equations for the following half-reactions.
    (a) $UO_2^+(aq) \rightarrow U^{4+}(aq)$ (acid solution)
    (b) $ClO_3^-(aq) \rightarrow Cl^-(aq)$ (acid solution)
    (c) $N_2H_4(aq) \rightarrow N_2(g)$ (basic solution)
    (d) $ClO^-(aq) \rightarrow Cl^-(aq)$ (basic solution)

50. Balance the following equations.
    (a) $Zn(s) + VO^{2+}(aq) \rightarrow$
       $Zn^{2+}(aq) + V^{3+}(aq)$ (acid solution)
    (b) $Zn(s) + VO_3^-(aq) \rightarrow$
       $V^{2+}(aq) + Zn^{2+}(aq)$ (acid solution)
    (c) $Zn(s) + ClO^-(aq) \rightarrow$
       $Zn(OH)_2(s) + Cl^-(aq)$ (basic solution)
    (d) $ClO^-(aq) + [Cr(OH)_4]^-(aq) \rightarrow$
       $Cl^-(aq) + CrO_4^{2-}(aq)$ (basic solution)

51. Magnesium metal is oxidized, and silver ions are reduced in a voltaic cell using $Mg^{2+}(aq, 1\ M)|Mg$ and $Ag^+(aq, 1\ M)|Ag$ half-cells.

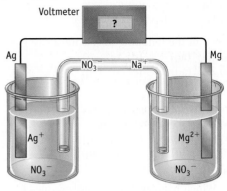

    (a) Label each part of the cell.
    (b) Write equations for the half-reactions occurring at the anode and the cathode, and write an equation for the net reaction in the cell.
    (c) Trace the movement of electrons in the external circuit. Assuming the salt bridge contains $NaNO_3$, trace the movement of the Na^+ and NO_3^- ions in the salt bridge that occurs when a voltaic cell produces current. Why is a salt bridge required in a cell?

52. You want to set up a series of voltaic cells with specific cell potentials. A $Zn^{2+}(aq, 1.0\ M)|Zn(s)$ half-cell is in one compartment. Identify several half-cells that you could use so that the cell potential will be close to (a) 1.1 V and (b) 0.50 V. Consider cells in which the zinc cell can be either the cathode or the anode.

53. You want to set up a series of voltaic cells with specific cell potentials. The $Ag^+(aq, 1.0\ M)|Ag(s)$ half-cell is one of the compartments. Identify several half-cells that you could use so that the cell potential will be close to (a) 1.7 V and (b) 0.50 V. Consider cells in which the silver cell can be either the cathode or the anode.

54. Which of the following reactions is (are) product-favored?
    (a) $Zn(s) + I_2(s) \rightarrow Zn^{2+}(aq) + 2\ I^-(aq)$
    (b) $2\ Cl^-(aq) + I_2(s) \rightarrow Cl_2(g) + 2\ I^-(aq)$
    (c) $2\ Na^+(aq) + 2\ Cl^-(aq) \rightarrow 2\ Na(s) + Cl_2(g)$
    (d) $2\ K(s) + 2\ H_2O(\ell) \rightarrow$
       $2\ K^+(aq) + H_2(g) + 2\ OH^-(aq)$

55. In the table of standard reduction potentials, locate the half-reactions for the reductions of the following metal ions to the metal: $Sn^{2+}(aq)$, $Au^+(aq)$, $Zn^{2+}(aq)$, $Co^{2+}(aq)$, $Ag^+(aq)$, $Cu^{2+}(aq)$. Among the metal ions and metals that make up these half-reactions:
    (a) Which metal ion is the weakest oxidizing agent?
    (b) Which metal ion is the strongest oxidizing agent?
    (c) Which metal is the strongest reducing agent?
    (d) Which metal is the weakest reducing agent?
    (e) Will $Sn(s)$ reduce $Cu^{2+}(aq)$ to $Cu(s)$?
    (f) Will $Ag(s)$ reduce $Co^{2+}(aq)$ to $Co(s)$?
    (g) Which metal ions on the list can be reduced by $Sn(s)$?
    (h) What metals can be oxidized by $Ag^+(aq)$?

56. ▲ In the table of standard reduction potentials, locate the half-reactions for the reductions of the following nonmetals: F_2, Cl_2, Br_2, I_2 (reduction to halide ions), and O_2, S, Se (reduction to H_2X in aqueous acid). Among the elements, ions, and compounds that make up these half-reactions:
(a) Which element is the weakest oxidizing agent?
(b) Which ion or H_2X is the weakest reducing agent?
(c) Which of the elements listed is (are) capable of oxidizing H_2O to O_2?
(d) Which of these elements listed is (are) capable of oxidizing H_2S to S?
(e) Is O_2 capable of oxidizing I^- to I_2, in acid solution?
(f) Is S capable of oxidizing I^- to I_2?
(g) Is the reaction $H_2S(aq) + Se(s) \rightarrow H_2Se(aq) + S(s)$ product-favored?
(h) Is the reaction $H_2S(aq) + I_2(s) \rightarrow 2\,H^+(aq) + 2\,I^-(aq) + S(s)$ product-favored?

57. Four voltaic cells are set up. In each, one half-cell contains a standard hydrogen electrode. The second half-cell is one of the following:
  (i) $Cr^{3+}(aq, 1.0\,M)\,|\,Cr(s)$
  (ii) $Fe^{2+}(aq, 1.0\,M)\,|\,Fe(s)$
  (iii) $Cu^{2+}(aq, 1.0\,M)\,|\,Cu(s)$
  (iv) $Mg^{2+}(aq, 1.0\,M)\,|\,Mg(s)$.
(a) In which of the voltaic cells does the hydrogen electrode serve as the cathode?
(b) Which voltaic cell produces the highest potential? Which produces the lowest potential?

58. The following half-cells are available:
  (i) $Ag^+(aq, 1.0\,M)\,|\,Ag(s)$
  (ii) $Zn^{2+}(aq, 1.0\,M)\,|\,Zn(s)$
  (iii) $Cu^{2+}(aq, 1.0\,M)\,|\,Cu(s)$
  (iv) $Co^{2+}(aq, 1.0\,M)\,|\,Co(s)$.

Linking any two half-cells makes a voltaic cell. Given four different half-cells, six voltaic cells are possible. These are labeled, for simplicity, Ag-Zn, Ag-Cu, Ag-Co, Zn-Cu, Zn-Co, and Cu-Co.
(a) In which of the voltaic cells does the copper electrode serve as the cathode? In which of the voltaic cells does the cobalt electrode serve as the anode?
(b) Which combination of half-cells generates the highest potential? Which combination generates the lowest potential?

59. The reaction occurring in the cell in which Al_2O_3 and aluminum salts are electrolyzed is $Al^{3+}(aq) + 3\,e^- \rightarrow Al(s)$. If the electrolysis cell operates at 5.0 V and 1.0×10^5 A, what mass of aluminum metal can be produced in a 24-hour day?

60. ▲ A cell is constructed using the following half-reactions:

$Ag^+(aq) + e^- \rightarrow Ag(s)$

$Ag_2SO_4(s) + 2\,e^- \rightarrow$
$\qquad 2\,Ag(s) + SO_4^{2-}(aq)$ $E° = 0.653$ V

(a) What reactions should be observed at the anode and cathode?
(b) Calculate the solubility product constant, K_{sp}, for Ag_2SO_4.

61. ▲ A potential of 0.142 V is recorded (under standard conditions) for a voltaic cell constructed using the following half reactions:

Cathode: $Pb^{2+}(aq) + 2\,e^- \rightarrow Pb(s)$
Anode: $PbCl_2(s) + 2\,e^- \rightarrow Pb(s) + 2\,Cl^-(aq)$
Net: $Pb^{2+}(aq) + 2\,Cl^-(aq) \rightarrow PbCl_2(s)$

(a) What is the standard reduction potential for the anode reaction?
(b) Calculate the solubility product, K_{sp}, for $PbCl_2$.

62. What is the value of $E°$ for the following half-reaction?

$$Ag_2CrO_4(s) + 2\,e^- \rightarrow 2\,Ag(s) + CrO_4^{2-}(aq)$$

63. The standard potential, $E°$, for the reaction of $Zn(s)$ and $Cl_2(g)$ is $+2.12$ V. What is the standard free energy change, $\Delta_rG°$, for the reaction?

64. ▲ An electrolysis cell for aluminum production operates at 5.0 V and a current of 1.0×10^5 A. Calculate the number of kilowatt-hours of energy required to produce 1 metric ton (1.0×10^3 kg) of aluminum. (1 kWh $= 3.6 \times 10^6$ J and 1 J $= 1$ C · V)

65. ▲ Electrolysis of molten NaCl is done in cells operating at 7.0 V and 4.0×10^4 A. What mass of Na(s) and $Cl_2(g)$ can be produced in 1 day in such a cell? What is the energy consumption in kilowatt-hours? (1 kWh $= 3.6 \times 10^6$ J and 1 J $= 1$ C · V)

66. ▲ A current of 0.0100 A is passed through a solution of rhodium sulfate, causing reduction of the metal ion to the metal. After 3.00 hours, 0.038 g of Rh has been deposited. What is the charge on the rhodium ion, Rh^{n+}? What is the formula for rhodium sulfate?

67. ▲ A current of 0.44 A is passed through a solution of ruthenium nitrate causing reduction of the metal ion to the metal. After 25.0 minutes, 0.345 g of Ru has been deposited. What is the charge on the ruthenium ion, Ru^{n+}? What is the formula for ruthenium nitrate?

68. The total charge that can be delivered by a large dry cell battery before its voltage drops too low is usually about 35 amp-hours. (One amp-hour is the charge that passes through a circuit when 1 A flows for 1 hour.) What mass of Zn is consumed when 35 amp-hours are drawn from the cell?

69. Chlorine gas is obtained commercially by electrolysis of brine (a concentrated aqueous solution of NaCl). If the electrolysis cells operate at 4.6 V and 3.0×10^5 A, what mass of chlorine can be produced in a 24-hour day?

70. Write equations for the half-reactions that occur at the anode and cathode in the electrolysis of *molten* KBr. What are the products formed at the anode and cathode in the electrolysis of *aqueous* KBr?

71. The products formed in the electrolysis of aqueous $CuSO_4$ are Cu(s) and $O_2(g)$. Write equations for the anode and cathode reactions.

72. Predict the products formed in the electrolysis of an aqueous solution of $CdSO_4$.

73. In the electrolysis of $HNO_3(aq)$, hydrogen is produced at the cathode. According to a table of reduction potentials, $NO_3^-(aq)$ is easier to reduce than $H^+(aq)$. Suggest a possible reason why H_2 formed rather than NO. What is the product formed at the anode? Write an equation for the anode reaction.

74. The metallurgy of aluminum involves electrolysis of Al_2O_3 dissolved in molten cryolyte (Na_3AlF_6) at about 950 °C. Aluminum metal is produced at the cathode. Predict the anode product and write equations for the reactions occurring at both electrodes.

75. Two half-cells, $Pt|Fe^{3+}(aq, 0.50 M)$, $Fe^{2+}(aq, 1.0 \times 10^{-5} M)$ and $Hg^{2+}(aq, 0.020 M)|Hg$, are constructed and then linked together to form a voltaic cell. Which electrode is the anode? What will be the potential of the voltaic cell at 298 K?

76. A voltaic cell is set up utilizing the reaction

$$Cu(s) + 2 Ag^+(aq) \rightarrow Cu^{2+}(aq) + 2 Ag(s)$$

$$Cu(s)|Cu^{2+}(aq, 1.0 M)||Ag^+(aq, 0.001 M)|Ag(s)$$

Under standard conditions, the expected potential is 0.45 V. Predict whether the potential for the voltaic cell will be higher, lower, or the same as the standard potential. Verify your prediction by calculating the new cell potential.

77. Calculate the cell potential for the following cell:

$$Pt|H_2(P = 1 \text{ bar})|H^+(aq, 1.0 M)||$$
$$Fe^{3+}(aq, 1.0M), Fe^{2+}(aq, 1.0M)|Pt$$

Will this reaction be more or less favorable at lower pH? To determine this, calculate the cell potential for a reaction in which $[H^+(aq)]$ is 1.0×10^{-7} M.

78. A voltaic cell set up utilizing the reaction

$$Cu(s) + 2 Ag^+(aq) \rightarrow Cu^{2+}(aq) + 2 Ag(s)$$

has a cell potential of 0.45 at 298 K. Describe how the potential of this cell will change as the cell is discharged. At what point does the cell potential reach a constant value? Explain your answer.

79. Two $Ag^+(aq)|Ag$ half-cells are constructed. The first has $[Ag^+] = 1.0$ M, the second has $[Ag^+] = 1.0 \times 10^{-5}$ M. When linked together with a salt bridge and external circuit, a cell potential is observed. (This kind of voltaic cell is referred to as a *concentration cell.*)
    (a) Draw a picture of this cell, labeling all components. Indicate the cathode and the anode, and indicate in which direction electrons flow in the external circuit.
    (b) Calculate the cell potential at 298 K.

80. Calculate equilibrium constants for the following reactions at 298 K. Indicate whether the equilibrium as written is reactant- or product-favored.
    (a) $Co(s) + Ni^{2+}(aq) \rightleftharpoons Co^{2+}(aq) + Ni(s)$
    (b) $Fe^{3+}(aq) + Cr^{2+}(aq) \rightleftharpoons Cr^{3+}(aq) + Fe^{2+}(aq)$

81. Calculate equilibrium constants for the following reactions at 298 K. Indicate whether the equilibrium as written is reactant- or product-favored.
    (a) $2 Cl^-(aq) + Br_2(\ell) \rightleftharpoons Cl_2(aq) + 2 Br^-(aq)$
    (b) $Fe^{2+}(aq) + Ag^+(aq) \rightleftharpoons Fe^{3+}(aq) + Ag(s)$

82. Use the table of standard reduction potentials (Appendix M) to calculate $\Delta_r G°$ for the following reactions at 298 K.
    (a) $ClO_3^-(aq) + 5 Cl^-(aq) + 6 H^+(aq) \rightarrow$
    $$3 Cl_2(g) + 3 H_2O(\ell)$$
    (b) $AgCl(s) + Br^-(aq) \rightarrow AgBr(s) + Cl^-(aq)$

83. Use the table of standard reduction potentials (Appendix M) to calculate $\Delta_r G°$ for the following reactions at 298 K.
    (a) $3 Cu(s) + 2 NO_3^-(aq) + 8 H^+(aq) \rightarrow$
    $$3 Cu^{2+}(aq) + 2 NO(g) + 4 H_2O(\ell)$$
    (b) $H_2O_2(aq) + 2 Cl^-(aq) + 2 H^+(aq) \rightarrow$
    $$Cl_2(g) + 2 H_2O(\ell)$$

84. ▲ Write balanced equations for the following reduction half-reactions involving organic compounds.
    (a) $HCO_2H \rightarrow CH_2O$ (acid solution)
    (b) $C_6H_5CO_2H \rightarrow C_6H_5CH_3$ (acid solution)
    (c) $CH_3CH_2CHO \rightarrow CH_3CH_2CH_2OH$ (acid solution)
    (d) $CH_3OH \rightarrow CH_4$ (acid solution)

85. ▲ Balance the following equations involving organic compounds.
    (a) $Ag^+(aq) + C_6H_5CHO(aq) \rightarrow$
    $$Ag(s) + C_6H_5CO_2H(aq) \quad \text{(acid solution)}$$
    (b) $CH_3CH_2OH + Cr_2O_7^{2-}(aq) \rightarrow$
    $$CH_3CO_2H(aq) + Cr^{3+}(aq) \quad \text{(acid solution)}$$

86. A voltaic cell is constructed in which one half-cell consists of a silver wire in an aqueous solution of $AgNO_3$. The other half-cell consists of an inert platinum wire in an aqueous solution containing $Fe^{2+}(aq)$ and $Fe^{3+}(aq)$.
    (a) Calculate the cell potential, assuming standard conditions.
    (b) Write the net ionic equation for the reaction occurring in the cell.
    (c) Which electrode is the anode and which is the cathode?
    (d) If $[Ag^+]$ is 0.10 M, and $[Fe^{2+}]$ and $[Fe^{3+}]$ are both 1.0 M, what is the cell potential? Is the net cell reaction still that used in part (a)? If not, what is the net reaction under the new conditions?

87. An expensive but lighter alternative to the lead storage battery is the silver-zinc battery.

$$Ag_2O(s) + Zn(s) + H_2O(\ell) \rightarrow Zn(OH)_2(s) + 2 Ag(s)$$

The electrolyte is 40% KOH, and silver–silver oxide electrodes are separated from zinc–zinc hydroxide electrodes by a plastic sheet that is permeable to hydroxide ions. Under normal operating conditions, the battery has a potential of 1.59 V.
    (a) How much energy can be produced per gram of reactants in the silver-zinc battery? Assume the battery produces a current of 0.10 A.

(b) How much energy can be produced per gram of reactants in the standard lead storage battery? Assume the battery produces a current of 0.10 A at 2.0 V.

(c) Which battery (silver-zinc or lead storage) produces the greater energy per gram of reactants?

88. The specifications for a lead storage battery include delivery of a steady 1.5 A of current for 15 hours.

(a) What is the minimum mass of lead that will be used in the anode?

(b) What mass of PbO_2 must be used in the cathode?

(c) Assume that the volume of the battery is 0.50 L. What is the minimum molarity of H_2SO_4 necessary?

89. Manganese may play an important role in chemical cycles in the oceans (page 922). Two reactions involving manganese (in acid solution) are the reduction of nitrate ions (to NO) with Mn^{2+} ions and the oxidation of ammonium ions (to N_2) with MnO_2.

(a) Write balanced chemical equations for these reactions (in acid solution).

(b) Calculate $E°_{cell}$ for the reactions. (One half-reaction potential you need is for the reduction of N_2 to NH_4^+, $E° = -0.272$ V.)

90. ▲ You want to use electrolysis to plate a cylindrical object (radius = 2.50 and length = 20.00 cm) with a coating of nickel metal, 4.0 mm thick. You place the object in a bath containing a salt (Na_2SO_4). One electrode is impure nickel, and the other is the object to be plated. The electrolyzing potential is 2.50 V.

(a) Which is the anode and which is the cathode in the experiment? What half-reaction occurs at each electrode?

(b) Calculate the number of kilowatt-hours (kWh) of energy required to carry out the electrolysis. (1 kWh = 3.6×10^6 J and 1 J = 1 C $\times$ 1 V)

91. ▲ Iron(II) ion undergoes a disproportionation reaction to give Fe(s) and the iron(III) ion. That is, iron(II) ion is both oxidized and reduced within the same reaction.

$$3\ Fe^{2+}(aq) \rightleftharpoons Fe(s) + 2\ Fe^{3+}(aq)$$

(a) What two half-reactions make up the disproportionation reaction?

(b) Use the values of the standard reduction potentials for the two half-reactions in part (a) to determine whether this disproportionation reaction is product-favored.

(c) What is the equilibrium constant for this reaction?

92. ▲ Copper(I) ion disproportionates to copper metal and copper(II) ion. (See Study Question 91.)

$$2\ Cu^+(aq) \rightleftharpoons Cu(s) + Cu^{2+}(aq)$$

(a) What two half-reactions make up the disproportionation reaction?

(b) Use values of the standard reduction potentials for the two half-reactions in part (a) to determine whether this disproportionation reaction is spontaneous.

(c) What is the equilibrium constant for this reaction? If you have a solution that initially contains 0.10 mol of Cu^+ in 1.0 L of water, what are the concentrations of Cu^+ and Cu^{2+} at equilibrium?

In the Laboratory

93. Consider an electrochemical cell based on the half-reactions $Ni^{2+}(aq) + 2\ e^- \rightarrow Ni(s)$ and $Cd^{2+}(aq) + 2\ e^- \rightarrow Cd(s)$.

(a) Diagram the cell, and label each of the components (including the anode, cathode, and salt bridge).

(b) Use the equations for the half-reactions to write a balanced, net ionic equation for the overall cell reaction.

(c) What is the polarity of each electrode?

(d) What is the value of $E°_{cell}$?

(e) In which direction do electrons flow in the external circuit?

(f) Assume that a salt bridge containing $NaNO_3$ connects the two half-cells. In which direction do the $Na^+(aq)$ ions move? In which direction do the $NO_3^-(aq)$ ions move?

(g) Calculate the equilibrium constant for the reaction.

(h) If the concentration of Cd^{2+} is reduced to 0.010 M and $[Ni^{2+}] = 1.0$ M, what is the value of E_{cell}? Is the net reaction still the reaction given in part (b)?

(i) If 0.050 A is drawn from the battery, how long can it last if you begin with 1.0 L of each of the solutions and each was initially 1.0 M in dissolved species? Each electrode weighs 50.0 g in the beginning.

94. An old method of measuring the current flowing in a circuit was to use a "silver coulometer." The current passed first through a solution of $Ag^+(aq)$ and then into another solution containing an electroactive species. The amount of silver metal deposited at the cathode was weighed. From the mass of silver, the number of atoms of silver was calculated. Since the reduction of a silver ion requires one electron, this value equaled the number of electrons passing through the circuit. If the time was noted, the average current could be calculated. If, in such an experiment, 0.052 g of Ag is deposited during 450 s, what was the current flowing in the circuit?

95. A "silver coulometer" (Study Question 94) was used in the past to measure the current flowing in an electrochemical cell. Suppose you found that the current flowing through an electrolysis cell deposited 0.089 g of Ag metal at the cathode after exactly 10 min. If this same current then passed through a cell containing gold(III) ion in the form of $[AuCl_4]^-$, how much gold was deposited at the cathode in that electrolysis cell?

96. ▲ Four metals, A, B, C, and D, exhibit the following properties:

(i)   Only A and C react with 1.0 M hydrochloric acid to give $H_2(g)$.

(ii) When C is added to solutions of the ions of the other metals, metallic B, D, and A are formed.

(iii) Metal D reduces B^{n+} to give metallic B and D^{n+}.

Based on this information, arrange the four metals in order of increasing ability to act as reducing agents.

97. ▲ A solution of KI is added dropwise to a pale blue solution of $Cu(NO_3)_2$. The solution changes to a brown color, and a precipitate of CuI forms. In contrast, no change is observed if solutions of KCl and KBr are added to aqueous $Cu(NO_3)_2$. Consult the table of standard reduction potentials to explain the dissimilar results seen with the different halides. Write an equation for the reaction that occurs when solutions of KI and $Cu(NO_3)_2$ are mixed.

98. ▲ The amount of oxygen, O_2, dissolved in a water sample at 25 °C can be determined by titration. The first step is to add solutions of $MnSO_4$ and NaOH to the water to convert the dissolved oxygen to MnO_2. A solution of H_2SO_4 and KI is then added to convert the MnO_2 to Mn^{2+}, and the iodide ion is converted to I_2. The I_2 is then titrated with standardized $Na_2S_2O_3$.
    (a) Balance the equation for the reaction of Mn^{2+} ions with O_2 in basic solution.
    (b) Balance the equation for the reaction of MnO_2 with I^- in acid solution.
    (c) Balance the equation for the reaction of $S_2O_3^{2-}$ with I_2.
    (d) Calculate the amount of O_2 in 25.0 mL of water if the titration requires 2.45 mL of 0.0112 M $Na_2S_2O_3$ solution.

Summary and Conceptual Questions

The following questions may use concepts from this and previous chapters.

99. Fluorinated organic compounds are used as herbicides, flame retardants, and fire-extinguishing agents, among other things. A reaction such as

$$CH_3SO_2F + 3\ HF \rightarrow CF_3SO_2F + 3\ H_2$$

is carried out electrochemically in liquid HF as the solvent.
    (a) If you electrolyze 150 g of CH_3SO_2F, what mass of HF is required, and what mass of each product can be isolated?
    (b) Is H_2 produced at the anode or the cathode of the electrolysis cell?
    (c) A typical electrolysis cell operates at 8.0 V and 250 A. How many kilowatt-hours of energy does one such cell consume in 24 hours?

100. ▲ The free energy change for a reaction, $\Delta_r G°$, is the maximum energy that can be extracted from the process, whereas $\Delta_r H°$ is the total chemical potential energy change. The efficiency of a fuel cell is the ratio of these two quantities.

$$\text{Efficiency} = \frac{\Delta_r G°}{\Delta_r H°} \times 100\%$$

Consider the hydrogen-oxygen fuel cell, where the net reaction is

$$H_2(g) + \tfrac{1}{2}\ O_2(g) \rightarrow H_2O(\ell)$$

   (a) Calculate the efficiency of the fuel cell under standard conditions.
   (b) Calculate the efficiency of the fuel cell if the product is water vapor instead of liquid water.
   (c) Does the efficiency depend on the state of the reaction product? Why or why not?

101. A hydrogen-oxygen fuel cell operates on the simple reaction

$$H_2(g) + \tfrac{1}{2}\ O_2(g) \rightarrow H_2O(\ell)$$

   If the cell is designed to produce 1.5 A of current and if the hydrogen is contained in a 1.0-L tank at 200 atm pressure at 25 °C, how long can the fuel cell operate before the hydrogen runs out? (Assume there is an unlimited supply of O_2.)

102. ▲ (a) Is it easier to reduce water in acid or base? To evaluate this, consider the half-reaction

$$2\ H_2O(\ell) + 2\ e^- \rightarrow 2\ OH^-(aq) + H_2(g)$$
$$E° = -0.83\ V$$

   (b) What is the reduction potential for water for solutions at pH = 7 (neutral) and pH = 1 (acid)? Comment on the value of $E°$ at pH = 1.

103. ▲ Living organisms derive energy from the oxidation of food, typified by glucose.

$$C_6H_{12}O_6(aq) + 6\ O_2(g) \rightarrow 6\ CO_2(g) + 6\ H_2O(\ell)$$

   Electrons in this redox process are transferred from glucose to oxygen in a series of at least 25 steps. It is instructive to calculate the total daily current flow in a typical organism and the rate of energy expenditure (power). (See T. P. Chirpich: *Journal of Chemical Education*, Vol. 52, p. 99, 1975.)
   (a) The molar enthalpy of combustion of glucose is −2800 kJ/mol-rxn. If you are on a typical daily diet of 2400 Cal (kilocalories), what amount of glucose (in moles) must be consumed in a day if glucose is the only source of energy? What amount of O_2 must be consumed in the oxidation process?
   (b) How many moles of electrons must be supplied to reduce the amount of O_2 calculated in part (a)?
   (c) Based on the answer in part (b), calculate the current flowing, per second, in your body from the combustion of glucose.
   (d) If the average standard potential in the electron transport chain is 1.0 V, what is the rate of energy expenditure in watts?

Applying Chemical Principles

Sacrifice!

In the latter half of the 18th century the British sheathed the hulls of their naval fleet with copper to protect the hulls from deterioration. Unfortunately, the copper corroded in sea water, so the navy called upon Sir Humphry Davy to determine the cause of the corrosion and to find a cure. Although Davy initially assumed that impurities in the copper caused the corrosion, he soon learned that high-purity copper corroded faster. Turning his attention to the sea water, Davy determined that the copper is oxidized by oxygen in the sea water. The overall reaction,

$$Cu(s) + \tfrac{1}{2} O_2(g) + H_2O(\ell) \rightarrow Cu(OH)_2(s)$$

produces copper(II) hydroxide which falls from the hull to the sea floor.

Davy, a pioneer in the field of electrochemistry, quickly determined that the corrosion of copper can be prevented by attaching small pieces of a more easily oxidized metal (such as zinc, tin, or iron) to the copper sheathing. The quantity of the metal may be small in comparison to the copper, but, to be effective, the metal must be positioned below the water line and in direct electrical contact with the copper.

Why is corrosion prevented by attaching a small piece of metal, such as zinc, to the copper? When the two different metals are submerged in sea water they form a galvanic cell. The copper serves as the cathode and the zinc as a "sacrificial" anode. The zinc anode is oxidized instead of the copper. Although the zinc anodes corrode over time and must be replaced, the cost is cheaper than replacing the copper on an entire ship's hull.

In modern fleets, copper-sheathed hulls have given way to steel hulls. Though surface coatings, such as paint, provide some protection against corrosion, sacrificial anodes are still used to protect the steel from corrosion. In addition, sacrificial anodes are now used to protect the steel in underground pipes, as well as in home water heaters, outboard motors, and boilers.

Questions:

1. If an electrically insulating material, such as paint, is placed between the zinc and the copper, the zinc will still corrode in seawater, but it will not protect the copper from corrosion. Explain.

2. Use standard reduction potentials to determine which of the following metals could serve as a sacrificial anode on a copper-sheathed hull. Indicate all correct responses.
   (a) tin   (c) iron   (e) chromium
   (b) silver   (d) nickel

Sacrificial anodes attached to a steel-hulled ship. The "patches" are zinc blocks. Sacrificial anodes of aluminum or magnesium are also used in domestic hot-water heaters to prevent corrosion in the heater.

3. Use standard reduction potentials to determine which of the following metals could serve as a sacrificial anode on a steel hull. Assume the standard reduction potential for steel is the same as that of iron. Indicate all correct responses.
   (a) tin   (c) iron   (e) chromium
   (b) silver   (d) nickel

4. The overall reaction for the production of $Cu(OH)_2$ from Cu in oxygenated water can be broken into three steps: an oxidation half-reaction, a reduction half-reaction, and a precipitation reaction.
   (a) Complete and balance the two missing half-reactions to give the overall equation for the oxidation of copper in seawater.
   1. Oxidation half-reaction: ?
   2. Reduction half-reaction: ?
   3. Precipitation: $Cu^{2+}(aq) + 2\ OH^-(aq) \rightarrow Cu(OH)_2(s)$
   4. Overall: $Cu(s) + \tfrac{1}{2} O_2(g) + H_2O(\ell) \rightarrow Cu(OH)_2(s)$
   (b) Determine the equilibrium constant for the overall reaction at 25 °C using standard reduction potentials and the solubility product constant (K_{sp}) of $Cu(OH)_2(s)$.

5. Assume the following electrochemical cell simulates the galvanic cell formed by copper and zinc in seawater at pH 7.90 and 25 °C.

$$Zn\,|\,Zn(OH)_2(s)\,|\,OH^-(aq)\,|\,Cu(OH)_2(s)\,|\,Cu(s)$$

   (a) Write a balanced equation for the reaction that occurs at the cathode.
   (b) Write a balanced equation for the reaction that occurs at the anode.
   (c) Write a balanced chemical equation for the overall reaction.
   (d) Determine the potential (in volts) of the cell.

The Chemistry of the Environment

Planet Earth can be discussed from many points of view: geological, political, historical, and environmental. The last of these has now become a main topic of concern. If we are to understand why this is so, we need to understand the chemical composition of our environment and the way it is changing.

Land, sea, air—continents, oceans, atmosphere—solid, liquid, gas. These are the three main components of the environment, and each is governed by the laws of chemistry that we associate with these physical states. Look a little closer at the continents, and we can see more and more space being devoted to human occupation and farming. We may classify the water on the planet as seawater, fresh water, or estuarine water, but how do we get from one to the other? We know the atmosphere is a mixture of gases and vapors and is restlessly in motion, sometimes violently so, but what will happen if its composition changes? Understanding the environment is crucial, but without a chemical perspective we are floundering.

In this interchapter, we look particularly at those parts of the environment that are most susceptible to change: the atmosphere and the aqua sphere (water). What humans are doing to the atmosphere appears to be leading to significant climate change. The water of the planet is also of concern: We often pollute it, and we need to purify it. Nature can supply water in abundance as rain, rivers, and lakes but not necessarily where it is most needed. While many in the developed world have a seemingly abundant supply of pure, fresh water, others obtain water only with difficulty—and even then it may not be fit to drink. As the world's population increases, many more people will find themselves having to rely on seawater for their supply of freshwater. Seawater, of course, is not drinkable, but chemistry can make it so.

If we are to understand atmospheric pollution and its effects on climate and water supplies and ways to make them drinkable, then we need to understand the chemistry that is involved.

The Atmosphere

The atmosphere may be the least weighty part of the environment, but this does not mean it has the least effect. In fact, it has a disproportionately large influence on our standard of living. We know it is changing because of what we are adding to it, and we fear the consequences of that change.

Earth has changed dramatically over the billions of years the planet has existed, and so has the atmosphere. The first atmosphere is thought to have been mainly ammonia, water vapor, and carbon dioxide. Today, it is mainly nitrogen, oxygen, and argon. At some stage, most of the water condensed onto the surface of the planet, and seas were formed. It was in the seas that life probably emerged, and life had to adapt to conditions as they changed. Sometimes the changes were so great that many species could not adapt and were wiped out. But, despite these mass extinctions, there were always a few survivors.

Table 1 gives the composition of the atmosphere in terms of the gases it contains. The values in the table are for dry air at sea level. Normally, air also contains water vapor, which can vary considerably from place to place and from day to day. It can be as high as 40,000 ppm (parts per million) but is generally about half this value.

In fact, there are many more components of the atmosphere than those listed in Table 1. There are trace amounts of chemicals emitted by plants, animals, and microbes, as well as those released by human activity. Our additions to

• **Sunrise over the Atlantic Ocean,** Sunday, April 4, 2010.

Table 1 The Gases of the Atmosphere*

Gases	Concentration (ppm)
Nitrogen (N_2)	780,840
Oxygen (O_2)	209,460
Argon (Ar)	9340
Carbon dioxide (CO_2)	385
Neon (Ne)	18
Helium (He)	5.2
Methane (CH_4)	1.7
Krypton (Kr)	1.1
Dinitrogen monoxide (nitrous oxide) (N_2O)	0.55
Hydrogen (H_2)	0.5
Ozone (O_3)	0.4
Carbon monoxide (CO)	0.25
Xenon (Xe)	0.086
Radon (Rn)	traces

*Data on gas concentrations refer to relative numbers of particles in dry air (and hence are related to mole fractions).

the atmosphere come from burning fuels to generate electricity, from vehicle exhausts, from industry, and from our day-to-day activities. The atmosphere is changing, and we need to understand what this means for the future.

We might imagine that air is a homogeneous mixture of gases and particles because it is constantly being stirred by the motion of the planet and the heat of the sun. In fact, this mixing is far from complete. There is relatively little exchange of air between the north and south regions of the planet, and there are distinct layers in the atmosphere (◀ page 528). As far as humans are concerned, the most important layer is the lower layer in which we live—the troposphere, which goes up to around 7 km at the poles and 17 km at the equator. Above the troposphere is the stratosphere; this extends to about 30 km, getting thinner and thinner as we rise to higher altitudes. There are even higher regions, but there the air is very thin, although not so thin it cannot interact with incoming space debris or vehicles like the Space Shuttle and cause them to glow red hot. In this interchapter, we concern ourselves only with the troposphere and the stratosphere.

The total mean mass of the atmosphere is estimated to be around 5.15×10^{18} kg (5.15×10^{15} metric tons, or 5.15×10^6 gigatons). (Gigatons are often used in environmental studies because the masses we are discussing are so large. A *metric ton* is 1000 kg, but a gigaton is a billion metric tons, that is, 10^9 metric tons.) Three quarters of the mass of the atmosphere is in the troposphere, and there its aver-

age temperature is 14 °C (but that is an average of a wide range of temperatures). It can be as low as −89 °C, the lowest temperature ever recorded, in Antarctica in 1983, or as high as 58 °C, the highest temperature ever recorded, in North Africa in 1922. After temperature, the next most obvious property of the atmosphere is the pressure it exerts, which at sea level is around 101 kPa (1 atmosphere).

Some of the gases of the atmosphere are unreactive and never change chemically. These are the noble gases: helium, neon, argon, krypton, and xenon. Two of these, namely, helium and argon, are being added continuously to the atmosphere because they are products of radioactive decay—helium comes from alpha particles emitted by elements such as uranium, and argon is produced by decay of ^{40}K, a long-lived radioactive isotope of potassium.

The other gases of the atmosphere, namely, oxygen, nitrogen, and carbon dioxide, are chemically reactive and can be changed into other molecules by reactions driven by lightning, ultraviolet rays from the sun, or the influence of living things, and especially the actions of humans.

Nitrogen and Nitrogen Oxides

The nitrogen of the atmosphere arose from the out-gassing of Earth when it was simply a molten mass. Even today, some nitrogen escapes when volcanoes erupt. Nitrogen gas is relatively unreactive, but every living thing on the planet needs to incorporate nitrogen into its cells as, among other compounds, amino acids, the building blocks of proteins. The process by which nitrogen gas is converted to useful nitrogen-containing compounds, such as ammonia (NH_3) and nitrate ions (NO_3^-), is known as **nitrogen fixation** (Figure 1). Bacteria in the soil and algae in the oceans are the primary "fixers" of nitrogen. On a global scale, the conversion of nitrogen to various compounds is accomplished to the extent of around 50% by biological processes, 10% by fertilizer manufacture, 10% by lightning, and 30% from the burning of fossil fuels. Once nitrogen is "fixed" it is incorporated into living things, passes through many other life forms, and ends up in the soil, which contains significant amounts of nitrogen-containing compounds such as ammonium salts, nitrates, and nitrites. The two anions (NO_3^- and NO_2^-) are converted back to nitrogen gas or to N_2O and returned to the atmosphere.

Dinitrogen monoxide (nitrous oxide), N_2O, is only one of several nitrogen oxides important in our environment. Others are nitrogen monoxide (nitric oxide), NO, and nitrogen dioxide, NO_2. Because they are readily interconverted, they are referred to collectively as NO_x compounds. There are a number of sources of NO_x compounds.

- NO produced from the combination of N_2 and O_2 when air is heated in an automobile engine or is sparked by a bolt of lighting

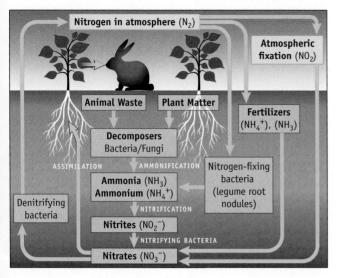

FIGURE 1 The nitrogen cycle. The nitrogen cycle involves nitrogen fixation by soil bacteria or, in aquatic environments, by cyanobacteria. The NH_4^+ ions produced are converted to nitrate ions, the main form of nitrogen absorbed by plants. Nitrogen is returned to the atmosphere by denitrifying bacteria, which convert nitrate ions to N_2.

- NO and NO_2 produced by the photochemical oxidation of N_2O in the atmosphere
- Oxidation of NH_3 in the atmosphere
- Production of NO and N_2O in soil by microbial processes

In addition, fossil fuel burning and biomass combustion by humans produce about 65% of the NO_x in the atmosphere.

The most abundant nitrogen oxide is dinitrogen monoxide because it is the least reactive. Most of this oxide comes from microbes in the soil. Ten million tons of N_2O are released each year, some from human activity.

The other nitrogen oxides make up only 0.00005 ppm of the atmosphere. While 100 million tons of NO_x come each year from vehicle exhaust, it is quickly washed out of the atmosphere by rain (and thus contributes to "acid rain"). When NO_x compounds do linger, particularly over cities in sunny climates, they can react with hydrocarbons in the atmosphere, such as traces of unburnt fuel, to produce irritating photochemical smog. Among the most polluting components of smog are PANs, peroxyacyl nitrates, represented here by peroxyacetyl nitrate.

One route to its formation is as follows:

(a) Organic compounds called *aldehydes* (such as CH_3CHO) are produced by complex reactions in smog. These molecules react with hydroxyl radicals ($OH\cdot$), which are also the result of photochemical reactions in the atmosphere (◀ page 363). Their interaction produces another radical species $CH_3CO\cdot$.

$$CH_3CHO + OH\cdot \rightarrow CH_3CO\cdot + H_2O$$

(b) The newly produced radical reacts with oxygen to produce the peroxyacetyl radical.

$$CH_3CO\cdot + O_2 \rightarrow CH_3COOO\cdot$$

(c) The peroxyacetyl radical reacts with NO_2 in polluted air to give peroxyacetyl nitrate.

$$CH_3COOO\cdot + NO_2 \rightarrow CH_3COOONO_2$$

PANs are toxic and irritating. At low concentrations, they irritate the eyes, but at higher concentrations they can cause more serious damage to both animals and vegetation. They are relatively stable, dissociating only slowly into radicals and NO_2. Thus, it is possible that they can travel some distance from where they are formed before dissociating into harmful radicals.

Oxygen

Plant life had a dramatic effect on the early atmosphere, changing it from a reducing to an oxidizing one, that is, from there being no oxygen present to one where this reactive gas is the second most abundant species present in the atmosphere. This change meant life had to change. Those species that could not live in the presence of this reactive gas either died out or were relegated to regions where oxygen is blocked out. The percent of oxygen in the air is now midway between two extremes that would make life on Earth impossible for humans: below 17% we would suffocate, and above 25% all organic material would burn easily.

The total mass of oxygen in the atmosphere is a million gigatons. Even though the burning of 7 gigatons of fossil fuel carbon per year uses up 18 gigatons of oxygen, this makes almost no discernible difference to the amount of oxygen in the atmosphere. Oxygen is also moderately soluble in water (◀ page 626), which makes life in rivers, lakes, and oceans possible.

Oxygen is a by-product of plant **photosynthesis**. Carbon dioxide is the source of the carbon that plants need and which they capture from the air and turn into carbohydrates such as glucose ($C_6H_{12}O_6$) by photosynthesis. The overall chemical reaction is

$$6\ CO_2 + 6\ H_2O \rightarrow C_6H_{12}O_6 + 6\ O_2$$

and the net result is the release of an oxygen molecule back into the atmosphere for each CO_2 absorbed. Oxygen

FIGURE 2 Cyanobacteria. Cyanobacteria, also known as blue-green algae, obtain their energy by photosynthesis. The name comes from the color of the material. Their importance lies in their production of oxygen by photosynthesis and their participation in the nitrogen-fixation cycle.

molecules released by photosynthesis remain in the atmosphere, on average, for around 3000 years before being reabsorbed.

Blue-green algae, or cyanobacteria (Figure 2), first began producing oxygen as long ago as 3.5 billion years. But, mysteriously, hundreds of millions of years elapsed before a significant amount of oxygen was present in the atmosphere. Astrobiologists are not at all certain why this occurred, but it does seem plausible that the oxygen first produced did not remain in the atmosphere because it reacted with metals, especially converting abundant iron(II) ions to iron(III) ions. This process continued for about a billion years, but then the level of oxygen in the atmosphere began to rise 2 billion years ago, and about 500 million years ago it rose relatively rapidly to around 20% when the first land plants started to appear.

There are three naturally occurring isotopes of oxygen: oxygen-16 accounts for 99.76% of O atoms, oxygen-17 for a mere 0.04%, and oxygen-18 for 0.2%. Because oxygen-18 is 12% heavier than oxygen-16, it can influence the behavior of water in the environment. The ratio of oxygen-18 to oxygen-16 in the world's oceans has varied slightly over geological time, and this has left an imprint on parts of the environment, providing evidence of past climates. When the world is in a cooler period, water molecules with oxygen-16 evaporate more easily from the oceans than their heavier oxygen-18 counterpart. Thus, snow is slightly richer in oxygen-16, and the water that remains in the oceans is slightly richer in oxygen-18. Marine creatures therefore lay down shells that have more oxygen-18 than expected, and these are preserved in sediments. Analyzing the ratio of the two isotopes in such deposits reveals the cycle of global cooling and warming that has characterized the past half million years with its five ice ages.

Ozone

Ozone (O_3) plays a key role for life on this planet, but it is also a threat. In the troposphere, it is a pollutant, while in the stratosphere it acts as a shield, protecting the planet from damaging ultraviolet rays from the sun. This shield is known as the **ozone layer** (Figure 3).

There is a natural low level of ozone in the air we breathe, about 0.02 ppm (parts per million), but in summer this can increase to 0.1 ppm or more as a result of sunlight acting on the nitrogen dioxide emitted by vehicles. In the presence of sunlight, NO_2 dissociates to NO and O atoms, and the O atoms can react with O_2 (in the presence of a third molecule acting as an energy "sink") to produce ozone.

$$NO_2 + \text{energy } (\lambda < 240 \text{ nm}) \rightarrow NO + O$$

$$O + O_2 \rightarrow O_3$$

Because ozone damages the lungs, the legal limit for exposure to ozone in the workplace is 0.1 ppm. Some growing plants are also susceptible to the gas, and even though they do not show visible signs of stress, their growth is reduced in proportion to the level of ozone in the air.

In contrast with ozone in the troposphere, O_3 in the stratosphere is vital to the planet because the molecules absorb ultraviolet radiation before it reaches Earth's surface. Radiation with wavelengths shorter than 240 nm interacts with O_2 molecules and cleaves them into two O

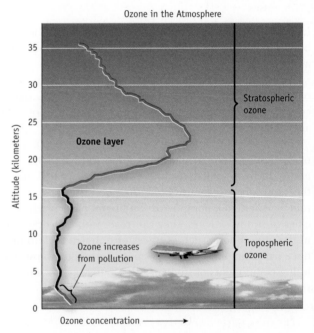

FIGURE 3 The ozone layer. Substantial concentrations of ozone exist between the 10 and 50 km above the Earth's surface (see page 528). About 90% of the ozone in the atmosphere is contained in the stratosphere (roughly 15–50 km above the surface). Concentrations range from 2 to 8 parts per million.

atoms. Each O atom combines with another O_2 molecule to produce an ozone molecule.

$$O_2 + energy \rightarrow O + O$$

$$O + O_2 \rightarrow O_3$$

Ozone in turn absorbs ultraviolet radiation with wavelengths less than 320 nm, and the O_3 is decomposed to O_2 and O atoms.

$$O_3 + energy (\lambda < 320 \text{ nm}) \rightarrow O_2 + O$$

$$O + O_3 \rightarrow 2 O_2$$

Without the ozone layer, dangerous radiation capable of harming living cells would penetrate to Earth's surface and could cause numerous human health and environmental effects. These effects include increased incidence of skin cancer and cataracts and suppression of the human immune response system. Damage to crops and marine phytoplankton and weathering of plastics are also caused by increased levels of ultraviolet radiation.

Chlorofluorocarbons and Ozone

From the late 1800s until about 1930 ammonia (NH_3), chloromethane (CH_3Cl), and sulfur dioxide (SO_2) were widely used as refrigerants. However, leakage from refrigerators caused several fatal accidents in the 1920s, so three American corporations, Frigidaire, General Motors, and DuPont, collaborated on the search for a less dangerous fluid. In 1928, Thomas Midgley, Jr., and his coworkers discovered a "miracle compound" as a substitute. This compound, dichlorodifluoromethane (CCl_2F_2), is a member of a large family of compounds called chlorofluorocarbons (CFCs). The two compounds shown here are CFC-114 ($C_2Cl_2F_4$) and CFC-12 (CCl_2F_2).

dichlorotetrafluoroethane   dichlorodifluoromethane

These compounds had exactly the physical and chemical properties needed for a refrigerant: appropriate critical temperatures and pressures, no toxicity, and apparent chemical inertness.

The uses of CFCs grew dramatically, not only in air conditioning and refrigeration equipment but also in applications such as propellants for aerosol cans, foaming agents in the production of expanded plastic foams, and inhalers for asthma sufferers.

Unfortunately, as the world has often learned about other "miracle compounds," the properties that made CFCs so useful also led to environmental problems. CFCs are unreactive in Earth's troposphere, which allows them to remain in the troposphere for hundreds of years. Over time, however, they slowly diffuse into the stratosphere where, as proposed by Sherwood Rowland and Mario Molina in 1974, solar radiation leads to their decomposition.

$$CF_2Cl_2(g) + UV \text{ radiation} \rightarrow CF_2Cl(g) + Cl(g)$$

They also proposed that the Cl atoms released in the decomposition of CFCs and other chlorine-containing compounds can destroy large numbers of ozone molecules. In this mechanism, Cl atoms react with O_3 molecules to produce the radical species ClO. This in turn intercepts O atoms from the decomposition of O_2 molecules, to produce Cl atoms, which then continue the cycle.

$$O_3(g) + Cl(g) \rightarrow ClO(g) + O_2(g)$$

$$O(g) + ClO(g) \rightarrow Cl(g) + O_2(g)$$

Net reaction: $\quad O_3(g) + O(g) \rightarrow O_2(g) + O_2(g)$

The two equations above represent steps of a *chain reaction*, which, when repeated over and over, means that the formation of one Cl atom can lead to the destruction of many ozone molecules.

In 1985 three British scientists of the British Antarctic Survey discovered that there was a significant reduction in the ozone concentration over the Antarctic continent, which has since been referred to as the "ozone hole" (Figure 4). In 1986, Susan Solomon and a team from the

FIGURE 4 **The "ozone hole" over the Antarctic continent.** During the Antarctic winter, when there are 24 hours of darkness, aerosols of HCl and $ClONO_2$ freeze and accumulate in the polar stratospheric clouds. During the Antarctic spring, these crystals melt, and Cl and ClO radicals are rapidly formed and lead to a depletion of stratospheric ozone over the continent.

National Center for Atmospheric Research went to Antarctica to investigate the "hole" and found that there were indeed higher levels of ClO than expected in the stratosphere.

Because of the damage caused to the stratospheric ozone layer, apparently by CFCs and related compounds, the United States banned the use of CFCs as aerosol propellants in 1978, and 68 nations followed suit in 1987 by signing the Montreal Protocol. This protocol called for an immediate reduction in nonessential uses of CFCs. In 1990, 100 nations met in London and decided to ban the production of CFCs. The United States and 140 other countries agreed to a complete halt in CFC manufacture as of December 31, 1995, and Rowland and Molina received the Nobel Prize for their work in that same year.

Carbon Dioxide

No element is more essential to life than carbon, and the reason is that only carbon has the ability to form long chains and rings of atoms that are stable. This is the basis of the structures for many compounds that comprise the living cell, of which the most important is DNA (◄ page 388). The food we eat—carbohydrates, oils, proteins, and fiber—is made up of compounds of carbon, and this carbon eventually returns to the atmosphere as CO_2 as part of the natural cycle. This cycle moves carbon between various compartments of the terrestrial ecosphere and so rules the tempo of life on Earth. The carbon cycle turns over 200 gigatons of carbon every year, and the amounts of carbon residing in the various compartments are, in order of increasing amounts:

> 40 gigatons in living things in the oceans
> 725 gigatons as CO_2 in the atmosphere
> 2000 gigatons in living things on land
> 39,000 gigatons as carbonate ions (CO_3^{2-}) dissolved in the oceans
> 20,000,000 gigatons as reduced carbon in fossil fuel deposits
> 100,000,000+ gigatons as carbonate minerals such as limestone

Reduced carbon in Earth's crust comes in various forms such as natural gas, which is largely CH_4; oil, which approximates to CH_2; and coal, a complex material with a carbon–hydrogen ratio corresponding to CH. Known reserves of these fossil fuels amount to a vast 1 trillion tons of coal, 160 billion tons of oil, and 180 trillion cubic meters of natural gas. A much larger amount of carbon in Earth's crust is also present but is too widely dispersed and inaccessible to be regarded as a potential energy resource. Human use of fossil fuels each year releases around 25 gigatons of CO_2 into the atmosphere.

Climate Change

The *Intergovernmental Panel on Climate Change* (IPCC) was set up in 1988 by members of the United Nations Environment Program and the World Meteorological Organization. To date, it has issued four Assessment Reports describing **global warming**. This term refers to the gradual warming of the surface air and oceans of the Earth. The best estimate is that the surface temperature of the Earth has increased 0.74 ± 0.18 °C during the last century and that it is continuing to increase.

Earth began to emerge from a cold period around 150 years ago. Will the natural cycle of temperature change create a warm period like those at the time of the Roman Empire and during the Middle Ages? Or has the increase in human population and its burning of fossil fuels, which increases the level of CO_2 in the atmosphere, made an additional contribution that will result in a much warmer period than those earlier ages experienced?

In the first three of the IPCC Assessment Reports, the authors warned that human activity might be partly responsible for raising the global temperature. While some heeded the IPCC warnings, little was done to check the use of fossil fuels, although some effort is now being directed into generating electricity by sustainable means such as wind power and solar panels. In 2007, the IPCC issued its *Fourth Assessment Report*. This report went further by saying that there is now little doubt the planet is warming and that additions of greenhouse gases to the atmosphere by humans are having a noticeable effect. (A fifth report is being prepared. To obtain the reports, see www.ipcc.ch.)

Greenhouse Gases

The greenhouse effect is the process by which radiation from the sun warms Earth's surface (◄ page 259). This is vital to life on Earth because the surface temperature is about 35 °C warmer than it would be without the effect.

The greenhouse effect is caused by certain gases in the troposphere. These gases are small molecules whose bonds vibrate with frequencies in the infrared region of the electromagnetic spectrum. Such a gas can trap infrared radiation, thus retaining energy that would otherwise be radiated into space.

Which gases can act as greenhouse gases depends solely on their chemistry. Gases that are single atoms, like argon, have no chemical bonds and so cannot interact with infrared light. Homonuclear diatomic molecules such as nitrogen (N_2) and oxygen (O_2) also do not absorb infrared radiation. Since these three gases make up 99% of the atmosphere, it is clearly beneficial for us that they are not greenhouse gases.

On the other hand, molecules with bonds between different atoms, such as water (H_2O) and carbon dioxide (CO_2), are greenhouse gases and allow Earth to warm more than it would have based solely on its distance from the sun. (Water vapor is the main greenhouse gas and accounts for most of the observed effect.) In this respect, these gases are vital. If Earth did not retain some energy supplied by the sun, the average temperature would be like that of the moon, too hot when feeling the full glare of the sun and too cold when in shadow. Life would be impossible.

Other gases in the atmosphere can also act as greenhouse gases. Methane (CH_4) is a greenhouse gas much more powerful than CO_2. Nitrous oxide (N_2O) is also very powerful at retaining heat energy. These come partly from natural sources but in amounts too small to pose a threat. Methane is released by anaerobic bacteria (that is, those that do not use oxygen). Some anaerobic bacteria live at the bottom of lakes and swamps, some in termite mounds, and some in the guts of animals such as cows and humans. Human activities can also release large amounts of these gases. For example, methane is the natural gas we use in vast amounts, and some of this escapes from leaking pipelines. It also leaks from landfill sites and coal mines, as well as from agricultural sites such as rice fields. Nitrous oxide is released as a by-product of our abundant use of ammonium nitrate fertilizers.

The methane concentration in the atmosphere is now around 1.7 ppm, which is about double the "natural" level. The concentration of N_2O is around 0.55 ppm instead of 0.27 ppm. More significantly, the carbon dioxide concentration increased from around 280 ppm in 1750 to 388 in 2010 (Figure 5). The fourth IPCC report states that "Today's CO_2 concentration has not been exceeded during the past 420,000 years and likely not during the past 20 million years. The rate of increase over the past century is unprecedented, at least during the past 20,000 years."

Industry has added new greenhouse gases to the atmosphere such as the many CFCs and various chemicals known as *volatile organic compounds* (VOCs). Although VOCs, especially isoprene and terpenes, are given off by trees, VOCs are also given off by paints, adhesives, plastics, air fresheners, and cosmetics. The family of CFCs has been replaced by a new generation of hydrofluorocarbon (HFC) compounds such as $F_3C–CH_2F$, also called HFC-134a, a compound now commonly used in air conditioners and refrigerators. Although HFCs behave as greenhouse gases, they are much less persistent in the atmosphere than the long-lived CFCs.

The IPCC estimates that in the past 100 years the atmosphere has warmed by $0.74 \pm 0.18 \ °C$, and this might well have been higher had it not been offset by the release of soot and other chemicals into the atmosphere. These cause a certain amount of "global dimming."

So how much hotter will the world become if we continue to rely on fossil fuels? The IPCC has considered several predictions and reports two possible scenarios. One of these predicts a relatively low level warming, between 1.8 and 2.9 °C. The other predicts an increase of between 4 and 6.4 °C and is much more worrisome. The lower scenario would lead to sea level rises of 18–38 cm; the higher range would cause a rise of 26–59 cm. While advanced nations could protect vulnerable areas against such rises—the Dutch have been living below sea level for hundreds of years thanks to massive dikes—less-developed nations and especially those that occupy large river deltas in Asia and small island states would literally be swamped by the sea. We still have time to decide what action to take, but the longer we continue with our heavy reliance on natural gas, oil, and coal, the worse the risk becomes.

Some believe we can offset the amount of carbon dioxide we release into the atmosphere by planting trees to reabsorb the CO_2. The trees would be paid for by a levy assessed on those who drive cars or travel by plane. Therefore, our journeys would be "carbon-neutral." In fact, very large areas around the world have been planted with trees. Unfortunately, it now appears that trees planted in temperate regions and especially those at higher latitudes might actually contribute to climate warming by absorbing more heat from the sun than the land they occupy would otherwise absorb. However, trees planted in the tropics do have the desired effect and absorb carbon dioxide while not contributing to this heating effect.

The Aqua Sphere (Water)

Most of the planet is covered by water, and for centuries humans have treated it as an inexhaustible source of food and the easiest place to dump our waste. That is now changing. The aqua sphere is a major asset but will remain so only if we treat it with respect.

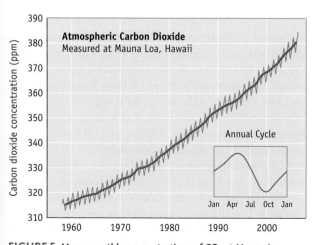

FIGURE 5 Mean monthly concentrations of CO_2 at Mauna Loa, Hawaii.

The Oceans

The quantity of minerals dissolved in the oceans is vast, and, even when the concentration is low (Table 2), the total can still be quite surprising. For example, though something may be present at only 5 ppm in seawater, its total mass is almost 7 trillion tons (7000 gigatons.) The lure of vast amounts of dissolved metals has tantalized people through the ages, and the amount of gold in the sea particularly so. At a concentration of only 10 parts per trillion (or 10 g in 1 trillion g of water), even this amounts to more than 13 million tons. Although some have tried, no method has been found by which it can be extracted profitably.

Water has fascinated scientists through the ages, in part because water has some unusual features that are of critical importance to the environment. For example, when it freezes it expands in volume unlike most other materials that shrink as they solidify (◄ page 556). This is why ice floats instead of sinking. In fact, this was essential for the emergence of early forms of life. Because water freezes from the top down, it actually protects the creatures that live underneath the ice; otherwise, only a few microbes that can exist in ice would have survived.

The fact that ice is less dense than water also means that when it melts the volume of water it creates is smaller than the volume of ice. For example, if the North Polar ice melts, it will not raise sea level because this ice is already floating in water and will take up less space in the liquid state than in the solid state. On the other hand, ice stacked on land, such as that in Greenland, will cause an increase in sea level if it melts because its water will be added to the oceans. Thankfully, the ice at the South Pole is not melting (yet), and computer models show that this part of the planet is not likely to be affected by global warming to the same extent as the Northern Hemisphere.

Table 2 Concentrations of Some Cations and Anions in Seawater

Element	Dissolved Species	Concentrations (mmol/L)
Chlorine	Cl^-	550
Sodium	Na^+	460
Magnesium	Mg^{2+}	52
Calcium	Ca^{2+}	10
Potassium	K^+	10
Carbon	HCO_3^-, CO_3^{2-}	30
Phosphorus	HPO_4^{2-}	<1

Drinking Water

Water is as vital to life as food; indeed, you can survive for weeks without anything to eat, but you would not last a week if you had no water to drink. People in developed countries have clean, safe water supplied to their homes by pipe (although curiously many prefer to buy it in small bottles). Sadly, a large number of our fellow humans, generally in less-developed countries, have to make do with whatever water they can find, taking it from a well or even from a river, and then they are at risk of contracting a water-borne disease such as cholera, typhoid, gastroenteritis, or meningitis. More than 5000 people per day are thought to die from diseases from the water they drink.

Water Purification

Water purification began with the ancient Egyptians 3500 years ago. They discovered that when alum—potassium aluminum sulfate, $KAl(SO_4)_2$—was dissolved in water, all visible impurities were removed. This salt forms a voluminous precipitate of insoluble aluminum hydroxide, $Al(OH)_3$, which carries down any cloudiness as it settles. This is still the way that modern treatment plants produce crystal-clear water (Figure 6). Adding a small amount of *slaked lime* (CaO, calcium hydroxide) to raise the pH slightly and then a solution of aluminum sulfate creates a *floc* of $Al(OH)_3$, which removes many impurities as it precipitates. The water is then filtered through sand to remove any trace of the floc.

After treatment with alum and subsequent settling and filtration, the water is crystal clear and ready to be disinfected to destroy any pathogens that are still present. This can be done with a powerful oxidizing agent such as chlorine, sodium hypochlorite (NaClO), or ozone. Chlorine and hypochlorite have an advantage over ozone in that they are more persistent, meaning that the water will still be fit to drink even when it has been standing in a pipe for a long time. For those areas where the water supply cannot be assumed to be fit to drink, it is possible to treat local supplies with sanitizing tablets that react with the water to form a solution of hypochlorite ions (ClO^-) strong enough to make the water safe to drink. Boiling water also makes it potable, but this might not be an option.

Ozone (O_3) is the most commonly used water supply disinfectant in Europe. It is also currently used in Los Angeles and some smaller communities in the United States. Its advantages are that it does not produce trihalomethanes (such as $CHCl_3$), by-products of chlorine treatment; is more effective than chlorine at killing *Cryptosporidium* bacteria and destroying viruses; and does not leave a residual "chlorine" taste. However, due to its reactivity, ozone must be generated on site and is therefore more expensive. Also, it does not provide residual disinfection in the distribution system.

FIGURE 6 **A municipal water treatment plant.** The general steps in this process are (1) the removal of turbidity, (2) softening, (3) sedimentation and filtration, and (4) disinfection. The removal of turbidity (by addition of alum) and the disinfection of water are discussed in the text.

Ultraviolet (UV) light has been used to disinfect food products, such as milk, for some time. Wavelengths ranging from 200 to 295 nm are used, with maximum disinfection occurring at 253.7 nm (Figure 7). UV units are less expensive to install than ozone generators and have the advantage of requiring short contact times for disinfection. In addition, UV radiation disinfection is not pH or temperature dependent, and it leaves no toxic residues. Although no residual disinfection is left in the water distribution system, small amounts of chlorine can be added to address this issue.

In the United States, tap water from a municipality must meet standards at least as strict as those for bottled water. All municipalities publish annual reports of the water quality, many of them on the internet. Check the quality of the tap water in your municipality.

Reverse Osmosis for Water Purification

Pure water can also be obtained from undrinkable water in other ways. The one most used in areas with access to

FIGURE 7 Ultraviolet light (UV) is used to disinfect drinking water using this equipment in a large water treatment plant in Beijing, China.

seawater is desalination by **reverse osmosis**. Osmosis is the process whereby water in one solution moves across a membrane in such a way as to dilute a solution with a higher concentration (◄ page 635). The osmotic pressure can be measured by seeing to what extent water will continue to pass across a membrane, even when it has to push against a resisting pressure on the other side. Eventually, the pressure is such that the process of osmosis stops and can be reversed if even more pressure is applied. This is the basis of reverse osmosis, and it is the way that some cities near the sea get their water supplies (◄ page 637).

Chemistry is an important part of the reverse osmosis desalination apparatus because of the membranes that allow the passage of water molecules but not of dissolved salts. The membranes are made of polymers such as polyvinylidene fluoride and polypropylene with ultrafine pores. They have to withstand the high pumping pressures that are needed to force water against the osmotic pressure gradient. The cost is not excessive, and a cubic meter of water (1000 L) produced this way need cost only $1. Desalination systems are now a $1 billion per year industry and growing at a rate of 7% per year. And not only seawater can be purified this way; any waste water from a suspect source can be treated.

Diminishing Water Supplies

People also want water for washing themselves, their clothing, and their bed linens, or for watering the garden and flushing the lavatory. In developed countries with adequate rainfall, water can be collected and stored in vast reservoirs above or below ground. But such is the increase in global population that even those regions may one day have to conserve supplies; there are times when water use is restricted, and such restrictions are likely to increase as the effects of global warming come into play this century. Already 500 million people worldwide are affected by water shortages. Even in the Great Plains of

A CLOSER LOOK

Chlorination of Water Supplies

Chlorination is the oldest and most commonly used water disinfection method in the United States. Originally, chlorine gas was dissolved in water to yield hypochlorous acid (HClO),

$$Cl_2(g) + H_2O(\ell) \rightarrow HClO(aq) + HCl(aq)$$

which dissociates to yield the hypochlorite ion (ClO^-).

$$HClO(aq) + H_2O(\ell) \rightleftharpoons H_3O^+(aq) + ClO^-(aq)$$
$$K_a = 3.5 \times 10^{-8}$$

Two of the chemical species formed by chlorine in water—hypochlorous acid and the hypochlorite ion—are known to environmental engineers as **free available chlorine**, meaning they are available for disinfection. Because chlorine gas is quite toxic and can easily escape from damaged containers, many water treatment facilities are now switching to solid hypochlorite salts such as sodium or calcium hypochlorite [NaClO and Ca(ClO)$_2$, respectively].

Hypochlorous acid and hypochlorite ion are effective in killing bacteria. However, they will also oxidize reduced inorganic ions such as iron(II), manganese(II), and nitrite ion, as well as organic impurities. These compounds are collectively known as the **chlorine demand**. To be available to kill bacteria, sufficient chlorine must be added to exceed the chlorine demand.

The advantages of chlorination include its relatively low cost and simple application as well as its ability to maintain residual disinfection throughout the distribution system. However, there are also disadvantages. Chlorine can react with dissolved, naturally occurring organic compounds in the source water to form carcinogenic compounds such as trihalomethanes (of which chloroform, CHCl$_3$, is one example). Chlorination has also been blamed for causing an unpleasant taste and odor in some drinking water.

In 1998, the Disinfection Byproducts Rule (DBR), which restricts the presence of chlorinated organic compounds in water, was implemented in the United States. One way to comply with the DBR is to add ammonia to the water, and about 30% of major U.S. water companies currently use this technique. Ammonia and hypochlorous acid react to form chloramines such as NH$_2$Cl:

$$HClO(aq) + NH_3(aq) \rightarrow NH_2Cl(aq) + H_2O(\ell)$$

Chloramines are called **combined available chlorine**. Like free available chlorine, combined available chlorine is retained as a disinfectant throughout the water distribution system, but it is a weaker disinfectant overall. Combined available chlorine, however, has the advantage that it is less likely to lead to chlorinated organic compounds.

Recently, however, chemists in Washington, D.C., which uses the ammonia/chlorine method of water treatment, found increased lead levels in the drinking water in area homes. [Several hundred homes had lead levels of 300 parts per billion (ppb), whereas the allowed level is 15 ppb.] Water treated with only chlorine is highly oxidizing, and lead in the water is oxidized to lead(IV) oxide. This insoluble oxide is

Chlorine tanks in the water treatment plant of a small city.

© Cengage Learning/Charles D. Winters

trapped in the mineral scale that inevitably forms inside water pipes, and lead is thus removed from the water system. However, switching to the less-oxidizing ammonia/chlorine method apparently means lead ions are not removed by oxidation.

Yet another effective disinfectant is the odd-electron molecule chlorine dioxide (ClO$_2$). The primary advantage of ClO$_2$ is that it completely oxidizes organic compounds (forming CO$_2$ and H$_2$O) and therefore does not produce trihalomethanes. However, ClO$_2$ provides no residual disinfection in the distribution system. Also, ClO$_2$ must be generated on site because it is explosive when exposed to air.

---

the United States the underground sources of water, known as *aquifers,* are becoming seriously depleted, and lakes such as Lake Mead, which was created by the Hoover Dam (on the Colorado River on the border between Nevada and Arizona), that were once full to overflowing are now around 20 meters (60 feet) below the level of water they held in the 1980s.

Water Pollution

Water has been polluted by many things, mainly from activities such as farming, mining, papermaking, inadequate or nonexistent sewage treatment facilities, and the chemical industry. Protecting natural bodies of water is now high on the agenda of most developed societies, and this has been achieved mainly by banning the use of dangerous chemicals and by installing better sewage treatment facilities.

Phosphates

In the past, phosphate pollution on a massive scale was an environmental problem, such as that which afflicted Lake Erie, one of the Great Lakes, in the 1960s when it appeared it was no longer capable of supporting life owing to a lack of dissolved oxygen. This was due in part to an excess of nutrients, primarily phosphates, supplied by the rivers that drained into the lake. Where did these phosphates come from? While sewage treatment plants draining into the rivers removed most undesirables in water, they were not removing phosphates that had become a major component of household detergents. Phosphate fertilizers were also being used by farmers, and these also found their way into the surface water. Similar problems were being experienced in other parts of the world, notably in Europe.

Campaigns to control the use of phosphates were successful. These chemicals were taken out of household products, and phosphate was extracted at sewage plants before the waste water was released to rivers. The result was to discourage the growth of algae, and slowly Lake Erie and other lakes began to regenerate. In fact, phosphate was not entirely to blame for the pollution. Lack of zooplankton, which feed on algae, also contributed. These creatures were being killed by traces of pesticides and heavy metals. Without the zooplankton, the algae could breed unchecked.

Heavy Metals

Some metals, such as cadmium, mercury, lead, and chromium, can be highly toxic even in small amounts. Therefore, the United States Environmental Protection Agency (EPA) places limits on the amount of many metals allowed in drinking water and in foods. This also explains why there are sometimes warnings about eating fish from certain areas due to toxic levels of mercury.

Lead is a cumulative poison that has been linked to learning disabilities and may still be found in the water of older houses due to leaching from lead plumbing. Lead levels in water in the United States are currently required to be no more than 50 μg/L (or 50 ppb).

Knowledge of heavy metal toxicity even made its way to Hollywood. The movie "Erin Brockovich" is centered around water pollution from hexavalent chromium (Cr^{6+}, generally in the form of ions such as CrO_4^{2-} or $Cr_2O_7^{2-}$) (Figure 8). For chemists, chromium presents a good example of the importance of knowing the oxidation state of an element; chromium(VI) compounds are toxic whereas chromium(III) is an essential trace element that plays a role in human metabolism.

Emerging Pollutants

A pollutant is "any substance, as certain chemicals or waste products, that renders the air, soil, water, or other natural resource harmful or unsuitable for a specific purpose." However, what would you say if you were told that over-the-counter drugs or your favorite hand sanitizer may be a source of pollution? These compounds and many others termed *pharmaceutical and personal care products* (PPCPs) are present in some natural waters at high enough concentrations to affect the reproductive systems of fish and other aquatic life. Many of these PPCPs are categorized as endocrine disruptors and are the focus of much recent environmental research. Although the impact of these emerging pollutants on human health is not yet clear, their presence in human breast milk

© Universal/Courtesy Everett Collection

FIGURE 8 Erin Brockovich. The movie, which came out in 2000, portrayed the campaign of Erin Brockovich, a law office clerk who built a case against a large electric utility for contaminating the water supply with chromium(VI) compounds. (The source of the chromium was compounds used to combat corrosion in cooling towers.) The lawsuit resulted in a large judgment against the utility. The real Erin Brockovich has remained an environmental activist.

has been documented, and some drugs have been shown to increase the growth rate of cancer cells.

There is much work to be done in this area of environmental research and in fact the EPA will require municipalities to begin monitoring certain PPCPs by 2012.

Arsenic in Drinking Water

Even when drinking water appears to be safe, it may harbor unsuspected dangers acquired from the environment. One example is the occurrence of arsenic-containing compounds in water supplies in the Lagunera region of Mexico, the Antofagasta region of northern Chile, the Codoban region of Argentina, and especially in the West Bengal region of India and the neighboring country of Bangladesh. The effects of arsenic in drinking water can be very serious, and it is very unfortunate that this contamination often went unnoticed for many years.

In Taiwan, an epidemiological study in the 1960s showed that the prevalence of skin cancer was related to the amount of arsenic in water. In one region where the level of arsenic was 500 micrograms per liter (500 ppb), 10% of people aged 60 or over had cancers, mainly on their skin. Thankfully, these types of cancers are not usually fatal and can be removed. Internal cancers, however, are not as easy to diagnose or treat. In one part of Taiwan where the level of arsenic was 800 ppb, there was a high incidence of bladder cancer. Unfortunately, even when measures are taken to purify the water, the incidence of cancer can continue to be high for many years because of the long latency period before the disease appears.

The largest mass poisoning by arsenic involved more than 30 million people (Figure 9). People in West Bengal, India, and in Bangladesh got their drinking water from tube wells that were drilled in the 1970s. The wells were installed by the United Nations Children's Fund (UNICEF) to provide safe drinking water for a population that had traditionally taken its water from contaminated streams, rivers, and ponds and which had suffered accordingly from water-borne diseases such as gastroenteritis, typhoid, and cholera. Eventually, 5 million such wells were drilled, and they indeed served the purpose of bringing cholera under control. In its place, however, they unknowingly brought low-level arsenic poisoning to large areas of Bangladesh.

Tube wells are 5 cm in diameter and tap the abundant ground water about 200 meters below the surface. A few had been installed in Bangladesh in the 1930s when the region was part of the British Empire. Those villages that had installed them showed a decrease in illness, especially among children. UNICEF continued to support the program after independence, and by 1997 it could report that it had already surpassed its goal of providing 80% of the population in those regions with "safe" water. Such had been the success of the program that many villagers installed private wells. Then doctors began to notice a worrying increase in skin cancer and suspected that arsenic was the cause. Analysis of the water from the wells showed that more than 20 million people were drinking water containing arsenic at the 50 ppb level, and as many as 5 million were drinking water containing 300 ppb arsenic. It does appear, though, that 80% of the Bangladeshi population has access to safe drinking water.

In 1997, the Bangladesh government instituted a Rapid Action Program that focused on a group of villages where contamination was severe. Almost two thirds of the tube wells in these villages were delivering water with arsenic in excess of 100 ppb. A team from the Dhaka Community Hospital visited 18 affected areas and examined 2000 adults and children; they concluded that more than half had skin lesions due to arsenic.

So what can the people of this region do? One answer is to dig wells that go deeper than 200 meters or shallower wells that reach down only 20 meters. In this way, the contaminated layer of ground water can be avoided. Once people have access to uncontaminated water, the arsenic in their bodies is quickly lost.

Remediation steps have to be taken when drinking water is contaminated, and yet it is a problem that can be costly to solve. When half a million people in New Mexico were exposed to high arsenic levels in their drinking water, action was taken but at a cost of $100 million. Taking similar action in Bangladesh would be beyond the ability of that country to pay. Even replacing a shallow well with one that draws water from the lower, safer, water table costs $1000. (Shallow tube wells cost only $100 to drill, which is why they have proved so popular.) The alternative is to remove the arsenic from the water. Various simple and cheap devices have been designed by chemists for doing this, such as passing the water through layers of sand, pieces of iron, and charcoal. The inorganic arsenic, which is present as arsenite ions, AsO_3^{3-}, sticks to the pieces of iron while the organic forms of arsenic are absorbed into the charcoal.

Fluoride in Drinking Water

It is generally acknowledged that a little fluoride in drinking water strengthens tooth enamel and prevents decay, and to this end many public water supplies are fluoridated to a level of 1 ppm. Nevertheless, there are dangers in drinking water that has much higher levels, and in some localities the level of fluoride is naturally high. Humans, as well as animals, can be affected and suffer from *fluorosis* (Figure 10), which is a hardening of the bones leading to a deformed skeleton. In certain parts of India, such as the Punjab, the condition is endemic, especially where villagers drink water from wells with high levels of fluoride, up to 15 ppm. About 25 million Indians suffer a mild form of fluorosis, with many thousands showing skeletal deformities.

Green Chemistry

Our environment is a complex chemical system but not one that is so complex that we can never understand it. It is also a robust system that may be capable of being healed when it is damaged. (One example seems to be the slow reversal of

FIGURE 9 A Bangladesh villager shows his hands affected by arsenic contamination in the water supply.

© Sucheta Das/Reuters/Corbis

© Hardy Limeback. Used by permission of Kevin and Hardy Limeback.

FIGURE 10 Fluorosis. Here, the teeth have whitish patches, indicating mild fluorosis. Teeth and bones are hydroxyapatite, $Ca_5(OH)(PO_4)_3$. If you drink water with a high F^- ion concentration, the OH^- ion in apatite can be replaced by the F^- ion. This can have the beneficial effect of hardening the surface of teeth, but in excess it can lead to mottling. And in very high concentrations, skeletal deformities can result.

the Antarctic ozone hole when CFC production was stopped.) Our stewardship of Earth demands a good knowledge of chemistry and sensible behavior. Nothing less will suffice.

One way chemists have responded to environmental problems is by practicing **green chemistry**, which is also called "sustainable chemistry." You were introduced to its concepts in Chapter 1 (page 6), and you have seen examples of green chemistry in use throughout the book. The United States EPA has a Green Chemistry Program, which includes research, education, and outreach efforts as well as the Presidential Green Chemistry Challenge Awards, an annual program recognizing innovations in "cleaner, cheaper, smarter chemistry." The American Chemical Society actively promotes green chemistry, and the Royal Society of Chemistry in England publishes the research journal *Green Chemistry*. Some universities now offer degrees in green chemistry.

If we assume the word "green" means environmentally sound or friendly, how can chemistry be green? People have many different opinions concerning chemistry and chemicals. Some use the word "chemical" as a synonym for a toxic substance. Others believe that all our problems can be solved through research in chemistry and other sciences. Chemists realize that all *matter*, including our food, water, and bodies as well as toxic compounds, is composed of chemicals. The practice of chemistry, like most aspects of life, has created problems at times, but chemistry has also solved many, many others.

SUGGESTED READINGS

1. J. Emsley: *Nature's Building Blocks*. England: Oxford University Press, 2001.
2. S. Manahan, editor: *Environmental Chemistry*, 9th ed. Boca Raton: CRC Press, 2009.
3. Safe Drinking Water Act, including a list of current maximum contaminant levels: www.epa.gov/safewater/sdwa/sdwa.html
4. Green Chemistry Program: www.epa.gov/greenchemistry
5. To check on the quality of air in your community: airnow.gov; see also www.arl.noaa.gov/
6. Intergovernmental Panel on Climate Change: www.ipcc.ch/

STUDY QUESTIONS

Blue-numbered questions have answers in Appendix Q and fully worked solutions in the *Student Solutions Manual*.

1. Use the data in Table 2 (page 954) to calculate the molar concentrations of Na^+ and Cl^- in seawater. Which amount is larger?

2. Using the data in Table 2, estimate the minimum mass of solid that would remain after evaporation of 1.0 L of seawater.

3. What mass of NaCl could be obtained by evaporating 1.0 L of seawater? (*Note:* The amount of Na^+ ions in seawater limits the amount of NaCl that can be obtained; see Question 1.)

4. In any solution, there must be a balance between the positive and negative charges of the ions that are present. Use the data in Table 2 to determine how close to a balance of charge is achieved for the ions in seawater. (The table lists only the major ions in seawater, and the balance between positive and negative charge will only be approximate.)

5. In the discussion on the composition of air, mention is made of the fact that water vapor may have a concentration as high as 40,000 ppm. Calculate the pressure exerted by water vapor at this concentration. Assume that this represents a situation with 100% humidity. What temperature would be needed to achieve this value? (See Appendix G.)

6. Although there are a number of magnesium-containing minerals, the commercial source of this metal is seawater. Treatment of seawater with $Ca(OH)_2$ gives solid insoluble $Mg(OH)_2$. This reacts with HCl to produce $MgCl_2$, which is dried, and Mg is obtained by electrolysis of the molten salt. Write balanced net ionic equations for the three reactions described here.

7. Calculate the mass of Mg that could be obtained by the process described in Question 6 from 1.0 L of seawater. To prepare 100. kg of Mg, what volume of seawater would be needed? (The density of seawater is 1.025 g/cm^3.)

8. Assume the average CO_2 concentration in the atmosphere is 385 ppm. The actual concentration of CO_2 at different sites will vary. Speculate on whether the concentration of CO_2 would be expected to be higher, lower, or the same as this average value in a typical large city.

9. Imagine the following experiment. You have a large graduated cylinder containing 100. mL of liquid water at 0 °C. You drop an ice cube with a volume of 25 cm^3 into the cylinder. Ice has a density of 0.92 g/cm^3, less than the density of liquid water, so it floats with 92% being under water.
   (a) To what level will the water in the graduated cylinder rise after adding the ice?
   (b) Allow the ice to melt. What volume will now be occupied by the liquid water? (One consequence of global warming will be a rise in sea level as ice in the northern and southern regions of the planet melts. However, the effect relates only to melting of ice on land. Melting of floating ice will have no effect on sea levels.)

ACKNOWLEDGMENT

This article was originally written for the previous edition by Dr. John Emsley of the University of Cambridge, England. It has been revised and reorganized for this edition by the authors and Dr. Trudy Thomas-Smith.

21 The Chemistry of the Main Group Elements

Quartz (SiO_2), dry ice (solid CO_2), and pure silicon.

Carbon and Silicon

Carbon and silicon are both significant elements in the earth's crust. Mendeleev placed them in the same periodic group based on the similarity in stoichiometry of their simple compounds such as their oxides (CO_2 and SiO_2). We know now that carbon is the backbone of millions of organic compounds. As we will see in this chapter, silicon, the second most abundant element in the earth's crust, is vitally important in the structures of a large number of minerals.

Probe a bit further into silicon chemistry, however, and what emerges are the surprising differences between these elements. We get a hint of this when we compare the two oxides, CO_2, a gas above -78 °C and 1 atm pressure, and SiO_2, a rock hard solid with a very high melting point. Another interesting contrast can be made between the reactions of the two simple hydrogen compounds, CH_4 and SiH_4, with water. The reaction of methane with water is reactant-favored, whereas silane will explode on contact with water.

In this chapter, we will evaluate and summarize the inorganic chemistry of the main group elements and explore the similarities and differences between elements in each periodic group.

Questions:

1. Write balanced chemical equations for the reactions of $H_2O(\ell)$ with CH_4 (forming CO_2 and H_2) and SiH_4 (forming SiO_2 and H_2).
2. Using thermodynamic data, calculate the standard free energy change for the reactions in Question 1. Is either reaction product-favored at equilibrium?
3. Look up the electronegativities of carbon, silicon, and hydrogen. What conclusion can you draw concerning the polarity of C—H and Si—H bonds?
4. Carbon and silicon compounds with the formulas $(CH_3)_2CO$ (acetone) and $[(CH_3)_2SiO]_n$ (a silicone polymer) also have quite different structures (Chapter 10). Draw Lewis structures for these species. This difference, along with the difference between structures of CO_2 and SiO_2, suggests a general observation about silicon compounds. Based on that observation, do you expect that a silicon compound with a structure similar to ethene (C_2H_4) exists?

Answers to these questions are available in Appendix N.

CHAPTER GOALS

See Chapter Goals Revisited (page 1006) for Study Questions keyed to these goals.

- Relate the formulas and properties of compounds to the periodic table.

- Describe the chemistry of the main group or A-Group elements, particularly H; Na and K; Mg and Ca; B and Al; Si; N and P; O and S; and F and Cl.

- Apply the principles of stoichiometry, thermodynamics, and electrochemistry to the chemistry of the main group elements.

The main group or A-Group elements occupy an important place in the world of chemistry. Eight of the 10 most abundant elements on the earth are in these groups. Likewise, the top 10 chemicals produced by the U.S. chemical industry are all main group elements or their compounds.

Because main group elements and their compounds are economically important—and because they have interesting chemistries—we devote this chapter to a brief survey of these elements.

21.1 Element Abundances

The abundance of the first 18 elements in the solar system is plotted against their atomic numbers in Figure 21.1. Hydrogen and helium are the most abundant by a wide margin because most of the mass of the solar system resides in the sun, and these elements are the sun's primary components. Lithium, beryllium, and boron

OWL

Sign in to OWL at **www.cengage.com/owl** to view tutorials and simulations, develop problem-solving skills, and complete online homework assigned by your professor.

go Chemistry

Download mini lecture videos for key concept review and exam prep from OWL or purchase them from **www.cengagebrain.com**

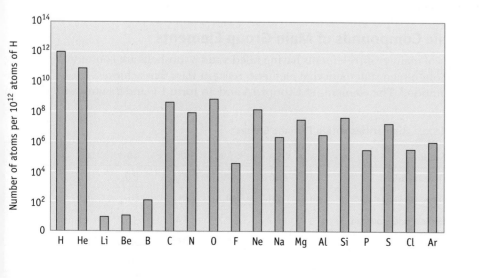

FIGURE 21.1 Abundance of elements 1–18 in the solar system. Li, Be, and B have relatively low abundances because they are circumvented when elements are made in stars. The common elements such as C, O, and Ne are made in stars by the accretion of alpha particles (helium nuclei). Helium has an atomic number of 2. If three He atoms combine, they produce an atom with atomic number 6 (carbon). Adding yet another He atom gives an atom with atomic number 8 (oxygen), and so on. (Notice that the vertical axis uses a logarithmic scale. This means, for example, there are 10^{12} H atoms for every 100 B atoms.)

Table 21.1 The 10 Most Abundant Elements in Earth's Crust

Rank	Element	Abundance (ppm)*
1	Oxygen	474,000
2	Silicon	277,000
3	Aluminum	82,000
4	Iron	56,300
5	Calcium	41,000
6	Sodium	23,600
7	Magnesium	23,300
8	Potassium	21,000
9	Titanium	5600
10	Hydrogen	1520

*ppm = g per 1000 kg. Most abundance data taken from J. Emsley: *The Elements*, New York, Oxford University Press, 3rd edition, 1998.

are low in abundance, but carbon's abundance is very high. From this point on, with the exception of iron and nickel, elemental abundances gradually decline as the atomic number increases.

Ten elements account for 99% of the aggregate mass of the earth's crust (Table 21.1), and oxygen, silicon, and aluminum represent more than 80% of this mass. Oxygen and nitrogen are the primary components of the atmosphere, and oxygen-containing water is highly abundant on the surface, underground, and as a vapor in the atmosphere. Many common minerals also contain these elements, including limestone ($CaCO_3$) and quartz or sand (SiO_2, ◄ Figure 2.8). Aluminum and silicon occur together in many minerals; among the more common ones are feldspar, granite, and clay.

21.2 The Periodic Table: A Guide to the Elements

The similarities in the properties of certain elements guided Mendeleev when he created the first periodic table (◄ page 59). He placed elements in groups based partly on the composition of their common compounds with oxygen and hydrogen (Table 21.2). We now understand that the elements are grouped according to the arrangements of their valence electrons.

Recall that the metallic character of the elements declines on moving from left to right in the periodic table. Elements in Group 1A, the alkali metals, are the most metallic elements in the periodic table. Elements on the far right are nonmetals, and in between are the metalloids. Metallic character also increases from the top of a group to the bottom. This is especially well illustrated by Group 4A. Carbon, at the top of the group, is a nonmetal; silicon and germanium are metalloids; and tin and lead are metals (Figure 21.2). The significance of metallic character in a discussion of the chemistry of the elements is readily apparent; metals typically form ionic compounds, whereas compounds composed only of nonmetals are covalent. Typically, ionic compounds are crystalline solids that have high melting points and conduct electricity in the molten state. Covalent compounds, on the other hand, can be gases, liquids, or solids and have low melting and boiling points.

Valence Electrons

The ns and np electrons are the valence electrons for main group elements (where n is the period in which the element is found) (◄ Section 7.3). The chemical behavior of an element is determined by the valence electrons.

When considering electronic structure, a useful reference point is the noble gases (Group 8A). Helium has an electron configuration of $1s^2$; the other noble gases have ns^2np^6 valence electron configurations. The dominant characteristic of the noble gases is their lack of reactivity. Indeed, the first two elements in the group do not form any compounds that can be isolated. The other four elements are now known to have limited chemistry, however, and the discovery of xenon compounds in the 1960s ranks as one of the most interesting developments in modern chemistry.

Ionic Compounds of Main Group Elements

Ions of main group elements having filled s and p subshells are common—justifying the often-seen statement that elements react in ways that achieve a "noble gas configuration." The elements in Groups 1A and 2A form 1+ and 2+ ions with electron

© Cengage Learning/Charles D. Winters

FIGURE 21.2 Group 4A elements. A nonmetal, carbon (graphite crucible); a metalloid, silicon (round, lustrous bar); and metals tin (chips of metal) and lead (a bullet, a toy, and a sphere).

Table 21.2 Similarities within Periodic Groups*

Group	1A	2A	3A	4A	5A	6A	7A
Common oxide	M_2O	MO	M_2O_3	EO_2	E_4O_{10}	EO_3	E_2O_7
Common hydride	MH	MH_2	MH_3	EH_4	EH_3	EH_2	EH
Highest oxidation state	+1	+2	+3	+4	+5	+6	+7
Common oxoanion			BO_3^{3-}	CO_3^{2-}	NO_3^-	SO_4^{2-}	ClO_4^-
				SiO_4^{4-}	PO_4^{3-}		

*M denotes a metal and E denotes a nonmetal or metalloid.

configurations that are the same as those for the previous noble gases. All common compounds of these elements (e.g., NaCl, $CaCO_3$) are ionic. The metallic elements in Group 3A (aluminum, gallium, indium, and thallium, but not the metalloid boron) form compounds containing $3+$ ions.

Elements of Groups 6A and 7A can achieve a noble gas configuration by adding electrons. The Group 7A elements (halogens) form anions with a $1-$ charge (the halide ions, F^-, Cl^-, Br^-, I^-), and the Group 6A elements form anions with a $2-$ charge (O^{2-}, S^{2-}, Se^{2-}, Te^{2-}). In Group 5A chemistry, $3-$ ions with a noble gas configuration (such as the nitride ion, N^{3-}) are also known. The energy required to form highly charged anions is large, however, which means that other types of chemical behavior will usually take precedence.

EXAMPLE 21.1   Reactions of Group 1A–3A Elements

Problem Give the formula and name for the product in each of the following reactions. Write a balanced chemical equation for the reaction.

(a) $Ca(s) + S_8(s)$

(b) $Rb(s) + I_2(s)$

(c)   lithium and chlorine

(d)   aluminum and oxygen

What Do You Know? The reactions listed are between metals in periodic groups 1A, 2A, and 3A and nonmetals in periodic groups 6A and 7A. The products formed will be ionic compounds made up of cations formed from metals by loss of electrons and anions formed from nonmetals by the gain of electrons. Remember that equations must be balanced.

Strategy Predictions are based on the assumption that ions are formed with the electron configuration of the nearest noble gas. Group 1A elements form $1+$ ions; Group 2A elements form $2+$ ions; and metals in Group 3A form $3+$ ions. In their reactions with metals, halogen atoms typically add a single electron to give anions with a $1-$ charge; Group 6A elements add two electrons to form anions with a $2-$ charge. For names of products, refer to the nomenclature discussion on page 75.

Solution

Balanced Equation	Product Name
(a) $8\ Ca(s) + S_8(s) \rightarrow 8\ CaS(s)$	Calcium sulfide
(b) $2\ Rb(s) + I_2(s) \rightarrow 2\ RbI(s)$	Rubidium iodide
(c) $2\ Li(s) + Cl_2(g) \rightarrow 2\ LiCl(s)$	Lithium chloride
(d) $4\ Al(s) + 3\ O_2(g) \rightarrow 2\ Al_2O_3(s)$	Aluminum oxide

Think about Your Answer It will be useful to review the formulas and names of common ions. These were given earlier in the text (Section 2.7).

Check Your Understanding

Write balanced chemical equations for the reactions forming the following compounds from the elements.

(a)   NaBr   (b)   CaSe   (c)   PbO   (d) $AlCl_3$

Molecular Compounds of Main Group Elements

Many avenues of reactivity are open to nonmetallic main group elements. Reactions with metals generally result in formation of ionic compounds, whereas compounds containing only metalloids and nonmetallic elements are generally molecular in nature.

Molecular compounds are encountered with the Group 3A element boron (Figure 21.3), and the chemistry of carbon in Group 4A is dominated by molecular

FIGURE 21.3 Boron halides. Liquid BBr_3 (left) and solid BI_3 (right). Formed from a metalloid and a nonmetal, both are molecular compounds. Both are sealed in glass ampules to prevent these boron compounds from reacting with H_2O in the air.

Table 21.3 Fluorine Compounds Formed by Main Group Elements

Group	Compound	Bonding
1A	NaF	Ionic
2A	MgF_2	Ionic
3A	AlF_3	Ionic
4A	SiF_4	Covalent
5A	PF_5	Covalent
6A	SF_6	Covalent
7A	IF_7	Covalent
8A	XeF_4	Covalent

compounds with covalent bonds (◄ Chapters 8 and 10). Similarly, nitrogen chemistry is dominated by molecular compounds. Consider ammonia, NH_3; the various nitrogen oxides (such as "laughing gas," N_2O); and nitric acid, HNO_3. In each of these species, nitrogen bonds covalently to another nonmetallic element. Also in Group 5A, phosphorus reacts with chlorine to produce the molecular compound PCl_3 (◄ page 111).

The valence electron configuration of an element determines the composition of its molecular compounds. Involving all the valence electrons in the formation of a compound is a frequent occurrence in main group element chemistry. We should not be surprised to discover compounds in which the central element has the highest possible oxidation number (such as P in PF_5). The highest oxidation number is readily predictable: it equals the group number. Thus, the highest (and only) oxidation number of sodium in its compounds is $+1$; the highest oxidation number of C is $+4$; and the highest oxidation number of phosphorus is $+5$ (Tables 21.2 and 21.3).

EXAMPLE 21.2 Predicting Formulas for Compounds of Main Group Elements

Problem Predict the formula for each of the following:

(a) The product of the reaction between germanium and excess oxygen

(b) The product of the reaction of arsenic and excess fluorine

(c) A compound formed from phosphorus and excess chlorine

(d) The fully deprotonated anion of selenic acid

What Do You Know? You know the symbol and location of each of the elements in the periodic table.

Strategy You can predict that in each reaction the element bonded to the halogen or oxygen in the product will achieve its most positive oxidation number, a value equal to the number of its periodic group.

Solution

(a) The Group 4A element germanium should have a maximum oxidation number of $+4$. Thus, its oxide has the formula GeO_2.

(b) Arsenic, in Group 5A, reacts vigorously with fluorine to form AsF_5, in which arsenic has an oxidation number of $+5$.

(c) PCl_5 is formed when the Group 5A element phosphorus reacts with excess chlorine.

(d) The chemistries of S and Se are similar. Sulfur, in Group 6A, has a maximum oxidation number of $+6$, so it forms SO_3 and sulfuric acid, H_2SO_4. Selenium, also in Group 6A, has analogous chemistry, forming SeO_3 and selenic acid, H_2SeO_4. The fully deprotonated anion of this acid is the selenate ion, SeO_4^{2-}.

Think about Your Answer Notice that in several questions the use of excess oxidizing agent was specified. This is important because, for most of the nonmetals, several different products were possible. For example, the oxidation of carbon can produce either CO_2 or CO depending on whether there is an excess or a deficiency of oxygen. You will learn more about this in later sections of this chapter.

Check Your Understanding

Write the formula for each of the following:

(a) hydrogen telluride

(b) sodium arsenate

(c) selenium hexachloride

(d) perbromic acid

There are many similarities among elements in the same periodic table group. This means you can use compounds of more common elements as examples when you encounter compounds of elements with which you are not familiar. For example, water, H_2O, is the simplest hydrogen compound of oxygen. You can reasonably expect the hydrogen compounds of other Group 6A elements to be H_2S, H_2Se, and H_2Te; all are well known.

EXAMPLE 21.3   Predicting Formulas

Problem Predict the formula for each of the following:

(a) A compound of hydrogen and phosphorus

(b) The hypobromite ion

(c) Germane (the simplest hydrogen compound of germanium)

(d) Two oxides of tellurium

What Do You Know? We expect the elements in a periodic group to behave similarly in their chemistry, in most instances. Thus, we can use known examples from the more common elements found early in the periodic table and extrapolate to predict the behavior of the less common elements found in the same group.

Strategy Recall as examples some of the compounds of lighter elements in a group, and then assume other elements in that group will form analogous compounds.

Solution

(a) Phosphine, PH_3, has a composition analogous to ammonia, NH_3.

(b) Hypobromite ion, BrO^-, is similar to the hypochlorite ion, ClO^-, the anion of hypochlorous acid ($HClO$).

(c) GeH_4 is analogous to CH_4 and SiH_4, other Group 4A hydrogen compounds.

(d) Te and S are in Group 6A. TeO_2 and TeO_3 are analogs of the oxides of sulfur, SO_2 and SO_3.

Think about Your Answer Keep in mind that there can be differences between elements within a periodic group. One difference is that second-period elements generally obey the octet rule, whereas in the third period and below, compounds with expanded octets can form (Section 8.5). For example, in reactions with fluorine, nitrogen forms NF_3 whereas phosphorus forms both PF_3 and PF_5.

Check Your Understanding

Identify a compound or ion based on a second-period element that has a formula and Lewis structure analogous to each of the following:

(a) PH_4^+ (b) S_2^{2-} (c) P_2H_4 (d) PF_3

EXAMPLE 21.4   Recognizing Incorrect Formulas

Problem One formula is incorrect in each of the following groups. Pick out the incorrect formula, and indicate why it is incorrect.

(a) $CsSO_4$, KCl, $NaNO_3$, Li_2O

(b) MgO, CaI_2, $BaPO_4$, $CaCO_3$

(c) CO, CO_2, CO_3

(d) PF_5, PF_4^+, PF_7, PF_6^-

What Do You Know? One formula in each set of four is wrong. You can determine which by applying the rules for oxidation states set forth in this section.

Strategy Look for errors such as incorrect charges on ions or an oxidation number exceeding the maximum possible for the periodic group.

Solution

(a)　$CsSO_4$. Sulfate ion has a 2− charge, so this formula would require a Cs^{2+} ion. Cesium, in Group 1A, forms only 1+ ions. The formula of cesium sulfate is Cs_2SO_4.

(b)　$BaPO_4$. This formula implies a Ba^{3+} ion (because the phosphate anion is PO_4^{3-}). The cation charge does not equal the group number. The formula of barium phosphate is $Ba_3(PO_4)_2$.

(c)　CO_3. Given that O has an oxidation number of −2, carbon would have to have an oxidation number of +6. Carbon is in Group 4A, however, and can have a maximum oxidation number of +4.

(d)　PF_7. The formula implies P has an oxidation state of +7, whereas +5 is expected for the maximum possible P oxidation state.

Think about Your Answer There are a lot of facts to learn in chemistry. Fortunately, many can be organized in ways that make learning easier. Using the periodic table to predict the chemistry of each element, and recognizing similarities among elements in groups, is one of the essential aspects of chemistry. This has been the goal of this section of the chapter.

Check Your Understanding

Explain why compounds with the following formulas would not be expected to exist: Na_2Cl, $CaCH_3CO_2$, Mg_2O.

REVIEW & CHECK FOR SECTION 21.2

1.　Which of the following formulas is incorrect?

　　(a)　CaH_2　　　　(b)　CaI_2　　　　(c)　CaS　　　　(d)　Ca_2O_3

2.　What is the name of the product of the reaction between elemental phosphorus and excess oxygen, P_4O_{10}?

　　(a)　phosphorus oxide　　　　　　　　(c)　phosphoric acid

　　(b)　phosphorus decaoxide　　　　　　(d)　tetraphosphorus decaoxide

3.　Like sulfur, selenium forms compounds in several different oxidation states. Which of the following is not likely to be an oxidation state of selenium in its compounds?

　　(a)　−2　　　　(b)　+3　　　　(c)　+6　　　　(d)　+4

4.　What is the highest oxidation state that antimony can have in its compounds?

　　(a)　0　　　　(b)　+1　　　　(c)　+3　　　　(d)　+5

21.3 **Hydrogen**

Chemical and Physical Properties of Hydrogen

Hydrogen has three isotopes, two of them stable (protium and deuterium) and one radioactive (tritium).

Isotopes of Hydrogen

Isotope Mass (u)	Symbol	Name
1.0078	^1H (H)	Hydrogen (protium)
2.0141	^2H (D)	Deuterium
3.0160	^3H (T)	Tritium

Of the three isotopes, only H and D are found in nature in significant quantities. Tritium, which is produced by cosmic ray bombardment of nitrogen in the atmosphere, is found to the extent of 1 atom per 10^{18} atoms of ordinary hydrogen. Tritium has a half-life of 12.26 years.

A CLOSER LOOK

Hydrogen, Helium, and Balloons

In 1783, Jacques Charles first used hydrogen to fill a balloon large enough to float above the French countryside (◀ page 518). In World War I, hydrogen-filled observation balloons were used. The Graf Zeppelin, a passenger-carrying dirigible built in Germany in 1928, was also filled with hydrogen. It carried more than 13,000 people between Germany and the United States until 1937, when it was replaced by the Hindenburg. The Hindenburg was designed to be filled with helium. At that time, World War II was approaching, and the United States, which has much of the world's supply of helium, would not sell the gas to Germany. As a consequence, the Hindenburg had to use hydrogen. The Hindenburg exploded and burned when landing in Lakehurst, New Jersey, in May 1937. Of the 62 people on

board, only about half escaped uninjured. As a result of this disaster, hydrogen has acquired a reputation as being a very dangerous substance. Actually, it is as safe to handle as many other fuels.

The Hindenburg. This hydrogen-filled dirigible crashed in Lakehurst, New Jersey, in May 1937. Some have speculated that the aluminum paint coating the skin of the dirigible was involved in sparking the fire.

Mary Evans Picture Library/Photo Researchers, Inc.

Under standard conditions, hydrogen is a colorless gas. Its very low boiling point, 20.7 K, reflects its nonpolar character and low molar mass. As the least dense gas known, it is ideal for filling lighter-than-air craft.

Deuterium compounds have been the subject of much research. One important observation is that, because D has twice the mass of H, reactions involving D atom transfer are slightly slower than those involving H atoms. This knowledge led to a way to produce D_2O or "heavy water." Hydrogen can be produced, albeit expensively, by electrolysis of water (Figure 21.4).

$$2 \ H_2O(\ell) + \text{electrical energy} \rightarrow 2 \ H_2(g) + O_2(g)$$

Any sample of natural water always contains a tiny concentration of D_2O. When electrolyzed, H_2O is electrolyzed more rapidly than D_2O. Thus, as the electrolysis proceeds, the liquid remaining is enriched in D_2O. Repeating this process many times will eventually give pure D_2O, often called "heavy water." Large amounts of D_2O are now produced because this compound is used as a moderator in some nuclear reactors that are used for power generation.

Hydrogen combines chemically with virtually every other element, except the noble gases. There are three different types of binary hydrogen-containing compounds.

Ionic metal hydrides are formed in the reaction of H_2 with a Group 1A or 2A metal.

$$2 \ Na(s) + H_2(g) \rightarrow 2 \ NaH(s)$$

$$Ca(s) + H_2(g) \rightarrow CaH_2(s)$$

These compounds contain the hydride ion, H^-, in which hydrogen has a -1 oxidation number.

Molecular compounds (such as H_2O, HF, and NH_3) are generally formed by direct combination of hydrogen with nonmetallic elements (Figure 21.5). The oxidation number of the hydrogen atom in these compounds is $+1$, but covalent bonds to hydrogen are the rule.

$$N_2(g) + 3 \ H_2(g) \rightarrow 2 \ NH_3(g)$$

$$F_2(g) + H_2(g) \rightarrow 2 \ HF(g)$$

© Cengage Learning/Charles D. Winters

FIGURE 21.4 Electrolysis of water. Electrolysis of water (containing dilute H_2SO_4 as an electrolyte) gives O_2 *(left)* and H_2 *(right)*.

FIGURE 21.5 The reaction of H_2 and Br_2. Hydrogen gas burns in an atmosphere of bromine vapor to give hydrogen bromide.

Hydrogen is absorbed by many metals to form *interstitial hydrides*, the third general class of hydrogen compounds. This name refers to the structures of these species, in which the hydrogen atoms reside in the spaces between the metal atoms (called *interstices*) in the crystal lattice. Palladium metal, for example, can soak up 1000 times its volume of hydrogen (at STP). Most interstitial hydrides are non-stoichiometric; that is, the ratio of metal and hydrogen is not a whole number. When interstitial metal hydrides are heated, H_2 is driven out. This phenomenon allows these materials to store H_2, just as a sponge can store water. It suggests one way to store hydrogen for use in automobiles (◄ page 912).

Preparation of Hydrogen

About 300 billion liters (STP) of hydrogen gas are produced annually worldwide, and virtually all is used immediately in the manufacture of ammonia (► Section 21.8), methanol (◄ Section 10.4), or other chemicals.

Some hydrogen is made from coal and steam, a reaction that has been used for more than 100 years.

$$C(s) + H_2O(g) \longrightarrow \underbrace{H_2(g) + CO(g)}_{\text{water gas or synthesis gas}}$$

$$\Delta_r H° = +131 \text{ kJ/mol-rxn}$$

The reaction is carried out by injecting water into a bed of red-hot coke. The mixture of gases produced, called *water gas* or *synthesis gas*, was used until about 1950 as a fuel for cooking, heating, and lighting. However, it has serious drawbacks. It produces only about half as much heat as an equal amount of methane does, and the flame is nearly invisible. Moreover, because it contains carbon monoxide, water gas is toxic.

The largest quantity of hydrogen is now produced by the *catalytic steam reformation of hydrocarbons* such as methane in natural gas (Figure 21.6). Methane reacts with steam at high temperature to give H_2 and CO.

$$CH_4(g) + H_2O(g) \rightarrow 3\ H_2(g) + CO(g) \qquad \Delta_r H° = +206 \text{ kJ/mol-rxn}$$

The reaction is rapid at 900–1000 °C and goes nearly to completion. More hydrogen can be obtained in a second step in which the CO formed in the first step reacts with more water. This so-called *water gas shift reaction* is run at 400–500 °C and is slightly exothermic.

$$H_2O(g) + CO(g) \rightarrow H_2(g) + CO_2(g) \qquad \Delta_r H° = -41 \text{ kJ/mol-rxn}$$

The CO_2 formed in the process is removed by reaction with CaO (to give solid $CaCO_3$), leaving fairly pure hydrogen.

Perhaps the cleanest way to make hydrogen on a relatively large scale is the electrolysis of water (Figure 21.4). This approach provides not only hydrogen gas but also high-purity O_2. Because electricity is quite expensive, however, this method is not generally used commercially.

Table 21.4 and Figure 21.7 give examples of reactions used to produce H_2 gas in the laboratory. The most often used method is the reaction of a metal with an acid. Alternatively, the reaction of aluminum with aqueous NaOH (Figure 21.7b) also generates hydrogen. During World War II, this reaction was used to obtain hydrogen to inflate small balloons for weather observation and to raise radio antennas. Metallic aluminum was plentiful at the time because it came from damaged aircraft.

The combination of a metal hydride and water (Figure 21.7c) is an efficient but expensive way to synthesize H_2 in the laboratory. The reaction is commonly used in laboratories to dry organic solvents because the metal hydride reacts with traces of water present in the solvent.

FIGURE 21.6 Production of water gas. Water gas, also called *synthesis gas*, is a mixture of CO and H_2. It is produced by treating coal, coke, or a hydrocarbon like methane with steam at high temperatures in plants such as that pictured here. Methane has the advantage that it gives more total H_2 per gram than other hydrocarbons, and the ratio of the by-product CO_2 to H_2 is lower.

Table 21.4 Methods for Preparing H₂ in the Laboratory

1. Metal + Acid ⟶ metal salt + H₂

   $Mg(s) + 2\,HCl(aq) \longrightarrow MgCl_2(aq) + H_2(g)$

2. Metal + H₂O ⟶ metal hydroxide or oxide + H₂

   $2\,Na(s) + 2\,H_2O(\ell) \longrightarrow 2\,NaOH(aq) + H_2(g)$

   $2\,Fe(s) + 3\,H_2O(\ell) \longrightarrow Fe_2O_3(s) + 3\,H_2(g)$

   $2\,Al(s) + 2\,KOH(aq) + 6\,H_2O(\ell) \longrightarrow 2\,K[Al(OH)_4](aq) + 3\,H_2(g)$

3. Metal hydride + H₂O ⟶ metal hydroxide + H₂

   $CaH_2(s) + 2\,H_2O(\ell) \longrightarrow Ca(OH)_2(s) + 2\,H_2(g)$

REVIEW & CHECK FOR SECTION 21.3

1. Which of the following elements does not react with hydrogen?

   (a) neon   (b) nitrogen   (c) potassium   (d) fluorine

2. Which of the methods below is the most suitable for the preparation of large quantities of hydrogen (such as the amounts needed as a reagent for the synthesis of compounds such as ammonia)?

   (a) Electrolysis of water

   (b) The reaction of metal hydrides with water

   (c) The high temperature reaction of methane and water

   (d) The reaction of zinc and hydrochloric acid

21.4 The Alkali Metals, Group 1A

Sodium and potassium are, respectively, the sixth and eighth most abundant elements in the earth's crust by mass. In contrast, lithium is relatively rare, as are rubidium and cesium. Only traces of radioactive francium occur in nature. Its longest-lived isotope (²²³Fr) has a half-life of only 22 minutes.

The Group 1A elements are metals, and all are highly reactive with oxygen, water, and other oxidizing agents (◄ Figure 7.13, page 324). In all cases, compounds

Group 1A
Alkali metals

| Lithium |
| 3 |
| **Li** |
| 20 ppm |

| Sodium |
| 11 |
| **Na** |
| 23,600 ppm |

| Potassium |
| 19 |
| **K** |
| 21,000 ppm |

| Rubidium |
| 37 |
| **Rb** |
| 90 ppm |

| Cesium |
| 55 |
| **Cs** |
| 0.0003 ppm |

| Francium |
| 87 |
| **Fr** |
| trace |

Element abundances are in **parts per million** *in the earth's crust.*

FIGURE 21.7
Producing hydrogen gas.

(a) The reaction of magnesium and acid. The products are hydrogen gas and a magnesium salt.

(b) The reaction of aluminum and NaOH. The products of this reaction are hydrogen gas and a solution of Na[Al(OH)₄].

(c) The reaction of CaH₂ and water. The products are hydrogen gas and Ca(OH)₂.

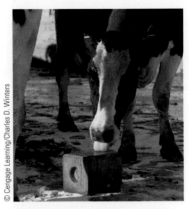

FIGURE 21.8 The importance of salt. All animals, including humans, need a certain amount of salt in their diet. Sodium ions are important in maintaining electrolyte balance and in regulating osmotic pressure. For an interesting account of the importance of salt in society, culture, history, and economy, see *Salt, A World History*, by M. Kurlansky, New York, Penguin Books, 2003.

of the Group 1A metals contain the element as a 1+ ion. The free metal is never found in nature. Most sodium and potassium compounds are water-soluble (◄ solubility guidelines, Figure 3.10), so it is not surprising that sodium and potassium compounds are found either in the oceans or in underground deposits that are the residue of ancient seas. To a much smaller extent, these elements are also found in minerals, such as Chile saltpeter ($NaNO_3$).

Despite the fact that sodium is only slightly more abundant than potassium on the earth, sea water contains significantly more sodium than potassium (2.8% NaCl versus 0.8% KCl). Why the great difference? Most compounds of both elements are water-soluble, so why didn't rain dissolve Na- and K-containing minerals over the centuries and carry them down to the sea, so that they appear in the same proportions in the oceans as on land? The answer lies in the fact that potassium is an important factor in plant growth. Most plants contain four to six times as much combined potassium as sodium. Thus, most of the potassium ions in groundwater from dissolved minerals are taken up preferentially by plants, whereas sodium salts continue on to the oceans. (Because plants require potassium, commercial fertilizers usually contain a significant amount of potassium salts.)

Some NaCl is essential in the diet of humans and other animals because many biological functions are controlled by the concentrations of Na^+ and Cl^- ions (Figure 21.8). The fact that salt has long been recognized as important is evident in surprising ways. For example, we are paid a "salary" for work done. This word is derived from the Latin *salarium*, which meant "salt money" because Roman soldiers were paid in salt.

Preparation of Sodium and Potassium

Sodium is produced by reducing sodium ions in sodium salts. However, because common chemical reducing agents are not powerful enough to convert sodium ions to sodium metal, the metal is usually prepared by electrolysis.

The English chemist Sir Humphry Davy first isolated sodium in 1807 by the electrolysis of molten sodium carbonate. However, the element remained a laboratory curiosity until 1824, when it was found sodium could be used to reduce aluminum chloride to aluminum metal. At that time, metallic aluminum was rare and very valuable, so this discovery inspired considerable interest in manufacturing sodium. By 1886, a practical method of sodium production had been devised (the reduction of NaOH with carbon). Unfortunately for sodium producers, in this same year Charles Hall and Paul Heroult invented the electrolytic method for aluminum production (► page 981), thereby eliminating this market for sodium.

Sodium is currently produced by the electrolysis of molten NaCl (◄ Section 20.7). The Downs cell for the electrolysis of molten NaCl operates at 7 to 8 V with currents of 25,000 to 40,000 amps (Figure 21.9). The cell is filled with a mixture of dry NaCl, $CaCl_2$, and $BaCl_2$. Adding other salts to NaCl lowers the melting point from that of pure NaCl (800.7 °C) to about 600 °C. [Recall that solutions have lower melting points than pure solvents (Chapter 14).] Sodium is produced at a copper or iron cathode that surrounds a circular graphite anode. Directly over the cathode is an inverted trough in which the low-density, molten sodium (melting point, 97.8 °C) collects. Chlorine, a valuable by-product, collects at the anode.

Potassium can also be made by electrolysis. Molten potassium is soluble in molten KCl, however, making separation of the metal difficult. The preferred method for preparation of potassium uses the reaction of sodium vapor with molten KCl, with potassium being continually removed from the equilibrium mixture.

$$Na(g) + KCl(\ell) \rightleftharpoons K(g) + NaCl(\ell)$$

Properties of Sodium and Potassium

Sodium and potassium are silvery metals that are soft and easily cut with a knife (◄ Figure 2.6). They are just a bit less dense than water. Their melting points are quite low, 97.8 °C for sodium and 63.7 °C for potassium.

● **Alkali Metals React with Water— Thermodynamics and Kinetics** The alkali metals all react vigorously with water, and it is easily observed that the violence of the reaction increases with atomic number. This seems counter to the argument presented in *A Closer Look* (page 972) that lithium is the best reducing agent. However, the reducing ability of a metal is a thermodynamic property, whereas the violence of the reaction is mainly a consequence of reaction rate.

FIGURE 21.9 A Downs cell for preparing sodium. A circular iron cathode is separated from the graphite anode by an iron screen. At the temperature of the electrolysis, about 600 °C, sodium is a liquid. It rises to the top and is drawn off periodically. Chlorine gas is produced at the anode and collected inside the inverted cone in the center of the cell.

All of the alkali metals are highly reactive. When exposed to moist air, the metal surface quickly becomes coated with a film of oxide or hydroxide. Consequently, the metals must be stored in a way that avoids contact with air, typically by placing them in kerosene or mineral oil.

The high reactivity of Group 1A metals is exemplified by their reaction with water, which generates an aqueous solution of the metal hydroxide and hydrogen gas (◀ Figure 7.13, page 324),

$$2 \text{ Na(s)} + 2 \text{ H}_2\text{O}(\ell) \rightarrow 2 \text{ Na}^+(\text{aq}) + 2 \text{ OH}^-(\text{aq}) + \text{H}_2(\text{g})$$

and their reaction with any of the halogens to yield a metal halide (◀ Figure 1.2),

$$2 \text{ Na(s)} + \text{Cl}_2(\text{g}) \rightarrow 2 \text{ NaCl(s)}$$

$$2 \text{ K(s)} + \text{Br}_2(\ell) \rightarrow 2 \text{ KBr(s)}$$

Chemistry often produces surprises. Group 1A metal oxides, M_2O, are known, but they are not the principal products of reactions between the Group 1A elements and oxygen. Instead, the primary product of the reaction of sodium and oxygen is sodium *peroxide*, Na_2O_2, whereas the principal product from the reaction of potassium and oxygen is KO_2, potassium *superoxide*.

$$2 \text{ Na(s)} + \text{O}_2(\text{g}) \rightarrow \text{Na}_2\text{O}_2(\text{s})$$

$$\text{K(s)} + \text{O}_2(\text{g}) \rightarrow \text{KO}_2(\text{s})$$

Both Na_2O_2 and KO_2 are ionic compounds. The Group 1A cation is paired with either the peroxide ion (O_2^{2-}) or the superoxide ion (O_2^-). These compounds are not merely laboratory curiosities. They are used in oxygen-generation devices in places where people are confined, such as submarines, aircraft, and spacecraft, or when an emergency supply is needed. When a person breathes, 0.82 L of CO_2 is exhaled for every 1 L of O_2 inhaled. Thus, a requirement of an O_2-generation system is that it should produce a larger volume of O_2 than the volume of CO_2 taken in. This requirement is met with superoxides (Figure 21.10). With KO_2 the reaction is

$$4 \text{ KO}_2(\text{s}) + 2 \text{ CO}_2(\text{g}) \rightarrow 2 \text{ K}_2\text{CO}_3(\text{s}) + 3 \text{ O}_2(\text{g})$$

Courtesy of Mine Safety Appliances Company

FIGURE 21.10 A closed-circuit breathing apparatus that generates its own oxygen. One source of oxygen is potassium superoxide (KO_2). Both carbon dioxide and moisture exhaled by the wearer into the breathing tube react with the KO_2 to generate oxygen. Because the rate of the chemical reaction is determined by the quantity of moisture and carbon dioxide exhaled, the production of oxygen is regulated automatically. With each exhalation, more oxygen is produced by volume than is required by the user.

A CLOSER LOOK

The Reducing Ability of the Alkali Metals

The uses of the Group 1A metals depend on their reducing ability. The values of $E°$ reveal that Li is the best reducing agent in the group, whereas Na is the poorest; the remainder of these metals have roughly comparable reducing abilities.

Reduction Potential

Element	$E°$ (V)
$Li^+(aq) + e^- \rightarrow Li(s)$	−3.045
$Na^+(aq) + e^- \rightarrow Na(s)$	−2.714
$K^+(aq) + e^- \rightarrow K(s)$	−2.925
$Rb^+(aq) + e^- \rightarrow Rb(s)$	−2.925
$Cs^+(aq) + e^- \rightarrow Cs(s)$	−2.92

Analysis of $E°$ is a thermodynamic problem, and to understand it better we can break the process of metal oxidation, $M(s) \rightarrow M^+(aq) + e^-$, into a series of steps. Here, we imagine that the metal sublimes to vapor, an electron is removed to form the gaseous cation, and the cation is hydrated. The first two steps require energy, but the last is exothermic. From Hess's law (page 230), we

know that the overall energy change should be

$$\Delta_r H_{net} = \Delta_{sub}H + IE + \Delta_{hyd}H$$

The element that is the best reducing agent should have the most negative (or least positive) value of $\Delta_r H$. Because it is exothermic, the hydration enthalpy serves to offset the energy of the endothermic steps ($\Delta_{sub}H$ and IE). Thus, a more exothermic hydration enthalpy leads to a more negative $\Delta_r H$. For the alkali metals, enthalpies of hydration range from −506 kJ/mol for Li^+ to −180 kJ/mol for Cs^+. The fact that $\Delta_{hyd}H$ is so much more exothermic for Li^+ than for Cs^+ largely

accounts for the difference in reducing ability.

While this analysis of the problem gives us a reasonable explanation for the great reducing ability of lithium, recall that $E°$ is directly related to $\Delta_r G°$ and not to $\Delta H°$. However, $\Delta_r G°$ is largely determined by $\Delta_r H°$ for these reactions, so it is possible to relate variations in $E°$ to variations in $\Delta_r H°$.

Potassium is a very good reducing agent and reacts vigorously with water.

Important Lithium, Sodium, and Potassium Compounds

Electrolysis of aqueous sodium chloride (*brine*) is the basis of one of the largest chemical industries in the United States.

$$2\ NaCl(aq) + 2\ H_2O(\ell) \rightarrow Cl_2(g) + 2\ NaOH(aq) + H_2(g)$$

Two of the products from this process—chlorine and sodium hydroxide—give the industry its name: the *chlor-alkali industry*. More than 10 billion kilograms of Cl_2 and NaOH is produced annually in the United States.

Sodium carbonate, Na_2CO_3, is another commercially important compound of sodium. It is also known by two common names, *soda ash* and *washing soda*. In the past, it was largely manufactured by combining NaCl, ammonia, and CO_2 in the *Solvay process* (which remains the method of choice in many countries). In the United States, however, sodium carbonate is obtained from naturally occurring deposits of the mineral *trona*, $Na_2CO_3 \cdot NaHCO_3 \cdot 2\ H_2O$ (Figure 21.11).

The chlor-alkali process has long used electrolysis cells with mercury cathodes. However, because of the environmental dangers of mercury, this process is largely being phased out, and there is considerable interest in the manufacture of sodium hydroxide by other methods. One approach is a revival of the old "soda-lime process," which produces NaOH from inexpensive lime (CaO) and soda ash (Na_2CO_3).

$$Na_2CO_3(aq) + CaO(s) + H_2O(\ell) \rightarrow 2\ NaOH(aq) + CaCO_3(s)$$

The insoluble calcium carbonate by-product is filtered off and then heated (calcining) to convert it to lime, which is recycled into the reaction system.

$$CaCO_3(s) \rightarrow CaO(s) + CO_2(g)$$

Sodium bicarbonate, $NaHCO_3$, also known as *baking soda*, is another common compound of sodium. Not only is $NaHCO_3$ used in cooking, but it is also added in

(a) *(above)* A mine in California. The mineral trona is taken from a mine 1600 feet deep.

(b) *(right)* Blocks of trona are cut from the face of the mine.

Courtesy of FMC Wyoming Corp.

FIGURE 21.11 Producing soda ash. Trona mined in Wyoming and California is processed into soda ash (Na_2CO_3) and other sodium-based chemicals. Soda ash is the ninth most widely used chemical in the United States. Domestically, about half of all soda ash production is used in making glass. The remainder goes to make chemicals such as sodium silicate, sodium phosphate, and sodium cyanide. Some is also used to make detergents, in the pulp and paper industry, and in water treatment.

small amounts to table salt. NaCl is often contaminated with small amounts of $MgCl_2$. The magnesium salt is hygroscopic; that is, it picks water up from the air and, in doing so, causes the NaCl to clump. Adding $NaHCO_3$ converts $MgCl_2$ to magnesium carbonate, a nonhygroscopic salt.

$$MgCl_2(s) + 2\,NaHCO_3(s) \rightarrow MgCO_3(s) + 2\,NaCl(s) + H_2O(\ell) + CO_2(g)$$

Large deposits of sodium nitrate, $NaNO_3$, are found in Chile, which explains its common name of "Chile saltpeter." These deposits are thought to have formed by bacterial action on organisms in shallow seas. The initial product was ammonia, which was subsequently oxidized to nitrate ion; combination with sea salt led to sodium nitrate. Because nitrates in general, and alkali metal nitrates in particular, are highly water-soluble, deposits of $NaNO_3$ are found only in areas with very little rainfall.

Sodium nitrate is important because it can be converted to potassium nitrate by an exchange reaction.

$$NaNO_3(aq) + KCl(aq) \rightleftharpoons KNO_3(aq) + NaCl(s)$$

Equilibrium favors the products here because, of the four salts involved in this reaction, NaCl is least soluble in hot water. Sodium chloride precipitates, and the KNO_3 that remains in solution can be recovered by evaporating the water.

Potassium nitrate has been used for centuries as the oxidizing agent in gunpowder (page 251). A mixture of KNO_3, charcoal, and sulfur will react when ignited.

$$2\,KNO_3(s) + 4\,C(s) \rightarrow K_2CO_3(s) + 3\,CO(g) + N_2(g)$$

$$2\,KNO_3(s) + 2\,S(s) \rightarrow K_2SO_4(s) + SO_2(g) + N_2(g)$$

Notice that both reactions (which are doubtless more complex than those written here) produce gases. These gases propel the bullet from a gun or cause a firecracker to explode.

In the past several years lithium has become a significant commodity because of its use in lithium ion batteries. In fact, there is some concern that shortages of lithium will arise if the use of lithium ion batteries in cars becomes widespread (◀ page 911). Currently, most lithium is obtained from concentrated brines in Chile and Bolivia, from which Li_2CO_3 is extracted. There are also ores from which lithium can be obtained. Similar to the other alkali metals, lithium metal is obtained from its compounds by molten salt electrolysis.

● **Gunpowder** Gunpowder was developed well over 1000 years ago by the Chinese. One of the three ingredients is KNO_3, commonly called *saltpeter*. Although there are places in the world where it is prevalent and can be mined, for centuries it was obtained by mixing manure or human waste with wood ashes. Animal and human waste contain ammonia, which is converted by bacterial oxidation to nitrates. Wood ashes contain potash, potassium carbonate, the source of potassium in KNO_3. Sodium nitrate will also work in gunpowder, but it is hygroscopic and the powder is not effective when damp. See *Gunpowder* by J. Kelly, Basic Books, 2004.

Group **2A**
Alkaline earths

| Beryllium |
| 4 |
| **Be** |
| 2.6 ppm |

| Magnesium |
| 12 |
| **Mg** |
| 23,300 ppm |

| Calcium |
| 20 |
| **Ca** |
| 41,000 ppm |

| Strontium |
| 38 |
| **Sr** |
| 370 ppm |

| Barium |
| 56 |
| **Ba** |
| 500 ppm |

| Radium |
| 88 |
| **Ra** |
| 6×10^{-7} ppm |

Element abundances are in **parts per million** *in the earth's crust.*

REVIEW & CHECK FOR SECTION 21.4

1. Which of the following is not a property of sodium?

   (a) Reacts with Cl_2 to form NaCl (c) Has a high melting point ($> 400\ °C$)

   (b) Has a silvery color (d) Conducts an electric current

2. Which Group 1A metal ion has the most negative enthalpy of hydration?

   (a) Li^+ (b) Na^+ (c) K^+ (d) Cs^+

3. The compound Na_2O_2 consists of

   (a) two Na^+ ions and two O^{2-} ions (c) two Na^+ ions and one O_2^{2-} ion

   (b) molecules of Na_2O_2 (d) Na^{2+} and O^{2-} ions

21.5 The Alkaline Earth Elements, Group 2A

The "earth" part of the name alkaline earth dates back to the days of medieval alchemy. To alchemists, any solid that did not melt and was not changed by fire into another substance was called an "earth." Compounds of the Group 2A elements, such as CaO, were alkaline according to experimental tests conducted by the alchemists: They had a bitter taste and neutralized acids. With very high melting points, these compounds were unaffected by fire.

Calcium and magnesium rank fifth and eighth, respectively, in abundance on the earth. Both elements form many commercially important compounds, and we shall focus our attention on these species.

Like the Group 1A elements, the Group 2A elements are very reactive, so they are found in nature as compounds. Unlike most of the compounds of the Group 1A metals, however, many compounds of the Group 2A elements have low water-solubility, which explains their occurrence in various minerals (Figure 21.12). Calcium minerals include limestone ($CaCO_3$), gypsum ($CaSO_4 \cdot 2\ H_2O$), and fluorite (CaF_2). Magnesite ($MgCO_3$), talc or soapstone ($3\ MgO \cdot 4\ SiO_2 \cdot H_2O$), and asbestos ($3\ MgO \cdot 4\ SiO_2 \cdot 2\ H_2O$) are common magnesium-containing minerals. The mineral dolomite, $MgCa(CO_3)_2$, contains both magnesium and calcium.

Limestone, a sedimentary rock, is found widely on the earth's surface. Many of these deposits contain the fossilized remains of marine life. Other forms of calcium carbonate include marble and Icelandic spar, the latter occurring as large, clear crystals with the interesting optical property of birefringence (Figure 21.12).

Limestone
$CaCO_3$

Gypsum
$CaSO_4 \cdot 2\ H_2O$

Fluorite
CaF_2

Common minerals of Group 2A elements.

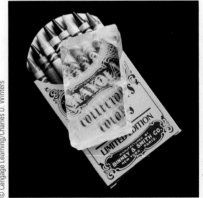

Icelandic spar. This mineral, one of a number of crystalline forms of $CaCO_3$, displays birefringence, a property in which a double image is formed when light passes through the crystal.

The walls of Arizona's Grand Canyon are largely limestone or dolomite.

FIGURE 21.12 Various minerals containing calcium and magnesium.

Properties of Calcium and Magnesium

Calcium and magnesium are fairly high-melting, silvery metals. The chemical properties of these elements present few surprises. They are oxidized by a wide range of oxidizing agents to form ionic compounds that contain the M^{2+} ion. For example, these elements combine with halogens to form MX_2, with oxygen or sulfur to form MO or MS, and with water to form hydrogen and the metal hydroxide, $M(OH)_2$ (Figure 21.13). With acids, hydrogen is evolved (Figure 21.7), and a salt of the metal cation and the anion of the acid results.

Metallurgy of Magnesium

Several hundred thousand tons of magnesium are produced annually, largely for use in lightweight alloys. (Magnesium has a very low density, 1.74 g/cm^3.) Most aluminum used today contains about 5% magnesium to improve its mechanical properties and to make it more resistant to corrosion. Other alloys having more magnesium than aluminum are used when a high strength-to-weight ratio is needed and when corrosion resistance is important, such as in aircraft and automotive parts and in lightweight tools.

Interestingly, magnesium-containing minerals are not the source of this element. Most magnesium is obtained from sea water, in which Mg^{2+} ion is present in a concentration of about 0.05 M. To obtain magnesium metal, magnesium ions in sea water are first precipitated (Figure 21.14) as the relatively insoluble hydroxide [K_{sp} for $Mg(OH)_2 = 5.6 \times 10^{-12}$]. Calcium hydroxide, the source of OH^- in this reaction, is prepared in a sequence of reactions beginning with $CaCO_3$, which may be in the form of seashells. Heating $CaCO_3$ gives CO_2 and CaO, and addition of water to CaO gives calcium hydroxide. When $Ca(OH)_2$ is added to sea water, $Mg(OH)_2$ precipitates:

$$Mg^{2+}(aq) + Ca(OH)_2(s) \rightleftharpoons Mg(OH)_2(s) + Ca^{2+}(aq)$$

Magnesium hydroxide is isolated by filtration and then converted to magnesium chloride by reaction with hydrochloric acid.

$$Mg(OH)_2(s) + 2 \text{ HCl}(aq) \rightarrow MgCl_2(aq) + 2 \text{ H}_2O(\ell)$$

After evaporating the water, anhydrous magnesium chloride remains. Solid $MgCl_2$ melts at 714 °C, and the molten salt is electrolyzed to give the metal and chlorine.

$$MgCl_2(\ell) \rightarrow Mg(s) + Cl_2(g)$$

FIGURE 21.13 The reaction of calcium and warm water. Hydrogen bubbles are seen rising from the metal surface. The other reaction product is $Ca(OH)_2$. The inset is a model of hexagonal close-packed calcium metal (◀ page 586).

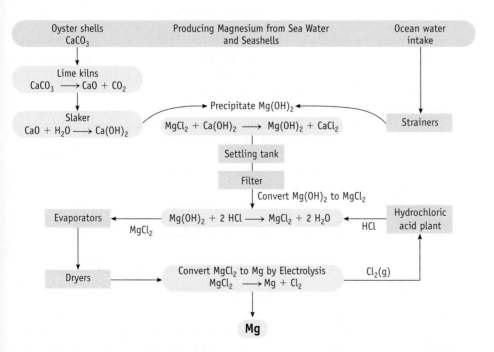

FIGURE 21.14 The process used to produce magnesium metal from the magnesium in sea water.

© Cengage Learning/Charles D. Winters

A CLOSER LOOK

Alkaline Earth Metals and Biology

Plants and animals derive energy from the oxidation of a sugar, glucose, with oxygen. Plants are unique, however, in being able to synthesize glucose from CO_2 and H_2O using sunlight as an energy source. This process is initiated by *chlorophyll*, a very large, magnesium-based molecule.

In your body, the alkaline earth metal ions Mg^{2+} and Ca^{2+} serve regulatory functions. Although the two metal ions are required by living systems, the other Group 2A elements are toxic. Beryllium compounds are carcinogenic, and soluble barium salts are poisons. You may be concerned if your physician asks you to drink a "barium cocktail" to check the condition of your digestive tract. Don't be afraid, because the "cocktail" contains very insoluble $BaSO_4$ ($K_{sp} = 1.1 \times 10^{-10}$), so it passes through your digestive tract without a significant amount being absorbed. Barium sulfate is opaque to x-rays, so its path through your organs appears on the developed x-ray image.

A molecule of chlorophyll. Magnesium is its central element.

X-ray of a gastrointestinal tract using $BaSO_4$ to make the organs visible.

The calcium-containing compound *hydroxyapatite* is the main component of tooth enamel. Cavities in your teeth form when acids (such as soft drinks) decompose the weakly basic hydroxyapatite coating.

$$Ca_5(OH)(PO_4)_3(s) + 4\ H_3O^+(aq) \rightarrow$$
$$5\ Ca^{2+}(aq) + 3\ HPO_4^{2-}(aq) + 5\ H_2O(\ell)$$

This reaction can be prevented by converting hydroxyapatite to the much more acid-resistant coating of fluoroapatite.

$$Ca_5(OH)(PO_4)_3(s) + F^-(aq) \rightarrow$$
$$Ca_5F(PO_4)_3(s) + OH^-(aq)$$

The source of the fluoride ion can be sodium fluoride or sodium monofluorophosphate (Na_2FPO_3, commonly known as MFP) in your toothpaste.

Calcium Minerals and Their Applications

The most common calcium minerals are the fluoride, phosphate, and carbonate salts of the element. Fluorite, CaF_2, and fluoroapatite, $Ca_5F(PO_4)_3$, are important as commercial sources of fluorine. Almost half of the CaF_2 mined is used in the steel industry, where it is added to the mixture of materials that is melted to make crude iron. The CaF_2 acts to remove some impurities and improves the separation of molten metal from silicates and other by-products resulting from the reduction of iron ore to the metal (Chapter 22). A second major use of fluorite is in the manufacture of hydrofluoric acid by a reaction of the mineral with concentrated sulfuric acid.

$$CaF_2(s) + H_2SO_4(\ell) \rightarrow 2\ HF(g) + CaSO_4(s)$$

Hydrofluoric acid is used to make cryolite, Na_3AlF_6, a material needed in aluminum production (▶ Section 21.6) and in the manufacture of fluorocarbons such as tetrafluoroethylene, the precursor to Teflon (Table 10.12).

Apatites have the general formula $Ca_5X(PO_4)_3$ (X = F, Cl, OH). More than 100 million tons of apatite is mined annually, with Florida alone accounting for about one third of the world's output. Most of this material is converted to phosphoric acid by reaction with sulfuric acid. Phosphoric acid is needed in the manufacture of a multitude of products, including fertilizers and detergents, baking powder, and various food products (▶ Section 21.8.).

Calcium carbonate and calcium oxide (*lime*) are of special interest. The thermal decomposition of $CaCO_3$ to give lime (and CO_2) is one of the oldest chemical reactions known. Lime is one of the top 10 industrial chemicals produced today, with about 20 billion kilograms produced annually.

Limestone, which consists mostly of calcium carbonate, has been used in agriculture for centuries. It is spread on fields to neutralize acidic compounds in the soil and to supply Ca^{2+}, an essential nutrient. Because magnesium carbonate is often present in limestone, "liming" a field also supplies Mg^{2+}, another important nutrient for plants.

For several thousand years, lime has been used in *mortar* (a lime, sand, and water paste) to secure stones to one another in building houses, walls, and roads. The

© Cengage Learning/Charles D. Winters

Apatite. The mineral has the general formula of $Ca_5X(PO_4)_3$ (X = F, Cl, OH). (The apatite is the elongated crystal in the center of a matrix of other rock.)

Susan Leavines/Science Source/Photo Researchers, Inc.

A CLOSER LOOK

Of Romans, Limestone, and Champagne

The stones of the Appian Way in Italy, a road conceived by the Roman senate in about 310 BC, are cemented with mortar made from limestone. The Appian Way was intended to serve as a military road linking Rome to seaports from which soldiers could embark to Greece and other Mediterranean countries. The road stretches 560 kilometers (350 miles) from Rome to Brindisi on the Adriatic Sea (at the heel of the Italian "boot"). It took almost 200 years to construct. The road had a standard width of 14 Roman feet, approximately 6 meters, large enough to allow two chariots to pass, and featured two sidewalks of 1.2 m each. Every 16 km or so, there were horse-changing stations with taverns, shops, and *latrinae*, the famous Roman restrooms.

All over the Roman Empire, buildings, temples, and aqueducts were constructed of blocks of limestone and marble, and the mortar to cement the blocks was made by heating the chips from stone cutting (to give CaO). In central France, the Romans dug chalk (also $CaCO_3$) from the ground for cementing sandstone blocks. This activity created huge caves that remain to this day and are used for aging and storing champagne.

The Appian Way in Italy.

Champagne in a limestone cave in France.

Chinese used it to set stones in the Great Wall. The Romans perfected its use, and the fact that many of their constructions still stand today is testament both to their skill and to the usefulness of lime. The famous Roman road, the Appian Way, used lime mortar between several layers of its stones.

The utility of mortar depends on some simple chemistry. Mortar consists of one part lime to three parts sand, with water added to make a thick paste. The first reaction, referred to as *slaking*, occurs after the solids are mixed with water. This produces a slurry containing calcium hydroxide, which is known as *slaked lime*.

$$CaO(s) + H_2O(\ell) \rightleftharpoons Ca(OH)_2(s)$$

When the wet mortar mix is placed between bricks or stone blocks, it slowly reacts with CO_2 from the air, and the slaked lime is converted to calcium carbonate.

$$Ca(OH)_2(s) + CO_2(g) \rightleftharpoons CaCO_3(s) + H_2O(\ell)$$

The sand grains are bound together by the particles of calcium carbonate.

REVIEW & CHECK FOR SECTION 21.5

1. Which of the following insoluble calcium compounds does not dissolve in hydrochloric acid?

   (a) limestone, $CaCO_3$

   (b) slaked lime, $Ca(OH)_2$

   (c) gypsum, $CaSO_4 \cdot 2H_2O$

   (d) hydroxyapatite, $Ca_5(OH)(PO_4)_3$

2. Calcium minerals are the raw materials for a variety of large-scale industrial processes. Which of the following is not an industrial process?

   (a) Converting limestone, $CaCO_3$, to lime

   (b) Converting fluorite, CaF_2, to HF

   (c) Converting slaked lime, $Ca(OH)_2$, to lime

   (d) Converting apatite minerals to phosphate fertilizers

Hard Water

No, hard water doesn't refer to ice. It is the name given to water containing high concentrations of $Ca^{2+}(aq)$ and, in some instances, $Mg^{2+}(aq)$ and other divalent metal cations. Accompanying these cations will be various anions, including in particular the hydrogen carbonate anion, $HCO_3^-(aq)$.

Water obtained from reservoirs that store rainwater does not usually contain high concentrations of these ions, and so is not classified as being "hard water." In many parts of the country, however, the municipal water supply is obtained from aquifers deep underground. If rainwater, containing some dissolved CO_2, has to percolate down through layers of limestone ($CaCO_3$) to get into the aquifer, a small amount of the solid will dissolve because of the following equilibrium:

$$CaCO_3(s) + CO_2(aq) + H_2O(\ell) \rightleftharpoons$$
$$Ca^{2+}(aq) + 2\ HCO_3^-(aq)$$

If hard water containing $Ca^{2+}(aq)$ and $HCO_3^-(aq)$ is heated, or even if it is left to stand in an open vessel, CO_2 will be expelled, and the equilibrium will shift, precipitating $CaCO_3(s)$ (◀ page 117). This can be a small problem in a teakettle but a bigger problem in an industrial setting, where the solid $CaCO_3$ can clog pipes. Another consequence of hard water is the formation of a scum when soaps are added to water. Soap is made by hydrolysis of fats, which produces long chain carboxylic acids. Soap scum is a precipitate of the calcium salt of these acids.

To avoid the problems associated with hard water, chemists and engineers have devised ways to soften water, that is, to decrease the concentration of the offending cations. In a water treatment plant for a municipality or a large industrial facility, most of the water hardness will be removed chemically, mainly by treatment with calcium oxide (lime, CaO). If HCO_3^- ions are present along with Ca^{2+} and/or Mg^{2+}, the following reactions occur:

$$Ca^{2+}(aq) + 2\ HCO_3^-(aq) + CaO(s) \rightarrow$$
$$2\ CaCO_3(s) + H_2O(\ell)$$

$$Mg^{2+}(aq) + 2\ HCO_3^-(aq) + CaO(s) \rightarrow$$
$$CaCO_3(s) + MgCO_3(s) + H_2O(\ell)$$

Although it seems odd to add CaO to remove calcium ions, notice that adding one mole of CaO leads to the precipitation of two moles of Ca^{2+} as $CaCO_3$.

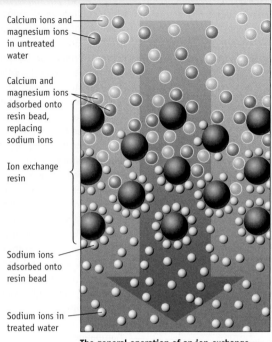

Calcium ions and magnesium ions in untreated water

Calcium and magnesium ions adsorbed onto resin bead, replacing sodium ions

Ion exchange resin

Sodium ions adsorbed onto resin bead

Sodium ions in treated water

The general operation of an ion-exchange resin. The ion exchange material is usually a polymeric material formed into small beads.

Water softening by ion exchange in the home.

On a smaller scale, most home water purification systems use *ion exchange* to soften water (Figure). This process involves the replacement of an ion adsorbed onto a solid ion exchange resin by an ion in solution. Zeolites (▶ page 987), naturally occurring aluminosilicate minerals, were at one time used as ion exchange materials. Now, synthetic organic polymers with negatively charged functional groups (such as carboxylate groups, $-CO_2^-$) are the most commonly used resins for this purpose. Sodium ions, Na^+, are present in the resin to balance the negative charges of the carboxylate groups. The affinity of a surface for multi-charged cations is greater than for monovalent cations. Therefore, when a solution of hard water is passed over the surface of the ion exchange resin, Ca^{2+} and Mg^{2+} (and other divalent ions if present) readily replace Na^+ ions in an ion exchange column. This process can be illustrated in a general way by the equilibrium

$$2\ NaX + Ca^{2+}(aq) \rightleftharpoons CaX_2 + 2\ Na^+(aq)$$

where X represents an adsorption site on the ion exchange resin. The equilibrium favors

adsorption of Ca^{2+} and release of Na^+. However, the equilibrium is reversed if $Na^+(aq)$ ions are present in high concentration, and this allows regeneration of the ion exchange resin. A solution containing a high concentration of Na^+ (usually from salt, NaCl) is passed through the resin to convert the resin back to its initial form.

Questions:

1. Assume that a sample of hard water contains 50. mg/L of Mg^{2+} and 150 mg/L of Ca^{2+}, with HCO_3^- as the accompanying anion. What mass of CaO should be added to 1.0 L of this aqueous solution to cause all of this Mg^{2+} and Ca^{2+} to precipitate as $CaCO_3$ and $MgCO_3$? What is the total mass of the two solids formed?

2. One way to remove the calcium carbonate residue in a teakettle is to add vinegar (a dilute solution of acetic acid). Write a chemical equation to explain this process. What kind of reaction is this?

Answers to these questions are available in Appendix N.

21.6 Boron, Aluminum, and the Group 3A Elements

With Group 3A, we see the first evidence of a change from metallic behavior of the elements at the left side of the periodic table to nonmetal behavior on the right side of the table. Boron is a metalloid, whereas all the other elements of Group 3A are metals.

The elements of Group 3A vary widely in their relative abundances on earth. Aluminum is the third most abundant element in the earth's crust (82,000 ppm), whereas the other elements of the group are relatively rare, and, except for boron, their compounds have limited commercial uses.

Chemistry of the Group 3A Elements

It is generally recognized that a chemical similarity exists between some elements diagonally situated in the periodic table. This diagonal relationship means that lithium and magnesium share some chemical properties, as do Be and Al, and B and Si. For example:

- Boric oxide, B_2O_3, and boric acid, $B(OH)_3$, are weakly acidic, as are SiO_2 and its acid, orthosilicic acid (H_4SiO_4). Boron–oxygen compounds, borates, are often chemically similar to silicon–oxygen compounds, silicates.
- Both $Be(OH)_2$ and $Al(OH)_3$ are amphoteric, dissolving in a strong base such as aqueous NaOH (◄ page 793).
- Chlorides, bromides, and iodides of boron and silicon (such as BCl_3 and $SiCl_4$) react vigorously with water.
- The hydrides of boron and silicon are simple, molecular species; are volatile and flammable; and react readily with water.
- Beryllium hydride and aluminum hydride are colorless, nonvolatile solids that are extensively polymerized through Be—H—Be and Al—H—Al three-center, two-electron bonds (◄ page 427).

Finally, the Group 3A elements are characterized by electron configurations of the type ns^2np^1. This means that each may lose three electrons to have a +3 oxidation number, although the heavier elements, especially thallium, also form compounds with an oxidation number of +1.

Boron Minerals and Production of the Element

Although boron has a low abundance on earth, its minerals are found in concentrated deposits. Large deposits of borax, $Na_2B_4O_7 \cdot 10\ H_2O$, are currently mined in the Mojave Desert near the town of Boron, California (Figure 21.15).

Group **3A**

Boron 5 **B** 10 ppm
Aluminum 13 **Al** 82,000 ppm
Gallium 31 **Ga** 18 ppm
Indium 49 **In** 0.05 ppm
Thallium 81 **Tl** 0.6 ppm

Element abundances are in **parts per million** *in the earth's crust.*

Diagonal Relationship

1A	2A	3A	4A
Li	Be	B	
	Mg	Al	Si

● **Diagonal Relationship** The chemistries of elements diagonally situated in the periodic table are often quite similar.

(a) A borax mine near the town of Boron, California.

(b) The mineral named ulexite, a form of crystalline borax, $Na_2B_4O_7 \cdot 10\ H_2O$.

(c) All four allotropes of elemental boron have an icosahedron (a 20-sided polyhedron) of 12 covalently linked boron atoms as a structural element.

FIGURE 21.15 Boron.

Gallium. Gallium, with a melting point of 29.8 °C, is one of the few metals that can be a liquid at or near room temperature. (Others are Hg and Cs.)

● **Boron, a Strange Element**
Within 1 week in 1808 three chemists claimed to have discovered boron: Sir Humphry Davy, J. Gay-Lussac, and L-J. Thenard. They had not; all were impure samples. One hundred years would pass before pure boron was finally isolated. But then the mystery began. What is its structure? Until recently three forms were known, but a fourth was discovered in 2009. The molecular structure of each of the forms has an icosahedron of twelve boron atoms (Figure 21.15).

Isolation of pure, elemental boron from boron-containing minerals is extremely difficult and is done in small quantities. Like most metals and metalloids, boron can be obtained by chemically or electrolytically reducing an oxide or halide. Magnesium has often been used for chemical reductions, but the product of this reaction is a noncrystalline boron of low purity.

$$B_2O_3(s) + 3\ Mg(s) \rightarrow 2\ B(s) + 3\ MgO(s)$$

Boron has several allotropes, all characterized by having an icosahedron of boron atoms as one structural element (Figure 21.15c). Partly as a result of extended covalent bonding, elemental boron is a very hard and refractory (resistant to heat) semiconductor. In this regard, it differs from the other Group 3A elements; Al, Ga, In, and Tl are all relatively low-melting, rather soft metals with high electrical conductivity.

Metallic Aluminum and Its Production

The low cost of aluminum and the excellent characteristics of its alloys with other metals (low density, strength, ease of handling in fabrication, and inertness toward corrosion, among others), have led to its widespread use. You know it best in the form of aluminum foil, aluminum cans, and parts of aircraft.

Pure aluminum is soft and weak; moreover, it loses strength rapidly at temperatures higher than 300 °C. What we call "aluminum" is actually aluminum alloyed with small amounts of other elements to strengthen the metal and improve its properties. A typical alloy may contain about 4% copper with smaller amounts of silicon, magnesium, and manganese. Softer, more corrosion-resistant alloys for window frames, furniture, highway signs, and cooking utensils may include only manganese.

The standard reduction potential of aluminum [$Al^{3+}(aq) + 3\ e^- \rightarrow Al(s)$; $E° = -1.66\ V$] tells you that aluminum is easily oxidized. From this, we might expect aluminum to be highly susceptible to corrosion but, in fact, it is quite resistant. Aluminum's corrosion resistance is due to the formation of a thin, tough, and transparent skin of Al_2O_3 that adheres to the metal surface. An important feature of the protective oxide layer is that it rapidly self-repairs. If you penetrate the surface coating by scratching it or using some chemical agent, the exposed metal surface immediately reacts with oxygen (or another oxidizing agent) to form a new layer of oxide over the damaged area (Figure 21.16).

Aluminum was first prepared by reducing $AlCl_3$ using sodium or potassium. This was a costly process, and, in the 19th century, aluminum was a precious metal.

FIGURE 21.16 Corrosion of aluminum.

(a) A ball of aluminum foil is added to a solution of copper(II) nitrate and sodium chloride. Normally, the coating of chemically inert Al_2O_3 on the surface of aluminum protects the metal from further oxidation.

(b) In the presence of the Cl^- ion, the coating of Al_2O_3 is breached, and aluminum reduces copper(II) ions to copper metal. The reaction is rapid and so exothermic that the water can boil on the surface of the foil. [The blue color of aqueous copper(II) ions will fade as these ions are consumed in the reaction.]

At the 1855 Paris Exposition, in fact, a sample of aluminum was exhibited along with the crown jewels of France. In an interesting coincidence, in 1886 Frenchman Paul Heroult (1863–1914) and American Charles Hall (1863–1914) simultaneously and independently conceived of the electrochemical method used today. The Hall–Heroult method bears the names of the two discoverers.

Aluminum is found in nature as aluminosilicates, minerals such as clay that are based on aluminum, silicon, and oxygen. As these minerals weather, they break down to various forms of hydrated aluminum oxide, $Al_2O_3 \cdot n\ H_2O$, called *bauxite*. Mined in huge quantities, bauxite is the raw material from which aluminum is obtained. The first step is to purify the ore, separating Al_2O_3 from iron and silicon oxides. This is done by the *Bayer process*, which relies on the amphoteric, basic, or acidic nature of the various oxides. (Silica, SiO_2, is an acidic oxide, whereas Al_2O_3 is amphoteric, and Fe_2O_3 is a basic oxide.) Silica and Al_2O_3 dissolve in a hot concentrated solution of caustic soda (NaOH), leaving insoluble Fe_2O_3 to be filtered out.

$$Al_2O_3(s) + 2\ NaOH(aq) + 3\ H_2O(\ell) \rightarrow 2\ Na[Al(OH)_4](aq)$$

$$SiO_2(s) + 2\ NaOH(aq) + 2\ H_2O(\ell) \rightarrow Na_2[Si(OH)_6](aq)$$

If a solution containing aluminate and silicate anions is treated with CO_2, Al_2O_3 precipitates, and the silicate ion remains in solution. Recall that CO_2 is an acidic oxide that forms the weak acid H_2CO_3 in water, so the Al_2O_3 precipitation in this step is an acid–base reaction.

$$H_2CO_3(aq) + 2\ Na[Al(OH)_4](aq) \rightarrow Na_2CO_3(aq) + Al_2O_3(s) + 5\ H_2O(\ell)$$

Metallic aluminum is obtained from purified bauxite by electrolysis (Figure 21.17). Bauxite is first mixed with cryolite, Na_3AlF_6, to give a lower-melting mixture (melting temperature = 980 °C) that is electrolyzed in a cell with graphite electrodes. The cell operates at a relatively low voltage (4.0–5.5 V) but with an extremely high current (50,000–150,000 A). Aluminum is produced at the cathode and oxygen at the anode. To produce 1 kg of aluminum requires 13 to 16 kilowatt-hours of energy plus the energy required to maintain the high temperature.

● **Charles Martin Hall (1863–1914)** Hall was only 22 years old when he worked out the electrolytic process for extracting aluminum from Al_2O_3 in a woodshed behind the family home in Oberlin, Ohio. He went on to found a company that eventually became ALCOA, the Aluminum Corporation of America.

Oesper Collection in the History of Chemistry/ University of Cincinnati

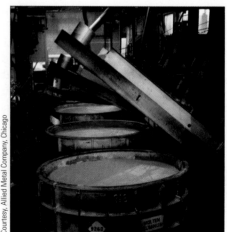

Courtesy, Allied Metal Company, Chicago

(a) Purified aluminum-containing ore (bauxite) is essentially Al_2O_3. In the Hall–Heroult process this is mixed with cryolite (Na_3AlF_6) and other fluorides such as AlF_3. (The additives serve to lower the melting point of the mixture and increase the conductivity). The aluminum-containing substances are reduced at a graphite cathode to give molten aluminum. Oxygen is produced at a graphite anode, and the gas reacts slowly with the carbon to give CO_2, leading to eventual destruction of the electrode.

(b) Molten aluminum alloy, produced from recycled metal, at 760 °C, in 1.6×10^4-kg capacity crucibles.

FIGURE 21.17 Industrial production of aluminum.

B atom surrounded by 4 electron pairs

B atom surrounded by 3 electron pairs

The borate ion of borax, [B₄O₅(OH)₄]²⁻.

Boron Compounds

Borax, $Na_2B_4O_7 \cdot 10\ H_2O$, is the most important boron–oxygen compound and is the form of the element most often found in nature. It has been used for centuries in metallurgy because of the ability of molten borax to dissolve other metal oxides. That is, borax is used as a *flux* that cleans the surfaces of metals to be joined and permits a good metal-to-metal contact.

The formula for borax gives little information about its structure. The anion is better described by the formula $[B_4O_5(OH)_4]^{2-}$, the structure of which illustrates two commonly observed structural features in inorganic chemistry. First, many minerals consist of MO_n groups that share O atoms. Second, the sharing of O atoms between two metals or metalloids often leads to MO rings.

After refinement, borax can be treated with sulfuric acid to produce boric acid, $B(OH)_3$.

$$Na_2B_4O_7 \cdot 10\ H_2O(s) + H_2SO_4(aq) \rightarrow 4\ B(OH)_3(aq) + Na_2SO_4(aq) + 5\ H_2O(\ell)$$

The chemistry of boric acid incorporates both Lewis and Brønsted acid behavior. Hydronium ions are produced by a Lewis acid–base interaction between boric acid and water.

$$K_a = 7.3 \times 10^{-10}$$

Because of its weak acid properties and slight biological activity, boric acid has been used for many years as an antiseptic. Furthermore, because boric acid is a weak acid, salts of borate ions, such as the $[B_4O_5(OH)_4]^{2-}$ ion in borax, are weak bases.

Boric acid is dehydrated to boric oxide when strongly heated.

$$2\ B(OH)_3(s) \rightarrow B_2O_3(s) + 3\ H_2O(\ell)$$

By far the largest use for the oxide is in the manufacture of borosilicate glass (the type of glass used in most laboratory glassware). This type of glass is composed of 76% SiO_2, 13% B_2O_3, and much smaller amounts of Al_2O_3 and Na_2O. The presence of boric oxide gives the glass a higher softening temperature, imparts a better resistance to attack by acids, and makes the glass expand less on heating.

Like its metalloid neighbor silicon, boron forms a series of molecular compounds with hydrogen. Because boron is slightly less electronegative than hydrogen, these compounds are described as hydrides, in which the H atoms bear a partial negative charge. More than 20 neutral boron hydrides, or boranes, with the general formula B_xH_y are known. The simplest of these is diborane, B_2H_6, where x is 2 and y is 6. This colorless, gaseous compound has a boiling point of $-92.6\ °C$. This molecule is described as electron deficient because there are apparently not enough electrons to attach all of the atoms using two-electron bonds. Instead, the description of bonding uses three-center two-electron bonds in the B—H—B bridges (◄ page 427).

Diborane has an endothermic enthalpy of formation ($\Delta_f H° = +41.0\ kJ/mol$), which contributes to the high exothermicity of oxidation of the compound. Diborane burns in air to give boric oxide and water vapor in an extremely exothermic reaction. It is not surprising that diborane and other boron hydrides were once considered as possible rocket fuels.

$$B_2H_6(g) + 3\ O_2(g) \rightarrow B_2O_3(s) + 3\ H_2O(g) \qquad \Delta_r H° = -2038\ kJ/mol\text{-rxn}$$

Diborane can be synthesized from sodium borohydride, $NaBH_4$, the only B—H compound produced in ton quantities.

$$2\ NaBH_4(s) + I_2(s) \rightarrow B_2H_6(g) + 2\ NaI(s) + H_2(g)$$

● **Borax in Fire Retardants** The second largest use for boric acid and borates is as a flame retardant for cellulose home insulation. Such insulation is often made of scrap paper, which is inexpensive but flammable. To control the flammability, 5%–10% of the weight of the insulation is boric acid.

133 pm

119 pm

97° 122°

The structure of diborane, B_2H_6, the simplest member of a family of boron hydrides. See also page 427.

Sodium borohydride, $NaBH_4$, a white, crystalline, water-soluble solid, is made from NaH and borate esters such as $B(OCH_3)_3$.

$$4\ NaH(s) + B(OCH_3)_3(g) \rightarrow NaBH_4(s) + 3\ NaOCH_3(s)$$

The main use of $NaBH_4$ is as a reducing agent in organic synthesis. We previously encountered its use to reduce aldehydes, carboxylic acids, and ketones in Chapter 10.

Aluminum Compounds

Aluminum is an excellent reducing agent, so it reacts readily with hydrochloric acid. In contrast, it does not react with nitric acid, a stronger oxidizing agent than hydrochloric acid. It turns out that nitric acid does rapidly oxidize the surface of aluminum, but the resulting film of Al_2O_3 that is produced protects the metal from further attack. In fact, this protection allows nitric acid to be shipped in aluminum tanks.

Various salts of aluminum dissolve in water, giving the hydrated $Al^{3+}(aq)$ ion. These solutions are acidic (◄ Table 17.3, page 766) because the hydrated ion is a weak Brønsted acid.

$$[Al(H_2O)_6]^{3+}(aq) + H_2O(\ell) \rightleftharpoons [Al(H_2O)_5(OH)]^{2+}(aq) + H_3O^+(aq)$$

Adding acid shifts the equilibrium to the left, whereas adding base causes the equilibrium to shift to the right. Addition of sufficient hydroxide ion results ultimately in precipitation of the hydrated oxide $Al_2O_3 \cdot 3\ H_2O$.

Aluminum oxide, Al_2O_3, formed by dehydrating the hydrated oxide, is quite insoluble in water and generally resistant to chemical attack. In the crystalline form, aluminum oxide is known as *corundum*. This material is extraordinarily hard, a property that leads to its use as an abrasive in grinding wheels, "sandpaper," and toothpaste.

Some gems are impure aluminum oxide. Rubies, beautiful red crystals prized for jewelry and used in some lasers, are composed of Al_2O_3 contaminated with a small amount of Cr^{3+} (Figure 21.18 and page 300). The Cr^{3+} ions replacing some of the Al^{3+} ions in the crystal lattice are the source of the red color. Synthetic rubies were first made in 1902, and the worldwide capacity is now about 200,000 kg/year; much of this production is used for jewel bearings in watches and instruments. Blue sapphires consist of Al_2O_3 with Fe^{2+} and Ti^{4+} impurities in place of Al^{3+} ions.

Boron forms halides such as gaseous BF_3 and BCl_3 that have the expected trigonal planar molecular geometry of halogen atoms surrounding an sp^2 hybridized boron atom. In contrast, the aluminum halides are all solids and have more interesting structures. Aluminum bromide, which is made by the very exothermic reaction of aluminum metal and bromine (◄ Figure 2.12, page 67),

$$2\ Al(s) + 3\ Br_2(\ell) \rightarrow Al_2Br_6(s)$$

is composed of two units of $AlBr_3$. That is, Al_2Br_6 is a dimer of $AlBr_3$ units. The structure resembles that of diborane in that bridging atoms appear between the two Al atoms. However, Al_2Br_6 is not electron deficient; the bridge is formed when a Br atom on one $AlBr_3$ uses a lone pair to form a coordinate covalent bond to a neighboring tetrahedral, sp^3-hybridized aluminum atom.

The structure of Al_2Br_6. The bonding in Al_2Br_6 is not unique to the aluminum halides. Metal−halogen−metal bridges are found in many other metal−halogen compounds.

Both aluminum bromide and aluminum iodide have this structure. Aluminum chloride has a different solid state structure, but it exists as dimeric molecules in the vapor state.

© Cengage Learning/Charles D. Winters

Aluminum does not react with nitric acid. Nitric acid, a strongly oxidizing acid, reacts vigorously with copper *(left)*, but aluminum *(right)* is untouched.

Photos © Chip Clark/Smithsonian Museum of Natural History

FIGURE 21.18 Forms of corundum. Corundum is a crystalline form of aluminum oxide. Both rubies and sapphires are a form of corundum in which a few Al^{3+} ions have been replaced by ions such as Cr^{3+}, Fe^{2+}, or Ti^{4+}. *(top)* The Star of Asia sapphire. *(middle)* Various sapphires. *(bottom)* Uncut corundum.

Aluminum chloride can react with a chloride ion to form the anion $[AlCl_4]^-$. Aluminum fluoride, in contrast, can accommodate three additional F^- ions to form an octahedral $[AlF_6]^{3-}$ ion. This anion is found in cryolite, Na_3AlF_6, the compound added to aluminum oxide in the electrolytic production of aluminum metal. Apparently, the Al^{3+} ion can bind to six of the smaller F^- ions, whereas only four of the larger Cl^-, Br^-, or I^- ions can surround an Al^{3+} ion.

REVIEW & CHECK FOR SECTION 21.6

1. In terms of abundance of the elements in the earth's crust, aluminum ranks

   (a) first   (b) second   (c) third   (d) fourth

2. The element below aluminum in Group 3A is gallium, and there are numerous similarities in the chemistry of these two elements. For example, the hydroxides of both elements are amphoteric. A consequence of this is that both gallium hydroxide and aluminum hydroxide

   (a) are insoluble   (c) dissolve only in base

   (b) dissolve only in acid   (d) dissolve in acid and in base

---

21.7 Silicon and the Group 4A Elements

Carbon is a nonmetal; silicon and germanium are classified as metalloids; and tin and lead are metals. As a result, the elements of Group 4A have a broad range of chemical behavior.

The Group 4A elements are characterized by half-filled valence shells with two electrons in the ns orbital and two electrons in np orbitals. The bonding in carbon and silicon compounds is largely covalent and involves sharing four electron pairs with neighboring atoms. In germanium compounds, the +4 oxidation state is common (GeO_2 and $GeCl_4$), but some +2 oxidation state compounds exist (GeI_2). Oxidation numbers of both +2 and +4 are common in compounds of tin and lead (such as $SnCl_2$, $SnCl_4$, PbO, and PbO_2). Oxidation numbers two units less than the group number are often encountered for heavier elements in Groups 3A–7A.

Silicon

Silicon is second after oxygen in abundance in the earth's crust, so it is not surprising that we are surrounded by silicon-containing materials: bricks, pottery, porcelain, lubricants, sealants, computer chips, and solar cells. The computer revolution is based on the semiconducting properties of silicon.

Reasonably pure silicon can be made in large quantities by heating pure silica sand with purified coke to approximately 3000 °C in an electric furnace.

$$SiO_2(s) + 2\ C(s) \rightarrow Si(\ell) + 2\ CO(g)$$

The molten silicon is drawn off the bottom of the furnace and allowed to cool to a shiny blue-gray solid. Because extremely high-purity silicon is needed for the electronics industry, purifying raw silicon requires several steps. First, the silicon in the impure sample is allowed to react with chlorine to convert the silicon to liquid silicon tetrachloride.

$$Si(s) + 2\ Cl_2(g) \rightarrow SiCl_4(\ell)$$

Silicon tetrachloride (boiling point of 57.6 °C) is carefully purified by distillation and then reduced to silicon using magnesium.

$$SiCl_4(g) + 2\ Mg(s) \rightarrow 2\ MgCl_2(s) + Si(s)$$

The magnesium chloride is washed out with water, and the silicon is remelted and cast into bars. A final purification is carried out by zone refining, a process in which a special heating device is used to melt a narrow segment of the silicon rod. The heater is moved slowly down the rod. Impurities contained in the silicon tend to

Group 4A

Carbon	6
C	480 ppm
Silicon	14
Si	277,000 ppm
Germanium	32
Ge	1.8 ppm
Tin	50
Sn	2.2 ppm
Lead	82
Pb	14 ppm

Element abundances are in **parts per million** *in the earth's crust.*

remain in the liquid phase because the melting point of a mixture is lower than that of the pure element (Chapter 14). The silicon that crystallizes above the heated zone is therefore of a higher purity (Figure 21.19).

Silicon Dioxide

The simplest oxide of silicon is SiO_2, commonly called *silica*, a constituent of many rocks such as granite and sandstone. Quartz is a pure crystalline form of silica, but impurities in quartz produce gemstones such as amethyst (Figure 21.20).

Silica and CO_2 are oxides of two elements in the same chemical group, so similarities between them might be expected. In fact, SiO_2 is a high-melting solid (quartz melts at 1610 °C), whereas CO_2 is a gas at room temperature and 1 atm. This great disparity arises from the different structures of the two oxides. Carbon dioxide is a molecular compound, with the carbon atom linked to each oxygen atom by a double bond. In contrast, SiO_2 is a network solid, which is the preferred structure because the bond energy of two Si=O double bonds is much less than the bond energy of four Si—O single bonds. The contrast between SiO_2 and CO_2 is an example of a more general phenomenon. Multiple bonds, often encountered between second-period elements, are rare among elements in the third period and beyond. There are many compounds with multiple bonds to carbon but very few compounds featuring multiple bonds to silicon.

Quartz crystals are used to control the frequency of radio and television transmissions. Because these and related applications use so much quartz, there is not enough natural quartz to fulfill demand, and quartz is therefore synthesized. Noncrystalline, or vitreous, quartz, made by melting pure silica sand, is placed in a steel "bomb," and dilute aqueous NaOH is added. A "seed" crystal is placed in the mixture, just as you might use a seed crystal in a hot sugar solution to grow rock candy. When the mixture is heated above the critical temperature of water (above 400 °C and 1700 atm) over a period of days, pure quartz crystallizes.

Silicon dioxide is resistant to attack by all acids except HF, with which it reacts to give SiF_4 and H_2O.

$$SiO_2(s) + 4\ HF(\ell) \rightarrow SiF_4(g) + 2\ H_2O(\ell)$$

Silicon dioxide also dissolves slowly in hot, molten NaOH or Na_2CO_3 to give Na_4SiO_4, sodium silicate.

$$SiO_2(s) + 2\ Na_2CO_3(\ell) \rightarrow Na_4SiO_4(s) + 2\ CO_2(g)$$

After the molten mixture has cooled, hot water under pressure is added. This partially dissolves the material to give a solution of sodium silicate. After filtering off insoluble sand or glass, the solvent is evaporated to leave sodium silicate, called *water glass*. The biggest single use of this material is in household and industrial detergents, in which it is included because a sodium silicate solution maintains pH by its

FIGURE 21.19 Pure silicon.
The manufacture of very pure silicon begins with producing the volatile liquid silanes $SiCl_4$ or $SiHCl_3$. After carefully purifying these by distillation, they are reduced to elemental silicon with extremely pure Mg or Zn. The resulting spongy silicon is purified by zone refining. The end result is a cylindrical rod of ultrapure silicon such as those seen in this photograph. Thin wafers of silicon are cut from the bars and are the basis for the semiconducting chips in computers and other devices.

Synthetic quartz. These crystals were grown from silica in sodium hydroxide. The colors come from added Co^{2+} ions (blue) or Fe^{2+} ions (brown).

FIGURE 21.20 Various forms of quartz.

(a) Pure quartz is colorless, but the presence of small amounts of impurities adds color. Purple amethyst and brown citrine crystals are quartz with iron impurities.

(b) Quartz is a network solid in which each Si atom is bound tetrahedrally to four O atoms, each O atom linked to another Si atom.

Silica gel. Silica gel is solid, noncrystalline SiO_2. Packages of the material are often used to keep electronic equipment dry when stored. Silica gel is also used to clarify beer; passing beer through a bed of silica gel removes minute particles that would otherwise make the brew cloudy. Yet another use is in kitty litter.

buffering ability. Additionally, sodium silicate is used in various adhesives and binders, especially for gluing corrugated cardboard boxes.

If sodium silicate is treated with acid, a gelatinous precipitate of SiO_2 called *silica gel* is obtained. Washed and dried, silica gel is a highly porous material with many uses. It is a drying agent, readily absorbing up to 40% of its own weight of water. Small packets of silica gel are often placed in packing boxes of merchandise during storage. The material is frequently stained with $(NH_4)_2CoCl_4$, a humidity detector that is pink when hydrated and blue when dry.

Silicate Minerals with Chain and Ribbon Structures

The structure and chemistry of silicate minerals is an enormous topic in geology and chemistry. Although all silicates are built from tetrahedral SiO_4 units, they have different properties and a wide variety of structures because of the way these tetrahedral SiO_4 units link together.

The simplest silicates, *orthosilicates*, contain SiO_4^{4-} anions. The 4– charge of the anion is balanced by four M^+ ions, two M^{2+} ions, or a combination of ions. Olivine, an important mineral in the earth's mantle, contains Mg^{2+} and Fe^{2+}, with the Fe^{2+} ion giving the mineral its characteristic olive color, and gem-like zircons are $ZrSiO_4$. Calcium orthosilicate, Ca_2SiO_4, is a component of Portland cement, the most common type of cement used in many parts of the world. (It consists mostly of a mixture of CaO and SiO_2 with the remainder largely aluminum and iron oxides.)

A group of minerals called *pyroxenes* have as their basic structural unit a chain of SiO_4 tetrahedra.

If two such chains are linked together by sharing oxygen atoms, the result is an *amphibole*, of which the asbestos minerals are one example. The molecular chain results in asbestos being a fibrous material.

Silicates with Sheet Structures and Aluminosilicates

Linking many silicate chains together produces a sheet of SiO_4 tetrahedra (Figure 21.21). This sheet is the basic structural feature of some of the earth's most important minerals, particularly the clay minerals (such as china clay), mica, talc, and

FIGURE 21.21 Mica, a sheet silicate. The sheet-like molecular structure of mica explains its physical appearance. As in the pyroxenes, each silicon is bonded to four oxygen atoms, but the Si and O atoms form a sheet of six-member rings of Si atoms with O atoms in each edge. The ratio of Si to O in this structure is 1 to 2.5. A formula of $SiO_{2.5}$ requires a positive ion, such as Na^+, to counterbalance the charge. Thus, mica and other sheet silicates, and aluminosilicates such as talc and many clays, have positive ions between the sheets. The sheet structure leads to the characteristic feature of mica, that it is often found as "books" of thin, silicate sheets. Mica is used in furnace windows and as insulation, and flecks of mica give the glitter to "metallic" paints.

the chrysotile form of asbestos. However, these minerals do not contain just silicon and oxygen. Rather, they are often referred to as *aluminosilicates* because they frequently have Al^{3+} ions in place of Si^{4+} (which means that other positive ions such as Na^+, K^+, and Mg^{2+} must also be present in the lattice to balance the net negative and positive charges). In kaolinite clay, for example, the sheet of SiO_4 tetrahedra is bonded to a sheet of AlO_6 octahedra. In addition, some Si^{4+} ions can be replaced by Al^{3+} atoms. Another example is muscovite, a form of mica. Aluminum ions have replaced some Si^{4+} ions, and there are charge-balancing K^+ ions, so it is best represented by the formula $KAl_2(OH)_2(Si_3AlO_{10})$.

There are some interesting uses of clays, one being in medicine (Figure 21.22). In certain cultures, clay is eaten for medicinal purposes. Several remedies for the relief of upset stomach contain highly purified clays that absorb excess stomach acid as well as potentially harmful bacteria and their toxins by exchanging the intersheet cations in the clays for the toxins, which are often organic cations.

Other aluminosilicates include the feldspars, common minerals that make up about 60% of the earth's crust, and zeolites (Figure 21.22). Both materials are composed of SiO_4 tetrahedra in which some of the Si atoms have been replaced by Al atoms, along with alkali and alkaline earth metal ions for charge balance. The main feature of zeolite structures is their regularly shaped tunnels and cavities. Hole diameters are between 300 and 1000 pm, and small molecules such as water can fit into the cavities of the zeolite structure. As a result, zeolites can be used as drying agents to selectively absorb water from air or a solvent. Small amounts of zeolites are often sealed into multipane windows to keep the air dry between the panes.

Zeolites are also used as catalysts. ExxonMobil, for example, has patented a process in which methanol, CH_3OH, is converted to gasoline in the presence of specially tailored zeolites. In addition, zeolites are added to detergents, where they function as water-softening agents because the sodium ions of the zeolite can be exchanged for Ca^{2+} ions in hard water, effectively removing Ca^{2+} ions from the water.

Kaolinite clay. The basic structural feature of many clays, and kaolinite in particular, is a sheet of SiO_4 tetrahedra (black and red spheres) bonded to a sheet of AlO_6 octahedra (gray and green spheres).

Silicone Polymers

Silicon and chloromethane (CH_3Cl) react at 300 °C in the presence of a catalyst, Cu powder. The primary product of this reaction is $(CH_3)_2SiCl_2$.

$$Si(s) + 2\ CH_3Cl(g) \rightarrow (CH_3)_2SiCl_2(\ell)$$

(a) Remedies for stomach upset. One of the ingredients in Kaopectate is kaolin, one form of clay. The off-white objects are pieces of clay purchased in a market in Ghana, West Africa. This clay was made to be eaten as a remedy for stomach ailments. Eating clay is widespread among the world's different cultures.

(b) The stucture of a zeolite. Zeolites, which have Si, Al, and O linked in a polyhedral framework, are often portrayed in drawings like this. Each edge consists of an Si—O—Si, Al—O—Si, or Al—O—Al bond. The channels in the framework can selectively capture small molecules or ions or act as catalytic sites.

(c) Apophyllite, a crystalline zeolite.

(d) Consumer products that remove odor-causing molecules from the air often contain zeolites.

FIGURE 21.22. Aluminosilicates.

Lead, Beethoven, and a Mystery Solved

Lead anchors the bottom of Group 4A. One of a handful of elements known since ancient times, it has a variety of modern uses. It ranks fifth among metals in usage behind iron, copper, aluminum, and zinc. The major uses of the metal and its compounds are in storage batteries (page 910), pigments, ammunition, solders, plumbing, and bearings.

Unfortunately, lead and its compounds are cumulative poisons, particularly in children. At a blood level as low as 50 ppb (parts per billion), blood pressure is elevated; intelligence is affected at 100 ppb; and blood levels higher than 800 ppb can lead to coma and possible death. Health experts believe that more than 200,000 children become ill from lead poisoning annually, a problem caused chiefly by children eating paint containing lead-based pigments. Older homes often contain lead-based paint because white lead [$2\ PbCO_3 \cdot Pb(OH)_2$] was the pigment used in white paint until about 40 years ago, when it was replaced by TiO_2. Lead salts have a sweet taste, which may contribute to the tendency of children to chew on painted objects.

The symptoms of lead poisoning include nausea, abdominal pain, irritability, headaches, and excess lethargy or hyperactivity. Indeed, these describe some of the symptoms of the illness that affected Ludwig van Beethoven. As a child, he was recognized as a musical prodigy and was thought to be the greatest pianist in Europe by the time he was 19. But then he fell ill, and, by the time he was 29, he wrote to his brother to say he

Erich Lessing/Art Resource, NY

Ludwig van Beethoven (1770–1827).

was considering suicide. By the time he died in 1827 at the age of 56, his belly, arms, and legs were swollen, and he complained constantly of pain in his joints and in his big toe. It is said he wandered the streets of Vienna with long, uncombed hair, dressed in a top hat and long coat, and scribbling in a notebook.

An autopsy at the time showed he died of kidney failure. Kidney stones had destroyed his kidneys, stones that presumably came from gout, the buildup of uric acid in his body. (Gout leads to joint pain, among other things.) But why did he have gout?

It was well known in the time of the Roman Empire that lead and its salts are toxic. The Romans drank wine sweetened with a very concentrated grape juice syrup that was prepared by boiling the juice in a

lead kettle. The resulting syrup, called *Sapa*, had a very high concentration of lead, and many Romans contracted gout. So, if Beethoven enjoyed drinking wine, which was often kept in lead-glass decanters, he could have contracted gout and lead poisoning. One scientist has also noted that he may have been one of a small number of people who have a "metal metabolism disorder," a condition that prevents the excretion of toxic metals like lead.

In 2005, scientists at Argonne National Laboratory examined fragments of Beethoven's hair and skull and found both were extremely high in lead. The hair sample, for example, had 60 ppm lead, about 100 times higher than normal.

The mystery of what caused Beethoven's death has been solved. But what remains a mystery is how he contracted lead poisoning.

Questions:

1. If blood contains 50. ppb lead, how many atoms of lead are there in 1.0 L of blood? (Assume d(blood) = 1.0 g/mL.)
2. Research has found that port wine stored for a year in lead-glass decanters contains 2000 ppm lead. If the decanter contains 750 mL of wine (d = 1.0 g/mL), what mass of lead has been extracted into the wine?

Answers to these questions are available in Appendix N.

© Cengage Learning/Charles D. Winters

Silicone. Some examples of products containing silicones, polymers with repeating —R_2Si—O— units.

Halides of Group 4A elements other than carbon hydrolyze readily. Thus, the reaction of $(CH_3)_2SiCl_2$ with water initially produces $(CH_3)_2Si(OH)_2$. On standing, these molecules combine to form a condensation polymer by eliminating water. The polymer is called polydimethylsiloxane, a member of the *silicone* family of polymers.

$$(CH_3)_2SiCl_2 + 2\ H_2O \rightarrow (CH_3)_2Si(OH)_2 + 2\ HCl$$

$$n\ (CH_3)_2Si(OH)_2 \rightarrow [—(CH_3)_2SiO—]_n + n\ H_2O$$

Silicone polymers are nontoxic and have good stability to heat, light, and oxygen; they are chemically inert and have valuable antistick and antifoam properties. They can take the form of oils, greases, and resins. Some have rubber-like properties ("Silly Putty," for example, is a silicone polymer). More than 1 million tons of silicone polymers is made worldwide annually. These materials are used in a wide variety of products: lubricants, peel-off labels, lipstick, suntan lotion, car polish, and building caulk.

21.8 Nitrogen, Phosphorus, and the Group 5A Elements

Group 5A elements are characterized by the ns^2np^3 configuration with its half-filled np subshell. In compounds of the Group 5A elements, the primary oxidation numbers are +3 and +5, although common nitrogen compounds display a range of oxidation numbers from −3 to +5. Once again, as in Groups 3A and 4A, the most positive oxidation number is less common for the heavier elements. In many arsenic, antimony, and bismuth compounds, the element has an oxidation number of +3. Not surprisingly, compounds of these elements with oxidation numbers of +5 are powerful oxidizing agents.

This part of our tour of the main group elements will concentrate on the chemistries of nitrogen and phosphorus. Nitrogen is found primarily as N_2 in the atmosphere, where it constitutes 78.1% by volume (75.5% by weight). In contrast, phosphorus occurs in the earth's crust in solids. More than 200 different phosphorus-containing minerals are known; all contain the tetrahedral phosphate ion, PO_4^{3-}, or a derivative of this ion. By far, the most abundant phosphorus-containing minerals are apatites (◄ page 976).

Nitrogen and its compounds play a key role in our economy, with ammonia making a particularly notable contribution. Phosphoric acid is an important commodity chemical, and it finds its greatest use in producing fertilizers.

Both phosphorus and nitrogen are part of every living organism. Phosphorus is contained in nucleic acids and phospholipids, and nitrogen occurs in proteins and nucleic acids (◄ *The Chemistry of Life: Biochemistry*, page 490).

Properties of Nitrogen and Phosphorus

Nitrogen (N_2) is a colorless gas that liquifies at 77 K (−196 °C) (◄ Figure 12.1, page 550). Its most notable feature is its reluctance to react with other elements or compounds because the N≡N triple bond has a large bond dissociation enthalpy (945 kJ/mol) and because the molecule is nonpolar. Nitrogen does, however, react with hydrogen to give ammonia in the presence of a catalyst (◄ Case Study, page 746) and with a few metals (notably lithium and magnesium) to give metal nitrides, compounds containing the N^{3-} ion.

$$3\ Mg(s) + N_2(g) \longrightarrow Mg_3N_2(s)$$

magnesium nitride

Elemental nitrogen is a very useful material. Because of its lack of reactivity, it is used to provide a nonoxidizing atmosphere for packaged foods and wine and to pressurize electric cables and telephone wires. Liquid nitrogen is valuable as a coolant in freezing biological samples such as blood and semen, in freeze-drying food, and for other applications that require extremely low temperatures.

Group **5A**
Nitrogen 7 **N** 25 ppm
Phosphorus 15 **P** 1000 ppm
Arsenic 33 **As** 1.5 ppm
Antimony 51 **Sb** 0.2 ppm
Bismuth 83 **Bi** 0.048 ppm

Element abundances are in **parts per million** *in the earth's crust.*

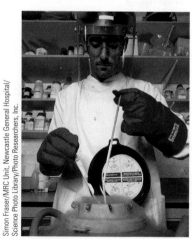

Simon Fraser/MRC Unit, Newcastle General Hospital/ Science Photo Library/Photo Researchers, Inc.

Liquid nitrogen. Biological samples—such as embryos or semen from animals or humans—can be stored in liquid nitrogen (at −196 °C) for long periods of time.

The red and white allotropes of phosphorus.

Elemental phosphorus was first derived from human waste (see *A Closer Look: Making Phosphorus*, page 993), but it is now produced by the reduction of phosphate minerals in an electric furnace.

$$2\ Ca_3(PO_4)_2(s) + 10\ C(s) + 6\ SiO_2(s) \rightarrow P_4(g) + 6\ CaSiO_3(s) + 10\ CO(g)$$

The phosphorus vapor can then be cooled under water, preventing its spontaneous combustion, and eventually yielding the solid forms of phosphorus present at room temperature. Waxy white phosphorus is the most common allotrope of phosphorus, but paradoxically it is the least stable thermodynamically. Rather than occurring as a diatomic molecule with a triple bond, like its second-period relative nitrogen (N_2), phosphorus is made up of tetrahedral P_4 molecules in which each P atom is joined to three others via single bonds. Red phosphorus is a polymer of P_4 units.

white phosphorus, P_4 polymeric red phosphorus

Nitrogen Compounds

A notable feature of the chemistry of nitrogen is the wide diversity of its compounds. Compounds with nitrogen in all oxidation numbers between -3 and $+5$ are known (Figure 21.23).

Hydrogen Compounds of Nitrogen: Ammonia and Hydrazine

Ammonia is a gas at room temperature and pressure. It has a very penetrating odor and condenses to a liquid at $-33\ °C$ under 1 atm of pressure. Solutions in water, often referred to as ammonium hydroxide, are basic due to the reaction of ammonia with water (◄ Section 17.4 and Figure 3.14).

$$NH_3(aq) + H_2O(\ell) \rightleftharpoons NH_4^+(aq) + OH^-(aq)\quad K_b = 1.8 \times 10^{-5}\ \text{at 25 °C}$$

Ammonia is a major industrial chemical and is prepared by the Haber process (◄ page 746), largely for use as a fertilizer.

Hydrazine, N_2H_4, is a colorless, fuming liquid with an ammonia-like odor (mp, 2.0 °C; bp, 113.5 °C). Almost 1 million kilograms of hydrazine is produced annually by the Raschig process—the oxidation of ammonia with alkaline sodium hypochlorite in the presence of gelatin (which is added to suppress metal-catalyzed side reactions that lower the yield of hydrazine).

$$2\ NH_3(aq) + NaClO(aq) \rightleftharpoons N_2H_4(aq) + NaCl(aq) + H_2O(\ell)$$

Hydrazine, like ammonia, is also a base,

$$N_2H_4(aq) + H_2O(\ell) \rightleftharpoons N_2H_5^+(aq) + OH^-(aq) \qquad K_b = 8.5 \times 10^{-7}$$

and it is a strong reducing agent, as reflected in the reduction potential for the following half-reaction in basic solution:

$$N_2(g) + 4\ H_2O(\ell) + 4\ e^- \rightarrow N_2H_4(aq) + 4\ OH^-(aq) \qquad E° = -1.15\ V$$

Hydrazine's reducing ability is exploited in its use in wastewater treatment for chemical plants. It removes oxidizing ions such as CrO_4^{2-} by reducing them, thus preventing them from entering the environment. A related use is the treatment of water boilers in large electric-generating plants. Oxygen dissolved in the water presents a serious problem in these plants because the dissolved gas can oxidize (corrode) the metal of the boiler and pipes. Hydrazine reduces the amount of dissolved oxygen in water.

$$N_2H_4(aq) + O_2(g) \rightarrow N_2(g) + 2\ H_2O(\ell)$$

Compound and Oxidation Number of N

Ammonia, -3

Hydrazine, -2

Dinitrogen, 0

Dinitrogen monoxide, $+1$

Nitrogen monoxide, $+2$

Nitrogen dioxide, $+4$

Nitric acid, $+5$

FIGURE 21.23 Compounds and oxidation numbers for nitrogen. In its compounds, the N atom can have oxidation states ranging from -3 to $+5$.

CASE STUDY

by Jeffrey Keaffaber, University of Florida

A Healthy Saltwater Aquarium and the Nitrogen Cycle

Large saltwater aquariums like those at Sea World in Florida, the Shedd Aquarium in Chicago, and the new Georgia Aquarium in Atlanta, are a continual source of enjoyment. So are smaller aquariums in your home. Maintaining these facilities is not trivial, however; a healthy environment for its marine inhabitants is essential. For this, chemistry plays an important role.

A key part of aquarium maintenance involves control of the concentrations of various dissolved nitrogen-containing species, including ammonia, nitrite ion, and nitrate ion, all of which are stressful to fish at low concentrations and toxic in higher concentrations. The chemistry that relates to maintaining proper balance among these species is called the *nitrogen cycle*.

© Avico Ltd/Alamy

Nitrification

The nitrogen cycle begins with the production of ammonia (and, in acid solution, its conjugate acid, the ammonium ion, NH_4^+), a fundamental waste product of protein metabolism in an aquarium habitat. Unless removed, the ammonia concentration will build up over time. To remove it, the aquarium water is cycled through sand filters infused with aerobic, oxygen-loving bacteria. These bacteria utilize enzymes that catalyze the oxidation of ammonia and ammonium ion by O_2 to form first nitrite ion and then nitrate ion. The overall process is called *nitrification*, and the saltwater bacteria that mediate each oxidation step are *Nitrosococcus sp.* and *Nitrococcus sp.*, respectively. Half-reactions representing this chemistry are as follows:

Oxidation half-reactions

$$NH_4^+(aq) + 8\ OH^-(aq) \longrightarrow$$
$$NO_2^-(aq) + 6\ H_2O(\ell) + 6\ e^-$$

$$NO_2^-(aq) + 2\ OH^-(aq) \longrightarrow$$
$$NO_3^-(aq) + H_2O(\ell) + 2\ e^-$$

Reduction half-reaction

$$O_2(aq) + 2\ H_2O(\ell) + 4\ e^- \longrightarrow 4\ OH^-(aq)$$

When setting up an aquarium at home, it is appropriate to monitor the concentrations of various nitrogen species. Initially, the NH_3/NH_4^+ concentration rises, but then it begins to fall as oxidation occurs. With time, the nitrite ion concentration builds up, peaks, and then decreases, with an accompanying increase in nitrate ion concentration. To reach a stable situation, as much as 6 weeks may be required.

Denitrification

Nitrate is much less toxic than ammonia and the nitrite ion, but its buildup must also be limited. In a small aquarium, nitrate ion concentration can be controlled by partial exchange of water. However, because of environmental restrictions this is not possible for large aquariums; they must use a closed water treatment process.

To remedy the buildup of the nitrate ion, another biologically catalyzed process is used that reduces the nitrate ion to nitrogen gas, N_2. A reducing agent is required, and early designs of denitrifying filters utilized methanol, CH_3OH, as the reducing agent. Among naturally occurring saltwater bacteria capable of nitrate reduction under low oxygen (anoxic) conditions, *Pseudomonas sp.* is commonly used. The bacteria, utilizing enzymes to catalyze reaction of nitrate and methanol to form N_2 and CO_2, are introduced to sand filters where methanol is added.

A stable pH is also important to the health of aquarium fish. Therefore, the marine environment in a saltwater aquarium is maintained at a relatively constant pH of 8.0–8.2. To aid in this, the CO_2 produced by methanol oxidation remains dissolved in solution, and increases the buffer capacity of the seawater.

Questions:

1. Write a balanced net ionic equation for the oxidation of NH_4^+ by O_2 to produce H_2O and NO_2^-.

2. Write half-reactions for the reduction of NO_3^- to N_2 and for the oxidation of CH_3OH to CO_2 in basic solution. Then, combine these half-reactions to obtain the balanced equation for the reduction of NO_3^- by CH_3OH.

3. Consider the carbon-containing species CO_2, H_2CO_3, HCO_3^-, and CO_3^{2-}. Which one is present in largest concentration at the pH conditions of the aquarium? Give a short explanation. K_a of $H_2CO_3 = 4.2 \times 10^{-7}$ and K_a of $HCO_3^- = 4.8 \times 10^{-11}$. (See Study Question 18.110.)

4. A large, 2.2×10^7 L, aquarium contains 1.7×10^4 kg of dissolved NO_3^-. Calculate concentrations in ppm (mg/L) N, ppm NO_3^-, and the molar concentration of NO_3^-.

Answers to these questions are available in Appendix N.

Oxides and Oxoacids of Nitrogen

Nitrogen is unique among all elements in the number of binary oxides it forms (Table 21.5). All are thermodynamically unstable with respect to decomposition to N_2 and O_2; that is, all have positive $\Delta_f G°$ values. Most are slow to decompose, however, and so are described as kinetically stable.

Dinitrogen monoxide, N_2O, commonly called *nitrous oxide*, is a nontoxic, odorless, and tasteless gas in which nitrogen has the lowest oxidation number (+1) among the nitrogen oxides. It can be made by the careful decomposition of ammonium nitrate at 250 °C.

$$NH_4NO_3(s) \rightarrow N_2O(g) + 2\ H_2O(g)$$

It is used as an anesthetic in minor surgery and has been called "laughing gas" because of its euphoriant effects. Because it is soluble in vegetable fats, the largest commercial use of N_2O is as a propellant and aerating agent in cans of whipped cream.

Nitrogen monoxide, NO, is an odd-electron molecule. It has 11 valence electrons, giving it one unpaired electron and making it a free radical. The compound has recently been the subject of intense research because it has been found to be important in a number of biochemical processes.

Nitrogen dioxide, NO_2, is the brown gas you see when a bottle of nitric acid is allowed to stand in the sunlight.

$$2\ HNO_3(aq) \rightarrow 2\ NO_2(g) + H_2O(\ell) + \tfrac{1}{2}\ O_2(g)$$

Nitrogen dioxide is also a culprit in air pollution (◀ page 948). Nitrogen monoxide forms when atmospheric nitrogen and oxygen are heated in internal combustion engines. Released into the atmosphere, NO rapidly reacts with O_2 to form NO_2.

$$2\ NO(g) + O_2(g) \rightarrow 2\ NO_2(g)$$

Table 21.5 Some Oxides of Nitrogen

Formula	Name	Structure	Nitrogen Oxidation Number	Description
N_2O	Dinitrogen monoxide (nitrous oxide)	:N≡N—O: (linear)	+1	Colorless gas (laughing gas)
NO	Nitrogen monoxide (nitric oxide)	*	+2	Colorless gas; odd-electron molecule (paramagnetic)
N_2O_3	Dinitrogen trioxide	N—N (planar)	+3	Blue solid (mp, −100.7 °C); reversibly dissociates to NO and NO_2 above its mp.
NO_2	Nitrogen dioxide	N	+4	Brown, paramagnetic gas; odd-electron molecule
N_2O_4	Dinitrogen tetraoxide	N—N (planar)	+4	Colorless liquid/gas; dissociates to NO_2 (◀ Figure 16.8)
N_2O_5	Dinitrogen pentaoxide	N N	+5	Colorless solid

*It is not possible to draw a Lewis structure that accurately represents the electronic structure of NO. ◀ Chapter 8. Also note that only one resonance structure is shown for each structure.

A CLOSER LOOK

Making Phosphorus

He stoked his small furnace with more charcoal and pumped the bellows until his retort glowed red hot. Suddenly something strange began to happen. Glowing fumes filled the vessel and from the end of the retort dripped a shining liquid that burst into flames.

J. Emsley: *The 13th Element*, p. 5.
New York, John Wiley, 2000.

John Emsley begins his story of phosphorus, its discovery, and its uses, by imagining what the German alchemist Hennig Brandt must have seen in his laboratory that day in 1669. (See page 334 for an artist's conception of the discovery of phosphorus by Brandt.) He was in search of the philosopher's stone, the magic elixir that would turn the crudest substance into gold. (Some may recall that the first Harry Potter novel was titled *Harry Potter and the Philosopher's Stone* when it was published in Great Britain.)

Brandt was experimenting with urine, which had served as the source of useful chemicals since Roman times. It is not surprising that phosphorus could be extracted from this source. Humans consume much more phosphorus, in the form of phosphate, than they require, and the excess phosphorus (about 1.4 g per day) is excreted in the urine. It is nonetheless extraordinary that Brandt was able to isolate the element. According to an 18th-century chemistry book, about 30 g of phosphorus could be obtained from 60 gallons of urine. And the process was not simple. Another 18th-century recipe states that "50 or 60 pails full" of urine was to be used. "Let it lie steeping . . . till it putrefy and breed worms." The chemist was then to reduce the whole to a paste and finally to heat the paste very strongly in a retort. After some days, phosphorus distilled from the mixture and was

collected in water. (We know now that carbon from the organic compounds in the urine would have reduced the phosphate to phosphorus.) Phosphorus was made in this manner for more than 100 years.

The glow of phosphorus burning in air.

Nitrogen dioxide has 17 valence electrons, so it is also an odd-electron molecule. Because the odd electron largely resides on the N atom, two NO_2 molecules can combine, forming an N—N bond and producing N_2O_4, *dinitrogen tetraoxide*.

$$2\ NO_2(g) \longrightarrow N_2O_4(g)$$

deep brown | colorless
gas | (mp, −11.2 °C)

Solid N_2O_4 is colorless and consists entirely of N_2O_4 molecules. However, as the solid melts and the temperature increases to the boiling point, the color darkens as N_2O_4 dissociates to form brown NO_2. At the normal boiling point (21.5 °C), the distinctly brown gas consists of 15.9% NO_2 and 84.1% N_2O_4.

When NO_2 is bubbled into water, nitric acid and nitrous acid form.

$$2\ NO_2(g) + H_2O(\ell) \rightarrow HNO_3(aq) + HNO_2(aq)$$

nitric acid | nitrous acid

Nitric acid has been known for centuries and has become an important compound in our modern economy. The oldest way to make the acid is to treat $NaNO_3$ with sulfuric acid (Figure 21.24).

$$2\ NaNO_3(s) + H_2SO_4(\ell) \rightarrow 2\ HNO_3(\ell) + Na_2SO_4(s)$$

Enormous quantities of nitric acid are now produced industrially by the oxidation of ammonia in the multistep *Ostwald process*. The acid has many applications, but by far the greatest amount is turned into ammonium nitrate (for use as a fertilizer) by the reaction of nitric acid and ammonia.

Nitric acid is a powerful oxidizing agent, as the large, positive $E°$ values for the following half-reactions illustrate:

$$NO_3{}^-(aq) + 4\ H_3O^+(aq) + 3\ e^- \rightarrow NO(g) + 6\ H_2O(\ell) \qquad E° = +0.96\ V$$

$$NO_3{}^-(aq) + 2\ H_3O^+(aq) + e^- \rightarrow NO_2(g) + 3\ H_2O(\ell) \qquad E° = +0.80\ V$$

Nitrous oxide, N_2O. This oxide readily dissolves in fats, so the gas is added, under pressure, to cans of cream. When the valve is opened, the gas expands, whipping the cream. N_2O is also an anesthetic and is considered safe for medical uses. However, significant dangers arise from using it as a recreational drug. Long-term use can induce nerve damage and cause problems such as weakness and loss of feeling.

FIGURE 21.24 The preparation and properties of nitric acid.

Photos © Cengage Learning/Charles D. Winters

(a) Nitric acid is prepared by the reaction of sulfuric acid and sodium nitrate. (Here the reactants were heated in the flask on the right, and HNO_3 was distilled and collected in the flask cooled with ice on the left.) Pure HNO_3 is colorless, but samples of the acid are often brown because of NO_2 formed by decomposition of the acid. In this photo this gas fills the apparatus and colors the liquid in the distillation flask.

(b) When concentrated nitric acid reacts with copper, the metal is oxidized to copper(II) ions, and NO_2 gas is a reaction product.

Concentrated nitric acid attacks and oxidizes most metals. (Aluminum is an exception; see page 983.) In this process, the nitrate ion is reduced to one of the nitrogen oxides. Which oxide is formed depends on the metal and on reaction conditions. In the case of copper, for example, either NO or NO_2 is produced, depending on the concentration of the acid (Figure 21.24b).

In dilute acid:

$$3\ Cu(s) + 8\ H_3O^+(aq) + 2\ NO_3^-(aq) \rightarrow 3\ Cu^{2+}(aq) + 12\ H_2O(\ell) + 2\ NO(g)$$

In concentrated acid:

$$Cu(s) + 4\ H_3O^+(aq) + 2\ NO_3^-(aq) \rightarrow Cu^{2+}(aq) + 6\ H_2O(\ell) + 2\ NO_2(g)$$

Four metals (Au, Pt, Rh, and Ir) that are not attacked by nitric acid are often described as the "noble metals." The alchemists of the 14th century, however, knew that if they mixed HNO_3 with HCl in a ratio of about 1:3, this aqua regia, or "kingly water," would attack even gold, the noblest of metals.

$$10\ Au(s) + 6\ NO_3^-(aq) + 40\ Cl^-(aq) + 36\ H_3O^+(aq) \rightarrow$$
$$10\ [AuCl_4]^-(aq) + 3\ N_2(g) + 54\ H_2O(\ell)$$

Hydrogen Compounds of Phosphorus and Other Group 5A Elements

The phosphorus analog of ammonia, phosphine (PH_3), is a poisonous, highly reactive gas with a faint garlic-like odor. Industrially, it is made by the reaction of white phosphorus and aqueous NaOH.

$$P_4(s) + 3\ KOH(aq) + 3\ H_2O(\ell) \rightarrow PH_3(g) + 3\ KH_2PO_2(aq)$$

The other hydrides of the heavier Group 5A elements are also toxic and become more unstable as the atomic number of the element increases. Nonetheless, arsine (AsH_3) is used in the semiconductor industry as a starting material in the preparation of gallium arsenide (GaAs) semiconductors.

Phosphorus Oxides and Sulfides

The most important compounds of phosphorus are those with oxygen, and there are at least six simple binary compounds containing just phosphorus and oxygen. All of them can be thought of as being derived structurally from the P_4 tetrahedron

P_4 221 pm

165.6 pm   127.0°   99.5°

O_2

P_4O_6

O_2

143 pm   123.0°   160 pm   102.0°

P_4O_{10}

H_2O

H_3PO_3
phosphorous acid

H_2O

H_3PO_4
phosphoric acid

FIGURE 21.25 Phosphorus oxides. Other binary P—O compounds have formulas between P_4O_6 and P_4O_{10}. They are formed by starting with P_4O_6 and adding O atoms successively to the P atom vertices.

of white phosphorus. For example, if P_4 is carefully oxidized, P_4O_6 is formed; an O atom has been placed into each P—P bond in the tetrahedron (Figure 21.25).

The most common and important phosphorus oxide is P_4O_{10}, a fine white powder commonly called *phosphorus pentaoxide* because its empirical formula is P_2O_5. In P_4O_{10}, each phosphorus atom is surrounded tetrahedrally by O atoms.

Phosphorus also forms a series of compounds with sulfur. Of these, the most important is P_4S_3. In this phosphorus sulfide, S atoms are placed into only three of the P—P bonds. The principal use of P_4S_3 is in "strike anywhere" matches, the kind that light when you rub the head against a rough object. The active ingredients are P_4S_3 and the powerful oxidizing agent potassium chlorate, $KClO_3$. The "safety match" is now more common than the "strike anywhere" match. In safety matches, the head is predominantly $KClO_3$, and the material on the match book is red phosphorus (about 50%), Sb_2S_3, Fe_2O_3, and glue.

© Cengage Learning/Charles D. Winters

Matches. The head of a "strike anywhere" match contains P_4S_3 and the oxidizing agent $KClO_3$. (Other components are ground glass, Fe_2O_3, ZnO, and glue.) Safety matches have sulfur (3–5%) and $KClO_3$ (45–55%) in the match head and red phosphorus in the striking strip.

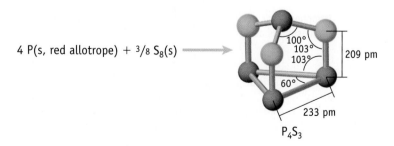

4 P(s, red allotrope) + 3/8 S_8(s) ⟶   100° 103° 103° 60°   209 pm   233 pm

P_4S_3

Enormous quantities of phosphorus compounds are used around the world, and most of this begins with phosphate rock, which is largely $Ca_3(PO_4)_2$ or apatite. As outlined in Figure 21.26, phosphate rock is converted to impure phosphoric acid and then to other products, or to elemental phosphorus, from which pure acid and other products are made.

(a) Mining phosphate rock. Phosphate rock is primarily $Ca_3(PO_4)_2$, and most mined in the United States comes from Florida.

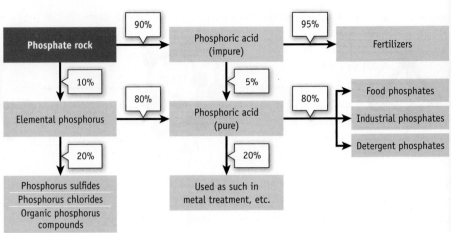

(b) Uses of phosphorus and phosphoric acid.

FIGURE 21.26 Uses of phosphate rock, phosphorus, and phosphoric acid.

Phosphorus Oxoacids and Their Salts

A few of the many known phosphorus oxoacids are illustrated in Table 21.6. Indeed, there are so many acids and their salts in this category that structural principles have been developed to organize and understand them.

(a) All P atoms in the oxoacids and their anions (conjugate bases) are four-coordinate and tetrahedral.

(b) All the P atoms in the acids have at least one P—OH group (and this occurs often in the anions as well). In every case, the H atom is ionizable as H^+.

(c) Some oxoacids have one or more P—H bonds. These H atoms are not ionizable as H^+.

(d) Polymerization can occur by P—O—P bond formation to give both linear and cyclic species. Two P atoms are never joined by more than one P—O—P bridge.

Table 21.6 **Phosphorus Oxoacids**

Formula	Name	Structure	pK_a
H_3PO_4	Orthophosphoric acid		2.21, 7.21, 12.67
$H_4P_2O_7$	Pyrophosphoric acid (diphosphoric acid)		0.85, 1.49, 5.77, 8.22
$(HPO_3)_3$	Metaphosphoric acid		
H_3PO_3	Phosphorous acid (phosphonic acid)		2.00, 6.59
H_3PO_2	Hypophosphorous acid (phosphinic acid)		1.24

(e) When a P atom is surrounded only by O atoms (as in H_3PO_4), its oxidation number is $+5$. For each P—OH that is replaced by P—H, the oxidation number drops by 2 (because P is considered more electronegative than H). For example, the oxidation number of P in H_3PO_2 is $+1$.

Orthophosphoric acid, H_3PO_4, and its salts are far more important commercially than other P—O acids. Millions of tons of phosphoric acid are made annually, some using white phosphorus as the starting material. The element is burned in oxygen to give P_4O_{10}, and the oxide reacts with water to produce the acid (Figure 21.27).

$$P_4O_{10}(s) + 6 \ H_2O(\ell) \rightarrow 4 \ H_3PO_4(aq)$$

This approach gives a pure product, so it is used to make phosphoric acid for use in food products in particular. The acid is nontoxic, and it gives the tart or sour taste to carbonated "soft drinks," such as various colas (about 0.05% H_3PO_4) or root beer (about 0.01% H_3PO_4).

A major use for phosphoric acid is to impart corrosion resistance to metal objects such as nuts and bolts, tools, and car-engine parts by plunging the object into a hot acid bath. Car bodies are similarly treated with phosphoric acid containing metal ions such as Zn^{2+}, and aluminum trim is "polished" by treating it with the acid.

The reaction of H_3PO_4 with strong bases produces salts such as NaH_2PO_4, Na_2HPO_4, and Na_3PO_4. In industry, the monosodium and disodium salts are produced using Na_2CO_3 as the base, but an excess of the stronger (and more expensive) base NaOH is required to remove the third proton to give Na_3PO_4.

Sodium phosphate (Na_3PO_4) is used in scouring powders and paint strippers because the anion PO_4^{3-} is a relatively strong base in water ($K_b = 2.8 \times 10^{-2}$). Sodium monohydrogen phosphate, Na_2HPO_4, which has a less basic anion than PO_4^{3-}, is widely used in food products. Kraft has patented a process using the salt in the manufacture of pasteurized cheese, for example. Thousands of tons of Na_2HPO_4 are still used for this purpose, even though the function of the salt in this process is not completely understood. In addition, a small amount of Na_2HPO_4 in pudding mixes enables the mix to gel in cold water, and the basic anion raises the pH of cereals to provide "quick-cooking" breakfast cereal. (The OH$^-$ ion from HPO_4^{2-} hydrolysis accelerates the breakdown of the cellulose material in the cereal.)

Calcium phosphates are used in a broad spectrum of products. For example, the weak acid $Ca(H_2PO_4)_2 \cdot H_2O$ is used as the acid leavening agent in baking powder. A typical baking powder contains (along with inert ingredients) 28% $NaHCO_3$, 10.7% $Ca(H_2PO_4)_2 \cdot H_2O$, and 21.4% $NaAl(SO_4)_2$ (also a weak acid). The weak acids react with sodium bicarbonate to produce CO_2 gas. For example,

$$Ca(H_2PO_4)_2 \cdot H_2O(s) + 2 \ NaHCO_3(aq) \rightarrow 2 \ CO_2(g) + 3 \ H_2O(\ell) + Na_2HPO_4(aq) + CaHPO_4(aq)$$

Finally, calcium monohydrogen phosphate, $CaHPO_4$, is used as an abrasive and polishing agent in toothpaste.

FIGURE 21.27 Reaction of P_4O_{10} and water. The white solid oxide reacts vigorously with water to give orthophosphoric acid, H_3PO_4. (The heat generated vaporizes the water, so steam is visible.)

REVIEW & CHECK FOR SECTION 21.8

1. Construct Lewis structures for the several resonance forms of N_2O. What is the predicted N—N bond order?

    (a) 1   (b) 2   (c) between 2 and 3   (d) 3

2. Which statement about ammonia is *not correct*?

    (a) Ammonia can be made by a direct reaction of the elements.

    (b) Solutions of ammonia are acidic.

    (c) Ammonia is a gas at room temperature and atmospheric pressure.

    (d) Ammonia is used as a reactant in the synthesis of nitric acid.

3. What is the oxidation state of phosphorus in phosphorous acid, $HPO(OH)_2$?

    (a) 0   (b) +1   (c) +3   (d) +5

Group **6A**
Oxygen 8 **O** 474,000 ppm
Sulfur 16 **S** 260 ppm
Selenium 34 **Se** 0.5 ppm
Tellurium 52 **Te** 0.005 ppm
Polonium 84 **Po** trace

Element abundances are in **parts per million** *in the earth's crust.*

21.9 Oxygen, Sulfur, and the Group 6A Elements

Oxygen is by far the most abundant element in the earth's crust, representing slightly less than 50% of it by weight. It is present as elemental oxygen in the atmosphere and is combined with other elements in water and in many minerals. Scientists believe that elemental oxygen did not appear on this planet until about 3.5 billion years ago, when it was formed on the planet by plants through the process of photosynthesis.

Sulfur, seventeenth in abundance in the earth's crust, is also found in its elemental form in nature, but only in certain concentrated deposits. Sulfur-containing compounds occur in natural gas, coal, and oil. In minerals, sulfur occurs as the sulfide ion (for example, in cinnabar, HgS, and galena, PbS), as the disulfide ion (in iron pyrite, FeS_2, or "fool's gold"), and as sulfate ion (e.g., in gypsum, $CaSO_4 \cdot 2 H_2O$). Sulfur oxides (SO_2 and SO_3) also occur in nature, primarily as products of volcanic activity (Figure 21.28).

In the United States, sulfur—several million tons per year—is obtained from deposits of the element found along the Gulf of Mexico. These deposits occur typically at a depth of 150 to 750 m below the surface in layers about 30 m thick. They are thought to have been formed by anaerobic ("without elemental oxygen") bacteria acting on sedimentary sulfate deposits such as gypsum.

Preparation and Properties of the Elements

Pure oxygen is obtained by the fractional distillation of air and is among the top five industrial chemicals produced in the United States. Oxygen can be made in the laboratory by electrolysis of water (Figure 21.4) and by the catalyzed decomposition of metal chlorates such as $KClO_3$.

$$2 \ KClO_3(s) \xrightarrow{\text{catalyst}} 2 \ KCl(s) + 3 \ O_2(g)$$

At room temperature and pressure, oxygen is a colorless gas, but it is pale blue when condensed to a liquid at $-183 \ °C$ (◄ Figure 9.12). As described in Section 9.3, diatomic oxygen is paramagnetic because it has two unpaired electrons.

An allotrope of oxygen, ozone (O_3), is a blue, diamagnetic gas with an odor so strong that it can be detected in concentrations as low as 0.05 ppm. Ozone is synthesized by passing O_2 through an electric discharge or by irradiating O_2 with ultraviolet light. It is often in the news because of the realization that the earth's protective layer of ozone in the stratosphere is being disrupted by chlorofluorocarbons and other chemicals (◄ page 951).

Sulfur has numerous allotropes. The most common and most stable allotrope is the yellow, orthorhombic form, which consists of S_8 molecules with the sulfur atoms arranged in a crown-shaped ring (Figure 21.29a). Less stable allotropes are known that have rings of 6 to 20 sulfur atoms. Another form of sulfur, called plastic sulfur, has a molecular structure with chains of sulfur atoms (Figure 21.29b).

Selenium and tellurium are comparatively rare on earth, having abundances about the same as those of silver and gold, respectively. Because their chemistry is similar to that of sulfur, they are often found in minerals associated with the sulfides of copper, silver, iron, and arsenic, and they are recovered as by-products of the industries devoted to those elements.

Selenium has a range of uses, including in glass making. A cadmium sulfide/selenide mixture is added to glass to give it a brilliant red color (Figure 21.30a). The most familiar use of selenium is in xerography, a word meaning "dry printing" and a process at the heart of the modern copy machine. Most photocopy machines use an aluminum plate or roller coated with selenium. Light coming from the imaging lens selectively discharges a static electric charge on the selenium surface, and the black toner sticks only on the areas that remain charged. A copy is made when the toner is transferred to a sheet of plain paper.

The heaviest element of Group 6A, polonium, is radioactive and found only in trace amounts on earth. It was discovered in Paris, France, in 1898 by Marie Sklodowska Curie (1867–1934) and her husband Pierre Curie (1859–1906). The Curies painstakingly separated this element from a large quantity of pitchblende, a uranium-containing ore.

© Mitchell Kanashkevich/Corbis

FIGURE 21.28 Sulfur spewing from a volcano in Indonesia.

(a)   (b)

FIGURE 21.29 Sulfur allotropes. **(a)** At room temperature, sulfur exists as a bright yellow solid composed of S_8 rings. **(b)** When heated, the rings break open and eventually form chains of S atoms in a material described as "plastic sulfur."

Sulfur Compounds

Hydrogen sulfide, H_2S, has a bent molecular geometry, like water. Unlike water, however, H_2S is a gas under standard conditions (mp, $-85.6\ °C$; bp, $-60.3\ °C$) because its intermolecular forces are weak compared with the strong hydrogen bonding in water (◄ Figure 12.6). Hydrogen sulfide is poisonous, comparable in toxicity to hydrogen cyanide, but fortunately it has a terrible odor and is detectable in concentrations as low as 0.02 ppm. You must be careful with H_2S, though. Because it has an anesthetic effect, your nose rapidly loses its ability to detect it. Death occurs at H_2S concentrations of 100 ppm.

Sulfur is often found as the sulfide ion in conjunction with metals because all metal sulfides (except those based on Group 1A metals) are insoluble. The recovery of metals from their sulfide ores usually begins by heating the ore in air.

$$2\ PbS(s) + 3\ O_2(g) \rightarrow 2\ PbO(s) + 2\ SO_2(g)$$

Here, lead(II) sulfide is converted to lead(II) oxide, and this is then reduced to lead using carbon or carbon monoxide in a blast furnace.

$$PbO(s) + CO(g) \rightarrow Pb(\ell) + CO_2(g)$$

● **Bad Breath** Halitosis or "bad breath" is due to three sulfur-containing compounds: H_2S, CH_3SH (methyl mercaptan), and $(CH_3)_2S$ (dimethyl sulfide). All three can be detected in very tiny concentrations. For example, your nose knows if as little as 0.2 microgram of CH_3SH is present per liter of air. The compounds result from bacteria's attack on the sulfur-containing amino acids cysteine and methionine in food particles in the mouth.

(a) Glass takes on a brilliant red color when a mixture of cadmium sulfide/selenide (CdS, CdSe) is added to it.

(b) These sample bottles hold suspensions of quantum dots, nanometer-sized crystals of CdSe dispersed in a polymer matrix. The crystals emit light in the visible range when excited by ultraviolet light. Light emission at different wavelengths is achieved by changing the particle size. Crystals of PbS and PbSe can be made that emit light in the infrared range.

FIGURE 21.30 Uses of selenium.

Common household products containing sulfur or sulfur-based compounds.

Alternatively, the oxide can be reduced to elemental lead by combining it with fresh lead sulfide.

$$2\ PbO(s) + PbS(s) \rightarrow 3\ Pb(s) + SO_2(g)$$

Models of some common sulfur-containing molecules: H_2S, SO_2, SO_3, and H_2SO_4.

Sulfur dioxide (SO_2), a colorless, toxic gas with a sharp odor, is produced on an enormous scale by the combustion of sulfur and by roasting sulfide ores in air. The combustion of sulfur in sulfur-containing coal and fuel oil creates particularly large environmental problems. It has been estimated that about 2.0×10^8 tons of sulfur oxides (primarily SO_2) are released into the atmosphere each year by human activities; this is more than half of the total emitted by all other natural sources of sulfur in the environment.

Sulfur dioxide readily dissolves in water. The most important reaction of this gas is its oxidation to SO_3.

$$SO_2(g) + \tfrac{1}{2}\ O_2(g) \rightarrow SO_3(g) \qquad \Delta_rH° = -98.9\ \text{kJ/mol-rxn}$$

Sulfur trioxide is almost never isolated but is converted directly to sulfuric acid by reaction with water in the "contact process."

The largest use of sulfur is the production of sulfuric acid, H_2SO_4, the compound produced in largest quantity by the chemical industry (◄ page 133). In the United States, roughly 70% of the acid is used to manufacture superphosphate fertilizer from phosphate rock. Plants need a soluble form of phosphorus for growth, but calcium phosphate and apatite [$Ca_5X(PO_4)_3$, X = F, OH, Cl] are insoluble. Treating phosphate-containing minerals with sulfuric acid produces a mixture of soluble phosphates. The balanced equation for the reaction of excess sulfuric acid and calcium phosphate, for example, is

$$Ca_3(PO_4)_2(s) + 3\ H_2SO_4(\ell) \rightarrow 2\ H_3PO_4(\ell) + 3\ CaSO_4(s)$$

but it does not tell the whole story. Concentrated superphosphate fertilizer is actually mostly $CaHPO_4$ or $Ca(H_2PO_4)_2$ plus some H_3PO_4 and $CaSO_4$. (Notice that the chemical principle behind this reaction is that sulfuric acid is a stronger acid than H_3PO_4 (◄ Table 17.3), so the PO_4^{3-} ion is protonated by sulfuric acid.)

Smaller amounts of sulfuric acid are used in the conversion of ilmenite, a titanium-bearing ore, to TiO_2, which is then used as a white pigment in paint, plastics, and paper. The acid is also used to manufacture iron and steel as well as petroleum products, synthetic polymers, and paper.

REVIEW & CHECK FOR SECTION 21.9

1. Which of the following is not a common oxidation number for sulfur in its compounds?

    (a) −2　　　　　(b) +6　　　　　(c) +3　　　　　(d) +4

2. Which statement about oxygen is *not* true?

    (a) Liquid oxygen is attracted to a magnet.

    (b) The allotropes of oxygen are O_2 and O_3.

    (c) Oxygen is the most abundant element in the earth's crust.

    (d) All electrons in O_2 are paired.

Snot-tites and Sulfur Chemistry

Sulfur chemistry can be important in cave formation, as a spectacular example in the jungles of southern Mexico amply demonstrates. Toxic hydrogen sulfide gas spews from the Cueva de Villa Luz along with water that is milky white with suspended sulfur particles. The cave can be followed downward to a large underground stream and a maze of actively enlarging cave passages. Water rises into the cave from underlying sulfur-bearing strata, releasing hydrogen sulfide at concentrations up to 150 ppm. Yellow sulfur crystallizes on the cave walls around the inlets. The sulfur and sulfuric acid are produced by the following reactions:

$$2\ H_2S(g) + O_2(g) \rightarrow 2\ S(s) + 2\ H_2O(\ell)$$

$$2\ S(s) + 2\ H_2O(\ell) + 3\ O_2(g) \rightarrow$$
$$2\ H_2SO_4(aq)$$

The cave atmosphere is poisonous to humans, so gas masks are essential for would-be explorers. But surprisingly, the cave is teeming with life. Several species of bacteria thrive on sulfur compounds in acidic environments. The chemical energy released in their metabolism is used to obtain carbon for their bodies from calcium carbonate and carbon dioxide, both of which are abundant in the cave. One result is that bacterial filaments hang from the walls and ceilings in bundles. Because the filaments look like something coming from a runny nose, cave explorers refer to them as "snot-tites." Other microbes feed on the bacteria, and so on up the food chain—which includes spiders, gnats, and pygmy snails—all the way to sardine-like fish that swim in the cave stream. This entire ecosystem is supported by reactions involving sulfur within the cave.

Snot-tites. Filaments of sulfur-oxidizing bacteria (dubbed "snot-tites") hang from the ceiling of a Mexican cave containing an atmosphere rich in hydrogen sulfide. The bacteria thrive on the energy released by oxidation of the hydrogen sulfide, forming the base of a complex food chain. Droplets of sulfuric acid on the filaments have an average pH of 1.4, with some as low as zero! Drops that landed on explorers in the cave burned their skin and disintegrated their clothing.

Arthur N. Palmer

21.10 The Halogens, Group 7A

Fluorine and chlorine are the most abundant halogens in the earth's crust, with fluorine somewhat more abundant than chlorine. If their abundance in sea water is measured, however, the situation is quite different. Chlorine has an abundance in sea water of 18,000 ppm, whereas the abundance of fluorine in the same source is only 1.3 ppm. This variation is a result of the differences in the solubility of their salts and plays a role in the methods used to recover the elements themselves.

Preparation of the Elements

Fluorine

The water-insoluble mineral fluorspar (calcium fluoride, CaF_2) is one of the many sources of fluorine. Because the mineral was originally used as a flux in metalworking, its name comes from the Latin word meaning "to flow." In the 17th century, it was discovered that solid CaF_2 would emit light when heated, and the phenomenon was called *fluorescence*. In the early 1800s, when it was recognized that a new element was contained in fluorspar, A. M. Ampère (1775–1836) suggested that the element be called fluorine.

Although fluorine was recognized as an element by 1812, it was not until 1886 that it was isolated by the French chemist Henri Moisson (1852–1907) in elemental form as a very pale yellow gas by the electrolysis of KF dissolved in anhydrous HF. Indeed, because F_2 is such a powerful oxidizing agent, chemical oxidation of F^- to F_2 is not feasible, and electrolysis is the only practical way to obtain gaseous F_2 (Figure 21.31).

Fluorine is still prepared by the Moisson method, but the preparation is difficult because F_2 is so reactive. It corrodes the equipment and reacts violently with traces of grease or other contaminants. Furthermore, the products of electrolysis,

Group 7A
Halogens

Fluorine
9
F
950 ppm

Chlorine
17
Cl
130 ppm

Bromine
35
Br
0.37 ppm

Iodine
53
I
0.14 ppm

Astatine
85
At
trace

Element abundances are in **parts per million** *in the earth's crust.*

FIGURE 21.31 Schematic of an electrolysis cell for producing fluorine.

F_2 and H_2, can recombine explosively, so they must not be allowed to come into contact with each other. (Compare with the reaction of H_2 and Br_2 in Figure 21.5.) Current U.S. production of fluorine is approximately 5000 metric tons per year.

Chlorine

Chlorine is a strong oxidizing agent, and to prepare this element from chloride ion by a chemical reaction requires an even stronger oxidizing agent. In the laboratory permanganate ions or dichromate ions in acid solution will serve this purpose (Figure 21.32). Elemental chlorine was first made by the Swedish chemist Karl Wilhelm Scheele (1742–1786) in 1774, who combined sodium chloride with an oxidizing agent in an acidic solution.

Industrially, chlorine is made by electrolysis of brine (concentrated aqueous NaCl). The other product of the electrolysis, NaOH, is also a valuable industrial chemical. About 80% of the chlorine produced is made using an electrochemical cell similar to the one depicted in Figure 21.33. Oxidation of chloride ion to Cl_2 gas occurs at the anode and reduction of water occurs at the cathode.

Anode reaction (oxidation): $2 \; Cl^-(aq) \rightarrow Cl_2(g) + 2 \; e^-$

Cathode reaction (reduction): $2 \; H_2O(\ell) + 2 \; e^- \rightarrow H_2(g) + 2 \; OH^-(aq)$

Activated titanium is used for the anode, and stainless steel or nickel is preferred for the cathode. The anode and cathode compartments are separated by a membrane that is not permeable to water but allows Na^+ ions to pass to maintain the charge balance. Thus, the membrane functions as a "salt" bridge between the anode and cathode compartments. The energy consumption of these cells is in the range of 2000–2500 kWh per ton of NaOH produced.

Bromine

The standard reduction potentials of the halogens indicate that their strength as oxidizing agents decreases going from F_2 to I_2.

Half-Reaction	Reduction Potential ($E°$, V)
$F_2(g) + 2 \; e^- \rightarrow 2 \; F^-(aq)$	2.87
$Cl_2(g) + 2 \; e^- \rightarrow 2 \; Cl^-(aq)$	1.36
$Br_2(\ell) + 2 \; e^- \rightarrow 2 \; Br^-(aq)$	1.08
$I_2(s) + 2 \; e^- \rightarrow 2 \; I^-(aq)$	0.535

This means that Cl_2 will oxidize Br^- ions to Br_2 in aqueous solution, for example.

$$Cl_2(aq) + 2 \; Br^-(aq) \rightarrow 2 \; Cl^-(aq) + Br_2(aq)$$

$$E°_{net} = E°_{cathode} - E°_{anode} = 1.36 \; V - (1.08 \; V) = +0.28 \; V$$

In fact, this is the commercial method of preparing bromine when NaBr is obtained from natural brine wells in Arkansas and Michigan.

Iodine

Iodine is a lustrous, purple-black solid, easily sublimed at room temperature and atmospheric pressure (◄ Figure 13.20). The element was first isolated in 1811 from seaweed and kelp, extracts of which had long been used for treatment of goiter, the enlargement of the thyroid gland. It is now known that the thyroid gland produces a growth-regulating hormone (thyroxine) that contains iodine. Consequently, most table salt in the United States has 0.01% NaI added to provide the necessary iodine in the diet.

A laboratory method for preparing I_2 is illustrated in Figure 21.34. The commercial preparation depends on the source of I^- and its concentration. One method is interesting because it involves some chemistry described earlier in this book. Iodide ions are first precipitated with silver ions to give insoluble AgI.

$$I^-(aq) + Ag^+(aq) \rightarrow AgI(s)$$

© Cengage Learning/Charles D. Winters

FIGURE 21.32 Chlorine preparation. Chlorine is prepared by oxidation of chloride ion using a strong oxidizing agent. Here, oxidation of NaCl is accomplished using $K_2Cr_2O_7$ in H_2SO_4. (The Cl_2 gas is bubbled into water in a receiving flask.)

FIGURE 21.33 A membrane cell for the production of NaOH and Cl_2 gas from a saturated, aqueous solution of NaCl (brine). Here, the anode and cathode compartments are separated by a water-impermeable but ion-conducting membrane. A widely used membrane is made of Nafion, a fluorine-containing polymer that is a relative of polytetrafluoroethylene (Teflon). Brine is fed into the anode compartment and dilute sodium hydroxide or water into the cathode compartment. Overflow pipes carry the evolved gases and NaOH away from the chambers of the electrolysis cell.

This is reduced by clean scrap iron to give iron(II) iodide and metallic silver.

$$2\ AgI(s) + Fe(s) \rightarrow FeI_2(aq) + 2\ Ag(s)$$

The silver is recycled by oxidizing it with nitric acid (forming silver nitrate) which is then reused. Finally, iodide ion from water-soluble FeI_2 is oxidized to iodine with chlorine [with iron(III) chloride as a by-product].

$$2\ FeI_2(aq) + 3\ Cl_2(aq) \rightarrow 2\ I_2(s) + 2\ FeCl_3(aq)$$

Fluorine Compounds

Fluorine is the most reactive of all of the elements, forming compounds with every element except He and Ne. In most cases, the elements combine directly, and some reactions can be so vigorous as to be explosive. This reactivity can be explained by at least two features of fluorine chemistry: the relatively weak F—F bond compared with chlorine and bromine, and, in particular, the relatively strong bonds formed by

FIGURE 21.34 The preparation of iodine. A mixture of sodium iodide and manganese(IV) oxide was placed in the flask *(left)*. On adding concentrated sulfuric acid *(right)*, brown iodine vapor is evolved.

$$2\ NaI(s) + 2\ H_2SO_4(aq) + MnO_2(s) \rightarrow$$
$$Na_2SO_4(aq) + MnSO_4(aq)$$
$$+ 2\ H_2O(\ell) + I_2(g)$$

Photos © Cengage Learning/Charles D. Winters

Bond Dissociation Enthalpies of Some Halogen Compounds (kJ/mol)

X	X—X	H—X	C—X (in CX_4)
F	155	565	485
Cl	242	432	339
Br	193	366	285
I	151	299	213

fluorine to other elements. This is illustrated by the table of bond dissociation enthalpies in the margin.

In addition to its oxidizing ability, another notable characteristic of fluorine is its small size. These properties lead to the formation of compounds where a number of F atoms can be bonded to a central element in a high oxidation state. Examples include PtF_6, UF_6, IF_7, and XeF_4.

Hydrogen fluoride is an important industrial chemical. More than 1 million tons of hydrogen fluoride is produced annually worldwide, almost all by the action of concentrated sulfuric acid on fluorspar.

$$CaF_2(s) + H_2SO_4(\ell) \rightarrow CaSO_4(s) + 2\ HF(g)$$

The U.S. capacity for HF production is approximately 210,000 metric tons, but demand often exceeds supply for this chemical. Anhydrous HF is used in a broad range of industries: in the production of refrigerants, herbicides, pharmaceuticals, high-octane gasoline, aluminum, plastics, electrical components, and fluorescent lightbulbs.

The fluorspar used to produce HF must be very pure and free of SiO_2 because HF reacts readily with silicon dioxide.

$$SiO_2(s) + 4\ HF(aq) \rightarrow SiF_4(g) + 2\ H_2O(\ell)$$

$$SiF_4(g) + 2\ HF(aq) \rightarrow H_2SiF_6(aq)$$

This series of reactions explains why HF can be used to etch or frost glass (such as the inside of fluorescent light bulbs). It also explains why HF is not shipped in glass containers (unlike HCl, for example).

The aluminum industry consumes about 10–40 kg of cryolite, Na_3AlF_6, per metric ton of aluminum produced. The reason is that cryolite is added to aluminum oxide to produce a lower-melting mixture that can be electrolyzed. Cryolite is found in only small quantities in nature, so it is made in various ways, among them the following reaction:

$$6\ HF(aq) + Al(OH)_3(s) + 3\ NaOH(aq) \rightarrow Na_3AlF_6(s) + 6\ H_2O(\ell)$$

About 3% of the hydrofluoric acid produced is used in uranium fuel production. To separate uranium isotopes in a gas centrifuge (▶ page 1079), the uranium must be in the form of a volatile compound. Naturally occurring uranium is processed to give UO_2. This oxide is treated with hydrogen fluoride to give UF_4, which is then reacted with F_2 to produce the volatile solid UF_6.

$$UO_2(s) + 4\ HF(aq) \rightarrow UF_4(s) + 2\ H_2O(\ell)$$

$$UF_4(s) + F_2(g) \rightarrow UF_6(s)$$

This last step consumes 70%–80% of the fluorine produced annually.

Chlorine Compounds

Hydrogen Chloride

Hydrochloric acid, an aqueous solution of hydrogen chloride, is a valuable industrial chemical. Hydrogen chloride gas can be prepared by the reaction of hydrogen and chlorine, but the rapid, exothermic reaction is difficult to control. The classical method of making HCl in the laboratory uses the reaction of NaCl and sulfuric acid, a procedure that takes advantage of the facts that HCl is a gas and that H_2SO_4 will not oxidize the chloride ion.

$$2\ NaCl(s) + H_2SO_4(\ell) \rightarrow Na_2SO_4(s) + 2\ HCl(g)$$

Hydrogen chloride gas has a sharp, irritating odor. Both gaseous and aqueous HCl react with metals and metal oxides to give metal chlorides and, depending on the reactant, hydrogen or water.

$$Mg(s) + 2\ HCl(aq) \rightarrow MgCl_2(aq) + H_2(g)$$

$$ZnO(s) + 2\ HCl(aq) \rightarrow ZnCl_2(aq) + H_2O(\ell)$$

Oxoacids of Chlorine

Oxoacids of chlorine range from HClO, in which chlorine has an oxidation number of +1, to $HClO_4$, in which the oxidation number is equal to the group number, +7. All are strong oxidizing agents.

Oxoacids of Chlorine

Acid	Name	Anion	Name
HClO	Hypochlorous	ClO^-	Hypochlorite
$HClO_2$	Chlorous	ClO_2^-	Chlorite
$HClO_3$	Chloric	ClO_3^-	Chlorate
$HClO_4$	Perchloric	ClO_4^-	Perchlorate

Hypochlorous acid, HClO, forms when chlorine dissolves in water. In this reaction, half of the chlorine is oxidized to hypochlorite ion and half is reduced to chloride ion in a **disproportionation reaction**.

$$Cl_2(g) + 2\ H_2O(\ell) \rightleftharpoons H_3O^+(aq) + HClO(aq) + Cl^-(aq)$$

If Cl_2 is dissolved in cold aqueous NaOH instead of in pure water, hypochlorite ion and chloride ion form.

$$Cl_2(g) + 2\ OH^-(aq) \rightleftharpoons ClO^-(aq) + Cl^-(aq) + H_2O(\ell)$$

Under basic conditions, the equilibrium lies far to the right. The resulting alkaline solution is the "liquid bleach" used in home laundries. The bleaching action of this solution is a result of the oxidizing ability of ClO^-. Most dyes are colored organic compounds, and hypochlorite ion oxidizes dyes to colorless products.

When calcium hydroxide is combined with Cl_2, solid $Ca(ClO)_2$ is the product. This compound is easily handled and is the "chlorine" that is sold for swimming pool disinfection.

When a basic solution of hypochlorite ion is heated, another disproportionation occurs, forming chlorate ion and chloride ion:

$$3\ ClO^-(aq) \rightarrow ClO_3^-(aq) + 2\ Cl^-(aq)$$

Sodium and potassium chlorates are made in large quantities this way. The sodium salt can be reduced to ClO_2, a compound used for bleaching paper pulp. Some $NaClO_3$ is also converted to potassium chlorate, $KClO_3$, the preferred oxidizing agent in fireworks and a component of safety matches.

Perchlorates, salts containing ClO_4^-, are powerful oxidants. Pure perchloric acid, $HClO_4$, is a colorless liquid that explodes if shocked. It explosively oxidizes organic materials and rapidly oxidizes silver and gold. Dilute aqueous solutions of the acid are safe to handle, however.

Perchlorate salts of most metals are usually relatively stable, albeit unpredictable. Great care should be used when handling any perchlorate salt. Ammonium perchlorate, for example, bursts into flame if heated above 200 °C.

$$2\ NH_4ClO_4(s) \rightarrow N_2(g) + Cl_2(g) + 2\ O_2(g) + 4\ H_2O(g)$$

The strong oxidizing ability of the ammonium salt accounts for its use as the oxidizer in the solid booster rockets for the Space Shuttle. The solid propellant in these rockets is largely NH_4ClO_4, the remainder being the reducing agent, powdered aluminum. Each launch requires about 750 tons of ammonium perchlorate, and more than half of the sodium perchlorate currently manufactured is converted to the ammonium salt. The process for making this conversion is an exchange reaction that takes advantage of the fact that ammonium perchlorate is less soluble in water than sodium perchlorate:

$$NaClO_4(aq) + NH_4Cl(aq) \rightleftharpoons NaCl(aq) + NH_4ClO_4(s)$$

● **Disproportionation** A reaction in which an element or compound is simultaneously oxidized and reduced is called a disproportionation reaction. Here, Cl_2 is oxidized to ClO^- and reduced to Cl^-.

Use of a perchlorate salt. The solid-fuel booster rockets of the Space Shuttle utilize a mixture of NH_4ClO_4 (oxidizing agent) and Al powder (reducing agent).

NASA

REVIEW & CHECK FOR SECTION 21.10

1. Which halogen has the highest bond dissociation enthalpy?

   (a) F_2 (b) Cl_2 (c) Br_2 (d) I_2

2. Which of the following statements is *not* correct?

   (a) The ease of oxidation of the halide ions is $F^- < Cl^- < Br^- < I^-$.

   (b) Fluorine is the most abundant halogen in the earth's crust.

   (c) F_2 is prepared industrially by electrolysis of aqueous NaF.

   (d) HF is used to etch glass.

OWL and **go Chemistry**

Sign in at **www.cengage.com/owl** to:
- View tutorials and simulations, develop problem-solving skills, and complete online homework assigned by your professor.
- For quick review and exam prep, download Go Chemistry mini lecture modules from OWL (or purchase them at **www.cengagebrain.com**)

Access **How Do I Solve It?** tutorials on how to approach problem solving using concepts in this chapter.

CHAPTER GOALS REVISITED

Now that you have studied this chapter, you should ask whether you have met the chapter goals. In particular, you should be able to:

Relate the formulas and properties of compounds to the periodic table

a.   Predict several chemical reactions of the Group A elements (Section 21.2). **Study Questions: 13, 14.**

b.   Predict similarities and differences among the elements in a given group, based on periodic properties (Section 21.2). **Study Questions: 22, 64, 65.**

c.   Know which reactions produce ionic compounds, and predict formulas for common ions and common ionic compounds based on electron configurations (Section 21.2). **Study Questions: 5, 6, 16.**

d.   Recognize when a formula is incorrectly written, based on general principles governing electron configurations (Section 21.2).

Describe the chemistry of the main group or A-Group elements, particularly H; Na and K; Mg and Ca; B and Al; Si; N and P; O and S; and F and Cl

a.   Identify the most abundant elements, know how they are obtained, and list some of their common chemical and physical properties.

b.   Be able to summarize briefly a series of facts about the most common compounds of main group elements (ionic or covalent bonding, color, solubility, simple reaction chemistry) (Sections 21.3–21.10).

c.   Identify uses of common elements and compounds, and understand the chemistry that relates to their usage (Sections 21.3–21.10).

Apply the principles of stoichiometry, thermodynamics, and electrochemistry to the chemistry of the main group elements Study Questions: 18, 24, 29, 32, 34, 43, 48, 50, 54, 58, 61, 75, 92, 94.

Study Questions

Practicing Skills

Properties of the Elements
(See Sections 21.1 and 21.2.)

1. Give examples of two basic oxides. Write equations illustrating the formation of each oxide from its component elements. Write another chemical equation that illustrates the basic character of each oxide.

2. Give examples of two acidic oxides. Write equations illustrating the formation of each oxide from its component elements. Write another chemical equation that illustrates the acidic character of each oxide.

3. Give the name and symbol of each element having the valence configuration [noble gas] ns^2np^1.

4. Give symbols and names for four monatomic ions that have the same electron configuration as argon.

5. Select one of the alkali metals, and write a balanced chemical equation for its reaction with chlorine. Is the reaction likely to be exothermic or endothermic? Is the product ionic or molecular?

6. Select one of the alkaline earth metals and write a balanced chemical equation for its reaction with oxygen. Is the reaction likely to be exothermic or endothermic? Is the product ionic or molecular?

7. For the product of the reaction you selected in Study Question 5, predict the following physical properties: color, state of matter (s, ℓ, or g), solubility in water.

8. For the product of the reaction you selected in Study Question 6, predict the following physical properties: color, state of matter (s, ℓ, or g), solubility in water.

9. Would you expect to find calcium occurring naturally in the earth's crust as a free element? Why or why not?

10. Which of the first 10 elements in the periodic table are found as free elements in the earth's crust? Which elements in this group occur in the earth's crust only as part of a chemical compound?

11. Place the following oxides in order of increasing basicity: CO_2, SiO_2, SnO_2.

12. Place the following oxides in order of increasing basicity: Na_2O, Al_2O_3, SiO_2, SO_3.

13. Complete and balance the equations for the following reactions. [Assume an excess of oxygen for (d).]
    (a) $K(s) + Br_2(\ell) \rightarrow$
    (b) $Mg(s) + O_2(g) \rightarrow$
    (c) $Al(s) + F_2(g) \rightarrow$
    (d) $C(s) + O_2(g) \rightarrow$

14. Complete and balance the equations for the following reactions:
    (a) $K(s) + I_2(g) \rightarrow$
    (b) $Ba(s) + O_2(g) \rightarrow$
    (c) $Al(s) + S_8(s) \rightarrow$
    (d) $Si(s) + Cl_2(g) \rightarrow$

Hydrogen
(See Section 21.3.)

15. Write balanced chemical equations for the reaction of hydrogen gas with oxygen, chlorine, and nitrogen.

16. Write an equation for the reaction of potassium and hydrogen. Name the product. Is it ionic or covalent? Predict one physical property and one chemical property of this compound.

17. Write a balanced chemical equation for the preparation of H_2 (and CO) by the reaction of CH_4 and water. Using data in Appendix L, calculate $\Delta_rH°$, $\Delta_rG°$, and $\Delta_rS°$ for this reaction at 298 K.

18. Using data in Appendix L, calculate $\Delta_rH°$, $\Delta_rG°$, and $\Delta_rS°$ for the reaction of carbon and water to give CO and H_2 at 298 K.

19. A method recently suggested for the preparation of hydrogen (and oxygen) from water proceeds as follows:
    (a) Sulfuric acid and hydrogen iodide are formed from sulfur dioxide, water, and iodine.
    (b) The sulfuric acid from the first step is decomposed by heat to water, sulfur dioxide, and oxygen.
    (c) The hydrogen iodide from the first step is decomposed with heat to hydrogen and iodine.

    Write a balanced equation for each of these steps, and show that their sum is the decomposition of water to form hydrogen and oxygen.

20. Compare the mass of H_2 expected from the reaction of steam (H_2O) per mole of methane, petroleum, and coal. (Assume complete reaction in each case. Use CH_2 and CH as representative formulas for petroleum and coal, respectively.)

Alkali Metals
(See Section 21.4.)

21. Write equations for the reaction of sodium with each of the halogens. Predict at least two physical properties that are common to all of the alkali metal halides.

22. Write balanced equations for the reaction of lithium, sodium, and potassium with O_2. Specify which metal forms an oxide, which forms a peroxide, and which forms a superoxide.

23. The electrolysis of aqueous NaCl gives NaOH, Cl_2, and H_2.
    (a) Write a balanced equation for the process.
    (b) In the United States, 1.19×10^{10} kg of NaOH and 1.14×10^{10} kg of Cl_2 were produced in a recent year. Does the ratio of masses of NaOH and Cl_2 produced agree with the ratio of masses expected from the balanced equation? If not, what does this tell you about the way in which NaOH and Cl_2 are actually produced? Is the electrolysis of aqueous NaCl the only source of these chemicals?

24. (a) Write equations for the half-reactions that occur at the cathode and the anode when an aqueous solution of KCl is electrolyzed. Which chemical species is oxidized, and which chemical species is reduced in this reaction?
    (b) Predict the products formed when an aqueous solution of CsI is electrolyzed.

Alkaline Earth Elements
(See Section 21.5.)

25. When magnesium burns in air, it forms both an oxide and a nitride. Write balanced equations for the formation of both compounds.

26. Calcium reacts with hydrogen gas at 300–400 °C to form a hydride. This compound reacts readily with water, so it is an excellent drying agent for organic solvents.
    (a) Write a balanced equation showing the formation of calcium hydride from Ca and H_2.
    (b) Write a balanced equation for the reaction of calcium hydride with water (Figure 21.7).

27. Name three uses of limestone. Write a balanced equation for the reaction of limestone with CO_2 in water.

28. Explain what is meant by "hard water." What causes hard water, and what problems are associated with it?

29. Calcium oxide, CaO, is used to remove SO_2 from power plant exhaust. These two compounds react to give solid $CaSO_3$. What mass of SO_2 can be removed using 1.2×10^3 kg of CaO?

30. $Ca(OH)_2$ has a K_{sp} of 5.5×10^{-5}, whereas K_{sp} for $Mg(OH)_2$ is 5.6×10^{-12}. Calculate the equilibrium constant for the reaction

    $$Ca(OH)_2(s) + Mg^{2+}(aq) \rightleftharpoons Ca^{2+}(aq) + Mg(OH)_2(s)$$

    Explain why this reaction can be used in the commercial isolation of magnesium from sea water.

Boron and Aluminum
(See Section 21.6.)

31. Draw a possible structure for the cyclic anion in the salt $K_3B_3O_6$ and the anion in $Ca_2B_2O_5$.

32. The boron trihalides (except BF_3) hydrolyze completely to boric acid and the acid HX.
    (a) Write a balanced equation for the reaction of BCl_3 with water.
    (b) Calculate $\Delta_r H°$ for the hydrolysis of BCl_3 using data in Appendix L and the following information: $\Delta_f H°$ [$BCl_3(g)$] $= -403$ kJ/mol; $\Delta_f H°$ [$B(OH)_3(s)$] $= -1094$ kJ/mol.

33. When boron hydrides burn in air, the reactions are very exothermic.
    (a) Write a balanced equation for the combustion of $B_5H_9(g)$ in air to give $B_2O_3(s)$ and $H_2O(g)$.
    (b) Calculate the enthalpy of combustion for $B_5H_9(g)$ ($\Delta_f H° = 73.2$ kJ/mol), and compare it with the enthalpy of combustion of B_2H_6 on page 982. (The enthalpy of formation of $B_2O_3(s)$ is -1271.9 kJ/mol.)
    (c) Compare the enthalpy of combustion of $C_2H_6(g)$ with that of $B_2H_6(g)$. Which transfers more energy as heat per gram?

34. Diborane can be prepared by the reaction of $NaBH_4$ and I_2. Which substance is oxidized, and which is reduced?

35. Write balanced equations for the reactions of aluminum with HCl(aq), Cl_2, and O_2.

36. (a) Write a balanced equation for the reaction of Al and $H_2O(\ell)$ to produce H_2 and Al_2O_3.
    (b) Using thermodynamic data in Appendix L, calculate $\Delta_r H°$, $\Delta_r S°$, and $\Delta_r G°$ for this reaction. Do these data indicate that the reaction should favor the products?
    (c) Why is aluminum metal unaffected by water?

37. Aluminum dissolves readily in hot aqueous NaOH to give the aluminate ion, $[Al(OH)_4]^-$, and H_2. Write a balanced equation for this reaction. If you begin with 13.2 g of Al, what volume (in liters) of H_2 gas is produced when the gas is measured at 22.5 °C and a pressure of 735 mm Hg?

38. Alumina, Al_2O_3, is amphoteric. Among examples of its amphoteric character are the reactions that occur when Al_2O_3 is heated strongly or "fused" with acidic oxides and basic oxides.
    (a) Write a balanced equation for the reaction of alumina with silica, an acidic oxide, to give aluminum metasilicate, $Al_2(SiO_3)_3$.
    (b) Write a balanced equation for the reaction of alumina with the basic oxide CaO to give calcium aluminate, $Ca(AlO_2)_2$.

39. Aluminum sulfate is the most commercially important aluminum compound, after aluminum oxide and aluminum hydroxide. It is produced from the reaction of aluminum oxide and sulfuric acid. What masses (in kilograms) of aluminum oxide and sulfuric acid must be used to manufacture 1.00 kg of aluminum sulfate?

40. "Aerated" concrete bricks are widely used building materials. They are obtained by mixing gas-forming additives with a moist mixture of lime, cement, and possibly sand. Industrially, the following reaction is important:

$$2\ Al(s) + 3\ Ca(OH)_2(s) + 6\ H_2O(\ell) \rightarrow$$
$$3\ CaO \cdot Al_2O_3 \cdot 6\ H_2O(s) + 3\ H_2(g)$$

Assume the mixture of reactants contains 0.56 g of Al (as well as excess calcium hydroxide and water) for each brick. What volume of hydrogen gas do you expect at 26 °C and a pressure of 745 mm Hg?

Silicon
(See Section 21.7.)

41. Describe the structure of pyroxenes (see page 986). What is the ratio of silicon to oxygen in this type of silicate?

42. Describe how ultrapure silicon can be produced from sand.

43. Silicate structures: Draw a structure, and give the charge for a silicate anion with the formula $[Si_6O_{18}]^{n-}$.

44. Silicates often have chain, ribbon, or sheet structures. One of the simpler ribbon structures is $[Si_2O_5{}^{2-}]_n$. Draw a structure for this anionic material.

Nitrogen and Phosphorus
(See Section 21.8.)

45. Consult the data in Appendix L. Are any of the nitrogen oxides listed there stable with respect to decomposition to N_2 and O_2?

46. Use data in Appendix L to calculate the enthalpy and free energy change for the reaction

$$2\ NO_2(g) \rightarrow N_2O_4(g)$$

Is this reaction exothermic or endothermic? Is the reaction product- or reactant-favored?

47. Use data in Appendix L to calculate the enthalpy and free energy change for the reaction

$$2\ NO(g) + O_2(g) \rightarrow 2\ NO_2(g)$$

Is this reaction exothermic or endothermic? Is the reaction product- or reactant-favored at equilibrium?

48. The overall reaction involved in the industrial synthesis of nitric acid is

$$NH_3(g) + 2\ O_2(g) \rightarrow HNO_3(aq) + H_2O(\ell)$$

Calculate $\Delta_r G°$ for this reaction and its equilibrium constant at 25 °C.

49. A major use of hydrazine, N_2H_4, is in steam boilers in power plants.
   (a) The reaction of hydrazine with O_2 dissolved in water gives N_2 and water. Write a balanced equation for this reaction.
   (b) O_2 dissolves in water to the extent of 0.0044 g in 100. mL of water at 20 °C. What mass of N_2H_4 is needed to consume all of the dissolved O_2 in 3.00×10^4 L of water (enough to fill a small swimming pool)?

50. Before hydrazine came into use to remove dissolved oxygen in the water in steam boilers, Na_2SO_3 was commonly used for this purpose:

$$2\ Na_2SO_3(aq) + O_2(aq) \rightarrow 2\ Na_2SO_4(aq)$$

What mass of Na_2SO_3 is required to remove O_2 from 3.00×10^4 L of water as outlined in Study Question 49?

51. Review the structure of phosphorous acid in Table 21.6.
   (a) What is the oxidation number of the phosphorus atom in this acid?
   (b) Draw the structure of diphosphorous acid, $H_4P_2O_5$. What is the maximum number of ionizable protons in a molecule of this acid?

52. Unlike carbon, which can form extended chains of atoms, nitrogen can form chains of very limited length. Draw the Lewis electron dot structure of the azide ion, $N_3{}^-$. Is the ion linear or bent?

Oxygen and Sulfur
(See Section 21.9.)

53. In the "contact process" for making sulfuric acid, sulfur is first burned to SO_2. Environmental restrictions allow no more than 0.30% of this SO_2 to be vented to the atmosphere.
   (a) If enough sulfur is burned in a plant to produce 1.80×10^6 kg of pure, anhydrous H_2SO_4 per day, what is the maximum amount of SO_2 that is allowed to be exhausted to the atmosphere?
   (b) One way to prevent any SO_2 from reaching the atmosphere is to "scrub" the exhaust gases with slaked lime, $Ca(OH)_2$:

$$Ca(OH)_2(s) + SO_2(g) \rightarrow CaSO_3(s) + H_2O(\ell)$$
$$2\ CaSO_3(s) + O_2(g) \rightarrow 2\ CaSO_4(s)$$

What mass of $Ca(OH)_2$ (in kilograms) is needed to remove the SO_2 calculated in part (a)?

54. A sulfuric acid plant produces an enormous amount of heat. To keep costs as low as possible, much of this heat is used to make steam to generate electricity. Some of the electricity is used to run the plant, and the excess is sold to the local electrical utility. Three reactions are important in sulfuric acid production: (1) burning S to SO_2; (2) oxidation of SO_2 to SO_3; and (3) reaction of SO_3 with H_2O:

$$SO_3(g) + H_2O\ (in\ 98\%\ H_2SO_4) \rightarrow H_2SO_4(\ell)$$

The enthalpy change of the third reaction is -130 kJ/mol. Estimate the enthalpy change when 1.00 mol of S is used to produce 1.00 mol of H_2SO_4. How much energy is produced per metric ton (1000 kg exactly) of H_2SO_4?

55. Sulfur forms anionic chains of S atoms called polysulfides. Draw a Lewis electron dot structure for the $S_2{}^{2-}$ ion. The $S_2{}^{2-}$ ion is the disulfide ion, an analogue of the peroxide ion. It occurs in iron pyrites, FeS_2.

56. Sulfur forms a range of compounds with fluorine. Draw Lewis electron dot structures for S_2F_2 (connectivity is FSSF), SF_2, SF_4, SF_6, and S_2F_{10}. What is the oxidation number of sulfur in each of these compounds?

Fluorine and Chlorine
(See Section 21.10.)

57. The halogen oxides and oxoanions are good oxidizing agents. For example, the reduction of bromate ion has an $E°$ value of 1.44 V in acid solution:

$$2\ BrO_3^-(aq) + 12\ H^+(aq) + 10\ e^- \rightarrow$$
$$Br_2(aq) + 6\ H_2O(\ell)$$

Is it possible to oxidize aqueous 1.0 M Mn^{2+} to aqueous MnO_4^- with 1.0 M bromate ion?

58. The hypohalite ions, XO^-, are the anions of weak acids. Calculate the pH of a 0.10 M solution of NaClO. What is the concentration of HClO in this solution?

59. Bromine is obtained from brine wells. The process involves treating water containing bromide ion with Cl_2 and extracting the Br_2 from the solution using an organic solvent. Write a balanced equation for the reaction of Cl_2 and Br^-. What are the oxidizing and reducing agents in this reaction? Using the table of standard reduction potentials (Appendix M), verify that this is a product-favored reaction.

60. To prepare chlorine from chloride ion a strong oxidizing agent is required. The dichromate ion, $Cr_2O_7^{2-}$, is one example (Figure 21.32). Consult the table of standard reduction potentials (Appendix M), and identify several other oxidizing agents that may be suitable. Write balanced equations for the reactions of these substances with chloride ion.

61. If an electrolytic cell for producing F_2 (Figure 21.31) operates at 5.00×10^3 A (at 10.0 V), what mass of F_2 can be produced per 24-hour day? Assume the conversion of F^- to F_2 is 100%.

62. Halogens combine with one another to produce *interhalogens* such as BrF_3. Sketch a possible molecular structure for this molecule, and decide if the F—Br—F bond angles will be less than or greater than ideal.

General Questions

The questions are not designated as to type or location in the chapter. They may combine several concepts.

63. For each of the third-period elements (Na through Ar), identify the following:
(a) whether the element is a metal, nonmetal, or metalloid
(b) the color and appearance of the element
(c) the state of the element (s, ℓ, or g) under standard conditions

64. Consider the chemistries of C, Si, Ge, and Sn.
(a) Write a balanced chemical equation to depict the reaction of each element with elemental chlorine.
(b) Describe the bonding in each of the products of the reactions with chlorine as ionic or covalent.
(c) Compare the reactions, if any, of some Group 4A chlorides —CCl_4, $SiCl_4$, and $SnCl_4$— with water.

65. Consider the chemistries of the elements potassium, calcium, gallium, germanium, and arsenic.
(a) Write a balanced chemical equation depicting the reaction of each element with elemental chlorine.
(b) Describe the bonding in each of the products of the reactions with chlorine as ionic or covalent.
(c) Draw Lewis electron dot structures for the products of the reactions of gallium and arsenic with chlorine. What are their electron-pair and molecular geometries?

66. When BCl_3 gas is passed through an electric discharge, small amounts of the reactive molecule B_2Cl_4 are produced. (The molecule has a B—B covalent bond.)
(a) Draw a Lewis electron dot structure for B_2Cl_4.
(b) Describe the hybridization of the B atoms in the molecule and the geometry around each B atom.

67. Complete and balance the following equations.
(a) $KClO_3$ + heat $\rightarrow$
(b) $H_2S(g) + O_2(g) \rightarrow$
(c) $Na(s) + O_2(g) \rightarrow$
(d) $P_4(s) + KOH(aq) + H_2O(\ell) \rightarrow$
(e) $NH_4NO_3(s)$ + heat $\rightarrow$
(f) $In(s) + Br_2(\ell) \rightarrow$
(g) $SnCl_4(\ell) + H_2O(\ell) \rightarrow$

68. (a) Heating barium oxide in pure oxygen gives barium peroxide. Write a balanced equation for this reaction.
(b) Barium peroxide is an excellent oxidizing agent. Write a balanced equation for the reaction of iron with barium peroxide to give iron(III) oxide and barium oxide.

69. Worldwide production of silicon carbide, SiC, is several hundred thousand tons annually. If you want to produce 1.0×10^5 metric tons of SiC, what mass (metric tons) of silicon sand (SiO_2) will you use if 70% of the sand is converted to SiC? (A metric ton is exactly 1000 kg.)

70. To store 2.88 kg of gasoline with an energy equivalence of 1.43×10^8 J requires a volume of 4.1 L. In comparison, 1.0 kg of H_2 has the same energy equivalence. What volume is required if this quantity of H_2 is to be stored at 25 °C and 1.0 atm of pressure?

71. Using data in Appendix L, calculate $\Delta_rG°$ values for the decomposition of MCO_3 to MO and CO_2 where M = Mg, Ca, Ba. What is the relative tendency of these carbonates to decompose?

72. Ammonium perchlorate is used as the oxidizer in the solid-fuel booster rockets of the Space Shuttle. Assume that one launch requires 700. tons (6.35×10^5 kg) of the salt, and the salt decomposes according to the equation on page 1005.
(a) What mass of water is produced? What mass of O_2 is produced?
(b) If all the O_2 produced is assumed to react with the powdered aluminum present in the rocket engine, what mass of aluminum is required to use up all of the O_2?
(c) What mass of Al_2O_3 is produced?

73. ▲ Metals react with hydrogen halides (such as HCl) to give the metal halide and hydrogen:

$$M(s) + n\,HX(g) \rightarrow MX_n(s) + \tfrac{1}{2}n\,H_2(g)$$

The free energy change for the reaction is $\Delta_r G° = \Delta_f G°(MX_n) - n\,\Delta_f G°[HX(g)]$.
(a) $\Delta_f G°$ for HCl(g) is -95.1 kJ/mol. What must be the value for $\Delta_f G°$ for MX_n for the reaction to be product-favored?
(b) Which of the following metals is (are) predicted to have product-favored reactions with HCl(g): Ba, Pb, Hg, Ti?

74. Halogens form polyhalide ions. Sketch Lewis electron dot structures and molecular structures for the following ions:
(a) I_3^-
(b) $BrCl_2^-$
(c) ClF_2^+
(d) An iodide ion and two iodine molecules form the I_5^- ion. Here, the ion has five I atoms in a row, but the ion is not linear. Draw the Lewis dot structure for the ion, and propose a structure for the ion.

75. The standard enthalpy of formation of OF_2 gas is $+24.5$ kJ/mol. Calculate the average O—F bond enthalpy.

76. Calcium fluoride can be used in the fluoridation of municipal water supplies. If you want to achieve a fluoride ion concentration of 2.0×10^{-5} M, what mass of CaF_2 must you use for 1.0×10^6 L of water? (K_{sp} for CaF_2 is 5.3×10^{-11}.)

77. The steering rockets in the Space Shuttle use N_2O_4 and a derivative of hydrazine, 1,1-dimethylhydrazine (page 245). This mixture is called a *hypergolic fuel* because it ignites when the reactants come into contact:

$$H_2NN(CH_3)_2(\ell) + 2\,N_2O_4(\ell) \rightarrow$$
$$3\,N_2(g) + 4\,H_2O(g) + 2\,CO_2(g)$$

(a) Identify the oxidizing agent and the reducing agent in this reaction.
(b) The same propulsion system was used by the Lunar Lander on moon missions in the 1970s. If the Lander used 4100 kg of $H_2NN(CH_3)_2$, what mass (in kilograms) of N_2O_4 was required to react with it? What mass (in kilograms) of each of the reaction products was generated?

78. ▲ Liquid HCN is dangerously unstable with respect to trimer formation—that is, formation of $(HCN)_3$ with a cyclic structure.
(a) Propose a structure for this cyclic trimer.
(b) Estimate the energy of the trimerization reaction using bond dissociation enthalpies (◀ Table 8.9).

79. Use $\Delta_f H°$ data in Appendix L to calculate the enthalpy change of the reaction

$$2\,N_2(g) + 5\,O_2(g) + 2\,H_2O(\ell) \rightarrow 4\,HNO_3(aq)$$

Speculate on whether such a reaction could be used to "fix" nitrogen. Would research to find ways to accomplish this reaction be a useful endeavor?

80. ▲ Phosphorus forms an extensive series of oxoanions.
(a) Draw a structure, and give the charge for an oxophosphate anion with the formula $[P_4O_{13}]^{n-}$. How many ionizable H atoms should the completely protonated acid have?
(b) Draw a structure, and give the charge for an oxophosphate anion with the formula $[P_4O_{12}]^{n-}$. How many ionizable H atoms should the completely protonated acid have?

81. ▲ Boron and hydrogen form an extensive family of compounds, and the diagram below shows how they are related by reaction.

The following table gives the weight percent of boron in each of the compounds. Derive the empirical and molecular formulas of compounds A–E.

Substance	State (at STP)	Mass Percent B	Molar Mass (g/mol)
A	Gas	78.3	27.7
B	Gas	81.2	53.3
C	Liquid	83.1	65.1
D	Liquid	85.7	63.1
E	Solid	88.5	122.2

82. ▲ In 1774, C. Scheele obtained a gas by reacting pyrolusite (MnO_2) with sulfuric acid. The gas, which had been obtained that same year by Joseph Priestley by a different method, was an element, A.
(a) What is the element isolated by Scheele and Priestley?
(b) Element A combines with almost all other elements. For example, with cesium it gives a compound in which the mass percent of A is 19.39%. The element combines with hydrogen to give a compound with a mass percent of element A of 94.12%. Determine the formulas of the cesium and hydrogen compounds.
(c) The compounds of cesium and hydrogen with element A react with one another. Write a balanced equation for the reaction.

83. What current must be used in a Downs cell operating at 7.0 V to produce 1.00 metric ton (exactly 1000 kg) of sodium per day? Assume 100% efficiency.

84. The chemistry of gallium:
    (a) Gallium hydroxide, like aluminum hydroxide, is amphoteric. Write a balanced equation to show how this hydroxide can dissolve in both $HCl(aq)$ and $NaOH(aq)$.
    (b) Gallium ion in water, $Ga^{3+}(aq)$, has a K_a value of 1.2×10^{-3}. Is this ion a stronger or a weaker acid than $Al^{3+}(aq)$?

85. Silicon-oxygen rings are a common structural feature in silicate chemistry. Draw the structure for the anion $[Si_3O_9]^{6-}$, which is found in minerals such as benitoite. Is the ring expected to be planar?

86. Using enthalpy of formation data in Appendix L, determine whether the decomposition of $NH_4NO_3(s)$ to give $N_2O(g)$ and $H_2O(g)$ is endothermic or exothermic.

87. Metal sulfides roasted in air produce metal oxides.

    $$2\ ZnS(s) + 3\ O_2(g) \rightarrow 2\ ZnO(s) + 2\ SO_2(g)$$

    Use thermodynamics to decide if the reaction is product- or reactant-favored at equilibrium at 298 K. Will the reaction be more or less product-favored at a high temperature?

88. Metals generally react with hydrogen halides to give the metal halide and hydrogen. Determine whether this is true for silver by calculating $\Delta_r G°$ for the reaction with each of the hydrogen halides.

    $$Ag(s) + HX(g) \rightarrow AgX(s) + \tfrac{1}{2}\ H_2(g)$$

    The required free energies of formation are:

HX	$\Delta_f G°$(kJ/mol)	AgX	$\Delta_f G°$(kJ/mol)
HF	273.2	AgF	193.8
HCl	95.09	AgCl	109.76
HBr	53.45	AgBr	96.90
HI	1.56	AgI	66.19

In the Laboratory

89. One material needed to make silicones is dichlorodimethylsilane, $(CH_3)_2SiCl_2$. It is made by treating silicon powder at about 300 °C with CH_3Cl in the presence of a copper-containing catalyst.
    (a) Write a balanced equation for the reaction.
    (b) Assume you carry out the reaction on a small scale with 2.65 g of silicon. To measure the CH_3Cl gas, you fill a 5.60-L flask at 24.5 °C. What pressure of CH_3Cl gas must you have in the flask to have the stoichiometrically correct amount of the compound?
    (c) What mass of $(CH_3)_2SiCl_2$ can be produced from 2.65 g of Si and excess CH_3Cl?

90. Sodium borohydride, $NaBH_4$, reduces many metal ions to the metal.
    (a) Write a balanced equation for the reaction of $NaBH_4$ with $AgNO_3$ in water to give silver metal, H_2 gas, boric acid, and sodium nitrate. (The chemistry of $NaBH_4$ is described on pages 982–983.)
    (b) What mass of silver can be produced from 575 mL of 0.011 M $AgNO_3$ and 13.0 g of $NaBH_4$?

91. A common analytical method for hydrazine involves its oxidation with iodate ion, IO_3^-, in acid solution. In the process, hydrazine acts as a four-electron reducing agent.

    $$N_2(g) + 5\ H_3O^+(aq) + 4\ e^- \rightarrow$$
    $$N_2H_5^+(aq) + 5\ H_2O(\ell) \qquad E° = -0.23\ V$$

    Write the balanced equation for the reaction of hydrazine in acid solution $(N_2H_5^+)$ with $IO_3^-(aq)$ to give N_2 and I_2. Calculate $E°$ for this reaction.

92. When 1.00 g of a white solid A is strongly heated, you obtain another white solid, B, and a gas. An experiment is carried out on the gas, showing that it exerts a pressure of 209 mm Hg in a 450-mL flask at 25 °C. Bubbling the gas into a solution of $Ca(OH)_2$ gives another white solid, C. If the white solid B is added to water, the resulting solution turns red litmus paper blue. Addition of aqueous HCl to the solution of B and evaporation of the resulting solution to dryness yield 1.055 g of a white solid D. When D is placed in a Bunsen burner flame, it colors the flame green. Finally, if the aqueous solution of B is treated with sulfuric acid, a white precipitate, E, forms. Identify the lettered compounds in the reaction scheme.

The salts $CaCl_2$, $SrCl_2$, and $BaCl_2$ were suspended in methanol. When the methanol is set ablaze, the heat of combustion causes the salts to emit light of characteristic wavelengths: Calcium salts are yellow; strontium salts are red; and barium salts are green-yellow.

93. ▲ In 1937, R. Schwartz and M. Schmiesser prepared a yellow-orange bromine oxide (BrO_2) by treating Br_2 with ozone in a fluorocarbon solvent. Many years later, J. Pascal found that, on heating, this oxide decomposed to two other oxides, a less volatile golden yellow oxide (A) and a more volatile deep brown oxide (B). Oxide B was later identified as Br_2O. To determine the formula for oxide A, a sample was treated with sodium iodide. The reaction liberated iodine, which was titrated to an equivalence point with 17.7 mL of 0.065 M sodium thiosulfate.

$$I_2(aq) + 2\ S_2O_3^{2-}(aq) \rightarrow 2\ I^-(aq) + S_4O_6^{2-}(aq)$$

Compound A was also treated with $AgNO_3$, and 14.4 mL of 0.020 M $AgNO_3$ was required to completely precipitate the bromine from the sample.
(a) What is the formula of the unknown bromine oxide A?
(b) Draw Lewis structures for A and Br_2O. Speculate on their molecular geometry.

94. A mixture of PCl_5 (12.41 g) and excess NH_4Cl was heated at 145 °C for 6 hours. The two reacted in equimolar amounts and evolved 5.14 L of HCl (at STP). Three substances (A, B, and C) were isolated from the reaction mixture. The three substances had the same elemental composition but differed in their molar mass. Substance A had a molar mass of 347.7 g/mol and B had a molar mass of 463.5 g/mol. Give the empirical and molecular formulas for A and B and draw a reasonable Lewis structure for A.

Summary and Conceptual Questions

The following questions may use concepts from this and previous chapters.

95. Dinitrogen trioxide, N_2O_3, has the structure shown here.

The oxide is unstable, decomposing to NO and NO_2 in the gas phase at 25 °C.

$$N_2O_3(g) \rightarrow NO(g) + NO_2(g)$$

(a) Explain why one N—O bond distance in N_2O_3 is 114.2 pm, whereas the other two bonds are longer (121 pm) and nearly equal to each other.
(b) For the decomposition reaction, $\Delta_rH° = +40.5$ kJ/mol and $\Delta_rG° = -1.59$ kJ/mol. Calculate $\Delta S°$ and K for the reaction at 298 K.
(c) Calculate $\Delta_fH°$ for $N_2O_3(g)$.

96. ▲ The density of lead is 11.350 g/cm³, and the metal crystallizes in a face-centered cubic unit cell. Estimate the radius of a lead atom.

97. You have a 1.0-L flask that contains a mixture of argon and hydrogen. The pressure inside the flask is 745 mm Hg, and the temperature is 22 °C. Describe an experiment that you could use to determine the percentage of hydrogen in this mixture.

98. The boron atom in boric acid, $B(OH)_3$, is bonded to three —OH groups. In the solid state, the —OH groups are in turn hydrogen-bonded to —OH groups in neighboring molecules.
(a) Draw the Lewis structure for boric acid.
(b) What is the hybridization of the boron atom in the acid?
(c) Sketch a picture showing how hydrogen bonding can occur between neighboring molecules.

99. How would you extinguish a sodium fire in the laboratory? What is the worst thing you could do?

100. Tin(IV) oxide, cassiterite, is the main ore of tin. It crystallizes in a rutile-like unit cell (Question 4, page 609).
(a) How many tin(IV) ions and oxide ions are there per unit cell of this oxide?
(b) Is it thermodynamically feasible to transform solid SnO_2 into liquid $SnCl_4$ by reaction of the oxide with gaseous HCl? What is the equilibrium constant for this reaction at 25 °C?

101. You are given a stoppered flask that contains hydrogen, nitrogen, or oxygen. Suggest an experiment you could do to identify the gas.

102. The structure of nitric acid is illustrated on page 990.
(a) Why are the N—O bonds the same length, and why are both shorter than the N—OH bond length?
(b) Rationalize the bond angles in the molecule.
(c) What is the hybridization of the central N atom? Which orbitals overlap to form the N—O π bond?

103. Assume an electrolysis cell that produces chlorine from aqueous sodium chloride operates at 4.6 V (with a current of 3.0×10^5 A). Calculate the number of kilowatt-hours of energy required to produce 1.00 kg of chlorine (1 kWh = 1 kilowatt-hour = 3.6×10^6 J).

104. Sodium metal is produced by electrolysis of molten sodium chloride. The cell operates at 7.0 V with a current of 25×10^3 A.
(a) What mass of sodium can be produced in 1 hour?
(b) How many kilowatt-hours of electricity are used to produce 1.00 kg of sodium metal (1 kWh = 3.6×10^6 J)?

105. The reduction potentials for the Group 3A metals, $E°$, are given below. What trend or trends do you observe in these data? What can you learn about the chemistry of the Group 3A elements from these data?

Half-Reaction	Reduction Potential ($E°$, V)
$Al^{3+}(aq) + 3\ e^- \longrightarrow Al(s)$	−1.66
$Ga^{3+}(aq) + 3\ e^- \longrightarrow Ga(s)$	−0.53
$In^{3+}(aq) + 3\ e^- \longrightarrow In(s)$	−0.338
$Tl^{3+}(aq) + 3\ e^- \longrightarrow Tl(s)$	+0.72

106. (a) Magnesium is obtained from sea water. If the concentration of Mg^{2+} in sea water is 0.050 M, what volume of sea water (in liters) must be treated to obtain 1.00 kg of magnesium metal? What mass of lime (CaO; in kilograms) must be used to precipitate the magnesium in this volume of sea water?

(b) When 1.2×10^3 kg of molten $MgCl_2$ is electrolyzed to produce magnesium, what mass (in kilograms) of metal is produced at the cathode? What is produced at the anode? What is the mass of this product? What is the total number of Faradays of electricity used in the process?

(c) One industrial process has an energy consumption of 18.5 kWh/kg of Mg. How many joules are required per mole (1 kWh = 1 kilowatt-hour = 3.6×10^6 J)? How does this energy compare with the energy of the following process?

$$MgCl_2(s) \rightarrow Mg(s) + Cl_2(g)$$

Applying Chemical Principles

van Arkel Triangles and Bonding

Two types of bonding, covalent and ionic, involve localized electrons. On one extreme are nonpolar covalent bonds, where electrons are equally shared between two atoms. On the other extreme are ionic bonds, where no sharing of electrons occurs. However, there are many bonds that fall between these extremes, and predictions of the extent of the polarity of a bond can be made using the electronegativity of the individual atoms. And finally, there is a third bonding type: metallic bonding, This raises the question of whether it is possible to develop an integrated picture wherein all three types of bonding, and their variations, can be represented. The answer is that it is possible, at least for binary compounds.

The first efforts in this direction were made by A. E. van Arkel in 1941 and modified later by J. A. A. Ketalaar. They summarized their findings in diagrams such as that shown in the Figure. Referred to now as van Arkel–Ketalaar triangles, the current version of this diagram portrays a wide variety of compounds composed of two different atoms within the boundary of an equilateral triangle. The corners represent the three types of bonding: metallic bonding at the lower left, covalent bonding on the lower right, and ionic bonding at the top. The least electronegative element (Cs), the most electronegative element (F), and the ionic compound formed from these elements are located at the corners of the triangle. All other binary compounds can be positioned inside the triangle.

Different versions of the van Arkel triangle have been developed, each using different scales on the axes. The one chosen for the Figure uses electronegativity values. Here, the x-axis is defined as the average of the electronegativities of the two atoms; as such, the x-axis is a measure of the localization of bonding electrons. The bonding electrons are completely delocalized in cesium, whereas the bonding electrons are completely localized in fluorine. The y-axis is defined as the difference in electronegativities. The greater the value in the y-axis, the greater the ionic character of the compound. With these parameters, the position of each binary compound can be assigned, associating the bond between elements with the degree of ionic/covalent/metallic character.

Questions:

1. Use electronegativity values (◀ Figure 8.11) to place the compounds GaAs, SBr$_2$, Mg$_3$N$_2$, BP, C$_3$N$_4$, CuZn, and SrBr$_2$ on the van Arkel diagram and use the results to answer the following questions:

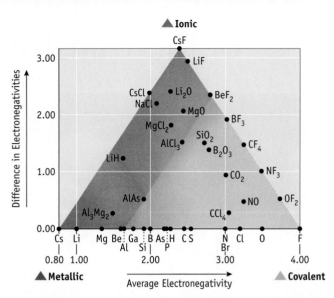

FIGURE A van Arkel–Ketalaar diagram. The four regions of this triangle represent the locations of metallic (blue), semiconducting (green), ionic (red), and covalent (orange) compounds

(a) Which of the compounds are metallic?

(b) Which of the compounds are semiconductors? Are either (or both) element(s) in these compounds metalloid(s)?

(c) Which of the compounds are ionic? Are the compounds composed of a metal and a nonmetal?

(d) Carbon nitride (C$_3$N$_4$) is predicted to be harder than diamond (which is currently the hardest known substance), but too little has been synthesized to enable a comparison. What type of bonding is predicted for C$_3$N$_4$?

(d) Which of the compounds are covalent? Are both elements in these compounds nonmetallic?

2. High boiling points are one characteristic of ionic compounds. For example, magnesium chloride boils at 1412 °C. Beryllium chloride, on the other hand, vaporizes at 520 °C. The boiling point of BeCl$_2$ is far lower than expected for an ionic compound, yet large for a covalent one. Determine where BeCl$_2$ lies on the van Arkel diagram.

Reference:

W. B. Jensen, *Journal of Chemical Education*, Vol. 72, pp. 395–398, 1995.

22 The Chemistry of the Transition Elements

Nitinol frames for glasses. Can you do this with your eye glasses? If you can, it is likely they are made of nitinol, a nickel–titanium alloy. They snap back to the proper fit even after they are twisted like a pretzel.

Memory Metal
In the 1960s, William J. Buehler, an engineer at the Naval Ordnance Laboratory in Maryland, was looking for a material for use in the nose cone of a Navy missile. It was important that the material be impact- and heat-resistant and not lose these properties when it was bent and shaped. He prepared long, thin strips of an alloy of nickel and titanium to demonstrate that they could be folded and unfolded many times without breaking. At a meeting to discuss this material, one of his associates held a cigarette lighter to a folded-up piece of metal and was amazed to observe that the metal strip immediately unfolded and assumed its original shape. Thus, memory metal was discovered. This unusual alloy is now called *nitinol*, a name constructed out of "nickel," "titanium," and "Naval Ordnance Laboratory."

Memory metal is an alloy with roughly the same number of Ni and Ti atoms. When the atoms are arranged in the

x, y, and z are not equal, γ about 96°

CsCl structure
$x = y = z$
$\alpha = \beta = \gamma = 90°$

Two phases of nitinol. The austenite form has a structure like CsCl.

highly symmetrical austenite phase, the alloy is relatively rigid. In this phase a specific shape is established that will be "remembered." If the alloy is cooled below its "phase transition temperature," it enters a less symmetrical but flexible phase (martensite). Below this transition temperature, the metal is fairly soft and may be bent and twisted out of shape. When warmed above the phase transition temperature, nitinol returns to its original shape. The temperature at which the change in shape occurs varies with small differences in the nickel-to-titanium ratio.

Besides eye glasses frames, nitinol is now used in stents to reinforce blood vessels and in orthodontics.

Questions:

1. What are the dimensions of the austenite unit cell? Assume the Ti and Ni atoms are just touching along the unit cell diagonal. (Atom radii: Ti = 145 pm; Ni = 125 pm.)
2. Calculate the density of nitinol based on the austenite unit cell parameters. Does the calculated density of the austenite unit cell agree with the reported density of 6.5 g/cm³?
3. Are Ti and Ni atoms paramagnetic or diamagnetic?

Answers to these questions are available in Appendix N.

CHAPTER GOALS

See Chapter Goals Revisited (page 1051) for Study Questions keyed to these goals.

- Identify and explain the chemical and physical properties of the transition elements.

- Understand the composition, structure, and bonding in coordination compounds.

- Relate ligand field theory to the magnetic and spectroscopic properties of the complexes.

- Apply the effective atomic number (EAN) rule to simple organometallic compounds of the transition metals.

The transition elements are the large block of elements in the central portion of the periodic table. All are metals and bridge the *s*-block elements at the left and the *p*-block elements on the right (Figure 22.1). The transition elements are often divided into two groups, depending on the valence electrons involved in their chemistry. The first group are the ***d*-block elements**, because their occurrence in the periodic table coincides with the filling of the *d* orbitals. The second group are the ***f*-block elements**, characterized by filling of the *f* orbitals. Contained within this group of elements are two subgroups: the *lanthanides*, elements that occur between La and Hf, and the *actinides*, elements that occur between Ac and Rf.

This chapter focuses primarily on the *d*-block elements, and within this group we concentrate mainly on the elements in the fourth period, that is, the elements of the first transition series, scandium to zinc.

Lanthanides
Actinides

d block

f block

Group **4B:** Titanium (Ti)

Group **5B:** Vanadium (V)

Group **6B:** Chromium (Cr)

Group **7B:** Manganese (Mn)

FIGURE 22.1
The transition metals. The *d*-block elements and *f*-block elements (the transition elements) are highlighted in a darker shade of blue.

Group **8B:** Iron (Fe)

Group **8B:** Cobalt (Co)

Group **8B:** Nickel (Ni)

Group **1B:** Copper (Cu)

Group **2B:** Zinc (Zn)

Photos © Cengage Learning/Charles D. Winters

22.1 Properties of the Transition Elements

The *d*-block metals include elements with a wide range of properties. They encompass the most common metal used in construction and manufacturing (iron), metals that are valued for their beauty (gold, silver, and platinum), and metals used in coins (nickel, copper, and zinc). There are metals used in modern technology (titanium) and metals known and used in early civilizations (copper, silver, gold, and iron). The *d*-block contains the densest elements (osmium, $d = 22.49$ g/cm^3, and iridium, $d = 22.41$ g/cm^3), the metals with the highest and lowest melting points (tungsten, mp = 3410 °C, and mercury, mp = −38.9 °C), and one of only two elements with atomic numbers less than 83 that have only radioactive isotopes [technetium (Tc), atomic number 43; promethium (Pm), atomic number 61, in the *f*-block].

With the exception of mercury, the transition elements are solids, often with high melting and boiling points. They have a metallic sheen and conduct electricity and heat. They react with various oxidizing agents to give ionic compounds. There is considerable variation in such reactions among the elements, however. Because silver, gold, and platinum resist oxidation, for example, they are used for jewelry and decorative items.

Certain *d*-block elements are particularly important in living organisms. Cobalt is the crucial element in vitamin B$_{12}$, which is part of a catalyst essential for several biochemical reactions. Hemoglobin and myoglobin, oxygen-carrying and storage proteins, contain iron (see page 1032). Molybdenum and iron, together with sulfur, form the reactive portion of nitrogenase, a biological catalyst used by nitrogen-fixing organisms to convert atmospheric nitrogen into ammonia.

Many transition metal compounds are highly colored, which makes them useful as pigments in paints and dyes (Figure 22.2). Prussian blue, Fe$_4$[Fe(CN)$_6$]$_3$ · 14 H$_2$O, is a "bluing agent" used in engineering blueprints and in the laundry to brighten yellowed white cloth. A common pigment (artist's cadmium yellow) contains cadmium sulfide (CdS), and the white in most white paints is titanium(IV) oxide, TiO$_2$.

The presence of transition metal ions in crystalline silicates or alumina transforms these common materials into gemstones. Iron(II) ions produce the yellow color in citrine, and chromium(III) ions produce the red color of a ruby. Transition metal compounds in small quantities add color to glass. Blue glass contains a small amount of a cobalt(III) oxide, and addition of chromium(III) oxide to glass gives a green color. Old window panes sometimes take on a purple color over time as a consequence of oxidation of traces of manganese(II) ion present in the glass to permanganate ion (MnO$_4^-$).

Prussian blue. When Fe^{3+} ions are added to [Fe(CN)$_6$]$^{4-}$ ions in water (or Fe^{2+} ions are added to [Fe(CN)$_6$]$^{3-}$ ions), a deep blue compound called Prussian blue forms. The formula of the compound is Fe$_4$[Fe(CN)$_6$]$_3$ · 14 H$_2$O. The color arises from electron transfer between the Fe(II) and Fe(III) ions in the compound.

(a) Paint pigments: yellow, CdS; green, Cr$_2$O$_3$; white, TiO$_2$ and ZnO; purple, Mn$_3$(PO$_4$)$_2$; blue, Co$_2$O$_3$ and Al$_2$O$_3$; ochre, Fe$_2$O$_3$.

(b) Small amounts of transition metal compounds are used to color glass: blue, Co$_2$O$_3$; green, copper or chromium oxides; purple, nickel or cobalt oxides; red, copper oxide; iridescent green, uranium oxide.

(c) Traces of transition metal ions are responsible for the colors of green jade (iron), red corundum (chromium), blue azurite, blue-green turquoise (copper), and purple amethyst (iron).

FIGURE 22.2 Colorful chemistry. Transition metal compounds are often colored, a property that leads to specific uses.

In the next few pages, we will examine the properties of the transition elements, concentrating on the underlying principles that govern these properties.

Electron Configurations

Because chemical behavior is related to electron structure, it is important to know the electron configurations of the *d*-block elements (Table 22.1) and their common ions (◄ Section 7.4). Recall that the configuration of these metals has the general form [noble gas core]$(n-1)d^b ns^a$; that is, valence electrons for the transition elements reside in the *ns* and $(n-1)d$ subshells.

Oxidation and Reduction

A characteristic chemical property of all metals is that they undergo oxidation by a wide range of oxidizing agents such as oxygen, the halogens, and aqueous acids. Standard reduction potentials for the elements of the first transition series can be used to predict which elements will be oxidized by a given oxidizing agent. For example, all of these metals except vanadium and copper are oxidized by aqueous HCl (Table 22.2). This feature, which dominates the chemistry of these elements, is sometimes highly undesirable (see *A Closer Look: Corrosion of Iron,* page 1021).

When a transition metal is oxidized, the outermost *s* electrons are removed, followed by one or more *d* electrons. With a few exceptions, transition metal ions have the electron configuration [noble gas core]$(n-1)d^x$. In contrast to ions formed by main group elements, transition metal cations often possess unpaired electrons, resulting in paramagnetism (◄ page 289). They are frequently colored as well, due to the absorption of light in the visible region of the electromagnetic spectrum. Color and magnetism figure prominently in a discussion of the properties and bonding of these elements, as you shall see shortly.

In the first transition series, the most commonly encountered metal ions have oxidation numbers of +2 and +3 (Table 22.2). With iron, for example, oxidation converts $Fe([Ar]3d^6 4s^2)$ to either $Fe^{2+}([Ar]3d^6)$ or $Fe^{3+}([Ar]3d^5)$. Iron reacts with chlorine to give $FeCl_3$, and it reacts with aqueous acids to produce $Fe^{2+}(aq)$ and H_2 (Figure 22.3). Despite the preponderance of 2+ and 3+ ions in compounds of the first transition metal series, the range of possible oxidation states for these compounds is broad (Figure 22.4). Earlier in this text, we encountered chromium with a +6 oxidation number (CrO_4^{2-}, $Cr_2O_7^{2-}$), manganese with an oxidation number of +7 (MnO_4^-), silver and copper as 1+ ions, and vanadium oxidation numbers that can range from +5 to +2 (◄ Figure 20.3).

Table 22.1 Electron Configurations of the Fourth-Period Transition Elements

	spdf Configu-ration	Box Notation	
		3d	4s
Sc	[Ar]$3d^1 4s^2$	↑ ☐ ☐ ☐ ☐	↑↓
Ti	[Ar]$3d^2 4s^2$	↑ ↑ ☐ ☐ ☐	↑↓
V	[Ar]$3d^3 4s^2$	↑ ↑ ↑ ☐ ☐	↑↓
Cr	[Ar]$3d^5 4s^1$	↑ ↑ ↑ ↑ ↑	↑
Mn	[Ar]$3d^5 4s^2$	↑ ↑ ↑ ↑ ↑	↑↓
Fe	[Ar]$3d^6 4s^2$	↑↓ ↑ ↑ ↑ ↑	↑↓
Co	[Ar]$3d^7 4s^2$	↑↓ ↑↓ ↑ ↑ ↑	↑↓
Ni	[Ar]$3d^8 4s^2$	↑↓ ↑↓ ↑↓ ↑ ↑	↑↓
Cu	[Ar]$3d^{10} 4s^1$	↑↓ ↑↓ ↑↓ ↑↓ ↑↓	↑
Zn	[Ar]$3d^{10} 4s^2$	↑↓ ↑↓ ↑↓ ↑↓ ↑↓	↑↓

Table 22.2 Products from Reactions of the Elements in the First Transition Series with O_2, Cl_2, or Aqueous HCl

Element	Reaction with O_2*	Reaction with Cl_2	Reaction with Aqueous HCl
Scandium	Sc_2O_3	$ScCl_3$	$Sc^{3+}(aq)$
Titanium	TiO_2	$TiCl_4$	$Ti^{3+}(aq)$
Vanadium	V_2O_5	VCl_4	NR†
Chromium	Cr_2O_3	$CrCl_3$	$Cr^{2+}(aq)$
Manganese	MnO_2	$MnCl_2$	$Mn^{2+}(aq)$
Iron	Fe_2O_3	$FeCl_3$	$Fe^{2+}(aq)$
Cobalt	Co_2O_3	$CoCl_2$	$Co^{2+}(aq)$
Nickel	NiO	$NiCl_2$	$Ni^{2+}(aq)$
Copper	CuO	$CuCl_2$	NR†
Zinc	ZnO	$ZnCl_2$	$Zn^{2+}(aq)$

* Product obtained with excess oxygen.

† NR = no reaction.

FIGURE 22.3 **Typical reactions of transition metals.** These metals react with oxygen, with halogens, and with acids under appropriate conditions.

Photos © Cengage Learning/Charles D. Winters

(a) Steel wool reacts with O_2.

(b) Steel wool reacts with chlorine gas, Cl_2.

(c) Iron chips react with aqueous HCl.

Higher oxidation numbers are more common in compounds of the elements in the second and third transition series. For example, the naturally occurring sources of molybdenum and tungsten are the ores molybdenite (MoS_2) and wolframite (WO_3). This general trend is carried over in the *f*-block. The lanthanides form primarily 3+ ions. In contrast, actinide elements usually have higher oxidation numbers in their compounds; +4 and even +6 are typical. For example, UO_3 is a common oxide of uranium, and UF_6 is a compound important in processing uranium fuel for nuclear reactors [▶ Section 23.6].

Periodic Trends in the *d*-Block: Size, Density, Melting Point

The periodic table is the most useful single reference source for a chemist. Not only does it provide data that have everyday use, but it also organizes the elements with respect to their chemical and physical properties. Let us look at three physical properties of the transition elements that vary periodically: atomic radii, density, and melting point.

(a) The most common oxidation states are indicated with *red squares;* less common oxidation states are indicated with *blue dots.*

(b) Aqueous solutions of chromium compounds with two different oxidation numbers: +3 in $Cr(NO_3)_3$ (violet) and $CrCl_3$ (green), and +6 in K_2CrO_4 (yellow) and $K_2Cr_2O_7$ (orange). The two Cr(III) species have different colors in solution because there are different complex ions in solution. The complex ion in the purple solution is $[Cr(H_2O)_6]^{3+}$; the complex ion in the green solution is $[Cr(H_2O)_4Cl_2]^+$.

FIGURE 22.4 **Oxidation states of the transition elements in the first transition series.**

A CLOSER LOOK

Corrosion of Iron

It is hard not to be aware of corrosion. Those of us who live in the northern part of the United States are well aware of the problems of rust on our automobiles. It is estimated that 20% of iron production each year goes solely to replace iron that has rusted away.

Qualitatively, we describe corrosion as the deterioration of metals by a product-favored oxidation reaction. The corrosion of iron, for example, converts iron metal to red-brown rust, which is hydrated iron(III) oxide, $Fe_2O_3 \cdot H_2O$. This process requires both air and water, and it is enhanced if the water contains dissolved ions and if the metal is stressed (e.g., if it has dents, cuts, and scrapes on the surface).

The corrosion process occurs in what is essentially a small electrochemical cell. There is an anode and a cathode, an electrical connection between the two (the metal itself), and an electrolyte in contact with both anode and cathode. When a metal corrodes, the metal is oxidized on anodic areas of the metal surface.

Anode, oxidation $\quad M(s) \longrightarrow M^{n+} + n\,e^-$

The electrons are consumed by several possible half-reactions in cathodic areas.

Cathode, reduction

$$2\,H_3O^+(aq) + 2\,e^- \longrightarrow H_2(g) + 2\,H_2O(\ell)$$

$$2\,H_2O(\ell) + 2\,e^- \longrightarrow H_2(g) + 2\,OH^-(aq)$$

$$O_2(g) + 2\,H_2O(\ell) + 4\,e^- \longrightarrow 4\,OH^-(aq)$$

The rate of iron corrosion is controlled by the rate of the cathodic process. Of the three possible cathodic reactions, the one that is fastest is determined by acidity and the amount of oxygen present. If little or no oxygen is present—as when a piece of iron is buried in soil such as moist clay—hydronium ions or water are reduced, and $H_2(g)$ and hydroxide ions are the products. Iron(II) hydroxide is relatively insoluble and will precipitate on the metal surface, inhibiting the further formation of Fe^{2+}.

Anode	$Fe(s) \longrightarrow Fe^{2+}(aq) + 2\,e^-$
Cathode	$2\,H_2O(\ell) + 2\,e^- \longrightarrow H_2(g) + 2\,OH^-(aq)$
Precipitation	$Fe^{2+}(aq) + 2\,OH^-(aq) \longrightarrow Fe(OH)_2(s)$
Net reaction	$Fe(s) + 2\,H_2O(\ell) \longrightarrow H_2(g) + Fe(OH)_2(s)$

If both water and O_2 are present, the chemistry of iron corrosion is somewhat different, and the corrosion reaction is about 100 times faster than without oxygen.

Anode	$2\,Fe(s) \longrightarrow 2\,Fe^{2+}(aq) + 4\,e^-$
Cathode	$O_2(g) + 2\,H_2O(\ell) + 4\,e^- \longrightarrow 4\,OH^-(aq)$
Precipitation	$2\,Fe^{2+}(aq) + 4\,OH^-(aq) \longrightarrow 2\,Fe(OH)_2(s)$
Net reaction	$2\,Fe(s) + 2\,H_2O(\ell) + O_2(g) \longrightarrow 2\,Fe(OH)_2(s)$

If oxygen is present but not in excess, further oxidation of the iron(II) hydroxide leads to the formation of magnetic iron oxide Fe_3O_4, (which can be thought of as a mixed oxide of Fe_2O_3 and FeO).

$$6\,Fe(OH)_2(s) + O_2(g) \longrightarrow 2\,Fe_3O_4 \cdot H_2O(s) + 4\,H_2O(\ell)$$
green hydrated magnetite

$$Fe_3O_4 \cdot H_2O(s) \longrightarrow H_2O(\ell) + Fe_3O_4(s)$$
black magnetite

It is the black magnetite that you find coating an iron object that has corroded by resting in moist soil.

If the iron object has free access to oxygen and water, as in the open or in flowing water, red-brown iron(III) oxide will form.

$$4\,Fe(OH)_2(s) + O_2(g) \longrightarrow 2\,Fe_2O_3 \cdot H_2O(s) + 2\,H_2O(\ell)$$
red-brown

This is the familiar rust you see on cars and buildings and the substance that colors the water red in some mountain streams or in your home.

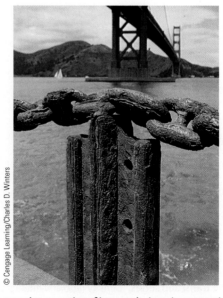

© Cengage Learning/Charles D. Winters

The corrosion or rusting of iron results in major economic loss.

© Cengage Learning/Charles D. Winters

Anode and cathode reactions in iron corrosion. Two iron nails were placed in an agar gel that contains phenolphthalein and $K_3[Fe(CN)_6]$. Iron(II) ion, formed at the tip and where the nail is bent, reacts with $[Fe(CN)_6]^{3-}$ to form blue-green $Fe_4[Fe(CN)_6]_3 \cdot 14\,H_2O$ (Prussian blue). Hydrogen and $OH^-(aq)$ are formed at the other parts of the surface of the nail, the latter being detected by the pink color of the acid–base indicator. In this electrochemical cell, regions of stress—the ends and the bent region of the nail—act as anodes, and the remainder of the surface serves as the cathode.

Titanium, a versatile element. Titanium takes it name from the Titans, a race of powerful gods in Greek mythology. It is the least dense metal in the *d*-block elements and is resistant to corrosion. For this reason it is used in aircraft and jet engines, not to mention golf clubs. Because it is also nonallergenic, it is used in jewelry and in artificial hip joints (shown here). It also forms many compounds, such as TiO_2. Titanium(IV) oxide is in the paper on which this book is printed. It prevents the type and figures on one side of the paper from being seen on the other side.

Metal Atom Radii

The variation in atomic radii for the transition elements in the fourth, fifth, and sixth periods is illustrated in Figure 7.9. The radii of the transition elements vary over a fairly narrow range, with a small decrease to a minimum being observed around the middle of this group of elements. This similarity of radii can be understood based on electron configurations. Atom size is determined by the electrons in the outermost orbital, which for these elements is the *ns* orbital ($n = 4, 5,$ or 6). Progressing from left to right in the periodic table, the size decline expected from increasing the number of protons in the nucleus is mostly canceled out by an opposing effect, repulsion from additional electrons in the $(n - 1)d$ orbitals.

The radii of the *d*-block elements in the fifth and sixth periods in each group are almost identical. The reason is that the lanthanide elements immediately precede the third series of *d*-block elements. The filling of 4*f* orbitals is accompanied by a steady contraction in size, consistent with the general trend of decreasing size from left to right in the periodic table. At the point where the 5*d* orbitals begin to fill again, the radii have decreased to a size similar to that of elements in the previous period. The decrease in size that results from the filling of the 4*f* orbitals is called the **lanthanide contraction**.

The similar sizes of the second and third series *d*-block elements have significant consequences for their chemistry. For example, the "platinum group metals" (Ru, Os, Rh, Ir, Pd, and Pt) form similar compounds. Thus, it is not surprising that minerals containing these metals are found in the same geological zones on earth. Nor is it surprising that it is difficult to separate these elements from one another.

Density

The variation in metal radii causes the densities of the transition elements to first increase and then decrease across a period (Figure 22.5). Although the overall change in radii among these elements is small, the effect is magnified because the volume is actually changing with the cube of the radius $[V = (4/3)\pi r^3]$.

The lanthanide contraction explains why elements in the sixth period have the highest density. The relatively small radii of sixth-period transition metals, combined with the fact that their atomic masses are considerably larger than their counterparts in the fifth period, causes sixth-period metal densities to be very large.

Melting Point

The melting point of any substance reflects the forces of attraction between the atoms, molecules, or ions that compose the solid. With transition elements, the

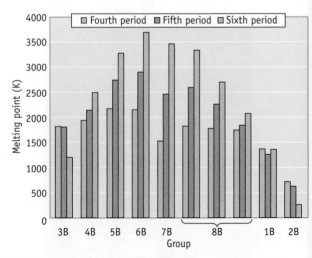

FIGURE 22.5 **Periodic properties in the transition series.** Density *(left)* and melting point *(right)* of the *d*-block elements.

melting points rise to a maximum around the middle of the series (Figure 22.5), then descend. Again, these elements' electron configurations provide us with an explanation. The variation in melting point indicates that the strongest metallic bonds occur when the d subshell is about half filled. This is also the point at which the largest number of electrons occupy the bonding molecular orbitals in the metal. (See the discussion of bonding in metals in Section 13.3.)

REVIEW & CHECK FOR SECTION 22.1

1. What is the maximum oxidation number that manganese can exhibit in its compounds?

   (a) +3   (b) +4   (c) +5   (d) +6   (e) +7

2. The "lanthanide contraction" is often given as an explanation for the fact that the sixth period transition elements have

   (a) densities smaller than that of the fifth period transition elements

   (b) atomic radii that are similar to the fifth period transition elements

   (c) melting points that are lower than the fifth period transition elements

---

22.2 Metallurgy

A few metals occur in nature as the free elements. This group includes copper (Figure 22.6), silver, and gold. Most metals, however, are found as oxides, sulfides, halides, carbonates, or other ionic compounds (Figure 22.7). Some metal-containing mineral deposits have little economic value, either because the concentration of the metal is too low or because the metal is difficult to separate from impurities. The relatively few minerals from which elements can be obtained profitably are called *ores* (Figure 22.7). **Metallurgy** is the general name given to the process of obtaining metals from their ores.

Very few ores are chemically pure substances. Instead, the desired mineral is usually mixed with large quantities of impurities such as sand and clay, called **gangue** (pronounced "gang"). Generally, the first step in a metallurgical process is to separate the mineral from the gangue. Then the ore is converted to the metal, a reduction process. Pyrometallurgy and hydrometallurgy are two methods of recovering metals from their ores. As the names imply, **pyrometallurgy** involves high temperatures and **hydrometallurgy** uses aqueous solutions (and thus is limited to the relatively low temperatures at which water is a liquid). Iron and copper metallurgy illustrate these two methods of metal production.

FIGURE 22.6 Naturally occurring copper. Copper occurs as the metal (native copper) and as minerals such as blue azurite [2 $CuCO_3 \cdot Cu(OH)_2$] and green malachite [$CuCO_3 \cdot Cu(OH)_2$].

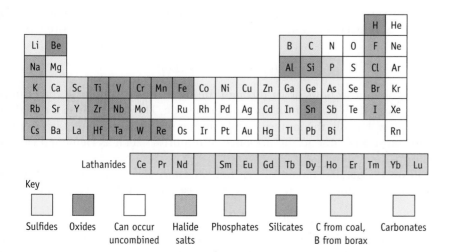

FIGURE 22.7 Sources of the elements. A few transition metals, such as copper and gold, occur naturally as the metal. Most other elements are found naturally as oxides, sulfides, or other salts.

FIGURE 22.8 A blast furnace.
The largest modern furnaces have hearths 14 meters in diameter. They can produce as much as 10,000 tons of iron per day.

Charge of ore, coke, and limestone

Flue gas

230 °C

525 °C

Hot gases used to preheat air

Reducing zone

945 °C

Heated air

1510 °C

Slag

Molten iron

Pyrometallurgy: Iron Production

● **Coke: A Reducing Agent** Coke is made by heating coal in a tall, narrow oven that is sealed to keep out oxygen. Heating drives off volatile chemicals, including benzene and ammonia. What remains is nearly pure carbon.

The production of iron from its ores is carried out in a blast furnace (Figure 22.8). The furnace is charged with a mixture of ore (usually hematite, Fe_2O_3), coke (which is primarily carbon), and limestone ($CaCO_3$). A blast of hot air forced in at the bottom of the furnace causes the coke to burn with such an intense heat that the temperature at the bottom is almost 1500 °C. The quantity of air input is controlled so that carbon monoxide is the primary product. Both carbon and carbon monoxide participate in the reduction of iron(III) oxide to give impure metal.

$$Fe_2O_3(s) + 3\ C(s) \longrightarrow 2\ Fe(\ell) + 3\ CO(g)$$

$$Fe_2O_3(s) + 3\ CO(g) \longrightarrow 2\ Fe(\ell) + 3\ CO_2(g)$$

Much of the carbon dioxide formed in the reduction process (and from heating the limestone) is reduced on contact with unburned coke and produces more reducing agent.

$$CO_2(g) + C(s) \longrightarrow 2\ CO(g)$$

The molten iron flows down through the furnace and collects at the bottom, where it is tapped off through an opening in the side. This impure iron is called *cast iron* or *pig iron*. Usually, the impure metal is either brittle or soft (undesirable properties for most uses) due to the presence of impurities such as elemental carbon, phosphorus, and sulfur.

Iron ores generally contain silicate minerals and silicon dioxide. Lime (CaO), formed when limestone is heated, reacts with these materials to give calcium silicate.

$$SiO_2(s) + CaO(s) \longrightarrow CaSiO_3(\ell)$$

This is an acid–base reaction because CaO is a basic oxide and SiO_2 is an acidic oxide. The calcium silicate, molten at the temperature of the blast furnace and less dense than molten iron, floats on the iron. Other nonmetal oxides dissolve in this layer and the mixture, called *slag*, is easily removed.

Pig iron from the blast furnace may contain as much as 4.5% carbon, 0.3% phosphorus, 0.04% sulfur, 1.5% silicon, and some other elements as well. The impure iron must be purified to remove these nonmetal components. Several processes are available to accomplish this task, but the most important uses the *basic oxygen furnace* (Figure 22.9). The process in the furnace removes much of the carbon and all of the phosphorus, sulfur, and silicon. Pure oxygen is blown into the molten pig iron and oxidizes phosphorus to P_4O_{10}, sulfur to SO_2, and carbon to CO_2. These nonmetal oxides either escape as gases or react with basic oxides such as CaO that are added or are used to line the furnace. For example,

$$P_4O_{10}(g) + 6\ CaO(s) \longrightarrow 2\ Ca_3(PO_4)_2(\ell)$$

The result is ordinary *carbon steel*. Almost any degree of flexibility, hardness, strength, and malleability can be achieved in carbon steel by reheating and cooling in a process called *tempering*. (See *Case Study: High Strength Steels and Unit Cells*, page 592.) The resulting material can then be used in a wide variety of applications. The major disadvantages of carbon steel are that it corrodes easily and that it loses its properties when heated strongly.

Other transition metals, such as chromium, manganese, and nickel, can be added during the steel-making process, giving *alloys* (solid solutions of two or more metals) that have specific physical, chemical, and mechanical properties. One well-known alloy is stainless steel, which contains 18% to 20% Cr and 8% to 12% Ni. Stainless steel is much more resistant to corrosion than carbon steel. Another alloy of iron is alnico V. Used in loudspeaker magnets because of its permanent magnetism, it contains five elements: Al (8%), Ni (14%), Co (24%), Cu (3%), and Fe (51%).

FIGURE 22.9 Molten iron being poured from a basic oxygen furnace.

Hydrometallurgy: Copper Production

In contrast to iron ores, which are mostly oxides, most copper minerals are sulfides. Copper-bearing minerals include chalcopyrite ($CuFeS_2$), chalcocite (Cu_2S), and covellite (CuS). Because ores containing these minerals generally have a very low percentage of copper, enrichment is necessary. This step is carried out by a process known as *flotation*. First, the ore is finely powdered. Next, oil is added and the mixture is agitated with soapy water in a large tank (Figure 22.10). At the same time, compressed air is forced through the mixture, so that the lightweight, oil-covered copper sulfide particles are carried to the top as a frothy mixture. The heavier gangue settles to the bottom of the tank, and the copper-laden froth is skimmed off.

Hydrometallurgy can be used to obtain copper from an enriched ore. In one method, enriched chalcopyrite ore is treated with a solution of copper(II) chloride. A reaction ensues that leaves copper in the form of solid, insoluble CuCl, which is easily separated from the iron that remains in solution as aqueous $FeCl_2$.

$$CuFeS_2(s) + 3\ CuCl_2(aq) \longrightarrow 4\ CuCl(s) + FeCl_2(aq) + 2\ S(s)$$

Aqueous NaCl is then added, and CuCl dissolves because of the formation of the complex ion $[CuCl_2]^-$.

$$CuCl(s) + Cl^-(aq) \longrightarrow [CuCl_2]^-(aq)$$

Copper(I) compounds in solution are unstable with respect to Cu(0) and Cu(II). Thus, $[CuCl_2]^-$ disproportionates to the metal and $CuCl_2$, and the latter is used to treat further ore.

$$2\ [CuCl_2]^-(aq) \longrightarrow Cu(s) + Cu^{2+}(aq) + 4\ Cl^-(aq)$$

Approximately 10% of the copper produced in the United States is obtained with the aid of bacteria. Acidified water is sprayed onto copper-mining wastes that contain low levels of copper. As the water trickles down through the crushed rock, the bacterium *Thiobacillus ferrooxidans* breaks down the iron sulfides in the rock and

FIGURE 22.10 Enriching copper ore by the flotation process. The less dense particles of Cu_2S are trapped in the soap bubbles and float. The denser gangue settles to the bottom.

FIGURE 22.11 Electrolytic refining of copper. (a) Slabs of impure copper, called *blister copper*, form the anode, and pure copper is deposited at the cathode. **(b)** The electrolysis cells at a copper refinery.

converts iron(II) to iron(III). Iron(III) ions oxidize the sulfide ion of copper sulfide to sulfate ions, leaving copper(II) ions in solution. Then the copper(II) ion is reduced to metallic copper by reaction with iron.

$$Cu^{2+}(aq) + Fe(s) \longrightarrow Cu(s) + Fe^{2+}(aq)$$

The purity of the copper obtained via these metallurgical processes is about 99%, but this is not acceptable because even traces of impurities greatly diminish the electrical conductivity of the metal. Consequently, a further purification step is needed—one involving electrolysis (Figure 22.11). Thin sheets of pure copper metal and slabs of impure copper are immersed in a solution containing $CuSO_4$ and H_2SO_4. The pure copper sheets serve as the cathode of an electrolysis cell, and the impure slabs are the anode. Copper in the impure sample is oxidized to copper(II) ions at the anode, and copper(II) ions in solution are reduced to pure copper at the cathode.

REVIEW & CHECK FOR SECTION 22.2

1. In the reaction between $CuFeS_2(s)$ and $CuCl_2(aq)$, what element is reduced and what element is oxidized?

    (a) Sulfur is reduced, iron is oxidized.

    (c) Sulfur is reduced, copper is oxidized.

    (b) Copper is reduced, sulfur is oxidized.

    (d) This is not a redox reaction.

2. What is the most common form in which iron is found in the earth's crust?

    (a) Iron is found in elemental form

    (c) Iron sulfide

    (b) Iron oxide

    (d) Iron silicate

22.3 Coordination Compounds

When metal salts dissolve, water molecules cluster around the ions (page 551). The negative end of each polar water molecule is attracted to the positively charged metal ion, and the positive end of the water molecule is attracted to the anion. As noted earlier (◄ Section 12.2), the energy of the ion–solvent interaction (solvation energy) is an important aspect of the solution process. But there is much more to this story.

Complexes and Ligands

A green solution formed by dissolving nickel(II) chloride in water contains $Ni^{2+}(aq)$ and $Cl^-(aq)$ ions (Figure 22.12). If the solvent is removed, a green crystalline solid is obtained. The formula of this solid is often written as $NiCl_2 \cdot 6\,H_2O$, and the compound is called nickel(II) chloride hexahydrate. Addition of ammonia to

FIGURE 22.12 **Coordination compounds of Ni²⁺ ion.** The transition metals and their ions form a wide range of compounds, often with beautiful colors and interesting structures. One purpose of this chapter is to explore some commonly observed structures and explain how these compounds can be so colorful.

[Ni(H₂O)₆]²⁺

Add NH₃

Add NaOH

[Ni(NH₃)₆]²⁺

Add ethylenediamine NH₂CH₂CH₂NH₂

Insoluble Ni(OH)₂

Add dimethylglyoxime (dmg)

[Ni(NH₂CH₂CH₂NH₂)₃]²⁺

Ni(dmg)₂

Photos © Cengage Learning/Charles D. Winters

Sum of metal ion and ligand charges

Coordination complex

2+

H

N

Ni²⁺

Coordinated metal ion

Ligand

$[Ni(NH_3)_6]^{2+}$

FIGURE 22.13 A coordination complex. In the $[Ni(NH_3)_6]^{2+}$ ion, the ligands are NH_3 molecules. Because the metal has a 2+ charge and the ligands have no charge, the charge on the complex ion is 2+.

● **Ligands Are Lewis Bases** Ligands are Lewis bases because they furnish the electron pair; the metal ion is a Lewis acid because it accepts electron pairs (◄ Section 17.11). Thus, the coordinate covalent bond between ligand and metal can be viewed as a Lewis acid–Lewis base interaction.

● **Bidentate Ligands** All common bidentate ligands bind to *adjacent* sites on the metal.

FIGURE 22.14 Common bidentate ligands. Coordination of these bidentate ligands to a transition metal ion results in five- or six-member metal-containing rings and no ring strain. (Only one resonance structure each of the acetylacetonate ion and phenanthroline are shown.)

the aqueous nickel(II) chloride solution gives a lilac-colored solution from which another compound, $NiCl_2 \cdot 6\ NH_3$, can be isolated. This formula looks very similar to the formula for the hydrate, with ammonia substituted for water.

What are these two nickel species? The formulas identify the compositions of the compounds but fail to give information about their structures. Because properties of compounds derive from their structures, we need to evaluate the structures in more detail. Typically, metal compounds are ionic, and solid ionic compounds have structures with cations and anions arranged in a regular array. The structure of hydrated nickel chloride contains cations with the formula $[Ni(H_2O)_6]^{2+}$ and chloride anions. The structure of the ammonia-containing compound is similar to the hydrate; it is made up of $[Ni(NH_3)_6]^{2+}$ cations and chloride anions.

Ions such as $[Ni(H_2O)_6]^{2+}$ and $[Ni(NH_3)_6]^{2+}$, in which a metal ion and either water or ammonia molecules compose a single structural unit, are examples of **coordination complexes**, also known as **complex ions** (Figure 22.13). Compounds containing a coordination complex as part of the structure are called **coordination compounds**, and their chemistry is known as **coordination chemistry**. Although the older "hydrate" formulas are still used, the preferred method of writing the formula for coordination compounds places the metal atom or ion and the molecules or anions directly bonded to it within brackets to show that it is a single structural entity. Thus, the formula for the nickel(II)–ammonia compound is better written as $[Ni(NH_3)_6]Cl_2$.

All coordination complexes contain a metal atom or ion as the central part of the structure. Bonded to the metal are molecules or ions called **ligands** (from the Latin verb *ligare*, meaning "to bind"). In the preceding examples, water and ammonia are the ligands. The number of ligand atoms attached to the metal defines the **coordination number** of the metal. The geometry described by the attached ligands is called the **coordination geometry**. In the nickel complex ion $[Ni(NH_3)_6]^{2+}$ (Figure 22.12), the six ligands are arranged in a regular octahedral geometry around the central metal ion.

Ligands can be either neutral molecules or anions (or, in rare instances, cations). The characteristic feature of a ligand is that it contains a lone pair of electrons. In the classic description of bonding in a coordination complex, the lone pair of electrons on a ligand is shared with the metal ion. The attachment is a coordinate covalent bond (◄ Section 8.5), because the electron pair being shared was originally on the ligand. The name "coordination complex" derives from the name given to this kind of bonding.

The net charge on a coordination complex is the sum of the charges on the metal and its attached groups. Complexes can be cations (as in the two nickel complexes used as examples here), anions, or uncharged.

Ligands such as H_2O and NH_3, which coordinate to the metal via a single Lewis base atom, are termed **monodentate**. The word "dentate" comes from the Latin *dentis*, meaning "tooth," so NH_3 is a "one-toothed" ligand. Some ligands attach to the metal with more than one donor atom. These ligands are called **polydentate**. Ethylenediamine (1,2-diaminoethane), $H_2NCH_2CH_2NH_2$, often abbreviated as en; oxalate ion, $C_2O_4^{2-}$ (ox^{2-}); and phenanthroline, $C_{12}H_8N_2$ (phen), are examples of the wide variety of **bidentate** ligands (Figure 22.14). Structures and examples of some complex ions with bidentate ligands are shown in Figure 22.15.

(a) $H_2NCH_2CH_2NH_2$, en
ethylenediamine

(b) $C_2O_4^{2-}$, ox
oxalate ion

(c) $CH_3COCHCOCH_3^-$, acac$^-$
acetylacetonate ion

(d) $C_{12}H_8N_2$, phen
phenanthroline

FIGURE 22.15 Complex ions with bidentate ligands. See Figure 22.14 for abbreviations.

$[Fe(C_2O_4)_3]^{3-}$ $\qquad$ $[Co(en)_3]^{3+}$ $\qquad$ $Cr(acac)_3$

Polydentate ligands are also called **chelating ligands**, or just *chelates* (pronounced "key-lates"). The name derives from the Greek *chele*, meaning "claw." Because two or more bonds are broken to separate the ligand from the metal, complexes with chelated ligands often have greater stability than those with monodentate ligands. Chelated complexes are important in everyday life. One way to clean the rust out of water-cooled automobile engines and steam boilers is to add a solution of oxalic acid. Iron(III) oxide reacts with oxalic acid to give a water-soluble iron oxalate complex ion:

$$3\ H_2O(\ell) + Fe_2O_3(s) + 6\ H_2C_2O_4(aq) \longrightarrow 2\ [Fe(C_2O_4)_3]^{3-}(aq) + 6\ H_3O^+(aq)$$

Ethylenediaminetetraacetate ion ($EDTA^{4-}$), a hexadentate ligand, is an excellent chelating ligand (Figure 22.16). It can wrap around a metal ion, encapsulating it. Salts of this anion are often added to commercial salad dressings to remove traces of free metal ions from solution; otherwise, these metal ions can act as catalysts for the oxidation of the oils in the dressing. Without $EDTA^{4-}$, the dressing would quickly become rancid. Another use is in bathroom cleansers. The $EDTA^{4-}$ ion removes deposits of $CaCO_3$ and $MgCO_3$ left by hard water by coordinating to Ca^{2+} or Mg^{2+} to create soluble complex ions.

Complexes with polydentate ligands play particularly important roles in biochemistry, one example of which is described in *A Closer Look: Hemoglobin*, page 1032.

Formulas of Coordination Compounds

It is useful to be able to predict the formula of a coordination complex, given the metal ion and ligands, and to derive the oxidation number of the coordinated metal ion, given the formula of a coordination compound. The following examples explore these issues.

(a) ethylenediaminetetraacetate, $EDTA^{4-}$ $\qquad$ **(b)** $[Co(EDTA)]^-$

FIGURE 22.16 $EDTA^{4-}$, a hexadentate ligand. (a) Ethylenediaminetetraacetate, $EDTA^{4-}$. **(b)** $[Co(EDTA)]^-$. Notice the five-member rings created when this ligand bonds to the metal.

EXAMPLE 22.1   Formulas of Coordination Complexes

Problem Give the formulas of the following coordination complexes:

(a) A Ni^{2+} ion is bound to two water molecules and two bidentate oxalate ions.

(b) A Co^{3+} ion is bound to one Cl^- ion, one ammonia molecule, and two bidentate ethylenediamine (en) molecules.

What Do You Know? The composition of the coordination complex is given for each part of the question.

Strategy The problem requires determining the net charge, which equals the sum of the charges of the various component parts of the complex ion. With that information, the metal and ligands can be assembled in the formula, which is placed in brackets, and the net charge indicated.

Solution

(a) This complex ion is constructed from two neutral H_2O molecules, two $C_2O_4^{2-}$ ions, and one Ni^{2+} ion, so the net charge on the complex is $2-$. The formula for the complex ion is

$$[Ni(C_2O_4)_2(H_2O)_2]^{2-}$$

(b) This cobalt(III) complex ion combines two en molecules and one NH_3 molecule, both having no charge, as well as one Cl^- ion and a Co^{3+} ion. The net charge is $2+$. The formula for this complex (writing out the entire formula for ethylenediamine) is

$$[Co(H_2NCH_2CH_2NH_2)_2(NH_3)Cl]^{2+}$$

Think about Your Answer Enclosing the formula of a complex in brackets is done to designate that this is a single unit. Species shown outside the brackets are counterions (when shown).

Check Your Understanding

(a) What is the formula of a complex ion composed of one Co^{3+} ion, three ammonia molecules, and three Cl^- ions?

(b) What is the formula for the coordination complex of iron (II) having two ethylenediamine ligands and two bromide ion ligands?

EXAMPLE 22.2   Coordination Compounds

Problem In each of the following coordination complexes, determine the metal's oxidation number and coordination number.

(a) $[Co(en)_2(NO_2)_2]Cl$ (c) $Pt(NH_3)_2Cl_4$

(b) $Pt(NH_3)_2(C_2O_4)$ (d) $[Co(NH_3)_5Cl]SO_4$

What Do You Know? You are given the formulas of compounds involving complex ions. The oxidation number is the charge that must be present on the metal. The coordination number is the number of ligand attachments to the metal. Remember that bidentate ligands coordinate in two positions.

Strategy Each formula consists of a complex ion or molecule made up of the metal ion, neutral, and anionic ligands. Counterions (shown outside the square brackets) may also be present. The oxidation number of the metal is the charge necessary to balance the sum of the negative charges associated with the anionic ligands and counterion. The coordination number is the number of donor atoms in the ligands that are bonded to the metal. Remember that the bidentate ligands in these examples (en, oxalate ion) attach to the metal at two sites and that any counterions present are not part of the complex ion—that is, they are not ligands.

Solution

(a) A chloride ion with a 1− charge is outside the brackets, showing that the charge on the complex ion must be 1+. There are two nitrite ions (NO_2^-) and two neutral bidentate ethylenediamine ligands in the complex. To give a 1+ charge on the complex ion, the cobalt ion must have a charge of 3+; that is, the sum of 2− (two nitrites), 0 (two en ligands), and 3+ (the cobalt ion) equals 1+. Each en ligand fills two coordination positions, and the two nitrite ions fill two more positions. The coordination number of the metal is 6.

(b) There is an oxalate ion ($C_2O_4^{2-}$) and two neutral ammonia ligands. To balance the charge on the oxalate ion, platinum must have a 2+ charge; that is, it has an oxidation number of +2. The coordination number is 4, with an oxalate ligand filling two coordination positions and each ammonia molecule filling one.

(c) There are four chloride ions (Cl^-) and two neutral ammonia ligands. In this complex, the oxidation number of the metal is +4, and the coordination number is 6.

(d) A sulfate ion with a 2− charge is outside the brackets, showing that the charge on the complex ion must be 2+. There is one chloride ion (Cl^-) and five neutral ammonia ligands in the complex ion. To give a 2+ charge on the complex ion, the cobalt must be 3+; the sum of 1− (one chloride), zero (five NH_3 ligands), and 3+ (the cobalt ion) equals 2+. The oxidation number of the metal is +3 and the coordination number is 6 (sulfate is not coordinated to the metal).

Think about Your Answer Knowing the oxidation state of the metal in a coordination compound is important. From this, you can determine the electron configuration of the metal. As we shall see in Section 22.5, this information will be needed to determine important properties of a complex such as magnetism and color.

Check Your Understanding

(a) Determine the metal's oxidation number and coordination number in (i) $K_3[Co(NO_2)_6]$ and in (ii) $Mn(NH_3)_4Cl_2$.

(b) Determine the oxidation number and coordination number of cobalt in the complex $NH_4[Co(edta)]$.

Naming Coordination Compounds

Coordination compounds are named according to an established system. The three compounds below are named according to the rules that follow.

Compound	Systematic Name
$[Ni(H_2O)_6]SO_4$	Hexaaquanickel(II) sulfate
$[Cr(en)_2(CN)_2]Cl$	Dicyanobis(ethylenediamine)chromium(III) chloride
$K[Pt(NH_3)Cl_3]$	Potassium amminetrichloroplatinate(II)

1. In naming a coordination compound that is a salt, name the cation first and then the anion. (This is how all salts are commonly named.)
2. When giving the name of the complex ion or molecule, name the ligands first, in alphabetical order, followed by the name of the metal. (When determining alphabetical order, any prefix is not considered part of the name.)
3. Ligands and their names:
   (a) If a ligand is an anion whose name ends in *-ite* or *-ate*, the final *e* is changed to *o* (sulfate $\longrightarrow$ sulfato or nitrite $\longrightarrow$ nitrito).
   (b) If the ligand is an anion whose name ends in *-ide*, the ending is changed to *o* (chloride $\longrightarrow$ chloro, cyanide $\longrightarrow$ cyano).
   (c) If the ligand is a neutral molecule, its common name is usually used with several important exceptions: Water as a ligand is referred to as *aqua;* ammonia is called *ammine;* and CO is called *carbonyl.*

Common Monodentate Ligands and Their Names

Ligand	Name
F^-	fluoro
Cl^-	chloro
Br^-	bromo
I^-	iodo
H_2O	aqua
NH_3	ammine
CO	carbonyl
CN^-	cyano
OH^-	hydroxo
$-NO_2^-$	nitro

A CLOSER LOOK

Hemoglobin

Metal-containing coordination compounds figure prominently in many biochemical reactions. Perhaps the best-known example is hemoglobin, the chemical in the blood responsible for O_2 transport. It is also one of the most thoroughly studied bioinorganic compounds.

As described in *The Chemistry of Life: Biochemistry* (page 493), hemoglobin (Hb) is a large iron-containing protein. It includes four polypeptide segments, each containing an iron(II) ion locked inside a porphyrin ring system and coordinated to a nitrogen atom from another part of the protein. A sixth site is available to attach to oxygen.

FIGURE A Porphyrin ring of the heme group. The tetradentate ligand surrounding the iron(II) ion in hemoglobin is a dianion of a substituted molecule called a *porphyrin*. Because of the double bonds in this structure, all of the carbon and nitrogen atoms in the dianion of the porphyrin lie in a plane. In addition, the nitrogen lone pairs are directed toward the center of the molecule, and the molecular dimensions are such that a metal ion may fit nicely into the cavity.

One segment of the hemoglobin molecule resembles the myoglobin structure shown below. (Myoglobin, the oxygen-storage protein in muscle, has only one polypeptide chain with an enclosed heme group.) In myoglobin, the heme group (the name given to the metal and porphyrin ring system) is enclosed within a polypeptide chain. The iron ion in the porphyrin ring is shown in Figure B. The first and sixth coordination positions are taken up by nitrogen atoms from amino acids of the polypeptide chain.

Hemoglobin functions by reversibly adding oxygen to the sixth coordination position of each iron, giving a complex called *oxyhemoglobin*.

Because hemoglobin features four iron centers, a maximum of four molecules of oxygen can bind to the molecule. The binding to oxygen is cooperative; that is, binding one molecule enhances the tendency to bind the second, third, and fourth molecules. Formation of the oxygenated complex is favored, but not too highly, because oxy-

Heme group with iron cation
Protein chain

Myoglobin (Mb)

FIGURE B The heme group in myoglobin. This protein is a close relative of hemoglobin. The heme group with its iron ion is shown.

gen must also be released by the molecule to body tissues. Interestingly, an increase in acidity leads to a decrease in the stability of the oxygenated complex. This phenomenon is known as the *Bohr effect*, named for Christian Bohr, Niels Bohr's father (page 342). Release of oxygen in tissues is facilitated by an increase in acidity that results from the presence of CO_2 formed by metabolism.

Among the notable properties of hemoglobin is its ability to form a complex with carbon monoxide. This complex is very stable, with the equilibrium constant for the following reaction being about 200 (where Hb is hemoglobin):

$$HbO_2(aq) + CO(g) \rightleftharpoons HbCO(aq) + O_2(g)$$

When CO complexes with iron, the oxygen-carrying capacity of hemoglobin is lost. Consequently, CO (and the isoelectronic CN^- ion) is highly toxic to humans. Exposure to even small amounts greatly reduces the capacity of the blood to transport oxygen.

Hemoglobin abnormalities are well known. One of the most common abnormalities causes sickle cell anemia and was described on page 494.

$120°$

Fe

Base from protein

FIGURE C Oxygen binding. Oxygen binds to the iron of the heme group in oxyhemoglobin (and in myoglobin). Interestingly, the Fe—O—O angle is bent.

(d) When there is more than one of a particular monodentate ligand with a simple name, the number of ligands is designated by the appropriate prefix: *di, tri, tetra, penta,* or *hexa.* If the ligand name is complicated, the prefix changes to *bis, tris, tetrakis, pentakis,* or *hexakis,* followed by the ligand name in parentheses.

4. If the coordination complex is an anion, the suffix *-ate* is added to the metal name.

5. Following the name of the metal, the oxidation number of the metal is given in Roman numerals.

EXAMPLE 22.3   Naming Coordination Compounds

Problem Name the following compounds:

(a) $[Cu(NH_3)_4]SO_4$

(b) $K_2[CoCl_4]$

(c) $Co(phen)_2Cl_2$

(d) $[Co(en)_2(H_2O)Cl]Cl_2$

What Do You Know? Formulas of each compound are given.

Strategy Apply the rules for nomenclature given above.

Solution

(a) The complex ion (in square brackets) is composed of four NH_3 molecules (named *ammine* in a complex) and the copper ion. To balance the 2− charge on the sulfate counterion, copper must have a 2+ charge. The compound's name is

tetraamminecopper(II) sulfate

(b) The complex ion $[CoCl_4]^{2-}$ has a 2− charge. With four Cl^- ligands, the cobalt ion must have a 2+ charge, so the sum of charges is 2−. The name of the compound is

potassium tetrachlorocobaltate(II)

(c) This is a neutral coordination compound. The ligands include two Cl^- ions and two neutral bidentate *phen* (phenanthroline) ligands (page 1028). The metal ion must have a 2+ charge (Co^{2+}). The name, listing ligands in alphabetical order, is

dichlorobis(phenanthroline)cobalt(II)

(d) The complex ion has a 2+ charge because it is paired with two uncoordinated Cl^- ions. The cobalt ion is Co^{3+} because it is bonded to two neutral en ligands, one neutral water, and one Cl^-. The name is

aquachlorobis(ethylenediamine)cobalt(III) chloride

Think about Your Answer The earliest studies of coordination compounds created a colorful array of names, and a few of these are still used (Prussian Blue, mentioned earlier, and Zeise's salt, $K[Pt(C_2H_4)Cl_3]$, are two examples). However, a systematic nomenclature is essential to communication among scientists working in the area. The rules of nomenclature make it possible for any scientist to derive a formula from the name, or to name a compound if given its formula.

Check Your Understanding

Name the following coordination compounds.

(a) $[Ni(H_2O)_6]SO_4$ (b) $[Cr(en)_2(CN)_2]Cl$ (c) $K[Pt(NH_3)Cl_3]$ (d) $K[CuCl_2]$

REVIEW & CHECK FOR SECTION 22.3

1. What is the coordination number for the metal in the compound tetraaquaoxalatoiron(III) chloride?

   (a) 4   (b) 6   (c) 7   (d) 2

2. What is the oxidation number of the metal in $(NH_4)_3[Fe(CN)_6]$?

   (a) 0   (b) +1   (c) +2   (d) +3

3. Which of the following is a complex ion based on an iron(II) ion?

   (a) $[Fe(H_2O)_4Cl_2]ClO_4$ (c) $Fe(acac)_3$

   (b) $Na_4[Fe(C_2O_4)_3]$ (d) $[Fe(NH_3)_5Cl]SO_4$

4. In which of the following complexes is the metal 6-coordinate?

    (a) lithium tetrachlorocobaltate(II)

    (b) pentaamminehydroxochromium(III) chloride

    (c) bis(ethylenediamine)silver(I) chloride

    (d) diamminedichlorozinc(II)

22.4 **Structures of Coordination Compounds**

Common Coordination Geometries

The geometry of a coordination complex is defined by the arrangement of donor atoms of the ligands around the central metal ion. Metal ions in coordination compounds can have coordination numbers ranging from 2 to 12. Only complexes with coordination numbers of 2, 4, and 6 are common, however, so we will concentrate on species such as $[ML_2]^{n\pm}$, $[ML_4]^{n\pm}$, and $[ML_6]^{n\pm}$, where M is the metal ion and L is a *monodentate* ligand. Within these stoichiometries, the following geometries are encountered:

[Ag(NH$_3$)$_2$]$^+$ — linear

- All $[ML_2]^{n\pm}$ complexes are linear. The two ligands are on opposite sides of the metal, and the L—M—L bond angle is 180°. Common examples include $[Ag(NH_3)_2]^+$ and $[CuCl_2]^-$.
- Tetrahedral geometry occurs in many $[ML_4]^{n\pm}$ complexes. Examples include $TiCl_4$, $[CoCl_4]^{2-}$, $[NiCl_4]^{2-}$, and $[Zn(NH_3)_4]^{2+}$.
- Some $[ML_4]^{n\pm}$ complexes can have square planar geometry. This geometry is most often seen with metal ions that have eight d electrons. Examples include $Pt(NH_3)_2Cl_2$, $[Ni(CN)_4]^{2-}$, and the nickel complex with the dimethylglyoximate (dmg$^-$) ligand in Figure 22.12.
- Octahedral geometry is found in complexes with the stoichiometry $[ML_6]^{n\pm}$ (Figure 22.12).

Isomerism

Isomerism is one of the most interesting aspects of molecular structure. Recall that the chemistry of organic compounds is greatly enlivened by the multitude of isomeric compounds that are known.

    Isomers are classified as follows:

- *Structural isomers* have the same molecular formula but different bonding arrangements of atoms.
- *Stereoisomers* have the same atom-to-atom bonding sequence, but the atoms differ in their arrangement in space. There are two types of stereoisomers: geometric isomers (such as *cis* and *trans* alkenes, page 449) and optical isomers (nonsuperimposable mirror images that have the unique property that they rotate the plane of plane-polarized light, page 442).

All three types of isomerism—structural, geometric, and optical—are encountered in coordination chemistry.

Structural Isomerism

The two most important types of structural isomerism in coordination chemistry are coordination isomerism and linkage isomerism. **Coordination isomerism** occurs when it is possible to exchange a coordinated ligand and the uncoordinated counterion. For example, dark violet [Co(NH$_3$)$_5$Br]SO$_4$ and red [Co(NH$_3$)$_5$SO$_4$]Br are coordination isomers. In the first compound, bromide ion is a ligand and sulfate is a counterion; in the second, sulfate is a ligand and bromide is the counterion. A diagnostic test for this kind of isomer is often made based on chemical reactions. For example, these two compounds can be distinguished by precipitation reactions.

Pt(NH$_3$)$_2$Cl$_2$ — square planar

[NiCl$_4$]$^{2-}$ — tetrahedral

[Ni(H$_2$O)$_6$]$^{2+}$ — octahedral

Common Coordination Geometries

pink-orange, O-bonded NO_2^-

© Cengage Learning/
Charles D. Winters

yellow-orange, N-bonded NO_2^-

FIGURE 22.17 Linkage isomers, $[Co(NH_3)_5ONO]^{2+}$ and $[Co(NH_3)_5NO_2]^{2+}$. These complex ions, whose systematic names are pentaamminenitritocobalt(III) and pentaamminenitrocobalt(III), respectively, were the first known examples of this type of isomerism. (Each compound has a Cl^- as a counterion.)

Addition of $Ba^{2+}(aq)$ to a solution of $[Co(NH_3)_5Br]SO_4$ gives a precipitate of $BaSO_4$, indicating the presence of sulfate ion in solution. In contrast, no reaction occurs if $Ba^{2+}(aq)$ is added to a solution of $[Co(NH_3)_5SO_4]Br$. In this complex, sulfate ion is attached to Co^{3+} and is not a free ion in solution.

$$[Co(NH_3)_5Br]SO_4 + Ba^{2+}(aq) \longrightarrow BaSO_4(s) + [Co(NH_3)_5Br]^{2+}(aq)$$

$$[Co(NH_3)_5SO_4]Br + Ba^{2+}(aq) \longrightarrow \text{no reaction}$$

Linkage isomerism occurs when it is possible to attach a ligand to the metal through different atoms. The two most common ligands with which linkage isomerism arises are thiocyanate, SCN^-, and nitrite, NO_2^-. The Lewis structure of the thiocyanate ion shows that there are lone pairs of electrons on sulfur and nitrogen. The ligand can attach to a metal either through sulfur (called *S-bonded thiocyanate*) or through nitrogen (called *N-bonded thiocyanate*). Nitrite ion can attach either at oxygen or at nitrogen. The former are called nitrito complexes; the latter are nitro complexes (Figure 22.17).

Ligands forming linkage isomers

:S—C≡N: Bind to metal ion using either lone pair.

:O⟍N⟍O: Bind to metal ion using either lone pair.

Bind to metal ion using either lone pair.

Geometric Isomerism

Geometric isomerism results when the atoms bonded directly to the metal have a different spatial arrangement. The simplest example of geometric isomerism in coordination chemistry is *cis–trans* isomerism, which occurs in both square-planar and octahedral complexes. An example of *cis–trans* isomerism is seen in the square-planar complex $Pt(NH_3)_2Cl_2$ (Figure 22.18a). In this complex, the two Cl^- ions can be either adjacent to each other (*cis*) or on opposite sides of the metal (*trans*). The

● **Cis–Trans Isomerism** *Cis–trans* isomerism is not possible for tetrahedral complexes. All L—M—L angles are 109.5°, and all positions are equivalent in this three-dimensional structure.

cis isomer   *trans* isomer

(a) The square-planar complex $Pt(NH_3)_2Cl_2$ can exist in two geometries, *cis* and *trans*.

cis isomer, purple   *trans* isomer, green

(b) *Cis* and *trans* octahedral isomers are possible for $[Co(en)_2Cl_2]^+$.

FIGURE 22.18 *Cis–trans* isomers.

fac isomer

mer isomer

FIGURE 22.19 *Fac* and *mer* isomers of Cr(NH₃)₃Cl₃. In the *fac* isomer, the three chloride ligands (and the three ammonia ligands) are arranged at the corners of a triangular face. In the *mer* isomer, the three similar ligands follow a meridian.

cis isomer is effective in the treatment of testicular, ovarian, bladder, and osteogenic sarcoma cancers, but the *trans* isomer has no effect on these diseases.

Cis–trans isomerism in an octahedral complex is illustrated by a complex ion with two bidentate ethylenediamine ligands and two chloride ligands, $[Co(H_2NCH_2CH_2NH_2)_2Cl_2]^+$. In this complex, the two Cl^- ions occupy positions that are either adjacent (the purple *cis* isomer) or opposite (the green *trans* isomer) (Figure 22.18b).

Another common type of geometric isomerism occurs for octahedral complexes with the general formula MX_3Y_3. A *fac* isomer has three identical ligands lying at the corners of a triangular face of an octahedron defined by the ligands (*fac* = facial), whereas the ligands follow a meridian in the *mer* isomer (*mer* = meridional). *Fac* and *mer* isomers of $Cr(NH_3)_3Cl_3$ are shown in Figure 22.19.

Optical Isomerism

Optical isomerism (chirality) occurs for octahedral complexes when the metal ion coordinates to three bidentate ligands or when the metal ion coordinates to two bidentate ligands and two monodentate ligands in a *cis* position. The complexes $[Co(en)_3]^{3+}$ and *cis*-$[Co(en)_2Cl_2]^+$, illustrated in Figure 22.20, are examples of chiral complexes. The diagnostic test for chirality is met with both species: Mirror images of these molecules are not superimposable (page 442). Solutions of the optical isomers rotate plane-polarized light in opposite directions.

EXAMPLE 22.4 Isomerism in Coordination Chemistry

Problem For which of the following compounds or complex ions do isomers exist? If isomers are possible, identify the type of isomerism (structural, geometric, or optical).

(a) $[Co(NH_3)_4Cl_2]^+$

(b) $Pt(NH_3)_2(CN)_2$ (square-planar)

(c) $Co(NH_3)_3Cl_3$

(d) $K_3[Fe(C_2O_4)_3]$

(e) $Zn(NH_3)_2Cl_2$ (tetrahedral)

(f) $[Co(NH_3)_5SCN]^{2+}$

What Do You Know? From the formulas, which are given, you can infer coordination number and geometry. Structural isomers are those for which there are different attachments of atoms; geometric isomers are those where the spatial arrangement of atoms is different. Complexes that are optically active have nonsuperimposable mirror images.

Strategy Determine the number of ligands attached to the metal and decide whether the ligands are monodentate or bidentate. Knowing how many donor atoms are coordinated to the metal (the coordination number) will allow you to establish the metal geometry. At that point, it is necessary to recall the possible types of isomers for each geometry. The only isomerism possible for square-planar complexes is geometric (*cis* and *trans*). Tetrahedral complexes do not have geometric or optical isomers. Six-coordinate complexes of the formula MA_4B_2 can be either *cis* or *trans*. *Mer* and *fac* isomers are possible with a stoichiometry of MA_3B_3. Optical activity arises for metal complexes of the formula *cis*-$M(bidentate)_2X_2$ and $M(bidentate)_3$ (among others). Drawing pictures of the molecules will help you visualize the isomers.

$[Co(en)_3]^{3+}$

$[Co(en)_3]^{3+}$ mirror image

cis-$[Co(en)_2Cl_2]^+$

cis-$[Co(en)_2Cl_2]^+$ mirror image

FIGURE 22.20 Chiral metal complexes. Both $[Co(en)_3]^{3+}$ and *cis*-$[Co(en)_2Cl_2]^+$ are chiral. Notice that the mirror images of the two compounds are not superimposable.

Solution

(a) Two geometric isomers can be drawn for octahedral complexes with a formula of MA_4B_2. One isomer has two Cl^- ions in *cis* positions (adjacent positions, at a 90° angle), and the other isomer has the Cl^- ligands in *trans* positions (with a 180° angle between the ligands). Optical isomers are not possible.

cis isomer   *trans* isomer

(b) In this square-planar complex, the two NH_3 ligands (and the two CN^- ligands) can be either *cis* or *trans*. These are geometric isomers. Optical isomers are not possible.

cis isomer   *trans* isomer

● **Optical Isomerism** Square-planar complexes are incapable of optical isomerism based at the metal center; mirror images are always superimposable. Chiral tetrahedral complexes are possible, but examples of complexes with a metal bonded tetrahedrally to four different monodentate ligands are rare.

(c) Two geometric isomers of this octahedral complex, with chloride ligands either *fac* or *mer*, are possible. In the *fac* isomer, the three Cl^- ligands are all at 90° to each other; in the *mer* isomer, two Cl^- ligands are at 180°, and the third is 90° from the other two. Optical isomers are not possible.

fac isomer   *mer* isomer

(d) Ignore the counterions, K^+. The anion is an octahedral complex. Remember that the bidentate oxalate ion occupies two coordination sites of the metal, and that three oxalate ligands means that the metal has a coordination number of 6. Mirror images of complexes of the stoichiometry M(bidentate)$_3$ are not superimposable; therefore, two optical isomers are possible. (Here the ligands, $C_2O_4^{2-}$, are drawn abbreviated as O—O.)

nonsuperimposable mirror images of $[Fe(ox)_3]^{3-}$

(e) Only a single structure is possible for tetrahedral complexes such as $Zn(NH_3)_2Cl_2$.

(f) Only linkage isomerism (structural isomerism) is possible for this octahedral cobalt complex. Either the sulfur or the nitrogen of the SCN^- anion can be attached to the cobalt(III) ion in this complex.

S-bonded SCN^- N-bonded SCN^-

Think about Your Answer More complex situations occur when a complex has three or more different ligands. In those instances it is important to be able to visualize the three dimensional molecule and to organize your approach.

Check Your Understanding

What types of isomers are possible for the following compounds or complex ions?

(a) $K[Co(NH_3)_2Cl_4]$

(b) $Pt(en)Cl_2$ (square-planar)

(c) $[Co(NH_3)_5Cl]^{2+}$

(d) $[Ru(phen)_3]Cl_3$

(e) $Na_2[MnCl_4]$ (tetrahedral)

(f) $[Co(NH_3)_5NO_2]^{2+}$

REVIEW & CHECK FOR SECTION 22.4

1. Which of the following complexes cannot exist as *cis–trans* isomers?

   (a) $Fe(NH_3)_4Cl_2$

   (b) $Ni(H_2O)_4(C_2O_4)$ ($C_2O_4^{2-}$ = oxalate)

   (c) Square-planar $[PtCl_2(CN)_2]^{2-}$

   (d) $Mn(en)_2Cl_2$ (en = ethylenediamine)

2. Which of the following complexes can exist as optical isomers?

   (a) Square-planar $Pt(NH_3)(H_2O)(CN)Cl$

   (b) $Fe(en)_2(CN)_2$ (en = ethylenediamine)

   (c) $Fe(NH_3)_4Cl_2$

   (d) $Cr(NH_3)_3Cl_3$

3. Which statement best describes the isomers for the complex $Fe(en)_2Cl_2$? (en = ethylenediamine)

   (a) Only a single structure can be drawn.

   (b) There are two geometric isomers, one of which has an optical isomer.

   (c) The compound exists as a pair of optical isomers.

   (d) This compound exists as two structural isomers.

4. How many geometric isomers are possible for $Fe(en)(NH_3)_2Cl_2$? (To answer this question, try to draw out possible structures in an organized manner. Start by placing the bidentate ethylenediamine ligand in two coordination sites, then add chloride and ammonia ligands into the remaining positions in various ways.)

   (a) 0   (b) 1   (c) 2   (d) 3

22.5 Bonding in Coordination Compounds

Metal–ligand bonding in a coordination complex was described earlier in this chapter as being covalent, resulting from the sharing of an electron pair between the metal and the ligand donor atom. Although frequently used, this description is not capable of explaining the color and magnetic behavior of these complexes. As a consequence, the covalent bonding picture has now largely been superseded by two other bonding models: molecular orbital theory and ligand field theory.

The bonding model based on molecular orbital theory assumes that the metal and the ligand bond through the molecular orbitals formed by atomic orbital overlap between metal and ligand. The **ligand field model**, in contrast, focuses on repulsion (and destabilization) of electrons in the metal coordination sphere. The ligand field model also assumes that the positive metal ion and the negative ligand lone pair are attracted electrostatically; that is, the bond arises when a positively charged metal ion attracts a negative ion or the negative end of a polar molecule. For the most part, the molecular orbital and ligand field models predict similar, qualitative results regarding color and magnetic behavior. Here, we will focus on the ligand field approach and illustrate how it explains color and magnetism of transition metal complexes.

The *d* Orbitals: Ligand Field Theory

To understand ligand field theory, it is necessary to look at the *d* orbitals, particularly with regard to their orientation relative to the positions of ligands in a metal complex.

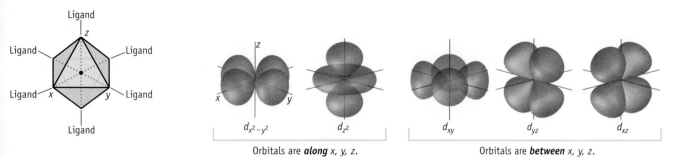

FIGURE 22.21 The *d* orbitals. The five *d* orbitals and their spatial relation to the ligands on the *x*-, *y*-, and *z*-axes.

We look first at octahedral complexes. Assume the ligands in an octahedral complex lie along the *x*-, *y*-, and *z*-axes. This results in the five *d* orbitals (Figure 22.21) being subdivided into two sets: the $d_{x^2-y^2}$ and d_{z^2} orbitals in one set and the d_{xy}, d_{xz}, and d_{yz} orbitals in the second. The $d_{x^2-y^2}$ and d_{z^2} orbitals are directed along the *x*-, *y*-, and *z*-axes, whereas the orbitals of the second group are aligned between these axes.

In an isolated atom or ion, the five *d* orbitals have the same energy. For a metal atom or ion in a coordination complex, however, the *d* orbitals have different energies. According to the ligand field model, repulsion between *d* electrons on the metal and electron pairs of the ligands destabilizes electrons that reside in the *d* orbitals; that is, it causes their energy to increase. Electrons in the various *d* orbitals are not affected equally, however, because of their different orientations in space relative to the position of the ligand lone pairs (Figure 22.22). Electrons in the $d_{x^2-y^2}$ and d_{z^2} orbitals experience a larger repulsion because these orbitals point directly at the incoming ligand electron pairs. A smaller repulsive effect is experienced by electrons in the d_{xy}, d_{xz}, and d_{yz} orbitals. The difference in degree of repulsion means that an energy difference exists between the two sets of orbitals in an octahedral complex. This difference, called the **ligand field splitting** and denoted by the symbol Δ_0, is a function of the metal and the ligands and varies predictably from one complex to another.

A different splitting pattern is encountered with square-planar complexes (Figure 22.23). Assume that the four ligands are along the *x*- and *y*-axes. The $d_{x^2-y^2}$ orbital also points along these axes, so it has the highest energy. The d_{xy} orbital (which also lies in the *xy*-plane, but does not point at the ligands) is next highest in energy, followed by the d_{z^2} orbital. The d_{xz} and d_{yz} orbitals, both of which partially point in the *z*-direction, have the lowest energy.

The *d*-orbital splitting pattern for a tetrahedral complex is the reverse of the pattern observed for octahedral complexes. Three orbitals (d_{xz}, d_{xy}, d_{yz}) are higher in energy, whereas the $d_{x^2-y^2}$ and d_{z^2} orbitals are below them in energy (Figure 22.23).

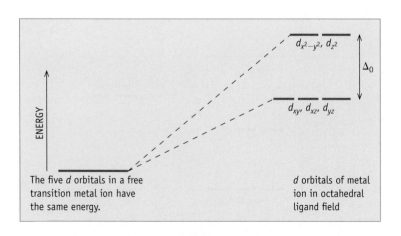

FIGURE 22.22 Ligand field splitting for an octahedral complex. The *d*-orbital energies increase as the ligands approach the metal along the *x*-, *y*-, and *z*-axes. The d_{xy}, d_{xz}, and d_{yz} orbitals, not pointed toward the ligands, are less destabilized than the $d_{x^2-y^2}$ and d_{z^2} orbitals. Thus, the d_{xy}, d_{xz}, and d_{yz} orbitals are at lower energy. (Δ_0 stands for the splitting in an octahedral ligand field.)

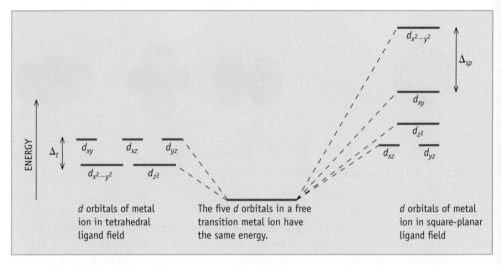

FIGURE 22.23 Splitting of the d orbitals in *(left)* tetrahedral and *(right)* square-planar geometries. (Δ_t and Δ_{sp} are, respectively, the splitting in tetrahedral and square-planar ligand fields.)

Electron Configurations and Magnetic Properties

The d-orbital splitting in coordination complexes provides the means to explain both the magnetic behavior and the color of these complexes. To understand this explanation, however, we must first understand how to assign electrons to the various orbitals in each geometry.

A gaseous Cr^{2+} ion has the electron configuration $[Ar]3d^4$. The term *gaseous* in this context is used to denote a single, isolated atom or ion with all other particles located an infinite distance away. In this situation, the five $3d$ orbitals have the same energy. The four electrons reside singly in different d orbitals, according to Hund's rule, and the Cr^{2+} ion has four unpaired electrons.

Cr(II) electron configuration

Cr^{2+} $[Ar]3d^4$

$3d$ $4s$

When the Cr^{2+} ion is part of an octahedral complex, the five d orbitals do not have identical energies. As illustrated in Figure 22.22, these orbitals divide into two sets, with the d_{xy}, d_{xz}, and d_{yz} orbitals having a lower energy than the $d_{x^2-y^2}$ and d_{z^2} orbitals. Having two sets of orbitals means that two different electron configurations are possible (Figure 22.24). Three of the four d electrons in Cr^{2+} are assigned to the lower-energy d_{xy}, d_{xz}, and d_{yz} orbitals. The fourth electron either can be assigned to an orbital in the higher-energy $d_{x^2-y^2}$ and d_{z^2} set or can pair up with an electron already in the lower-energy set. The first arrangement is called **high spin**, because it has the maximum number of unpaired electrons, four in the case of Cr^{2+}. The second arrangement is called **low spin**, because it has the minimum number of unpaired electrons possible.

FIGURE 22.24 High- and low-spin cases for an octahedral chromium(II) complex. *(left, high spin)* If the ligand field splitting (Δ_0) is smaller than the pairing energy (P), the electrons are placed in different orbitals, and the complex has four unpaired electrons. *(right, low spin)* If the splitting is larger than the pairing energy, all four electrons will be in the lower-energy orbital set. This requires pairing two electrons in one of the orbitals, so the complex will have two unpaired electrons.

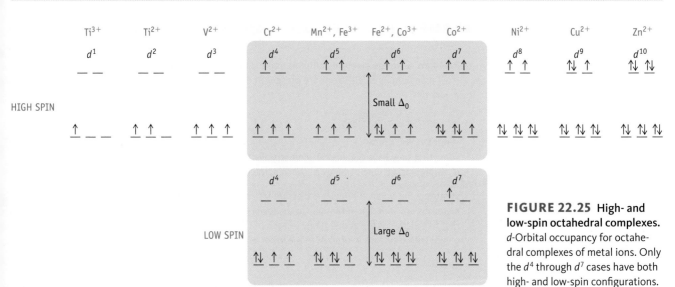

HIGH SPIN

LOW SPIN

FIGURE 22.25 High- and low-spin octahedral complexes. d-Orbital occupancy for octahedral complexes of metal ions. Only the d^4 through d^7 cases have both high- and low-spin configurations.

At first glance, a high-spin configuration appears to contradict conventional thinking. It seems logical that the most stable situation would occur when electrons occupy the lowest-energy orbitals. A second factor intervenes, however. Because electrons are negatively charged, repulsion increases when they are assigned to the same orbital. This destabilizing effect bears the name **pairing energy (P)**. The preference for an electron to be in the lowest-energy orbital and the pairing energy have opposing effects (Figure 22.24). Low-spin complexes arise when the splitting of the d orbitals by the ligand field is large—that is, when Δ_0 has a large value. The energy gained by putting all of the electrons in the lowest-energy level is the dominant effect when $\Delta_0 > P$. In contrast, high-spin complexes occur if the value of Δ_0 is smaller than the energy required to pair electrons ($\Delta_0 < P$).

For octahedral complexes, high- and low-spin complexes can occur only for configurations d^4 through d^7 (Figure 22.25). Complexes of the d^6 metal ion, Fe^{2+}, for example, can have either high spin or low spin. The complex formed when the Fe^{2+} ion is placed in water, $[Fe(H_2O)_6]^{2+}$, is high spin, whereas the $[Fe(CN)_6]^{4-}$ complex ion is low spin.

Electron configuration for Fe^{2+} in an octahedral complex

$$\frac{\uparrow\quad\uparrow}{d_{x^2-y^2},\, d_{z^2}} \Big\updownarrow \Delta_0(H_2O)$$
$$\frac{\text{⇅}\ \uparrow\ \uparrow}{d_{xy},\, d_{xz},\, d_{yz}}$$
high spin
$[Fe(H_2O)_6]^{2+}$

$$\frac{\overline{\ }\ \overline{\ }}{d_{x^2-y^2},\, d_{z^2}} \Big\updownarrow \Delta_0(CN^-)$$
$$\frac{\text{⇅}\ \text{⇅}\ \text{⇅}}{d_{xy},\, d_{xz},\, d_{yz}}$$
low spin
$[Fe(CN)_6]^{4-}$

It is possible to tell whether a complex is high or low spin by examining its magnetic behavior. The high-spin complex $[Fe(H_2O)_6]^{2+}$ has four unpaired electrons and is *paramagnetic* (attracted by a magnet), whereas the low-spin $[Fe(CN)_6]^{4-}$ complex has no unpaired electrons and is *diamagnetic* (repelled by a magnet) (◄ page 289).

Most complexes of Pd^{2+} and Pt^{2+} ions are square-planar, the electron configuration of these metals being [noble gas]$(n - 1)d^8$. In a square-planar complex, there are four sets of orbitals (Figure 22.23). For square-planar d^8 complexes, all except the highest-energy orbital are filled, and all electrons are paired, resulting in diamagnetic (low-spin) complexes.

Nickel, which is found above palladium in the periodic table, forms both square-planar and tetrahedral complexes (as well as octahedral complexes). For example, the complex ion $[Ni(CN)_4]^{2-}$ is square-planar, whereas the $[NiCl_4]^{2-}$ ion is tetrahedral. Magnetism allows us to differentiate between these two geometries. Based on the ligand field splitting pattern, the cyanide complex is expected to be diamagnetic, whereas the chloride complex is paramagnetic with two unpaired electrons.

Nickel(II) complexes and magnetism. The anion $[NiCl_4]^{2-}$ is a paramagnetic tetrahedral complex. In contrast, $[Ni(CN)_4]^{2-}$ is a diamagnetic square-planar complex.

EXAMPLE 22.5   High- and Low-Spin Complexes and Magnetism

Problem Give the electron configuration for the metal ion in each of the following complexes. How many unpaired electrons are present in each? Are the complexes paramagnetic or diamagnetic?

(a) Low-spin $[Co(NH_3)_6]^{3+}$ (b) High-spin $[CoF_6]^{3-}$

What Do You Know? From their formulas, we know that these have six ligands and we can presume that they have octahedral geometry. Both are complexes of cobalt(III), a metal ion with a d^6 configuration. One complex is low spin, the other high spin.

Strategy Set up an energy-level diagram for an octahedral complex. In low-spin complexes, the electrons are added preferentially to the lower-energy set of orbitals. In high-spin complexes, the first five electrons are added singly to each of the five orbitals, then additional electrons are paired with electrons in orbitals in the lower-energy set.

Solution

(a) The six electrons of the Co^{3+} ion fill the lower-energy set of orbitals entirely. This d^6 complex ion has no unpaired electrons and is diamagnetic.

(b) To obtain the electron configuration in high-spin $[CoF_6]^{3-}$, place one electron in each of the five d orbitals, and then place the sixth electron in one of the lower-energy orbitals. The complex has four unpaired electrons and is paramagnetic.

Electron configuration of low-spin, octahedral $[Co(NH_3)_6]^{3+}$

(a)

Electron configuration of high-spin, octahedral $[CoF_6]^{3-}$

(b)

Think about Your Answer The two complexes have different magnetic properties; low-spin $[Co(NH_3)_6]^{3+}$ is diamagnetic and high-spin $[CoF_6]^{3-}$ is paramagnetic. As expected, the low-spin complex has fewer unpaired electrons than the high-spin complex.

Check Your Understanding

For each of the following complex ions, give the oxidation number of the metal, depict possible low- and high-spin configurations, give the number of unpaired electrons in each configuration, and tell whether each is paramagnetic or diamagnetic.

(a) $[Ru(H_2O)_6]^{2+}$ (b) $[Ni(NH_3)_6]^{2+}$

REVIEW & CHECK FOR SECTION 22.5

1. Which of the following complexes has the greatest number of unpaired electrons?

(a) Low-spin $[Fe(CN)_6]^{4-}$ (c) $[V(H_2O)_6]^{3+}$

(b) High-spin $[Mn(NH_3)_6]^{2+}$ (d) $[Ni(en)_3]^{2+}$ (en = ethylenediamine)

2. Which of the following complexes is diamagnetic?

(a) Square-planar $[PtCl_4]^{2-}$ (c) $[Fe(H_2O)_6]^{3+}$

(b) Tetrahedral $[NiCl_4]^{2-}$ (d) High-spin $[CoF_6]^{3-}$

© Cengage Learning/Charles D. Winters

Fe³⁺(aq)   Co²⁺(aq)   Ni²⁺(aq)   Cu²⁺(aq)   Zn²⁺(aq)

FIGURE 22.26 Aqueous solutions of some transition metal ions. Compounds of transition metal elements are often colored, whereas those of main group metals are usually colorless. Pictured here, from *left* to *right*, are solutions of the nitrate salts of Fe^{3+}, Co^{2+}, Ni^{2+}, Cu^{2+}, and Zn^{2+}.

22.6 Colors of Coordination Compounds

The range of colors observed for compounds of the transition elements is one of their most interesting features (Figure 22.26). In contrast, compounds of main group metals are usually colorless. The underlying reason for this difference is that the color of transition metal compounds results from *d*-orbital splitting. Before discussing how *d*-orbital splitting is involved, however, we need to look more closely at what we mean by color.

Color

Visible light, consisting of radiation with wavelengths from 400 to 700 nm (◄ Section 6.1), represents a very small portion of the electromagnetic spectrum. Within this region are all the colors you see when white light passes through a prism: red, orange, yellow, green, blue, indigo, and violet (ROY G BIV). Each color is identified with a portion of the wavelength range.

Isaac Newton did experiments with light and established that the mind's perception of color requires only three colors! When we see white light, we are seeing a mixture of all of the colors—in other words, the superposition of red, green, and blue. If one or more of these colors is absent, the light of the other colors that reaches your eyes is interpreted by your mind as color.

Figure 22.27 will help you in analyzing perceived colors. This color wheel shows the three primary colors—red, green, and blue—as overlapping disks arranged in a triangle. The secondary colors—cyan, magenta, and yellow—appear where two disks overlap. The overlap of all three disks in the center produces white light.

The colors we perceive are determined as follows:

- Light of a single primary color is perceived as that color: Red light is perceived as red, green light as green, blue light as blue.
- Light made up of two primary colors is perceived as the color shown where the disks in Figure 22.27 overlap: Red and green light together appear yellow, green and blue light together are perceived as cyan; and red and blue light are perceived as magenta.
- Light made up of the three primary colors is white (colorless).

In discussing the color of a substance such as a coordination complex *in solution*, these guidelines are turned around because the color we see is the color of light *not* absorbed by the solution.

- Red color is the result of the absence of green and blue light from white light.
- Green color results if red and blue light are absent from white light.
- Blue color results if red and green light are absent.

λ (nm)

700

600

Wavelength increases

500

Energy increases

400

The ROY G BIV spectrum of colors of visible light. The colors used in printing this book are cyan, magenta, yellow, and black. The blue in ROY G BIV is actually cyan, according to color industry standards. Magenta doesn't have its own wavelength region. Rather, it is a mixture of blue and red.

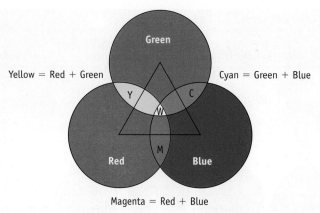

FIGURE 22.27 Using color disks to analyze colors. The three primary colors are red, green, and blue. Adding light of two primary colors gives the secondary colors yellow (= red + green), cyan (= green + blue), and magenta (= red + blue). Adding all three primary colors results in white light.

The secondary colors are rationalized similarly. Absorption of blue light gives yellow (the color across from it in Figure 22.27); absorption of red light results in cyan; and absorption of green light results in magenta.

Now we can apply these ideas to explain colors in transition metal complexes. Focus on what kind of light is *absorbed*. A solution of $[Ni(H_2O)_6]^{2+}$ is green. Green light is the result of removing red and blue light from white light. As white light passes through an aqueous solution of Ni^{2+}, red and blue light are absorbed, and green light is allowed to pass (Figure 22.28). Similarly, the $[Co(NH_3)_6]^{3+}$ ion is yellow because blue light has been absorbed and red and green light pass through.

The Spectrochemical Series

Recall that atomic spectra are obtained when electrons are excited from one energy level to another (◀ Section 6.3). The energy of the light absorbed or emitted is related to the energy levels of the atom or ion under study. The concept that light is absorbed when electrons move from lower to higher energy levels applies to all substances, not just atoms. It is the basic premise for the absorption of light for transition metal coordination complexes.

In coordination complexes, the splitting between *d* orbitals often corresponds to the energy of visible light, so light in the visible region of the spectrum is absorbed when electrons move from a lower-energy *d* orbital to a higher-energy *d* orbital. This change, as an electron moves between two orbitals having different energies in a complex, is called a **d-to-d transition**. Qualitatively, such a transition for $[Co(NH_3)_6]^{3+}$ might be represented using an energy-level diagram such as that shown here.

FIGURE 22.28 Light absorption and color. The color of a solution is due to the color of the light *not* absorbed by the solution. Here, a solution of Ni^{2+} ion in water absorbs red and blue light and so appears green. See also Figures 4.15–4.19.

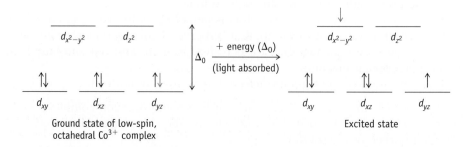

Experiments with coordination complexes reveal that, for a given metal ion, some ligands cause a small energy separation of the *d* orbitals, whereas others cause a large separation. In other words, some ligands create a small ligand field, and

© Cengage Learning/Charles D. Winters

Table 22.3 The Colors of Some Co^{3+} Complexes*

Complex Ion	Wavelength of Light Absorbed (nm)	Color of Light Absorbed	Color of Complex
$[CoF_6]^{3-}$	700	Red	Blue
$[Co(C_2O_4)_3]^{3-}$	600, 420	Yellow, violet	Dark green
$[Co(H_2O)_6]^{3+}$	600, 400	Yellow, violet	Blue-green
$[Co(NH_3)_6]^{3+}$	475, 340	Blue, ultraviolet	Yellow-orange
$[Co(en)_3]^{3+}$	470, 340	Blue, ultraviolet	Yellow-orange
$[Co(CN)_6]^{3-}$	310	Ultraviolet	Pale yellow

*The complex with fluoride ion, $[CoF_6]^{3-}$, is high spin and has one absorption band. The other complexes are low spin and have two absorption bands. In all but one case, one of these absorptions occurs in the visible region of the spectrum. The wavelengths are measured at the top of that absorption band.

others create a large one. An example is seen in the spectroscopic data for several cobalt(III) complexes presented in Table 22.3.

- Both $[Co(NH_3)_6]^{3+}$ and $[Co(en)_3]^{3+}$ are yellow-orange, because they absorb light in the blue portion of the visible spectrum. These compounds have very similar spectra, to be expected because both have six amine-type donor atoms (H—NH_2 or R—NH_2).
- Although $[Co(CN)_6]^{3-}$ does not have an absorption band whose maximum falls in the visible region, it is pale yellow. The peak of the absorption band occurs in the ultraviolet region, but the absorption band is broad and extends minimally into the visible (blue) region.
- $[Co(C_2O_4)_3]^{3-}$ and $[Co(H_2O)_6]^{3+}$ have similar absorptions, in the yellow and violet regions. Their colors are shades of green with a small difference due to the relative amount of light of each color being absorbed.

The wavelength of maximum absorption among the listed complexes ranges from 700 nm for $[CoF_6]^{3-}$ to 310 nm for $[Co(CN)_6]^{3-}$. The ligands change from member to member of this series, and we can conclude that the energy of the light absorbed by the complex is related to the different ligand field splittings, Δ_0, caused by the different ligands. Fluoride ion causes the smallest splitting of the d orbitals among the complexes listed in Table 22.3, whereas cyanide causes the largest splitting.

Spectra of complexes of other metals provide similar results. Based on this information, ligands can be listed in order of their ability to split the d orbitals. This list is called the **spectrochemical series** because it was determined by spectroscopy. A short list, with some of the more common ligands, follows:

$$F^-, Cl^-, Br^-, I^- < C_2O_4^{2-} < H_2O < NH_3 = en < phen < CN^-$$

small orbital splitting   large orbital splitting
small Δ_0 large Δ_0

The spectrochemical series is applicable to a wide range of metal complexes. Indeed, the ability of ligand field theory to explain the differences in the colors of the transition metal complexes is one of the strengths of this theory.

Based on the relative position of a ligand in the series, predictions can be made about a compound's magnetic behavior. Recall that d^4, d^5, d^6, and d^7 complexes can be high or low spin, depending on the ligand field splitting, Δ_0. Complexes formed with ligands near the left end of the spectrochemical series are expected to have small Δ_0 values and, therefore, are likely to be high spin. In contrast, complexes with ligands near the right end are expected to have large Δ_0 values and low-spin configurations. The complex $[CoF_6]^{3-}$ is high spin, whereas $[Co(NH_3)_6]^{3+}$ and the other complexes in Table 22.3 are low spin.

PROBLEM SOLVING TIP 22.1

Ligand Field Theory

This summary of the concepts of ligand field theory may help you to keep the broader picture in mind.

- Ligand–metal bonding results from the electrostatic attraction between a metal cation and either an anion or a polar molecule.
- The ligands define a coordination geometry. Common geometries are linear (coordination number = 2), tetrahedral and square-planar (coordination number = 4), and octahedral (coordination number = 6).
- The placement of the ligands around the metal causes the d orbitals on the metal

to have different energies. In an octahedral complex, for example, the d orbitals divide into two groups: a higher-energy group ($d_{x^2-y^2}$ and d_{z^2}) and a lower-energy group (d_{xy}, d_{xz}, and d_{yz}).

- Electrons are placed in the metal d orbitals in a manner that leads to the lowest total energy. Two competing features determine the placement: the relative energy of the sets of orbitals and the electron pairing energy.
- For the electron configurations of d^4, d^5, d^6, and d^7 in octahedral complexes, two electron configurations are possible:

high spin, which occurs when the orbital splitting is small, and low spin, which occurs with a large orbital splitting. To determine whether a complex is high spin or low spin, measure its magnetism to determine the number of unpaired electrons.

- The d-orbital splitting (the energy difference between the metal d-orbital energies) often corresponds to the energy associated with visible light. As a consequence, many metal complexes absorb visible light and thus are colored.

EXAMPLE 22.6 Spectrochemical Series

Problem An aqueous solution of $[Fe(H_2O)_6]^{2+}$ is light blue-green. Do you expect the d^6 Fe^{2+} ion in this complex to have a high- or low-spin configuration? How could you test your prediction experimentally?

What Do You Know? This is an octahedral complex of Fe^{2+}, an ion with a d^6 configuration. The blue-green color is the result of the absorption of visible light due to a d-to-d transition. The complex could be either low spin (no unpaired electrons) or high spin (four unpaired electrons).

Strategy Use the color wheel in Figure 22.27 to determine what color light is transmitted and therefore what color of light has been absorbed. Based on the energy of the light absorbed, determine if Δ_0 is high or low. If it is low, then the complex is high spin. If it is high, then the complex is low spin.

Solution In this case, the blue-green color of the solution indicates that blue and green light is transmitted. This implies that red light was absorbed. The low energy of the light absorbed suggests that $[Fe(H_2O)_6]^{2+}$ is likely to be a high-spin complex. If the complex is high spin, it will have four unpaired electrons and be paramagnetic; if, contrary to our prediction, it is low spin, it will have no unpaired electrons and be diamagnetic. Thus, identifying the presence of four unpaired electrons by measuring the compound's magnetism can be used to verify the high-spin configuration experimentally.

Think about Your Answer The spectrochemical series was generated by measuring the absorptions for a series of complexes of a given metal, varying the ligands. As in the example here, the spectrochemical series is useful because it allows you to predict whether a complex is likely to be high or low spin. The more definitive evidence for high or low spin comes from information on the magnetism of the complex.

Check Your Understanding

1. The complex $[Co(NH_3)_5OH]^{2+}$ has an absorption maximum at 500 nm. What color of light is absorbed and what color is the complex?

2. Figure 22.17 shows a sample of yellow $[Co(NH_3)_5NO_2]^{2+}$. What color of light is absorbed by this complex? Predict whether this is a high-spin or low-spin complex.

REVIEW & CHECK FOR SECTION 22.6

Solutions of each of the following complexes absorb light in the visible region of the spectrum. Predict which complex will absorb light of the longest wavelength.

(a) $[Cr(H_2O)_6]^{3+}$ (b) $[Cr(NH_3)_6]^{3+}$ (c) $[CrF_6]^{3-}$ (d) $[Cr(CN)_6]^{3-}$

CASE STUDY

Accidental Discovery of a Chemotherapy Agent

There are many naturally occurring metal-based molecules such as heme, vitamin B_{12}, and the enzyme involved in fixing nitrogen (nitrogenase). Chemists have also synthesized various metal-based compounds for medical purposes. One of these, *cisplatin* [$PtCl_2(NH_3)_2$], was known for many years, but it was discovered serendipitously to be effective in treatment of certain kinds of cancers.

In 1965, Barnett Rosenberg, a biophysicist at Michigan State University, set out to study the effect of electric fields on living cells, but the results of his experiments were very different from his expectations. He and his students had placed an aqueous suspension of live *Escherichia coli* bacteria in an electric field between supposedly inert platinum electrodes. Much to their surprise, they found that cell growth was significantly affected. After careful experimentation, the effect on cell division was found to be due to a trace of a complex of platinum, ammonia, and chloride ion formed by an electrolytic process involving the platinum electrode in the presence of ammonia in the growth medium.

To follow up on this interesting discovery, Rosenberg and his students tested the effect of *cis-* and *trans-*$PtCl_2(NH_3)_2$ on cell growth and found that only the *cis* isomer

was effective. This led Rosenberg and others to study the effect of so-called *cisplatin* on cancer cell growth, and the result is that cisplatin and similar compounds are now used to treat genitourinary tumors. In fact, testicular cancer in particular is now considered largely curable because of cisplatin chemotherapy.

The chemistry of cisplatin has now been thoroughly studied and illustrates many of the principles of transition metal coordination chemistry. It has been found that cisplatin has a half-life of 2.5 hours for the replacement of a Cl^- ligand by water at 310 K (in a first order reaction) and that the replacement of a second Cl^- ligand by water is slightly faster.

The aqua species are acidic and damaging to the kidneys, so cisplatin is generally used in a saline solution to prevent the hydrolysis reactions. It has been found that, in blood plasma at pH 7.4 and with a Cl^- ion concentration of about 1.04×10^{-5} M, $PtCl_2(NH_3)_2$

and $PtCl(OH)(NH_3)_2$ are the dominant species. In the cell nucleus, however, the Cl^- ion concentration is lower, and the aqua species are present in higher concentration.

Question:
If a patient is given 10.0 mg of cisplatin, what quantity remains as cisplatin at 24 hours?

The answer to this question is available in Appendix N.

$k = 7.6 \times 10^{-5}$ s^{-1}

$k = 2.3 \times 10^{-4}$ s^{-1}

$pK_a = 6.6$

$pK_a = 5.5$

$pK_a = 7.3$

22.7 Organometallic Chemistry: Compounds with Metal–Carbon Bonds

One of the largest and most active areas of chemistry over the past half-century has been the field of organometallic chemistry, the study of molecules having metal–carbon bonds. Thousands of such compounds have been made and characterized, and much of the activity has involved transition metals. Many have unique bonding modes and structures. In recent years, organometallic compounds have also found particularly widespread use as reagents in organic synthesis and as catalysts for economically important chemical reactions.

Carbon Monoxide Complexes of Metals

In the earlier discussion of hemoglobin (page 1032), you learned that the iron in this biologically important complex binds not only to O_2 but also to CO. Our understanding of metal–CO complexes, however, emerged from the solution to a problem in industrial chemistry at the end of the 19th century.

The synthesis of sodium carbonate from NaCl, CO_2, NH_3, and H_2O by the Solvay process was an important chemical industry in the late 19th century (and remains so today in some parts of the world; page 972). In the late 1800s, a Solvay plant in England had a problem: The valves used to conduct the gaseous reactants and products rapidly corroded. A German chemist, Ludwig Mond (1839–1909), traced this problem to a small quantity of CO in the gas stream. Carbon monoxide gas reacted with nickel metal in the valves to form $Ni(CO)_4$ (Figure 22.29), tetracarbonyl nickel, a volatile liquid with a low boiling point (bp 47 °C). The

FIGURE 22.29 Metals carbonyls. $Ni(CO)_4$ is a tetrahedral molecule. Pentacarbonyliron(O) [$Fe(CO)_5$] is trigonal bipyramidal, whereas $Mo(CO)_6$ is octahedral, and the geometry around the manganese atom in $Mn_2(CO)_{10}$ is likewise octahedral (with the sixth position being an Mn—Mn bond).

$Ni(CO)_4$ $Fe(CO)_5$ $Mo(CO)_6$ $Mn_2(CO)_{10}$

deterioration of the valves occurred when the gaseous $Ni(CO)_4$ that formed was carried away in the effluent gas stream.

$$Ni(s) + 4\ CO(g) \rightleftharpoons Ni(CO)_4(g)$$

Mond determined that the reaction forming $Ni(CO)_4$ is reversible; at moderate temperatures or at low pressures, CO is liberated, and nickel metal re-forms. He then exploited the formation and decomposition reactions in a process to obtain pure nickel. Nickel and cobalt are generally found together in nature. Because of this, the two metals are obtained together when ores are refined, and they are difficult to separate. However, if a mixture of the metals is exposed to CO, nickel is converted to $Ni(CO)_4$ whereas cobalt is unchanged. Volatile $Ni(CO)_4$ is easily separated from solid cobalt metal. The $Ni(CO)_4$ can then be decomposed to give pure nickel. The Mond process, as it is now known, was the preferred procedure to obtain pure nickel for the first half of the 20th century.

Nickel is unique among metals in its facile reaction with CO, but many other transition metal carbonyl compounds are now known and can be synthesized by a variety of procedures. One of the most common is reductive carbonylation, in which a metal salt is reduced in the presence of CO, usually under high pressure. In effect, reduction of the metal salt gives metal atoms. Before these very reactive atoms aggregate to form the unreactive bulk metal, however, they react with CO. Metal carbonyls of most of the transition metals can be made by this route. Simple examples include hexacarbonyls of the Group 6B metals [$Cr(CO)_6$, $Mo(CO)_6$, and $W(CO)_6$,] as well as $Fe(CO)_5$ and $Mn_2(CO)_{10}$ (Figure 22.29).

The Effective Atomic Number Rule and Bonding in Organometallic Compounds

● **Terminology in Organometallic Chemistry** The standard terminology of coordination chemistry applies to metal carbonyls. In tetracarbonylnickel(0), for example, the metal is formally zerovalent, and CO molecules are ligands. The metal has a coordination number of 4 and a tetrahedral coordination geometry.

An important observation has guided researchers studying these metal–CO complexes and other organometallic compounds. The **effective atomic number (EAN) rule**, now often referred to as the **18-electron rule**, states that compounds in which the sum of the metal valence electrons plus the electrons donated by the ligand groups totals 18 are likely to be stable. Thus, the 18-electron rule predicts the stoichiometry of a number of compounds. Iron(0), for example, which has eight valence electrons, would be expected to coordinate to five CO ligands. Each CO donates two electrons for a total of 10; adding these to the eight valence electrons on the metal gives 18 electrons around the Fe atom (Figure 22.30). We now recognize that the 18-electron rule is similar to the octet rule in main group chemistry, in that it defines the likely number of bonds to an element.

5 **CO** ligands donate a total of **10** electrons.

Each **CO** donates 2 electrons.

The **Fe** atom has 8 valence electrons.

FIGURE 22.30 The EAN rule and $Fe(CO)_5$. The EAN or 18-electron rule states that stable organometallic compounds frequently have 18 valence electrons around the central metal. (There are also many 16-electron molecules, particularly of the heavier transition metals. See Study Question 22.34.) Here, the zerovalent Fe atom has the configuration [Ar]$3d^6 4s^2$, so eight valence electrons are available for bonding.

The bonding in traditional coordination compounds is described as being due to attractive forces between a positively charged metal ion and a polar molecule or an anion, and the properties of these species are in accord with substantial ionic character to the metal–ligand bond. In metal carbonyls, the zerovalent metal lacks a charge, and CO is only slightly polar. Both features argue against ionic bonding. The best model for these species instead describes the bonding between the metal and CO as covalent. Each CO donates a C-atom lone pair to the metal atom to form a sigma bond (Figure 22.31). However, carbon monoxide is a very poor donor, and this alone would not lead to these species being stable. Rather, in conjunction with

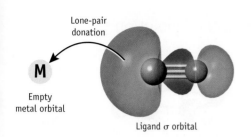

Lone-pair donation

M

Empty metal orbital

Ligand σ orbital

Ligand to metal sigma bonding.
Donation of **CO** lone pair to empty orbital on **M**.

Electron donation

M

Metal d orbital

Empty ligand π^* orbital

Metal to ligand pi bonding.
Donation of electrons from filled **M** d orbital to empty π^* antibonding orbital on **CO**.

FIGURE 22.31 Bonding in metal carbonyls. The current understanding is that the CO ligand donates a lone pair of electrons to the low-valent metal to form a sigma bond. The electron-rich metal then donates electrons from a d orbital to the antibonding π^* orbital of the CO. There is a "synergistic" effect; the sigma and pi bonds complement each other.

the sigma bond, the electron-rich metal donates a pair of electrons to form a π bond formed by overlap of a d orbital of the metal and a π^* antibonding orbital of CO. The latter interaction is described as $d\pi$–$p\pi$ bonding. Based on this model of bonding, carbon monoxide in these compounds is best described as a σ donor and π acceptor ligand.

Ligands in Organometallic Compounds

The bonding model for metal–CO complexes leads to important conclusions: Only metals of low charge and with filled or partially filled d orbitals can form stable bonds to CO, and only ligands capable of forming π bonds with the metal are capable of forming low-valent metal compounds. Thus, this area is dominated by low-valent metals and special types of ligands that are capable of π bonding.

Some of the most common ligands in coordination chemistry cannot engage in π bonding and thus cannot form low-valent compounds with transition metals. For example, low-valent metal complexes with NH_3 or amines (such as $N(CH_3)_3$) do not exist, but phosphine complexes of zerovalent metals are well known. Phosphines, such as $P(CH_3)_3$, are the phosphorus analogs of amines and so have a lone pair of electrons on the P atom. Thus, phosphines can donate this lone pair to a metal to form a sigma bond. In addition, phosphorus atoms have empty $3d$ orbitals, and these can overlap with the filled d orbitals of a low-valent metal. Ammonia, with no empty valence orbitals to overlap with a filled metal d orbitals cannot form such π bonds.

Yet another class of molecules that can serve as ligands in organometallic compounds are organic species such as ethylene (C_2H_4) and benzene (C_6H_6). For example, in the anion of Zeise's salt, ethylene binds to a Pt^{2+} ion through donation of the two π electrons of the double bond (Figure 22.32). As in metal carbonyls, there is also a metal-to-ligand π bond formed by overlap of filled metal d orbitals with the antibonding π orbitals from the ligand. This combination of bonding modes strengthens the metal–ligand bond.

Benzene can be thought of as a tridentate ligand capable of donating three π electron pairs to a metal atom (which then donates d electrons back to the ligand in a π-type interaction). Such molecules also obey the 18-electron rule. For example, in dibenzenechromium (Figure 22.33), the Cr(0) atom with six valence electrons is bound to two ligands, each donating six π electrons.

Dibenzenechromium is one of many organometallic compounds often referred to as "sandwich" compounds. (See *Case Study: Ferrocene—The Beginning of a Chemical Revolution*, page 1051.) These are molecular compounds in which a low-valent metal atom is "sandwiched" between two organic ligands. In addition, they are often referred to as π complexes because the π electrons of the ligand are involved in bonding. Modern terminology uses the Greek letter eta (η) to indicate this type of attachment, so dibenzenechromium is properly symbolized as $Cr(\eta^6\text{-}C_6H_6)_2$ (where the superscript 6 indicates the number of carbon atoms involved in bonding on each ligand).

Zeise's salt
$[(C_2H_4)PtCl_3]^-$

Electron density transferred from π bonding MO of C_2H_4 to Pt^{2+}

C_2H_4
π_{2p}

Pt^{2+}

Electron density transferred from Pt^{2+} to π antibonding MO of C_2H_4

C_2H_4
π^*_{2p}

Pt^{2+}

FIGURE 22.32 Bonding in the anion of Zeise's salt.

Cr

FIGURE 22.33 Dibenzenechromium. Two views of the molecule. *(top)*: A computer-generated model. *(bottom)*: A line drawing typically used by chemists.

CASE STUDY

Unexpected discoveries open up new areas of science.

Ferrocene—The Beginning of a Chemical Revolution

One example was the synthesis of compounds of Xe (page 400), a result that destroyed the myth that the noble gases were unreactive and led to a rich chemistry of these elements. At approximately the same time, another discovery, the synthesis of ferrocene, $Fe(C_5H_5)_2$, set the stage for the rapid and exciting growth of organometallic chemistry, the chemistry of compounds containing metal–carbon bonds. This destroyed another common myth of the time, that metal–carbon bonds are inherently unstable. Xenon compounds and ferrocene spearheaded a renaissance in inorganic chemistry that continues to this day.

The synthesis of ferrocene in two quite dissimilar research laboratories was accidental and unexpected. The first report, from an academic laboratory, described the reaction of the cyclopentadienide anion, $[C_5H_5]^-$ with $FeCl_2$. This reaction was intended to provide a precursor to an elusive organic compound fulvalene, $(C_5H_4)_2$ but a completely new substance—ferrocene—was obtained instead.

$2\ C_5H_5MgCl + FeCl_2 \rightarrow Fe(\eta^5\text{-}C_5H_5)_2 + 2\ MgCl_2$
(in diethyl ether)

The second report, from an industrial laboratory, described a high-temperature process in which cyclopentadiene was passed over a catalyst that contained, among other things, iron(II) oxide.

$2\ C_5H_6(g) + FeO(s) \rightarrow$
$\qquad Fe(\eta^5\text{-}C_5H_5)_2(s) + H_2O(g)$
(at high temperature)

The properties of ferrocene were unexpected. Ferrocene is a diamagnetic orange solid, has a relatively low melting point (mp 173 °C), and is soluble in organic solvents but not in water. Most striking is its thermal and oxidative stability. Ferrocene is unaffected by oxygen, water, aqueous bases and nonoxidizing acids under ambient conditions, and can be heated to over 450 °C without decomposing. These observations contradicted conventional wisdom that held that metal–carbon bonds were weak and unstable, hard to make, and reactive.

The structure of ferrocene was quickly established by x-ray crystallography. Like dibenzenechromium (Figure 22.33), ferrocene is a molecular "sandwich" compound, containing an iron atom sandwiched between two planar hydrocarbon rings (Figure). Iron(II), a d^6 metal ion, is in its low-spin configuration. The cyclopentadienyl anions can be thought of as tridentate ligands with the six π electrons (three pairs) of each organic ring being donated to the metal ion.

Once the structure of ferrocene was known, the race was on to make other complexes with unsaturated hydrocarbon ligands. Synthesis of cyclopentadienyl compounds of other metals soon followed, and now hundreds are known in combination with CO, benzene, ethylene, and many other carbon-containing compounds. The discovery of ferrocene was one of the keys that unlocked the field of organometallic chemistry.

The structure of ferrocene, $Fe(\eta^5\text{-}C_5H_5)_2$

Questions:

1. Rationalize ferrocene's diamagnetism.
2. Dibenzenechromium is also a "sandwich" compound. What is the oxidation state of chromium in this compound? Is it diamagnetic or paramagnetic?
3. Do ferrocene and dibenzenechromium obey the 18-electron rule (page 1048)?
4. Ferrocene can be oxidized to form the ferrocenium cation, $[Fe(\eta\text{-}C_5H_5)_2]^+$. The standard reduction potential for the ferrocenium–ferrocene half-reaction is 0.400 V. Identify several oxidizing agents in Appendix M that are capable of oxidizing ferrocene. Is elemental chlorine, Cl_2, a sufficiently strong oxidizing agent to carry out this oxidation?
5. Write an equation for one way to synthesize nickelocene, $Ni(\eta^5\text{-}C_5H_5)_2$. Nickelocene is paramagnetic. Predict the number of unpaired electrons in this compound.

Answers to these questions are available in Appendix N.

EXAMPLE 22.7   The Effective Atomic Number Rule

Problem Show that each of the following molecules or ions satisfies the EAN rule.

(a) $[Fe(CO)_2(\eta^5\text{-}C_5H_5)]^-$ (b) $[Mn(CO)_5]^-$ (c) $Co(C_2H_4)_2(\eta^5\text{-}C_5H_5)$

What Do You Know? The formulas of the several complexes are given. Recognize that CO and C_2H_4 are both two-electron donors and that the $C_5H_5^-$ ion is a six-electron donor.

Strategy A complex obeys the EAN rule if the total number of electrons around the metal (valence electrons from the metal plus electrons donated by the ligands) equals 18. For the metal center, take its total number of valence electrons, and add or subtract electrons as necessary to adjust for negative or positive charges.

Solution

(a) The overall charge is 1−, which is equal to the charge on the $C_5H_5^-$ group. Thus, the Fe atom must have no charge.

6 electrons for $C_5H_5^-$ + 8 electrons for Fe + 4 electrons for 2 CO groups = 18 electrons

(b) Because CO is neutral the Mn center must have a negative charge. This means the manganese center has effectively eight valence electrons. Together with the five CO groups, each donating two electrons, the total is 18 electrons.

(c) This is a neutral molecule, so the negative charge on the $C_5H_5^-$ group must be balanced by a positive charge on Co. The Co^+ ion has eight valence electrons. Each C_2H_4 molecule donates two electrons.

6 electrons for $C_5H_5^-$ + 8 electrons for Co^+ + 4 electrons for 2 C_2H_4 molecules = 18 electrons

Think about Your Answer The octet rule and the 18-electron rule have similar rationales. According to the octet rule, 8 electrons (4 pairs) are required to fill all the bonding and non-bonding orbitals for main group elements. By analogy, complexes obeying the 18-electron rule will have 18 electrons (9 pairs) filling all the bonding and nonbonding orbitals for *d*-block elements.

Check Your Understanding

What must the charge of the metal in each species be for the species to satisfy the EAN rule?

REVIEW & CHECK FOR SECTION 22.7

Which of the following formulas does not obey the 18-electron rule?

(a) $Mn(CO)_5H$

(b) $[V(CO)_6]^-$

(c) $[Co(\eta^5-C_5H_5)_2]^+$

(d) The anion in Zeise's salt, $[Pt(\eta^2-C_2H_4)Cl_3]^-$

CHAPTER GOALS REVISITED

Now that you have studied this chapter, you should ask whether you have met the chapter goals. In particular, you should be able to:

Identify and explain the chemical and physical properties of the transition elements
a. Identify the general classes of transition elements (Section 22.1).
b. Identify the transition metals from their symbols and positions in the periodic table, and recall some physical and chemical properties (Section 22.1).
c. Understand the electrochemical nature of corrosion (Section 22.1).
d. Describe the metallurgy of iron and copper (Section 22.2).

Understand the composition, structure, and bonding in coordination compounds
a. Given the formula for a coordination complex, identify the metal and its oxidation state, the ligands, the coordination number and coordination geometry, and the overall charge on the complex (Section 22.3). Relate names and formulas of complexes. **Study Questions: 9–18, 48, 49, 57.**
b. Given the formula for a complex, be able to recognize whether isomers will exist, and draw their structures (Section 22.4). **Study Questions: 41, 44, 45, 47, 48.**

Sign in at **www.cengage.com/owl** to:
- View tutorials and simulations, develop problem-solving skills, and complete online homework assigned by your professor.
- For quick review and exam prep, download Go Chemistry mini lecture modules from OWL (or purchase them at **www.cengagebrain.com**)

Access **How Do I Solve It?** tutorials on how to approach problem solving using concepts in this chapter.

c. Describe the bonding in coordination complexes (Section 22.5). Study Question: 42.

d. Apply the principles of stoichiometry, thermodynamics, and equilibrium to transition metal compounds. Study Questions: 64, 67, 68, 70.

Relate ligand field theory to the magnetic and spectroscopic properties of the complexes

a. Understand why substances are colored (Section 22.6). Study Questions: 31, 32, 43.

b. Understand the relationship between the ligand field splitting, magnetism, and color of complexes (Sections 22.5–22.6). Study Questions: 23–30, 36, 37, 44, 45, 52, 55, 56, 60, 63.

Apply the effective atomic number (EAN) rule to simple organometallic compounds of the transition metals

a. Apply the EAN rule to molecules containing a low-valent metal and ligands such as C_6H_6, C_2H_4, and CO (Section 22.7). Study Questions: 33, 34, 68, 71.

Study Questions

ʊWL Interactive versions of these questions are assignable in OWL.

▲ denotes challenging questions.

Blue-numbered questions have answers in Appendix R and fully worked solutions in the *Student Solutions Manual*.

Practicing Skills

Properties of Transition Elements
(See Section 22.1 and Example 7.3.)

1. Give the electron configuration for each of the following ions, and tell whether each is paramagnetic or diamagnetic.
   (a) Cr^{3+} (b) V^{2+} (c) Ni^{2+} (d) Cu^+

2. Identify two transition metal cations with each of the following electron configurations.
   (a) $[Ar]3d^6$ (b) $[Ar]3d^{10}$ (c) $[Ar]3d^5$ (d) $[Ar]3d^8$

3. Identify a cation of a first series transition metal that is isoelectronic with each of the following.
   (a) Fe^{3+} (b) Zn^{2+} (c) Fe^{2+} (d) Cr^{3+}

4. Match up the isoelectronic ions on the following list.
   $$Cu^+ \ Mn^{2+} \ Fe^{2+} \ Co^{3+} \ Fe^{3+} \ Zn^{2+} \ Ti^{2+} \ V^{3+}$$

5. The following equations represent various ways of obtaining transition metals from their compounds. Balance each equation.
   (a) $Cr_2O_3(s) + Al(s) \longrightarrow Al_2O_3(s) + Cr(s)$
   (b) $TiCl_4(\ell) + Mg(s) \longrightarrow Ti(s) + MgCl_2(s)$
   (c) $[Ag(CN)_2]^-(aq) + Zn(s) \longrightarrow$
   $$Ag(s) + [Zn(CN)_4]^{2-}(aq)$$
   (d) $Mn_3O_4(s) + Al(s) \longrightarrow Mn(s) + Al_2O_3(s)$

6. Identify the products of each reaction, and balance the equation.
   (a) $CuSO_4(aq) + Zn(s) \longrightarrow$
   (b) $Zn(s) + HCl(aq) \longrightarrow$
   (c) $Fe(s) + Cl_2(g) \longrightarrow$
   (d) $V(s) + O_2(g) \longrightarrow$

Formulas of Coordination Compounds
(See Examples 22.1 and 22.2.)

7. Which of the following ligands is expected to be monodentate, and which might be polydentate?
   (a) CH_3NH_2 (d) en
   (b) CH_3CN (e) Br^-
   (c) N_3^- (f) phen

8. One of the following nitrogen compounds or ions is not capable of serving as a ligand: NH_4^+, NH_3, NH_2^-. Identify this species, and explain your answer.

9. Give the oxidation number of the metal ion in each of the following compounds.
   (a) $[Mn(NH_3)_6]SO_4$ (c) $[Co(NH_3)_4Cl_2]Cl$
   (b) $K_3[Co(CN)_6]$ (d) $Cr(en)_2Cl_2$

10. Give the oxidation number of the metal ion in each of the following complexes.
    (a) $[Fe(NH_3)_6]^{2+}$ (c) $[Co(NH_3)_5(NO_2)]^+$
    (b) $[Zn(CN)_4]^{2-}$ (d) $[Cu(en)_2]^{2+}$

11. Give the formula of a complex constructed from one Ni^{2+} ion, one ethylenediamine ligand, three ammonia molecules, and one water molecule. Is the complex neutral or is it charged? If charged, give the charge.

12. Give the formula of a complex constructed from one Cr^{3+} ion, two ethylenediamine ligands, and two ammonia molecules. Is the complex neutral or is it charged? If charged, give the charge.

Naming Coordination Compounds
(See Example 22.3.)

13. Write formulas for the following ions or compounds.
    (a) dichlorobis(ethylenediamine)nickel(II)
    (b) potassium tetrachloroplatinate(II)
    (c) potassium dicyanocuprate(I)
    (d) tetraamminediaquairon(II)

14. Write formulas for the following ions or compounds.
    (a) diamminetriaquahydroxochromium(II) nitrate
    (b) hexaammineiron(III) nitrate
    (c) pentacarbonyliron(0) (where the ligand is CO)
    (d) ammonium tetrachlorocuprate(II)

15. Name the following ions or compounds.
    (a) $[Ni(C_2O_4)_2(H_2O)_2]^{2-}$ (c) $[Co(en)_2(NH_3)Cl]^{2+}$
    (b) $[Co(en)_2Br_2]^+$ (d) $Pt(NH_3)_2(C_2O_4)$

16. Name the following ions or compounds.
    (a) $[Co(H_2O)_4Cl_2]^+$ (c) $[Pt(NH_3)Br_3]^-$
    (b) $Co(H_2O)_3F_3$ (d) $[Co(en)(NH_3)_3Cl]^{2+}$

17. Give the name or formula for each ion or compound, as appropriate.
    (a) pentaaquahydroxoiron(III) ion
    (b) $K_2[Ni(CN)_4]$
    (c) $K[Cr(C_2O_4)_2(H_2O)_2]$
    (d) ammonium tetrachloroplatinate(II)

18. Give the name or formula for each ion or compound, as appropriate.
    (a) tetraaquadichlorochromium(III) chloride
    (b) $[Cr(NH_3)_5SO_4]Cl$
    (c) sodium tetrachlorocobaltate(II)
    (d) $[Fe(C_2O_4)_3]^{3-}$

Isomerism
(See Example 22.4.)

19. Draw all possible geometric isomers of the following.
    (a) $Fe(NH_3)_4Cl_2$
    (b) $Pt(NH_3)_2(SCN)(Br)$ (SCN^- is bonded to Pt^{2+} through S)
    (c) $Co(NH_3)_3(NO_2)_3$ (NO_2^- is bonded to Co^{3+} through N)
    (d) $[Co(en)Cl_4]^-$

20. In which of the following complexes are geometric isomers possible? If isomers are possible, draw their structures and label them as *cis* or *trans,* or as *fac* or *mer.*
    (a) $[Co(H_2O)_4Cl_2]^+$ (c) $[Pt(NH_3)Br_3]^-$
    (b) $Co(NH_3)_3F_3$ (d) $[Co(en)_2(NH_3)Cl]^{2+}$

21. Determine whether the following complexes have a chiral metal center.
    (a) $[Fe(en)_3]^{2+}$
    (b) *trans*-$[Co(en)_2Br_2]^+$
    (c) *fac*-$[Co(en)(H_2O)Cl_3]$
    (d) square-planar $Pt(NH_3)(H_2O)(Cl)(NO_2)$

22. Four geometric isomers are possible for $[Co(en)(NH_3)_2(H_2O)Cl]^+$. Draw the structures of all four. (Two of the isomers are chiral, meaning that each has a non-superimposable mirror image.)

Magnetic Properties of Complexes
(See Example 22.5.)

23. The following are low-spin complexes. Use the ligand field model to find the electron configuration of the central metal ion in each ion. Determine which are diamagnetic. Give the number of unpaired electrons for the paramagnetic complexes.
    (a) $[Mn(CN)_6]^{4-}$ (c) $[Fe(H_2O)_6]^{3+}$
    (b) $[Co(NH_3)_6]Cl_3$ (d) $[Cr(en)_3]SO_4$

24. The following are high-spin complexes. Use the ligand field model to find the electron configuration of the central metal ion in each ion. Determine the number of unpaired electrons, if any, in each.
    (a) $K_4[FeF_6]$ (c) $[Cr(H_2O)_6]^{2+}$
    (b) $[MnF_6]^{4-}$ (d) $(NH_4)_3[FeF_6]$

25. Determine the number of unpaired electrons in the following tetrahedral complexes. All tetrahedral complexes are high spin.
    (a) $[FeCl_4]^{2-}$ (c) $[MnCl_4]^{2-}$
    (b) $Na_2[CoCl_4]$ (d) $(NH_4)_2[ZnCl_4]$

26. Determine the number of unpaired electrons in the following tetrahedral complexes. All tetrahedral complexes are high spin.
    (a) $[Zn(H_2O)_4]^{2+}$ (c) $Mn(NH_3)_2Cl_2$
    (b) $VOCl_3$ (d) $[Cu(en)_2]^{2+}$

27. For the high-spin complex $[Fe(H_2O)_6]SO_4$, identify the following:
    (a) the coordination number of iron
    (b) the coordination geometry for iron
    (c) the oxidation number of iron
    (d) the number of unpaired electrons
    (e) whether the complex is diamagnetic or paramagnetic

28. For the low-spin complex $[Co(en)(NH_3)_2Cl_2]ClO_4$, identify the following:
    (a) the coordination number of cobalt
    (b) the coordination geometry for cobalt
    (c) the oxidation number of cobalt
    (d) the number of unpaired electrons
    (e) whether the complex is diamagnetic or paramagnetic
    (f) Draw any geometric isomers.

29. The anion $[NiCl_4]^{2-}$ is paramagnetic, but when CN^- ions are added, the product, $[Ni(CN)_4]^{2-}$, is diamagnetic. Explain this observation.

$$[NiCl_4]^{2-}(aq) + 4\ CN^-(aq) \longrightarrow$$
paramagnetic
$$[Ni(CN)_4]^{2-}(aq) + 4\ Cl^-(aq)$$
diamagnetic

30. An aqueous solution of iron(II) sulfate is paramagnetic. If NH_3 is added, the solution becomes diamagnetic. Why does the magnetism change?

Spectroscopy of Complexes
(See Example 22.6.)

31. In water, the titanium(III) ion, $[Ti(H_2O)_6]^{3+}$, has a broad absorption band centered at about 500 nm. What color light is absorbed by the ion?

32. In water, the chromium(II) ion, $[Cr(H_2O)_6]^{2+}$, absorbs light with a wavelength of about 700 nm. What color is the solution?

Organometallic Compounds
(See Example 22.7.)

33. Show that the molecules and ions below satisfy the EAN rule.
    (a) $[Mn(CO)_6]^+$ (b)   (c)

(In (b) PR_3 is a phosphine such as $P(C_6H_5)_3$, a two-electron donor ligand.)

34. Many organometallic compounds of the transition metals satisfy the 18-electron rule. However, there also are many other stable molecules that have only 16-valence electrons. These often have the capability of adding more ligands and function as catalysts in chemical reactions (see Study Question 71). (In the molecules below, PR_3 is a phosphine such as $P(C_6H_5)_3$, a two-electron donor ligand. For electron counting purposes, the CH_3 or methyl group is considered an anion, $(CH_3)^-$, and also a two-electron donor ligand.) Which molecules below have 18-valence electrons and which have 16?

General Questions

These questions are not designated as to type or location in the chapter. They may contain several concepts.

35. Describe an experiment that would determine whether nickel in $K_2[NiCl_4]$ is square-planar or tetrahedral.

36. Which of the following high-spin complexes has the greatest number of unpaired electrons?
    (a) $[Cr(H_2O)_6]^{3+}$ (c) $[Fe(H_2O)_6]^{2+}$
    (b) $[Mn(H_2O)_6]^{2+}$ (d) $[Ni(H_2O)_6]^{2+}$

37. How many unpaired electrons are expected for high-spin and low-spin complexes of Fe^{2+}?

38. Excess silver nitrate is added to a solution containing 1.0 mol of $[Co(NH_3)_4Cl_2]Cl$. What amount of AgCl (in moles) will precipitate?

39. Which of the following complex ions is (are) square-planar?
    (a) $[Ti(CN)_4]^{2-}$ (c) $[Zn(CN)_4]^{2-}$
    (b) $[Ni(CN)_4]^{2-}$ (d) $[Pt(CN)_4]^{2-}$

40. Which of the following complex ions containing the oxalate ion is (are) chiral?
    (a) $[Fe(C_2O_4)Cl_4]^{2-}$
    (b) *cis*-$[Fe(C_2O_4)_2Cl_2]^{2-}$
    (c) *trans*-$[Fe(C_2O_4)_2Cl_2]^{2-}$

41. How many geometric isomers are possible for the square-planar complex ion $[Pt(NH_3)(CN)Cl_2]^-$?

42. For a tetrahedral complex of a metal in the first transition series, which of the following statements concerning energies of the $3d$ orbitals is correct?
    (a) The five d orbitals have the same energy.
    (b) The $d_{x^2-y^2}$ and d_{z^2} orbitals are higher in energy than the d_{xz}, d_{yz}, and d_{xy} orbitals.
    (c) The d_{xz}, d_{yz}, and d_{xy} orbitals are higher in energy than the $d_{x^2-y^2}$ and d_{z^2} orbitals.
    (d) The d orbitals all have different energies.

43. A transition metal coordination compound absorbs 425-nm light. What is its color?
    (a) red   (c) yellow
    (b) green   (d) blue

44. For the low-spin coordination compound $[Fe(en)_2Cl_2]Cl$, identify the following.
    (a) the oxidation number of iron
    (b) the coordination number for iron
    (c) the coordination geometry for iron
    (d) the number of unpaired electrons per metal atom
    (e) whether the complex is diamagnetic or paramagnetic
    (f) the number of geometric isomers

45. For the high-spin coordination compound $Mn(NH_3)_4Cl_2$, identify the following.
    (a) the oxidation number of manganese
    (b) the coordination number for manganese
    (c) the coordination geometry for manganese
    (d) the number of unpaired electrons per metal atom
    (e) whether the complex is diamagnetic or paramagnetic
    (f) the number of geometric isomers

46. A platinum-containing compound, known as Magnus's green salt, has the formula $[Pt(NH_3)_4][PtCl_4]$ (in which both platinum ions are Pt^{2+}). Name the cation and the anion.

47. Early in the 20th century, coordination compounds sometimes were given names based on their colors. Two compounds with the formula $CoCl_3 \cdot 4\,NH_3$ were named praseo-cobalt chloride (*praseo* = green) and violio-cobalt chloride (violet color). We now know that these compounds are octahedral cobalt complexes and that they are *cis* and *trans* isomers. Draw the structures of these two compounds, and name them using systematic nomenclature.

48. Give the formula and name of a square-planar complex of Pt^{2+} with one nitrite ion (NO_2^-, which binds to Pt^{2+} through N), one chloride ion, and two ammonia molecules as ligands. Are isomers possible? If so, draw the structure of each isomer, and tell what type of isomerism is observed.

49. Give the formula of the coordination complex formed from one Co^{3+} ion, two ethylenediamine molecules, one water molecule, and one chloride ion. Is the complex neutral or charged? If charged, give the net charge on the ion.

50. ▲ How many geometric isomers of the complex ion $[Cr(dmen)_3]^{3+}$ can exist? (dmen is the bidentate ligand 1,1-dimethylethylenediamine.)

$$(CH_3)_2\ddot{N}CH_2CH_2\ddot{N}H_2$$

1,1-Dimethylethylenediamine, dmen.

51. ▲ Diethylenetriamine (dien) is capable of serving as a tridentate ligand.

$$H_2\ddot{N}CH_2CH_2-\overset{..}{\underset{\underset{H}{|}}{N}}-CH_2CH_2\ddot{N}H_2$$

Diethylenetriamine, dien.

(a) Draw the structures of *fac*-Cr(dien)Cl₃ and *mer*-Cr(dien)Cl₃.

(b) Two different geometric isomers of *mer*-Cr(dien) Cl₂Br are possible. Draw the structure for each.

(c) Three different geometric isomers are possible for $[Cr(dien)_2]^{3+}$. Two have the dien ligand in a *fac* configuration, and one has the ligand in a *mer* orientation. Draw the structure of each isomer.

52. From experiment, we know that $[CoF_6]^{3-}$ is paramagnetic and $[Co(NH_3)_6]^{3+}$ is diamagnetic. Using the ligand field model, depict the electron configuration for each ion, and use this model to explain the magnetic property. What can you conclude about the effect of the ligand on the magnitude of Δ_o?

53. Three geometric isomers are possible for $[Co(en)(NH_3)_2(H_2O)_2]^{3+}$. One of the three is chiral; that is, it has a nonsuperimposable mirror image. Draw the structures of the three isomers. Which one is chiral?

54. The square-planar complex Pt(en)Cl₂ has chloride ligands in a *cis* configuration. No *trans* isomer is known. Based on the bond lengths and bond angles of carbon and nitrogen in the ethylenediamine ligand, explain why the *trans* compound is not possible.

55. The complex $[Mn(H_2O)_6]^{2+}$ has five unpaired electrons, whereas $[Mn(CN)_6]^{4-}$ has only one. Using the ligand field model, depict the electron configuration for each ion. What can you conclude about the effects of the different ligands on the magnitude of Δ_o?

56. Experiments show that K₄[Cr(CN)₆] is paramagnetic and has two unpaired electrons. The related complex K₄[Cr(SCN)₆] is paramagnetic and has four unpaired electrons. Account for the magnetism of each compound using the ligand field model. Predict where the SCN⁻ ion occurs in the spectrochemical series relative to CN⁻.

57. Give a systematic name or the formula for the following:

(a) (NH₄)₂[CuCl₄]

(b) Mo(CO)₆

(c) tetraaquadichlorochromium(III) chloride

(d) aquabis(ethylenediamine)thiocyanatocobalt(III) nitrate

58. When CrCl₃ dissolves in water, three different species can be obtained.

(a) $[Cr(H_2O)_6]Cl_3$, violet

(b) $[Cr(H_2O)_5Cl]Cl_2$, pale green

(c) $[Cr(H_2O)_4Cl_2]Cl$, dark green

If diethyl ether is added, a fourth complex can be obtained: Cr(H₂O)₃Cl₃ (brown). Describe an experiment that will allow you to differentiate these complexes.

59. ▲ The complex ion $[Co(CO_3)_3]^{3-}$, an octahedral complex with bidentate carbonate ions as ligands, has one absorption in the visible region of the spectrum at 640 nm. From this information,

(a) Predict the color of this complex, and explain your reasoning.

(b) Is the carbonate ion a weak- or strong-field ligand?

(c) Predict whether $[Co(CO_3)_3]^{3-}$ will be paramagnetic or diamagnetic.

60. The glycinate ion, $H_2NCH_2CO_2^-$, formed by deprotonation of the amino acid glycine, can function as a bidentate ligand, coordinating to a metal through the nitrogen of the amino group and one of the oxygen atoms.

Glycinate ion, a bidentate ligand

Site of bonding to transition metal ion

A copper complex of this ligand has the formula Cu(H₂NCH₂CO₂)₂(H₂O)₂. For this complex, determine the following:

(a) the oxidation state of copper

(b) the coordination number of copper

(c) the number of unpaired electrons

(d) whether the complex is diamagnetic or paramagnetic

61. ▲ Draw structures for the five possible geometric isomers of Cu(H₂NCH₂CO₂)₂(H₂O)₂. Are any of these species chiral? (See the structure of the ligand in Study Question 60.)

62. Chromium forms two anionic carbonyls, $[Cr(CO)_5]^{x-}$ and $[Cr(CO)_4]^{y-}$. What are the values of x and y?

63. Nickel and palladium both form complexes of the general formula M(PR₃)₂Cl₂ (where PR₃ is a phosphine such as P(C₆H₅)₃, triphenylphosphine). The nickel(II) compound is paramagnetic whereas the palladium(II) compound is diamagnetic.

(a) Explain the magnetic properties of these compounds.

(b) How many isomers of each compound are expected?

64. ▲ The transition metals form a class of compounds called metal carbonyls, an example of which is the tetrahedral complex Ni(CO)₄. Given the following thermodynamic data (at 298 K):

	$\Delta_f H°$ (kJ/mol)	$S°$ (J/K · mol)
Ni(s)	0	29.87
CO(g)	−110.525	+197.674
Ni(CO)₄(g)	−602.9	+410.6

(a) Calculate the equilibrium constant for the formation of Ni(CO)₄(g) from nickel metal and CO gas.

(b) Is the reaction of Ni(s) and CO(g) product- or reactant-favored at equilibrium?

(c) Is the reaction more or less product-favored at higher temperatures? How could this reaction be used in the purification of nickel metal?

In the Laboratory

65. Two different coordination compounds containing one cobalt(III) ion, five ammonia molecules, one bromide ion, and one sulfate ion exist. The dark violet form (A) gives a precipitate upon addition of aqueous $BaCl_2$. No reaction is seen upon addition of aqueous $BaCl_2$ to the violet-red form (B). Suggest structures for these two compounds, and write a chemical equation for the reaction of (A) with aqueous $BaCl_2$.

66. Three different compounds of chromium(III) with water and chloride ion have the same composition: 19.51% Cr, 39.92% Cl, and 40.57% H_2O. One of the compounds is violet and dissolves in water to give a complex ion with a 3+ charge and three chloride ions. All three chloride ions precipitate immediately as AgCl on adding $AgNO_3$. Draw the structure of the complex ion, and name the compound. Write a net ionic equation for the reaction of this compound with silver nitrate.

67. ▲ A 0.213-g sample of uranyl(VI) nitrate, $UO_2(NO_3)_2$, is dissolved in 20.0 mL of 1.0 M H_2SO_4 and shaken with Zn. The zinc reduces the uranyl ion, UO_2^{2+}, to a uranium ion, U^{n+}. To determine the value of n, this solution is titrated with $KMnO_4$. Permanganate is reduced to Mn^{2+} and U^{n+} is oxidized back to UO_2^{2+}.
    (a) In the titration, 12.47 mL of 0.0173 M $KMnO_4$ was required to reach the equivalence point. Use this information to determine the charge on the ion U^{n+}.
    (b) With the identity of U^{n+} now established, write a balanced net ionic equation for the reduction of UO_2^{2+} by zinc (assume acidic conditions).
    (c) Write a balanced net ionic equation for the oxidation of U^{n+} to UO_2^{2+} by MnO_4^- in acid.

68. ▲ You have isolated a solid organometallic compound containing manganese, some number of CO ligands, and one or more CH_3 ligands. To find the molecular formula of the compound, you burn 0.225 g of the solid in oxygen and isolate 0.283 g of CO_2 and 0.0290 g of H_2O. The molar mass of the compound is 210 g/mol. Suggest a plausible formula and structure for the molecule. (Make sure it satisfies the EAN rule. The CH_3 group can be thought of as a CH_3^- ion, a two-electron donor ligand.)

Summary and Conceptual Questions

The following questions may use concepts from this and previous chapters.

69. The stability of analogous complexes $[ML_6]^{n+}$ (relative to ligand dissociation) is in the general order $Mn^{2+} < Fe^{2+} < Co^{2+} < Ni^{2+} < Cu^{2+} > Zn^{2+}$. This order of ions is called the Irving–Williams series. Look up the values of the formation constants for the ammonia complexes of Co^{2+}, Ni^{2+}, Cu^{2+}, and Zn^{2+} in Appendix K, and verify this statement.

70. ▲ In this question, we explore the differences between metal coordination by monodentate and bidentate ligands. Formation constants, K_f, for $[Ni(NH_3)_6]^{2+}(aq)$ and $[Ni(en)_3]^{2+}(aq)$ are as follows:

$$Ni^{2+}(aq) + 6\,NH_3(aq) \longrightarrow [Ni(NH_3)_6]^{2+}(aq)$$
$$K_f = 10^8$$

$$Ni^{2+}(aq) + 3\,en(aq) \longrightarrow [Ni(en)_3]^{2+}(aq)$$
$$K_f = 10^{18}$$

The difference in K_f between these complexes indicates a higher thermodynamic stability for the chelated complex, caused by the *chelate effect*. Recall that K is related to the standard free energy of the reaction by $\Delta_r G° = -RT \ln K$ and $\Delta_r G° = \Delta_r H° - T\Delta_r S°$. We know from experiment that $\Delta_r H°$ for the NH_3 reaction is -109 kJ/mol-rxn, and $\Delta_r H°$ for the ethylenediamine reaction is -117 kJ/mol-rxn. Is the difference in $\Delta_r H°$ sufficient to account for the 10^{10} difference in K_f? Comment on the role of entropy in the second reaction.

71. As mentioned on page 1047, transition metal organometallic compounds have found use as catalysts. One example is Wilkinson's catalyst, a rhodium compound $[RhCl(PR_3)_3]$ used in the hydrogenation of alkenes. The steps involved in the catalytic process are outlined below. Indicate whether the rhodium compounds in each step have 18- or 16-valence electrons. (See Study Question 34.)

Step 1. Addition of H_2 to the rhodium center of Wilkinson's catalyst. (For electron-counting purposes H is considered a hydride ion, H^-, a two-electron donor.)

Step 2. Loss of a PR_3 ligand (a two-electron donor) to open a coordination site. (PR_3 is a phosphine such as $P(C_6H_5)_3$, triphenylphosphine.)

Step 3. Addition of the alkene to the open site.

Step 4. Rearrangement to add H to the double bond. (Here the $-CH_2CH_3$ group is a two-electron donor and can be thought of as a $[CH_2CH_3]^-$ anion for electron counting purposes.)

Step 5. Loss of the alkane.

Step 6. Regeneration of the catalyst.

Net reaction: $CH_2{=}CH_2 + H_2 \longrightarrow CH_3CH_3$

Applying Chemical Principles

Green Catalysts

You were introduced to "green chemistry" in Chapter 1 and have seen several instances of it throughout the book. The important objective of this field is that a process that creates a useful product must have a negligible impact on the environment. Thus, important goals of green chemistry include eliminating the use of toxic substances as reactants and reducing the quantity of unwanted reaction by-products.

Catalysts can play an important role in green chemistry processes. Catalysts increase reaction rates sufficiently so that reactions can often be run at lower temperatures, thereby reducing energy usage. Catalysts may also improve the reaction specificity, yielding higher percentages of products, often in fewer synthetic steps. A specific area where green catalytic alternatives are needed is in oxidation reactions. At present these are often carried out by environmentally unfriendly compounds such as chlorine or chlorine dioxide.

Terry Collins, Professor of Chemistry at the Carnegie Mellon Institute for Green Chemistry, has designed a family of iron-based coordination complexes that are promising oxidation catalysts. Named Fe-TAML® (where TAML stands for tetraamido-macrocyclic ligand), these complexes catalyze reactions using hydrogen peroxide as an oxidizing agent. Hydrogen peroxide is an environmentally friendly oxidizing agent. However, when H_2O_2 decomposes it tends to produce hydroxyl radicals that indiscriminately attack organic molecules when used without a suitable catalyst.

Recently, this catalyst has shown positive results in the treatment of waste water from wood pulp treatment plants. Wood pulp consists of two naturally occurring polymers, cellulose and lignin. Cellulose is used for making white paper, whereas lignin is a dark colored polymer that must be removed. Current practice is to oxidize the lignin with chlorine dioxide before releasing it into waste water. Not all the lignin is destroyed in this process. The remaining lignin darkens the water and affects the quantity of light absorbed by aquatic life. Low concentrations of Fe-TAML (500 nanomolar) combined with small amounts of hydrogen peroxide have been shown to destroy the majority of lignin quickly at room temperature.

Questions:

Answer the following questions concerning the Fe-TAML catalyst in the Figure.

1. What is the coordination number of the metal in the Fe-TAML catalyst?

The prototype TAML activator or a relative *plus* hydrogen peroxide

The prototype TAML activator. A model of hydrogen peroxide is also shown. The central iron cation is coordinated to four nitrogen atoms and a water molecule. The geometry around the central iron atom is square pyramidal geometry. (Model from the Institute for Green Science: www.chem.cmu.edu/groups/collins.)

2. Fe-TAML, as pictured here, is a complex ion of a macrocyclic ligand (with a charge of 4–), a water molecule, and an iron(III) ion. What is the overall charge on the Fe-TAML complex ion?

3. TAML is a tetra_____ macrocyclic ligand, meaning it has four "teeth" than can bond to the metal.

4. What is the geometry of the coordinating atoms around the Fe^{3+} ion in the Fe-TAML complex ion: tetrahedral, square pyramidal, or octahedral?

5. What is the geometry of the coordinating atoms around the Fe^{3+} ion in the Fe-TAML complex ion if the water is removed: tetrahedral, square planar, square pyramidal, or octahedral?

6. Can this metal–ligand complex have any isomers?

References and Notes:

1. Professor Terry Collins, whose research group developed the Fe-TAML catalyst, received the 1999 Presidential Green Chemistry Award.

2. See an outline of the Twelve Principles of green chemistry on page 6. See also the U. S. Environmental Protection Agency website: www.epa.gov/greenchemistry/pubs/principles.html.

23 Nuclear Chemistry

A Primordial Nuclear Reactor

The natural nuclear reactors in West Africa have been called "one of the greatest natural phenomena that ever occurred." In 1972, a French scientist noticed that the uranium taken from a mine in Oklo, Gabon, was strangely deficient in ^{235}U. Uranium exists in nature as two principal isotopes, ^{238}U (99.275% abundant) and ^{235}U (0.72% abundant). It is ^{235}U that most readily undergoes nuclear fission and is used to fuel nuclear power plants around the world. But the uranium found in the Oklo mines had an isotope ratio like that of the spent fuel that comes from modern reactors. Based on this and other evidence, scientists concluded that ^{235}U at the Oklo mine was once about 3% of the total and that a "natural" fission process occurred in the bed of uranium ore nearly 2 billion years ago.

But intriguing questions remained: Why could fission occur to a significant extent in this natural deposit of uranium and why didn't the "reactor" explode? Apparently, there must have been a moderator of neutron energy and a regulation mechanism. In a modern nuclear power reactor, control rods slow down the neutrons from nuclear fission so that they can induce fission in other ^{235}U nuclei; that is, they moderate the neutron energy. Without a moderator, the neutrons just fly off. In the Oklo reactors, water seeping into the bed of uranium ore could have acted as a moderator.

The reason the Oklo reactor did not explode is that water could have also been the regulator. As the fission process heated the water, it boiled off as steam. This caused the fission to stop, but it began again when more water seeped in.

Courtesy of Francois Gauthier-Lafaye

The natural nuclear reactor in Oklo, Gabon (West Africa). Nearly 2 billion years ago, a natural formation containing uranium oxide (the yellow material) underwent fission that started and stopped over a period of a million years.

Scientists now believe this natural reactor would turn on for about 30 minutes and then shut down for several hours before turning on again. There is evidence these natural reactors functioned intermittently for about 1 million years, until the concentration of uranium isotopes was too low to keep the reaction going.

Questions:

1. How many protons and neutrons are there in the ^{235}U and ^{238}U nuclei?
2. Although plutonium does not occur naturally on earth now, it is thought to have been produced in the Oklo reactor (and then decayed). Write balanced nuclear equations for:
   (a) the reaction of ^{238}U and a neutron to give ^{239}U
   (b) the decay of ^{239}U to ^{239}Np and then to ^{239}Pu by beta emission
   (c) the decay of ^{239}Pu to ^{235}U by alpha emission

Answers to these questions are available in Appendix N.

CHAPTER GOALS

See Chapter Goals Revisited (page 1088) for Study Questions keyed to these goals.

- Identify radioactive elements, and describe natural and artificial nuclear reactions.

- Calculate the binding energy and binding energy per nucleon for a particular isotope.

- Understand rates of radioactive decay.

- Understand artificial nuclear reactions.

- Understand issues of health and safety with respect to radioactivity.

- Be aware of some uses of radioactive isotopes in science and medicine.

History of science scholars cite areas of study out of which modern chemistry arose: technology, medicine, and alchemy. The third of these pillars, alchemy, was pursued in many cultures on three continents for well over 1000 years. Simply stated, the goal of the ancient alchemists was to turn less valuable materials into gold. We now recognize the futility of these efforts, because this goal is not reachable by chemical processes. But we now also know that their dream of transmuting one element into another can be achieved by means of nuclear reactions. This happens naturally in the decomposition of uranium and other radioactive elements, and scientists can intentionally carry out such reactions in the laboratory. The goal is no longer to make gold, however. Far more important and valuable products of nuclear reactions are possible.

Nuclear chemistry encompasses a wide range of topics that share one thing in common: they involve changes in the nucleus of an atom. While nuclear "chemistry" is a major focus in this chapter, this subject cuts across many areas of science and modern society. Radioactive isotopes are used in medicine. Nuclear power provides a sizable fraction of energy for modern society. And, then there are nuclear weapons. . . .

23.1 Natural Radioactivity

In the late 19th century, while studying radiation emanating from uranium and thorium, Ernest Rutherford (1871–1937) stated, "There are present at least two distinct types of radiation—one that is readily absorbed, which will be termed for convenience α (alpha) radiation, and the other of a more penetrative character, which will be termed β (beta) radiation." Subsequently, charge-to-mass ratio measurements showed that α radiation is composed of helium nuclei (He^{2+}) and β radiation is composed of electrons (e^-) (Table 23.1).

Table 23.1 Characteristics of α, β, and γ Radiation

Name	Symbols	Charge	Mass (g/particle)
Alpha	^4_2He, $^4_2\alpha$	2+	6.65×10^{-24}
Beta	$^0_{-1}e$, $^0_{-1}\beta$	1−	9.11×10^{-28}
Gamma	γ	0	0

OWL

Sign in to OWL at **www.cengage.com/owl** to view tutorials and simulations, develop problem-solving skills, and complete online homework assigned by your professor.

go Chemistry

Download mini lecture videos for key concept review and exam prep from OWL or purchase them from **www.cengagebrain.com**

● **Discovery of Radioactivity** The discovery of radioactivity by Henri Becquerel and the isolation of radium and polonium from pitchblende, a uranium ore, by Marie Curie were described in *Milestones in the Development of Chemistry*, page 338.

FIGURE 23.1 The relative
penetrating ability of α, β, and γ
radiation. Highly charged α particles interact strongly with matter
and are stopped by a piece of paper.
Beta particles, with less mass and a
lower charge, interact to a lesser
extent with matter and thus can
penetrate farther. Gamma radiation
is the most penetrating.

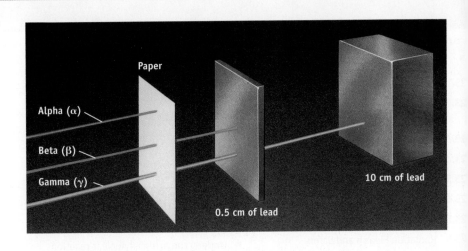

Paper

Alpha (α)

Beta (β)

Gamma (γ)

0.5 cm of lead

10 cm of lead

● **Common Symbols: α and β**
Symbols used to represent alpha and
beta particles do not include a plus or
minus superscript, respectively, to
show that they have a charge.

Rutherford hedged his bet when he said at least two types of radiation existed.
A third type was later discovered by the French scientist Paul Villard (1860–1934);
he named it **γ (gamma) radiation**, using the third letter in the Greek alphabet in
keeping with Rutherford's scheme. Unlike α and β radiation, γ radiation is not affected by electric and magnetic fields. Rather, it is a form of electromagnetic radiation like x-rays but even more energetic.

Early studies measured the penetrating power of the three types of radiation
(Figure 23.1). Alpha radiation is the least penetrating; it can be stopped by several
sheets of ordinary paper or clothing. Beta particles can penetrate several millimeters of living bone or tissue, but about 0.5 cm of lead will stop the particles. Gamma
radiation is the most penetrating. Thick layers of lead or concrete are required to
shield the body from this radiation, and γ-rays can pass completely through the human body.

Alpha and β particles typically possess high kinetic energies. The energy of
γ radiation is similarly very high. The energy associated with this radiation is transferred to any material used to stop the particle or absorb the radiation. This fact is
important because the damage caused by radiation is related to the energy
absorbed (see Section 23.8).

23.2 Nuclear Reactions and Radioactive Decay

Equations for Nuclear Reactions

● **Symbols Used in Nuclear
Equations** The mass number is included as a superscript, and the atomic
number is included as a subscript preceding the symbols for reactants and
products. This is done to facilitate balancing these equations.

In 1903, Rutherford and Frederick Soddy (1877–1956) proposed that radioactivity
is the result of a natural change of an isotope of one element into an isotope of a
different element. Such processes are called **nuclear reactions**.

Consider a reaction in which radium-226 (the isotope of radium with mass number 226) emits an α particle to form radon-222. The equation for this reaction is

$$^{226}_{88}\text{Ra} \rightarrow \,^{4}_{2}\alpha + \,^{222}_{86}\text{Rn}$$

In a nuclear reaction, the sum of the mass numbers of reacting particles must
equal the sum of the mass numbers of products. Furthermore, to maintain nuclear
charge balance, the sum of the atomic numbers of the products must equal the sum
of the atomic numbers of the reactants. These principles are illustrated using the
preceding nuclear equation:

	$^{226}_{88}\text{Ra}$		$^{4}_{2}\alpha$		$^{222}_{86}\text{Rn}$
	radium-226	$\rightarrow$	α particle	+	radon-222
Mass number: (protons + neutrons)	226	=	4	+	222
Atomic number: (protons)	88	=	2	+	86

Alpha-particle emission causes a decrease of two units in atomic number and four units in the mass number.

Similarly, nuclear mass and nuclear charge balance accompany β-particle emission, as illustrated by the decomposition of uranium-239:

	$^{239}_{92}\text{U}$	$\rightarrow$	$^{0}_{-1}\beta$	+	$^{239}_{93}\text{Np}$
	uranium-239	$\rightarrow$	β particle	+	neptunium-239
Mass number: (protons + neutrons)	239	=	0	+	239
Atomic number: (protons)	92	=	−1	+	93

The β particle has a charge of $1-$. Charge balance requires that the atomic number of the product be one unit greater than the atomic number of the reacting nucleus. The mass number does not change in this process.

How does a nucleus, composed of protons and neutrons, eject an electron? It is a complex process, but the net result is the conversion within the nucleus of a neutron to a proton and an electron.

$$^{1}_{0}\text{n} \longrightarrow {}^{0}_{-1}\text{e} + {}^{1}_{1}\text{p}$$

neutron　　　electron　　　proton

Notice that the mass and charge numbers balance in this equation.

What is the origin of the gamma radiation that accompanies many nuclear reactions? Recall that a photon of visible light is emitted when an atom undergoes a transition from an excited electronic state to a lower energy state (◄ Section 6.3). Gamma radiation originates from transitions between nuclear energy levels. Nuclear reactions often result in the formation of a product nucleus in an excited nuclear state. One option is to return to the ground state by emitting a photon. The energy of γ radiation is a measure of the large energy difference between the energy levels in the nucleus.

Radioactive Decay Series

Several naturally occurring radioactive isotopes decay to form a product that is also radioactive. When this happens, the initial nuclear reaction is followed by a second nuclear reaction; if the situation is repeated, a third and a fourth nuclear reaction occur; and so on. Eventually, a nonradioactive isotope is formed to end the series. Such a sequence of nuclear reactions is called a **radioactive decay series**. In each step of this sequence, the reactant nucleus is called the *parent,* and the product is called the *daughter.*

Uranium-238, the most abundant of three naturally occurring uranium isotopes, heads one of four radioactive decay series. This series begins with the loss of an α particle from $^{238}_{92}\text{U}$ to form radioactive $^{234}_{90}\text{Th}$. Thorium-234 then decomposes by β emission to $^{234}_{91}\text{Pa}$, which emits a β particle to give $^{234}_{92}\text{U}$. Uranium-234 is an α emitter, forming $^{230}_{90}\text{Th}$. Further α and β emissions follow, until the series ends with formation of the stable, nonradioactive isotope, $^{206}_{82}\text{Pb}$. In all, this radioactive decay series converting $^{238}_{92}\text{U}$ to $^{206}_{82}\text{Pb}$ is made up of 14 reactions, with eight α and six β particles being emitted. The series is portrayed graphically by plotting atomic number versus mass number (Figure 23.2). An equation can be written for each step in the sequence. Equations for the first four steps in the uranium-238 radioactive decay series are as follows:

Step 1.　$^{238}_{92}\text{U} \rightarrow {}^{234}_{90}\text{Th} + {}^{4}_{2}\alpha$

Step 2.　$^{234}_{90}\text{Th} \rightarrow {}^{234}_{91}\text{Pa} + {}^{0}_{-1}\beta$

Step 3.　$^{234}_{91}\text{Pa} \rightarrow {}^{234}_{92}\text{U} + {}^{0}_{-1}\beta$

Step 4.　$^{234}_{92}\text{U} \rightarrow {}^{230}_{90}\text{Th} + {}^{4}_{2}\alpha$

Uranium ore contains trace quantities of the radioactive elements formed in the radioactive decay series. A significant development in nuclear chemistry was Marie Curie's discovery in 1898 of radium and polonium as trace components of

FIGURE 23.2 The uranium-238 radioactive decay series. The steps in this radioactive decay series are shown graphically in this plot of mass number versus atomic number. Each α-decay step lowers the atomic number by two units and the mass number by four units. Beta-particle emission does not change the mass but raises the atomic number by one unit. Half-lives of the isotopes are included on the chart. Notice that several of the isotopes in this series decompose by two different pathways.

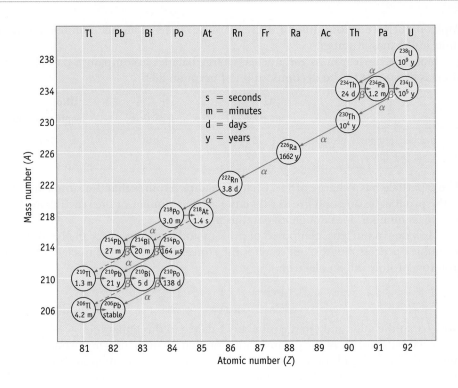

pitchblende, a uranium ore. The amount of each of these elements is small because the isotopes of these elements have short half-lives. Marie Curie isolated only a single gram of radium from 7 tons of ore. It is a credit to her skills as a chemist that she extracted sufficient amounts of radium and polonium from uranium ore to identify these elements.

The uranium-238 radioactive decay series is also the source of the environmental hazard radon. Trace quantities of uranium are often present naturally in the soil and rocks, and radon-222 is being continuously formed. Because radon is chemically inert, it is not trapped by chemical processes in soil or water and is free to seep into mines or into homes through pores in cement block walls, through cracks in the basement floor or walls, or around pipes. Because it is more dense than air, radon tends to collect in low spots, and its concentration can build up in a basement if steps are not taken to remove it.

The major health hazard from radon, when it is inhaled by humans, arises not from radon itself but from its decomposition product, polonium.

$$^{222}_{86}\text{Rn} \rightarrow {}^{218}_{84}\text{Po} + {}^{4}_{2}\alpha \qquad t_{1/2} = 3.82 \text{ days}$$

$$^{218}_{84}\text{Po} \rightarrow {}^{214}_{82}\text{Pb} + {}^{4}_{2}\alpha \qquad t_{1/2} = 3.04 \text{ minutes}$$

Radon does not undergo chemical reactions or form compounds that can be taken up in the body. Polonium, however, is not chemically inert. Polonium-218 can lodge in body tissues, where it undergoes α decay to give lead-214, another radioactive isotope. The range of an α particle in body tissue is quite small, perhaps 0.7 mm. This is approximately the thickness of the epithelial cells of the lungs, however, so α-particle radiation can cause serious damage to lung tissues.

Virtually every home in the United States has some level of radon, and kits can be purchased to test for the presence of this gas. If a significant amount of radon gas is detected in your home, you should take corrective actions such as sealing cracks around the foundation and in the basement. It may be reassuring to know that the health risks associated with radon are low. The likelihood of getting lung cancer from exposure to radon is about the same as the likelihood of dying in an accident in your home.

Radon detector. This kit is intended for use in the home to detect radon gas. The small device is placed in the home's basement for a given time period and is then sent to a laboratory to measure the amount of radon that might be present.

EXAMPLE 23.1   Radioactive Decay Series

Problem A second radioactive decay series begins with $^{235}_{92}U$ and ends with $^{207}_{82}Pb$.

(a) How many α and β particles are emitted in this series?

(b) The first three steps of this series are (in order) α, β, and α emission. Write an equation for each of these steps.

What Do You Know? You are given the starting (long-lived radioactive) isotope and the final (stable) isotope. A series of alpha and beta reactions is the link between these two species.

Strategy First, find the total change in atomic number and mass number. A combination of α and β particles is required that will decrease the total nuclear mass by 28 (235 − 207) and at the same time decrease the atomic number by 10 (92 − 82). Each equation must give symbols for the parent and daughter nuclei and the emitted particle. In the equations, the sums of the atomic numbers and mass numbers for reactants and products must be equal.

Solution

(a) Mass declines by 28 mass units (235 − 207). Because a decrease of 4 mass units occurs with each α emission, 7 α particles must be emitted. Also, for each α emission, the atomic number decreases by 2. Emission of 7 α particles would cause the atomic number to decrease by 14, but the actual decrease in atomic number is 10 (92 − 82). This means that 4 β particles must also have been emitted because each β emission increases the atomic number of the product by one unit. Thus, the radioactive decay sequence involves emission of 7 α and 4 β particles.

(b) Step 1. $^{235}_{92}U \rightarrow {}^{231}_{90}Th + {}^{4}_{2}\alpha$

  Step 2. $^{231}_{90}Th \rightarrow {}^{231}_{91}Pa + {}^{0}_{-1}\beta$

  Step 3. $^{231}_{91}Pa \rightarrow {}^{227}_{89}Ac + {}^{4}_{2}\alpha$

Think about Your Answer

Because the mass number changes in these series only when an alpha particle is lost, all of the mass numbers in a given decay series are some multiple of four less than the first isotope in the series. For the series beginning with U-238, the mass numbers are in the series 238, 234, 230, . . . , 206. This series is sometimes called the $4n + 2$ *series* because each mass number (M) fits the equation $4n + 2 = M$, where n is an integer (n is 59 for the first member of this series and 51 for the last member). For the series headed by $^{235}_{92}U$, the mass numbers are 235, 231, 227, . . . , 207; this is the $4n + 3$ *series*.

Two other decay series are possible. One, called the $4n$ *series* and beginning with ^{232}Th, is found in nature; the other, the $4n + 1$ series, is not. No member of this series has a very long half-life. During the 4.5 billion years since this planet was formed, all radioactive members of this series have completely decayed to the end product of this series, ^{209}Bi.

Check Your Understanding

(a) Six α and four β particles are emitted in the thorium-232 radioactive decay series before a stable isotope is reached. What is the final product in this series?

(b) The first three steps in the thorium-232 decay series (in order) are α, β, and β emission. Write an equation for each step.

Other Types of Radioactive Decay

Most naturally occurring radioactive elements decay by emission of α, β, and γ radiation. Other nuclear decay processes became known, however, when new radioactive elements were synthesized by artificial means. These include **positron ($^{0}_{+1}\beta$) emission** and **electron capture**.

Positrons ($^{0}_{+1}\beta$) and electrons have the same mass but opposite charge. The positron is the antimatter analog to an electron. *Positron emission* by polonium-207, for example, results in the formation of bismuth-207.

● **Positrons** Positrons were discovered by Carl Anderson (1905–1991) in 1932. The positron is one of a group of particles that are known as *antimatter*. If matter and antimatter particles collide, mutual annihilation occurs, with energy being emitted.

	$^{207}_{84}Po$	$\rightarrow$	$^{0}_{+1}\beta$	+	$^{207}_{83}Bi$
	polonium-207	$\rightarrow$	positron	+	bismuth-207
Mass number: (protons + neutrons)	207	=	0	+	207
Atomic number: (protons)	84	=	1	+	83

To retain charge balance, positron decay results in a decrease in the atomic number.

In *electron capture*, an extranuclear electron is captured by the nucleus. The mass number is unchanged, and the atomic number is reduced by 1. (In an old nomenclature, the innermost electron shell was called the *K shell,* and electron capture was called *K capture.*)

● **Neutrinos and Antineutrinos** Beta particles having a wide range of energies are emitted. To balance the energy associated with β decay, it is necessary to postulate the concurrent emission of another particle, the *antineutrino*. Similarly, neutrino emission accompanies positron emission. Much study has gone into detecting neutrinos and antineutrinos. These massless, chargeless particles are not included when writing nuclear equations.

	$^{7}_{4}Be$	+	$^{0}_{-1}e$	$\rightarrow$	$^{7}_{3}Li$
	beryllium-7	+	electron	$\rightarrow$	lithium-7
Mass number: (protons + neutrons)	7	+	0	=	7
Atomic number: (protons)	4	+	-1	=	3

In summary, most unstable nuclei decay by one of four paths: α or β decay, positron emission, or electron capture. Gamma radiation often accompanies these processes. Section 23.6 introduces a fifth way that nuclei decompose, *fission*.

EXAMPLE 23.2 Nuclear Reactions

Problem Complete the following equations. Give the symbol, mass number, and atomic number of the product species.

(a) $^{37}_{18}Ar + ^{0}_{-1}e \rightarrow ?$ (c) $^{35}_{16}S \rightarrow ^{35}_{17}Cl + ?$

(b) $^{11}_{6}C \rightarrow ^{11}_{5}B + ?$ (d) $^{30}_{15}P \rightarrow ^{0}_{+1}\beta + ?$

What Do You Know? You are given the reactant and one of two products formed in these nuclear reactions. You know that both the masses and charges must balance in a balanced nuclear equation.

Strategy The missing product in each reaction can be determined by recognizing that the sums of mass numbers and atomic numbers for products and reactants must be equal. When you know the nuclear mass and nuclear charge of the product, you can identify it with the appropriate symbol.

Solution

(a) This is an electron capture reaction. The product has a mass number of 37 + 0 = 37 and an atomic number of 18 − 1 = 17. Therefore, the symbol for the product is $^{37}_{17}Cl$.

(b) This missing particle has a mass of zero and a charge of 1+; these are the characteristics of a positron, $^{0}_{+1}\beta$. If this particle is included in the equation, the sums of the atomic numbers (6 = 5 + 1) and the mass numbers (11) on either side of the equation are equal.

(c) A beta particle, $^{0}_{-1}\beta$, is required to balance the mass numbers (35) and atomic numbers (16 = 17 − 1) in the equation.

(d) The product nucleus has mass number 30 and atomic number 14. This identifies the unknown as $^{30}_{14}Si$.

Think about Your Answer The product in each reaction is a stable isotope. As we will see in the next section, there is a narrow range of neutron-to-proton ratios for stable products. Spontaneous nuclear reactions always occur in a way that moves either into or closer to the narrow range of stable isotopes.

Check Your Understanding

Indicate the symbol, the mass number, and the atomic number of the missing product in each of the following nuclear reactions.

(a) $^{13}_{7}N \rightarrow ^{13}_{6}C + ?$ (b) $^{41}_{20}Ca + ^{0}_{-1}e \rightarrow ?$ (c) $^{90}_{38}Sr \rightarrow ^{90}_{39}Y + ?$ (d) $^{22}_{11}Na \rightarrow ? + ^{0}_{+1}\beta$

23.3 Stability of Atomic Nuclei

We can learn something about nuclear stability from Figure 23.3. In this plot, the horizontal axis represents the number of protons, and the vertical axis gives the number of neutrons for known isotopes. Each circle represents an isotope identified by the number of neutrons and protons contained in its nucleus. The black circles represent stable (nonradioactive) isotopes, about 300 in number, and the red circles represent some of the known radioactive isotopes. For example, the three isotopes of hydrogen are $^{1}_{1}H$ and $^{2}_{1}H$ (neither is radioactive) and $^{3}_{1}H$ (tritium, radioactive). For lithium, the third element, isotopes with mass numbers 4, 5, 6, and 7 are known. The isotopes with masses of 6 and 7 (shown in black) are stable, whereas the other two isotopes (in red) are radioactive.

Figure 23.3 contains the following information about nuclear stability:

- Stable isotopes fall in a very narrow range called the **band of stability**. It is remarkable how few isotopes are stable.
- Only two stable isotopes ($^{1}_{1}H$ and $^{3}_{2}He$) have more protons than neutrons.
- Up to calcium ($Z = 20$), stable isotopes often have equal numbers of protons and neutrons or only one or two more neutrons than protons.
- Beyond calcium, the neutron-to-proton ratio is always greater than 1. As the mass increases, the band of stable isotopes deviates more and more from a 1:1 neutron-to-proton ratio (the line in Figure 23.3 for which $N/Z = 1$).
- Beyond bismuth (83 protons and 126 neutrons), all isotopes are unstable and radioactive. There is apparently no nuclear "superglue" strong enough to hold heavy nuclei together.
- Isotopes that fall farther from the band of stability tend to have shorter half-lives than do unstable isotopes nearer to the band of stability.
- Elements of even atomic number have more stable isotopes than do those of odd atomic number. More stable isotopes have an even number of neutrons than have an odd number. Roughly 200 isotopes have an even number of neutrons and an even number of protons, whereas only about 120 isotopes have an odd number of either protons or neutrons. Only five stable isotopes ($^{2}_{1}H$, $^{6}_{3}Li$, $^{10}_{5}B$, $^{14}_{7}N$, and $^{180}_{73}Ta$) have odd numbers of both protons and neutrons.

The Band of Stability and Radioactive Decay

Besides being a criterion for stability, the neutron-to-proton ratio can assist in predicting what type of radioactive decay will be observed. Unstable nuclei decay in a manner that brings them toward a stable neutron-to-proton ratio—that is, toward the band of stability.

FIGURE 23.3 **Stable and unstable isotopes.** A graph of the number of neutrons (N) versus the number of protons (Z) for stable (*black circles*) and radioactive (*red circles*) isotopes from hydrogen to bismuth. This graph is used to assess criteria for nuclear stability and to predict modes of decay for unstable nuclei.

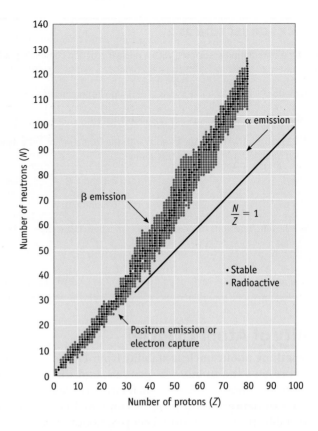

- All elements beyond bismuth ($Z = 83$) are unstable. To reach the band of stability starting with these elements, a process that decreases the atomic number is needed. Alpha emission is an effective way to lower Z, the atomic number, because each emission decreases the atomic number by 2. For example, americium, the radioactive element used in smoke detectors, decays by α emission:

$$^{243}_{95}\text{Am} \rightarrow {}^{4}_{2}\alpha + {}^{239}_{93}\text{Np}$$

- Beta emission occurs for isotopes that have a high neutron-to-proton ratio—that is, isotopes above the band of stability. With β decay, the atomic number increases by 1, and the mass number remains constant, resulting in a lower neutron-to-proton ratio:

$$^{60}_{27}\text{Co} \rightarrow {}^{0}_{-1}\beta + {}^{60}_{28}\text{Ni}$$

- Isotopes with a low neutron-to-proton ratio, below the band of stability, decay by positron emission or by electron capture. Both processes lead to product nuclei with a lower atomic number and the same mass number and move the product closer to the band of stability:

$$^{13}_{7}\text{N} \rightarrow {}^{0}_{+1}\beta + {}^{13}_{6}\text{C}$$

$$^{41}_{20}\text{Ca} + {}^{0}_{-1}\text{e} \rightarrow {}^{41}_{19}\text{K}$$

EXAMPLE 23.3   Predicting Modes of Radioactive Decay

Problem Identify probable mode(s) of decay for each isotope and write an equation for the decay process.

(a) oxygen-15, $^{15}_{8}\text{O}$

(b) uranium-234, $^{234}_{92}\text{U}$

(c) fluorine-20, $^{20}_{9}\text{F}$

(d) manganese-56, $^{56}_{25}\text{Mn}$

What Do You Know? You are given the formulas for four radioactive isotopes. The possible modes of decomposition are α, β, or positron emission and electron capture. The preferred mode will give a more stable isotope and create a nucleus that is closer to the band of stability.

Strategy In parts (a), (c), and (d), compare the mass number with the atomic mass. If the mass number of the isotope is higher than the atomic weight, then there are too many neutrons, and β emission is likely. If the mass number is lower than the atomic weight, then there are too few neutrons, and positron emission or electron capture is the more likely process. It is not possible to choose between the latter two modes of decay without further information. For part (b), note that isotopes with atomic number greater than 83 are likely to be α emitters.

Solution

(a) Oxygen-15 has 7 neutrons and 8 protons, so the neutron-to-proton (n/p) ratio is less than 1—too low for ^{15}O to be stable. Nuclei with too few neutrons are expected to decay by either positron emission or electron capture. In this instance, the process is $^{0}_{+1}\beta$ emission, and the equation is $^{15}_{8}O \rightarrow {}^{0}_{+1}\beta + {}^{15}_{7}N$.

(b) Alpha emission is a common mode of decay for isotopes of elements with atomic numbers higher than 83. The decay of uranium-234 is one example:

$$^{234}_{92}U \rightarrow {}^{230}_{90}Th + {}^{4}_{2}\alpha$$

(c) Fluorine-20 has 11 neutrons and 9 protons, a high n/p ratio. The ratio is lowered by β emission:

$$^{20}_{9}F \rightarrow {}^{0}_{-1}\beta + {}^{20}_{10}Ne$$

(d) The atomic weight of manganese is 54.85. The higher mass number, 56, suggests that this radioactive isotope has an excess of neutrons, in which case it would be expected to decay by β emission:

$$^{56}_{25}Mn \rightarrow {}^{0}_{-1}\beta + {}^{56}_{26}Fe$$

Think about Your Answer Decomposition can occur by four possible paths, α and β emission, positron emission, and electron capture. Whether the decay follows beta emission or positron emission (or electron capture) is predicted by the neutron/proton ratio, relative to the n/p ratio in stable isotopes.

Check Your Understanding

Write an equation for the probable mode of decay for each of the following unstable isotopes, and write an equation for that nuclear reaction.

(a) silicon-32, $^{32}_{14}Si$

(b) titanium-45, $^{45}_{22}Ti$

(c) plutonium-239, $^{239}_{94}Pu$

(d) potassium-42, $^{42}_{19}K$

Nuclear Binding Energy

An atomic nucleus can contain as many as 83 protons and still be stable. For stability, nuclear binding (attractive) forces must be greater than the electrostatic repulsive forces between the closely packed protons in the nucleus. **Nuclear binding energy**, E_b, is defined as the energy required to separate the nucleus of an atom into protons and neutrons. For example, the nuclear binding energy for deuterium is the energy required to convert one mole of deuterium (^2_1H) nuclei into one mole of protons and one mole of neutrons.

$$^{2}_{1}H \rightarrow {}^{1}_{1}p + {}^{1}_{0}n \qquad E_b = 2.15 \times 10^8 \text{ kJ/mol}$$

The positive sign for E_b indicates that energy is required for this process. A deuterium nucleus is more stable than an isolated proton and an isolated neutron, just as the H_2 molecule is more stable than two isolated H atoms. Recall, however, that the H—H bond energy is only 436 kJ/mol. The energy holding a proton and a neutron together in a deuterium nucleus, 2.15×10^8 kJ/mol, is about 500,000 times larger than the typical covalent bond energies.

To further understand nuclear binding energy, we turn to an experimental observation and a theory. The experimental observation is that the mass of a nucleus is always less than the sum of the masses of its constituent protons and neutrons. The theory is that the "missing mass," called the **mass defect**, is equated with the energy that holds the nuclear particles together.

The mass defect for deuterium is the difference between the mass of a deuterium nucleus and the sum of the masses of a proton and a neutron. Mass spectrometric measurements (◀ Section 2.3) give the masses of these particles to a high level of accuracy, providing the numbers needed to carry out calculations of mass defects.

Masses of atomic nuclei are not generally listed in reference tables, but masses of atoms are. Calculation of the mass defect can be carried out using masses of atoms instead of masses of nuclei. By using atomic masses, we are including in this calculation the masses of extranuclear electrons in the reactants and the products. Because the same number of extranuclear electrons appears in products and reactants, this does not affect the result. Thus, for one mole of deuterium nuclei, the mass defect is found as follows:

$$\overset{2}{\underset{1}{}}\text{H} \quad \longrightarrow \quad \overset{1}{\underset{1}{}}\text{H} \quad + \quad \overset{1}{\underset{0}{}}\text{n}$$

$$2.01410 \text{ g/mol} \qquad 1.007825 \text{ g/mol} \qquad 1.008665 \text{ g/mol}$$

Mass defect $= \Delta m =$ mass of products $-$ mass of reactants

$$= [1.007825 \text{ g/mol} + 1.008665 \text{ g/mol}] - 2.01410 \text{ g/mol}$$

$$= 0.00239 \text{ g/mol}$$

The relationship between mass and energy is contained in Albert Einstein's 1905 theory of special relativity, which holds that mass and energy are different manifestations of the same quantity. Einstein defined the energy–mass relationship: Energy is equivalent to mass times the square of the speed of light; that is, $E = mc^2$. In the case of atomic nuclei, it is assumed that the missing mass (the mass defect, Δm) is equated with the binding energy holding the nucleus together.

$$E_b = (\Delta m)c^2 \tag{23.1}$$

If Δm is given in kilograms and the speed of light is given in meters per second, E_b will have units of joules (because $1 \text{ J} = 1 \text{ kg} \cdot \text{m}^2/\text{s}^2$). For the decomposition of one mole of deuterium nuclei to one mole of protons and one mole of neutrons, we have

$$E_b = (2.39 \times 10^{-6} \text{ kg/mol})(2.998 \times 10^8 \text{ m/s})^2$$

$$= 2.15 \times 10^{11} \text{ J/mol of } \overset{2}{\underset{1}{}}\text{H nuclei } (= 2.15 \times 10^8 \text{ kJ/mol of } \overset{2}{\underset{1}{}}\text{H nuclei})$$

The nuclear stabilities of different elements are compared using the **binding energy per mole of nucleons**. (**Nucleon** is the general name given to nuclear particles—that is, protons and neutrons.) A deuterium nucleus contains two nucleons, so the binding energy per mole of nucleons, E_b/n, is 2.15×10^8 kJ/mol divided by 2, or 1.08×10^8 kJ/mol nucleon.

$$E_b/n = \left(\frac{2.15 \times 10^8 \text{ kJ}}{\text{mol } \overset{2}{\underset{1}{}}\text{H nuclei}} \right) \left(\frac{1 \text{ mol } \overset{2}{\underset{1}{}}\text{H nuclei}}{2 \text{ mol nucleons}} \right)$$

$$E_b/n = 1.08 \times 10^8 \text{ kJ/mol nucleons}$$

The binding energy per nucleon can be calculated for any atom whose mass is known. Then, to compare nuclear stabilities, we can plot binding energies per nucleon as a function of mass number (Figure 23.4). The greater the binding energy per nucleon, the greater the stability of the nucleus. From the graph in Figure 23.4, the point of maximum nuclear stability occurs at a mass of 56 (i.e., at iron in the periodic table).

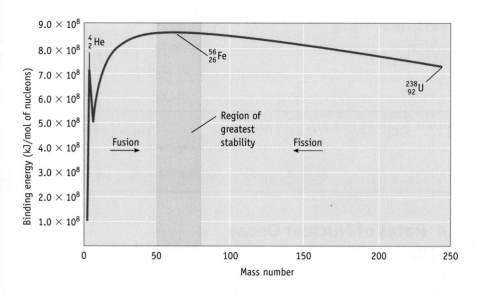

EXAMPLE 23.4 Nuclear Binding Energy

Problem Calculate the binding energy, E_b (in kJ/mol), and the binding energy per nucleon, E_b/n (in kJ/mol nucleon), for carbon-12.

What Do You Know? The mass of carbon-12 is, by definition, exactly 12 g/mol. You will need the molar masses of hydrogen atoms (^1_1H) and neutrons (1.007825 g/mol and 1.008665 g/mol respectively), to determine the mass defect.

Strategy The mass defect is the difference between the mass of carbon-12 and the masses of 6 protons, 6 neutrons, and 6 electrons. The mass of 1 mol of protons and 1 mol of electrons can be taken into account by using the molar mass of ^1_1H. Use the values given to calculate the mass defect (in g/mol). The binding energy is calculated from the mass defect using Equation 23.1.

Solution The mass of ^1_1H is 1.007825 g/mol, and the mass of ^1_0n is 1.008665 g/mol. Carbon-12, $^{12}_6C$, is the standard for the atomic masses in the periodic table, and its mass is defined as exactly 12 g/mol

$$\Delta m = [(6 \times \text{mass } ^1_1H) + (6 \times \text{mass } ^1_0n)] - \text{mass } ^{12}_6C$$

$$= [(6 \times 1.007825 \text{ g/mol}) + (6 \times 1.008665 \text{ g/mol})] - 12.000000 \text{ g/mol}$$

$$= 9.8940 \times 10^{-2} \text{ g/mol nuclei}$$

The binding energy is calculated using Equation 23.1. Using the mass in kilograms and the speed of light in meters per second gives the binding energy in joules:

$$E_b = (\Delta m)c^2$$

$$= (9.8940 \times 10^{-5} \text{ kg/mol})(2.99792 \times 10^8 \text{ m/s})^2$$

$$= 8.8923 \times 10^{12} \text{ J/mol nuclei } (= 8.8923 \times 10^9 \text{ kJ/mol nuclei})$$

The binding energy per nucleon, E_b/n, is determined by dividing the binding energy by 12 (the number of nucleons)

$$\frac{E_b}{n} = \frac{8.8923 \times 10^9 \text{ kJ/mol nuclei}}{12 \text{ mol nucleons/mol nuclei}}$$

$$= 7.4102 \times 10^8 \text{ kJ/mol nucleons}$$

Think about Your Answer Be sure that the units of mass and the speed of light are in kg and m/s, respectively, in this calculation. (Note that 1 kg · m²/s² = 1 J.) The binding energy is a very large quantity of energy compared to those of ordinary chemical reactions. Compare binding energy to the very exothermic reaction of hydrogen and oxygen to form water vapor, for which $\Delta_r H°$ is only −242 kJ per mol of water vapor formed at 25 °C.

Check Your Understanding

Calculate the binding energy per nucleon, in kilojoules per mole, for lithium-6. The molar mass of ^6_3Li is 6.015125 g/mol.

REVIEW & CHECK FOR SECTION 23.3

Among the listed species, which has the highest binding energy per nucleon?

(a) ^2_1D (b) $^{20}_{10}Ne$ (c) $^{56}_{26}Fe$ (d) $^{238}_{92}U$

23.4 **Rates of Nuclear Decay**

Half-Life

When a new radioactive isotope is identified, its *half-life* is usually measured. Half-life ($t_{1/2}$) is used in nuclear chemistry in the same way it is used when discussing the kinetics of first-order chemical reactions (◀ Section 15.4): It is the time required for half of a sample to decay to products (Figure 23.5). Recall that for first-order kinetics the half-life is independent of the amount of sample.

Half-lives for radioactive isotopes cover a wide range of values. Uranium-238 has one of the longer half-lives, 4.47×10^9 years, a length of time close to the age of the earth (estimated at $4.5–4.6 \times 10^9$ years). Thus, roughly half of the uranium-238 present when the planet was formed is still around. At the other end of the range of half-lives are isotopes such as the 277 isotope of element 112 (recently named copernicium, ^{277}Cn), which has a half-life of 240 microseconds (1 $\mu s = 1 \times 10^{-6} s$).

Half-life provides an easy way to estimate the time required before a radioactive element is no longer a health hazard. Strontium-90, for example, is a β emitter with a half-life of 29.1 years. Significant quantities of strontium-90 were dispersed into the environment in atmospheric nuclear bomb tests in the 1960s and 1970s, and, from the half-life, we know that almost one half is still around. The health problems associated with strontium-90 arise because calcium and strontium have similar chemical properties. Strontium-90 is taken into the body and deposited in bone, taking the place of calcium. Radiation damage by strontium-90 (a β emitter) in bone has been directly linked to bone-related cancers.

FIGURE 23.5 Decay of 20.0 mg of oxygen-15. After each half-life period of 2.0 minutes, the mass of oxygen-15 decreases by one half. (Oxygen-15 decays by positron emission.)

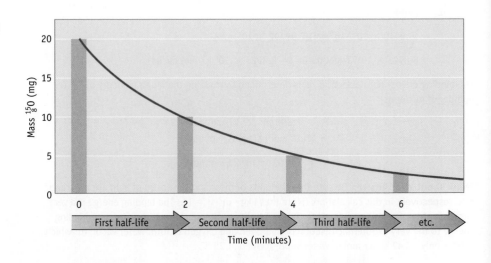

EXAMPLE 23.5   Using Half-Life

Problem Radioactive iodine-131, used to treat hyperthyroidism, has a half-life of 8.04 days.

(a)   If you have 8.8 μg (micrograms) of this isotope, what mass remains after 32.2 days?

(b)   How long will it take for a sample of iodine-131 to decay to one eighth of its activity?

(c)   Estimate the length of time necessary for the sample to decay to 10% of its original activity.

What Do You Know? The half-life of ^{131}I, 8.04 days, is given in the problem. Estimates of the masses remaining are made based on this value.

Strategy This problem asks you to use half-life to qualitatively assess the rate of decay. After one half-life, half of the sample remains. After another half-life, the amount of sample is again decreased by half to one fourth of its original value. To answer these questions, assess the number of half-lives that have elapsed and use this information to determine the amount of sample remaining.

Solution

(a)   The time elapsed, 32.2 days, is 4 half-lives (32.2/8.04 = 4). The amount of iodine-131 has decreased to 1/16 of the original amount [1/2 × 1/2 × 1/2 × 1/2 = $(1/2)^4$ = 1/16]. The amount of iodine remaining is 8.8 μg × $(1/2)^4$ or 0.55 μg.

(b)   After 3 half-lives, the amount of iodine-131 remaining is 1/8 [= $(1/2)^3$] of the original amount. The amount remaining is 8.8 μg × $(1/2)^3$ = 1.1 μg.

(c)   After 3 half-lives, 1/8 (12.5%) of the sample remains; after 4 half-lives, 1/16 (6.25%) remains. It will take between 3 and 4 half-lives, between 24.15 and 32.2 days, to decrease the amount of sample to 10% of its original value.

Think about Your Answer You will find it useful to make approximations as we have done in (c). An exact time can be calculated from the first-order rate law (page 681 and Equation 23.5).

Check Your Understanding

Tritium ($^{3}_{1}$H), a radioactive isotope of hydrogen, has a half-life of 12.3 years.

(a)   Starting with 1.5 mg of this isotope, what mass (mg) remains after 49.2 years?

(b)   How long will it take for a sample of tritium to decay to one eighth of its activity?

(c)   Estimate the length of time necessary for the sample to decay to 1% of its original activity.

Kinetics of Nuclear Decay

The rate of nuclear decay is determined from measurements of the **activity** (A) of a sample. Activity refers to the number of disintegrations observed per unit of time, a quantity that can be measured readily with devices such as a Geiger–Müller counter (Figure 23.6). *Activity is proportional to the number of radioactive atoms present (N).*

$$A \propto N \qquad (23.2)$$

If the number of radioactive nuclei N is reduced by half, the activity of the sample will be half as large. Doubling N will double the activity. This evidence indicates that the rate of decomposition is first order with respect to N. Consequently, the equations describing rates of radioactive decay are the same as those used to describe the kinetics of first-order chemical reactions; the change in the number of radioactive atoms N per unit of time is proportional to N:

$$\frac{\Delta N}{\Delta t} = -kN \qquad (23.3)$$

Thin window
through which
radiation enters

FIGURE 23.6 A Geiger–Müller counter. A charged particle (an α or β particle) enters the gas-filled tube (diagram at the *right*) and ionizes the gas. The gaseous ions migrate to electrically charged plates and are recorded as a pulse of electric current. The current is amplified and used to operate a counter. A sample of carnotite, a mineral containing uranium oxide, is also shown in the photograph.

The integrated rate equation can be written in two ways depending on the data used:

$$\ln\left(\frac{N}{N_0}\right) = -kt \tag{23.4}$$

or

$$\ln\left(\frac{A}{A_0}\right) = -kt \tag{23.5}$$

Here, N_0 and A_0 are the number of atoms and the activity of the sample initially, respectively, and N and A are the number of atoms and the activity of the sample after time t, respectively. Thus, N/N_0 is the fraction of atoms remaining after a given time (t), and A/A_0 is the fraction of the activity remaining after the same period. In these equations, k is the rate constant (decay constant) for the isotope in question. The relationship between half-life and the first-order rate constant is the same as seen with chemical kinetics (Equation 15.4, page 686):

$$t_{1/2} = \frac{0.693}{k} \tag{23.6}$$

Equations 23.3–23.6 are useful in several ways:

- If the activity (A) or the number of radioactive nuclei (N) is measured in the laboratory over some period t, then k can be calculated. The decay constant k can then be used to determine the half-life of the sample.
- If k is known, the fraction of a radioactive sample (N/N_0) still present after some time t has elapsed can be calculated.
- If k is known, the time required for that isotope to decay to a fraction of the original activity (A/A_0) can be calculated.

EXAMPLE 23.6   Kinetics of Radioactive Decay

Problem A sample of radon-222 has an initial α-particle activity (A_0) of 7.0×10^4 dps (disintegrations per second). After 6.6 days, its activity (A) is 2.1×10^4 dps. What is the half-life of radon-222?

What Do You Know? You are given the initial and final activities of the sample of ^{222}Rn and the time elapsed.

Strategy Values for A, A_0, and t are given. The problem can be solved using Equation 23.5 with k as the unknown. Once k is found, the half-life can be calculated using Equation 23.6.

Solution

$$\ln(2.1 \times 10^4 \text{ dps}/7.0 \times 10^4 \text{ dps}) = -k \text{ (6.6 day)}$$

$$\ln(0.30) = -k(6.6 \text{ day})$$

$$k = 0.18 \text{ days}^{-1}$$

From k we obtain $t_{1/2}$:

$$t_{1/2} = 0.693/0.18 \text{ days}^{-1} = 3.8 \text{ days}$$

Think about Your Answer Notice that the activity decreased to between one half and one fourth of its original value. The 6.6 days of elapsed time represents one full half-life and part of another half-life.

Check Your Understanding

(a) A sample of $Ca_3(PO_4)_2$ containing phosphorus-32 has an activity of 3.35×10^3 dpm. Exactly 2 days later, the activity is 3.18×10^3 dpm. Calculate the half-life of phosphorus-32.

(b) A highly radioactive sample of nuclear waste products with a half-life of 200. years is stored in an underground tank. How long will it take for the activity to diminish from an initial activity of 6.50×10^{12} dpm to a fairly harmless activity of 3.00×10^3 dpm?

Radiocarbon Dating

In certain situations, the age of a material can be determined based on the rate of decay of a radioactive isotope. The best-known example of this procedure is the use of carbon-14 to date historical artifacts.

Naturally occurring carbon is primarily carbon-12 and carbon-13 with isotopic abundances of 98.9% and 1.1%, respectively. In addition, traces of a third isotope, carbon-14, are present to the extent of about 1 in 10^{12} atoms in atmospheric CO_2 and in living materials. Carbon-14 is a β emitter with a half-life of 5730 years. A 1-gram sample of carbon from living material will show about 14 disintegrations per minute, not a lot of radioactivity but nevertheless detectable by modern methods.

Carbon-14 is formed in the upper atmosphere by nuclear reactions initiated by neutrons in cosmic radiation:

$$^{14}_{7}\text{N} + ^{1}_{0}\text{n} \rightarrow ^{14}_{6}\text{C} + ^{1}_{1}\text{H}$$

Once formed, carbon-14 is oxidized to $^{14}CO_2$. This product enters the carbon cycle, circulating through the atmosphere, oceans, and biosphere.

The usefulness of carbon-14 for dating comes about in the following way. Plants absorb CO_2 and convert it to organic compounds, thereby incorporating carbon-14 into living tissue. As long as a plant remains alive, this process will continue, and the percentage of carbon that is carbon-14 in the plant will equal the percentage in the atmosphere. When the plant dies, carbon-14 will no longer be taken up. Radioactive decay continues, however, with the carbon-14 activity decreasing over time. After 5730 years, the activity will be 7 dpm/g; after 11,460 years, it will be 3.5 dpm/g; and so on. By measuring the activity of a sample, and knowing the half-life of carbon-14, it is possible to calculate when a plant (or an animal that was eating plants) died.

As with all experimental procedures, carbon-14 dating has limitations. Although the procedure assumes that the amount of carbon-14 in the atmosphere hundreds or thousands of years ago is the same as it is now, in fact the percentage has varied by as much as 10% (Figure 23.7). Furthermore, it is not possible to use carbon-14 to date an object that is less than about 100 years old; the radiation level

FIGURE 23.7 Variation of atmospheric carbon-14 activity.
The amount of carbon-14 has changed with the variation in cosmic ray activity. To obtain the data for the pre-1990 part of the curve shown in this graph, scientists carried out carbon-14 dating of artifacts for which the age was accurately known (often through written records). Data for this figure were obtained using carbon-14 dating of tree rings.

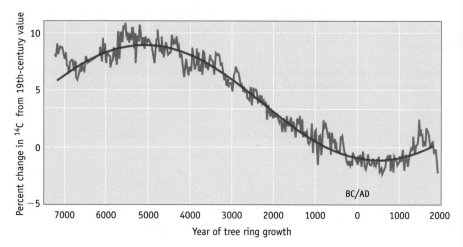

Source: Hans E. Suess, La Jolla Radiocarbon Laboratory

● **Willard Libby (1908–1980)**
Libby received the 1960 Nobel Prize in chemistry for developing carbon-14 dating techniques. Carbon-14 dating is widely used in fields such as anthropology.

Oesper Collection in the History of Chemistry, University of Cincinnati

from carbon-14 will not change enough in this short time period to permit accurate detection of a difference from the initial value. In most instances, the accuracy of the measurement is, in fact, only about ±100 years. Finally, it is not possible to determine ages of objects much older than about 40,000 years. By then, after nearly seven half-lives, the radioactivity will have decreased virtually to zero. But for the span of time between 100 and 40,000 years, this technique has provided important information (Figure 23.8).

EXAMPLE 23.7 Radiochemical Dating

Problem To test the concept of carbon-14 dating, J. R. Arnold and W. F. Libby applied this technique to analyze samples of acacia and cyprus wood whose ages were already known. (The acacia wood, which was supplied by the Metropolitan Museum of Art in New York, came from the tomb of Zoser, the first Egyptian pharaoh to be entombed in a pyramid. The cyprus wood was from the tomb of Sneferu.) The average activity based on five determinations on one of these wood samples was 7.04 dpm per gram of carbon. Assume (as Arnold and Libby did) that the original activity of carbon-14, A_0, was 12.6 dpm per gram of carbon. Calculate the approximate age of the sample.

What Do You Know? You are given the initial and final ^{14}C activity. The first-order rate constant can be calculated from the half-life.

Strategy First, determine the rate constant for the decay of carbon-14 from its half-life ($t_{1/2}$ for ^{14}C is 5.73×10^3 years). Then, use Equation 23.5.

Solution

$$k = 0.693/t_{1/2} = 0.693/5730 \text{ yr}$$

$$= 1.21 \times 10^{-4} \text{ yr}^{-1}$$

$$\ln(A/A_0) = -kt$$

$$\ln\left(\frac{7.04 \text{ dpm/g}}{12.6 \text{ dpm/g}}\right) = (-1.21 \times 10^{-4} \text{ yr}^{-1})t$$

$$t = 4.8 \times 10^3 \text{ yr}$$

The wood is about 4800 years old.

Think about Your Answer This problem uses real data from an early research paper in which the carbon-14 dating method was being tested. The age of the wood was known to be 4750 ± 250 years. (See J. R. Arnold and W. F. Libby: *Science*, Vol. 110, p. 678, 1949.)

FIGURE 23.8 The Iceman.
The world's oldest preserved human remains were discovered in the ice of a glacier high in the Alps. Carbon-14 dating techniques allowed scientists to determine that he lived about 5300 years ago. See pages 58 and 1 for more information on the Iceman.

© JEAN LOUIS PRADELS/PHOTOPOR/ LA DEPECHE DU MIDI/NEWSCOM

Check Your Understanding

A sample of the inner part of a redwood tree felled in 1874 was shown to have ^{14}C activity of 9.32 dpm/g. Calculate the approximate age of the tree when it was cut down. Compare this age with that obtained from tree ring data, which estimated that the tree began to grow in 979 ± 52 BC. Use 13.4 dpm/g for the value of A_0.

REVIEW & CHECK FOR SECTION 23.4

1. The age of the earth is thought to be 4.5 billion years. Approximately what percentage of ^{232}Th has decomposed during this period of time? The half-life of ^{232}Th is 1.4×10^{10} years.

   (a) 20%   (b) 40%   (c) 60%   (d) 80%

2. The half-life of ^{32}P is 14.3 days. How much ^{32}P in a sample will remain after 71.5 days have elapsed?

   (a) 1/4   (b) 1/8   (c) 1/16   (d) 1/32

23.5 Artificial Nuclear Reactions

How many different isotopes are found on earth? All of the stable isotopes occur naturally. A few unstable (radioactive) isotopes that have long half-lives are found in nature; the best-known examples are uranium-235, uranium-238, and thorium-232. Trace quantities of other radioactive isotopes with short half-lives are present because they are being formed continuously by nuclear reactions. They include isotopes of radium, polonium, and radon, along with other elements produced in various radioactive decay series, and carbon-14, formed in a nuclear reaction initiated by cosmic radiation.

Naturally occurring isotopes account for only a very small fraction of the currently known radioactive isotopes, however. The rest—several thousand—have been synthesized via artificial nuclear reactions, sometimes referred to as transmutation.

The first artificial nuclear reaction was identified by Rutherford about 90 years ago. Recall the classic experiment that led to the nuclear model of the atom (◄ *Milestones in the Development of Chemistry,* page 340) in which gold foil was bombarded with α particles. In the years following that experiment, Rutherford and his coworkers bombarded many other elements with α particles. In 1919, one of these experiments led to an unexpected result: When nitrogen atoms were bombarded with α particles, protons were detected among the products. Rutherford correctly concluded that a nuclear reaction had occurred. Nitrogen had undergone a *transmutation* to oxygen:

$$^{4}_{2}He + ^{14}_{7}N \rightarrow ^{17}_{8}O + ^{1}_{1}H$$

During the next decade, other nuclear reactions were discovered by bombarding other elements with α particles. Progress was slow, however, because in most cases α particles are simply scattered by target nuclei. The bombarding particles cannot get close enough to the nucleus to react because of the strong repulsive forces between the positively charged α particle and the positively charged atomic nucleus.

Two advances were made in 1932 that greatly extended nuclear reaction chemistry. The first involved the use of particle accelerators to create high-energy particles as projectiles. The second was the use of neutrons as the bombarding particles.

The α particles used in the early studies on nuclear reactions came from naturally radioactive materials such as uranium and had relatively low energies, at least by today's standards. Particles with higher energy were needed, so J. D. Cockcroft (1897–1967) and E. T. S. Walton (1903–1995), working in Rutherford's laboratory in Cambridge, England, turned to protons. Protons are formed when hydrogen atoms ionize in a cathode-ray tube, and it was known that they could be accelerated to

● **Discovery of Neutrons** Neutrons had been predicted to exist for more than a decade before they were identified in 1932 by James Chadwick (1891–1974) (page 343). Chadwick produced neutrons in a nuclear reaction between α particles and beryllium: $^{4}_{2}\alpha + ^{9}_{4}Be \rightarrow ^{12}_{6}C + ^{1}_{0}n$.

● **Glenn T. Seaborg (1912–1999)** Seaborg figured out that thorium and the elements that followed it fit under the lanthanides in the periodic table. For this insight, he and Edwin McMillan shared the 1951 Nobel Prize in chemistry. Over a 21-year period, Seaborg and his colleagues synthesized 10 new transuranium elements. To honor Seaborg's scientific contributions, the name "seaborgium" was assigned to element 106. It marked the first time an element was named for a living person.

Lawrence Berkeley Laboratory

A CLOSER LOOK

The Search for New Elements

By 1936, guided first by Mendeleev's predictions and later by atomic theory, chemists had identified all but two of the elements with atomic numbers between 1 and 92. From this point onward, all new elements to be discovered came from artificial nuclear reactions. Two gaps in the periodic table were filled when radioactive technetium and promethium, the last two elements with atomic numbers less than 92, were identified in 1937 and 1942, respectively. The first success in the search for elements with atomic numbers higher than 92 came with the 1940 discovery of neptunium and plutonium.

Since 1950, laboratories in the United States (Lawrence Berkeley National Laboratory), Russia (Joint Institute for Nuclear Research at Dubna, near Moscow), and Europe (Institute for Heavy Ion Research at Darmstadt, Germany) have competed to make new elements. Syntheses of new transuranium elements use a standard methodology. An element of fairly high atomic number is bombarded with a beam of high-energy particles. Initially, neutrons were used; later, helium nuclei and then larger nuclei such as ^{11}B and ^{12}C were used; and, more recently, highly charged ions of elements such as calcium, chromium, cobalt, and zinc have been chosen. The bombarding particle fuses with the nucleus of the target atom, forming a new nucleus that lasts for a short time before decomposing. New elements are detected by their decomposition products, a signature of particles with specific masses and energies.

By using bigger particles and higher energies, the list of known elements reached 106 by the end of the 1970s. To further extend the search, Russian scientists used a new idea, matching precisely the energy of the bombarding particle with the energy required to fuse the nuclei. This technique enabled the synthesis of elements 107, 108, and 109 in Darmstadt in the early 1980s, and the synthesis of elements 110, 111, and 112 in the following decade. Lifetimes of these elements were in the millisecond range; copernicium-277, $^{277}_{112}Cn$, for example, has a half-life of 240 μs.

Yet another breakthrough was needed to extend the list further. Scientists have long known that isotopes with specific so-called *magic numbers* of neutrons and protons are more stable. Elements with 2, 8, 20, 50, and 82 protons are members of this category, as are elements with 126 neutrons. The magic numbers correspond to filled shells in the nucleus. Their significance is analogous to the significance of filled shells for electronic structure. Theory had predicted that the next magic numbers would be 114 protons and 184 neutrons. Using this information, researchers discovered element 114 in early 1999. The Dubna group reporting this discovery found that the mass 289 isotope had an exceptionally long half-life, about 20 seconds.

Work along these lines is continuing and has resulted in the discovery of elements 113, 115, 116 and 118. Then, as we were preparing this edition of the book, the discovery of element 117, Uus, was announced (on April 19, 2010). An international team working at the Flerov Laboratories in Dubna, Russia, described the formation of 6 atoms of this element by bombarding ^{249}Bk with ^{48}Ca atoms. (The isotopes ^{293}Uus and ^{294}Uus were detected.) Assuming confirmation of this element from other labs will follow, the periodic table now includes all the elements from 1 to 118!

Footnote: Until an official name is chosen for element 117, it will be known by a placeholder name, ununseptium, and the corresponding three-letter symbol Uus. This name simply stands for "one-one-seven," because the atomic number of the element is 117.

Discovery of element 117. Scientists at the Flerov Laboratories in Dubna, Russia, used radioactive berkelium-249 as the starting material to make two isotopes of element 117. Berkelium-249 is contained in the greenish fluid in the tip of the vial. It was made in the research reactor at Oak Ridge National Laboratory.

higher energy by applying a high voltage. Cockcroft and Walton found that when energetic protons struck a lithium target, the following reaction occurs:

$$^{7}_{3}Li + ^{1}_{1}p \rightarrow 2\,^{4}_{2}He$$

This was the first example of a reaction initiated by a particle that had been artificially accelerated to high energy. Since this experiment was conducted, the technique has been developed much further, and the use of particle accelerators in nuclear chemistry is now commonplace. Particle accelerators operate on the principle that a charged particle placed between charged plates will be accelerated to a high speed and high energy. Modern examples of this process are seen in the synthesis of the transuranium elements, several of which are described in more detail in *A Closer Look: The Search for New Elements*, on the previous page.

Experiments using neutrons as bombarding particles were first carried out in both the United States and Great Britain in 1932. Nitrogen, oxygen, fluorine, and neon were bombarded with energetic neutrons, and α particles were detected among the products. Using neutrons made sense: Because neutrons have no charge, it was reasoned that these particles would not be repelled by the positively charged nuclear particles. Thus, neutrons did not need high energies to react.

In 1934, Enrico Fermi (1901–1954) and his coworkers showed that nuclear reactions using neutrons are more favorable if the neutrons have low energy. A low-energy neutron is simply captured by the nucleus, giving a product in which the mass number is increased by one unit. Because of the low energy of the bombarding particle, the product nucleus does not have sufficient energy to fragment in these reactions. The new nucleus is produced in an excited state, however; when the nucleus returns to the ground state, a γ-ray is emitted. Reactions in which a neutron is captured and a γ-ray is emitted are called **(n, γ) reactions**.

The (n, γ) reactions are the source of many of the radioisotopes used in medicine and chemistry. An example is radioactive phosphorus, $^{32}_{15}P$, which is used in chemical studies such as tracing the uptake of phosphorus in the body.

$$^{31}_{15}P + ^{1}_{0}n \rightarrow ^{32}_{15}P + \gamma$$

Transuranium elements, elements with an atomic number greater than 92, were first made in a nuclear reaction sequence beginning with an (n, γ) reaction. Scientists at the University of California at Berkeley bombarded uranium-238 with neutrons. Among the products identified were neptunium-239 and plutonium-239. These new elements were formed when ^{239}U decayed by β radiation.

$$^{238}_{92}U + ^{1}_{0}n \rightarrow ^{239}_{92}U$$

$$^{239}_{92}U \rightarrow ^{239}_{93}Np + ^{0}_{-1}\beta$$

$$^{239}_{93}Np \rightarrow ^{239}_{94}Pu + ^{0}_{-1}\beta$$

Four years later, a similar reaction sequence was used to make americium-241. Plutonium-239 was found to add two neutrons to form plutonium-241, which decays by β emission to give americium-241.

● **Transuranium Elements in Nature** Neptunium, plutonium, and americium were unknown prior to their preparation via these nuclear reactions. Later, these elements were found to be present in trace quantities in uranium ores.

EXAMPLE 23.8 Nuclear Reactions

Problem Write equations for the nuclear reactions described below.

(a) Fluorine-19 undergoes an (n, γ) reaction to give a radioactive product that decays by β emission. (Write equations for both nuclear reactions.)

(b) When an atom of beryllium-9 (the only stable isotope of beryllium) reacts with an alpha particle emitted by a plutonium atom, a neutron is ejected.

What Do You Know? Reactants and one of two products are given for each reaction.

Strategy The equations are written so that both mass and charge are balanced.

Solution

(a) $^{19}_{9}F + ^{1}_{0}n \rightarrow ^{20}_{9}F + \gamma$

$^{20}_{9}F \rightarrow ^{20}_{10}Ne + ^{0}_{-1}\beta$

(b) $^{239}_{94}Pu \rightarrow ^{235}_{92}U + ^{4}_{2}\alpha$

$^{4}_{2}\alpha + ^{9}_{4}Be \rightarrow ^{12}_{6}C + ^{1}_{0}n$

Think about Your Answer Both answers deal with neutrons. The equation given for part (a), an (n, γ) reaction, illustrates a process that is easy to carry out. In a lab, the neutrons might be produced in a small device called a *Pu-Be neutron source*. The answer to part (b) of this question describes the nuclear reactions in such a device.

Check Your Understanding

Technetium is one of the two elements with atomic numbers less than 83 for which there is no stable isotope (promethium, element 61, is the other). Nevertheless, technetium is a very important element because of its extensive use in medical imaging (page 1085). It is produced in a two-step process. First, ^{98}Mo undergoes an (n, γ) reaction; then, the resulting unstable isotope decomposes to ^{99}Tc. Write equations for these two reactions.

REVIEW & CHECK FOR SECTION 23.5

Which of the following is seldom used as a bombarding particle to initiate a nuclear reaction?

(a) protons   (b) neutrons   (c) electrons   (d) alpha particles

23.6 Nuclear Fission

In 1938, two chemists, Otto Hahn (1879–1968) and Fritz Strassman (1902–1980), isolated and identified barium in a sample of uranium that had been bombarded with neutrons. How was barium formed? The answer to that question explained one of the most significant scientific discoveries of the 20th century. The uranium nucleus had split into smaller pieces in the process we now call **nuclear fission**.

The details of nuclear fission were unraveled through the work of a number of scientists. They determined that a uranium-235 nucleus initially captured a neutron to form uranium-236. This isotope underwent nuclear fission to produce two new nuclei, one with a mass number around 140 and the other with a mass around 90, along with several neutrons (Figure 23.9). The nuclear reactions that led to formation of barium when a sample of ^{235}U was bombarded with neutrons are

$$^{235}_{92}\text{U} + ^{1}_{0}\text{n} \rightarrow ^{236}_{92}\text{U}$$

$$^{236}_{92}\text{U} \rightarrow ^{141}_{56}\text{Ba} + ^{92}_{36}\text{Kr} + 3\,^{1}_{0}\text{n}$$

An important aspect of fission reactions is that they produce more neutrons than are used to initiate the process. Under the right circumstances, these neutrons then serve to continue the reaction. If one or more of these neutrons are captured by another ^{235}U nucleus, then a further reaction can occur, releasing still more neutrons. This sequence repeats over and over. Such a mechanism, in which each step generates a reactant to continue the reaction, is called a **chain reaction**.

● **The Atomic Bomb** In an atomic bomb, each nuclear fission step produces 3 neutrons, which leads to about 3 more fissions and 9 more neutrons, which leads to 9 more fission steps and 27 more neutrons, and so on. The rate of fission depends on the number of neutrons, so the nuclear reaction occurs faster and faster as more and more neutrons are formed, leading to an enormous output of energy in a short time span.

FIGURE 23.9 **Nuclear fission.** Neutron capture by $^{235}_{92}$U produces $^{236}_{92}$U. This isotope undergoes fission, which yields several fragments along with several neutrons. These neutrons initiate further nuclear reactions by adding to other $^{235}_{92}$U nuclei. The process is highly exothermic, producing about 2×10^{10} kJ/mol.

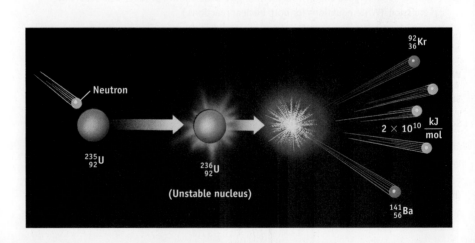

$^{92}_{36}$Kr

Neutron

$2 \times 10^{10}\ \dfrac{\text{kJ}}{\text{mol}}$

$^{235}_{92}$U

$^{236}_{92}$U

(Unstable nucleus)

$^{141}_{56}$Ba

A nuclear fission chain reaction has three general steps:

1. *Initiation.* The reaction of a single atom is needed to start the chain. Fission of ^{235}U is initiated by the absorption of a neutron.
2. *Propagation.* This part of the process repeats itself over and over, with each step yielding more product. The fission of ^{236}U releases neutrons that initiate the fission of other uranium atoms.
3. *Termination.* Eventually, the chain will end. Termination could occur if the reactant (^{235}U) is used up, or if the neutrons that continue the chain escape from the sample without being captured by ^{235}U.

To harness the energy produced in a nuclear reaction, it is necessary to control the rate at which a fission reaction occurs. This is managed by balancing the propagation and termination steps by limiting the number of neutrons available. In a nuclear reactor, this balance is accomplished by using cadmium rods to absorb neutrons. By withdrawing or inserting the rods, the number of neutrons available to propagate the chain can be changed, and the rate of the fission reaction (and the rate of energy production) can be increased or decreased.

Uranium-235 and plutonium-239 are the fissionable isotopes most commonly used in power reactors. Natural uranium contains only 0.72% of uranium-235; more than 99% of the natural element is uranium-238. The percentage of uranium-235 in natural uranium is too small to sustain a chain reaction, however, so the uranium used for nuclear fuel must be enriched in this isotope. One way to do so is by gaseous centrifugation (Figure 23.10). Plutonium, on the other hand, occurs naturally in only trace quantities and so must be made by a nuclear reaction. The raw material for this nuclear synthesis is the more abundant uranium isotope, ^{238}U. Addition of a neutron to ^{238}U gives ^{239}U, which, as noted earlier, undergoes two β emissions to form ^{239}Pu.

Currently, there are over 100 operating nuclear power plants in the United States and more than 400 worldwide. About 20% of this country's electricity (and 17% of the world's energy) comes from nuclear power (Figure 23.11). Although one might imagine that nuclear energy would be called upon to meet the ever-increasing needs of society, no new nuclear power plants are under construction in the United States. Among other things, the disasters at Chernobyl (in the former Soviet Union) in 1986 and Three Mile Island (in Pennsylvania) in 1979 have sensitized the public to the issue of safety. The cost to construct a nuclear power plant (measured in terms of dollars per kilowatt-hour of power) is considerably more than the cost for a natural gas–powered facility, and there are severe regulatory restrictions for nuclear power. Disposal of highly radioactive nuclear waste is another

● **Lise Meitner (1878–1968)**
Meitner's greatest contribution to 20th-century science was her explanation of the process of nuclear fission. She and her nephew, Otto Frisch, also a physicist, published a paper in 1939 that was the first to use the term *nuclear fission*. Element number 109 is named meitnerium to honor Meitner's contributions. The leader of the team that discovered this element said that "She should be honored as the most significant woman scientist of [the 20th] century."

AIP-Emilio Segré Visual Archives, Herzfeld Collection

FIGURE 23.10 **Isotope separation.** *(left)* Separation of uranium isotopes for use in atomic weaponry or in nuclear power plants is done with gas centrifuges. *(right)* UF_6 gas is injected into the centrifuge from a tube passing down through the center of a tall, spinning cylinder. The heavier $^{238}UF_6$ molecules experience more centrifugal force and move to the outer wall of the cylinder; the lighter $^{235}UF_6$ molecules stay closer to the center. A temperature difference inside the rotor causes the $^{235}UF_6$ molecules to move to the top of the cylinder and the $^{238}UF_6$ molecules to move to the bottom. (See the *New York Times*, page F1, March 23, 2004.)

FIGURE 23.11 Percentage of electricity generation by nuclear power in various countries. This varies from 76.2% in France, to 19.7% in the United States, to a little more than 2% in China and India. (Data from "Energy, Electricity and Nuclear Power Estimates for the Period up to 2030" from the International Atomic Energy Agency, 2009 edition.)

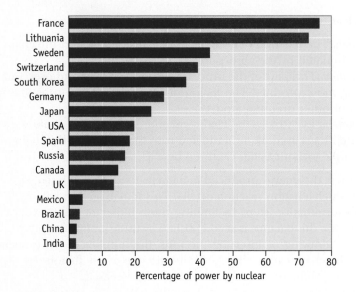

thorny problem, with 20 metric tons of waste being generated per year at each reactor.

In addition to technical problems, nuclear energy production brings with it significant geopolitical security concerns. The process for enriching uranium for use in a reactor is the same process used for generating weapons-grade uranium. Also, some nuclear reactors are designed so that one by-product of their operation is the isotope plutonium-239, which can be removed and used in a nuclear weapon. Despite these problems, nuclear fission is an important part of the energy profile in a number of countries. For example, 76.2% of power production in France and 24.9% in Japan is nuclear generated.

REVIEW & CHECK FOR SECTION 23.6

Identify the other element generated in this fission reaction: $^{235}_{92}U + ^{1}_{0}n \rightarrow ^{141}_{55}Cs + ? + 2^{1}_{0}n$

(a) $^{93}_{37}Rb$ (b) $^{141}_{56}Ba$ (c) $^{92}_{36}Kr$

23.7 Nuclear Fusion

In a **nuclear fusion** reaction, several small nuclei react to form a larger nucleus. Tremendous amounts of energy can be generated by such reactions. An example is the fusion of deuterium and tritium nuclei to form $^{4}_{2}He$ and a neutron:

$$^{2}_{1}H + ^{3}_{1}H \rightarrow ^{4}_{2}He + ^{1}_{0}n \qquad \Delta E = -1.7 \times 10^9 \text{ kJ/mol}$$

Fusion reactions provide the energy of our sun and other stars. Scientists have long dreamed of being able to harness fusion to provide power. To do so, a temperature of 10^6 to 10^7 K, like that in the interior of the sun, would be required to bring the positively charged nuclei together with enough energy to overcome nuclear repulsions. At the very high temperatures needed for a fusion reaction, matter does not exist as atoms or molecules; instead, matter is in the form of a *plasma* made up of unbound nuclei and electrons.

Three critical requirements must be met before nuclear fusion could represent a viable energy source. First, the temperature must be high enough for fusion to occur. The fusion of deuterium and tritium, for example, requires a temperature of 10^7 K or more. Second, the plasma must be confined long enough to release a net output of energy. Third, the energy must be recovered in some usable form.

Harnessing a nuclear fusion reaction for a peaceful use has not yet been achieved. Nevertheless, many attractive features encourage continuing research in this field. The hydrogen used as "fuel" is cheap and available in almost unlimited amounts. As a further benefit, most radioisotopes produced by fusion have short half-lives, so they remain a radiation hazard for only a short time.

23.8 Radiation Health and Safety

Units for Measuring Radiation

Several units of measurement are used to describe levels and doses of radioactivity. Generally the units used in the United States are not the same as the SI units of measurement.

In the United States, the degree of radioactivity is often measured in **curies** (Ci). Less commonly used in the United States is the SI unit, the **becquerel** (Bq). Both units measure the number of disintegrations per second; 1 Ci is 3.7×10^{10} dps (disintegrations per second), while 1 Bq represents 1 dps. The curie and the becquerel are used to report the amount of radioactivity when multiple kinds of unstable nuclei are decaying and to report amounts necessary for medical purposes.

By itself, the degree of radioactivity does not provide a good measure of the amount of energy in the radiation or the amount of damage that the radiation can cause to living tissue. Two additional kinds of information are necessary. The first is the amount of energy absorbed; the second is the effectiveness of the particular kind of radiation in causing tissue damage. The amount of energy absorbed by living tissue is measured in **rads**. *Rad* is an acronym for "radiation absorbed dose." One rad represents 0.01 J of energy absorbed per kilogram of tissue. Its SI equivalent is the **gray** (Gy); 1 Gy denotes the absorption of 1 J per kilogram of tissue.

Different forms of radiation cause different amounts of biological damage. The amount of damage depends on how strongly a form of radiation interacts with matter. Alpha particles cannot penetrate the body any farther than the outer layer of skin. If α particles are emitted within the body, however, they will cause between 10 and 20 times the amount of damage done by γ-rays, which can go entirely through a human body without being stopped. In determining the amount of biological damage to living tissue, differences in damaging power are accounted for using a "quality factor." This quality factor has been set at 1 for β and γ radiation, 5 for low-energy protons and neutrons, and 20 for α particles or high-energy protons and neutrons.

Biological damage is quantified in a unit called the **rem** (an acronym for "roentgen equivalent man"). A dose of radiation in rem is determined by multiplying the energy absorbed in rads by the quality factor for that kind of radiation. The rad and the rem are very large in comparison to normal exposures to radiation, so it is more common to express exposures in millirems (mrem). The SI equivalent of the rem is the **sievert** (Sv), determined by multiplying the dose in grays by the quality factor.

Radiation: Doses and Effects

Exposure to a small amount of radiation is unavoidable. Earth is constantly being bombarded with radioactive particles from outer space. There is also some exposure to radioactive elements that occur naturally on earth, including ^{14}C, ^{40}K (a radioactive isotope that occurs naturally in 0.0117% abundance), ^{238}U, and ^{232}Th. Radioactive elements in the environment that were created artificially (in the fallout from nuclear bomb tests, for example) also contribute to this exposure. For some people, medical procedures using radioisotopes are a major contributor.

The average dose of background radioactivity to which a person in the United States is exposed is about 200 mrem per year (Table 23.2). Well over half of that amount comes from natural sources over which we have no control. Of the 60–70 mrem per year exposure that comes from artificial sources, nearly 90% is delivered in medical procedures such as x-ray examinations and radiation therapy. Considering the controversy surrounding nuclear power, it is interesting to note that less than 0.5% of the total annual background dose of radiation that the average person receives can be attributed to the nuclear power industry.

● **The Roentgen** The roentgen (R) is an older unit of radiation exposure. It is defined as the amount of x-rays or γ radiation that will produce 2.08×10^9 ions in 1 cm³ of dry air. The roentgen and the rad are similar in size. Wilhelm Roentgen (1845–1923) first produced and detected x radiation. Element 111 has been named roentgenium in his honor.

Table 23.2 Radiation Exposure of an Individual for One Year from Natural and Artificial Sources

	Millirem/Year	Percentage
Natural Sources		
Cosmic radiation	50.0	25.8
The earth	47.0	24.2
Building materials	3.0	1.5
Inhaled from the air	5.0	2.6
Elements found naturally in human tissue	21.0	10.8
Subtotal	**126.0**	**64.9**
Medical Sources		
Diagnostic x-rays	50.0	25.8
Radiotherapy	10.0	5.2
Internal diagnosis	1.0	0.5
Subtotal	**61.0**	**31.5**
Other Artificial Sources		
Nuclear power industry	0.85	0.4
Luminous watch dials, TV tubes	2.0	1.0
Fallout from nuclear tests	4.0	2.1
Subtotal	**6.9**	**3.5**
Total	**193.9**	**99.9**

Describing the biological effects of a dose of radiation precisely is not a simple matter. The amount of damage done depends not only on the kind of radiation and the amount of energy absorbed, but also on the particular tissues exposed and the rate at which the dose builds up. A great deal has been learned about the effects of radiation on the human body by studying the survivors of the bombs dropped over Japan in World War II and the workers exposed to radiation from the reactor disaster at Chernobyl. From studies of the health of these survivors, we have learned that the effects of radiation are not generally observable below a single dose of 25 rem. At the other extreme, a single dose of >200 rem will be fatal to about half the population (Table 23.3).

Our information is more accurate when dealing with single, large doses than it is for the effects of chronic, smaller doses of radiation. One current issue of debate in the scientific community is how to judge the effects of multiple smaller doses or long-term exposure (see *A Closer Look: What Is A Safe Exposure?*).

Table 23.3 Effects of a Single Dose of Radiation

Dose (rem)	Effect
0–25	No effect observed
26–50	Small decrease in white blood cell count
51–100	Significant decrease in white blood cell count, lesions
101–200	Loss of hair, nausea
201–500	Hemorrhaging, ulcers, death in 50% of population
500	Death

What Is a Safe Exposure?

Is the exposure to natural background radiation totally without effect? Can you equate the effect of a single dose and the effect of cumulative, smaller doses that are spread out over a long period of time? The assumption generally made is that no "safe maximum dose," or level below which absolutely no damage will occur, exists. However, the accuracy of this assumption has come into question. These issues are not testable with human subjects, and tests based on animal studies are not completely reliable because of the uncertainty of species-to-species variations.

The model used by government regulators to set exposure limits assumes that the relationship between exposure to radiation and incidence of radiation-induced problems, such as cancer, anemia, and immune

system problems, is linear. Under this assumption, if a dose of $2x$ rem causes damage in 20% of the population, then a dose of x rem will cause damage in 10% of the population. But is this true? Cells do possess mechanisms for repairing damage. Many scientists believe that this self-repair mechanism renders the human body less susceptible to damage from smaller doses of radiation, because the damage will be repaired as part of the normal course of events. They argue that, at extremely low doses of radiation, the self-repair response results in less damage.

The bottom line is that much still remains to be learned in this area. And the stakes are significant.

The film badge. These badges, worn by scientists using radioactive materials, are used to monitor cumulative exposure to radiation.

23.9 Applications of Nuclear Chemistry

We tend to think about nuclear chemistry in terms of power plants and bombs. In truth, radioactive elements are now used in many areas of science and medicine, and they are of ever-increasing importance to our lives. Because describing all of their uses would take several books, we have selected just a few examples to illustrate the diversity of applications of radioactivity.

Nuclear Medicine: Medical Imaging

Diagnostic procedures using nuclear chemistry are essential in medical imaging, which entails the creation of images of specific parts of the body. There are three principal components to constructing a radioisotope-based image:

- A radioactive isotope, administered as the element or incorporated into a compound, that concentrates the radioactive isotope in the tissue to be imaged
- A method of detecting the type of radiation involved
- A computer to assemble the information from the detector into a meaningful image

The choice of a radioisotope and the manner in which it is administered are determined by the tissue in question. A compound containing the isotope must be absorbed more by the target tissue than by the rest of the body. Table 23.4 lists radioisotopes that are commonly used in nuclear imaging processes, their half-lives, and

Table 23.4 Radioisotopes Used in Medical Diagnostic Procedures

Radioisotope	Half-Life (h)	Imaging
^{99m}Tc	6.0	Thyroid, brain, kidneys
^{201}Tl	73.0	Heart
^{123}I	13.2	Thyroid
^{67}Ga	78.2	Various tumors and abscesses
^{18}F	1.8	Brain, sites of metabolic activity

A CLOSER LOOK

Technetium-99m

Technetium was the first new element to be made artificially. One might think that this element would be a chemical rarity, but this is not so: Its importance in medical imaging has brought a great deal of attention to it. Although all the technetium in the world must be synthesized by nuclear reactions, the element is readily available and even inexpensive; its price is about $60 per gram, only a bit more than gold (in 2010).

Technetium-99m is formed when molybdenum-99 decays by β emission. Technetium-99m then decays to its ground state with a half-life of 6.01 hours, giving off a 140-KeV γ-ray in the process. (Technetium-99 is itself unstable, decaying to stable ^{99}Ru with a half-life of 2.1×10^5 years.)

Technetium-99m is produced in hospitals using a molybdenum–technetium generator. Sheathed in lead shielding, the generator contains the artificially synthesized isotope ^{99}Mo in the form of molybdate ion, MoO_4^{2-}, adsorbed on a column of alumina, Al_2O_3. The MoO_4^{2-} is continually being converted into the pertechnate ion, $^{99m}TcO_4^-$ by β emission. When it is needed, the $^{99m}TcO_4^-$ is washed from the column using a saline solution. Technetium-99m may be used directly as the pertechnate ion or converted into other compounds. The pertechnate ion or radiopharmaceuticals made from it are administered intravenously to the patient. Such small quantities are needed that 1 μg (microgram) of technetium-99m is sufficient for the average hospital's daily imaging needs.

One use of ^{99m}Tc is for imaging the thyroid gland. Because I^-(aq) and TcO_4^-(aq) ions have very similar sizes, the thyroid will (mistakenly) take up TcO_4^-(aq) along with iodide ion. This uptake concentrates ^{99m}Tc in the thyroid and allows a physician to obtain images such as the one shown in the accompanying Figure.

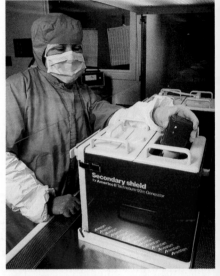

Technetium-99m generator. A technician is handling a sample containing the MoO_4^{2-} that will be converted to $^{99m}TcO_4^-$.

(a) Healthy human thyroid gland.

(b) Thyroid gland showing effect of hyperthyroidism.

Thyroid imaging. Technetium-99m concentrates in sites of high activity. Images of this gland, which is located at the base of the neck, were obtained by recording γ-ray emission after the patient was given radioactive technetium-99m. Current technology creates a computer color-enhanced scan.

---

the tissues they are used to image. All of the isotopes in Table 23.4 are γ emitters; γ radiation is preferred for imaging because it is less damaging to the body in small doses than either α or β radiation.

Technetium-99m is used in more than 85% of the diagnostic scans done in hospitals each year (see *A Closer Look: Technetium-99m*. The "m" stands for *metastable*, a term used to identify an unstable state that exists for a finite period of time. Recall that atoms in excited electronic states emit visible, infrared, and ultraviolet radiation (◄ Chapter 6). Similarly, a nucleus in an excited state gives up its excess energy, but in this case a much higher energy is involved, and the emission occurs as γ radiation. The γ-rays given off by ^{99m}Tc are detected to produce the image (Figure 23.12).

Another medical imaging technique based on nuclear chemistry is *positron emission tomography* (PET). In PET, an isotope that decays by positron emission is incorporated into a carrier compound and given to the patient. When emitted, the positron travels no more than a few millimeters before undergoing matter–antimatter annihilation.

$$^{0}_{+1}\beta + \,^{0}_{-1}e \rightarrow 2\gamma$$

The two emitted γ-rays travel in opposite directions. By determining where high numbers of γ-rays are being emitted, one can construct a map showing where the positron emitter is located in the body.

An isotope often used in PET is ^{15}O. A patient is given gaseous O_2 that contains ^{15}O. This isotope travels throughout the body in the bloodstream, allowing images of the brain and bloodstream to be obtained (Figure 23.13). Because positron emitters are typically very short-lived, PET facilities must be located near a cyclotron where the radioactive nuclei are prepared and then immediately incorporated into a carrier compound.

Nuclear Medicine: Radiation Therapy

To treat most cancers, it is necessary to use radiation that can penetrate the body to the location of the tumor. Gamma radiation from a cobalt-60 source is commonly used. Unfortunately, the penetrating ability of γ-rays makes it virtually impossible to destroy diseased tissue without also damaging healthy tissue in the process. Nevertheless, this technique is a regularly sanctioned procedure, and its successes are well known.

Analytical Methods: The Use of Radioactive Isotopes as Tracers

Radioactive isotopes can be used to help determine the fate of compounds in the body or in the environment. These studies begin with a compound that contains a radioactive isotope of one of its component elements. In biology, for example, scientists can use radioactive isotopes to measure the uptake of nutrients. Plants take up phosphorus-containing compounds from the soil through their roots. By adding a small amount of radioactive ^{32}P, a β emitter with a half-life of 14.3 days, to fertilizer and then measuring the rate at which the radioactivity appears in the leaves, plant biologists can determine the rate at which phosphorus is taken up. The outcome can assist scientists in identifying hybrid strains of plants that can absorb phosphorus quickly, resulting in faster-maturing crops, better yields per acre, and more food or fiber at less expense.

To measure pesticide levels, a pesticide can be tagged with a radioisotope and then applied to a test field. By counting the disintegrations of the radioactive tracer, information can be obtained about how much pesticide accumulates in the soil, is taken up by the plant, and is carried off in runoff surface water. After these tests are completed, the radioactive isotope decays to harmless levels in a few days or a few weeks because of the short half-lives of the isotopes used.

Analytical Methods: Isotope Dilution

Imagine, for the moment, that you wanted to estimate the volume of blood in an animal subject. How might you do this? Obviously, draining the blood and measuring its volume in volumetric glassware is not a desirable option.

One technique uses a method called *isotope dilution*. In this process, a small amount of radioactive isotope is injected into the bloodstream. After a period of time to allow the isotope to become distributed throughout the body, a blood sample is taken and its radioactivity measured. The calculation used to determine the total blood volume is illustrated in the next example.

John C. Katz

FIGURE 23.12 Heart imaging with technetium-99m. The radioactive element technetium-99m, a γ emitter, is injected into a patient's vein in the form of the pertechnetate ion (TcO_4^-) or as a complex ion with an organic ligand. A series of scans of the γ emissions of the isotope are made while the patient is resting and then again after strenuous exercise. Bright areas in the scans indicate that the isotope is binding to the tissue in that area. The scans in this figure show a normal heart function for one of the authors of this book.

Wellcome Department of Neurology/Science Photo Library/Photo Researchers, Inc.

FIGURE 23.13 PET scans of the brain. These scans show the left side of the brain; *red* indicates an area of highest activity. *(upper left) Sight* activates the visual area in the occipital cortex at the back of the brain. *(upper right) Hearing* activates the auditory area in the superior temporal cortex of the brain. *(lower left) Speaking* activates the speech centers in the insula and motor cortex. *(lower right) Thinking* about verbs, and speaking them, generates high activity, including in the hearing, speaking, temporal, and parietal areas.

EXAMPLE 23.9 Analysis Using Radioisotopes

Problem A 1.00-mL solution containing 0.240 μCi of tritium is injected into a dog's bloodstream. After a period of time to allow the isotope to be dispersed, a 1.00-mL sample of blood is drawn. The radioactivity of this sample is found to be 4.3×10^{-4} μCi/mL. What is the total volume of blood in the dog?

What Do You Know? You know the concentration (activity) and volume of a concentrated solution and you then measure the concentration of the dilute solution. The unknown is the volume of the dilute solution.

Strategy In this problem, we relate the activity of the sample (in Ci) to the amount of the radioisotope present. The total amount of solute is 0.240 μCi, and the concentration (measured on the small sample of blood) is 4.3×10^{-4} μCi/mL. The unknown is the total volume of blood, V.

● **Boron Neutron Capture Therapy (BNCT).** To avoid the side effects associated with more traditional forms of radiation therapy, BNCT is an experimental treatment that has been explored in the last 10 to 15 years. BNCT is unusual in that boron-10, the isotope of boron used as part of the treatment, is not radioactive. This isotope is highly effective in capturing neutrons, however: 2500 times better than boron-11 and eight times better than uranium-235. When the nucleus of a boron-10 atom captures a neutron, the resulting boron-11 nucleus has so much energy that it fragments to form an α particle and a lithium-7 atom. Although the α particles do a great deal of damage, because their penetrating power is so low, the damage remains confined to an area not much larger than one or two cells in diameter.

Solution The blood contains a total of 0.240 μCi of radioactive material. Exactly 1.00 mL containing this amount was injected. After dilution in the bloodstream, 1.00 mL of blood, representative of the total volume V, is found to have an activity of 4.3×10^{-4} μCi/mL.

$$(0.240 \ \mu Ci/mL)(1.00 \ mL) = (4.3 \times 10^{-4} \ \mu Ci/mL)(V)$$

$$V = 560 \ mL$$

Think about Your Answer This is solved as a classic dilution problem, by equating $C_{dil} \times V_{dil} = C_{conc} \times V_{conc}$

Check Your Understanding

To measure the solubility for $PbCrO_4$ you mix a small amount of a lead(II) salt having radioactive ^{212}Pb with a lead salt containing 0.0100 g of lead. To this mixture you add enough K_2CrO_4 to completely precipitate the lead(II) ions as $PbCrO_4$. The supernatant solution still contains a trace of lead, of course, and when you evaporate 10.00 mL of this solution to solid $PbCrO_4$, you find a radioactivity that is 4.17×10^{-5} of what it is for the pure ^{212}Pb salt. Calculate the solubility of $PbCrO_4$ in mol/L. (Adapted from C. E. Housecraft and A. G. Sharpe, *Inorganic Chemistry*, Pearson, 3rd edition, 2008, p. 84.)

Space Science: Neutron Activation Analysis and the Moon Rocks

The first manned space mission to the moon brought back a number of samples of soil and rock—a treasure trove for scientists. One of their first tasks was to analyze these samples to determine their identity and composition. Most analytical methods require chemical reactions using at least a small amount of material; however, this was not a desirable option, considering that the moon rocks were at the time the most valuable rocks in the world.

A few scientists got a chance to work on this unique project, and one of the analytical tools they used was **neutron activation analysis**. In this nondestructive process, a sample is irradiated with neutrons. Most isotopes add a neutron to form a new isotope that is one mass unit higher in an excited nuclear state. When the nucleus decays to its ground state, it emits a γ-ray. The energy of the γ-ray identifies the element, and the number of γ-rays can be counted to determine the amount of the element in the sample. Using neutron activation analysis, it is possible to analyze for a number of elements in a single experiment (Table 23.5).

Neutron activation analysis has many other uses. This analytical procedure yields a kind of fingerprint that can be used to identify a substance. For example, this technique has been applied in determining whether an art work is real or fraudulent. Analysis of the pigments in paints on a painting can be carried out without damaging the painting to determine whether the composition resembles modern paints or paints used hundreds of years ago.

Food Science: Food Irradiation

Refrigeration, canning, and chemical additives provide significant protection in terms of food preservation, but in some parts of the world these procedures are unavailable, and stored-food spoilage may claim as much as 50% of the food crop. Irradiation with γ-rays from sources such as ^{60}Co and ^{137}Cs is an option for prolonging the shelf life of foods. Relatively low levels of radiation may retard the growth of organisms, such as bacteria, molds, and yeasts, that can cause food spoilage. After irradiation, milk in a sealed container has a minimum shelf life of 3 months without refrigeration. Chicken normally has a 3-day refrigerated shelf life; after irradiation, it may have a 3-week refrigerated shelf life.

Higher levels of radiation, in the 1- to 5-Mrad (1 Mrad = 1×10^6 rad) range, will kill every living organism. Foods irradiated at these levels will keep indefinitely when sealed in plastic or aluminum-foil packages. Ham, beef, turkey, and corned beef

Table 23.5 Rare Earth Analysis of Moon Rock Sample 10022 (Fine-Grain Igneous Rock)

Element	Concentration (ppm)
La	26.4
Ce	68
Nd	66
Sm	21.2
Eu	2.04
Gd	25
Tb	4.7
Dy	31.2
Ho	5.5
Er	16
Yb	17.7
Lu	2.55

Source: L. A. Haskin, P. A, Helmke, and R. O. Allen: *Science,* Vol. 167, p. 487, 1970. The concentrations of rare earths in moon rocks were quite similar to the values in terrestrial rocks except that the europium concentration is much depleted. The January 30, 1970, issue of *Science* was devoted to analysis of moon rocks.

CASE STUDY

Nuclear Medicine and Hyperthyroidism

The primary function of the thyroid gland, located in your neck, is the production of thyroxine (3,5,3′,5′-tetraiodothyronine) and 3,5,3′-triiodothyronine. These chemical compounds are hormones that help to regulate the rate of metabolism (page 504), a term that refers to all of the chemical reactions that take place in the body. In particular, the thyroid hormones play an important role in the processes that release energy from food.

Abnormally low levels of thyroxine result in a condition known as *hypothyroidism*. Its symptoms include lethargy and feeling cold much of the time. The remedy for this condition is medication, consisting of thyroxine pills. The opposite condition, hyperthyroidism, also occurs in some people. In this condition, the body produces too much of the hormone. Hyperthyroidism is diagnosed by symptoms such as nervousness, heat intolerance, increased appetite, and muscle weakness and fatigue when blood sugar is too rapidly depleted. The standard remedy for hyperthyroidism is to destroy part of the thyroid gland, and one way to do so is to use a compound containing radioactive iodine-123 or iodine-131.

To understand this procedure, you need to know something about iodine in the body. Iodine is an essential element. Some diets provide iodine naturally (seaweed, for example, is a good source of iodine), but in the Western world most iodine taken up by the body comes from iodized salt, NaCl containing a few percent of NaI. An adult man or woman of average size should take in about 150 μg (micrograms) of iodine

Thyroxine. The hormone 3,5,3′,5′-tetraiodothyronine (thyroxine) exerts a stimulating effect on metabolism.

(1 μg $= 10^{-6}$ g) in the daily diet. In the body, iodide ion is transported to the thyroid, where it serves as one of the raw materials in making thyroxine.

The fact that iodine concentrates in the thyroid tissue is essential to the procedure for using radioiodine therapy as a treatment for hyperthyroidism. Typically, an aqueous NaI solution is used in which a small fraction of iodide is the radioactive isotope iodine-131 or iodine-123, and the rest is nonradioactive iodine-127. The radioactivity destroys thyroid tissue, resulting in a decrease in thyroid activity.

Questions:

1. ^{131}I decays by beta emission. What is the product of this decay? Write a balanced nuclear equation for this process.

2. The half-life of ^{131}I is 8.04 days, and that of ^{123}I is 13.3 hours. If you begin with an equal number of moles of each isotope, at the end of 7 days what are their relative amounts?

Answers to these questions are available in Appendix N.

---

sterilized by radiation have been used on many Space Shuttle flights, for example. An astronaut said, "The beautiful thing was that it didn't disturb the taste, which made the meals much better than the freeze-dried and other types of foods we had."

These procedures are not without their opponents, and the public has not fully embraced irradiation of foods. An interesting argument favoring this technique is that radiation is less harmful than other methodologies for food preservation. This type of sterilization offers greater safety to food workers because it lessens chances of exposure to harmful chemicals, and it protects the environment by avoiding contamination of water supplies with toxic chemicals.

Food irradiation is commonly used in European countries, Canada, and Mexico. Its use in the United States is currently regulated by the U.S. Food and Drug Administration (FDA) and Department of Agriculture (USDA). In 1997, the FDA approved the irradiation of refrigerated and frozen uncooked meat to control pathogens and extend shelf-life, and in 2000 the USDA approved the irradiation of eggs to control *Salmonella* infection.

and

CHAPTER GOALS REVISITED

Now that you have studied this chapter, you should ask whether you have met the chapter goals. In particular, you should be able to:

Identify radioactive elements, and describe natural and artificial nuclear reactions

a. Identify α, β, and γ radiation, the three major types of radiation in natural radioactive decay (Section 23.1), and write balanced equations for nuclear reactions (Section 23.2). **Study Questions: 11–16, 32, 41.**

b. Predict whether a radioactive isotope will decay by α or β emission, or by positron emission or electron capture (Sections 23.2 and 23.3). **Study Questions: 17–22.**

Calculate the binding energy and binding energy per nucleon for a particular isotope

a. Understand how binding energy per nucleon is defined (Section 23.3) and recognize the significance of a graph of binding energy per nucleon versus mass number (Section 23.3). **Study Questions: 23–28, 52.**

Understand rates of radioactive decay

a. Understand and use mathematical equations that characterize the radioactive decay process (Section 23.4). **Study Questions: 29–38, 47, 50, 54, 58.**

Understand artificial nuclear reactions

a. Describe nuclear chain reactions, nuclear fission, and nuclear fusion (Sections 23.6 and 23.7). **Study Questions: 39–46.**

Understand issues of health and safety with respect to radioactivity

a. Describe the units used to measure intensity, and understand how they pertain to health issues (Sections 23.8 and 23.9).

Be aware of some uses of radioactive isotopes in science and medicine

Key Equations

Equation 23.1 (page 1068): The equation relating interconversion of mass (m) and energy (E). This equation is applied in the calculation of binding energy (E_b) for nuclei.

$$E_b = (\Delta m)c^2$$

Equation 23.2 (page 1071): The activity of a radioactive sample (A) is proportional to the number of radioactive atoms (N).

$$A \propto N$$

Equation 23.3 (page 1071): The change in the number of radioactive elements with time is equal to the product of the rate constant (k, decay constant) and number of atoms present (N).

$$\Delta N/\Delta t = -kN$$

Equation 23.4 (page 1072): The rate law for nuclear decay based on number of radioactive atoms initially present (N_0) and the number N after time t.

$$\ln(N/N_0) = -kt$$

Equation 23.5 (page 1072): The rate law for nuclear decay based on the measured activity of a sample (A).

$$\ln(A/A_0) = -kt$$

Equation 23.6 (page 1072): The relationship between the half-life and the rate constant for a nuclear decay process.

$$t_{1/2} = 0.693/k$$

Study Questions

⏻WL Interactive versions of these questions are assignable in OWL.

▲ denotes challenging questions.

Blue-numbered questions have answers in Appendix R and fully worked solutions in the *Student Solutions Manual*.

Practicing Skills

Important Concepts

1. Some important discoveries in scientific history that contributed to the development of nuclear chemistry are listed below. Briefly, describe each discovery, identify prominent scientists who contributed to it, and comment on the significance of the discovery to the development of this field.
   (a) 1896, the discovery of radioactivity
   (b) 1898, the identification of radium and polonium
   (c) 1919, the first artificial nuclear reaction
   (d) 1932, (n, γ) reactions
   (e) 1939, fission reactions

2. In Chapter 3, the law of conservation of mass was introduced as an important principle in chemistry. The discovery of nuclear reactions forced scientists to modify this law. Explain why, and give an example illustrating that mass is not conserved in a nuclear reaction.

3. A graph of binding energy per nucleon is shown in Figure 23.4. Explain how the data used to construct this graph were obtained.

4. How is Figure 23.3 used to predict the type of decomposition for unstable (radioactive) isotopes?

5. Outline how nuclear reactions are carried out in the laboratory. Describe the artificial nuclear reactions used to make an element with an atomic number greater than 92.

6. What mathematical equations define the rates of decay for radioactive elements?

7. Explain how carbon-14 is used to estimate the ages of archeological artifacts. What are the limitations for use of this technique?

8. Describe how the concept of half-life for nuclear decay is used.

9. What is a radioactive decay series? Explain why radium and polonium are found in uranium ores.

10. The interaction of radiation with matter has both positive and negative consequences. Discuss briefly the hazards of radiation and the way that radiation can be used in medicine.

Nuclear Reactions

(See Section 23.2 and Examples 23.1 and 23.2.)

11. Complete the following nuclear equations. Write the mass number and atomic number for the remaining particle, as well as its symbol.
    (a) $^{54}_{26}\text{Fe} + ^{4}_{2}\text{He} \longrightarrow 2\,^{1}_{0}\text{n} + ?$
    (b) $^{27}_{13}\text{Al} + ^{4}_{2}\text{He} \longrightarrow ^{30}_{15}\text{P} + ?$
    (c) $^{32}_{16}\text{S} + ^{1}_{0}\text{n} \longrightarrow ^{1}_{1}\text{H} + ?$
    (d) $^{96}_{42}\text{Mo} + ^{2}_{1}\text{H} \longrightarrow ^{1}_{0}\text{n} + ?$
    (e) $^{98}_{42}\text{Mo} + ^{1}_{0}\text{n} \longrightarrow ^{99}_{43}\text{Tc} + ?$
    (f) $^{18}_{9}\text{F} \longrightarrow ^{18}_{8}\text{O} + ?$

12. Complete the following nuclear equations. Write the mass number, atomic number, and symbol for the remaining particle.
    (a) $^{9}_{4}\text{Be} + ? \longrightarrow ^{6}_{3}\text{Li} + ^{4}_{2}\text{He}$
    (b) $? + ^{1}_{0}\text{n} \longrightarrow ^{24}_{11}\text{Na} + ^{4}_{2}\text{He}$
    (c) $^{40}_{20}\text{Ca} + ? \longrightarrow ^{40}_{19}\text{K} + ^{1}_{1}\text{H}$
    (d) $^{241}_{95}\text{Am} + ^{4}_{2}\text{He} \longrightarrow ^{243}_{97}\text{Bk} + ?$
    (e) $^{246}_{96}\text{Cm} + ^{12}_{6}\text{C} \longrightarrow 4\,^{1}_{0}\text{n} + ?$
    (f) $^{238}_{92}\text{U} + ? \longrightarrow ^{249}_{100}\text{Fm} + 5\,^{1}_{0}\text{n}$

13. Complete the following nuclear equations. Write the mass number, atomic number, and symbol for the remaining particle.
    (a) $^{111}_{47}\text{Ag} \longrightarrow ^{111}_{48}\text{Cd} + ?$
    (b) $^{87}_{36}\text{Kr} \longrightarrow ^{0}_{-1}\beta + ?$
    (c) $^{231}_{91}\text{Pa} \longrightarrow ^{227}_{89}\text{Ac} + ?$
    (d) $^{230}_{90}\text{Th} \longrightarrow ^{4}_{2}\text{He} + ?$
    (e) $^{82}_{35}\text{Br} \longrightarrow ^{82}_{36}\text{Kr} + ?$
    (f) $? \longrightarrow ^{24}_{12}\text{Mg} + ^{0}_{-1}\beta$

14. Complete the following nuclear equations. Write the mass number, atomic number, and symbol for the remaining particle.
    (a) $^{19}_{10}\text{Ne} \longrightarrow ^{0}_{+1}\beta + ?$
    (b) $^{59}_{26}\text{Fe} \longrightarrow ^{0}_{-1}\beta + ?$
    (c) $^{40}_{19}\text{K} \longrightarrow ^{0}_{-1}\beta + ?$
    (d) $^{37}_{18}\text{Ar} + ^{0}_{-1}\text{e} \text{ (electron capture)} \longrightarrow ?$
    (e) $^{55}_{26}\text{Fe} + ^{0}_{-1}\text{e} \text{ (electron capture)} \longrightarrow ?$
    (f) $^{26}_{13}\text{Al} \longrightarrow ^{25}_{12}\text{Mg} + ?$

15. The uranium-235 radioactive decay series, beginning with $^{235}_{92}\text{U}$ and ending with $^{207}_{82}\text{Pb}$, occurs in the following sequence: α, β, α, β, α, α, α, α, β, β, α. Write an equation for each step in this series.

16. The thorium-232 radioactive decay series, beginning with $^{232}_{90}\text{Th}$ and ending with $^{208}_{82}\text{Pb}$, occurs in the following sequence: α, β, β, α, α, α, α, β, β, α. Write an equation for each step in this series.

Nuclear Stability and Nuclear Decay
(See Section 23.3 and Examples 23.3 and 23.4.)

17. What particle is emitted in the following nuclear reactions? Write an equation for each reaction.
    (a) Gold-198 decays to mercury-198.
    (b) Radon-222 decays to polonium-218.
    (c) Cesium-137 decays to barium-137.
    (d) Indium-110 decays to cadmium-110.

18. What is the product of the following nuclear decay processes? Write an equation for each process.
    (a) Gallium-67 decays by electron capture.
    (b) Potassium-38 decays with positron emission.
    (c) Technetium-99m decays with γ emission.
    (d) Manganese-56 decays by β emission.

19. Predict the probable mode of decay for each of the following radioactive isotopes, and write an equation to show the products of decay.
    (a) bromine-80   (c) cobalt-61
    (b) californium-240   (d) carbon-11

20. Predict the probable mode of decay for each of the following radioactive isotopes, and write an equation to show the products of decay.
    (a) manganese-54   (c) silver-110
    (b) americium-241   (d) mercury-197m

21. (a) Which of the following nuclei decay by $_{-1}^{0}\beta$ decay?

    $$^3\text{H} \quad ^{16}\text{O} \quad ^{20}\text{F} \quad ^{13}\text{N}$$

    (b) Which of the following nuclei decays by $_{+1}^{0}\beta$ decay?

    $$^{238}\text{U} \quad ^{19}\text{F} \quad ^{22}\text{Na} \quad ^{24}\text{Na}$$

22. (a) Which of the following nuclei decay by $_{-1}^{0}\beta$ decay?

    $$^1\text{H} \quad ^{23}\text{Mg} \quad ^{32}\text{P} \quad ^{20}\text{Ne}$$

    (b) Which of the following nuclei decay by $_{+1}^{0}\beta$ decay?

    $$^{235}\text{U} \quad ^{35}\text{Cl} \quad ^{38}\text{K} \quad ^{24}\text{Na}$$

23. Boron has two stable isotopes, ^{10}B and ^{11}B. Calculate the binding energies per mole of nucleons of these two nuclei. The required masses (in g/mol) are $_1^1\text{H} = 1.00783$, $_0^1\text{n} = 1.00867$, $_5^{10}\text{B} = 10.01294$, and $_5^{11}\text{B} = 11.00931$.

24. Calculate the binding energy in kilojoules per mole of nucleons of P for the formation of ^{30}P and ^{31}P. The required masses (in g/mol) are $_1^1\text{H} = 1.00783$, $_0^1\text{n} = 1.00867$, $_{15}^{30}\text{P} = 29.97832$, and $_{15}^{31}\text{P} = 30.97376$.

25. Calculate the binding energy per mole of nucleons for calcium-40, and compare your result with the value in Figure 23.4. Masses needed for this calculation are (in g/mol) $_1^1\text{H} = 1.00783$, $_0^1\text{n} = 1.00867$, and $_{20}^{40}\text{Ca} = 39.96259$.

26. Calculate the binding energy per mole of nucleons for iron-56. Masses needed for this calculation (in g/mol) are $_1^1\text{H} = 1.00783$, $_0^1\text{n} = 1.00867$, and $_{26}^{56}\text{Fe} = 55.9349$. Compare the result of your calculation to the value for iron-56 in the graph in Figure 23.4.

27. Calculate the binding energy per mole of nucleons for $_8^{16}\text{O}$. Masses needed for this calculation are $_1^1\text{H} = 1.00783$, $_0^1\text{n} = 1.00867$, and $_8^{16}\text{O} = 15.99492$.

28. Calculate the binding energy per mole of nucleons for nitrogen-14. The mass of nitrogen-14 is 14.003074.

Rates of Radioactive Decay
(See Section 23.4 and Examples 23.5–23.7.)

29. Copper(II) acetate containing ^{64}Cu is used to study brain tumors. This isotope has a half-life of 12.7 hours. If you begin with 25.0 μg of ^{64}Cu, what mass remains after 63.5 hours?

30. Gold-198 is used in the diagnosis of liver problems. The half-life of ^{198}Au is 2.69 days. If you begin with 2.8 μg of this gold isotope, what mass remains after 10.8 days?

31. Iodine-131 is used to treat thyroid cancer.
    (a) The isotope decays by β-particle emission. Write a balanced equation for this process.
    (b) Iodine-131 has a half-life of 8.04 days. If you begin with 2.4 μg of radioactive ^{131}I, what mass remains after 40.2 days?

32. Phosphorus-32 is used in the form of Na_2HPO_4 in the treatment of chronic myeloid leukemia, among other things.
    (a) The isotope decays by β-particle emission. Write a balanced equation for this process.
    (b) The half-life of ^{32}P is 14.3 days. If you begin with 4.8 μg of radioactive ^{32}P in the form of Na_2HPO_4, what mass remains after 28.6 days (about one month)?

33. Gallium-67 ($t_{1/2}$ = 78.25 hours) is used in the medical diagnosis of certain kinds of tumors. If you ingest a compound containing 0.015 mg of this isotope, what mass (in milligrams) remains in your body after 13 days? (Assume none is excreted.)

34. Iodine-131 ($t_{1/2}$ = 8.04 days), a β emitter, is used to treat thyroid cancer.
    (a) Write an equation for the decomposition of ^{131}I.
    (b) If you ingest a sample of NaI containing ^{131}I, how much time is required for the activity to decrease to 35.0% of its original value?

35. Radon has been the focus of much attention recently because it is often found in homes. Radon-222 emits α particles and has a half-life of 3.82 days.
    (a) Write a balanced equation to show this process.
    (b) How long does it take for a sample of ^{222}Rn to decrease to 20.0% of its original activity?

36. Strontium-90 is a hazardous radioactive isotope that resulted from atmospheric testing of nuclear weapons. A sample of strontium carbonate containing ^{90}Sr is found to have an activity of 1.0×10^3 dpm. One year later, the activity of this sample is 975 dpm.
    (a) Calculate the half-life of strontium-90 from this information.
    (b) How long will it take for the activity of this sample to drop to 1.0% of the initial value?

37. Radioactive cobalt-60 is used extensively in nuclear medicine as a γ-ray source. It is made by a neutron capture reaction from cobalt-59 and is a β emitter; β emission is accompanied by strong γ radiation. The half-life of cobalt-60 is 5.27 years.
    (a) How long will it take for a cobalt-60 source to decrease to one eighth of its original activity?
    (b) What fraction of the activity of a cobalt-60 source remains after 1.0 year?

38. Scandium occurs in nature as a single isotope, scandium-45. Neutron irradiation produces scandium-46, a β emitter with a half-life of 83.8 days. If the initial activity is 7.0×10^4 dpm, draw a graph showing disintegrations per minute as a function of time during a period of 1 year.

Nuclear Reactions

(See Section 23.5 and Example 23.9.)

39. Americium-240 is made by bombarding plutonium-239 with α particles. In addition to ^{240}Am, the products are a proton and two neutrons. Write a balanced equation for this process.

40. There are two isotopes of americium, both with half-lives sufficiently long to allow the handling of large quantities. Americium-241, with a half-life of 432 years, is an α emitter. It is used in smoke detectors. The isotope is formed from ^{239}Pu by absorption of two neutrons followed by emission of a β particle. Write a balanced equation for this process.

41. The superheavy element ^{287}Uuq (element 114) was made by firing a beam of ^{48}Ca ions at ^{242}Pu. Three neutrons were ejected in the reaction. Write a balanced nuclear equation for the synthesis of ^{287}Uuq.

42. To synthesize the heavier transuranium elements, a nucleus must be bombarded with a relatively large particle. If you know the products are californium-246 and four neutrons, with what particle would you bombard uranium-238 atoms?

43. Deuterium nuclei ($^2_1$H) are particularly effective as bombarding particles to carry out nuclear reactions. Complete the following equations:
(a) $^{114}_{48}$Cd $+ ^2_1$H $\longrightarrow$? $+ ^1_1$H
(b) $^6_3$Li $+ ^2_1$H $\longrightarrow$? $+ ^1_0$n
(c) $^{40}_{20}$Ca $+ ^2_1$H $\longrightarrow$ $^{38}_{19}$K $+$?
(d) ? $+ ^2_1$H $\longrightarrow$ $^{65}_{30}$Zn $+ \gamma$

44. Element $^{287}_{114}$Uuq decays by α emission with a half-life of about 5 seconds. Write an equation for this process.

45. Boron is an effective absorber of neutrons. When boron-10 is bombarded by neutrons, an α particle is emitted. Write an equation for this nuclear reaction.

46. Some of the reactions explored by Ernest Rutherford (page 339) and others are listed below. Identify the unknown species in each reaction.
(a) $^{14}_7$N $+ ^4_2$He $\longrightarrow$ $^{17}_8$O $+$?
(b) $^9_4$Be $+ ^4_2$He $\longrightarrow$? $+ ^1_0$n
(c) ? $+ ^4_2$He $\longrightarrow$ $^{30}_{15}$P $+ ^1_0$n
(d) $^{239}_{94}$Pu $+ ^4_2$He $\longrightarrow$? $+ ^1_0$n

General Questions

These questions are not designated as to type or location in the chapter. They may combine several concepts.

47. ▲ A technique to date geological samples uses rubidium-87, a long-lived radioactive isotope of rubidium ($t_{1/2} = 4.8 \times 10^{10}$ years). Rubidium-87 decays by β emission to strontium-87. If rubidium-87 is part of a rock or mineral, then strontium-87 will remain trapped within the crystalline structure of the rock. The age of the rock dates back to the time when the rock solidified. Chemical analysis of the rock gives the amounts of ^{87}Rb and ^{87}Sr. From these data, the fraction of ^{87}Rb that remains can be calculated. Suppose analysis of a stony meteorite determined that 1.8 mmol of ^{87}Rb and 1.6 mmol of ^{87}Sr (the portion of ^{87}Sr formed by decomposition of ^{87}Rb) were present. Estimate the age of the meteorite. (*Hint:* The amount of ^{87}Rb at t_0 is moles ^{87}Rb + moles ^{87}Sr.)

48. Tritium, $^3_1$H, is one of the nuclei used in fusion reactions. This isotope is radioactive, with a half-life of 12.3 years. Like carbon-14, tritium is formed in the upper atmosphere from cosmic radiation, and it is found in trace amounts on earth. To obtain the amounts required for a fusion reaction, however, it must be made via a nuclear reaction. The reaction of $^6_3$Li with a neutron produces tritium and an α particle. Write an equation for this nuclear reaction.

49. Phosphorus occurs in nature as a single isotope, phosphorus-31. Neutron irradiation of phosphorus-31 produces phosphorus-32, a β emitter with a half-life of 14.28 days. Assume you have a sample containing phosphorus-32 that has a rate of decay of 3.2×10^6 dpm. Draw a graph showing disintegrations per minute as a function of time during a period of 1 year.

50. In June 1972, natural fission reactors, which operated billions of years ago, were discovered in Oklo, Gabon (page 1058). At present, natural uranium contains 0.72% ^{235}U. How many years ago did natural uranium contain 3.0% ^{235}U, the amount needed to sustain a natural reactor? ($t_{1/2}$ for ^{235}U is 7.04×10^8 years.)

51. If a shortage in worldwide supplies of fissionable uranium arose, it would be possible to use other fissionable nuclei. Plutonium, one such fuel, can be made in "breeder" reactors that manufacture more fuel than they consume. The sequence of reactions by which plutonium is made is as follows:
(a) A ^{238}U nucleus undergoes an (n, γ) reaction to produce ^{239}U.
(b) ^{239}U decays by β emission ($t_{1/2} = 23.5$ min) to give an isotope of neptunium.
(c) This neptunium isotope decays by β emission to give a plutonium isotope.
(d) The plutonium isotope is fissionable. On collision of one of these plutonium isotopes with a neutron, fission occurs, with at least two neutrons and two other nuclei as products.
Write an equation for each of the nuclear reactions.

52. When a neutron is captured by an atomic nucleus, energy is released as γ radiation. This energy can be calculated based on the change in mass in converting reactants to products.

For the nuclear reaction $^6_3$Li $+ ^1_0$n $\longrightarrow$ $^7_3$Li $+ \gamma$:

(a) Calculate the energy evolved in this reaction (per atom). Masses needed (in g/mol) are $^6_3$Li = 6.01512, $^1_0$n = 1.00867, and $^7_3$Li = 7.01600.
(b) Use the answer in part (a) to calculate the wavelength of the γ-rays emitted in the reaction.

In the Laboratory

53. A piece of charred bone found in the ruins of a Native American village has a $^{14}C:^{12}C$ ratio that is 72% of the ratio found in living organisms. Calculate the age of the bone fragment. ($t_{1/2}$ for ^{14}C is 5.73×10^3 years.)

54. A sample of wood from a Thracian chariot found in an excavation in Bulgaria has a ^{14}C activity of 11.2 dpm/g. Estimate the age of the chariot and the year it was made. ($t_{1/2}$ for ^{14}C is 5.73×10^3 years, and the activity of ^{14}C in living material is 14.0 dpm/g.)

55. The isotope of polonium that was most likely isolated by Marie Curie in her pioneering studies is polonium-210. A sample of this element was prepared in a nuclear reaction. Initially, its activity (α emission) was 7840 dpm. Measuring radioactivity over time produced the data below. Determine the half-life of polonium-210.

Activity (dpm)	Time (days)
7840	0
7570	7
7300	14
5920	56
5470	72

56. Sodium-23 (in a sample of NaCl) is subjected to neutron bombardment in a nuclear reactor to produce ^{24}Na. When removed from the reactor, the sample is radioactive, with β activity of 2.54×10^4 dpm. The decrease in radioactivity over time was studied, producing the following data:

Activity (dpm)	Time (hours)
2.54×10^4	0
2.42×10^4	1
2.31×10^4	2
2.00×10^4	5
1.60×10^4	10
1.01×10^4	20

(a) Write equations for the neutron capture reaction and for the reaction in which the product of this reaction decays by β emission.

(b) Determine the half-life of sodium-24.

57. The age of minerals can sometimes be determined by measuring the amounts of ^{206}Pb and ^{238}U in a sample. This determination assumes that all of the ^{206}Pb in the sample comes from the decay of ^{238}U. The date obtained identifies when the rock solidified. Assume that the ratio of ^{206}Pb to ^{238}U in an igneous rock sample is 0.33. Calculate the age of the rock. ($t_{1/2}$ for ^{238}U is 4.5×10^9 years.)

58. The oldest-known fossil found in South Africa has been dated based on the decay of Rb-87.

$$^{87}Rb \longrightarrow {}^{87}Sr + {}_{-1}^{0}\beta \qquad t_{1/2} = 4.8 \times 10^{10} \text{ years}$$

If the ratio of the present quantity of ^{87}Rb to the original quantity is 0.951, calculate the age of the fossil.

Summary and Conceptual Questions

The following questions may use concepts from this and previous chapters.

59. The average energy output of a good grade of coal is 2.6×10^7 kJ/ton. Fission of 1 mol of ^{235}U releases 2.1×10^{10} kJ. Find the number of tons of coal needed to produce the same energy as 1 lb of ^{235}U. (See Appendix C for conversion factors.)

60. Collision of an electron and a positron results in formation of two γ-rays. In the process, their masses are converted completely into energy.
(a) Calculate the energy evolved from the annihilation of an electron and a positron, in kilojoules per mole.
(b) Using Planck's equation (Equation 6.2), determine the frequency of the γ-rays emitted in this process.

61. The principle underlying the isotope dilution method of analysis can be applied to many kinds of problems. Suppose that you, a marine biologist, want to estimate the number of fish in a lake. You release 1000 tagged fish, and after allowing an adequate amount of time for the fish to disperse evenly in the lake, you catch 5250 fish and find that 27 of them have tags. How many fish are in the lake?

62. ▲ Radioactive isotopes are often used as "tracers" to follow an atom through a chemical reaction. The following is an example of this process: Acetic acid reacts with methanol, CH_3OH, by eliminating a molecule of H_2O to form methyl acetate, $CH_3CO_2CH_3$. Explain how you would use the radioactive isotope ^{15}O to show whether the oxygen atom in the water product comes from the —OH of the acid or the —OH of the alcohol.

63. ▲ Radioactive decay series begin with a very long-lived isotope. For example, the half-life of ^{238}U is 4.5×10^9 years. Each series is identified by the name of the long-lived parent isotope of highest mass.
(a) The uranium-238 radioactive decay series is sometimes referred to as the $4n + 2$ series because the masses of all 13 members of this series can be expressed by the equation $m = 4n + 2$, where m is the mass number and n is an integer. Explain why the masses are correlated in this way.
(b) Two other radioactive decay series identified in minerals in the earth's crust are the thorium-232 series and the uranium-235 series. Do the masses of the isotopes in these series conform to a simple mathematical equation? If so, identify the equation.
(c) Identify the radioactive decay series to which each of the following isotopes belongs: $^{226}_{88}Ra$, $^{215}_{86}At$, $^{228}_{90}Th$, $^{210}_{83}Bi$.
(d) Evaluation reveals that one series of elements, the $4n + 1$ series, is not present in the earth's crust. Speculate why.

64. ▲ The thorium decay series includes the isotope $^{228}_{90}Th$. Determine the sequence of nuclei on going from $^{232}_{90}Th$ to $^{228}_{90}Th$.

65. ▲ The last unknown element between bismuth and uranium was discovered by Lise Meitner (1878–1968) and Otto Hahn (1879–1968) in 1918. They obtained ^{231}Pa by chemical extraction of pitchblende, in which its concentration is about 1 ppm (part per million). This isotope, an α emitter, has a half-life of 3.27×10^4 years.
    (a) Which radioactive decay series (the uranium-235, uranium-238, or thorium-232 series) contains ^{231}Pa as a member?
    (b) Suggest a possible sequence of nuclear reactions starting with the long-lived isotope that eventually forms this isotope.
    (c) What quantity of ore would be required to isolate 1.0 g of ^{231}Pa, assuming 100% yield?
    (d) Write an equation for the radioactive decay process for ^{231}Pa.

66. ▲ You might wonder how it is possible to determine the half-life of long-lived radioactive isotopes such as ^{238}U. With a half-life of more than 10^9 years, the radioactivity of a sample of uranium will not measurably change in your lifetime. In fact, you can calculate the half-life using the mathematics governing first-order reactions.

    It can be shown that a 1.0-mg sample of ^{238}U decays at the rate of 12 α emissions per second. Set up a mathematical equation for the rate of decay, $\Delta N / \Delta t = -kN$, where N is the number of nuclei in the 1.0-mg sample and $\Delta N / \Delta t$ is 12 dps. Solve this equation for the rate constant for this process, and then relate the rate constant to the half-life of the reaction. Carry out this calculation, and compare your result with the literature value, 4.5×10^9 years.

67. ▲ Marie and Pierre Curie isolated radium and polonium from uranium ore (pitchblende, which contains ^{238}U and ^{235}U). Which of the following isotopes of radium and polonium can be found in the uranium ore? (*Hint:* Consider both the isotope half-lives and the decay series starting with ^{238}U and ^{235}U.)

Isotope	Half-Life
^{226}Ra	1620 y
^{225}Ra	14.8 d
^{228}Ra	6.7 y
^{216}Po	0.15 s
^{210}Po	138.4 d

68. To measure the volume of the blood system of an animal, the following experiment was done. A 1.0-mL sample of an aqueous solution containing tritium, with an activity of 2.0×10^6 dps, was injected into the animal's bloodstream. After time was allowed for complete circulatory mixing, a 1.0-mL blood sample was withdrawn and found to have an activity of 1.5×10^4 dps. What was the volume of the circulatory system? (The half-life of tritium is 12.3 years, so this experiment assumes that only a negligible amount of tritium has decayed in the time of the experiment.)

Applying Chemical Principles

The Age of Meteorites

Meteorites have a significant value for collectors, but they are also of scientific interest. Meteorites are generally regarded as some of the oldest materials in the solar system. And this raises the obvious question: How is the age of a meteorite determined? By age, we are referring to the time since the meteor condensed to a solid, locking the components into a solid matrix so they cannot escape. There are a number of methods to measure the age of a meteor, all involving the decay of long-lived radioactive elements.

One dating procedure involves vaporizing samples of the material and measuring the amounts of ^{86}Sr, ^{87}Sr, and ^{87}Rb by mass spectrometry. Both ^{86}Sr and ^{87}Sr are stable isotopes. The rubidium isotope, which decays to ^{87}Sr, has a half-life of 4.88×10^{10} years. The amount of ^{87}Sr measured includes the amount of ^{87}Sr initially present (^{87}Sr°) when the meteorite was formed plus the amount formed by decay of ^{87}Rb. The ^{86}Sr remains constant and is used as a check on the original amounts of the other isotopes. The three measured amounts are related by an equation (which can be derived from the first-order rate law):

$$[^{87}Sr/^{86}Sr] = (e^{kt} - 1)\,[^{87}Rb/^{86}Sr] + [^{87}Sr°/^{86}Sr]$$

The equation has the form of the equation of a straight line, $y = mx + b$. Multiple samples are analyzed from each meteorite. The amounts of each isotope may vary between samples, but a graph of $[^{87}Sr/^{86}Sr]$ versus $[^{87}Rb/^{86}Sr]$ will give a straight line with a slope $m = (e^{kt} - 1)$ and a y-intercept of $[^{87}Sr°/^{86}Sr]$. The symbol k refers to the rate constant for the radioactive decomposition. This method is called *isochron dating*.

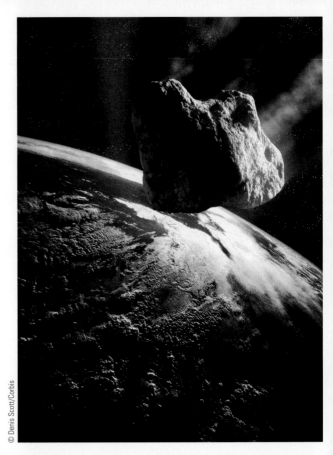

Meteorites. Meteorites are materials that originate in outer space and survive the fall to the earth's surface. They can be large or small, but as they enter Earth's atmosphere they are warmed to a high temperature by friction in the atmosphere and emit light, forming a fireball. They are classified as stony meteorites, which are silicate minerals; iron meteorites, largely composed of iron and nickel; and stony-iron meteorites. (See also the photo of an iron meteorite on page 316.)

Questions:

1. Write a balanced equation for the radioactive decomposition of ^{87}Rb.
2. The decomposition of ^{87}Rb occurs by which of the following processes?
   (a) alpha emission   (d) electron capture
   (b) beta emission   (e) positron emission
   (c) gamma emission
3. Determine the rate constant for the radioactive decay of ^{87}Rb.
4. The oldest dated meteorites have ages of about 4.5 billion years. What fraction of the initial ^{87}Rb has decayed?
5. The relative abundances of ^{86}Sr, ^{87}Sr, and ^{87}Rb were measured for four samples of a meteorite; the results were tabulated below. Make a strontium-rubidium isochron plot of these data, then use the slope of the line to determine the age of the meteorite.

Relative Abundance

Sample #	^{86}Sr	^{87}Sr	^{87}Rb
1	1.000	0.819	0.839
2	1.063	0.855	0.506
3	0.950	0.824	1.929
4	1.011	0.809	0.379

6. Derive the equation given above for $[^{87}Sr/^{86}Sr]$. (*Hint:* Start with the rate equation in the form $[^{87}Rb°] = [^{87}Rb]\,e^{kt}$.)

A Using Logarithms and Solving Quadratic Equations

An introductory chemistry course requires basic algebra plus a knowledge of (1) exponential (or scientific) notation, (2) logarithms, and (3) quadratic equations. The use of exponential notation was reviewed on pages 33–35, and this appendix reviews the last two topics.

A.1 Logarithms

Two types of logarithms are used in this text: (1) common logarithms (abbreviated log) whose base is 10 and (2) natural logarithms (abbreviated ln) whose base is e ($= 2.71828$):

$$\log x = n, \text{ where } x = 10^n$$
$$\ln x = m, \text{ where } x = e^m$$

Most equations in chemistry and physics were developed in natural, or base e, logarithms, and we follow this practice in this text. The relation between log and ln is

$$\ln x = 2.303 \log x$$

Despite the different bases of the two logarithms, they are used in the same manner. What follows is largely a description of the use of common logarithms.

A common logarithm is the power to which you must raise 10 to obtain the number. For example, the log of 100 is 2, since you must raise 10 to the second power to obtain 100. Other examples are

$$\log 1000 = \log (10^3) = 3$$
$$\log 10 = \log (10^1) = 1$$
$$\log 1 = \log (10^0) = 0$$
$$\log 0.1 = \log (10^{-1}) = -1$$
$$\log 0.0001 = \log (10^{-4}) = -4$$

To obtain the common logarithm of a number other than a simple power of 10, you must resort to a log table or an electronic calculator. For example,

$$\log 2.10 = 0.322, \text{ which means that } 10^{0.322} = 2.10$$
$$\log 5.16 = 0.713, \text{ which means that } 10^{0.713} = 5.16$$
$$\log 3.125 = 0.4949, \text{ which means that } 10^{0.4949} = 3.125$$

To check this on many calculators, enter the number, and then press the "log" key. You should make sure that you understand how to use your particular calculator.

To obtain the natural logarithm ln of the numbers shown here, use a calculator having this function. Enter each number, and press "ln:"

$$\ln 2.10 = 0.742, \text{ which means that } e^{0.742} = 2.10$$
$$\ln 5.16 = 1.641, \text{ which means that } e^{1.641} = 5.16$$

To find the common logarithm of a number greater than 10 or less than 1 with a log table, first express the number in scientific notation. Then find the log of each part of the number and add the logs. For example,

$$\log 241 = \log (2.41 \times 10^2) = \log 2.41 + \log 10^2$$
$$= 0.382 + 2 = 2.382$$
$$\log 0.00573 = \log (5.73 \times 10^{-3}) = \log 5.73 + \log 10^{-3}$$
$$= 0.758 + (-3) = -2.242$$

Significant Figures and Logarithms

Notice that the mantissa has as many significant figures as the number whose log was found.

Obtaining Antilogarithms

If you are given the logarithm of a number, and find the number from it, you have obtained the "antilogarithm," or "antilog," of the number. Two common procedures used by electronic calculators to do this are as follows:

Procedure A	Procedure B
1. Enter the value of the log or ln.	1. Enter value of the log or ln.
2. Press 2ndF.	2. Press INV.
3. Press 10^x or e^x.	3. Press log or ln x.

Make sure you can properly perform this operation on your calculator by working the following examples:

1. Find the number whose log is 5.234:
    Recall that $\log x = n$, where $x = 10^n$. In this case, $n = 5.234$. Find the value of 10^n, the antilog. In this case,

$$10^{5.234} = 10^{0.234} \times 10^5 = 1.71 \times 10^5$$

    Notice that the characteristic (5) sets the decimal point; it is the power of 10 in the exponential form. The mantissa (0.234) gives the value of the number x, 1.71 in this case.

2. Find the number whose log is -3.456:

$$10^{-3.456} = 10^{0.544} \times 10^{-4} = 3.50 \times 10^{-4}$$

Notice here that -3.456 is expressed as the sum of -4 and $+0.544$.

Mathematical Operations Using Logarithms

Because logarithms are exponents, operations involving them follow the same rules used for exponents. Thus, multiplying two numbers can be done by adding logarithms:

$$\log xy = \log x + \log y$$

For example, we multiply 563 by 125 by adding their logarithms and finding the antilogarithm of the result:

$$\log 563 = 2.751$$
$$\log 125 = \underline{2.097}$$
$$\log xy = 4.848$$
$$xy = 10^{4.848} = 10^{0.848} \times 10^4 = 7.05 \times 10^4$$

One number (x) can be divided by another (y) by subtraction of their logarithms:

$$\log \frac{x}{y} = \log x - \log y$$

For example, to divide 125 by 742,

$$\log 125 = 2.097$$
$$-\log 742 = \underline{2.870}$$
$$\log \frac{x}{y} = -0.773$$
$$\frac{x}{y} = 10^{-0.773} = 10^{0.227} \times 10^{-1} = 1.68 \times 10^{-1}$$

● **Logarithms and Nomenclature** The number to the left of the decimal in a logarithm is called the **characteristic**, and the number to the right of the decimal is the **mantissa**.

Similarly, powers and roots of numbers can be found using logarithms.

$$\log x^y = y(\log x)$$

$$\log \sqrt[y]{x} = \log x^{1/y} = \frac{1}{y} \log x$$

As an example, find the fourth power of 5.23. We first find the log of 5.23 and then multiply it by 4. The result, 2.874, is the log of the answer. Therefore, we find the antilog of 2.874:

$$(5.23)^4 = ?$$

$$\log (5.23)^4 = 4 \log 5.23 = 4(0.719) = 2.874$$

$$(5.23)^4 = 10^{2.874} = 748$$

As another example, find the fifth root of 1.89×10^{-9}:

$$\sqrt[5]{1.89 \times 10^{-9}} = (1.89 \times 10^{-9})^{1/5} = ?$$

$$\log (1.89 \times 10^{-9})^{1/5} = \frac{1}{5} \log (1.89 \times 10^{-9}) = \frac{1}{5}(-8.724) = -1.745$$

The answer is the antilog of -1.745:

$$\left(1.89 \times 10^{-9}\right)^{1/5} = 10^{-1.745} = 1.80 \times 10^{-2}$$

A.2   Quadratic Equations

Algebraic equations of the form $ax^2 + bx + c = 0$ are called **quadratic equations**. The coefficients a, b, and c may be either positive or negative. The two roots of the equation may be found using the *quadratic formula:*

$$x = \frac{-b \pm \sqrt{b^2 - 4ac}}{2a}$$

As an example, solve the equation $5x^2 - 3x - 2 = 0$. Here $a = 5$, $b = -3$, and $c = -2$. Therefore,

$$x = \frac{3 \pm \sqrt{(-3)^2 - 4(5)(-2)}}{2(5)}$$

$$= \frac{3 \pm \sqrt{9 - (-40)}}{10} = \frac{3 \pm \sqrt{49}}{10} = \frac{3 \pm 7}{10}$$

$$= 1 \text{ and } -0.4$$

How do you know which of the two roots is the correct answer? Mathematically, both roots are possible, but in chemistry problems you have to decide in each case which root has physical significance. It is *usually* true in this course, however, that negative values are not significant.

When you have solved a quadratic expression, you should always check your values by substitution into the original equation. In the previous example, we find that $5(1)^2 - 3(1) - 2 = 0$ and that $5(-0.4)^2 - 3(-0.4) - 2 = 0$.

The most likely place you will encounter quadratic equations is in the chapters on chemical equilibria, particularly in Chapters 16 through 18. Here, you will often be faced with solving an equation such as

$$1.8 \times 10^{-4} = \frac{x^2}{0.0010 - x}$$

This equation can certainly be solved using the quadratic formula (to give $x = 3.4 \times 10^{-4}$). You may find the **method of successive approximations** to be especially convenient, however. Here we begin by making a reasonable approximation of x. This approximate value is substituted into the original equation, which is then solved to give what is hoped to be a more correct value of x. This process is repeated until the answer converges on a particular value of x—that is, until the value of x derived from two successive approximations is the same.

Step 1: First, assume that x is so small that $(0.0010 - x) \approx 0.0010$. This means that

$$x^2 = 1.8 \times 10^{-4}\,(0.0010)$$
$$x = 4.2 \times 10^{-4} \text{ (to 2 significant figures)}$$

Step 2: Substitute the value of x from Step 1 into the denominator of the original equation, and again solve for x:

$$x^2 = 1.8 \times 10^{-4}(0.0010 - 0.00042)$$
$$x = 3.2 \times 10^{-4}$$

Step 3: Repeat Step 2 using the value of x found in that step:

$$x = \sqrt{1.8 \times 10^{-4}(0.0010 - 0.00032)} = 3.5 \times 10^{-4}$$

Step 4: Continue repeating the calculation, using the value of x found in the previous step:

$$x = \sqrt{1.8 \times 10^{-4}(0.0010 - 0.00035)} = 3.4 \times 10^{-4}$$

Step 5: $\qquad x = \sqrt{1.8 \times 10^{-4}(0.0010 - 0.00034)} = 3.4 \times 10^{-4}$

Here, we find that iterations after the fourth step give the same value for x, indicating that we have arrived at a valid answer (and the same one obtained from the quadratic formula).

Here are some final thoughts on using the method of successive approximations. First, in some cases the method does not work. Successive steps may give answers that are random or that diverge from the correct value. In Chapters 16 through 18, you confront quadratic equations of the form $K = x^2/(C - x)$. The method of successive approximations works as long as $K < 4C$ (assuming one begins with $x = 0$ as the first guess, that is, $K \approx x^2/C$). This is always going to be true for weak acids and bases (the topic of Chapters 17 and 18), but it may *not* be the case for problems involving gas phase equilibria (Chapter 16), where K can be quite large.

Second, values of K in the equation $K = x^2/(C - x)$ are usually known only to two significant figures. We are therefore justified in carrying out successive steps until two answers are the same to two significant figures.

Finally, we highly recommend this method of solving quadratic equations, especially those in Chapters 17 and 18. If your calculator has a memory function, successive approximations can be carried out easily and rapidly.

B* Some Important Physical Concepts

B.1 Matter

The tendency to maintain a constant velocity is called *inertia*. Thus, unless acted on by an unbalanced force, a body at rest remains at rest, and a body in motion remains in motion with uniform velocity. Matter is anything that exhibits inertia; the quantity of matter is its mass.

B.2 Motion

Motion is the change of position or location in space. Objects can have the following classes of motion:

- Translation occurs when the center of mass of an object changes its location. Example: a car moving on the highway.
- Rotation occurs when each point of a moving object moves in a circle about an axis through the center of mass. Examples: a spinning top, a rotating molecule.
- Vibration is a periodic distortion and then recovery of original shape. Examples: a struck tuning fork, a vibrating molecule.

B.3 Force and Weight

Force is that which changes the velocity of a body; it is defined as

$$\text{Force} = \text{mass} \times \text{acceleration}$$

The SI unit of force is the **newton**, N, whose dimensions are kilograms times meter per second squared ($kg \cdot m/s^2$). A newton is therefore the force needed to change the velocity of a mass of 1 kilogram by 1 meter per second in a time of 1 second.

Because the earth's gravity is not the same everywhere, the weight (a force) corresponding to a given mass is not a constant. At any given spot on earth, gravity is constant, however, and therefore weight is proportional to mass. When a balance tells us that a given sample (the "unknown") has the same weight as another sample (the "weights," as given by a scale reading or by a total of counterweights), it also tells us that the two masses are equal. The balance is therefore a valid instrument for measuring the mass of an object independently of slight variations in the force of gravity.

B.4 Pressure[†]

Pressure is force per unit area. The SI unit, called the *pascal*, Pa, is

$$1\ \text{pascal} = \frac{1\ \text{newton}}{m^2} = \frac{1\ kg \cdot m/s^2}{m^2} = \frac{1\ kg}{m \cdot s^2}$$

The International System of Units also recognizes the bar, which is 10^5 Pa and which is close to standard atmospheric pressure (Table 1).

Chemists also express pressure in terms of the heights of liquid columns, especially water and mercury. This usage is not completely satisfactory because the

---

*Adapted from F. Brescia, J. Arents, H. Meislich, et al.: *General Chemistry,* 5th ed. Philadelphia: Harcourt Brace, 1988.
†See Section 11.1.

Table 1 Pressure Conversions

From	To	Multiply By
atmosphere	mm Hg	760 mm Hg/atm (exactly)
atmosphere	lb/in²	14.6960 lb/(in² · atm)
atmosphere	kPa	101.325 kPa/atm
bar	Pa	10^5 Pa/bar (exactly)
bar	lb/in²	14.5038 lb/(in² · bar)
mm Hg	torr	1 torr/mm Hg (exactly)

pressure exerted by a given column of a given liquid is not a constant but depends on the temperature (which influences the density of the liquid) and the location (which influences the magnitude of the force exerted by gravity). Such units are therefore not part of the SI, and their use is now discouraged. The older units are still used in books and journals, however, and chemists must be familiar with them.

The pressure of a liquid or a gas depends only on the depth (or height) and is exerted equally in all directions. At sea level, the pressure exerted by the earth's atmosphere supports a column of mercury about 0.76 m (76 cm, or 760 mm) high.

One **standard atmosphere** (atm) is the pressure exerted by exactly 76 cm of mercury at 0 °C (density, 13.5951 g/cm³) and at standard gravity, 9.80665 m/s². The **bar** is equivalent to 0.9869 atm. One **torr** is the pressure exerted by exactly 1 mm of mercury at 0 °C and standard gravity.

B.5 Energy and Power

The SI unit of energy is the product of the units of force and distance, or kilograms times meter per second squared (kg · m/s²) times meters (× m), which is kg · m²/s²; this unit is called the **joule**, J. The joule is thus the work done when a force of 1 newton acts through a distance of 1 meter.

Work may also be done by moving an electric charge in an electric field. When the charge being moved is 1 coulomb (C) and the potential difference between its initial and final positions is 1 volt (V), the work is 1 joule. Thus,

$$1 \text{ joule} = 1 \text{ coulomb volt (CV)}$$

Another unit of electric work that is not part of the International System of Units but is still in use is the **electron volt**, eV, which is the work required to move an electron against a potential difference of 1 volt. (It is also the kinetic energy acquired by an electron when it is accelerated by a potential difference of 1 volt.) Because the charge on an electron is 1.602×10^{-19} C, we have

$$1 \text{ eV} = 1.602 \times 10^{-19} \text{ CV} \times \frac{1 \text{ J}}{1 \text{ CV}} = 1.602 \times 10^{-19} \text{ J}$$

If this value is multiplied by Avogadro's number, we obtain the energy involved in moving 1 mol of electron charges (1 faraday) in a field produced by a potential difference of 1 volt:

$$1\frac{\text{eV}}{\text{particle}} = \frac{1.602 \times 10^{-19} \text{ J}}{\text{particle}} \times \frac{6.022 \times 10^{23} \text{ particles}}{\text{mol}} \cdot \frac{1 \text{ kJ}}{1000 \text{ J}} = 96.49 \text{ kJ/mol}$$

Power is the amount of energy delivered per unit time. The SI unit is the watt, W, which is 1 joule per second. One kilowatt, kW, is 1000 W. Watt-hours and kilowatt-hours are therefore units of energy (Table 2). For example, 1000 watt-hours, or 1 kilowatt-hour, is

$$1.0 \times 10^3 \text{ W} \cdot \text{h} \times \frac{1 \text{ J}}{1 \text{ W} \cdot \text{s}} \times \frac{3.6 \times 10^3 \text{ s}}{1 \text{ h}} = 3.6 \times 10^6 \text{ J}$$

Table 2 Energy Conversions

From	To	Multiply By
calorie (cal)	joule	4.184 J/cal (exactly)
kilocalorie (kcal)	cal	10^3 cal/kcal (exactly)
kilocalorie	joule	4.184×10^3 J/kcal (exactly)
liter atmosphere (L · atm)	joule	101.325 J/L · atm
electron volt (eV)	joule	1.60218×10^{-19} J/eV
electron volt per particle	kilojoules per mole	96.485 kJ · particle/eV · mol
coulomb volt (CV)	joule	1 CV/J (exactly)
kilowatt-hour (kW-h)	kcal	860.4 kcal/kW-h
kilowatt-hour	joule	3.6×10^6 J/kW-h (exactly)
British thermal unit (BTU)	calorie	252 cal/BTU

C Abbreviations and Useful Conversion Factors

Table 3 Some Common Abbreviations and Standard Symbols

Term	Abbreviation	Term	Abbreviation
Activation energy	E_a	Equilibrium constant	K
Ampere	A	Concentration basis	K_c
Aqueous solution	aq	Pressure basis	K_p
Atmosphere, unit of pressure	atm	Ionization weak acid	K_a
Atomic mass unit	u	Ionization weak base	K_b
Avogadro's constant	N	Solubility product	K_{sp}
Bar, unit of pressure	bar	Formation constant	K_f
Body-centered cubic	bcc	Ethylenediamine	en
Bohr radius	a_0	Face-centered cubic	fcc
Boiling point	bp	Faraday constant	F
Celsius temperature	°C	Gas constant	R
Charge number of an ion	z	Gibbs free energy	G
Coulomb, electric charge	C	Standard free energy	$G°$
Curie, radioactivity	Ci	Standard free energy of formation	$\Delta_f G°$
Cycles per second, hertz	Hz	Standard free energy change for reaction	$\Delta_r G°$
Debye, unit of electric dipole	D	Half-life	$t_{1/2}$
Electron	e^-	Heat	q
Electron volt	eV	Hertz	Hz
Electronegativity	χ	Hour	h
Energy	E	Joule	J
Enthalpy	H	Kelvin	K
Standard enthalpy	$H°$	Kilocalorie	kcal
Standard enthalpy of formation	$\Delta_f H°$	Liquid	ℓ
Standard enthalpy of reaction	$\Delta_r H°$	Logarithm, base 10	log
Entropy	S	Logarithm, base e	ln
Standard entropy	$S°$	Millimeters of mercury, unit of pressure	mm Hg
Entropy change for reaction	$\Delta_r S°$	Minute	min

(continued)

Table 3 Some Common Abbreviations and Standard Symbols (continued)

Term	Abbreviation	Term	Abbreviation
Molar	M	Pressure	P
Molar mass	M	Proton number	Z
Mole	mol	Rate constant	k
Osmotic pressure	Π	Standard temperature and pressure	STP
Pascal, unit of pressure	Pa	Temperature	T
Planck's constant	h	Volt	V
Pound	lb	Watt	W
Primitive cubic (unit cell)	pc	Wavelength	λ

C.1   Fundamental Units of the SI System

The metric system was begun by the French National Assembly in 1790 and has undergone many modifications. The International System of Units or *Système International* (SI), which represents an extension of the metric system, was adopted by the 11th General Conference of Weights and Measures in 1960. It is constructed from seven base units, each of which represents a particular physical quantity (Table 4).

Table 4 SI Fundamental Units

Physical Quantity	Name of Unit	Symbol
Length	meter	m
Mass	kilogram	kg
Time	second	s
Temperature	kelvin	K
Amount of substance	mole	mol
Electric current	ampere	A
Luminous intensity	candela	cd

The first five units listed in Table 4 are particularly useful in general chemistry and are defined as follows:

1. The *meter* was redefined in 1960 to be equal to 1,650,763.73 wavelengths of a certain line in the emission spectrum of krypton-86.
2. The *kilogram* represents the mass of a platinum–iridium block kept at the International Bureau of Weights and Measures at Sèvres, France.
3. The *second* was redefined in 1967 as the duration of 9,192,631,770 periods of a certain line in the microwave spectrum of cesium-133.
4. The *kelvin* is 1/273.16 of the temperature interval between absolute zero and the triple point of water.
5. The *mole* is the amount of substance that contains as many entities as there are atoms in exactly 0.012 kg of carbon-12 (12 g of ^{12}C atoms).

C.2 Prefixes Used with Traditional Metric Units and SI Units

Decimal fractions and multiples of metric and SI units are designated by using the prefixes listed in Table 5. Those most commonly used in general chemistry appear in italics.

Table 5 Traditional Metric and SI Prefixes

Factor	Prefix	Symbol	Factor	Prefix	Symbol
10^{12}	tera	T	10^{-1}	*deci*	d
10^{9}	giga	G	10^{-2}	*centi*	c
10^{6}	mega	M	10^{-3}	*milli*	m
10^{3}	*kilo*	k	10^{-6}	micro	μ
10^{2}	hecto	h	10^{-9}	nano	n
10^{1}	deka	da	10^{-12}	pico	p
			10^{-15}	femto	f
			10^{-18}	atto	a

C.3 Derived SI Units

In the International System of Units, all physical quantities are represented by appropriate combinations of the base units listed in Table 4. A list of the derived units frequently used in general chemistry is given in Table 6.

Table 6 Derived SI Units

Physical Quantity	Name of Unit	Symbol	Definition
Area	square meter	m^2	
Volume	cubic meter	m^3	
Density	kilogram per cubic meter	kg/m^3	
Force	newton	N	$kg \cdot m/s^2$
Pressure	pascal	Pa	N/m^2
Energy	joule	J	$kg \cdot m^2/s^2$
Electric charge	coulomb	C	$A \cdot s$
Electric potential difference	volt	V	$J/(A \cdot s)$

Table 7 Common Units of Mass and Weight

1 pound = 453.39 grams
1 kilogram = 1000 grams = 2.205 pounds
1 gram = 1000 milligrams
1 gram = 6.022×10^{23} atomic mass units
1 atomic mass unit = 1.6605×10^{-24} gram
1 short ton = 2000 pounds = 907.2 kilograms
1 long ton = 2240 pounds
1 metric tonne = 1000 kilograms = 2205 pounds

Table 8 Common Units of Length

1 inch = 2.54 centimeters (exactly)
1 mile = 5280 feet = 1.609 kilometers
1 yard = 36 inches = 0.9144 meter
1 meter = 100 centimeters = 39.37 inches = 3.281 feet = 1.094 yards
1 kilometer = 1000 meters = 1094 yards = 0.6215 mile
1 Ångstrom = 1.0×10^{-8} centimeter = 0.10 nanometer = 100 picometers $= 1.0 \times 10^{-10}$ meter = 3.937×10^{-9} inch

Table 9 Common Units of Volume

1 quart = 0.9463 liter   **1 liter = 1.0567 quarts**
1 liter = 1 cubic decimeter = 1000 cubic centimeters = 0.001 cubic meter
1 milliliter = 1 cubic centimeter = 0.001 liter = 1.056×10^{-3} quart
1 cubic foot = 28.316 liters = 29.924 quarts = 7.481 gallons

D Physical Constants

Table 10 Physical Constants

Quantity	Symbol	Traditional Units	SI Units
Acceleration of gravity	g	980.6 cm/s^2	9.806 m/s^2
Atomic mass unit (1/12 the mass of ^{12}C atom)	u	1.6605×10^{-24} g	1.6605×10^{-27} kg
Avogadro's number	N	$6.02214179 \times 10^{23}$ particles/mol	$6.02214179 \times 10^{23}$ particles/mol
Bohr radius	a_0	0.052918 nm 5.2918×10^{-9} cm	5.2918×10^{-11} m
Boltzmann constant	k	1.3807×10^{-16} erg/K	1.3807×10^{-23} J/K
Charge-to-mass ratio of electron	e/m	1.7588×10^8 C/g	1.7588×10^{11} C/kg
Electron rest mass	m_e	9.1094×10^{-28} g 0.00054858 u	9.1094×10^{-31} kg
Electronic charge	e	1.6022×10^{-19} C 4.8033×10^{-10} esu	1.6022×10^{-19} C
Faraday constant	F	96,485 C/mol e$^-$ 23.06 kcal/V · mol e$^-$	96,485 C/mol e$^-$ 96,485 J/V · mol e$^-$
Gas constant	R	$0.082057 \dfrac{L \cdot atm}{mol \cdot K}$ $1.987 \dfrac{cal}{mol \cdot K}$	$8.3145 \dfrac{Pa \cdot dm^3}{mol \cdot K}$ 8.3145 J/mol · K
Molar volume (STP)	V_m	22.414 L/mol	22.414×10^{-3} m^3/mol 22.414 dm^3/mol
Neutron rest mass	m_n	1.67493×10^{-24} g 1.008665 u	1.67493×10^{-27} kg
Planck's constant	h	6.6261×10^{-27} erg · s	$6.6260693 \times 10^{-34}$ J · s
Proton rest mass	m_p	1.6726×10^{-24} g 1.007276 u	1.6726×10^{-27} kg
Rydberg constant	R Rhc	—	1.0974×10^7 m^{-1} 2.1799×10^{-18} J
Velocity of light (in a vacuum)	c	2.9979×10^{10} cm/s (186,282 miles/s)	2.9979×10^8 m/s
$\pi = 3.1416$			
$e = 2.7183$			
$\ln X = 2.303 \log X$			

Table 11 **Specific Heats and Heat Capacities for Some Common Substances at 25 °C**

Substance	Specific Heat (J/g · K)	Molar Heat Capacity (J/mol · K)
Al(s)	0.897	24.2
Ca(s)	0.646	25.9
Cu(s)	0.385	24.5
Fe(s)	0.449	25.1
Hg(ℓ)	0.140	28.0
H_2O(s), ice	2.06	37.1
H_2O(ℓ), water	4.184	75.4
H_2O(g), steam	1.86	33.6
C_6H_6(ℓ), benzene	1.74	136
C_6H_6(g), benzene	1.06	82.4
C_2H_5OH(ℓ), ethanol	2.44	112.3
C_2H_5OH(g), ethanol	1.41	65.4
$(C_2H_5)_2O$(ℓ), diethyl ether	2.33	172.6
$(C_2H_5)_2O$(g), diethyl ether	1.61	119.5

Table 12 **Heats of Transformation and Transformation Temperatures of Several Substances**

Substance	MP (°C)	Heat of Fusion		BP (°C)	Heat of Vaporization	
		J/g	kJ/mol		J/g	kJ/mol
Elements*						
Al	660	395	10.7	2518	12083	294
Ca	842	212	8.5	1484	3767	155
Cu	1085	209	13.3	2567	4720	300
Fe	1535	267	13.8	2861	6088	340
Hg	−38.8	11	2.29	357	295	59.1
Compounds						
H_2O	0.00	333	6.01	100.0	2260	40.7
CH_4	−182.5	58.6	0.94	−161.5	511	8.2
C_2H_5OH	−114	109	5.02	78.3	838	38.6
C_6H_6	5.48	127.4	9.95	80.0	393	30.7
$(C_2H_5)_2O$	−116.3	98.1	7.27	34.6	357	26.5

*Data for the elements are taken from J. A. Dean: *Lange's Handbook of Chemistry,* 15th ed. New York: McGraw-Hill Publishers, 1999.

E A Brief Guide to Naming Organic Compounds

It seems a daunting task to devise a systematic procedure that gives each organic compound a unique name, but that is what has been done. A set of rules was developed to name organic compounds by the International Union of Pure and Applied Chemistry (IUPAC). The IUPAC nomenclature allows chemists to write a name for any compound based on its structure or to identify the formula and structure for a compound from its name. In this book, we have generally used the IUPAC nomenclature scheme when naming compounds.

In addition to the systematic names, many compounds have common names. The common names came into existence before the nomenclature rules were developed, and they have continued in use. For some compounds, these names are so well entrenched that they are used most of the time. One such compound is acetic acid, which is almost always referred to by that name and not by its systematic name, ethanoic acid.

The general procedure for systematic naming of organic compounds begins with the nomenclature for hydrocarbons. Other organic compounds are then named as derivatives of hydrocarbons. Nomenclature rules for simple organic compounds are given in the following section.

E.1 Hydrocarbons

Alkanes

The names of alkanes end in "-ane." When naming a specific alkane, the root of the name identifies the longest carbon chain in the compound. Specific substituent groups attached to this carbon chain are identified by name and position.

Alkanes with chains of one to ten carbon atoms are given in Table 10.2. After the first four compounds, the names derive from Greek and Latin numbers—pentane, hexane, heptane, octane, nonane, decane—and this regular naming continues for higher alkanes. For substituted alkanes, the substituent groups on a hydrocarbon chain must be identified both by a name and by the position of substitution; this information precedes the root of the name. The position is indicated by a number that refers to the carbon atom to which the substituent is attached. (Numbering of the carbon atoms in a chain should begin at the end of the carbon chain that allows the substituent groups to have the lowest numbers.)

Names of hydrocarbon substituents are derived from the name of the hydrocarbon. The group $-CH_3$, derived by taking a hydrogen from methane, is called the *methyl group;* the $-C_2H_5$ group is the *ethyl group.* The nomenclature scheme is easily extended to derivatives of hydrocarbons with other substituent groups such as $-Cl$ (chloro), $-NO_2$ (nitro), $-CN$ (cyano), $-D$ (deuterio), and so on (Table 13). If two or more of the same substituent groups occur, the prefixes "di-," "tri-," and "tetra-" are added. When different substituent groups are present, they are generally listed in alphabetical order.

Table 13 Names of Common Substituent Groups

Formula	Name	Formula	Name
—CH_3	methyl	—D	deuterio
—C_2H_5	ethyl	—Cl	chloro
—$CH_2CH_2CH_3$	propyl (*n*-propyl)	—Br	bromo
—$CH(CH_3)_2$	1-methylethyl (isopropyl)	—F	fluoro
—$CH=CH_2$	ethenyl (vinyl)	—CN	cyano
—C_6H_5	phenyl	—NO_2	nitro
—OH	hydroxo		
—NH_2	amino		

Example:
$$CH_3 \quad\quad C_2H_5$$
$$\underset{|}{} \quad\quad \underset{|}{}$$
$$CH_3CH_2CHCH_2CHCH_2CH_3$$

Step	Information to Include	Contribution to Name
1	An alkane	Name will end in "-ane"
2	Longest chain is 7 carbons	Name as a *heptane*
3	—CH_3 group at carbon 3	3-*methyl*
4	—C_2H_5 group at carbon 5	5-*ethyl*
Name:		5-ethyl-3-methylheptane

Cycloalkanes are named based on the ring size and by adding the prefix "cyclo"; for example, the cycloalkane with a six-member ring of carbons is called *cyclohexane.*

Alkenes

Alkenes have names ending in "-ene." The name of an alkene must specify the length of the carbon chain and the position of the double bond (and when appropriate, the configuration, either *cis* or *trans*). As with alkanes, both identity and position of substituent groups must be given. The carbon chain is numbered from the end that gives the double bond the lowest number.

Compounds with two double bonds are called *dienes,* and they are named similarly—specifying the positions of the double bonds and the name and position of any substituent groups.

For example, the compound $H_2C=C(CH_3)CH(CH_3)CH_2CH_3$ has a five-carbon chain with a double bond between carbon atoms 1 and 2 and methyl groups on carbon atoms 2 and 3. Its name using IUPAC nomenclature is **2,3-dimethyl-1-pentene**. The compound $CH_3CH=CHCCl_3$ with a *cis* configuration around the double bond is named **1,1,1-trichloro-*cis*-2-butene**. The compound $H_2C=C(Cl)CH=CH_2$ is **2-chloro-1,3-butadiene**.

Alkynes

The naming of alkynes is similar to the naming of alkenes, except that *cis–trans* isomerism isn't a factor. The ending "-yne" on a name identifies a compound as an alkyne.

Benzene Derivatives

The carbon atoms in the six-member ring are numbered 1 through 6, and the name and position of substituent groups are given. The two examples shown here are **1-ethyl-3-methylbenzene** and **1,4-diaminobenzene**.

CH$_3$

C$_2$H$_5$

1-ethyl-3-methylbenzene

NH$_2$

NH$_2$

1,4-diaminobenzene

E.2 Derivatives of Hydrocarbons

The names for alcohols, aldehydes, ketones, and acids are based on the name of the hydrocarbon with an appropriate suffix to denote the class of compound, as follows:

- **Alcohols:** Substitute "-ol" for the final "-e" in the name of the hydrocarbon, and designate the position of the —OH group by the number of the carbon atom. For example, $CH_3CH_2CHOHCH_3$ is named as a derivative of the 4-carbon hydrocarbon butane. The —OH group is attached to the second carbon, so the name is **2-butanol**.
- **Aldehydes:** Substitute "-al" for the final "-e" in the name of the hydrocarbon. The carbon atom of an aldehyde is, by definition, carbon-1 in the hydrocarbon chain. For example, the compound $CH_3CH(CH_3)CH_2CH_2CHO$ contains a 5-carbon chain with the aldehyde functional group being carbon-1 and the —CH$_3$ group at position 4; thus, the name is **4-methylpentanal**.
- **Ketones:** Substitute "-one" for the final "-e" in the name of the hydrocarbon. The position of the ketone functional group (the carbonyl group) is indicated by the number of the carbon atom. For example, the compound $CH_3COCH_2CH(C_2H_5)CH_2CH_3$ has the carbonyl group at the 2 position and an ethyl group at the 4 position of a 6-carbon chain; its name is **4-ethyl-2-hexanone**.
- **Carboxylic acids (organic acids):** Substitute "-oic" for the final "-e" in the name of the hydrocarbon. The carbon atoms in the longest chain are counted beginning with the carboxylic carbon atom. For example, *trans*-$CH_3CH{=}CHCH_2CO_2H$ is named as a derivative of *trans*-3-pentene—that is, ***trans*-3-pentenoic acid**.

An **ester** is named as a derivative of the alcohol and acid from which it is made. The name of an ester is obtained by splitting the formula RCO_2R' into two parts, the RCO_2— portion and the —R' portion. The —R' portion comes from the alcohol and is identified by the hydrocarbon group name; derivatives of ethanol, for example, are called *ethyl* esters. The acid part of the compound is named by dropping the "-oic" ending for the acid and replacing it by "-oate." The compound $CH_3CH_2CO_2CH_3$ is named **methyl propanoate**.

Notice that an anion derived from a carboxylic acid by loss of the acidic proton is named the same way. Thus, $CH_3CH_2CO_2{}^-$ is the **propanoate anion**, and the sodium salt of this anion, $Na(CH_3CH_2CO_2)$, is **sodium propanoate**.

F Values for the Ionization Energies and Electron Attachment Enthalpies of the Elements

First Ionization Energies for Some Elements (kJ/mol)

1A (1)	2A (2)	3B (3)	4B (4)	5B (5)	6B (6)	7B (7)	8B (8,9,10)			1B (11)	2B (12)	3A (13)	4A (14)	5A (15)	6A (16)	7A (17)	8 (18)
H 1312																	He 2371
Li 520	Be 899											B 801	C 1086	N 1402	O 1314	F 1681	Ne 2081
Na 496	Mg 738											Al 578	Si 786	P 1012	S 1000	Cl 1251	Ar 1521
K 419	Ca 599	Sc 631	Ti 658	V 650	Cr 652	Mn 717	Fe 759	Co 758	Ni 757	Cu 745	Zn 906	Ga 579	Ge 762	As 947	Se 941	Br 1140	Kr 1351
Rb 403	Sr 550	Y 617	Zr 661	Nb 664	Mo 685	Tc 702	Ru 711	Rh 720	Pd 804	Ag 731	Cd 868	In 558	Sn 709	Sb 834	Te 869	I 1008	Xe 1170
Cs 377	Ba 503	La 538	Hf 681	Ta 761	W 770	Re 760	Os 840	Ir 880	Pt 870	Au 890	Hg 1007	Tl 589	Pb 715	Bi 703	Po 812	At 890	Rn 1037

Table 14 Electron Attachment Enthalpy Values for Some Elements (kJ/mol)*

H −72.77						
Li −59.63	Be 0†	B −26.7	C −121.85	N 0	O −140.98	F −328.0
Na −52.87	Mg 0	Al −42.6	Si −133.6	P −72.07	S −200.41	Cl −349.0
K −48.39	Ca 0	Ga −30	Ge −120	As −78	Se −194.97	Br −324.7
Rb −46.89	Sr 0	In −30	Sn −120	Sb −103	Te −190.16	I −295.16
Cs −45.51	Ba 0	Tl −20	Pb −35.1	Bi −91.3	Po −180	At −270

*Derived from data taken from H. Hotop and W. C. Lineberger: *Journal of Physical Chemistry, Reference Data,* Vol. 14, p. 731, 1985. (This paper also includes data for the transition metals.) Some values are known to more than two decimal places. See also: http://en.wikipedia.org/wiki/Electron_affinity_(data_page)
†Elements with an electron attachment enthalpy of zero indicate that a stable anion A⁻ of the element does not exist in the gas phase.

G Vapor Pressure of Water at Various Temperatures

Table 15 Vapor Pressure of Water at Various Temperatures

Temperature (°C)	Vapor Pressure (torr)	Temperature (°C)	Vapor Pressure (torr)	Temperature (°C)	Vapor Pressure (torr)	Temperature (°C)	Vapor Pressure (torr)
−10	2.1	21	18.7	51	97.2	81	369.7
−9	2.3	22	19.8	52	102.1	82	384.9
−8	2.5	23	21.1	53	107.2	83	400.6
−7	2.7	24	22.4	54	112.5	84	416.8
−6	2.9	25	23.8	55	118.0	85	433.6
−5	3.2	26	25.2	56	123.8	86	450.9
−4	3.4	27	26.7	57	129.8	87	468.7
−3	3.7	28	28.3	58	136.1	88	487.1
−2	4.0	29	30.0	59	142.6	89	506.1
−1	4.3	30	31.8	60	149.4	90	525.8
0	4.6	31	33.7	61	156.4	91	546.1
1	4.9	32	35.7	62	163.8	92	567.0
2	5.3	33	37.7	63	171.4	93	588.6
3	5.7	34	39.9	64	179.3	94	610.9
4	6.1	35	42.2	65	187.5	95	633.9
5	6.5	36	44.6	66	196.1	96	657.6
6	7.0	37	47.1	67	205.0	97	682.1
7	7.5	38	49.7	68	214.2	98	707.3
8	8.0	39	52.4	69	223.7	99	733.2
9	8.6	40	55.3	70	233.7	100	760.0
10	9.2	41	58.3	71	243.9	101	787.6
11	9.8	42	61.5	72	254.6	102	815.9
12	10.5	43	64.8	73	265.7	103	845.1
13	11.2	44	68.3	74	277.2	104	875.1
14	12.0	45	71.9	75	289.1	105	906.1
15	12.8	46	75.7	76	301.4	106	937.9
16	13.6	47	79.6	77	314.1	107	970.6
17	14.5	48	83.7	78	327.3	108	1004.4
18	15.5	49	88.0	79	341.0	109	1038.9
19	16.5	50	92.5	80	355.1	110	1074.6
20	17.5						

H Ionization Constants for Aqueous Weak Acids at 25 °C

Table 16 Ionization Constants for Aqueous Weak Acids at 25 °C

Acid	Formula and Ionization Equation	K_a
Acetic	$CH_3CO_2H \rightleftarrows H^+ + CH_3CO_2^-$	1.8×10^{-5}
Arsenic	$H_3AsO_4 \rightleftarrows H^+ + H_2AsO_4^-$ $H_2AsO_4^- \rightleftarrows H^+ + HAsO_4^{2-}$ $HAsO_4^{2-} \rightleftarrows H^+ + AsO_4^{3-}$	$K_1 = 5.8 \times 10^{-3}$ $K_2 = 1.1 \times 10^{-7}$ $K_3 = 3.2 \times 10^{-12}$
Arsenous	$H_3AsO_3 \rightleftarrows H^+ + H_2AsO_3^-$ $H_2AsO_3^- \rightleftarrows H^+ + HAsO_3^{2-}$	$K_1 = 6.0 \times 10^{-10}$ $K_2 = 3.0 \times 10^{-14}$
Benzoic	$C_6H_5CO_2H \rightleftarrows H^+ + C_6H_5CO_2^-$	6.3×10^{-5}
Boric	$H_3BO_3 \rightleftarrows H^+ + H_2BO_3^-$ $H_2BO_3^- \rightleftarrows H^+ + HBO_3^{2-}$ $HBO_3^{2-} \rightleftarrows H^+ + BO_3^{3-}$	$K_1 = 7.3 \times 10^{-10}$ $K_2 = 1.8 \times 10^{-13}$ $K_3 = 1.6 \times 10^{-14}$
Carbonic	$H_2CO_3 \rightleftarrows H^+ + HCO_3^-$ $HCO_3^- \rightleftarrows H^+ + CO_3^{2-}$	$K_1 = 4.2 \times 10^{-7}$ $K_2 = 4.8 \times 10^{-11}$
Citric	$H_3C_6H_5O_7 \rightleftarrows H^+ + H_2C_6H_5O_7^-$ $H_2C_6H_5O_7^- \rightleftarrows H^+ + HC_6H_5O_7^{2-}$ $HC_6H_5O_7^{2-} \rightleftarrows H^+ + C_6H_5O_7^{3-}$	$K_1 = 7.4 \times 10^{-3}$ $K_2 = 1.7 \times 10^{-5}$ $K_3 = 4.0 \times 10^{-7}$
Cyanic	$HOCN \rightleftarrows H^+ + OCN^-$	3.5×10^{-4}
Formic	$HCO_2H \rightleftarrows H^+ + HCO_2^-$	1.8×10^{-4}
Hydrazoic	$HN_3 \rightleftarrows H^+ + N_3^-$	1.9×10^{-5}
Hydrocyanic	$HCN \rightleftarrows H^+ + CN^-$	4.0×10^{-10}
Hydrofluoric	$HF \rightleftarrows H^+ + F^-$	7.2×10^{-4}
Hydrogen peroxide	$H_2O_2 \rightleftarrows H^+ + HO_2^-$	2.4×10^{-12}
Hydrosulfuric	$H_2S \rightleftarrows H^+ + HS^-$ $HS^- \rightleftarrows H^+ + S^{2-}$	$K_1 = 1 \times 10^{-7}$ $K_2 = 1 \times 10^{-19}$
Hypobromous	$HOBr \rightleftarrows H^+ + OBr^-$	2.5×10^{-9}
Hypochlorous	$HOCl \rightleftarrows H^+ + OCl^-$	3.5×10^{-8}
Nitrous	$HNO_2 \rightleftarrows H^+ + NO_2^-$	4.5×10^{-4}
Oxalic	$H_2C_2O_4 \rightleftarrows H^+ + HC_2O_4^-$ $HC_2O_4^- \rightleftarrows H^+ + C_2O_4^{2-}$	$K_1 = 5.9 \times 10^{-2}$ $K_2 = 6.4 \times 10^{-5}$
Phenol	$C_6H_5OH \rightleftarrows H^+ + C_6H_5O^-$	1.3×10^{-10}
Phosphoric	$H_3PO_4 \rightleftarrows H^+ + H_2PO_4^-$ $H_2PO_4^- \rightleftarrows H^+ + HPO_4^{2-}$ $HPO_4^{2-} \rightleftarrows H^+ + PO_4^{3-}$	$K_1 = 7.5 \times 10^{-3}$ $K_2 = 6.2 \times 10^{-8}$ $K_3 = 3.6 \times 10^{-13}$
Phosphorous	$H_3PO_3 \rightleftarrows H^+ + H_2PO_3^-$ $H_2PO_3^- \rightleftarrows H^+ + HPO_3^{2-}$	$K_1 = 1.6 \times 10^{-2}$ $K_2 = 7.0 \times 10^{-7}$
Selenic	$H_2SeO_4 \rightleftarrows H^+ + HSeO_4^-$ $HSeO_4^- \rightleftarrows H^+ + SeO_4^{2-}$	$K_1 = $ very large $K_2 = 1.2 \times 10^{-2}$

Table 16 Ionization Constants for Aqueous Weak Acids at 25 °C (continued)

Acid	Formula and Ionization Equation	K_a
Selenous	$H_2SeO_3 \rightleftharpoons H^+ + HSeO_3^-$ $HSeO_3^- \rightleftharpoons H^+ + SeO_3^{2-}$	$K_1 = 2.7 \times 10^{-3}$ $K_2 = 2.5 \times 10^{-7}$
Sulfuric	$H_2SO_4 \rightleftharpoons H^+ + HSO_4^-$ $HSO_4^- \rightleftharpoons H^+ + SO_4^{2-}$	$K_1 = $ very large $K_2 = 1.2 \times 10^{-2}$
Sulfurous	$H_2SO_3 \rightleftharpoons H^+ + HSO_3^-$ $HSO_3^- \rightleftharpoons H^+ + SO_3^{2-}$	$K_1 = 1.2 \times 10^{-2}$ $K_2 = 6.2 \times 10^{-8}$
Tellurous	$H_2TeO_3 \rightleftharpoons H^+ + HTeO_3^-$ $HTeO_3^- \rightleftharpoons H^+ + TeO_3^{2-}$	$K_1 = 2 \times 10^{-3}$ $K_2 = 1 \times 10^{-8}$

I Ionization Constants for Aqueous Weak Bases at 25 °C

Table 17 Ionization Constants for Aqueous Weak Bases at 25 °C

Base	Formula and Ionization Equation	K_b
Ammonia	$NH_3 + H_2O \rightleftharpoons NH_4^+ + OH^-$	1.8×10^{-5}
Aniline	$C_6H_5NH_2 + H_2O \rightleftharpoons C_6H_5NH_3^+ + OH^-$	4.0×10^{-10}
Dimethylamine	$(CH_3)_2NH + H_2O \rightleftharpoons (CH_3)_2NH_2^+ + OH^-$	7.4×10^{-4}
Ethylamine	$C_2H_5NH_2 + H_2O \rightleftharpoons C_2H_5NH_3^+ + OH^-$	4.3×10^{-4}
Ethylenediamine	$H_2NCH_2CH_2NH_2 + H_2O \rightleftharpoons H_2NCH_2CH_2NH_3^+ + OH^-$ $H_2NCH_2CH_2NH_3^+ + H_2O \rightleftharpoons H_3NCH_2CH_2NH_3^{2+} + OH^-$	$K_1 = 8.5 \times 10^{-5}$ $K_2 = 2.7 \times 10^{-8}$
Hydrazine	$N_2H_4 + H_2O \rightleftharpoons N_2H_5^+ + OH^-$ $N_2H_5^+ + H_2O \rightleftharpoons N_2H_6^{2+} + OH^-$	$K_1 = 8.5 \times 10^{-7}$ $K_2 = 8.9 \times 10^{-16}$
Hydroxylamine	$NH_2OH + H_2O \rightleftharpoons NH_3OH^+ + OH^-$	6.6×10^{-9}
Methylamine	$CH_3NH_2 + H_2O \rightleftharpoons CH_3NH_3^+ + OH^-$	5.0×10^{-4}
Pyridine	$C_5H_5N + H_2O \rightleftharpoons C_5H_5NH^+ + OH^-$	1.5×10^{-9}
Trimethylamine	$(CH_3)_3N + H_2O \rightleftharpoons (CH_3)_3NH^+ + OH^-$	7.4×10^{-5}

J Solubility Product Constants for Some Inorganic Compounds at 25 °C

Table 18A Solubility Product Constants at 25 °C

Cation	Compound	K_{sp}	Cation	Compound	K_{sp}
Ba^{2+}	*$BaCrO_4$	1.2×10^{-10}	Hg_2^{2+}	*Hg_2Br_2	6.4×10^{-23}
	$BaCO_3$	2.6×10^{-9}		Hg_2Cl_2	1.4×10^{-18}
	BaF_2	1.8×10^{-7}		*Hg_2I_2	2.9×10^{-29}
	*$BaSO_4$	1.1×10^{-10}		Hg_2SO_4	6.5×10^{-7}
Ca^{2+}	$CaCO_3$ (calcite)	3.4×10^{-9}	Ni^{2+}	$NiCO_3$	1.4×10^{-7}
	*CaF_2	5.3×10^{-11}		$Ni(OH)_2$	5.5×10^{-16}
	*$Ca(OH)_2$	5.5×10^{-5}	Ag^+	*$AgBr$	5.4×10^{-13}
	$CaSO_4$	4.9×10^{-5}		*$AgBrO_3$	5.4×10^{-5}
Cu^+, Cu^{2+}	$CuBr$	6.3×10^{-9}		$AgCH_3CO_2$	1.9×10^{-3}
	CuI	1.3×10^{-12}		$AgCN$	6.0×10^{-17}
	$Cu(OH)_2$	2.2×10^{-20}		Ag_2CO_3	8.5×10^{-12}
	$CuSCN$	1.8×10^{-13}		*$Ag_2C_2O_4$	5.4×10^{-12}
Au^+	$AuCl$	2.0×10^{-13}		*$AgCl$	1.8×10^{-10}
Fe^{2+}	$FeCO_3$	3.1×10^{-11}		Ag_2CrO_4	1.1×10^{-12}
	$Fe(OH)_2$	4.9×10^{-17}		*AgI	8.5×10^{-17}
Pb^{2+}	$PbBr_2$	6.6×10^{-6}		$AgSCN$	1.0×10^{-12}
	$PbCO_3$	7.4×10^{-14}		*Ag_2SO_4	1.2×10^{-5}
	$PbCl_2$	1.7×10^{-5}	Sr^{2+}	$SrCO_3$	5.6×10^{-10}
	$PbCrO_4$	2.8×10^{-13}		SrF_2	4.3×10^{-9}
	PbF_2	3.3×10^{-8}		$SrSO_4$	3.4×10^{-7}
	PbI_2	9.8×10^{-9}	Tl^+	$TlBr$	3.7×10^{-6}
	$Pb(OH)_2$	1.4×10^{-15}		$TlCl$	1.9×10^{-4}
	$PbSO_4$	2.5×10^{-8}		TlI	5.5×10^{-8}
Mg^{2+}	$MgCO_3$	6.8×10^{-6}	Zn^{2+}	$Zn(OH)_2$	3×10^{-17}
	MgF_2	5.2×10^{-11}		$Zn(CN)_2$	8.0×10^{-12}
	$Mg(OH)_2$	5.6×10^{-12}			
Mn^{2+}	$MnCO_3$	2.3×10^{-11}			
	*$Mn(OH)_2$	1.9×10^{-13}			

The values reported in this table were taken from J. A. Dean: *Lange's Handbook of Chemistry,* 15th ed. New York: McGraw-Hill Publishers, 1999. Values have been rounded off to two significant figures.

*Calculated solubility from these K_{sp} values will match experimental solubility for this compound within a factor of 2. Experimental values for solubilities are given in R. W. Clark and J. M. Bonicamp: *Journal of Chemical Education,* Vol. 75, p. 1182, 1998.

Table 18B K_{spa} **Values* for Some Metal Sulfides at 25 °C**

Substance	K_{spa}
HgS (red)	4×10^{-54}
HgS (black)	2×10^{-53}
Ag_2S	6×10^{-51}
CuS	6×10^{-37}
PbS	3×10^{-28}
CdS	8×10^{-28}
SnS	1×10^{-26}
FeS	6×10^{-19}

*The equilibrium constant value K_{spa} for metal sulfides refers to the equilibrium $MS(s) + H_2O(\ell) \rightleftharpoons M^{2+}(aq) + OH^-(aq) + HS^-(aq)$; see R. J. Myers, *Journal of Chemical Education,* Vol. 63, p. 687, 1986.

K Formation Constants for Some Complex Ions in Aqueous Solution at 25 °C

Table 19 Formation Constants for Some Complex Ions in Aqueous Solution at 25 °C*

Formation Equilibrium	K
$Ag^+ + 2\ Br^- \rightleftharpoons [AgBr_2]^-$	2.1×10^7
$Ag^+ + 2\ Cl^- \rightleftharpoons [AgCl_2]^-$	1.1×10^5
$Ag^+ + 2\ CN^- \rightleftharpoons [Ag(CN)_2]^-$	1.3×10^{21}
$Ag^+ + 2\ S_2O_3^{2-} \rightleftharpoons [Ag(S_2O_3)_2]^{3-}$	2.9×10^{13}
$Ag^+ + 2\ NH_3 \rightleftharpoons [Ag(NH_3)_2]^+$	1.1×10^7
$Al^{3+} + 6\ F^- \rightleftharpoons [AlF_6]^{3-}$	6.9×10^{19}
$Al^{3+} + 4\ OH^- \rightleftharpoons [Al(OH)_4]^-$	1.1×10^{33}
$Au^+ + 2\ CN^- \rightleftharpoons [Au(CN)_2]^-$	2.0×10^{38}
$Cd^{2+} + 4\ CN^- \rightleftharpoons [Cd(CN)_4]^{2-}$	6.0×10^{18}
$Cd^{2+} + 4\ NH_3 \rightleftharpoons [Cd(NH_3)_4]^{2+}$	1.3×10^7
$Co^{2+} + 6\ NH_3 \rightleftharpoons [Co(NH_3)_6]^{2+}$	1.3×10^5
$Cu^+ + 2\ CN^- \rightleftharpoons [Cu(CN)_2]^-$	1.0×10^{24}
$Cu^+ + 2\ Cl^- \rightleftharpoons [CuCl_2]^-$	3.2×10^5
$Cu^{2+} + 4\ NH_3 \rightleftharpoons [Cu(NH_3)_4]^{2+}$	2.1×10^{13}
$Fe^{2+} + 6\ CN^- \rightleftharpoons [Fe(CN)_6]^{4-}$	1.0×10^{35}
$Hg^{2+} + 4\ Cl^- \rightleftharpoons [HgCl_4]^{2-}$	1.2×10^{15}
$Ni^{2+} + 4\ CN^- \rightleftharpoons [Ni(CN)_4]^{2-}$	2.0×10^{31}
$Ni^{2+} + 6\ NH_3 \rightleftharpoons [Ni(NH_3)_6]^{2+}$	5.5×10^8
$Zn^{2+} + 4\ OH^- \rightleftharpoons [Zn(OH)_4]^{2-}$	4.6×10^{17}
$Zn^{2+} + 4\ NH_3 \rightleftharpoons [Zn(NH_3)_4]^{2+}$	2.9×10^9

*Data reported in this table are taken from J. A. Dean: *Lange's Handbook of Chemistry,* 15th ed. New York: McGraw-Hill Publishers, 1999.

L Selected Thermodynamic Values

Table 20 **Selected Thermodynamic Values***

Species	$\Delta_f H°$ (298.15 K) (kJ/mol)	$S°$ (298.15 K) (J/K · mol)	$\Delta_f G°$ (298.15 K) (kJ/mol)
Aluminum			
Al(s)	0	28.3	0
AlCl$_3$(s)	−705.63	109.29	−630.0
Al$_2$O$_3$(s)	−1675.7	50.92	−1582.3
Barium			
BaCl$_2$(s)	−858.6	123.68	−810.4
BaCO$_3$(s)	−1213	112.1	−1134.41
BaO(s)	−548.1	72.05	−520.38
BaSO$_4$(s)	−1473.2	132.2	−1362.2
Beryllium			
Be(s)	0	9.5	0
Be(OH)$_2$(s)	−902.5	51.9	−815.0
Boron			
BCl$_3$(g)	−402.96	290.17	−387.95
Bromine			
Br(g)	111.884	175.022	82.396
Br$_2$(ℓ)	0	152.2	0
Br$_2$(g)	30.91	245.47	3.12
BrF$_3$(g)	−255.60	292.53	−229.43
HBr(g)	−36.29	198.70	−53.45
Calcium			
Ca(s)	0	41.59	0
Ca(g)	178.2	158.884	144.3
Ca^{2+}(g)	1925.90	—	—
CaC$_2$(s)	−59.8	70.	−64.93
CaCO$_3$(s, calcite)	−1207.6	91.7	−1129.16
CaCl$_2$(s)	−795.8	104.6	−748.1
CaF$_2$(s)	−1219.6	68.87	−1167.3
CaH$_2$(s)	−186.2	42	−147.2
CaO(s)	−635.09	38.2	−603.42
CaS(s)	−482.4	56.5	−477.4
Ca(OH)$_2$(s)	−986.09	83.39	−898.43
Ca(OH)$_2$(aq)	−1002.82	—	−868.07
CaSO$_4$(s)	−1434.52	106.5	−1322.02

*Most thermodynamic data are taken from the NIST Chemistry WebBook at http://webbook.nist.gov.

Table 20 Selected Thermodynamic Values (continued)

Species	$\Delta_f H°$ (298.15 K) (kJ/mol)	$S°$ (298.15 K) (J/K · mol)	$\Delta_f G°$ (298.15 K) (kJ/mol)
Carbon			
C(s, graphite)	0	5.6	0
C(s, diamond)	1.8	2.377	2.900
C(g)	716.67	158.1	671.2
$CCl_4(\ell)$	−128.4	214.39	−57.63
$CCl_4(g)$	−95.98	309.65	−53.61
$CHCl_3(\ell)$	−134.47	201.7	−73.66
$CHCl_3(g)$	−103.18	295.61	−70.4
CH_4(g, methane)	−74.87	186.26	−50.8
C_2H_2(g, ethyne)	226.73	200.94	209.20
C_2H_4(g, ethene)	52.47	219.36	68.35
C_2H_6(g, ethane)	−83.85	229.2	−31.89
C_3H_8(g, propane)	−104.7	270.3	−24.4
$C_6H_6(\ell$, benzene)	48.95	173.26	124.21
$CH_3OH(\ell$, methanol)	−238.4	127.19	−166.14
CH_3OH(g, methanol)	−201.0	239.7	−162.5
$C_2H_5OH(\ell$, ethanol)	−277.0	160.7	−174.7
C_2H_5OH(g, ethanol)	−235.3	282.70	−168.49
CO(g)	−110.525	197.674	−137.168
CO_2(g)	−393.509	213.74	−394.359
$CS_2(\ell)$	89.41	151	65.2
CS_2(g)	116.7	237.8	66.61
$COCl_2$(g)	−218.8	283.53	−204.6
Cesium			
Cs(s)	0	85.23	0
Cs^+(g)	457.964	—	—
CsCl(s)	−443.04	101.17	−414.53
Chlorine			
Cl(g)	121.3	165.19	105.3
Cl^-(g)	−233.13	—	—
Cl_2(g)	0	223.08	0
HCl(g)	−92.31	186.2	−95.09
HCl(aq)	−167.159	56.5	−131.26
Chromium			
Cr(s)	0	23.62	0
Cr_2O_3(s)	−1134.7	80.65	−1052.95
$CrCl_3$(s)	−556.5	123.0	−486.1

(continued)

Table 20 Selected Thermodynamic Values (continued)

Species	$\Delta_f H°$ (298.15 K) (kJ/mol)	$S°$ (298.15 K) (J/K · mol)	$\Delta_f G°$ (298.15 K) (kJ/mol)
Copper			
Cu(s)	0	33.17	0
CuO(s)	−156.06	42.59	−128.3
CuCl$_2$(s)	−220.1	108.07	−175.7
CuSO$_4$(s)	−769.98	109.05	−660.75
Fluorine			
F$_2$(g)	0	202.8	0
F(g)	78.99	158.754	61.91
F$^-$(g)	−255.39	—	—
F$^-$(aq)	−332.63	—	−278.79
HF(g)	−273.3	173.779	−273.2
HF(aq)	−332.63	88.7	−278.79
Hydrogen			
H$_2$(g)	0	130.7	0
H(g)	217.965	114.713	203.247
H$^+$(g)	1536.202	—	—
H$_2$O(ℓ)	−285.83	69.95	−237.15
H$_2$O(g)	−241.83	188.84	−228.59
H$_2$O$_2$(ℓ)	−187.78	109.6	−120.35
Iodine			
I$_2$(s)	0	116.135	0
I$_2$(g)	62.438	260.69	19.327
I(g)	106.838	180.791	70.250
I$^-$(g)	−197	—	—
ICl(g)	17.51	247.56	−5.73
Iron			
Fe(s)	0	27.78	0
FeO(s)	−272	—	—
Fe$_2$O$_3$(s, hematite)	−825.5	87.40	−742.2
Fe$_3$O$_4$(s, magnetite)	−1118.4	146.4	−1015.4
FeCl$_2$(s)	−341.79	117.95	−302.30
FeCl$_3$(s)	−399.49	142.3	−344.00
FeS$_2$(s, pyrite)	−178.2	52.93	−166.9
Fe(CO)$_5$(ℓ)	−774.0	338.1	−705.3
Lead			
Pb(s)	0	64.81	0
PbCl$_2$(s)	−359.41	136.0	−314.10
PbO(s, yellow)	−219	66.5	−196
PbO$_2$(s)	−277.4	68.6	−217.39
PbS(s)	−100.4	91.2	−98.7

Table 20 Selected Thermodynamic Values (continued)

Species	$\Delta_f H°$ (298.15 K) (kJ/mol)	$S°$ (298.15 K) (J/K · mol)	$\Delta_f G°$ (298.15 K) (kJ/mol)
Lithium			
Li(s)	0	29.12	0
Li$^+$(g)	685.783	—	—
LiOH(s)	−484.93	42.81	−438.96
LiOH(aq)	−508.48	2.80	−450.58
LiCl(s)	−408.701	59.33	−384.37
Magnesium			
Mg(s)	0	32.67	0
MgCl$_2$(s)	−641.62	89.62	−592.09
MgCO$_3$(s)	−1111.69	65.84	−1028.2
MgO(s)	−601.24	26.85	−568.93
Mg(OH)$_2$(s)	−924.54	63.18	−833.51
MgS(s)	−346.0	50.33	−341.8
Mercury			
Hg(ℓ)	0	76.02	0
HgCl$_2$(s)	−224.3	146.0	−178.6
HgO(s, red)	−90.83	70.29	−58.539
HgS(s, red)	−58.2	82.4	−50.6
Nickel			
Ni(s)	0	29.87	0
NiO(s)	−239.7	37.99	−211.7
NiCl$_2$(s)	−305.332	97.65	−259.032
Nitrogen			
N$_2$(g)	0	191.56	0
N(g)	472.704	153.298	455.563
NH$_3$(g)	−45.90	192.77	−16.37
N$_2$H$_4$(ℓ)	50.63	121.52	149.45
NH$_4$Cl(s)	−314.55	94.85	−203.08
NH$_4$Cl(aq)	−299.66	169.9	−210.57
NH$_4$NO$_3$(s)	−365.56	151.08	−183.84
NH$_4$NO$_3$(aq)	−339.87	259.8	−190.57
NO(g)	90.29	210.76	86.58
NO$_2$(g)	33.1	240.04	51.23
N$_2$O(g)	82.05	219.85	104.20
N$_2$O$_4$(g)	9.08	304.38	97.73
NOCl(g)	51.71	261.8	66.08
HNO$_3$(ℓ)	−174.10	155.60	−80.71
HNO$_3$(g)	−135.06	266.38	−74.72
HNO$_3$(aq)	−207.36	146.4	−111.25

(continued)

Table 20 Selected Thermodynamic Values (continued)

Species	$\Delta_f H°$ (298.15 K) (kJ/mol)	$S°$ (298.15 K) (J/K · mol)	$\Delta_f G°$ (298.15 K) (kJ/mol)
Oxygen			
$O_2(g)$	0	205.07	0
$O(g)$	249.170	161.055	231.731
$O_3(g)$	142.67	238.92	163.2
Phosphorus			
$P_4(s, white)$	0	41.1	0
$P_4(s, red)$	−17.6	22.80	−12.1
$P(g)$	314.64	163.193	278.25
$PH_3(g)$	5.47	210.24	6.64
$PCl_3(g)$	−287.0	311.78	−267.8
$P_4O_{10}(s)$	−2984.0	228.86	−2697.7
$H_3PO_4(\ell)$	−1279.0	110.5	−1119.1
Potassium			
$K(s)$	0	64.63	0
$KCl(s)$	−436.68	82.56	−408.77
$KClO_3(s)$	−397.73	143.1	−296.25
$KI(s)$	−327.90	106.32	−324.892
$KOH(s)$	−424.72	78.9	−378.92
$KOH(aq)$	−482.37	91.6	−440.50
Silicon			
$Si(s)$	0	18.82	0
$SiBr_4(\ell)$	−457.3	277.8	−443.9
$SiC(s)$	−65.3	16.61	−62.8
$SiCl_4(g)$	−662.75	330.86	−622.76
$SiH_4(g)$	34.31	204.65	56.84
$SiF_4(g)$	−1614.94	282.49	−1572.65
$SiO_2(s, quartz)$	−910.86	41.46	−856.97
Silver			
$Ag(s)$	0	42.55	0
$Ag_2O(s)$	−31.1	121.3	−11.32
$AgCl(s)$	−127.01	96.25	−109.76
$AgNO_3(s)$	−124.39	140.92	−33.41
Sodium			
$Na(s)$	0	51.21	0
$Na(g)$	107.3	153.765	76.83
$Na^+(g)$	609.358	—	—
$NaBr(s)$	−361.02	86.82	−348.983
$NaCl(s)$	−411.12	72.11	−384.04
$NaCl(g)$	−181.42	229.79	−201.33
$NaCl(aq)$	−407.27	115.5	−393.133

Table 20 Selected Thermodynamic Values (continued)

Species	$\Delta_f H°$ (298.15 K) (kJ/mol)	$S°$ (298.15 K) (J/K · mol)	$\Delta_f G°$ (298.15 K) (kJ/mol)
Sodium (continued)			
NaOH(s)	−425.93	64.46	−379.75
NaOH(aq)	−469.15	48.1	−418.09
Na₂CO₃(s)	−1130.77	134.79	−1048.08
Sulfur			
S(s, rhombic)	0	32.1	0
S(g)	278.98	167.83	236.51
S₂Cl₂(g)	−18.4	331.5	−31.8
SF₆(g)	−1209	291.82	−1105.3
H₂S(g)	−20.63	205.79	−33.56
SO₂(g)	−296.84	248.21	−300.13
SO₃(g)	−395.77	256.77	−371.04
SOCl₂(g)	−212.5	309.77	−198.3
H₂SO₄(ℓ)	−814	156.9	−689.96
H₂SO₄(aq)	−909.27	20.1	−744.53
Tin			
Sn(s, white)	0	51.08	0
Sn(s, gray)	−2.09	44.14	0.13
SnCl₄(ℓ)	−511.3	258.6	−440.15
SnCl₄(g)	−471.5	365.8	−432.31
SnO₂(s)	−577.63	49.04	−515.88
Titanium			
Ti(s)	0	30.72	0
TiCl₄(ℓ)	−804.2	252.34	−737.2
TiCl₄(g)	−763.16	354.84	−726.7
TiO₂(s)	−939.7	49.92	−884.5
Zinc			
Zn(s)	0	41.63	0
ZnCl₂(s)	−415.05	111.46	−369.398
ZnO(s)	−348.28	43.64	−318.30
ZnS(s, sphalerite)	−205.98	57.7	−201.29

M Standard Reduction Potentials in Aqueous Solution at 25 °C

Table 21 Standard Reduction Potentials in Aqueous Solution at 25 °C

Acidic Solution	Standard Reduction Potential $E°$ (volts)
$F_2(g) + 2\,e^- \longrightarrow 2\,F^-(aq)$	2.87
$Co^{3+}(aq) + e^- \longrightarrow Co^{2+}(aq)$	1.82
$Pb^{4+}(aq) + 2\,e^- \longrightarrow Pb^{2+}(aq)$	1.8
$H_2O_2(aq) + 2\,H^+(aq) + 2\,e^- \longrightarrow 2\,H_2O$	1.77
$NiO_2(s) + 4\,H^+(aq) + 2\,e^- \longrightarrow Ni^{2+}(aq) + 2\,H_2O$	1.7
$PbO_2(s) + SO_4^{2-}(aq) + 4\,H^+(aq) + 2\,e^- \longrightarrow PbSO_4(s) + 2\,H_2O$	1.685
$Au^+(aq) + e^- \longrightarrow Au(s)$	1.68
$2\,HClO(aq) + 2\,H^+(aq) + 2\,e^- \longrightarrow Cl_2(g) + 2\,H_2O$	1.63
$Ce^{4+}(aq) + e^- \longrightarrow Ce^{3+}(aq)$	1.61
$NaBiO_3(s) + 6\,H^+(aq) + 2\,e^- \longrightarrow Bi^{3+}(aq) + Na^+(aq) + 3\,H_2O$	≈ 1.6
$MnO_4^-(aq) + 8\,H^+(aq) + 5\,e^- \longrightarrow Mn^{2+}(aq) + 4\,H_2O$	1.51
$Au^{3+}(aq) + 3\,e^- \longrightarrow Au(s)$	1.50
$ClO_3^-(aq) + 6\,H^+(aq) + 5\,e^- \longrightarrow \frac{1}{2}\,Cl_2(g) + 3\,H_2O$	1.47
$BrO_3^-(aq) + 6\,H^+(aq) + 6\,e^- \longrightarrow Br^-(aq) + 3\,H_2O$	1.44
$Cl_2(g) + 2\,e^- \longrightarrow 2\,Cl^-(aq)$	1.36
$Cr_2O_7^{2-}(aq) + 14\,H^+(aq) + 6\,e^- \longrightarrow 2\,Cr^{3+}(aq) + 7\,H_2O$	1.33
$N_2H_5^+(aq) + 3\,H^+(aq) + 2\,e^- \longrightarrow 2\,NH_4^+(aq)$	1.24
$MnO_2(s) + 4\,H^+(aq) + 2\,e^- \longrightarrow Mn^{2+}(aq) + 2\,H_2O$	1.23
$O_2(g) + 4\,H^+(aq) + 4\,e^- \longrightarrow 2\,H_2O$	1.229
$Pt^{2+}(aq) + 2\,e^- \longrightarrow Pt(s)$	1.2
$IO_3^-(aq) + 6\,H^+(aq) + 5\,e^- \longrightarrow \frac{1}{2}\,I_2(aq) + 3\,H_2O$	1.195
$ClO_4^-(aq) + 2\,H^+(aq) + 2\,e^- \longrightarrow ClO_3^-(aq) + H_2O$	1.19
$Br_2(\ell) + 2\,e^- \longrightarrow 2\,Br^-(aq)$	1.08
$AuCl_4^-(aq) + 3\,e^- \longrightarrow Au(s) + 4\,Cl^-(aq)$	1.00
$Pd^{2+}(aq) + 2\,e^- \longrightarrow Pd(s)$	0.987
$NO_3^-(aq) + 4\,H^+(aq) + 3\,e^- \longrightarrow NO(g) + 2\,H_2O$	0.96
$NO_3^-(aq) + 3\,H^+(aq) + 2\,e^- \longrightarrow HNO_2(aq) + H_2O$	0.94
$2\,Hg^{2+}(aq) + 2\,e^- \longrightarrow Hg_2^{2+}(aq)$	0.920
$Hg^{2+}(aq) + 2\,e^- \longrightarrow Hg(\ell)$	0.855
$Ag^+(aq) + e^- \longrightarrow Ag(s)$	0.7994
$Hg_2^{2+}(aq) + 2\,e^- \longrightarrow 2\,Hg(\ell)$	0.789
$Fe^{3+}(aq) + e^- \longrightarrow Fe^{2+}(aq)$	0.771

Table 21 Standard Reduction Potentials in Aqueous Solution at 25 °C (continued)

Acidic Solution	Standard Reduction Potential $E°$ (volts)
$SbCl_6^-(aq) + 2\,e^- \longrightarrow SbCl_4^-(aq) + 2\,Cl^-(aq)$	0.75
$[PtCl_4]^{2-}(aq) + 2\,e^- \longrightarrow Pt(s) + 4\,Cl^-(aq)$	0.73
$O_2(g) + 2\,H^+(aq) + 2\,e^- \longrightarrow H_2O_2(aq)$	0.682
$[PtCl_6]^{2-}(aq) + 2\,e^- \longrightarrow [PtCl_4]^{2-}(aq) + 2\,Cl^-(aq)$	0.68
$I_2(aq) + 2\,e^- \longrightarrow 2\,I^-(aq)$	0.621
$H_3AsO_4(aq) + 2\,H^+(aq) + 2\,e^- \longrightarrow H_3AsO_3(aq) + H_2O$	0.58
$I_2(s) + 2\,e^- \longrightarrow 2\,I^-(aq)$	0.535
$TeO_2(s) + 4\,H^+(aq) + 4\,e^- \longrightarrow Te(s) + 2\,H_2O$	0.529
$Cu^+(aq) + e^- \longrightarrow Cu(s)$	0.521
$[RhCl_6]^{3-}(aq) + 3\,e^- \longrightarrow Rh(s) + 6\,Cl^-(aq)$	0.44
$Cu^{2+}(aq) + 2\,e^- \longrightarrow Cu(s)$	0.337
$Hg_2Cl_2(s) + 2\,e^- \longrightarrow 2\,Hg(\ell) + 2\,Cl^-(aq)$	0.27
$AgCl(s) + e^- \longrightarrow Ag(s) + Cl^-(aq)$	0.222
$SO_4^{2-}(aq) + 4\,H^+(aq) + 2\,e^- \longrightarrow SO_2(g) + 2\,H_2O$	0.20
$SO_4^{2-}(aq) + 4\,H^+(aq) + 2\,e^- \longrightarrow H_2SO_3(aq) + H_2O$	0.17
$Cu^{2+}(aq) + e^- \longrightarrow Cu^+(aq)$	0.153
$Sn^{4+}(aq) + 2\,e^- \longrightarrow Sn^{2+}(aq)$	0.15
$S(s) + 2\,H^+ + 2\,e^- \longrightarrow H_2S(aq)$	0.14
$AgBr(s) + e^- \longrightarrow Ag(s) + Br^-(aq)$	0.0713
$2\,H^+(aq) + 2\,e^- \longrightarrow H_2(g)\text{(reference electrode)}$	0.0000
$N_2O(g) + 6\,H^+(aq) + H_2O + 4\,e^- \longrightarrow 2\,NH_3OH^+(aq)$	−0.05
$Pb^{2+}(aq) + 2\,e^- \longrightarrow Pb(s)$	−0.126
$Sn^{2+}(aq) + 2\,e^- \longrightarrow Sn(s)$	−0.14
$AgI(s) + e^- \longrightarrow Ag(s) + I^-(aq)$	−0.15
$[SnF_6]^{2-}(aq) + 4\,e^- \longrightarrow Sn(s) + 6\,F^-(aq)$	−0.25
$Ni^{2+}(aq) + 2\,e^- \longrightarrow Ni(s)$	−0.25
$Co^{2+}(aq) + 2\,e^- \longrightarrow Co(s)$	−0.28
$Tl^+(aq) + e^- \longrightarrow Tl(s)$	−0.34
$PbSO_4(s) + 2\,e^- \longrightarrow Pb(s) + SO_4^{2-}(aq)$	−0.356
$Se(s) + 2\,H^+(aq) + 2\,e^- \longrightarrow H_2Se(aq)$	−0.40
$Cd^{2+}(aq) + 2\,e^- \longrightarrow Cd(s)$	−0.403
$Cr^{3+}(aq) + e^- \longrightarrow Cr^{2+}(aq)$	−0.41
$Fe^{2+}(aq) + 2\,e^- \longrightarrow Fe(s)$	−0.44
$2\,CO_2(g) + 2\,H^+(aq) + 2\,e^- \longrightarrow H_2C_2O_4(aq)$	−0.49
$Ga^{3+}(aq) + 3\,e^- \longrightarrow Ga(s)$	−0.53
$HgS(s) + 2\,H^+(aq) + 2\,e^- \longrightarrow Hg(\ell) + H_2S(g)$	−0.72
$Cr^{3+}(aq) + 3\,e^- \longrightarrow Cr(s)$	−0.74
$Zn^{2+}(aq) + 2\,e^- \longrightarrow Zn(s)$	−0.763
$Cr^{2+}(aq) + 2\,e^- \longrightarrow Cr(s)$	−0.91

(continued)

Table 21 Standard Reduction Potentials in Aqueous Solution at 25 °C (continued)

Acidic Solution	Standard Reduction Potential $E°$ (volts)
$FeS(s) + 2\,e^- \longrightarrow Fe(s) + S^{2-}(aq)$	-1.01
$Mn^{2+}(aq) + 2\,e^- \longrightarrow Mn(s)$	-1.18
$V^{2+}(aq) + 2\,e^- \longrightarrow V(s)$	-1.18
$CdS(s) + 2\,e^- \longrightarrow Cd(s) + S^{2-}(aq)$	-1.21
$ZnS(s) + 2\,e^- \longrightarrow Zn(s) + S^{2-}(aq)$	-1.44
$Zr^{4+}(aq) + 4\,e^- \longrightarrow Zr(s)$	-1.53
$Al^{3+}(aq) + 3\,e^- \longrightarrow Al(s)$	-1.66
$Mg^{2+}(aq) + 2\,e^- \longrightarrow Mg(s)$	-2.37
$Na^+(aq) + e^- \longrightarrow Na(s)$	-2.714
$Ca^{2+}(aq) + 2\,e^- \longrightarrow Ca(s)$	-2.87
$Sr^{2+}(aq) + 2\,e^- \longrightarrow Sr(s)$	-2.89
$Ba^{2+}(aq) + 2\,e^- \longrightarrow Ba(s)$	-2.90
$Rb^+(aq) + e^- \longrightarrow Rb(s)$	-2.925
$K^+(aq) + e^- \longrightarrow K(s)$	-2.925
$Li^+(aq) + e^- \longrightarrow Li(s)$	-3.045

Basic Solution	Standard Reduction Potential $E°$ (volts)
$ClO^-(aq) + H_2O + 2\,e^- \longrightarrow Cl^-(aq) + 2\,OH^-(aq)$	0.89
$OOH^-(aq) + H_2O + 2\,e^- \longrightarrow 3\,OH^-(aq)$	0.88
$2\,NH_2OH(aq) + 2\,e^- \longrightarrow N_2H_4(aq) + 2\,OH^-(aq)$	0.74
$ClO_3^-(aq) + 3\,H_2O + 6\,e^- \longrightarrow Cl^-(aq) + 6\,OH^-(aq)$	0.62
$MnO_4^-(aq) + 2\,H_2O + 3\,e^- \longrightarrow MnO_2(s) + 4\,OH^-(aq)$	0.588
$MnO_4^-(aq) + e^- \longrightarrow MnO_4^{2-}(aq)$	0.564
$NiO_2(s) + 2\,H_2O + 2\,e^- \longrightarrow Ni(OH)_2(s) + 2\,OH^-(aq)$	0.49
$Ag_2CrO_4(s) + 2\,e^- \longrightarrow 2\,Ag(s) + CrO_4^{2-}(aq)$	0.446
$O_2(g) + 2\,H_2O + 4\,e^- \longrightarrow 4\,OH^-(aq)$	0.40
$ClO_4^-(aq) + H_2O + 2\,e^- \longrightarrow ClO_3^-(aq) + 2\,OH^-(aq)$	0.36
$Ag_2O(s) + H_2O + 2\,e^- \longrightarrow 2\,Ag(s) + 2\,OH^-(aq)$	0.34
$2\,NO_2^-(aq) + 3\,H_2O + 4\,e^- \longrightarrow N_2O(g) + 6\,OH^-(aq)$	0.15
$N_2H_4(aq) + 2\,H_2O + 2\,e^- \longrightarrow 2\,NH_3(aq) + 2\,OH^-(aq)$	0.10
$[Co(NH_3)_6]^{3+}(aq) + e^- \longrightarrow [Co(NH_3)_6]^{2+}(aq)$	0.10
$HgO(s) + H_2O + 2\,e^- \longrightarrow Hg(\ell) + 2\,OH^-(aq)$	0.0984
$O_2(g) + H_2O + 2\,e^- \longrightarrow OOH^-(aq) + OH^-(aq)$	0.076
$NO_3^-(aq) + H_2O + 2\,e^- \longrightarrow NO_2^-(aq) + 2\,OH^-(aq)$	0.01
$MnO_2(s) + 2\,H_2O + 2\,e^- \longrightarrow Mn(OH)_2(s) + 2\,OH^-(aq)$	-0.05
$CrO_4^{2-}(aq) + 4\,H_2O + 3\,e^- \longrightarrow Cr(OH)_3(s) + 5\,OH^-(aq)$	-0.12
$Cu(OH)_2(s) + 2\,e^- \longrightarrow Cu(s) + 2\,OH^-(aq)$	-0.36
$S(s) + 2\,e^- \longrightarrow S^{2-}(aq)$	-0.48
$Fe(OH)_3(s) + e^- \longrightarrow Fe(OH)_2(s) + OH^-(aq)$	-0.56
$2\,H_2O + 2\,e^- \longrightarrow H_2(g) + 2\,OH^-(aq)$	-0.8277

Table 21 Standard Reduction Potentials in Aqueous Solution at 25 °C (continued)

Basic Solution	Standard Reduction Potential $E°$ (volts)
$2\ NO_3^-(aq) + 2\ H_2O + 2\ e^- \longrightarrow N_2O_4(g) + 4\ OH^-(aq)$	−0.85
$Fe(OH)_2(s) + 2\ e^- \longrightarrow Fe(s) + 2\ OH^-(aq)$	−0.877
$SO_4^{2-}(aq) + H_2O + 2\ e^- \longrightarrow SO_3^{2-}(aq) + 2\ OH^-(aq)$	−0.93
$N_2(g) + 4\ H_2O + 4\ e^- \longrightarrow N_2H_4(aq) + 4\ OH^-(aq)$	−1.15
$[Zn(OH)_4]^{2-}(aq) + 2\ e^- \longrightarrow Zn(s) + 4\ OH^-(aq)$	−1.22
$Zn(OH)_2(s) + 2\ e^- \longrightarrow Zn(s) + 2\ OH^-(aq)$	−1.245
$[Zn(CN)_4]^{2-}(aq) + 2\ e^- \longrightarrow Zn(s) + 4\ CN^-(aq)$	−1.26
$Cr(OH)_3(s) + 3\ e^- \longrightarrow Cr(s) + 3\ OH^-(aq)$	−1.30
$SiO_3^{2-}(aq) + 3\ H_2O + 4\ e^- \longrightarrow Si(s) + 6\ OH^-(aq)$	−1.70

N Answers to Chapter Opening Questions and Case Study Questions

Chapter 1
Chapter Opening: Gold!

1. 5.2×10^5 g Au; $19 million

2. Gold = Au; copper = Cu; zinc = Zn

3. 1337 K

4. (a) No, gold is not the most dense element.

   (b) 0.217 cm^3 Au

Case Study: CO_2 in the Oceans

1. Carbon dioxide

2. Calcium: Ca; copper: Cu; manganese: Mn; iron: Fe

3. Most dense: copper, least dense: calcium

4. Elements: calcium, carbon, oxygen

   Compound name: calcium carbonate

Let's Review
Case Study: Out of Gas!

1. Fuel density in kg/L: (1.77 lb/L) (0.4536 kg/lb) = 0.803 kg/L

2. Mass of fuel already in tank: 7682 L (0.803 kg/L) = 6170 kg

   Mass of fuel needed: 22,300 kg − 6,170 kg = 16,100 kg (answer to three significant figures)

   Volume of fuel needed: 16,130 kg (1 L/0.803 kg) = 20,100 L

Chapter 2
Chapter Opening: The Periodic Table, the Central Icon of Chemistry

1. Eka-silicon is germanium. Its atomic weight is 72.61 (predicted 72), and its density is 5.32 g/cm^3 (predicted value 5.5 g/cm^3).

2. Other elements missing from Mendeleev's periodic table include Sc, Ga, the noble gases (He, Ne, Ar, Kr, Xe), and all of the radioactive elements except Th and U.

Case Study: Using Isotopes: Ötzi, the Iceman of the Alps

1. ^{18}O: 18 − 8 = 10 neutrons

   ^{204}Pb: 204 − 82 = 122 neutrons

   ^{206}Pb: 206 − 82 = 124 neutrons

2. ^{14}C: 14 − 6 = 8 neutrons

3. ^{87}Sr/^{86}Sr = 0.710

   The ratio found in the Iceman is slightly higher.

Case Study: Mummies, Bangladesh, and the Formula of Compound 606

1. Amount As: 19.024 g As × (1 mol As/74.9216 g As) = 0.25392 mol As

   Amount Cu: 48.407 g Cu × (1 mol Cu/63.546 g Cu) = 0.76176 mol Cu

   Amount S: 32.569 g S × (1 mol S/32.066 g S) = 1.0157 mol S

   Mole ratio Cu/As: 0.76176 mol Cu/0.25392 mol As = 3.0000 mol Cu/1 mol As

   Mole ratio S/As: 1.0157 mol S/0.25392 mol As = 4.0001 mol S/1 mol As

   Empirical formula: Cu_3AsS_4

2. Amount C: 39.37 g C × (1 mol C/12.011 g C) = 3.278 mol C

   Amount H: 3.304 g H × (1 mol H/1.0079 g H) = 3.278 mol H

   Amount O: 8.741 g O × (1 mol O/15.999 g O) = 0.5463 mol O

   Amount N: 7.652 g N × (1 mol N/14.007 g N) = 0.5463 mol N

   Amount As: 40.932 g As × (1 mol As/74.9216 g As) = 0.54633 mol As

   Mole ratio C/O and H/O: 3.278 mol C/0.5463 mol O = 6.000 mol C/1 mol O. A similar calculation yields 6.000 mol H/1 mol O.

Mole ratio N/O and As/O: 0.5463 mol N/ 0.5463 mol O = 1.000 mol N/1 mol O. A similar calculation yields 1.000 mol As/1 mol O.

Empirical formula: C_6H_6AsNO

Molar mass of C_6H_6AsNO: 183.0 g/mol

Compound 1: 549/183.0 = 3.00; therefore, the molecular formula is $C_{18}H_{18}As_3N_3O_3$.

Compound 2: 915/183.0 = 5.00; therefore, the molecular formula is $C_{30}H_{30}As_5N_5O_5$.

Chapter 3
Chapter Opening: Black Smokers and Volcanoes

$$Fe^{2+}(aq) + H_2S(aq) + 2\,H_2O(\ell) \rightarrow FeS(s) + 2\,H_3O^+(aq)$$

$$2\,Bi^{3+}(aq) + 3\,H_2S(aq) + 6\,H_2O(\ell) \rightarrow Bi_2S_3(s) + 6\,H_3O^+(aq)$$

$$Ca^{2+}(aq) + SO_4^{2-}(aq) \rightarrow CaSO_4(s)$$

Case Study: Killing Bacteria with Silver

1. 100×10^{15} Ag^+ ions (1 mol/6.022×10^{23} ions) = 2×10^{-7} mol Ag^+

2. 2×10^{-7} mol Ag^+ (107.9 g Ag^+/1 mol Ag^+) = 2×10^{-5} g Ag^+ ions

Chapter 4
Chapter Opening: The Chemistry of Pyrotechnics

1. 1.0 g Fe (1 mol Fe/55.85 g Fe)(2 mol Fe_2O_3/ 4 mol Fe)(159.7 g Fe_2O_3/1 mol Fe_2O_3) = 1.4 g Fe_2O_3

2. 10.0 g Fe_2O_3 (1 mol Fe_2O_3/159.7 g Fe_2O_3) (2 mol Al/1 mol Fe_2O_3)(26.98 g Al/1 mol Al) = 3.38 g Al

3. 20 g Al (1 mol Al/26.98 g Al) = 0.7 mol Al 10 g Fe_2O_3 (1 mol Fe_2O_3/159.7 g Fe_2O_3) = 0.06 mol Fe_2O_3

   Mole ratio from balanced equation: 2 mol Al/ 1 mol Fe_2O_3

   Mole ratio actually present: 0.7 mol Al/0.06 mol Fe_2O_3 = 1×10^1 mol Al/1 mol Fe_2O_3

   There is an excess of Al compared to what the balanced equation requires, so Fe_2O_3 is the limiting reactant.

Case Study: Green Chemistry and Atom Economy

Reactant molecules contain 5 C, 10 H, 3 O. Combined molar mass = 118.1 g/mol

Desired product (methyl methacrylate) contains 5 C, 8 H, 2 O. Molar mass = 100.1 g/mol

% Atom economy = (100.1/118.1) × 100 = 84.75%

Case Study: How Much Salt Is There in Seawater?

1. Step 1: Calculate the amount of Cl^- in the diluted solution from titration data.

   Mol Cl^- in 50 mL of dilute solution = mol Ag^+ = (0.100 mol/L)(0.02625 L) = 2.63×10^{-3} mol Cl^-

   Step 2: Calculate the concentration of Cl^- in the dilute solution.

   Concentration of Cl^- in dilute solution = 2.63×10^{-3} mol/0.0500 L = 5.25×10^{-2} M

   Step 3: Calculate the concentration of Cl^- in seawater.

   Seawater was initially diluted to one hundredth its original concentration. Thus, the concentration of Cl^- in seawater (undiluted) = 5.25 M

Case Study: Forensic Chemistry: Titrations and Food Tampering

1. Step 1: Calculate the amount of I_2 in solution from titration data.

   Amount I_2 = (0.0425 mol $S_2O_3^{2-}$/L)(0.0253 L) (1 mol I_2/2 mol $S_2O_3^{2-}$) = 5.38×10^{-4} mol I_2

   Step 2: Calculate the amount of NaClO present based on the amount of I_2 formed, and from that value calculate the mass of NaClO.

   Mass NaClO = 5.38×10^{-4} mol I_2 (1 mol HClO/ 1 mol I_2)(1 mol NaClO/1 mol HClO)(74.44 g NaClO/1 mol NaClO) = 0.0400 g NaClO

Chapter 5
Chapter Opening: Energy and Your Diet

1. Orange, all commercial varieties (197 kJ) < apple, raw with skin (218 kJ) < potato, flesh and skin, raw (321 kJ) < rice, brown, long grain, uncooked (1548 kJ) < popcorn, unpopped kernels (1568 kJ) < glazed doughnut, yeast-leavened, unenriched (1686 kJ) < peanut M&Ms (2156 kJ) < mixed nuts, dry roasted, with peanuts, with salt (2485 kJ)

2. In the following, we assume water vapor, $H_2O(g)$, is formed upon oxidation.

   Balanced Equation: $C_2H_5OH(\ell) + 3\,O_2(g) \rightarrow 2\,CO_2(g) + 3\,H_2O(g)$

   $\Delta_rH° = (2$ mol CO_2/1 mol-rxn)$[\Delta_fH°\ CO_2(g)]$ + (3 mol H_2O/1 mol-rxn)$[\Delta_fH°\ H_2O(g)]$ − {(1 mol C_2H_5OH/1 mol-rxn)$[\Delta_fH°\ C_2H_5OH(\ell)]$ + (3 mol O_2/1 mol-rxn)$[\Delta_fH°\ O_2(g)]$}

$\Delta_r H° = (2 \text{ mol } CO_2/1 \text{ mol-rxn})[-393.5 \text{ kJ}/\text{mol } CO_2] + (3 \text{ mol } H_2O/1 \text{ mol-rxn})[-241.8 \text{ kJ}/\text{mol } H_2O] - \{(1 \text{ mol } C_2H_5OH/1 \text{ mol-rxn})[-277.0 \text{ kJ/mol } C_2H_5OH] + (3 \text{ mol } O_2/1 \text{ mol-rxn})[0 \text{ kJ/mol } O_2]\} = -1235.4 \text{ kJ/mol-rxn}$

100. g C_2H_5OH $(1 \text{ mol } C_2H_5OH/46.07 \text{ g } C_2H_5OH)(1 \text{ mol-rxn}/1 \text{ mol } C_2H_5OH)(-1235.4 \text{ kJ/mol-rxn}) = -2680 \text{ kJ}$

The energy evolved as heat is 2680 kJ. This is more energy than all of the foods pictured except for the mixed nuts.

Case Study: The Fuel Controversy–Alcohol and Gasoline

In the following, we assume water vapor, $H_2O(g)$, is formed upon oxidation.

1. Burning ethanol: $C_2H_5OH(\ell) + 3 \text{ } O_2(g) \rightarrow 2 \text{ } CO_2(g) + 3 \text{ } H_2O(g)$

   $\Delta_r H° = (2 \text{ mol } CO_2/\text{mol-rxn})[\Delta_f H°(CO_2)] + (3 \text{ mol } H_2O/\text{mol-rxn})[\Delta_f H°(H_2O)] - (1 \text{ mol } C_2H_5OH/\text{mol-rxn})[\Delta_f H°(C_2H_5OH)]$

   $\Delta_r H° = (2 \text{ mol } CO_2/\text{mol-rxn})[-393.5 \text{ kJ/mol } CO_2] + (3 \text{ mol } H_2O/\text{mol-rxn})[-241.8 \text{ kJ/mol } H_2O] - (1 \text{ mol } C_2H_5OH/\text{mol-rxn})[-277.0 \text{ kJ/mol } C_2H_5OH] = -1235.4 \text{ kJ/mol-rxn}$

   1 mol ethanol per 1 mol-rxn; therefore, q per mol is -1235.4 kJ/mol

   q per gram: $-1235.4 \text{ kJ/mol} (1 \text{ mol } C_2H_5OH/46.07 \text{ g } C_2H_5OH) = -26.80 \text{ kJ/g } C_2H_5OH$

   Burning octane: $C_8H_{18}(\ell) + 12.5 \text{ } O_2(g) \rightarrow 8 \text{ } CO_2(g) + 9 \text{ } H_2O(g)$

   $\Delta_r H° = (8 \text{ mol } CO_2/\text{mol-rxn})[\Delta_f H°(CO_2)] + (9 \text{ mol } H_2O/\text{mol-rxn})[\Delta_f H°(H_2O)] - (1 \text{ mol } C_8H_{18}/\text{mol-rxn})[\Delta_f H°(C_8H_{18})]$

   $\Delta_r H° = (8 \text{ mol } CO_2/\text{mol-rxn})[-393.5 \text{ kJ/mol } CO_2] + (9 \text{ mol } H_2O/\text{mol-rxn})[-241.8 \text{ kJ/mol } H_2O] - (1 \text{ mol } C_8H_{18}/\text{mol-rxn})[-250.1 \text{ kJ/mol } C_8H_{18}] = -5074.1 \text{ kJ/mol-rxn}$

   1 mol octane per mol-rxn; therefore, q per mol is -5074.1 kJ/mol

   q per gram: $-5074.1 \text{ kJ}/1 \text{ mol } C_8H_{18} (1 \text{ mol } C_8H_{18}/114.2 \text{ g } C_8H_{18}) = -44.43 \text{ kJ/g } C_8H_{18}$

2. For ethanol, per liter: $q = -26.80 \text{ kJ/g}$ $(785 \text{ g/L}) = -2.10 \times 10^4 \text{ kJ/L}$

   For octane, per liter: $q = -44.43 \text{ kJ/g}$ $(699 \text{ g/L}) = -3.11 \times 10^4 \text{ kJ/L}$

   Octane produces almost 50% more energy per liter of fuel.

3. Mass of CO_2 per liter of ethanol = 1.000 L $(785 \text{ g } C_2H_5OH/L)(1 \text{ mol } C_2H_5OH/46.07 \text{ g } C_2H_5OH)(2 \text{ mol } CO_2/1 \text{ mol } C_2H_5OH)(44.01 \text{ g } CO_2/1 \text{ mol } CO_2) = 1.50 \times 10^3 \text{ g } CO_2$

   Mass of CO_2 per liter of octane = 1.000 L $(699 \text{ g } C_8H_{18}/L)(1 \text{ mol } C_8H_{18}/114.2 \text{ g } C_8H_{18})(8 \text{ mol } CO_2/1 \text{ mol } C_8H_{18})(44.01 \text{ g } CO_2/1 \text{ mol } CO_2) = 2.16 \times 10^3 \text{ g } CO_2$

4. Volume of ethanol needed to obtain 3.11×10^4 kJ of energy from oxidation: 2.10×10^4 kJ/L $C_2H_5OH)(x) = 3.11 \times 10^4$ kJ (where x is volume of ethanol)

   Volume of ethanol = $x = 1.48$ L

   Mass of CO_2 produced by burning 1.48 L of ethanol = $(1.50 \times 10^3 \text{ g } CO_2/L \text{ } C_2H_5OH)(1.48 \text{ L } C_2H_5OH) = 2.22 \times 10^3 \text{ g } CO_2$

   To obtain the same amount of energy, slightly more CO_2 is produced by burning ethanol than by burning octane.

5. Your car will travel about 50% farther on a liter of octane, and it will produce slightly less CO_2 emissions, than if you burned 1.0 L of ethanol.

Chapter 6
Chapter Opening: Fireworks

1. Yellow light has a longer wavelength than blue light.

2. Blue light has a greater energy per photon than yellow light.

3. The energy of light emitted by atoms is determined by the energy levels of the electrons in an atom. See discussion in the text, Section 6.3.

Case Study: What Makes the Colors in Fireworks?

1. Yellow light is from the 589 and 590 nm emissions.

2. Primary emission for Sr is red. This has a longer wavelength than yellow light.

3. $4 \text{ Mg}(s) + KClO_4(s) \rightarrow KCl(s) + 4 \text{ MgO}(s)$

Chapter 7
Chapter Opening: Rubies and Sapphires— Pretty Stones

1. Cr: $[Ar]3d^5 4s^1$; Cr^{3+}: $[Ar]3d^3$

2. Cr^{2+} is paramagnetic with four unpaired electrons. Cr^{3+} is paramagnetic with three unpaired electrons.

3. The radius of Al^{3+} is 57 pm. The radius of Cr^{3+} is thus only 7 pm larger than that of Al^{3+}.

4. Fe^{2+}: $[Ar]3d^6$; Ti^{4+}: $[Ar]$

Case Study: Metals in Biochemistry and Medicine

1. Fe: $[Ar]3d^64s^2$; Fe^{2+}: $[Ar]3d^6$; Fe^{3+}: $[Ar]3d^5$

2. Both iron ions are paramagnetic.

3. Cu: $[Ar]3d^{10}4s^1$; Cu^+: $[Ar]3d^{10}$; Cu^{2+}: $[Ar]3d^9$; Cu^{2+} is paramagnetic; Cu^+ is diamagnetic.

4. The slightly larger size of Cu compared to Fe is related to greater electron–electron repulsions.

5. Fe^{2+} is larger than Fe^{3+} and will fit less well into the structure. As a result, some distortion of the ring structure from planarity occurs.

Chapter 8

Chapter Opening: Chemical Bonding in DNA

1. Carbon and phosphorus (in phosphate) achieve the noble gas configuration by forming four bonds.

2. In each instance, there are four bonds to the element; VSEPR predicts that these atoms will have tetrahedral geometry with 109.5° angles.

3. Bond angles in these rings are 120°. To achieve this preferred bond angle, the rings must be planar.

4. Thymine and cytosine are polar molecules.

Case Study: Hydroxyl Radicals, Atmospheric Chemistry, and Hair Dyes

1. 18 valence electrons

$$H-\ddot{O}-\ddot{N}=\ddot{O}$$

All atoms have a formal charge of zero. There are no equivalent resonance structures.

2. 30 valence electrons

All atoms have zero formal charge except for those indicated.

Case Study: Ibuprofen, A Study in Green Chemistry

1. The Lewis structures for the key portions of the molecules where the reaction takes place are the following:

Bond broken: 1 C—O and 1 C≡O

(1 mol C—O/1 mol-rxn)(358 kJ/mol C—O) + (1 mol C≡O/1 mol-rxn)(1046 kJ/mol C≡O) = 1404 kJ/mol-rxn

Bonds formed: 1 C—C, 1 C=C, and 1 C—O

(1 mol C—C/1 mol-rxn)(346 kJ/mol C—C) + (1 mol C=O/1 mol-rxn)(745 kJ/mol C=O) + (1 mol C—O/1 mol-rxn)(358 kJ/mol C—O) = 1449 kJ/mol-rxn

$\Delta_r H° \approx$ 1404 kJ/mol-rxn − 1449 kJ/mol-rxn = −45 kJ/mol-rxn

The reaction is thus predicted to be exothermic.

2. All of the atoms in ibuprofen have a formal charge of zero.

3. The most polar bond in the molecule is the O—H bond.

4. The molecule is not symmetrical and so is polar.

5. The shortest bond in the molecule is the O—H bond.

6. The C=O bond has the highest bond order. The C=C bonds in the ring have an order of 1.5.

7. Yes, there are 120° bond angles present: the bond angles around the C atoms in the ring and those around the C atom in the −CO₂H group are all 120°. There are no 180° angles in this molecule.

8. There is one acid group in ibuprofen (−CO₂H), therefore 1 mol of ibuprofen will react with 1 mol of NaOH.

200. mg ibuprofen (1 g/1000 mg)(1 mol ibuprofen/206.3 g ibuprofen)(1 mol NaOH/ 1 mol ibuprofen)(1 L/0.0259 mol NaOH) (1000 mL/1 L) = 37.4 mL

Therefore 37.4 mL of the NaOH solution would be required.

Chapter 9

Chapter Opening: The Noble Gases: Not So Inert

1. XeF_2 is linear. The electron-pair geometry is trigonal-bipyramidal. Three lone pairs are located in the equatorial plane, and the two F atoms are located in the axial positions. This symmetrical structure will not have a dipole.

2. The Xe atom is sp^3d hybridized. Xe—F bonds: overlap of Xe sp^3d orbitals with F 2p orbital. 3 lone pairs in Xe sp^3d orbitals.

3. This 36-electron molecule has a bent molecular structure.

Case Study: Green Chemistry, Safe Dyes, and Molecular Orbitals

1. C_8H_4BrNO

2. The energy per photon is inversely proportional to wavelength. The light absorbed by butter yellow has a smaller wavelength than that absorbed by nitrated butter yellow; therefore butter yellow absorbs higher energy light than does nitrated butter yellow.

3. Tyrian purple: 9

   Nitrated butter yellow: 8

Chapter 10

Chapter Opening: The Food of the Gods

1. The only structural difference between theobromine and caffeine occurs on the N in the six-member ring that is between the two $C=O$ groups. In theobromine, there is an H atom attached to this N. In caffeine, there is a CH_3 group attached.

2. 5.00 g sample (2.16 g theobromine/100 g sample) = 0.108 g theobromine

Case Study: An Awakening with L-DOPA

1. L-DOPA is chiral. Its chiral center is indicated in the following structural formula.

2. Dopamine is not chiral. Epinephrine is chiral. Its chiral center is indicated in the following structural formula.

3. 5.0 g L-DOPA (1 mol L-DOPA/197.2 g L-DOPA) = 0.025 mol L-DOPA

Case Study: Green Adhesives

1. Structural formulas:

phenol   urea   formaldehyde

2. The electron-pair and molecular geometries are both trigonal-planar. The C—H σ bonds are each formed by the overlap of an sp^2 hybrid orbital on the C atom with the $1s$ orbital of the H atom. The σ bond between the C and O is formed by the overlap of an sp^2 hybrid orbital on the C with an sp^2 hybrid orbital on the O. The π bond between the C and O is formed by the overlap of a $2p$ orbital on C with a $2p$ orbital on O.

3. Similarity: Both nylon-6,6 and proteins are polyamides.

   Differences:

   1. In proteins there is one direction for the amide linkage: CONH. In nylon-6,6 two orientations are present: CONH and NHCO.

   2. In proteins there is only one C between the amide linkages. In nylon-6,6 there are four or six carbons between amide linkages.

   3. Proteins have numerous R groups that can be attached to the carbon in between the amide groups, whereas nylon-6,6 has only hydrogen atoms attached to the carbons in between the amide groups.

   4. Proteins are chiral, whereas nylon-6,6 is not.

Chapter 11

Chapter Opening: The Atmosphere and Altitude Sickness

1. $P(O_2)$ at 3000 m is 70% of 0.21 atm, the value of $P(O_2)$ at sea level. Thus, $P(O_2)$ at 3000 m = 0.21 atm $\times$ 0.70 = 0.15 atm (110 mm Hg). At the top of Everest, $P(O_2)$ = 0.21 atm $\times$ 0.29 = 0.061 atm (46 mm Hg).

2. Blood saturation levels (estimated from table): at 3000 m, >95%; at top of Everest, 75%.

Case Study: What to Do with All of that CO_2? More on Green Chemistry

1. 9.1×10^9 g C (1 mol C/12.0 g C) (1 mol CO_2/1 mol C) (44.0 g CO_2/1 mol CO_2) = 3.3×10^{10} g CO_2

2. 1.0×10^6 g CO_2 (1 mol CO_2/44.0 g CO_2)
(1 mol $(NH_4)_2CO_3$/1 mol CO_2)
(96.1 g $(NH_4)_2CO_3$/1 mol $(NH_4)_2CO_3$) =
2.2×10^6 g $(NH_4)_2CO_3$

Chapter 12
Case Study: Methane Hydrates

1. One CH_4 molecule is contained in a clathrate cage that has 12 faces, 20 apexes, and 30 edges; each edge is an O—H—O unit, so there are 30 hydrogen bonds.

2. 164 m³ = 1.64×10^5 L of CH_4. Use the ideal gas law to calculate n ($n = 7.32 \times 10^3$ mol CH_4). Using $\Delta_f H°$ values, calculate the enthalpy change for the combustion of 1.00 mole of CH_4 to form $CO_2(g)$ and $H_2O(g)$ ($\Delta_r H° = -802$ kJ/mol). $\Delta_r H°$ for 164 m³ of CH_4 = (-802 kJ/mol) (7.32×10^3 mol) = -5.87×10^6 kJ.

Case Study: A Pet Food Catastrophe

1. % N in melamine = 84/126 × 100 = 67%

% N in cyanuric acid = 42/129 × 100 = 33%

Both of these compounds have a greater percentage of nitrogen than the average protein.

2. 454 g sample (0.14 g melamine/1,000,000 g sample) = 6.4×10^{-5} g melamine = 0.064 mg melamine = 64 μg melamine

Chapter 13
Chapter Opening: Lithium and "Green Cars"

1. 73,000,000 metric tons Li_2CO_3 (13.88 metric tons Li/73.89 metric tons Li_2CO_3) = 1.4×10^7 metric tons Li (= 14 million metric tons Li)

2. The unit cell for lithium metal is body-centered cubic. (There are atoms at each of the corners of a cube and one atom embedded in the middle of the cube.)

3. 351 pm (1 m/10^{12} pm) (100 cm/1 m) = 3.51×10^{-8} cm

V of unit cell = (3.51×10^{-8} cm)³ = 4.32×10^{-23} cm³

Mass of unit cell = 6.941 g Li/mol (1 mol/6.022×10^{23} atoms) (2 atoms/unit cell) = 2.305×10^{-23} g/unit cell

Density = mass/volume = 2.305×10^{-23} g/4.32×10^{-23} cm³ = 0.533 g/cm³

4. One method is to carry out the following gas-forming reaction:

$Li_2CO_3(aq)$ + 2 $HCl(aq)$ → 2 $LiCl(aq)$ + $H_2O(\ell)$ + $CO_2(g)$

Case Study: High-Strength Steel and Unit Cells

1. Ferrite has a body-centered cubic unit cell.

2. Austenite has a face-centered cubic unit unit cell of iron atoms with a carbon atom embedded in the body of the cell.

3. The face-centered unit cell of austenite transforms into a body-centered unit cell, but this unit cell is not cubic because it is longer in one dimension than the other two (this is called a *body-centered tetragonal unit cell*). The carbon atoms remain embedded in the lattice.

Case Study: Graphene—The Hottest New Network Solid

1. We want to know the distance x in the diagram of the hexagon. You know the interior angles in a hexagon are all 120°. To find x, we can find the distance y in the figure and then double it ($x = 2y$). The angle bounded by the side of the hexagon and y is 30°, and, from geometry, cos 30° = y/(hexagon side) so y = (cos 30°) (139 pm) = (0.866)(139 pm) = 120. pm. Finally, x = 241 pm.

2. 1.0 μm (1 m/10^6 μm)(10^{12} pm/1 m)(1 C_6-ring/241 pm) = 4.1×10^3 C_6-rings

3. The thickness would be approximately 150 pm. This corresponds to the diameter of a carbon atom, found by multiplying the radius of a carbon atom (given in Figure 7.6) by 2 and rounding off to two significant figures.

Chapter 14
Chapter Opening: Survival at Sea

$\Pi = cRT$ = (1.15 mol/L)(0.082057 L atm/mol · K)(298 K) = 28.1 atm

Case Study: Exploding Lakes and Diet Coke

1. $PV = nRT$

4.0 atm(0.025 L) = n(0.08206 L · atm/mol · K) 298 K; $n = 4.1 \times 10^{-3}$ mol

2. $P_1 V_1 = P_2 V_2$

4.0 atm(0.025 L) = 3.7×10^{-4} atm (V_2); V_2 = 270 L

The gas expanded by a factor of 11,000 (= 270 L/0.025 L).

3. Solubility of $CO_2 = k_H P_g = 0.034$ mol/kg · bar $(3.7 \times 10^{-4}$ bar) $= 1.3 \times 10^{-5}$ mol/kg

4. Before opening: Solubility of CO_2 before opening $= k_H P_g = 0.034$ mol/kg · bar (4.0 bar) $= 0.14$ mol/kg

Assume the density of the solution is 1.0 g/cm³, therefore 1.0 L corresponds to 1.0 kg. The amount of CO_2 dissolved is 0.14 mol.

After opening: Solubility of $CO_2 = 1.3 \times 10^{-5}$ mol/kg as calculated in part 3 above. The amount of CO_2 in 1.0 kg is 1.3×10^{-5} mol.

Mass of CO_2 released $= (0.14$ mol $CO_2 - 1.3 \times 10^{-5}$ mol $CO_2)(44.01$ g $CO_2/1$ mol $CO_2)$ $= 6.0$ g CO_2

Chapter 15

Chapter Opening: Where Did the Indicator Go?

See the answer to Study Question 75 for this chapter in Appendix R.

Case Study: Enzymes—Nature's Catalysts

1. To decompose an equivalent amount of H_2O_2 catalytically would take 1.0×10^{-7} years; this is equivalent to 3.2 seconds.

2.

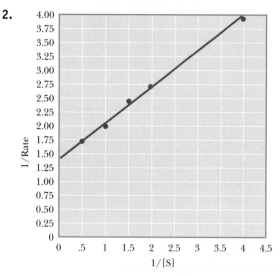

[S]	1/[S]	Rate	1/Rate
2.50	0.400	0.588	1.70
1.00	1.00	0.500	2.00
0.714	1.40	0.417	2.40
0.526	1.90	0.370	2.70
0.250	4.00	0.256	3.91

From the graph, we obtain a value of 1/Rate = 1.47 when 1/[S] = 0. From this, $R_{max} = 0.68$ mmol/min.

Chapter 16

Chapter Opening: Dynamic and Reversible

1. Endothermic. Raising the temperature (adding energy as heat) leads to conversion of reactants to products.

2. Apply LeChatelier's Principle: Increasing the concentration of Cl^- by adding HCl results in a shift to the right to produce more $[CoCl_4]^{2-}$. Decreasing the concentration of Cl^- by addition of water results in a shift to the left and the formation of more $[Co(H_2O)_6]^{2+}$.

3. The various stresses applied have caused the system to adjust in either direction. (Better evidence: Show that when heating and cooling the system is *repeated several times* the system cycles back and forth between the two colors.)

Case Study: Applying Equilibrium Concepts— The Haber–Bosch Ammonia Process

1. (a) Oxidize part of the NH_3 to HNO_3, then react NH_3 and HNO_3 (an acid–base reaction) to form NH_4NO_3.

$$4\ NH_3 + 5\ O_2 \rightarrow 4\ NO_2 + 6\ H_2O$$

$$2\ NO_2 + H_2O \rightarrow HNO_3 + HNO_2$$

$$HNO_3 + NH_3 \rightarrow NH_4NO_3$$

(b) $\Delta_r H° = (1$ mol $(NH_2)_2CO/$mol-rxn) $[\Delta_f H°\{(NH_2)_2CO\}] + (1$ mol $H_2O/$mol-rxn) $[\Delta_f H°(H_2O)] - (2$ mol $NH_3/$mol-rxn) $[\Delta_f H°(NH_3)] - (1$ mol $CO_2/$mol-rxn) $[\Delta_f H°(CO_2)]$

$\Delta_r H° = (1$ mol $(NH_2)_2CO/$mol-rxn) $(-333.1$ kJ/mol) $+ (1$ mol $H_2O/$mol-rxn) $(-241.8$ kJ/mol) $- (2$ mol $NH_3/$mol-rxn) $(-45.90$ kJ/mol) $- (1$ mol $CO_2/$mol-rxn) $(-393.5$ kJ/mol)

$$\Delta_r H° = -89.6 \text{ kJ/mol-rxn.}$$

The reaction as written is exothermic, so the equilibrium will be more favorable for product formation at a low temperature. The reaction converts three moles of gaseous reactants to one mole of gaseous products; thus, high pressure will be more favorable to product formation.

2. (a) For $CH_4(g) + H_2O(g) \rightarrow CO(g) + 3\ H_2(g)$

$\Delta_r H° = (1$ mol $CO/$mol-rxn) $[\Delta_f H°(CO)] - (1$ mol $CH_4/$mol-rxn) $[\Delta_f H°(CH_4)] - (1$ mol $H_2O/$mol-rxn) $[\Delta_f H°(H_2O)]$

$\Delta_r H° = (1$ mol $CO/$mol-rxn) $(-110.5$ kJ/mol) $- (1$ mol $CH_4/$mol-rxn) $(-74.87$ kJ/mol) $- (1$ mol $H_2O/$mol-rxn) $(-241.8$ kJ/mol) $= 206.2$ kJ/mol-rxn (endothermic)

For $CO(g) + H_2O(g) \rightarrow CO_2(g) + H_2(g)$

$\Delta_r H° = (1\ mol\ CO_2/mol\text{-}rxn)[\Delta_f H°(CO_2)] - (1\ mol\ CO/mol\text{-}rxn)[\Delta_f H°(CO)] - (1\ mol\ H_2O/mol\text{-}rxn)[\Delta_f H°(H_2O)]$

$\Delta_r H° = (1\ mol\ CO_2/mol\text{-}rxn)(-393.5\ kJ/mol) - (1\ mol\ CO/mol\text{-}rxn)(-110.5\ kJ/mol) - (1\ mol\ H_2O/mol\text{-}rxn)(-241.8\ kJ/mol) = -41.2\ kJ/mol\text{-}rxn$ (exothermic)

(b) (15 billion kg = 1.5×10^{13} g)

Add the two equations:
$CH_4(g) + 2\ H_2O(g) \rightarrow CO_2(g) + 4\ H_2(g)$

CH_4 required = $(1.5 \times 10^{13}\ g\ NH_3)(1\ mol\ NH_3/17.03\ g\ NH_3)(3\ mol\ H_2/2\ mol\ NH_3)(1\ mol\ CH_4/4\ mol\ H_2)(16.04\ g\ CH_4/1\ mol\ CH_4) = 5.3 \times 10^{12}\ g\ CH_4$

CO_2 formed = $(1.5 \times 10^{13}\ g\ NH_3)(1\ mol\ NH_3/17.03\ g\ NH_3)(3\ mol\ H_2/2\ mol\ NH_3)(1\ mol\ CO_2/4\ mol\ H_2)(44.01\ g\ CO_2/1\ mol\ CO_2) = 1.5 \times 10^{13}\ g\ CO_2$

Chapter 17

Chapter Opening: Aspirin is More Than 100 Years Old!

1. Aspirin, with a smaller pK_a, is a stronger acid than acetic acid.

2. The acidic hydrogen is the H on the $-CO_2H$ (carboxylic acid) functional group.

3. $C_6H_4(CO_2CH_3)CO_2H + H_2O \rightarrow C_6H_4(CO_2CH_3)CO_2^- + H_3O^+$

Case Study: Would You Like Some Belladonna Juice in Your Drink?

1. $(100.\ mg\ C_{17}H_{23}NO_3)(1\ g/1000\ mg)(1\ mol\ C_{17}H_{23}NO_3/289.4\ g\ C_{17}H_{23}NO_3) = 3.46 \times 10^{-4}$ mol $C_{17}H_{23}NO_3$

2. The proton will attach to the N.

3. The pK_a of protonated atropine (4.35) is less than that of the ammonium ($pK_a = 9.26$), methylammonium ($pK_a = 10.70$), and anilinium ($pK_a = 4.60$) ions.

4. The site of chirality is a carbon atom with four different groups attached; this is the carbon atom that has the $-CH_2OH$ group attached.

Chapter 18

Chapter Opening: Nature's Acids

1. (a) $H_2C_2O_4(aq) + 2\ NaOH(aq) \rightarrow Na_2C_2O_4(aq) + 2\ H_2O(\ell)$

28 g rhubarb $(1.2\ g\ H_2C_2O_4/100\ g\ rhubarb)(1\ mol\ H_2C_2O_4/90.04\ g\ H_2C_2O_4)(2\ mol\ NaOH/1\ mol\ H_2C_2O_4)(1\ L/0.25\ mol\ NaOH)(1000\ mL/1\ L) = 30.\ mL$

(b) $Ca^{2+}(aq) + H_2C_2O_4(aq) + 2\ H_2O(\ell) \rightarrow CaC_2O_4(s) + 2\ H_3O^+(aq)$

28 g rhubarb $(1.2\ g\ H_2C_2O_4/100\ g\ rhubarb)(1\ mol\ H_2C_2O_4/90.04\ g\ H_2C_2O_4)(1\ mol\ CaC_2O_4/1\ mol\ H_2C_2O_4)(128.1\ CaC_2O_4/1\ mol\ CaC_2O_4) = 0.48\ g\ CaC_2O_4$

2. $CaC_2O_4(s) \rightleftharpoons Ca^{2+}(aq) + C_2O_4^{2-}(aq)$

$K_{sp} = 4 \times 10^{-9} = [Ca^{2+}][C_2O_4^{2-}]$

Let x = solubility of CaC_2O_4

$4 \times 10^{-9} = x^2$

$x = 6 \times 10^{-5}$ mol/L

Solubility in g/L = 6×10^{-5} mol/L (128.1 g $CaC_2O_4/1\ mol\ CaC_2O_4) = 0.008$ g/L

Case Study: Take a Deep Breath!

1. $pH = pK_a + \log[HPO_4^{2-}]/[H_2PO_4^-]$

$7.4 = 7.20 + \log[HPO_4^{2-}]/[H_2PO_4^-]$

$[HPO_4^{2-}]/[H_2PO_4^-] = 1.6$

2. Assign $x = [HPO_4^{2-}]$, then $[H_2PO_4^-] = (0.020 - x)$

$1.6 = x/(0.020 - x);\ x = 0.012$

$[HPO_4^{2-}] = x = 0.012$ mol/L

$[H_2PO_4^-] = 0.020 - x = 0.008$ mol/L

Case Study: Chemical Equilibria in the Oceans

For both of these compounds, the chemical equilibrium is:

$CaCO_3(s) \rightleftharpoons Ca^{2+}(aq) + CO_3^{2-}(aq)$

$K_{sp} = [Ca^{2+}][CO_3^{2-}]$ and the solubility (in mol/L) is equal to $(K_{sp})^{1/2}$.

Aragonite:

Solubility (in g/L) = $[(6.0 \times 10^{-9})^{1/2}$ mol $CaCO_3/L](100.1\ g\ CaCO_3/1\ mol\ CaCO_3) = 7.8 \times 10^{-3}$ g $CaCO_3/L$

Calcite:

Solubility (in g/L) = $[(3.4 \times 10^{-9})^{1/2}$ mol $CaCO_3/L](100.1\ g\ CaCO_3/1\ mol\ CaCO_3) = 5.8 \times 10^{-3}$ g $CaCO_3/L$

Aragonite is 7.8×10^{-3} g/L/5.8×10^{-3} g/L = 1.3 times more soluble than calcite.

Chapter 19
Chapter Opening: Hydrogen for the Future?

1. $\Delta_r H° = (2 \text{ mol } H_2/\text{mol-rxn}) \Delta_f H° [H_2(g)] +$
$(1 \text{ mol } O_2/\text{mol-rxn}) \Delta_f H° [O_2(g)] -$
$(2 \text{ mol } H_2O/\text{mol-rxn}) \Delta_f H° [H_2O(\ell)]$
$= (2 \text{ mol } H_2/\text{mol-rxn}) [0 \text{ kJ/mol } H_2] +$
$(1 \text{ mol } O_2/\text{mol-rxn}) [0 \text{ kJ/mol } O_2] -$
$(2 \text{ mol } H_2O/\text{mol-rxn}) [-285.83 \text{ kJ/mol } H_2O]$
$= +571.66 \text{ kJ/mol-rxn}$

$\Delta_r S° = (2 \text{ mol } H_2/\text{mol-rxn}) S° [H_2(g)] +$
$(1 \text{ mol } O_2/\text{mol-rxn}) S° [O_2(g)] -$
$(2 \text{ mol } H_2O/\text{mol-rxn}) S° [H_2O(\ell)]$
$= (2 \text{ mol } H_2/\text{mol-rxn}) [130.7 \text{ J/K} \cdot \text{mol } H_2] +$
$(1 \text{ mol } O_2/\text{mol-rxn}) [205.07 \text{ J/K} \cdot \text{mol } O_2] -$
$(2 \text{ mol } H_2O/\text{mol-rxn}) [69.95 \text{ J/K} \cdot \text{mol } H_2O]$
$= +326.6 \text{ J/K} \cdot \text{mol-rxn} =$
$+0.3266 \text{ kJ/K} \cdot \text{mol-rxn}$

$\Delta_r G° = \Delta_r H° - T \Delta_r S°$
$= 571.66 \text{ kJ/mol-rxn} - 298.15 \text{ K} (0.3266 \text{ kJ/K} \cdot$
$\text{mol-rxn}) = +474.29 \text{ kJ/mol-rxn}$

2. $\Delta_r H° = (3 \text{ mol } H_2/\text{mol-rxn}) \Delta_f H° [H_2(g)] +$
$(1 \text{ mol } CO/\text{mol-rxn}) \Delta_f H° [CO(g)] -$
$\{(1 \text{ mol } CH_4/\text{mol-rxn}) \Delta_f H° [CH_4(g)] +$
$(1 \text{ mol } H_2O/\text{mol-rxn}) \Delta_f H° [H_2O(g)]\}$
$= (3 \text{ mol } H_2/\text{mol-rxn}) [0 \text{ kJ/mol } H_2] +$
$(1 \text{ mol } CO/\text{mol-rxn}) [-110.525 \text{ kJ/mol } CO] -$
$\{(1 \text{ mol } CH_4/\text{mol-rxn}) [-74.87 \text{ kJ/mol } CH_4] +$
$(1 \text{ mol } H_2O/\text{mol-rxn}) [-241.83 \text{ kJ/mol } H_2O]\}$
$= +206.18 \text{ kJ/mol-rxn}$

$\Delta_r S° = (3 \text{ mol } H_2/\text{mol-rxn}) S° [H_2(g)] +$
$(1 \text{ mol } CO/\text{mol-rxn}) S° [CO(g)] -$
$\{(1 \text{ mol } CH_4/\text{mol-rxn}) S° [CH_4(g)] +$
$(1 \text{ mol } H_2O/\text{mol-rxn}) S° [H_2O(g)]\}$
$= (3 \text{ mol } H_2/\text{mol-rxn}) [130.7 \text{ J/K} \cdot \text{mol } H_2] +$
$(1 \text{ mol } CO/\text{mol-rxn}) [197.674 \text{ J/K} \cdot \text{mol } CO] -$
$\{(1 \text{ mol } CH_4/\text{mol-rxn}) [186.26 \text{ J/K} \cdot \text{mol } CH_4] +$
$(1 \text{ mol } H_2O/\text{mol-rxn}) [188.84 \text{ J/K} \cdot \text{mol } H_2O]\}$
$= +214.7 \text{ J/K} \cdot \text{mol-rxn} =$
$+0.2147 \text{ kJ/K} \cdot \text{mol-rxn}$

$\Delta_r G° = \Delta_r H° - T \Delta_r S° = 206.18 \text{ kJ/mol-rxn} -$
$298.15 \text{ K} (0.2147 \text{ kJ/K} \cdot \text{mol-rxn})$
$= +142.17 \text{ kJ/mol-rxn}$

Case Study: Thermodynamics and Living Things

1. Creatine phosphate $+ H_2O \rightarrow$ creatine $+ HP_i$
$\Delta G° = -43.3 \text{ kJ/mol}$

Adenosine $+ HP_i \rightarrow$ adenosine monophosphate $+ H_2O$ $\Delta G° = +9.2 \text{ kJ/mol}$

Net reaction (sum of the two reactions):

Creatine phosphate $+$ adenosine $\rightarrow$
creatine $+$ adenosine monophosphate

For this, $\Delta G° = -43.3 \text{ kJ/mol} + 9.2 \text{ kJ/mol} = -34.1 \text{ kJ/mol}$. The negative value indicates that the transfer of phosphate from creatine phosphate to adenosine is product-favored.

2. $\Delta G°' = \Delta G° + RT \ln [C][H_3O^+]/[A][B] =$
$\Delta G° + (8.31 \times 10^{-3} \text{ kJ/mol} \cdot \text{K}) (298 \text{ K})$
$\ln [1][1 \times 10^{-7}]/[1][1]$

$\Delta G°' = \Delta G° - 39.9 \text{ kJ/mol}$

Chapter 20
Chapter Opening: Battery Power

1. (a) The oxidation number of cobalt in CoO_2 is $+4$ and in $LiCoO_2$ is $+3$.

   (b) Cobalt(IV) is reduced in this reaction, so CoO_2 is the cathode, and Li is the anode.

   (c) Lithium in the battery is elemental Li in a carbon matrix. Elemental Li reacts readily with water (◄ page 324).

2. (a) (1 hour) (3600 s/1 hour) (7.5 C/s) (1 mol e^-/ 96,485 C) $= 0.28 \text{ mol } e^-$

   (b) (0.28 mol e^-) (1 mol Li/1 mol e^-) (6.941 g Li/1 mol Li) $= 1.9 \text{ g Li}$

Case Study: Manganese in the Oceans

1. Cathode reaction: $Mn^{3+} + e^- \rightarrow Mn^{2+}$

   Anode reaction: $Mn^{3+} + 2 H_2O \rightarrow MnO_2 + 4 H^+ + e^-$

   Net reaction: $2 Mn^{3+} + 2 H_2O \rightarrow MnO_2 + Mn^{2+} + 4 H^+$

   $E°_{cell} = E°(\text{cathode}) - E°(\text{anode}) = 1.50 \text{ V} - 0.95 \text{ V} = 0.55 \text{ V}$

   The positive value associated with dispropor-tionation (the net reaction) is positive, indicat-ing a product-favored reaction.

2. (a) $MnO_2 + HS^- + 3 H^+ \rightarrow Mn^{2+} + S + 2 H_2O$

   (b) $2 Mn^{2+} + O_2 + 2 H_2O \rightarrow 2 MnO_2 + 4 H^+$

3. Cathode reaction: $O_2 + 4 H^+ + 4 e^- \rightarrow 2 H_2O$ $(E° = 1.229 \text{ V})$

   Anode reaction: $Mn^{2+} + 2 H_2O \rightarrow MnO_2 + 4 H^+ + 2 e^-$ $(E° = 1.23 \text{ V}, \text{ from Appendix M})$

   $E°_{cell} = E°(\text{cathode}) - E°(\text{anode}) = 1.229 \text{ V} - 1.23 \text{ V} = 0 \text{ V}.$

Chapter 21

Chapter Opening: Carbon and Silicon

1. $CH_4(g) + 2\,H_2O(\ell) \rightarrow CO_2(g) + 4\,H_2(g)$

   $SiH_4(g) + 2\,H_2O(\ell) \rightarrow SiO_2(s) + 4\,H_2(g)$

2. For CH_4:

   $\Delta_r G° = (1\text{ mol } CO_2/\text{mol-rxn})\Delta_f G°[CO_2(g)] + (4\text{ mol } H_2/\text{mol-rxn})\Delta_f G°[H_2(g)] - \{(1\text{ mol } CH_4/\text{mol-rxn})\Delta_f G°[CH_4(g)] + (2\text{ mol } H_2O/\text{mol-rxn})\Delta_f G°[H_2O(\ell)]\}$

   $\Delta_r G° = (1\text{ mol } CO_2/\text{mol-rxn})(-394.359\text{ kJ/mol } CO_2) + (4\text{ mol } H_2/\text{mol-rxn})(0\text{ kJ/mol } H_2) - \{(1\text{ mol } CH_4/\text{mol-rxn})(-50.8\text{ kJ/mol } CH_4) + (2\text{ mol } H_2O/\text{mol-rxn})(-237.15\text{ kJ/mol } H_2O)\}$
   $= 130.7\text{ kJ/mol-rxn}$

   For SiH_4:

   $\Delta_r G° = (1\text{ mol } SiO_2/\text{mol-rxn})\Delta_f G°[SiO_2(s)] + (4\text{ mol } H_2/\text{mol-rxn})\Delta_f G°[H_2(g)] - \{(1\text{ mol } SiH_4/\text{mol-rxn})\Delta_f G°[SiH_4(g)] + (2\text{ mol } H_2O/\text{mol-rxn})\Delta_f G°[H_2O(\ell)]\}$

   $\Delta_r G° = (1\text{ mol } SiO_2/\text{mol-rxn})(-856.97\text{ kJ/mol } SiO_2) + (4\text{ mol } H_2/\text{mol-rxn})(0\text{ kJ/mol } H_2) - \{(1\text{ mol } SiH_4/\text{mol-rxn})(56.84\text{ kJ/mol } SiH_4) + (2\text{ mol } H_2O/\text{mol-rxn})(-237.15\text{ kJ/mol } H_2O)\}$
   $= -439.51\text{ kJ/mol-rxn}$

   The reaction involving SiH_4 is product-favored at equilibrium, whereas the reaction involving CH_4 is reactant-favored at equilibrium.

3. Electronegativities: C 2.5, Si 1.9, H 2.2. From this we conclude that the polarities of C—H and Si—H bonds are in the opposite directions. In SiH_4, the H has a slight negative charge, and in CH_4 the H has a slight positive charge.

4. General observation from these examples: Carbon often bonds to other atoms via double bonds, whereas Si does not. We would not expect $H_2Si{=}SiH_2$ to exist as a molecular species; instead a polymeric structure $+SiH_2SiH_2{-}\!\frac{}{n}$ is predicted.

Case Study: Hard Water

1. For Mg^{2+}: $(50.\text{ mg})(1\text{ mmol } Mg^{2+}/24.31\text{ mg})(1\text{ mmol } CaO/\text{mmol } Mg^{2+})(56.08\text{ mg } CaO/1\text{ mmol } CaO) = 120\text{ mg } CaO$

   For Ca^{2+}: $(150\text{ mg})(1\text{ mmol } Ca^{2+}/40.08\text{ mg})(1\text{ mmol } CaO/\text{mmol } Ca^{2+})(56.08\text{ mg } CaO/1\text{ mmol } CaO) = 210\text{ mg } CaO$

Total $CaO = 120\text{ mg} + 210\text{ mg} = 330\text{ mg}$ (two significant figures)

We get 2 mol $CaCO_3$ per mole Ca^{2+} and 1 mol each of $CaCO_3$ and $MgCO_3$ per mole Mg^{2+}

$CaCO_3$ from Ca^{2+} reaction: $(0.15\text{ g } Ca^{2+})(1\text{ mol}/40.08\text{ g } Ca^{2+})(2\text{ mol } CaCO_3/1\text{ mol } Ca^{2+})(100.1\text{ g } CaCO_3/1\text{ mol } CaCO_3) = 0.75\text{ g}$

$CaCO_3$ from Mg^{2+} reaction: $(0.050\text{ g } Mg^{2+})(1\text{ mol}/24.31\text{ g } Mg^{2+})(1\text{ mol } CaCO_3/1\text{ mol } Mg^{2+})(100.1\text{ g } CaCO_3/1\text{ mol } CaCO_3) = 0.21\text{ g}$

$MgCO_3$ from Mg^{2+} reaction: $(0.050\text{ g } Mg^{2+})(1\text{ mol}/24.31\text{ g } Mg^{2+})(1\text{ mol } MgCO_3/1\text{ mol } Mg^{2+})(84.31\text{ g } MgCO_3/1\text{ mol } MgCO_3) = 0.17\text{ g}$

Total mass of solids $= 0.75\text{ g} + 0.21\text{ g} + 0.17\text{ g} = 1.1\text{ g}$ (two significant figures)

2. $CaCO_3(s) + 2\,CH_3CO_2H(aq)$
   $Ca(CH_3CO_2H)_2(aq) + H_2O(\ell) + CO_2(g)$

   This is a gas-forming reaction.

Case Study: Lead, Beethoven, and a Mystery Solved

1. 50 ppb is 50 g in 1×10^9 g of blood. Assume the density of blood is 1.0 g/mL. In 1.0×10^3 mL (i.e., 1.0 L) of blood, there will be 50×10^{-6} g of Pb. From this:

   $(50 \times 10^{-6}\text{ g})(1\text{ mol Pb}/207.2\text{ g Pb})(6.022 \times 10^{23}\text{ atoms Pb/mol Pb}) = 1.5 \times 10^{17}$ atoms Pb

2. $(750\text{ mL wine})(1.0\text{ g wine/mL wine})(2000\text{ g Pb}/1,000,000\text{ g wine}) = 1.5\text{ g Pb}$

Case Study: A Healthy Saltwater Aquarium and the Nitrogen Cycle

1. $2\,NH_4^+(aq) + 4\,OH^-(aq) + 3\,O_2(aq) \rightarrow 2\,NO_2^-(aq) + 6\,H_2O(\ell)$

2. Reduction half-reaction: $2\,NO_3^-(aq) + 6\,H_2O(\ell) + 10\,e^- \rightarrow N_2(g) + 12\,OH^-(aq)$

   Oxidation half-reaction: $CH_3OH(aq) + 6\,OH^-(aq) \rightarrow CO_2(aq) + 5\,H_2O(\ell) + 6\,e^-$

   Net: $6\,NO_3^-(aq) + 5\,CH_3OH \rightarrow 3\,N_2(g) + 5\,CO_2(aq) + 6\,OH^-(aq) + 7\,H_2O(\ell)$

3. HCO_3^- is the predominant species. Recall that when acid and base concentrations are equal, pH = pK_a. If H_2CO_3 and HCO_3^- are present in equal concentrations, the pH would be about 6.4. If HCO_3^- and CO_3^{2-} are present in equal concentrations, the pH would be 10.2. For the pH to be about 8 (in a salt water aquarium), $[HCO_3^-]$ would have to be higher than either of the other carbonate species.

4. Concentration of N in ppm (mg N/L) =
   $[(1.7 \times 10^4 \text{ kg NO}_3^-)(10^6 \text{ mg NO}_3^-/\text{kg NO}_3^-)$
   $(14.0 \text{ mg N}/62.0 \text{ mg NO}_3^-)]/(2.2 \times 10^7 \text{ L}) =$
   $1.7 \times 10^2 \text{ mg/L} = 1.7 \times 10^2 \text{ ppm}$

   Concentration of NO_3^- in ppm (mg/L) =
   $(1.7 \times 10^4 \text{ kg})(10^6 \text{ mg/kg})/(2.2 \times 10^7 \text{ L}) =$
   770 mg/L

   Concentration of NO_3^- in mol/L =
   $[(1.7 \times 10^4 \text{ kg})(10^3 \text{ g/kg})(1 \text{ mol}/62.0 \text{ g})]/$
   $(2.2 \times 10^7 \text{ L}) = 0.012 \text{ mol/L}$

Chapter 22
Chapter Opening: Memory Metal

1. Define length of the side of the cube as x, then the length of the diagonal across the cube is $x\sqrt{3}$. This is set equal to: $2\,r_{Ti} + 2\,r_{Ni}$, i.e., $x\sqrt{3} = 2\,r_{Ti} + 2\,r_{Ni} = 540$ pm; $x = 312$ pm $(a = b = c = 3.12 \times 10^{-8}$ cm)

2. Calculated density:

   Mass of one unit cell is the mass of one Ti and one Ni atom = $(47.87 \text{ g/mol})(1 \text{ mol}/6.022 \times 10^{23} \text{ atoms Ti}) + (58.69 \text{ g/mol})(1 \text{ mol}/6.022 \times 10^{23} \text{ atoms Ti}) = 1.77 \times 10^{-22}$ g

   Volume of the unit cell is $x^3 = (3.12 \times 10^{-8} \text{ cm})^3 = 3.04 \times 10^{-23} \text{ cm}^3$

   Calculated density = $1.77 \times 10^{-22} \text{ g}/3.04 \times 10^{-23} \text{ cm}^3 = 5.82 \text{ g/cm}^3$

   The agreement is not very good, probably because atoms don't pack together as tightly as is assumed.

3. As free atoms, both Ti and Ni are paramagnetic.

Case Study: Accidental Discovery of a Chemotherapy Drug

1. First-order kinetics: $\ln[x/x_o] = -kt$

   $\ln[x/10 \text{ mg}] = -7.6 \times 10^{-5} \text{ s}^{-1}[24 \text{ h} \times 3600 \text{ s/h}]$

   $x/10 \text{ mg} = 1.4 \times 10^{-3}$; $x = 1.4 \times 10^{-2}$ mg remain

Case Study: Ferrocene—The Beginning of a Chemical Revolution

1. Fe^{2+} in ferrocene has an electron configuration [Ar] $3d^6$ and is present in the low-spin state.

2. Cr(0). Cr(0) in this compound is assumed to have an electron configuration [Ar] $3d^6$, is present in the low-spin state, and so is diamagnetic.

3. Both are in accordance with the 18-electron rule.

4. Select oxidizing agents from Table 20.1 (page 917) based on the northeast–southwest rule (above $E° = 0.400$ v). Common oxidizing agents include the halogens H_2O_2 and MnO_4^-. Cl_2 is a sufficiently strong oxidizing agent to carry out this oxidation.

5. $NiCl_2 + 2 \text{ Na}[C_5H_5] \rightarrow Ni(\eta\text{-}C_5H_5)_2 + 2 \text{ NaCl}$. Nickelocene is predicted to have two unpaired electrons (Ni^{2+}, with a d^8 configuration, in an octahedral environment.)

Chapter 23
Chapter Opening: A Primordial Nuclear Reactor

1. ^{235}U: 92 protons, $235 - 92 = 143$ neutrons

   ^{238}U: 92 protons, 146 neutrons

2. (a) $^{238}U + {}_0^1n \rightarrow {}^{239}U$

   (b) $^{239}U \rightarrow {}^{239}Np + {}_{-1}^0\beta$

   $^{239}Np \rightarrow {}^{239}Pu + {}_{-1}^0\beta$

   (c) $^{239}Pu \rightarrow {}^{235}U + {}_2^4\alpha$

Case Study: Nuclear Medicine and Hyperthyroidism

1. $^{131}I \rightarrow {}^{131}Xe + {}_{-1}^0\beta$

2. Calculate the fraction ($= f$) of each remaining after 7 days

   For ^{123}I: $k = 0.693/t_{1/2} = 0.693/13.3 \text{ h} = 0.0521 \text{ h}^{-1}$

   $\ln(f) = -0.0521 \text{ h}^{-1}[7 \text{ d}(24 \text{ h/d})]$

   $f = 1.6 \times 10^{-4}$

   For ^{131}I: $k = 0.693/t_{1/2} = 0.693/8.04 \text{ d} = 0.0862 \text{ d}^{-1}$

   $\ln(f) = -0.0862 \text{ d}^{-1}(7 \text{ d})$

   $f = 0.55$

   Ratio of amounts remaining, $[^{131}I]/[^{123}I] = 0.55/(1.6 \times 10^{-4}) = 3400$

   The amount of ^{131}I isotope is 3400 times greater than the amount of ^{123}I.

O Answers to Check Your Understanding Questions

Let's Review

LR 1 0.154 nm (1 m/10^9 nm) (10^{12} pm/1 m) = 154 pm

0.154 nm (1 m/10^9 nm) (100 cm/1 m) = 1.54×10^{-8} cm

LR 2 Student A: average = −0.1 °C; percent error
= {[(−0.1 + 273.15) K − 273.15 K]/273.15 K} × 100%
= −0.04%

Student B: average = +0.01 °C; percent error
= {[(0.01 + 273.15) K − 273.15 K]/273.15 K} × 100%
= 0.004%

Student B has the smaller error.

LR 3 $x = 3.9 \times 10^5$. The difference between 110.7 and 64 is 47. Dividing 47 by 0.056 and 0.00216 gives an answer with two significant figures.

LR 4 (19,320 kg/m³) (10^3 g/1 kg) (1 m³/10^6 cm³)
= 19.32 g/cm³

LR 5 Change all dimensions to centimeters: 7.6 m
= 760 cm; 2.74 m = 274 cm; 0.13 mm = 0.013 cm.

Volume of paint = (760 cm) (274 cm) (0.013 cm)
= 2.7×10^3 cm³

Volume (L) = (2.7×10^3 cm³) (1 L/10^3 cm³) = 2.7 L

Mass = (2.7×10^3 cm³) (0.914 g/cm³) = 2.5×10^3 g

Chapter 2

2.1 (1) Mass number with 26 protons and 30 neutrons is 56
(2) (59.930788 u) (1.661 × 10^{-24} g/u) = 9.955 × 10^{-23} g
(3) ^{64}Zn has 30 protons, 30 electrons, and (64 − 30)
= 34 neutrons.

2.2 Use Equation 2.2 for the calculation.

Atomic mass = (34.96885) (75.77/100) + (36.96590) (24.23/100) = 35.45. (Accuracy is limited by the value of the percent abundance to four significant figures.)

2.3 Use Equation 2.2 for the calculation. Let x = percent abundance of ^{20}Ne and y = percent abundance of ^{22}Ne.

20.1797 u = (x/100) (19.992435 u) + (0.27/100) (20.993843 u) + (y/100) (21.991383 u)

Because all the percent abundances must sum to 100%, y = 100 − x − 0.27 = 99.73 − x.

20.1797 u = (x/100) (19.992435 u) + (0.27/100) (20.993843 u) + [(99.73 − x)/100] (21.991383 u)

x = 90.5; therefore the percent abundance of ^{20}Ne = 90.5% and the percent abundance of ^{22}Ne = 9.2%.

2.4 (a) (1) NaF: 1 Na$^+$ and 1 F$^-$ ion. (2) Cu(NO$_3$)$_2$: 1 Cu^{2+} and 2 NO$_3^-$ ions. (3) NaCH$_3$CO$_2$: 1 Na$^+$ and 1 CH$_3$CO$_2^-$ ion.
(b) FeCl$_2$, FeCl$_3$

2.5 Na$_2$S, Na$_3$PO$_4$, BaS, Ba$_3$(PO$_4$)$_2$

2.6 (2.6 × 10^{24} atoms) (1.000 mol/6.022 × 10^{23} atoms) (197.0 g Au/1.000 mol) = 850 g Au

Volume = (850 g Au) (1.00 cm³/19.32 g) = 44 cm³

Volume = 44 cm³ = (thickness) (area) = (0.10 cm) (area)

Area = 440 cm²

Length = width = $\sqrt{440 \text{ cm}^2}$ = 21 cm

2.7 Molar mass H$_3$C$_6$H$_5$O$_7$ = 8(1.01) + 6(12.01) + 7(16.00) = 192.14 g/mol

(454 g H$_3$C$_6$H$_5$O$_7$) (1 mol H$_3$C$_6$H$_5$O$_7$/192.14 g H$_3$C$_6$H$_5$O$_7$) = 2.36 mol H$_3$C$_6$H$_5$O$_7$

(2.36 mol H$_3$C$_6$H$_5$O$_7$) (6.022 × 10^{23} molecules/1 mol) = 1.42 × 10^{24} molecules H$_3$C$_6$H$_5$O$_7$

(1.42 × 10^{24} molecules H$_3$C$_6$H$_5$O$_7$) (6 atoms C/1 molecule H$_3$C$_6$H$_5$O$_7$) = 8.54 × 10^{24} atoms C

2.8 (1) 1.00 mol (NH$_4$)$_2$CO$_3$ (molar mass 96.09 g/mol) has 28.0 g of N (29.2%), 8.06 g of H (8.39%), 12.0 g of C (12.5%), and 48.0 g of O (50.0%)
(2) 454 g C$_8$H$_{18}$ (1 mol C$_8$H$_{18}$/114.2 g) (8 mol C/1 mol C$_8$H$_{18}$) (12.01 g C/1 mol C) = 382 g C

2.9 (1) C$_5$H$_4$
(2) C$_2$H$_4$O$_2$
(3) (88.17 g C) (1 mol C/12.011 g C) = 7.341 mol C
(11.83 g H) (1 mol H/1.008 g H) = 11.74 mol H
11.74 mol H/7.341 mol C = 1.6 mol H/1 mol C
= (8/5); (mol H/1 mol C) = 8 mol H/5 mol C

The empirical formula is C$_5$H$_8$. The molar mass, 68.11 g/mol, closely matches this formula, so C$_5$H$_8$ is also the molecular formula.
(4) (78.90 g C) (1 mol C/12.011 g C) = 6.569 mol C
(10.59 g H) (1 mol H/1.008 g H) = 10.51 mol H
(10.51 g O) (1 mol O/16.00 g O) = 0.6569 mol O
10.51 mol H/0.6569 mol O = 16 mol H/1 mol O
6.569 mol C/0.6569 mol O = 10 mol C/1 mol O

The empirical formula is C$_{10}$H$_{16}$O.

2.10 $(1.25 \text{ g Ga})(1 \text{ mol Ga}/69.72 \text{ g Ga}) = 0.0179 \text{ mol Ga}$

$1.68 \text{ g product} - 1.25 \text{ g Ga} = 0.43 \text{ g O}$

$(0.43 \text{ g O})(1 \text{ mol O}/16.00 \text{ g O}) = 0.027 \text{ mol O}$

Mole ratio $= 0.027 \text{ mol O}/0.0179 \text{ mol Ga}$
$= 1.5 \text{ mol O}/1.0 \text{ mol Ga} = 3.0 \text{ mol O}/2.0 \text{ mol Ga}$

Empirical formula $= Ga_2O_3$

2.11 $(0.586 \text{ g K})(1 \text{ mol K}/39.10 \text{ g K}) = 0.0150 \text{ mol K}$

$(0.480 \text{ g O})(1 \text{ mol O}/16.00 \text{ g O}) = 0.0300 \text{ mol O}$

The ratio of moles K to moles O atoms is $1:2$; the empirical formula is KO_2.

2.12 Mass of water lost on heating is $0.235 \text{ g} - 0.128 \text{ g}$
$= 0.107 \text{ g}; 0.128 \text{ g NiCl}_2$ remain

$(0.107 \text{ g H}_2O)(1 \text{ mol H}_2O/18.016 \text{ g H}_2O)$
$= 0.00594 \text{ mol H}_2O$

$(0.128 \text{ g NiCl}_2)(1 \text{ mol NiCl}_2/129.6 \text{ g NiCl}_2)$
$= 0.000988 \text{ mol NiCl}_2$

Mole ratio $= 0.00594 \text{ mol H}_2O/0.000988 \text{ mol}$
$NiCl_2 = 6.01$: Therefore $x = 6$

The formula for the hydrate is $NiCl_2 \cdot 6 \text{ H}_2O$.

Chapter 3

3.1 (a) $2 \text{ C}_4H_{10}(g) + 13 \text{ O}_2(g) \longrightarrow$
$8 \text{ CO}_2(g) + 10 \text{ H}_2O(g)$

(b) $2 \text{ Pb}(C_2H_5)_4(\ell) + 27 \text{ O}_2(g) \longrightarrow$
$2 \text{ PbO}(s) + 16 \text{ CO}_2(g) + 20 \text{ H}_2O(g)$

3.2 (a) $LiNO_3$ is soluble and gives $Li^+(aq)$ and $NO_3^-(aq)$ ions.

(b) $CaCl_2$ is soluble and gives $Ca^{2+}(aq)$ and $Cl^-(aq)$ ions.

(c) CuO is not water soluble.

(d) $NaCH_3CO_2$ is soluble and gives $Na^+(aq)$ and $CH_3CO_2^-(aq)$ ions.

3.3 (a) $Na_2CO_3(aq) + CuCl_2(aq) \longrightarrow$
$2 \text{ NaCl}(aq) + CuCO_3(s)$

(b) No reaction; no insoluble compound is produced.

(c) $NiCl_2(aq) + 2 \text{ KOH}(aq) \longrightarrow$
$Ni(OH)_2(s) + 2 \text{ KCl}(aq)$

3.4 (a) $3 \text{ CaCl}_2(aq) + 2 \text{ Na}_3PO_4(aq) \longrightarrow$
$Ca_3(PO_4)_2(s) + 6 \text{ NaCl}(aq)$

$3 \text{ Ca}^{2+}(aq) + 2 \text{ PO}_4^{3-}(aq) \longrightarrow Ca_3(PO_4)_2(s)$

(b) $FeCl_3(aq) + 3 \text{ KOH}(aq) \longrightarrow$
$Fe(OH)_3(s) + 3 \text{ KCl}(aq)$

$Fe^{3+}(aq) + 3 \text{ OH}^-(aq) \longrightarrow Fe(OH)_3(s)$

(c) $Pb(NO_3)_2(aq) + 2 \text{ KCl}(aq) \longrightarrow$
$PbCl_2(s) + 2 \text{ KNO}_3(aq)$

$Pb^{2+}(aq) + 2 \text{ Cl}^-(aq) \longrightarrow PbCl_2(s)$

3.5 (a) $H_3PO_4(aq) + H_2O(\ell) \rightleftharpoons$
$H_3O^+(aq) + H_2PO_4^-(aq)$

(b) Acting as an acid:
$H_2PO_4^-(aq) + H_2O(\ell) \rightleftharpoons$
$HPO_4^{2-}(aq) + H_3O^+(\ell)$

Acting as a base:
$H_2PO_4^-(aq) + H_2O(\ell) \rightleftharpoons$
$H_3PO_4(aq) + OH^-(aq)$

Because $H_2PO_4^-(aq)$ can react as a Brønsted acid and as a base, it is said to be amphiprotic.

3.6 $Mg(OH)_2(s) + 2 \text{ HCl}(aq) \longrightarrow$
$MgCl_2(aq) + 2 \text{ H}_2O(\ell)$

Net ionic equation: $Mg(OH)_2(s) + 2 \text{ H}_3O^+(aq)$
$\longrightarrow Mg^{2+}(aq) + 4 \text{ H}_2O(\ell)$

3.7 $BaCO_3(s) + 2 \text{ HNO}_3(aq) \longrightarrow$
$Ba(NO_3)_2(aq) + CO_2(g) + H_2O(\ell)$

Barium carbonate and nitric acid produce barium nitrate, carbon dioxide, and water.

3.8 (a) Fe in Fe_2O_3, $+3$; (b) S in H_2SO_4, $+6$;
(c) C in CO_3^{2-}, $+4$; (d) N in NO_2^+, $+5$

3.9 Dichromate ion is the oxidizing agent and is reduced. (Cr with a $+6$ oxidation number is reduced to Cr^{3+} with a $+3$ oxidation number.) Ethanol is the reducing agent and is oxidized. (The C atoms in ethanol have an oxidation number of -2. The oxidation number is 0 in acetic acid.)

3.10 (a) Gas-forming reaction:
$CuCO_3(s) + H_2SO_4(aq) \longrightarrow$
$CuSO_4(aq) + H_2O(\ell) + CO_2(g)$

Net ionic equation:
$CuCO_3(s) + 2 \text{ H}_3O^+(aq) \longrightarrow$
$Cu^{2+}(aq) + 3 \text{ H}_2O(\ell) + CO_2(g)$

(b) Oxidation–reduction: $4 \text{ Ga}(s) + 3 \text{ O}_2(g) \longrightarrow$
$2 \text{ Ga}_2O_3(s)$

(c) Acid–base reaction:
$Ba(OH)_2(aq) + 2 \text{ HNO}_3(aq) \longrightarrow$
$Ba(NO_3)_2(aq) + 2 \text{ H}_2O(\ell)$

Net ionic equation:
$OH^-(aq) + H_3O^+(aq) \longrightarrow 2 \text{ H}_2O(\ell)$

(d) Precipitation reaction:
$CuCl_2(aq) + (NH_4)_2S(aq) \longrightarrow$
$CuS(s) + 2 \text{ NH}_4Cl(aq)$

Net ionic equation:
$Cu^{2+}(aq) + S^{2-}(aq) \longrightarrow CuS(s)$

Chapter 4

4.1 $(454 \text{ g C}_3H_8)(1 \text{ mol C}_3H_8/44.10 \text{ g C}_3H_8)$
$= 10.3 \text{ mol C}_3H_8$

$10.3 \text{ mol C}_3H_8 (5 \text{ mol O}_2/1 \text{ mol C}_3H_8)$
$(32.00 \text{ g O}_2/1 \text{ mol O}_2) = 1650 \text{ g O}_2$

$(10.3 \text{ mol C}_3H_8)(3 \text{ mol CO}_2/1 \text{ mol C}_3H_8)$
$(44.01 \text{ g CO}_2/1 \text{ mol CO}_2) = 1360 \text{ g CO}_2$

$(10.3 \text{ mol C}_3H_8)(4 \text{ mol H}_2O/1 \text{ mol C}_3H_8)$
$(18.02 \text{ g H}_2O/1 \text{ mol H}_2O) = 742 \text{ g H}_2O$

4.2 (a) Amount Al $= (50.0 \text{ g Al})(1 \text{ mol Al}/26.98 \text{ g Al})$
$= 1.85 \text{ mol Al}$

Amount $Fe_2O_3 = (50.0 \text{ g Fe}_2O_3)(1 \text{ mol Fe}_2O_3/$
$159.7 \text{ g Fe}_2O_3) = 0.313 \text{ mol Fe}_2O_3$

Mol Al/mol $Fe_2O_3 = 1.85/0.313 = 5.92$

This is more than the $2:1$ ratio required, so the limiting reactant is Fe_2O_3.

(b) Mass Fe $= (0.313 \text{ mol Fe}_2O_3)(2 \text{ mol Fe}/$
$1 \text{ mol Fe}_2O_3)(55.85 \text{ g Fe}/1 \text{ mol Fe}) = 35.0 \text{ g Fe}$

4.3 $(0.143 \text{ g O}_2)(1 \text{ mol O}_2/32.00 \text{ g O}_2)(3 \text{ mol TiO}_2/$
$3 \text{ mol O}_2)(79.87 \text{ g TiO}_2/1 \text{ mol TiO}_2) = 0.357 \text{ g TiO}_2$

Percent TiO_2 in sample $= (0.357 \text{ g}/2.367 \text{ g})(100\%)$
$= 15.1\%$

4.4 $(1.612 \text{ g } CO_2)(1 \text{ mol } CO_2/44.010 \text{ g } CO_2)(1 \text{ mol } C/1 \text{ mol } CO_2) = 0.03663 \text{ mol C}$

$(0.7425 \text{ g } H_2O)(1 \text{ mol } H_2O/18.015 \text{ g } H_2O)(2 \text{ mol } H/1 \text{ mol } H_2O) = 0.08243 \text{ mol H}$

$0.08243 \text{ mol H}/0.03663 \text{ mol} = 2.250 \text{ H}/1 \text{ C} = 9 \text{ H}/4 \text{ C}$

The empirical formula is C_4H_9, which has a molar mass of 57 g/mol. This is one half of the measured value of molar mass, so the molecular formula is C_8H_{18}.

4.5 $(0.240 \text{ g } CO_2)(1 \text{ mol } CO_2/44.01 \text{ g } CO_2)(1 \text{ mol } C/1 \text{ mol } CO_2)(12.01 \text{ g } C/1 \text{ mol } C) = 0.06549 \text{ g C}$

$(0.0982 \text{ g } H_2O)(1 \text{ mol } H_2O/18.02 \text{ g } H_2O)(2 \text{ mol } H/1 \text{ mol } H_2O)(1.008 \text{ g } H/1 \text{ mol } H) = 0.01099 \text{ g H}$

Mass O (by difference) =
$0.1342 \text{ g} - 0.06549 \text{ g} - 0.01099 \text{ g} = 0.0577 \text{ g}$

Amount C = $0.06549 \text{ g}(1 \text{ mol } C/12.01 \text{ g } C) = 0.00545 \text{ mol C}$

Amount H = $0.01099 \text{ g H}(1 \text{ mol } H/1.008 \text{ g } H) = 0.01090 \text{ mol H}$

Amount O = $0.0577 \text{ g O}(1 \text{ mol } O/16.00 \text{ g } O) = 0.00361 \text{ mol O}$

To find a whole-number ratio, divide each value by 0.00361; this gives 1.51 mol C : 3.02 mol H : 1 mol O. Multiply each value by 2, and round off to 3 mol C : 6 mol H : 2 mol O. The empirical formula is $C_3H_6O_2$; given the molar mass of 74.1, this is also the molecular formula.

4.6 $(26.3 \text{ g})(1 \text{ mol } NaHCO_3/84.01 \text{ g } NaHCO_3) = 0.313 \text{ mol } NaHCO_3$

$0.313 \text{ mol } NaHCO_3/0.200 \text{ L} = 1.57 \text{ M}$

Ion concentrations: $[Na^+] = [HCO_3^-] = 1.57 \text{ M}$

4.7 $(2.00 \text{ M})(V_{conc}) = (1.00 \text{ M})(0.250 \text{ L}); V_{conc} = 0.125 \text{ L}$

To prepare the solution, measure accurately 125 mL of 2.00 M NaOH into a 250-mL volumetric flask, and add water to give a total volume of 250 mL.

4.8 (a) pH = $-\log (2.6 \times 10^{-2}) = 1.59$
(b) $-\log [H^+] = 3.80; [H^+] = 1.6 \times 10^{-4} \text{ M}$

4.9 HCl is the limiting reagent.

$(0.350 \text{ mol } HCl/1 \text{ L})(0.0750 \text{ L})(1 \text{ mol } CO_2/2 \text{ mol } HCl)(44.01 \text{ g } CO_2/1 \text{ mol } CO_2) = 0.578 \text{ g } CO_2$

4.10 $(0.953 \text{ mol } NaOH/1 \text{ L})(0.02833 \text{ L } NaOH) = 0.0270 \text{ mol } NaOH$

$(0.0270 \text{ mol } NaOH)(1 \text{ mol } CH_3CO_2H/1 \text{ mol } NaOH) = 0.0270 \text{ mol } CH_3CO_2H$

$(0.0270 \text{ mol } CH_3CO_2H)(60.05 \text{ g/mol}) = 1.62 \text{ g } CH_3CO_2H$

$0.0270 \text{ mol } CH_3CO_2H/0.0250 \text{ L} = 1.08 \text{ M}$

4.11 $(0.100 \text{ mol } HCl/1 \text{ L})(0.02967 \text{ L}) = 0.00297 \text{ mol } HCl$

$(0.00297 \text{ mol } HCl)(1 \text{ mol } NaOH/1 \text{ mol } HCl) = 0.00297 \text{ mol } NaOH$

$0.00297 \text{ mol } NaOH/0.02500 \text{ L} = 0.119 \text{ M } NaOH$

4.12 Moles acid = moles base = $(0.323 \text{ mol/L})(0.03008 \text{ L}) = 9.716 \times 10^{-3} \text{ mol}$

Molar mass = $0.856 \text{ g acid}/9.716 \times 10^{-3} \text{ mol acid} = 88.1 \text{ g/mol}$

4.13 $(0.196 \text{ mol } Na_2S_2O_3/1 \text{ L})(0.02030 \text{ L}) = 0.00398 \text{ mol } Na_2S_2O_3$

$(0.00398 \text{ mol } Na_2S_2O_3)(1 \text{ mol } I_2/2 \text{ mol } Na_2S_2O_3) = 0.00199 \text{ mol } I_2$

0.00199 mol I_2 is in excess and was not used in the reaction with ascorbic acid.

I_2 originally added = $(0.0520 \text{ mol } I_2/1 \text{ L})(0.05000 \text{ L}) = 0.00260 \text{ mol } I_2$

I_2 used in reaction with ascorbic acid
$= 0.00260 \text{ mol} - 0.00199 \text{ mol} = 6.1 \times 10^{-4} \text{ mol } I_2$

$(6.1 \times 10^{-4} \text{ mol } I_2)(1 \text{ mol } C_6H_8O_6/1 \text{ mol } I_2)(176.1 \text{ g}/1 \text{ mol}) = 0.11 \text{ g } C_6H_8O_6$

4.14 A Beer's Law plot of the calibration data was constructed by plotting concentration of Cu^{2+} along the *x*-axis and the absorbance along the *y*-axis. The equation for the best-fit line is $y = 13.0x + 0.011$.

Substituting the absorbance for the solution of unknown concentration yields

$0.418 = 13.0x + 0.011$

$x = 0.0315$

Thus the concentration of Cu^{2+} in the solution of unknown concentration is 0.0315 M.

Chapter 5

5.1 $C = 59.8 \text{ J}/[(25.0 \text{ g})(1.00 \text{ K})] = 2.39 \text{ J/g} \cdot \text{K}$

5.2 $(15.5 \text{ g})(C_{metal})(18.9 \text{ °C} - 100.0 \text{ °C}) + (55.5 \text{ g})(4.184 \text{ J/g} \cdot \text{K})(18.9 \text{ °C} - 16.5 \text{ °C}) = 0$

$C_{metal} = 0.44 \text{ J/g} \cdot \text{K}$

5.3 $1.00 \text{ L} (1000 \text{ mL}/1 \text{ L})(0.7849 \text{ g/cm}^3) = 785 \text{ g}$

Heat liquid from 25.0 °C to 78.3 °C.

$\Delta T = 78.3 \text{ °C} - 25.0 \text{ °C} = 53.3 \text{ °C} = 53.3 \text{ K}$
$q = (2.44 \text{ J/g} \cdot \text{K})(785 \text{ g})(53.3 \text{ K}) = 1.02 \times 10^5 \text{ J} = 102 \text{ kJ}$

Boil the liquid.
$q = 38.56 \text{ kJ/mol} (785 \text{ g})(1 \text{ mol}/46.08 \text{ g}) = 657 \text{ kJ}$

Total = 102 kJ + 657 kJ = 759 kJ

5.4 Energy transferred as heat from tea + energy as heat expended to melt ice = 0.

$(250 \text{ g})(4.2 \text{ J/g} \cdot \text{K})(273.2 \text{ K} - 291.4 \text{ K}) + x \text{ g} (333 \text{ J/g}) = 0$

$x = 57 \text{ g}$

57 g of ice melts with energy supplied by cooling 250 g of tea from 18.2 °C (291.4 K) to 0 °C (273.2 K).

Mass of ice remaining = mass of ice initially − mass of ice melted

Mass of ice remaining = 75 g − 57 g = 18 g

5.5 $(15.0 \text{ g } C_2H_6)(1 \text{ mol } C_2H_6/30.07 \text{ g } C_2H_6) = 0.499 \text{ mol } C_2H_6$

$\Delta H° = 0.499 \text{ mol } C_2H_6(1 \text{ mol-rxn}/2 \text{ mol } C_2H_6)(-2857.3 \text{ kJ/mol-rxn})$

$= -713 \text{ kJ}$

5.6 Mass of final solution = 400. g

$\Delta T = 27.78\ °C - 25.10\ °C = 2.68\ °C = 2.68\ K$

Amount of HCl used = amount of NaOH used = $C \times V = (0.400\ mol/L) \times 0.200\ L = 0.0800\ mol$

Energy transferred as heat by acid–base reaction + energy gained as heat to warm solution = 0

$q_{rxn} + (4.20\ J/g \cdot K)(400.\ g)(2.68\ K) = 0$

$q_{rxn} = -4.50 \times 10^3\ J$

This represents the energy transferred as heat in the reaction of 0.0800 mol HCl.

Energy transferred as heat per mole = $\Delta_r H$ = $-4.50\ kJ/0.0800\ mol\ HCl = -56.3\ kJ/mol\ HCl$

5.7 (a) Energy evolved as heat in reaction + energy as heat absorbed by H_2O + energy as heat absorbed by bomb = 0

$q_{rxn} + (1.50 \times 10^3\ g)(4.20\ J/g \cdot K)(27.32\ °C - 25.00\ °C) + (837\ J/K)(27.32\ °C - 25.00\ °C) = 0$

$q_{rxn} = -16,600\ J$ (energy as heat evolved in burning 1.0 g sucrose)

(b) Energy evolved as heat per mole = $(-16.6\ kJ/g$ sucrose$)(342.3\ g$ sucrose$/1\ mol$ sucrose$) = -5670\ kJ/mol$ sucrose

5.8 $C(s) + O_2(g) \longrightarrow CO_2(g)$ $\quad \Delta_r H_1° = -393.5\ kJ$

$2\ [S(s) + O_2(g) \longrightarrow SO_2(g)]$
$\Delta_r H° = 2\ \Delta_r H_2° = 2(-296.8) = -593.6\ kJ$

$CO_2(g) + 2\ SO_2(g) \longrightarrow CS_2(g) + 3\ O_2(g)$
$\Delta_r H° = -\Delta_r H_3° = +1103.9\ kJ$

Net: $C(s) + 2\ S(s) \longrightarrow CS_2(g)$
$\Delta_r H°_{net} = -393.5\ kJ + -593.6\ kJ + 1103.9\ kJ = +116.8\ kJ$

5.9 $\Delta_r H° = (6\ mol\ CO_2/mol\text{-}rxn)\Delta_f H°[CO_2(g)] + (3\ mol\ H_2O/mol\text{-}rxn)\Delta_f H°[H_2O(\ell)] - \{(1\ mol\ C_6H_6/1\ mol\text{-}rxn)\Delta_f H°[C_6H_6(\ell)] + (^{15}\!/_2\ mol\ O_2/mol\text{-}rxn)\Delta_f H°[O_2(g)]\}$

$= (6\ mol/mol\text{-}rxn)(-393.5\ kJ/mol) + (3\ mol/mol\text{-}rxn)(-285.8\ J/mol) - (1\ mol/mol\text{-}rxn)(+49.0\ kJ/mol) - 0$

$= -3267.4\ kJ/mol\text{-}rxn$

Chapter 6

6.1 (a) Highest frequency, violet; lowest frequency, red
(b) The frequency of a microwave oven, 2.45 GHz, is higher than the FM radio frequency, 91.7 MHz.
(c) The wavelength of x-rays is shorter than the wavelength of ultraviolet light.

6.2 (a) E (per atom) = $-Rhc/n^2$
$= (-2.179 \times 10^{-18})/(3^2)\ J/atom$
$= -2.421 \times 10^{-19}\ J/atom$
(b) E (per mol) = $(-2.421 \times 10^{-19}\ J/atom)$
$(6.022 \times 10^{23}\ atoms/mol)$
$(1\ kJ/10^3\ J)$
$= -145.8\ kJ/mol$

6.3 The least energetic line is from the electron transition from $n = 2$ to $n = 1$.

$\Delta E = -Rhc[1/1^2 - 1/2^2]$
$= -(2.179 \times 10^{-18}\ J/atom)(3/4)$
$= -1.634 \times 10^{-18}\ J/atom$

The photon emitted thus has $E_{photon} = 1.634 \times 10^{-18}\ J$

$\nu = E_{photon}/h$
$= (1.634 \times 10^{-18}\ J)/(6.626 \times 10^{-34}\ J \cdot s)$
$= 2.466 \times 10^{15}\ s^{-1}$

$\lambda = c/\nu = (2.998 \times 10^8\ m/s^{-1})/(2.466 \times 10^{15}\ s^{-1})$
$= 1.216 \times 10^{-7}\ m$ (or 121.6 nm)

6.4 First, calculate the velocity of the neutron:
$v = [2E/m]^{1/2} = [2(6.21 \times 10^{-21}\ kg \cdot m^2\ s^{-2})/$
$(1.675 \times 10^{-27}\ kg)]^{1/2}$

$= 2720\ m \cdot s^{-1}$

Use this value in the de Broglie equation:
$\lambda = h/mv = (6.626 \times 10^{-34}\ kg \cdot m^2\ s^{-2} \cdot s)/$
$(1.675 \times 10^{-27}\ kg)(2720\ m\ s^{-1})$
$= 1.45 \times 10^{-10}\ m = 0.145\ nm$

Chapter 7

7.1 (a) chlorine (Cl)
(b) $1s^2 2s^2 2p^6 3s^2 3p^3$

7.2 Calcium has two valence electrons in the $4s$ subshell. Quantum numbers for these two electrons are $n = 4$, $\ell = 0$, $m_\ell = 0$, and $m_s = \pm 1/2$

7.3 Obtain the answers from Table 7.3.

7.4

All three ions are paramagnetic with three, two, and four unpaired electrons, respectively.

7.5 (a) Increasing atomic radius: C < B < Al
(b) Increasing ionization energy: Al < B < C
(c) Carbon is predicted to have the more negative electron attachment enthalpy.

Chapter 8

8.1

8.2

methanol   hydroxylamine

8.3 (a) CN^- : formal charge on C is -1; formal charge on N is 0.

(b) SO_3^{2-}: formal charge on S is $+1$; formal charge on each O is -1.

8.4 Resonance structures for the HCO_3^- ion:

$$\left[\ddot{O}=C-\ddot{O}:\atop{\atop:\ddot{O}-H}\right]^- \longleftrightarrow \left[:\ddot{O}-C=\ddot{O}\atop{\atop:\ddot{O}-H}\right]^-$$

(a) No. Three resonance structures are needed in the description of CO_3^{2-}; only two are needed to describe HCO_3^-.

(b) In each resonance structure: carbon's formal charge is 0; the oxygen of the $-OH$ group and the double-bonded oxygen have a formal charge of zero; the singly bonded oxygen has a formal charge of -1. The average formal charge on the latter two oxygen atoms is $-\frac{1}{2}$. In the carbonate ion, each of the three oxygen atoms has an average formal charge of $-\frac{2}{3}$.

(c) H^+ would be expected to add to one of the oxygens with a negative formal charge; that is, one of the oxygens with formal charge of $-\frac{1}{2}$ in this structure.

8.5 $\left[:\ddot{F}-\ddot{C}l-\ddot{F}:\right]^+$ ClF_2^+, 2 bond pairs and 2 lone pairs.

$\left[:\ddot{F}-\ddot{C}l-\ddot{F}:\right]^-$ ClF_2^-, 2 bond pairs and 3 lone pairs.

8.6 Tetrahedral geometry around carbon. The $Cl-C-Cl$ bond angle will be close to $109.5°$.

8.7 For each species, the electron-pair geometry and the molecular shape are the same. BF_3: trigonal-planar; BF_4^-: tetrahedral. Adding F^- to BF_3 adds an electron pair to the central atom and changes the shape.

8.8 The electron-pair geometry around I is trigonal-bipyramidal. The molecular geometry of the ion is linear.

$$\left[\begin{array}{c}:\ddot{C}l:\\ \\ :-I\\ \\ :\ddot{C}l:\end{array}\right]^-$$

8.9 (a) In PO_4^{3-}, there is tetrahedral electron-pair geometry. The molecular geometry is also tetrahedral.

$$\left[\begin{array}{c}:\ddot{O}:\\ :\ddot{O}-P-\ddot{O}:\\ :\ddot{O}:\end{array}\right]^{3-} \qquad \begin{array}{c}O\\ O-P\cdots\cdots O\\ O\end{array}$$

(b) In SO_3^{2-}, there is tetrahedral electron-pair geometry. The molecular geometry is trigonal-pyramidal.

$$\left[:\ddot{O}-S-\ddot{O}:\atop:\ddot{O}:\right]^{2-} \qquad \begin{array}{c}\\ O-S\cdots\cdots O\\ O\end{array}$$

(c) In IF_5, there is octahedral electron-pair geometry. The molecular geometry is square-pyramidal.

$$:\ddot{F}:\atop:\ddot{F}\diagdown{I}-\ddot{F}:\atop:\ddot{F}::\ddot{F}: \qquad \begin{array}{c}F\\ F_{\prime\prime\prime\prime}\,I\,_{\prime\prime\prime\prime}F\\ FF\end{array}$$

8.10 (a) The H atom is the positive pole in each case. $H-F$ ($\Delta\chi = 1.8$) is more polar than $H-I$ ($\Delta\chi = 0.5$).

(b) The B atom is the positive pole in each case. $B-F$ ($\Delta\chi = 2.0$) is more polar than $B-C$ ($\Delta\chi = 0.5$).

(c) $C-Si$ ($\Delta\chi = 0.6$) is more polar than $C-S$ ($\Delta\chi = 0.1$). In $C-Si$, C is the negative pole, and Si is the positive pole. In $C-S$, S is the negative pole, and C the positive pole.

8.11 16 valence electrons

$$\left[:S\equiv C-\ddot{N}:\right]^- \longleftrightarrow \left[:\ddot{S}=C=\ddot{N}:\right]^- \longleftrightarrow \left[:\ddot{S}-C\equiv N:\right]^-$$

Formal charges $\quad+\quad0\quad2-\qquad\qquad0\quad0\quad-\qquad\qquad-\quad0\quad0$

Formal charge considerations favor the middle structure because it has less formal charge than the left structure and, unlike the right structure, it has the negative formal charge on the most electronegative atom in the ion.

Bond polarity: For the C–N bond, $\Delta\chi = 0.5$, so this bond is polar and should have a partially positive C and a partially negative N. For the C–S bond, $\Delta\chi = 0.1$, so this bond should be only slightly polar with a partially positive C and a partially negative S. Comparison of formal charge and bond polarity: The bonding in SCN^- will be closest to the middle resonance structure with a smaller contribution of the resonance structure on the right. From this we conclude that both N and S will have a negative formal charge, with N having the more negative value. The polarities of the C–N and C–S bonds match this description, with N and S being the negative end of each polar bond.

8.12 (a) $BFCl_2$, polar, negative side is the F atom because F is the most electronegative atom in the molecule.

$$\begin{array}{c}F\uparrow\\ |\\ B\\ Cl\diagup\quad\diagdown Cl+\end{array}$$

(b) NH_2Cl, polar, negative side is the Cl atom.

$$\begin{array}{c}\ddot{N}\,_{\prime\prime\prime\prime}H^{\delta+}\\ \overset{\delta-}{Cl}\diagup|\\ H^{\delta+}\end{array}$$

(c) SCl_2, polar, Cl atoms are on the negative side.

$$\begin{array}{c}\ddot{S}\uparrow\\ Cl\diagup{}_{\delta+}\diagdown Cl\downarrow\\ _{\delta-}{}_{\delta-}\end{array}$$

8.13 (a)

$$:\overset{\displaystyle :\ddot{O}:}{\underset{}{\vert}}$$
$$:\ddot{C}l\!-\!S\!-\!\ddot{C}l:$$

Formal charges: S = +1, O = −1, Cl = 0

(b) Geometry: trigonal-pyramidal. The molecule is polar. The positive charge is on sulfur, the negative charge on oxygen.

8.14 $CH_4(g) + 2\ O_2(g) \longrightarrow CO_2(g) + 2\ H_2O(g)$

Break 4 C—H bonds and 2 O=O bonds:
(4 mol)(413 kJ/mol) + (2 mol)(498 kJ/mol) = 2648 kJ

Make 2 C=O bonds and 4 H—O bonds:
(2 mol)(745 kJ/mol) + (4 mol)(463 kJ/mol) = 3342 kJ

$\Delta_r H° = 2648$ kJ − 3342 kJ = −694 kJ/mol-rxn
(value calculated using enthalpies of formation = −802 kJ/mol-rxn)

Chapter 9

9.1 This molecule has a tetrahedral electron-pair geometry and also a tetrahedral molecular shape. The carbon is sp^3 hybridized. The C—H bond arises from overlap of a carbon sp^3 orbital and the hydrogen $1s$ orbital. The C—Cl bonds each arise from overlap of a carbon sp^3 orbital and a chlorine $3p$ orbital.

9.2 The carbon and nitrogen atoms in CH_3NH_2 are sp^3 hybridized. The C—H bonds arise from overlap of carbon sp^3 orbitals and hydrogen $1s$ orbitals. The bond between C and N is formed by overlap of sp^3 orbitals from these atoms. Overlap of nitrogen sp^3 and hydrogen $1s$ orbitals gives the two N—H bonds, and there is a lone pair in the remaining sp^3 orbital on nitrogen.

9.3 This molecule has a trigonal-bipyramidal electron-pair geometry and a linear molecular shape. The xenon is sp^3d hybridized. The Xe—F bonds each arise from the overlap of one of the axial sp^3d hybrid orbitals on Xe with a $2p$ orbital on the F. The three lone pairs around Xe are in the equatorial sp^3d hybrid orbitals.

9.4 (a) BH_4^-, tetrahedral electron-pair geometry, sp^3
(b) SF_5^-, octahedral electron-pair geometry, sp^3d^2
(c) OSF_4, trigonal-bipyramidal electron-pair geometry, sp^3d
(d) ClF_3, trigonal-bipyramidal electron-pair geometry, sp^3d
(e) BCl_3, trigonal-planar electron-pair geometry, sp^2
(f) XeO_6^{4-}, octahedral electron-pair geometry, sp^3d^2

9.5 The two CH_3 carbon atoms are sp^3 hybridized, and the center carbon atom is sp^2 hybridized. For each of the carbon atoms in the methyl groups, the sp^3 orbitals overlap with hydrogen $1s$ orbitals to form the three C—H bonds, and the fourth sp^3 orbital overlaps with an sp^2 orbital on the central carbon atom, forming a carbon–carbon sigma bond. Overlap of an sp^2 orbital on the central carbon and an oxygen sp^2 orbital gives the sigma bond between these elements. The π bond between carbon and oxygen arises by overlap of a p orbital from each element.

9.6 H_2^+: $(\sigma_{1s})^1$ The ion has a bond order of ½ and is expected to exist. A bond order of ½ is predicted for He_2^+ and H_2^-, both of which are predicted to have electron configurations $(\sigma_{1s})^2(\sigma^*_{1s})^1$.

9.7 Li_2^- is predicted to have an electron configuration $(\sigma_{1s})^2(\sigma^*_{1s})^2(\sigma_{2s})^2(\sigma^*_{2s})^1$ and a bond order of ½, the positive value implying that the ion might exist.

9.8 O_2^+: [core electrons] $(\sigma_{2s})^2(\sigma^*_{2s})^2(\sigma_{2p})^2(\pi_{2p})^4(\pi^*_{2p})^1$. The bond order is 2.5. The ion is paramagnetic with one unpaired electron.

Chapter 10

10.1 (a) Isomers of C_7H_{16}

$$CH_3CH_2CH_2CH_2CH_2CH_2CH_3 \qquad \text{heptane}$$

$$CH_3CH_2CH_2CH_2\overset{\overset{\displaystyle CH_3}{\vert}}{C}HCH_3 \qquad \text{2-methylhexane}$$

$$CH_3CH_2CH_2\overset{\overset{\displaystyle CH_3}{\vert}}{C}HCH_2CH_3 \qquad \text{3-methylhexane}$$

$$CH_3CH_2\overset{\overset{\displaystyle CH_3}{\vert}}{\underset{\underset{\displaystyle CH_3}{\vert}}{C}}HCHCH_3 \qquad \text{2,3-dimethylpentane}$$

$$CH_3CH_2CH_2\overset{\overset{\displaystyle CH_3}{\vert}}{\underset{\underset{\displaystyle CH_3}{\vert}}{C}}CH_3 \qquad \text{2,2-dimethylpentane}$$

$$CH_3CH_2\overset{\overset{\displaystyle CH_3}{\vert}}{\underset{\underset{\displaystyle CH_3}{\vert}}{C}}CH_2CH_3 \qquad \text{3,3-dimethylpentane}$$

$$CH_3\overset{\overset{\displaystyle CH_3}{\vert}}{\underset{\underset{\displaystyle CH_3}{\vert}}{C}}HCH_2CHCH_3 \qquad \text{2,4-dimethylpentane}$$

3-Ethylpentane is pictured on page 446.

$$CH_3\overset{\overset{\displaystyle H_3C}{\vert}}{\underset{\underset{\displaystyle CH_3}{\vert}}{C}}\!-\!\overset{\overset{\displaystyle CH_3}{\vert}}{C}HCH_3 \qquad \text{2,2,3-trimethylbutane}$$

(b) Two isomers, 3-methylhexane and 2,3-dimethylpentane, are chiral.

10.2 The names accompany the structures in the answer to Check Your Understanding 10.1.

10.3 Isomers of C_6H_{12} in which the longest chain has six C atoms:

Names (in order, top to bottom): 1-hexene, *cis*-2-hexene, *trans*-2-hexene, *cis*-3-hexene, *trans*-3-hexene. None of these isomers is chiral.

10.4 (a)

bromoethane

(b)

2,3-dibromobutane

10.5 1,4-diaminobenzene

10.6

$CH_3CH_2CH_2CH_2OH$ 1-butanol

$CH_3CH_2CHCH_3$ (OH)   2-butanol

CH_3CHCH_2OH (CH_3)   2-methyl-1-propanol

CH_3CCH_3 (OH)(CH_3)   2-methyl-2-propanol

10.7 (a) $CH_3CH_2CH_2OH$: 1-propanol, has an alcohol (—OH) group

CH_3CO_2H: ethanoic acid (acetic acid), has a carboxylic acid (—CO_2H) group

$CH_3CH_2NH_2$: ethylamine, has an amino (—NH_2) group

(b) 1-propyl ethanoate (propyl acetate)

(c) Oxidation of this primary alcohol first gives propanal, CH_3CH_2CHO. Further oxidation gives propanoic acid, $CH_3CH_2CO_2H$.

(d) *N*-ethylacetamide, $CH_3CONHCH_2CH_3$

(e) The amine is protonated by hydrochloric acid, forming ethylammonium chloride, $[CH_3CH_2NH_3]Cl$.

10.8 Kevlar is a condensation polymer, prepared by the reaction of terephthalic acid and 1,4-diaminobenzene.

$$n\, H_2NC_6H_4NH_2 + n\, HO_2CC_6H_4CO_2H \rightarrow \text{(}HNC_6H_4NHCOC_6H_4CO\text{)}_n + 2n\, H_2O$$

Chapter 11

11.1 0.83 bar (0.82 atm) > 75 kPa (0.74 atm) > 0.63 atm > 250 mm Hg (0.33 atm)

11.2 $V_2 = P_1V_1/P_2 = (745 \text{ mm Hg})(65.0 \text{ L})/[0.70(745 \text{ mm Hg})] = 93 \text{ L}$

11.3 $V_1 = 45 \text{ L}$ and $T_1 = 298 \text{ K}$; $V_2 = ?$ and $T_2 = 263 \text{ K}$

$V_2 = V_1(T_2/T_1) = (45 \text{ L})(263 \text{ K}/298 \text{ K}) = 40. \text{ L}$

11.4 $V_2 = V_1(P_1/P_2)(T_2/T_1)$

$= (22 \text{ L})(150 \text{ atm}/0.993 \text{ atm})(295 \text{ K}/304 \text{ K})$

$= 3200 \text{ L}$

At 5.0 L per balloon, there is sufficient He to fill 640 balloons.

11.5 44.8 L of O_2 is required; 44.8 L of $H_2O(g)$ and 22.4 L of $CO_2(g)$ are produced.

11.6 $PV = nRT$

$(750/760 \text{ atm})(V) = (1300 \text{ mol})(0.08206 \text{ L} \cdot \text{atm/mol} \cdot \text{K})(296 \text{ K})$

$V = 3.2 \times 10^4 \text{ L}$

11.7 $d = PM/RT$; $M = dRT/P$

$M = (5.02 \text{ g/L})(0.082057 \text{ L} \cdot \text{atm/mol} \cdot \text{K})(288.2 \text{ K})/(745/760 \text{ atm}) = 121 \text{ g/mol}$

11.8 $PV = (m/M)RT$; $M = mRT/PV$

$M = (0.105 \text{ g})(0.082057 \text{ L} \cdot \text{atm/mol} \cdot \text{K})(296.2 \text{ K})/[(561/760) \text{ atm} (0.125 \text{ L})] = 27.7 \text{ g/mol}$

11.9 $n(N_2) = PV/RT = (1.10 \text{ atm})(25.0 \text{ L})/(0.082057 \text{ L} \cdot \text{atm/mol} \cdot \text{K})(298.2 \text{ K}) = 1.12 \text{ mol } N_2$

$1.12 \text{ mol } N_2 (2 \text{ mol Na}/3 \text{ mol } N_2)(22.99 \text{ g Na}/1 \text{ mol Na}) = 17.2 \text{ g Na}$

11.10 $n(H_2) = PV/RT$

$= (542/760 \text{ atm})(355 \text{ L})/(0.08206 \text{ L} \cdot \text{atm/mol} \cdot \text{K})(298.2 \text{ K})$

$n(H_2) = 10.3 \text{ mol}$

$n(NH_3) = (10.3 \text{ mol } H_2)(2 \text{ mol } NH_3/3 \text{ mol } H_2)$

$= 6.90 \text{ mol } NH_3$

$P(125 \text{ L}) = (6.90 \text{ mol})(0.082057 \text{ L} \cdot \text{atm/mol} \cdot \text{K})(298.2 \text{ K})$

$P(NH_3) = 1.35 \text{ atm}$

11.11 $P_{halothane}$ (5.00 L)

$\quad$ = (0.0760 mol)(0.08206 L · atm/mol · K) (298.2 K)

$\quad P_{halothane}$ = 0.372 atm (or 283 mm Hg)

$\quad P_{oxygen}$ (5.00 L)

$\quad$ = (0.734 mol)(0.08206 L · atm/mol · K)(298.2 K)

$\quad P_{oxygen}$ = 3.59 atm (or 2730 mm Hg)

$\quad P_{total} = P_{halothane} + P_{oxygen}$

$\quad$ = 283 mm Hg + 2730 mm Hg = 3010 mm Hg

11.12 For He: Use Equation 11.9, with $M = 4.00 \times 10^{-3}$ kg/mol, $T = 298$ K, and $R = 8.314$ J/mol · K to calculate the rms speed of 1360 m/s. A similar calculation for N_2, with $M = 28.01 \times 10^{-3}$ kg/mol, gives an rms speed of 515 m/s.

11.13 The molar mass of CH_4 is 16.0 g/mol.

$$\frac{\text{Rate for } CH_4}{\text{Rate for unknown}} = \frac{n \text{ molecules/1.50 min}}{n \text{ molecules/4.73 min}} = \sqrt{\frac{M_{unknown}}{16.0}}$$

$M_{unknown} = 159$ g/mol

Chapter 12

12.1 Because F^- is the smaller ion, water molecules can approach more closely and interact more strongly. Thus, F^- should have the more negative enthalpy of hydration.

12.2

Hydrogen bonding in methanol entails the attraction of the hydrogen atom bearing a partial positive charge (δ^+) on one molecule to the oxygen atom bearing a partial negative charge (δ^-) on a second molecule. The strong attractive force of hydrogen bonding will cause the boiling point and the enthalpy of vaporization of methanol to be quite high.

12.3 Water is a polar solvent, while hexane and CCl_4 are nonpolar. London dispersion forces are the primary forces of attraction between all pairs of dissimilar solvents. For mixtures of water with the other solvents, dipole–induced dipole forces will also be important.

12.4 (a) O_2: induced dipole–induced dipole forces only.

(b) CH_3OH: strong hydrogen bonding (dipole–dipole forces) as well as induced dipole–induced dipole forces.

(c) Forces between water molecules: strong hydrogen bonding and induced dipole–induced dipole forces. Between N_2 and H_2O: dipole-induced dipole forces and induced dipole–induced dipole forces.

Relative strengths: a < forces between N_2 and H_2O in c < b < forces between water molecules in c.

12.5 (1.00 × 10³ g)(1 mol/32.04 g)(35.2 kJ/mol)

$\qquad\qquad\qquad\qquad\qquad$ = 1.10 × 10³ kJ

12.6 (a) At 40 °C, the vapor pressure of ethanol is about 120 mm Hg.

(b) The equilibrium vapor pressure of ethanol at 60 °C is about 320 mm Hg. At 60 °C and 600 mm Hg, ethanol is a liquid. If vapor is present, it will condense to a liquid.

Chapter 13

13.1 (a) The strategy to solve this problem is given in Example 13.1.

Step 1. Mass of the unit cell

= (197.0 g/mol)(1 mol/6.022 × 10²³ atom)

$\qquad\qquad\qquad\qquad$ (4 atoms/unit cell)

= 1.309 × 10⁻²¹ g/unit cell

Step 2. Volume of unit cell

= (1.309 × 10⁻²¹ g/unit cell)(1 cm³/19.32 g)

= 6.773 × 10⁻²³ cm³/unit cell

Step 3. Length of side of unit cell

= [6.773 × 10⁻²³ cm³/unit cell]^{1/3}

= 4.076 × 10⁻⁸ cm

Step 4. Calculate the radius from the edge dimension.

Diagonal distance = 4.076 × 10⁻⁸ cm (2^{½}) = 4 (r_{Au})

r_{Au} = 1.441 × 10⁻⁸ cm (= 144.1 pm)

(b) To verify a body-centered cubic structure, calculate the mass contained in the unit cell. If the structure is bcc, then the mass will be the mass of 2 Fe atoms. (Other possibilities: fcc − mass of 4 Fe; primitive cubic − mass of 1 Fe atom). This calculation uses the four steps from the previous exercise in reverse order.

Step 1. Use radius of Fe to calculate cell dimensions. In a body-centered cube, atoms touch across the diagonal of the cube.

Diagonal distance = side dimension ($\sqrt{3}$) = 4 r_{Fe}

Side dimension of cube = 4 (1.26 × 10⁻⁸ cm)/($\sqrt{3}$) = 2.910 × 10⁻⁸ cm

Step 2. Calculate unit cell volume

Unit cell volume = (2.910 × 10⁻⁸ cm)³

= 2.464 × 10⁻²³ cm³

Step 3. Combine unit cell volume and density to find the mass of the unit cell.

Mass of unit cell = 2.464 × 10⁻²³ cm³(7.8740 g/cm³)

= 1.940 × 10⁻²² g

Step 4. Calculate the mass of 2 Fe atoms, and compare this to the answer from step 3.

Mass of 2 Fe atoms

= 55.85 g/mol (1 mol/6.022 × 10²³ atoms)

$\qquad\qquad\qquad\qquad\qquad\qquad$ (2 atoms)

= 1.85 × 10⁻²² g.

This is a fairly good match, and clearly much better than the two other possibilities, primitive and fcc.

13.2 M_2X. In a face-centered cubic unit cell, there are four anions and eight tetrahedral holes in which to place metal ions. All of the tetrahedral holes are inside the unit cell, so the ratio of atoms in the unit cell is 2 : 1.

13.3 We need to calculate the mass and volume of the unit cell from the information given. The density of KCl will then be mass/volume. Select units so the density is calculated as g/cm^3

> Step 1. Mass: The unit cell contains 4 K^+ ions and 4 Cl^- ions
>
> Unit cell mass = $(39.10 \text{ g/mol})(1 \text{ mol}/6.022 \times 10^{23} \text{ K}^+ \text{ ions})(4 \text{ K}^+ \text{ ions}) + (35.45 \text{ g/mol})(1 \text{ mol}/6.022 \times 10^{23} \text{ Cl}^- \text{ ions})(4 \text{ Cl}^- \text{ ions})$
>
> $= 2.355 \times 10^{-22} \text{ g} + 2.597 \times 10^{-22} \text{ g}$
>
> $= 4.952 \times 10^{-22} \text{ g}$
>
> Step 2. Volume: Assuming K^+ and Cl^- ions touch along one edge of the cube, the side dimension = $2\,r_{K^+} + 2\,r_{Cl^-}$. The volume of the cube is the cube of this value. (Convert the ionic radius from pm to cm.)
>
> V = $[2(1.33 \times 10^{-8} \text{ cm}) + 2(1.81 \times 10^{-8} \text{ cm})]^3$
>
> $= 2.477 \times 10^{-22} \text{ cm}^3$
>
> Step 3. Density = mass/volume
>
> $= 4.952 \times 10^{-22} \text{ g}/2.477 \times 10^{-22} \text{ cm}^3)$
>
> $= 2.00 \text{ g/cm}^3$

Chapter 14

14.1 (a) 10.0 g sucrose = 0.0292 mol; 250. g H_2O = 13.9 mol

X_{sucrose} = $(0.0292 \text{ mol})/(0.0292 \text{ mol} + 13.9 \text{ mol})$
$= 0.00210$

c_{sucrose} = $(0.0292 \text{ mol sucrose})/(0.250 \text{ kg solvent})$
$= 0.117 \, m$

Weight % sucrose =
$(10.0 \text{ g sucrose}/260 \text{ g soln})(100\%) = 3.85\%$

(b) 1.08×10^4 ppm =
1.08×10^4 mg Na^+ per 1000 g soln

= $(1.08 \times 10^4 \text{ mg Na}^+/1000 \text{ g soln})$
$(1050 \text{ g soln}/1 \text{ L})$

= 1.13×10^4 mg Na^+/L

= 11.3 g Na^+/L

$(11.3 \text{ g Na}^+/\text{L})(58.44 \text{ g NaCl}/23.0 \text{ g Na}^+) =$
28.8 g NaCl/L

14.2 $\Delta_{\text{soln}}H^\circ = \Delta_f H^\circ[\text{NaOH(aq)}] - \Delta_f H^\circ[\text{NaOH(s)}]$
$= -469.2 \text{ kJ/mol} - (-425.9 \text{ kJ/mol})$
$= -43.3 \text{ kJ/mol}$

14.3 Solubility of CO_2 = $k_H P_g$ = 0.034 mol/kg $\cdot$ bar $\times$ 0.33 bar = 1.1×10^{-2} mol/kg

14.4 The solution contains sucrose $[(10.0 \text{ g})(1 \text{ mol}/342.3 \text{ g})$ = 0.0292 mol] in water $[(225 \text{ g})(1 \text{ mol}/18.02 \text{ g})$ = 12.5 mol].

X_{water} = $(12.5 \text{ mol H}_2\text{O})/(12.5 \text{ mol} + 0.0292 \text{ mol})$
$= 0.998$

P_{water} = $X_{\text{water}}P^\circ_{\text{water}}$ = 0.998(149.4 mm Hg)
$= 149 \text{ mm Hg}$

14.5 c_{glycol} = $\Delta T_{\text{bp}}/K_{\text{bp}}$ = 1.0 °C/(0.512 °C/m)
$= 2.0 \, m$ = 2.0 mol/kg

mass$_{\text{glycol}}$ = (2.0 mol/kg)(0.125 kg)(62.07 g/mol) = 15 g

14.6 c_{glycol} = $(525 \text{ g})(1 \text{ mol}/62.07 \text{ g})/(3.00 \text{ kg})$ = 2.82 m

ΔT_{fp} = $K_{\text{fp}} \times m$ = $(-1.86 °C/m)(2.82 \, m)$ = −5.24 °C

You will be protected only to about −5 °C and not to −25 °C.

14.7 c (mol/L) = 0.033 g bradykinin (1 mol bradykinin/1060 g bradykinin)/0.0500 L = 6.2×10^{-4} M

$\Pi = cRT$
$= (6.2 \times 10^{-4} \text{ mol/L})(0.082057 \text{ L} \cdot \text{atm/mol} \cdot \text{K})(293 \text{ K})$
$= 0.015 \text{ atm}$

14.8 ΔT_{fp} = 5.265 °C − 5.50 °C = −0.24 °C

ΔT_{fp} = $K_{\text{fp}} \times m_{\text{solute}}$

m_{solute} = −0.24 °C/−5.12 °C/m = 0.046 mol/kg

n_{solute} = (0.046 mol solute/kg benzene)(0.02346 kg benzene) = 0.0011 mol solute

M = 0.448 g/0.0011 mol = 4.2×10^2 g/mol

$M(\text{compound})/M(\text{empirical formula})$
$= 4.2 \times 10^2$ g/mol/104.1 g/mol = 4.0

Molecular formula = $(C_2H_5)_8Al_4F_4$

14.9 c (mol/L) = Π/RT = $[(1.86 \text{ mm Hg})(1 \text{ atm}/760 \text{ mm Hg})]/[(0.08206 \text{ L} \cdot \text{atm/mol} \cdot \text{K})(298 \text{ K})]$
$= 1.00 \times 10^{-4}$ M

$(1.00 \times 10^{-4} \text{ mol/L})(0.100 \text{ L})$ = 1.00×10^{-5} mol

Molar mass = 1.40 g/1.00×10^{-5} mol
$= 1.4 \times 10^5$ g/mol

(Assuming the polymer is composed of CH_2 units, the polymer is about 10,000 units long.)

14.10 c_{NaCl} = $(25.0 \text{ g NaCl})(1 \text{ mol}/58.44 \text{ g})/(0.525 \text{ kg})$
$= 0.815 \, m$

ΔT_{fp} = $K_{\text{fp}} \times m \times i$ = $(-1.86 °C/m)(0.815 \, m)(1.85)$
$= -2.80 °C$

Chapter 15

15.1 $-\frac{1}{2}(\Delta[\text{NOCl}]/\Delta t) = \frac{1}{2}(\Delta[\text{NO}]/\Delta t) = \Delta[\text{Cl}_2]/\Delta t$

15.2 For the first 2 hours:

$-\Delta[\text{sucrose}]/\Delta t = -[(0.033 - 0.050) \text{ mol/L}]/(2.0 \text{ h})$
$= 0.0085 \text{ mol/L} \cdot \text{h}$

For the last 2 hours:

$-\Delta[\text{sucrose}]/\Delta t = -[(0.010 - 0.015) \text{ mol/L}]/(2.0 \text{ h})$
$= 0.0025 \text{ mol/L} \cdot \text{h}$

Instantaneous rate at 4 hours = 0.0045 mol/L $\cdot$ h. (Calculated from the slope of a line tangent to the curve at the defined concentration.)

15.3 Compare experiments 1 and 2: Doubling $[O_2]$ causes the rate to double, so the rate is first order in $[O_2]$. Compare experiments 2 and 4: Doubling [NO] causes the rate to increase by a factor of 4, so the rate is second order in [NO]. Thus, the rate law is

Rate $= -(1/2)(\Delta[NO]/\Delta t) = k[NO]^2[O_2]$

Notice that stoichiometry requires the factor of $(1/2)$ in the reaction rate expression.

Using the data in experiment 1 to determine k:

$(1/2)0.028$ mol/L $\cdot$ s $= k[0.020$ mol/L$]^2[0.010$ mol/L$]$

$k = 3.5 \times 10^3$ L^2/mol$^2 \cdot$ s

15.4 Rate $= k[Pt(NH_3)_2Cl_2] = (0.27$ h$^{-1})(0.020$ mol/L$)$

$= 0.0054$ mol/L $\cdot$ h

15.5 ln $([sucrose]/[sucrose]_o) = -kt$

ln $([sucrose]/[0.010]) = -(0.21$ h$^{-1})(5.0$ h$)$

$[sucrose] = 0.0035$ mol/L

15.6 (a) The fraction remaining is $[CH_3N_2CH_3]/[CH_3N_2CH_3]_o$.

ln $([CH_3N_2CH_3]/[CH_3N_2CH_3]_o)$
$= -(3.6 \times 10^{-4}$ s$^{-1})(150$ s$)$

$[CH_3N_2CH_3]/[CH_3N_2CH_3]_o = 0.95$

(b) After the reaction is 99% complete
$[CH_3N_2CH_3]/[CH_3N_2CH_3]_o = 0.010$

ln $(0.010) = -(3.6 \times 10^{-4}$ s$^{-1})(t)$

$t = 1.3 \times 10^4$ s $(210$ min$)$

15.7 $1/[HI] - 1/[HI]_o = kt$

$1/[HI] - 1/[0.010$ M$] = (30.$ L/mol $\cdot$ min$)(12$ min$)$

$[HI] = 0.0022$ M

15.8 $(0.060$ M/0.24 M$) = 0.25$; thus $\frac{1}{4}$ of the original material remains and two half-lives have transpired.

$t_{1/2} = 141$ min.

$k = \ln 2/t_{1/2} = (\ln 2)/141$ min $= 4.9 \times 10^{-3}$ min^{-1}

Initial rate $= k[H_2O_2]_0$
$= 4.9 \times 10^{-3}$ min^{-1} $(0.24$ mol/L$)$
$= 1.2 \times 10^{-3}$ mol/L $\cdot$ min

15.9 (a) For ^{241}Am, $t_{1/2} = 0.693/k = 0.693/(0.0016$ y$^{-1})$
$= 430$ y

For ^{125}I, $t_{1/2} = 0.693/(0.011$ d$^{-1}) = 63$ d

(b) ^{125}I decays much faster.

(c) ln $[(n)/(1.6 \times 10^{15}$ atoms$)] = -(0.011$ d$^{-1})(2.0$ d$)$

$n/1.6 \times 10^{15}$ atoms $= 0.978$; $n = 1.57 \times 10^{15}$ atoms

Since the answer should have two significant figures, we should round this off to 1.6×10^{15} atoms. The approximately 2% that has decayed is not discernable within the limits of accuracy of the data presented.

15.10 An Arrhenius plot was constructed by plotting ln k on the y-axis and $1/T$ on the x-axis. Using Microsoft Excel, the equation of the best-fit line is $y = -22336x + 27.304$.

$E_a = -R \cdot$ (slope)
$= -(0.0083145$ kJ/mol $\cdot$ K$)(-22336$ K$)$
$= 1.9 \times 10^2$ kJ/mol

15.11 ln $(k_2/k_1) = (-E_a/R)(1/T_2 - 1/T_1)$

ln $[(1.00 \times 10^4)/(4.5 \times 10^3)]$
$= -(E_a/8.3145 \times 10^{-3}$ kJ/mol $\cdot$ K$)(1/283$ K $- 1/274$ K$)$

$E_a = 57$ kJ/mol

15.12 All three steps are bimolecular.

For step 3: Rate $= k[N_2O][H_2]$.

There are two intermediates, $N_2O_2(g)$ and $N_2O(g)$.

When the three equations are added, N_2O_2 (a product in the first step and a reactant in the second step) and N_2O (a product in the second step and a reactant in the third step) cancel, leaving the net equation:

2 NO$(g) + 2$ H$_2(g) \longrightarrow$ N$_2(g) + 2$ H$_2$O(g).

15.13 (a) 2 NH$_3$(aq) + OCl$^-$(aq) $\longrightarrow$
N_2H_4(aq) + Cl$^-$(aq) + H$_2$O(ℓ)

(b) The second step is the rate-determining step.

(c) Rate $= k[NH_2Cl][NH_3]$

(d) NH$_2$Cl, N$_2$H$_5^+$, and OH$^-$ are intermediates.

15.14 Overall reaction: 2 NO$_2$Cl$(g) \longrightarrow 2$ NO$_2(g) +$ Cl$_2(g)$

Rate $= k'[NO_2Cl]^2/[NO_2]$ (where $k' = k_1k_2/k_{-1}$)

Increasing $[NO_2]$ causes the reaction rate to decrease.

Chapter 16

16.1 (a) $K = [CO]^2/[CO_2]$

(b) $K = [Cu^{2+}][NH_3]^4/[Cu(NH_3)_4^{2+}]$

(c) $K = [H_3O^+][CH_3CO_2^-]/[CH_3CO_2H]$

16.2 (a) $Q = [2.18]/[0.97] = 2.2$. The system is not at equilibrium; $Q < K$. To reach equilibrium, [isobutane] will increase and [butane] will decrease.

(b) $Q = [2.60]/[0.75] = 3.5$. The system is not at equilibrium; $Q > K$. To reach equilibrium, [butane] will increase and [isobutane] will decrease.

16.3 (a)

Equation	$C_6H_{10}I_2 \rightleftharpoons$	$C_6H_{10} +$	I_2
Initial (M)	0.050	0	0
Change (M)	−0.035	+0.035	+0.035
Equilibrium (M)	0.015	0.035	0.035

(b) $K = (0.035)(0.035)/(0.015) = 0.082$

16.4

Equation	$PCl_5(g) \rightleftharpoons$	$PCl_3(g) +$	$Cl_2(g)$
Initial (atm)	2.000	0	0
Change (atm)	$-x$	$+x$	$+x$
Equilibrium (atm)	$2.000 - x$	x	x

The partial pressure of Cl$_2$ at equilibrium is 0.814 atm, so $x = 0.814$ atm.

$P(PCl_5) = 2.000$ atm $- 0.814$ atm $= 1.186$ atm

$P(PCl_3) = P(Cl_2) = 0.814$ atm

$K_p = (0.814)(0.814)/1.186 = 0.559$

16.5

Equation	H_2	$+$	I_2	$\rightleftharpoons$	$2\,HI$
Initial (M)	6.00×10^{-3}		6.00×10^{-3}		0
Change (M)	$-x$		$-x$		$+2x$
Equilibrium (M)	$0.00600 - x$		$0.00600 - x$		$+2x$

$$K_c = 33 = \frac{(2x)^2}{(0.00600 - x)^2}$$

$x = 0.0045$ M, so $[H_2] = [I_2] = 0.0015$ M and $[HI] = 0.0090$ M.

16.6

Equation	$PCl_5(g)$	$\rightleftharpoons$	$PCl_3(g)$	$+$	$Cl_2(g)$
Initial (M)	0.1000		0		0
Change (M)	$-x$		$+x$		$+x$
Equilibrium (M)	$0.1000 - x$		x		x

$K_c = [PCl_3][Cl_2]/[PCl_5]$

$33.3 = x^2/0.1000 - x$

We cannot use the simplifying assumption in this case (K is > 1 and $100 \cdot K > 0.1000$), so we must solve using the quadratic formula.

$x^2 + 33.3x - 3.33 = 0$

Using the quadratic formula, $x = 0.0997$ (the other root, $x = -33.4$, is not possible because it leads to negative concentrations).

$[PCl_3] = [Cl_2] = 0.0997$ M

$[PCl_5] = 0.1000$ M $- 0.0997$ M $= 0.0003$ M

16.7 (a) $K' = K^2 = (2.5 \times 10^{-29})^2 = 6.3 \times 10^{-58}$
(b) $K'' = 1/K^2 = 1/(6.3 \times 10^{-58}) = 1.6 \times 10^{57}$

16.8

Equation	Butane	$\rightleftharpoons$	Isobutane
Initial (M)	0.20		0.50
After adding 2.0 M more isobutane	0.20		$2.00 + 0.50$
Change (M)	$+x$		$-x$
Equilibrium (M)	$0.20 + x$		$2.50 - x$

$$K = \frac{[\text{isobutane}]}{[\text{butane}]} = \frac{(2.50 - x)}{(0.20 + x)} = 2.50$$

Solving for x gives $x = 0.57$ M. Therefore, [isobutane] $= 2.50 - 0.57 = 1.93$ M and [butane] $= 0.20 + 0.57 = 0.77$ M.

Chapter 17

17.1 $[H_3O^+] = 4.0 \times 10^{-3}$ M; $[OH^-] = K_w/[H_3O^+]$ $= 2.5 \times 10^{-12}$ M

17.2 (a) pH $= 7$
(b) pH < 7 (NH_4^+ is an acid)
(c) pH < 7 $[Al(H_2O)_6]^{3+}$ is an acid
(d) pH > 7 (HPO_4^{2-} is a stronger base than it is an acid)

17.3 (a) NH_4^+ is a stronger acid than HCO_3^-. CO_3^{2-}, the conjugate base of HCO_3^-, is a stronger base than NH_3, the conjugate base of NH_4^+.
(b) Reactant-favored; the reactants are the weaker acid and base.
(c) Reactant-favored; the reactants are the weaker acid and base, so reaction lies to the left.

17.4 From the pH, we can calculate $[H_3O^+] = 1.9 \times 10^{-3}$ M. Also, [butanoate$^-$] $= [H_3O^+] = 1.9 \times 10^{-3}$ M. Use these values along with [butanoic acid] to calculate K_a.
$K_a = [1.9 \times 10^{-3}][1.9 \times 10^{-3}]/(0.055 - 1.9 \times 10^{-3})$ $= 6.8 \times 10^{-5}$

17.5 $K_a = 1.8 \times 10^{-5} = [x][x]/(0.10 - x)$
$x = [H_3O^+] = [CH_3CO_2^-] = 1.3 \times 10^{-3}$ M;
$[CH_3CO_2H] = 0.099$ M; pH $= 2.87$

17.6 $HF(aq) + H_2O(\ell) \rightleftharpoons H_3O^+(aq) + F^-(aq)$
$K_a = 7.2 \times 10^{-4} = [x][x]/(0.00150 - x)$
The x in the denominator cannot be dropped. This equation must be solved with the quadratic formula or by successive approximations. Because this problem follows the section dealing with the method of successive approximations, that method will be used here.
$7.2 \times 10^{-4} = x^2/(0.00150); x = 1.0 \times 10^{-3}$
$7.2 \times 10^{-4} = x^2/(0.00150 - 1.0 \times 10^{-3}); x = 6.0 \times 10^{-4}$
$7.2 \times 10^{-4} = x^2/(0.00150 - 6.0 \times 10^{-4}); x = 8.0 \times 10^{-4}$
$7.2 \times 10^{-4} = x^2/(0.00150 - 8.0 \times 10^{-4}); x = 7.1 \times 10^{-4}$
$7.2 \times 10^{-4} = x^2/(0.00150 - 7.1 \times 10^{-4}); x = 7.5 \times 10^{-4}$
$7.2 \times 10^{-4} = x^2/(0.00150 - 7.5 \times 10^{-4}); x = 7.3 \times 10^{-4}$
$7.2 \times 10^{-4} = x^2/(0.00150 - 7.3 \times 10^{-4}); x = 7.4 \times 10^{-4}$
$7.2 \times 10^{-4} = x^2/(0.00150 - 7.4 \times 10^{-4}); x = 7.4 \times 10^{-4}$
The result has converged to two significant figures.
$[H_3O^+] = [F^-] = 7.4 \times 10^{-4}$ M
$[HF] = 0.00150$ M $- 7.4 \; 10^{-4}$ M $= 7.6 \times 10^{-4}$ M

17.7 $OCl^-(aq) + H_2O(\ell) \rightleftharpoons HOCl(aq) + OH^-(aq)$
$K_b = 2.9 \times 10^{-7} = [x][x]/(0.015 - x)$
$x = [OH^-] = [HOCl] = 6.6 \times 10^{-5}$ M
pOH $= 4.18$; pH $= 9.82$

17.8 Equivalent amounts of acid and base react to form water, $CH_3CO_2^-$ and Na^+. Acetate ion hydrolyzes to a small extent, giving CH_3CO_2H and OH^-. We need to determine $[CH_3CO_2^-]$ and then solve a weak base equilibrium problem to determine $[OH^-]$.
Amount $CH_3CO_2^-$ $=$ moles base $= 0.12$ mol/L $\times 0.015$ L $= 1.8 \times 10^{-3}$ mol
Total volume $= 0.030$ L, so $[CH_3CO_2^-] =$ $(1.8 \times 10^{-3}$ mol$)/0.030$ L $= 0.060$ M
$CH_3CO_2^-(aq) + H_2O(\ell) \rightleftharpoons$
$\qquad\qquad\qquad\qquad\qquad CH_3CO_2H(aq) + OH^-(aq)$
$K_b = 5.6 \times 10^{-10} = [x][x]/(0.060 - x)$
$x = [OH^-] = [CH_3CO_2H] = 5.8 \times 10^{-6}$ M
pOH $= 5.24$; pH $= 8.76$

17.9 $H_2C_2O_4(aq) + H_2O(\ell) \rightleftharpoons$
$$H_3O^+(aq) + HC_2O_4^-(aq)$$

$K_{a1} = 5.9 \times 10^{-2} = [x][x]/(0.10 - x)$

The x in the denominator cannot be dropped. This equation must be solved with the quadratic formula or by successive approximations.

$x = [H_3O^+] = [HC_2O_4^-] = 5.3 \times 10^{-2}$ M

pH = 1.28

$K_{a2} = [H_3O^+][C_2O_4^{2-}]/[HC_2O_4^-]$; because $[H_3O^+]$ = $[HC_2O_4^-]$

$[C_2O_4^{2-}] = K_{a2} = 6.4 \times 10^{-5}$ M

Chapter 18

18.1 pH of 0.30 M HCO_2H:

$K_a = [H_3O^+][HCO_2^-]/[HCO_2H]$

$1.8 \times 10^{-4} = [x][x]/[0.30 - x]$

$x = 7.3 \times 10^{-3}$ M; pH = 2.13

pH of 0.30 M formic acid + 0.10 M $NaHCO_2$

$K_a = [H_3O^+][HCO_2^-]/[HCO_2H]$

$1.8 \times 10^{-4} = [x][0.10 + x]/(0.30 - x)$

$x = 5.4 \times 10^{-4}$ M; pH = 3.27

18.2

Equation	$HCO_2H + H_2O \rightleftharpoons$	$H_3O^+ +$	HCO_2^-
Initial (M)	0.50	0	0.70
Change (M)	−x	+x	+x
Equilibrium (M)	0.50 − x	x	0.70 + x

$K_a = 1.8 \times 10^{-4} = (x)(0.70 + x)/(0.50 - x)$

The value of x will be insignificant compared to 0.50 M and 0.70 M.

$1.8 \times 10^{-4} = (x)(0.70)/(0.50)$

$x = [H_3O^+] = 1.3 \times 10^{-4}$ M

pH = $-\log[H_3O^+]$ = 3.89

18.3 $(15.0$ g $NaHCO_3)(1$ mol$/84.01$ g$) = 0.179$ mol $NaHCO_3$, and $(18.0$ g $Na_2CO_3)(1$ mol$/106.0$ g$)$ $= 0.170$ mol Na_2CO_3

pH = $pK_a + \log$ {[base]/[acid]}

pH = $-\log (4.8 \times 10^{-11}) + \log$ {[0.170]/[0.179]}

pH = 10.32 − 0.02 = 10.30

18.4 pH = $pK_a + \log$ {[base]/[acid]}

$5.00 = -\log (1.8 \times 10^{-5}) + \log$ {[base]/[acid]}

$5.00 = 4.74 + \log$ {[base]/[acid]}

[base]/[acid] = 1.8

To prepare this buffer solution, the ratio [base]/[acid] must equal 1.8. For example, you can dissolve 1.8 mol (148 g) of $NaCH_3CO_2$ and 1.0 mol (60.05 g) of CH_3CO_2H in enough water to make 1.0 L of solution.

18.5 Initial pH (before adding acid):

pH = $pK_a + \log$ {[base]/[acid]}

$= -\log (1.8 \times 10^{-4}) + \log$ {[0.70]/[0.50]}

$= 3.74 + 0.15 = 3.89$

After adding acid, the added HCl will react with the weak base (formate ion) and form more formic acid. The net effect is to change the ratio of [base]/[acid] in the buffer solution.

Initial amount HCO_2H = 0.50 mol/L × 0.500 L
$= 0.25$ mol

Initial amount HCO_2^- = 0.70 mol/L × 0.50 L
$= 0.35$ mol

Amount HCl added = 1.0 mol/L × 0.010 L
$= 0.010$ mol

Amount HCO_2H after HCl addition
$= 0.25$ mol + 0.010 mol = 0.26 mol

Amount HCO_2^- after HCl addition
$= 0.35$ mol − 0.010 mol = 0.34 mol

pH = $pK_a + \log$ {[base]/[acid]}

pH = $-\log (1.8 \times 10^{-4}) + \log$ {[0.34]/[0.26]}

pH = 3.74 + 0.12 = 3.86

18.6 35.0 mL base will partially neutralize the acid.

Initial amount CH_3CO_2H
$= (0.100$ mol/L$)(0.1000$ L$) = 0.0100$ mol

Amount NaOH added
$= (0.100$ mol/L$)(0.0350$ L$) = 0.00350$ mol

Amount CH_3CO_2H after reaction
$= 0.0100 - 0.00350 = 0.0065$ mol

Amount $CH_3CO_2^-$ after reaction = 0.0035 mol

$[CH_3CO_2H]$ after reaction = 0.0065 mol/0.1350 L
$= 0.048$ M

$[CH_3CO_2^-]$ after reaction = 0.00350 mol/0.1350 L
$= 0.0259$ M

$K_a = [H_3O^+][CH_3CO_2^-]/[CH_3CO_2H]$

$1.8 \times 10^{-5} = [x][0.0259 + x]/[0.048 - x]$

$x = [H_3O^+] = 3.3 \times 10^{-5}$ M; pH = 4.48

18.7 75.0 mL acid will partially neutralize the base.

Initial amount NH_3 = $(0.100$ mol/L$)(0.1000$ L$)$
$= 0.0100$ mol

Amount HCl added = $(0.100$ mol/L$)(0.0750$ L$)$
$= 0.00750$ mol

Amount NH_3 after reaction = 0.0100 − 0.00750
$= 0.0025$ mol

Amount NH_4^+ after reaction = 0.00750 mol

Solve using the Henderson–Hasselbach equation; use K_a for the weak acid NH_4^+:

pH = $pK_a + \log$ {[base]/[acid]}

pH = $-\log (5.6 \times 10^{-10}) + \log$ {[0.0025]/[0.00750]}

pH = 9.25 − 0.48 = 8.77

18.8 $BaF_2(s) \rightleftharpoons Ba^{2+}(aq) + 2 F^-(aq)$

$[F^-] = 2[Ba^{2+}] = 2(3.6 \times 10^{-3} \text{ M}) = 7.2 \times 10^{-3} \text{ M}$

$K_{sp} = [Ba^{2+}][F^-]^2 = (3.6 \times 10^{-3})(7.2 \times 10^{-3})^2$
$= 1.9 \times 10^{-7}$

18.9 $AgCN(s) \rightleftharpoons Ag^+(aq) + CN^-(aq)$

$K_{sp} = [Ag^+][CN^-]$

Let x = solubility of AgCN in mol/L

$6.0 \times 10^{-17} = x^2$

$x = 7.7 \times 10^{-9}$ mol/L

$(7.7 \times 10^{-9} \text{ mol AgCN/L})(133.9 \text{ g AgCN/1 mol AgCN}) = 1.0 \times 10^{-6}$ g/L

18.10 $Ca(OH)_2(s) \rightleftharpoons Ca^{2+}(aq) + 2 OH^-(aq)$

$K_{sp} = [Ca^{2+}][OH^-]^2; K_{sp} = 5.5 \times 10^{-5}$

$5.5 \times 10^{-5} = [x][2x]^2$ (where x = solubility in mol/L)

$x = 2.4 \times 10^{-2}$ mol/L

Solubility in g/L =
$(2.4 \times 10^{-2} \text{ mol/L})(74.1 \text{ g/mol}) = 1.8$ g/L

18.11 (a) In pure water:

$K_{sp} = [Ba^{2+}][SO_4{}^{2-}]; 1.1 \times 10^{-10} = [x][x];$

$x = 1.0 \times 10^{-5}$ mol/L

(b) In 0.010 M $Ba(NO_3)_2$, which furnishes 0.010 M Ba^{2+} in solution:

$K_{sp} = [Ba^{2+}][SO_4{}^{2-}]$
$1.1 \times 10^{-10} = [0.010 + x][x]$
$x = 1.1 \times 10^{-8}$ mol/L

18.12 (a) In pure water:

$K_{sp} = [Zn^{2+}][CN^-]^2; 8.0 \times 10^{-12} = [x][2x]^2 = 4x^3$

Solubility = $x = 1.3 \times 10^{-4}$ mol/L

(b) In 0.10 M $Zn(NO_3)_2$, which furnishes 0.10 M Zn^{2+} in solution:

$K_{sp} = [Zn^{2+}][CN^-]^2; 8.0 \times 10^{-12} = [0.10 + x][2x]^2$

Solubility = $x = 4.5 \times 10^{-6}$ mol/L

18.13 When $[Pb^{2+}] = 1.1 \times 10^{-3}$ M, $[I^-] = 2.2 \times 10^{-3}$ M.

$Q = [Pb^{2+}][I^-]^2 = [1.1 \times 10^{-3}][2.2 \times 10^{-3}]^2$
$= 5.3 \times 10^{-9}$

This value is less than K_{sp}, which means that the system has not yet reached equilibrium and more PbI_2 will dissolve.

18.14 $K_{sp} = [Pb^{2+}][I^-]^2$. Let x be the concentration of I^- required at equilibrium.

$9.8 \times 10^{-9} = [0.050][x]^2$

$x = [I^-] = 4.4 \times 10^{-5}$ mol/L. A concentration greater than this value will result in precipitation of PbI_2.

Let x be the concentration of Pb^{2+} in solution, in equilibrium with 0.0015 M I^-.

$9.8 \times 10^{-9} = [x][1.5 \times 10^{-3}]^2$

$x = [Pb^{2+}] = 4.4 \times 10^{-3}$ M

18.15 First, determine the concentrations of Ag^+ and Cl^-; then calculate Q, and see whether it is greater than or less than K_{sp}. Concentrations are calculated using the final volume, 105.0 mL, in the equation $C_{dil} \times V_{dil} = C_{conc} \times V_{conc}$.

$[Ag^+](0.1050 \text{ L}) = (0.0010 \text{ mol/L})(0.1000 \text{ L})$

$[Ag^+] = 9.5 \times 10^{-4}$ M

$[Cl^-](0.1050 \text{ L}) = (0.025 \text{ M})(0.0050 \text{ L})$

$[Cl^-] = 1.2 \times 10^{-3}$ M

$Q = [Ag^+][Cl^-] = [9.5 \times 10^{-4}][1.2 \times 10^{-3}]$
$= 1.1 \times 10^{-6}$

Because $Q > K_{sp}$, precipitation occurs.

18.16

Equation	$Ag(NH_3)_2{}^+$	$\rightleftharpoons$	Ag^+ +	$2 NH_3$
Initial (M)	0.0050		0	$1.00 - 2(0.0050)$
Change	$-x$		$+x$	$+2x$
Equilibrium (M)	$0.0050 - x$		x	$0.99 + 2x$

$K = 1/K_f = 1/1.1 \times 10^7 = [x][0.99]^2/0.0050$
$x = [Ag^+] = 4.6 \times 10^{-10}$ mol/L

18.17 $Cu(OH)_2(s) \rightleftharpoons Cu^{2+}(aq) + 2 OH^-(aq)$

$K_{sp} = [Cu^{2+}][OH^-]^2$

$Cu^{2+}(aq) + 4 NH_3(aq) \rightleftharpoons Cu(NH_3)_4{}^{2+}(aq)$

$K_{form} = [Cu(NH_3)_4{}^{2+}]/[Cu^{2+}][NH_3]^4$

Net: $Cu(OH)_2(s) + 4 NH_3(aq) \rightleftharpoons Cu(NH_3)_4{}^{2+}(aq) + 2 OH^-(aq)$

$K_{net} = K_{sp} \times K_f = (2.2 \times 10^{-20})(2.1 \times 10^{13})$
$= 4.6 \times 10^{-7}$

Chapter 19

19.1 (a) O_3; larger molecules generally have higher entropies than smaller molecules.

(b) $SnCl_4(g)$; gases have higher entropies than liquids.

19.2 (a) $\Delta_r S° = \Sigma n S°(\text{products}) - \Sigma n S°(\text{reactants})$

$\Delta_r S° = (1 \text{ mol/mol-rxn}) \, S°[NH_4Cl(aq)])$
$\qquad - (1 \text{ mol/mol-rxn}) \, S°[NH_4Cl(s)]$

$\Delta_r S° = (1 \text{ mol/mol-rxn})(169.9 \text{ J/mol} \cdot \text{K})$
$\qquad - (1 \text{ mol/mol-rxn})(94.85 \text{ J/mol} \cdot \text{K})$

$= 75.1 \text{ J/K} \cdot \text{mol-rxn}$

A gain in entropy for the formation of a mixture (solution) is expected.

(b) $\Delta_r S° = (2 \text{ mol } CO_2/\text{mol-rxn}) \, S°(CO_2) + (3 \text{ mol } H_2O/\text{mol-rxn}) \, S°(H_2O) - [(1 \text{ mol } C_2H_5OH/\text{mol-rxn}) \, S°(C_2H_5OH) + (3 \text{ mol } O_2/\text{mol-rxn}) \, S°(O_2)]$

$\Delta_r S° = (2 \text{ mol/mol-rxn})(213.74 \text{ J/mol} \cdot \text{K})$
$\qquad + (3 \text{ mol/mol-rxn})(188.84 \text{ J/mol} \cdot \text{K})$
$\qquad - [(1 \text{ mol/mol-rxn})(282.70 \text{ J/mol} \cdot \text{K})$
$\qquad + (3 \text{ mol/mol-rxn})(205.07 \text{ J/mol} \cdot \text{K})]$

$\Delta_r S° = +96.09 \text{ J/K} \cdot \text{mol-rxn}$

An increase in entropy is expected because there is a increase in the number of moles of gases.

19.3 $\Delta S°$(system) $= \Delta_r S°$
$$= \Sigma n S°(\text{products}) - \Sigma n S°(\text{reactants})$$

$\Delta_r S° = (2 \text{ mol HCl/mol-rxn}) \, S°[\text{HCl(g)}]$
$\quad - \{(1 \text{ mol H}_2/\text{mol-rxn}) \, S°[\text{H}_2(\text{g})]$
$\quad + (1 \text{ mol Cl}_2/\text{mol-rxn}) \, S°[\text{Cl}_2(\text{g})]\}$

$\quad = (2 \text{ mol HCl/mol-rxn})(186.2 \text{ J/K} \cdot \text{mol HCl})$
$\quad - \{(1 \text{ mol H}_2/\text{mol-rxn})(130.7 \text{ J/K} \cdot \text{mol H}_2)$
$\quad + (1 \text{ mol Cl}_2/\text{mol-rxn}) \, (223.08 \text{ J/K} \cdot \text{mol Cl}_2(\text{g})\}$

$\quad = 18.6 \text{ J/K} \cdot \text{mol-rxn}$

$\Delta_r H° = \Sigma n \Delta_f H°(\text{products}) - \Sigma n \Delta_f H°(\text{reactants})$

$\Delta_r H° = (2 \text{ mol HCl/mol-rxn}) \, \Delta_f H°[\text{HCl(g)}]$
$\quad - \{(1 \text{ mol H}_2/\text{mol-rxn}) \, \Delta_f H°[\text{H}_2(\text{g})]$
$\quad + (1 \text{ mol Cl}_2/\text{mol-rxn}) \, \Delta_f H°[\text{Cl}_2(\text{g})]\}$

$\quad = (2 \text{ mol HCl/mol-rxn})(-92.31 \text{ kJ/mol HCl})$
$\quad - \{(1 \text{ mol H}_2/\text{mol-rxn})(0 \text{ kJ/mol H}_2)$
$\quad + (1 \text{ mol Cl}_2/\text{mol-rxn})(0 \text{ kJ/mol Cl}_2(\text{g})\}$

$\quad = -184.62 \text{ kJ/mol-rxn}$

Both $\Delta_r H°$ (< 0) and $\Delta_r S°$ (> 0) are favorable, so this reaction is predicted to be spontaneous under standard conditions.

$\Delta S°$(surroundings) $= -\Delta_r H°/\text{T}$
$= -(-184.62 \text{ kJ/mol-rxn})/298.15 \text{ K}$
$= 0.61922 \text{ kJ/K} \cdot \text{mol-rxn} = 619.22 \text{ J/K} \cdot \text{mol-rxn}$

$\Delta S°$(universe) $= \Delta S°$(system) $+ \Delta S°$(surroundings)
$= 18.6 \text{ J/K} \cdot \text{mol-rxn} + 619.22 \text{ J/K} \cdot \text{mol-rxn}$
$= 637.8 \text{ J/K} \cdot \text{mol-rxn}$

$\Delta S°$(universe) > 0, so the reaction is spontaneous under standard conditions.

19.4 For the reaction $N_2(\text{g}) + 3 \, H_2(\text{g}) \longrightarrow 2 \, NH_3(\text{g})$:

$\Delta_r H° = (2 \text{ mol/mol-rxn}) \, \Delta_f H°$ for $\text{NH}_3(\text{g})$
$= (2 \text{ mol/mol-rxn})(-45.90 \text{ kJ/mol})$
$= -91.80 \text{ kJ/mol-rxn}$

$\Delta_r S° = (2 \text{ mol/mol-rxn}) \, S°(\text{NH}_3) - [(1 \text{ mol/mol-rxn})$
$S°(\text{N}_2) + (3 \text{ mol/mol-rxn}) \, S°(\text{H}_2)]$

$\Delta_r S° = (2 \text{ mol/mol-rxn})(192.77 \text{ J/ mol} \cdot \text{K})$
$\quad - [(1 \text{ mol/mol-rxn})(191.56 \text{ J/mol} \cdot \text{K})$
$\quad + (3 \text{ mol/mol-rxn})(130.7 \text{ J/mol} \cdot \text{K})]$

$\Delta_r S° = -198.1 \text{ J/K} \cdot \text{mol-rxn} \, (= 0.1981 \text{ kJ/K} \cdot \text{mol-rxn})$

$\Delta_r G° = \Delta_r H° - T\Delta_r S° =$
$-91.80 \text{ kJ/mol-rxn} - (298 \text{ K})(-0.1981 \text{ kJ/K} \cdot \text{mol-rxn})$

$\Delta_r G° = -32.8 \text{ kJ/mol-rxn}$

19.5 $SO_2(\text{g}) + \frac{1}{2} \, O_2(\text{g}) \longrightarrow SO_3(\text{g})$

$\Delta_r G° = \Sigma n \Delta_f G°(\text{products}) - \Sigma n \Delta_f G°(\text{reactants})$

$\Delta_r G° = (1 \text{ mol/mol-rxn}) \Delta_f G°[\text{SO}_3(\text{g})]$
$\quad - \{(1 \text{ mol/mol-rxn}) \Delta_f G°[\text{SO}_2(\text{g})]$
$\quad + (0.5 \text{ mol/mol-rxn}) \Delta_f G°[\text{O}_2(\text{g})]\}$

$\Delta_r G° = -371.04 \text{ kJ/mol-rxn}$
$\quad - (-300.13 \text{ kJ/mol-rxn} + 0 \text{ kJ/mol-rxn})$

$\quad = -70.91 \text{ kJ/mol-rxn}$

19.6 $HgO(\text{s}) \longrightarrow Hg(\ell) + \frac{1}{2} \, O_2(\text{g})$; determine the temperature at which $\Delta_r G° = \Delta_r H° - T\Delta_r S° = 0$. T is the unknown in this problem.

$\Delta_r H° = [-\Delta_f H°$ for $\text{HgO(s)}] = 90.83 \text{ kJ/mol-rxn}$

$\Delta_r S° = S°[\text{Hg}(\ell)] + \frac{1}{2} \, S°(\text{O}_2) - S°[\text{HgO(s)}]$

$\Delta_r S° = (1 \text{ mol/mol-rxn})(76.02 \text{ J/mol} \cdot \text{K})$
$\quad + [(0.5 \text{ mol/mol-rxn})(205.07 \text{ J/mol} \cdot \text{K})$
$\quad - (1 \text{ mol/mol-rxn})(70.29 \text{ J/mol} \cdot \text{K})]$
$\quad = 108.26 \text{ J/K} \cdot \text{mol-rxn}$

$\Delta_r H° - T(\Delta_r S°) = 0$
$= 90,830 \text{ J/mol-rxn} - T(108.26 \text{ J/K} \cdot \text{mol-rxn})$

$T = 839 \text{ K} \, (566 \, °\text{C})$

19.7 $CaCO_3(\text{s}) \rightleftharpoons CaO(\text{s}) + CO_2(\text{g})$

$\Delta_r G° = \Sigma \, n \Delta_f G°(\text{products}) - \Sigma \, n \Delta_f G°(\text{reactants})$

$\Delta_r G° = \Delta_f G°(\text{CaO}) + \Delta_f G°(\text{CO}_2) - \Delta_f G°(\text{CaCO}_3)$

$\Delta_r G° = (1 \text{ mol CaO/mol-rxn})(-603.42 \text{ kJ/mol CaO})$
$\quad + (1 \text{ mol CO}_2/\text{mol-rxn})(-394.359 \text{ kJ/mol CO}_2)$
$\quad - (1 \text{ mol CaCO}_3/\text{mol-rxn})$
$\quad \quad (-1129.16 \text{ kJ/mol CaCO}_3)$

$\Delta_r G° = 131.38 \text{ kJ/mol-rxn}$

$\Delta_r G° = -RT \ln K$

$131,380 \text{ J/mol-rxn}$
$\quad = -(8.3145 \text{ J/mol-rxn} \cdot \text{K})(298 \text{ K})(\ln K)$

$K_p = 9.37 \times 10^{-24}$

19.8 $C(\text{s}) + CO_2(\text{g}) \rightleftharpoons 2 \, CO(\text{g})$

$\Delta_r G° = \Sigma \, n \Delta_f G°(\text{products}) - \Sigma \, n \Delta_f G°(\text{reactants})$

$\Delta_r G° = 2 \, \Delta_f G°(\text{CO}) - \Delta_f G°(\text{CO}_2)$

$\Delta_r G° = (2 \text{ mol/mol-rxn})(-137.17 \text{ kJ/mol})$
$\quad - (1 \text{ mol/mol-rxn})(-394.36 \text{ kJ/mol})$

$\Delta_r G° = 120.02 \text{ kJ/mol-rxn}$

$\Delta_r G° = -RT \ln K$

$120,020 \text{ J/mol-rxn}$
$\quad = -(8.3145 \text{ J/mol-rxn} \cdot \text{K})(298 \text{ K})(\ln K)$

$K = 9.18 \times 10^{-22}$

Chapter 20

20.1 Oxidation half-reaction: $Al(\text{s}) \longrightarrow Al^{3+}(\text{aq}) + 3 \, e^-$
Reduction half-reaction: $2 \, H^+(\text{aq}) + 2 \, e^- \longrightarrow H_2(\text{g})$
Overall reaction: $2 \, Al(\text{s}) + 6 \, H^+(\text{aq}) \longrightarrow$
$$2 \, Al^{3+}(\text{aq}) + 3 \, H_2(\text{g})$$

Al is the reducing agent and is oxidized; $H^+(\text{aq})$ is the oxidizing agent and is reduced.

20.2 (1) $2 \, VO^{2+}(\text{aq}) + Zn(\text{s}) + 4 \, H^+(\text{aq}) \longrightarrow$
$$Zn^{2+}(\text{aq}) + 2 \, V^{3+}(\text{aq}) + 2 \, H_2O(\ell)$$
$2 \, V^{3+}(\text{aq}) + Zn(\text{s}) \longrightarrow 2 \, V^{2+}(\text{aq}) + Zn^{2+}(\text{aq})$
(2) Oxidation (Fe^{2+}, the reducing agent, is oxidized):
$$Fe^{2+}(\text{aq}) \longrightarrow Fe^{3+}(\text{aq}) + e^-$$
Reduction (MnO_4^-, the oxidizing agent, is reduced)
$$MnO_4^-(\text{aq}) + 8 \, H^+(\text{aq}) + 5 \, e^- \longrightarrow$$
$$Mn^{2+}(\text{aq}) + 4 \, H_2O(\ell)$$

Overall reaction:

$$MnO_4^-(\text{aq}) + 8 \, H^+(\text{aq}) + 5 \, Fe^{2+}(\text{aq}) \longrightarrow$$
$$Mn^{2+}(\text{aq}) + 5 \, Fe^{3+}(\text{aq}) + 4 \, H_2O(\ell)$$

20.3 (a) Oxidation half-reaction:

$$Al(s) + 3\ OH^-(aq) \longrightarrow Al(OH)_3(s) + 3\ e^-$$

Reduction half-reaction:

$$S(s) + H_2O(\ell) + 2\ e^- \longrightarrow HS^-(aq) + OH^-(aq)$$

Overall reaction:

$$2\ Al(s) + 3\ S(s) + 3\ H_2O(\ell) + 3\ OH^-(aq) \longrightarrow$$
$$2\ Al(OH)_3(s) + 3\ HS^-(aq)$$

(b) Aluminum is the reducing agent and is oxidized; sulfur is the oxidizing agent and is reduced.

20.4 Construct two half-cells, the first with a silver electrode and a solution containing $Ag^+(aq)$, and the second with a nickel electrode and a solution containing $Ni^{2+}(aq)$. Connect the two half-cells with a salt bridge. When the electrodes are connected through an external circuit, electrons will flow from the anode (the nickel electrode) to the cathode (the silver electrode). The overall cell reaction is $Ni(s) + 2\ Ag^+(aq) \longrightarrow Ni^{2+}(aq) + 2\ Ag(s)$. To maintain electrical neutrality in the two half-cells, negative ions will flow from the $Ag\ |\ Ag^+$ half-cell to the $Ni\ |\ Ni^{2+}$ half-cell, and positive ions will flow in the opposite direction.

20.5 (a) Using Appendix M, the order determined for these metals from least strong reducing agent to strongest reducing agent is Hg < Pb < Sn. (The further down the table, the stronger the metal is as a reducing agent.)

(b) F_2, Cl_2, and Br_2 all can oxidize mercury to mercury(II); Hg is located "southeast" of them on the table. I_2 cannot oxidize mercury to mercury(II); mercury is located "northeast" rather than "southeast" of it.

20.6 Overall reaction: $2\ Al(s) + 3\ Fe^{2+}(aq) \longrightarrow$
$$2\ Al^{3+}(aq) + 3\ Fe(s)$$

$(E°_{cell} = 1.22\ V,\ n = 6)$

$E_{cell} = E°_{cell} - (0.0257/n)\ \ln\ \{[Al^{3+}]^2/[Fe^{2+}]^3\}$

$= 1.22 - (0.0257/6)\ \ln\ \{[0.025]^2/[0.50]^3\}$

$= 1.22\ V - (-0.023)\ V = 1.24\ V$

20.7 Overall reaction: $Fe(s) + 2\ H^+(aq) \longrightarrow$
$$Fe^{2+}(aq) + H_2(g)$$

$(E°_{cell} = 0.44\ V,\ n = 2)$

$E_{cell} = E°_{cell} - (0.0257/n)\ \ln\ \{[Fe^{2+}]P_{H_2}/[H^+]^2\}$

$= 0.44 - (0.0257/2)\ \ln\ \{[0.024]1.0/[0.056]^2\}$

$= 0.44\ V - 0.026\ V = 0.41\ V$

20.8 $\Delta_rG° = -nFE°$

$= -(2\ mol\ e^-)(96,500\ C/mol\ e^-)$
$$(-0.76\ V)(1\ J/1\ C \cdot V)$$

$= 146,680\ J = 150\ kJ$

The negative value of $E°$ and the positive value of $\Delta G°$ both indicate a reactant-favored reaction.

20.9 $E°_{cell} = E°_{cathode} - E°_{anode} = 0.799\ V - 0.855\ V$
$= -0.056\ V;\ n = 2$

$E° = (0.0257/n)\ \ln\ K$

$-0.056 = (0.0257/2)\ \ln\ K$

$K = 0.013$

20.10 Cathode: $2\ H_2O(\ell) + 2\ e^- \longrightarrow 2\ OH^-(aq) + H_2(g)$

$E°_{cathode} = -0.83\ V$

Anode: $4\ OH^-(aq) \longrightarrow O_2(g) + 2\ H_2O(\ell) + 4\ e^-$

$E°_{anode} = 0.40\ V$

Overall: $2\ H_2O(\ell) \longrightarrow 2\ H_2(g) + O_2(g)$

$E°_{cell} = E°_{cathode} - E°_{anode} = -0.83\ V - 0.40\ V = -1.23\ V$

The minimum voltage needed to cause this reaction to occur is 1.23 V.

20.11 (1) O_2 is formed at the anode, by the reaction

$$2\ H_2O(\ell) \longrightarrow 4\ H^+(aq) + O_2(g) + 4\ e^-.$$

$(0.445\ A)(45\ min)(60\ s/min)(1\ C/1\ A \cdot s)(1\ mol\ e^-/96,500\ C)(1\ mol\ O_2/4\ mol\ e^-)(32\ g\ O_2/1\ mol\ O_2) = 0.10\ g\ O_2$

(2) The cathode reaction (electrolysis of molten NaCl) is

$$Na^+(melt) + e^- \longrightarrow Na(\ell).$$

$(25 \times 10^3\ A)(60\ min)(60\ s/min)(1\ C/1\ A \cdot s)$
$(1\ mol\ e^-/96,500\ C)(1\ mol\ Na/mol\ e^-)(23\ g\ Na/1\ mol\ Na) = 21,450\ g\ Na = 21\ kg$

Chapter 21

21.1 (a) $2\ Na(s) + Br_2(\ell) \longrightarrow 2\ NaBr(s)$

(b) $Ca(s) + Se(s) \longrightarrow CaSe(s)$

(c) $2\ Pb(s) + O_2(g) \longrightarrow 2\ PbO(s)$

Lead(II) oxide, a red compound commonly called *litharge*, is the most widely used inorganic lead compound. Maroon-colored lead(IV) oxide is the product of lead oxidation in lead-acid storage batteries (Chapter 20). Other oxides such as Pb_3O_4 also exist.

(d) $2\ Al(s) + 3\ Cl_2(g) \longrightarrow 2\ AlCl_3(s)$

21.2 (a) H_2Te

(b) Na_3AsO_4

(c) $SeCl_6$

(d) $HBrO_4$

21.3 (a) NH_4^+ (ammonium ion)

(b) O_2^{2-} (peroxide ion)

(c) N_2H_4 (hydrazine)

(d) NF_3 (nitrogen trifluoride)

21.4 (a) In Na_2Cl, chlorine would have the unlikely charge of 2− (to balance the two positive charges of the two Na^+ ions).

(b) This compound would require either the calcium ion to have the formula Ca^+ or the acetate ion to have the formula $CH_3CO_2^{2-}$. In all of its compounds, calcium occurs as the Ca^{2+} ion. The acetate ion, formed from acetic acid by loss of H^+, has a 1− charge.

(c) In Mg_2O, the magnesium ions would need to have the incorrect charge of 1+ to balance charge of the O^{2-} ion or else the oxygen would need to have the incorrect charge of 4− to balance the charge of the two Mg^{2+} ions. Neither of these possiblities is acceptable.

Chapter 22

22.1 (a) $Co(NH_3)_3Cl_3$
(b) $Fe(H_2NCH_2CH_2NH_2)_2Br_2 = Fe(en)_2Br_2$

22.2 (a) (i) $K_3[Co(NO_2)_6]$: a complex of cobalt(III) with a coordination number of 6
(ii) $Mn(NH_3)_4Cl_2$: a complex of manganese(II) with a coordination number of 6
(b) $NH_4[Co(edta)]$: a complex of cobalt(III) with a co-ordination number of 6

22.3 (a) hexaaquanickel(II) sulfate
(b) dicyanobis(ethylenediamine)chromium(III) chloride
(c) potassium amminetrichloroplatinate(II)
(d) potassium dichlorocuprate(I)

22.4 (a) Geometric isomers are possible (with the NH_3 ligands in *cis* and *trans* positions).
(b) Only a single structure is possible.
(c) Only a single structure is possible.
(d) This compound is chiral; there are two optical isomers.
(e) Only a single structure is possible.
(f) Two structural isomers are possible based on coordination of the NO_2^- ligand through oxygen or nitrogen.

22.5 (a) $[Ru(H_2O)_6]^{2+}$: an octahedral complex of ruthenium(II) (d^6). A low-spin complex has no unpaired electrons and is diamagnetic. A high-spin complex has four unpaired electrons and is paramagnetic.

high-spin Ru^{2+} low-spin Ru^{2+}

(b) $[Ni(NH_3)_6]^{2+}$: an octahedral complex of nickel(II) (d^8). Only one electron configuration is possible; it has two unpaired electrons and is paramagnetic.

Ni^{2+} ion (d^8)

22.6 (1) A wavelength of 500 nm corresponds to green light being absorbed. The complex ion will appear magenta.
(2) The complex appears yellow because blue light is being absorbed. The high energy of blue light indicates that Δ_o is large and the complex is therefore low spin.

22.7 (a) The $C_5H_5^-$ ligand is an anion (6 π electrons), C_6H_6 is a neutral ligand (6 π electrons), so Mn must be +1 (6 valence electrons). There is a total of 18 valence electrons.
(b) The ligands in this complex all are neutral, so the Mo atom must have no charge. The C_6H_6 ligand contributes six electrons, each CO contributes two electrons for a total of six, and Mo has six valence electrons. The total is 18 electrons.

Chapter 23

23.1 (a) Emission of six α particles leads to a decrease of 24 in the mass number and a decrease of 12 in the atomic number. Emission of four β particles increases the atomic number by 4 but doesn't affect the mass. The final product of this process has a mass number of $232 - 24 = 208$ and an atomic number of $90 - 12 + 4 = 82$, identifying it as $^{208}_{82}Pb$.
(b) Step 1: $^{232}_{90}Th \longrightarrow {}^{228}_{88}Ra + {}^{4}_{2}\alpha$
Step 2: $^{228}_{88}Ra \longrightarrow {}^{228}_{89}Ac + {}^{0}_{-1}\beta$
Step 3: $^{228}_{89}Ac \longrightarrow {}^{228}_{90}Th + {}^{0}_{-1}\beta$

23.2 (a) $^{0}_{+1}\beta$ (b) $^{41}_{19}K$ (c) $^{0}_{-1}\beta$ (d) $^{22}_{10}Ne$

23.3 (a) $^{32}_{14}Si \longrightarrow {}^{32}_{15}P + {}^{0}_{-1}\beta$
(b) $^{45}_{22}Ti \longrightarrow {}^{45}_{21}Sc + {}^{0}_{+1}\beta$ or
$^{45}_{22}Ti + {}^{0}_{-1}e \longrightarrow {}^{45}_{21}Sc$
(c) $^{239}_{94}Pu \longrightarrow \alpha + {}^{235}_{92}U$
(d) $^{42}_{19}K \longrightarrow {}^{42}_{20}Ca + {}^{0}_{-1}\beta$

23.4 $\Delta m = 0.03435$ g/mol
$\Delta E = (3.435 \times 10^{-5}$ kg/mol$)(2.998 \times 10^8$ m/s$)^2$
$= 3.087 \times 10^{12}$ J/mol $(= 3.087 \times 10^9$ kJ/mol$)$
$E_b = 5.146 \times 10^8$ kJ/mol nucleons

23.5 (a) 49.2 years is exactly four half-lives; quantity remaining $= 1.5$ mg$(1/2)^4 = 0.094$ mg
(b) Three half-lives, 36.9 years
(c) 1% is between six half-lives, 73.8 years (1/64 remains), and seven half-lives, 86.1 years (1/128 remains). [Using the integrated first-order rate equation with $[R]/[R]_0 = 0.010$ and $k = (\ln 2)/t_{1/2} = 0.0564$ y^{-1}, the amount of time is calculated to be 81.7 years.]

23.6 (a) $\ln ([A]/[A_o]) = -kt$
$\ln ([3.18 \times 10^3]/[3.35 \times 10^3]) = -k(2.00$ d$)$
$k = 0.0260$ d^{-1}
$t_{1/2} = 0.693/k = 0.693/(0.0260$ d$^{-1}) = 26.7$ d
(b) $k = 0.693/t_{1/2} = 0.693/200$ y $= 3.47 \times 10^{-3}$ y^{-1}
$\ln ([A]/[A_o]) = -kt$
$\ln ([3.00 \times 10^3]/[6.50 \times 10^{12}]) =$
$-(3.47 \times 10^{-3}$ y$^{-1})t$
$\ln (4.62 \times 10^{-10}) = -(3.47 \times 10^{-3}$ y$^{-1})t$
$t = 6190$ y

23.7 $\ln ([A]/[A_o]) = -kt$
$\ln ([9.32]/[13.4]) = -(1.21 \times 10^{-4}$ y$^{-1})t$
$t = 3.00 \times 10^3$ y
This compares quite well with the estimated date.

23.8 $^{98}_{42}Mo + {}^{1}_{0}n \rightarrow {}^{99}_{42}Mo + \gamma$
$^{99}_{42}Mo \rightarrow {}^{99}_{43}Tc + {}^{0}_{-1}\beta$

23.9 $4.17 \times 10^{-5}(0.0100$ g $Pb^{2+}) = 4.17 \times 10^{-7}$ g Pb^{2+}
Solubility $= [4.17 \times 10^{-7}$ g Pb^{2+} (1 mol $Pb^{2+}/$ 207.2 g Pb)(1 mol $PbCrO_4/1$ mol Pb^{2+})$]/$ 0.01000 L $= 2.01 \times 10^{-7}$ mol $PbCrO_4/L$

P Answers to Review & Check Questions

Chapter 1

Section 1.4

1. (b) Na
2. (d) silicon

Section 1.5

1. (d) water
2. (c) potassium

Section 1.6

1. (c) gasoline burns in air
2. (b) polypropylene < water < soda bottle plastic
3. (d) volume = 13.6 cm^3

Section 1.7

(b) The campfire wood burns.

Section 1.8

1. (d) 1.0 g of water vapor at 100 °C
2. (a) A mixture of H_2 and O_2 has lower chemical potential energy than H_2O.

Let's Review

Section 1

1. (b) -196 °C
2. (c) 0.16 cm^3
3. (a) 0.750 L
4. (c) 1.9 L
5. (a) 5.59×10^3 mg
6. (d) 2×10^{-8} g/L
7. (c) 1050 kJ

Section 2

1. (c) 0.03 g
2. (b) Student B

Section 3

1. (c) 3
2. (a) 1
3. (b) 10.32 g
4. (c) 0.65 cm^2

Section 4

1. (a) 23.3 km^2
2. (c) 2.8×10^{17} km

Section 5

1. (a) 2.4
2. (d) 78 g

Section 6

(c) 130 m

Chapter 2

Section 2.2

1. (b) 30 neutrons
2. (c) Na

Section 2.3

(d) $^{109}_{47}$Ag , 48.161%

Section 2.4

1. (a) ^{63}Cu
2. (b) 40%

Section 2.5

1.   (a) Ge

2.   (a) Si

3.   (c) O

4.   (c) allotropes

Section 2.6

(b) $C_3H_7NO_2S$

Section 2.7

1.   (b) 2+

2.   (a) loses 3 electrons

3.   (b) ammonium sulfide

4.   (a) $Ba(CH_3CO_2)_2$

5.   (a) vanadium(III) oxide

6.   (a) MgO

Section 2.8

1.   (a) O_2F_2

2.   (b) nitrogen pentaoxide, N_2O_5

3.   (c) dinitrogen tetrafluoride

4.   (b) tetraphosphorus decaoxide

Section 2.9

1.   (c) 164.09 g/mol

2.   (b) 4.0 g H_2

3.   (c) 0.40 mol Ca

4.   (d) 30 g HF

5.   (a) 6.0×10^{23} atoms O

Section 2.10

1.   (d) butane, C_4H_{10}

2.   (a) benzene, C_6H_6

3.   (b) $C_6H_{12}O_6$

4.   (b) C_5H_6O, $C_{10}H_{12}O_2$

Section 2.11

(d) $MgSO_4 \cdot 3H_2O$

Chapter 3

Section 3.1

1.   (b) 2, 3, 1

2.   (c) 12,000

Section 3.2

(b) 9 O_2, 8 H_2O

Section 3.3

(d) All chemical equilibria are product-favored.

Section 3.4

1.   (a) $Ba(NO_3)_2$

2.   (b) Ca^{2+} and 2 NO_3^-

3.   (b) acetic acid

Section 3.5

1.   (b) Ag_2S

2.   (d) 1, 2, 3, and 4

3.   (c) $2\,Ag^+(aq) + CO_3^{2-}(aq) \rightarrow Ag_2CO_3(s)$

Section 3.6

1.   (d) H_2SO_4

2.   (d) PO_4^{3-}

3.   (c) $CH_3CO_2H(aq) + OH^-(aq) \rightarrow$
     $$H_2O(\ell) + CH_3CO_2^-(aq)$$

4.   (b) BaO

Section 3.7

(b) Na_2CO_3

Section 3.8

1.   (c) +6

2.   (c) 2 and 4

3.   (c) $KMnO_4$

Section 3.9

(c) acid–base and precipitation

Chapter 4

Section 4.1

1.   (b) 0.60 moles Cl_2

2.   (a) 0.60 g Mg

Section 4.2

(b) O_2

Section 4.3

1. (c) 41.8 g
2. (c) 32.5%

Section 4.4

(c) C_4H_4O

Section 4.5

1. (c) 0.080 M
2. (b) 0.010 M
3. (b) 15 mL of 0.20 M KOH

Section 4.6

1. (a) 0.10 M HCl
2. (c) 1.301

Section 4.7

1. (a) acidic
2. (a) 80.0 mL

Section 4.8

(b) A is reduced to half the original value.

Chapter 5

Section 5.1

(a) melting of ice at 0 °C

Section 5.2

1. (b) warming 2.0 g of copper by 10 °C
2. (c) 20 g of water at 20 °C + 10 g of water at 30 °C

Section 5.3

1. (a) Raising the temperature of 100 g of water by 1.0 °C
2. (b) All of the ice melts; liquid water is at a temperature between 0 °C and 10 °C.

Section 5.4

1. (b) 2 and 4
2. (c) 2 C(s) + O_2(g) → 2 CO(g)

Section 5.5

1. (c) 90.8 kJ
2. (b) −425 kJ

Section 5.6

1. (b) endothermic
2. (b) The calculated value of $\Delta_{solution}H°$ will be too small.

Section 5.7

1. (d) Al(s) + 3/2 Cl_2(g) → $AlCl_3$(s)
2. (c) $1/2\ \Delta_rH_1° - \Delta_rH_2° + 1/2\ \Delta_rH_3°$

Chapter 6

Section 6.1

(d) microwaves from a microwave oven

Section 6.2

1. (a) 3.9×10^5 J/mol
2. (a) UVB

Section 6.3

1. (d) from $n = 6$ to $n = 2$
2. (b) from $n = 4$ to $n = 2$

Section 6.4

(b) Wavelength will be shorter.

Section 6.5

1. (b) $4p$
2. (d) 16
3. (c) both n and ℓ

Section 6.6

1. (d) $3f$
2. (b) $n = 4$, $\ell = 1$, $m_\ell = 0$
3. (c) 2

Chapter 7

Section 7.1

(d) 98

Section 7.2

(a) $4s$
(b) $6s$
(c) $5s$

Section 7.3

1. (c) $3d^{10}4s^2 4p^4$
2. (c) Ni

Section 7.4

1. (d) Fe^{2+}
2. (c) Co^{3+}

Section 7.5

1. (d) $S^{2-} > Cl^- > K^+$
2. (c) N highest, Si lowest

Section 7.6

1. (a) MgCl
2. (d) S^{3-}

Chapter 8

Section 8.1

(c) $SiBr_4$

Section 8.2

1. (a) Sulfur has three single bonds to oxygen and a lone pair.
2. (c) O_3
3. (b) OCN^-

Section 8.3

(c) +1

Section 8.4

1. (b) SO_2 and SO_3
2. (b) Formal charge on each N is +1, formal charge on each oxygen is $-1/2$.

Section 8.5

1. (b) SF_4, SF_5^+, SF_6
2. (d) 3

Section 8.6

1. (a) PCl_3
2. (c) square pyramidal
3. (c) $120°$
4. (a) linear, $180°$ angle

Section 8.7

1. (d) Al—Cl
2. (c) The I—Cl bond is polar with I being the positive end.
3. (a) $:N\equiv N-\ddot{\underset{..}{O}}:$

Section 8.8

1. (a) HF
2. (a) BCl_3

Section 8.9

1. (d) H_2NOH
2. (a) CN^-
3. (b) -206 kJ/mol-rxn

Chapter 9

Section 9.2

1. (b) $sp^3 d$
2. (a) boron sp^3 + fluorine $2p$
3. (c) The hybridization of I in ICl_4^- is sp^3.
4. (d) p on atom A with p on atom B
5. (b) The nitrogens are attached by one σ and two π bonds.

Section 9.3

1. (b) 2.5
2. (b) π^*_{2p}
3. (c) C_2
4. (a) O_2^+

Chapter 10

Section 10.1

1. (c) b and c
2. (a) a and b
3. (c) 2

Section 10.2

1. (c) 2,5-dimethylheptane
2. (c) The compound is an isomer of hexane, is not chiral, and is named 2,2-dimethylbutane.

3. **(i)** (c) only 3

    (ii) (c) 1 and 2

4. (a)
$$Br-\underset{\underset{\displaystyle CH_3}{|}}{\overset{\overset{\displaystyle CH_3}{|}}{C}}-\underset{\underset{\displaystyle H}{|}}{\overset{\overset{\displaystyle CH_2CH_3}{|}}{C}}-H$$

5. (c) 3

Section 10.3

1. (d) more than 4
2. (a) 2-propanol
3. (a) sp^3
4. (d) NaOH

Section 10.4

1. (d) 1 aldehyde and 2 ketones
2. (b) 2-butanone
3. (d) 120°, sp^2 hybridized
4. (c) ethyl ethanoate

Section 10.5

(c)
$$CH_2{=}\underset{\underset{\displaystyle CH}{}}{\overset{\overset{\displaystyle CO_2H}{|}}{}}$$

Chapter 11

Section 11.1

1. (b) 16 kPa
2. (b) 7.8 m

Section 11.2

1. (b) 463 mL
2. (d) 120. °C
3. (d) none of the above (pressure = 0.458 atm)

Section 11.3

1. (e) Xe
2. (b) B
3. (b) D

Section 11.4

1. (d) 0.88 g
2. (a) 0.18 mol

Section 11.5

(c) 40. mm Hg C_2H_2 and 100. mm Hg O_2

Section 11.6

(a) A = Xe, B = O_2, C = Ne, D = He

Section 11.7

(c) rms for HCl/rms for NH_3 = 0.68

Section 11.8

(a) 18.0 atm

Chapter 12

Section 12.2

(b) $AlCl_3$

Section 12.3

1. (b) CH_3OH
2. (a) H_2O

Section 12.4

1. (d) I_2
2. (d) octane, C_8H_{18}

Section 12.5

(a) He < SO_2 < CH_3OH

Section 12.6

1. (b) All the water evaporates.
2. (a) 29.1 kJ/mol

Chapter 13

Section 13.1

1. (b) body-centered cubic
2. (a) 0.858 g/cm^3

Section 13.2

1. (c) face-centered cubic
2. (c) 3.21 g/cm^3

Section 13.3

(a) 1800 nm, infrared

Section 13.4

1.   (d) NaF

2.   (c) $Na^+(g) + Cl^-(g) \rightarrow NaCl(s)$

3.   (c) -287 kJ/mol

Section 13.5

1.   (c) buckyballs (C_{60})

2.   (b) an amorphous solid

Section 13.6

1.   (a) NaCl

2.   (b) 15 g

Section 13.7

1.   (d) Supercritical CO_2 can be obtained at 25 °C if a high enough pressure is applied.

2.   (b) At 66 K and 0.50 atm N_2 is a gas.

Chapter 14

Section 14.1

1.   (b) 0.063

      (b) 3.7

2.   (a) weight percent

Section 14.2

      (c) -23.55 kJ/mol

Section 14.3

      (b) 0.097 mol

Section 14.4

1.   (b) Na_2SO_4 < sugar < KBr < $C_2H_4(OH)_2$

2.   (d) naphthalene, $C_{10}H_8$

3.   (c) 1.0 g propylene glycol, $C_3H_6(OH)_2$

4.   (c) 122 g/mol

Section 14.5

      (b) 40 million atoms

Chapter 15

Section 15.1

1.   (b) The rate of disappearance of NO(g) is twice the rate of disappearance of $O_2(g)$.

2.   (c) 0.6×10^{-5} mol/L · min

Section 15.2

      (e) all of the above

Section 15.3

      (b) 1.24×10^{-5} mol/L·s

Section 15.4

1.   (b) between 6 and 7

2.   (d) A graph of $\ln[SO_2Cl_2]$ vs. time gives a straight line.

3.   (b) second order

Section 15.5

1.   (c) $\ln k$ vs. $1/T$

2.   (b) A higher proportion of reactant molecules exceeds the activation energy.

Section 15.6

1.   (b) This reaction might occur in a single elementary step.

2.   (c) Rate $= k[A]^2[B]$

Chapter 16

Section 16.1

      (a) More $CaCO_3$ would precipitate.

Section 16.2

1.   (b) $K = [SO_2]^2[O_2]/[SO_3]^2$

2.   (b) No, it is not at equilibrium, and the reaction proceeds further to the right.

Section 16.3

      (b) 6.1×10^{-4}

Section 16.4

      (b) 0.011 M

Section 16.5

(c) $K_p = 2.7 \times 10^{33}$

Section 16.6

1. (b) shift right

2. (a) shift left

3. (a) exothermic

Chapter 17

Section 17.1

(c) H_2CO_3, CH_3CO_2H, H_3PO_4

Section 17.2

1. (c) amphiprotic

2. (b) base

3. (b) acid = HNO_3 and conjugate base = NO_3^-

   (a) base = NH_3 and conjugate acid = NH_4^+

4. (c) HF/F^- and $CH_3CO_2H/CH_3CO_2^-$

Section 17.3

1. (b) 11.08

2. (a) 4.8×10^{-5} M

3. (d) 1.4×10^{-4} M

Section 17.4

1. (a) HF

2. (c) HCN

3. (a) $C_6H_5CO_2H$

4. (b) 9.25

5. (c) 10.15

Section 17.5

1. (b) decrease

2. (a) increase

Section 17.6

1. (b) product-favored

2. (b) right

Section 17.7

1. (a) acidic

2. (a) acidic

3. (b) basic

Section 17.8

1. (b) 6.3×10^{-6} M

2. (a) 2.3×10^{-5}

3. (b) pH = 8.37, $[Na^+]$ = 0.10 M, $[CHO_2^-]$ = 0.10 M, $[OH^-] = 2.4 \times 10^{-6}$ M

4. (c) greater than 7

Section 17.9

(c) 10.16

Section 17.10

1. (a) H_2SeO_4

2. (b) $[Fe(H_2O)_6]^{3+}$

3. (a) HOCl

Section 17.11

1. (b) BCl_3

2. (c) Brønsted base and (d) Lewis base

Chapter 18

Section 18.1

(b) 5.05

Section 18.2

1. (a) 0.20 M HCN and 0.10 M KCN

2. (d) 18 mL

3. (b) 9.25

4. (c) 1/1.8

Section 18.3

1. (b) 1.48

2. (d) 11.29

3. (c) methyl red

Section 18.4

1. (b) $K_{sp} = [Ag^+]^2[CO_3^{2-}]$

2. (a) AgCl
   (b) $Ca(OH)_2$
   (c) $Ca(OH)_2$

3. (b) 1.6×10^{-4} M

4. (a) 1.0×10^{-7} M

5. (a) $FeCO_3$

Section 18.5

(b) no

Section 18.6

(b) 1.9×10^{-36} M

Section 18.7

(c) 1.1×10^5

Chapter 19

Section 19.1

1. (b) toward equilibrium
2. (b) false
3. (b) sometimes spontaneous

Section 19.2

1. (c) > 0
2. (c) dispersed
3. (b) 3.19 J/K

Section 19.3

1. (b) increases
2. (c) 2.5×10^{-23} J/K

Section 19.4

1. (c) $NaCl(s) < H_2O(\ell) < NH_3(g)$
2. (c) $\Delta_r S° > 0$
3. (a) -326.6 J/K·mol-rxn

Section 19.5

1. (b) -121.6 J/K·mol-rxn
2. (d) 1320 J/K·mol-rxn
3. (b) at higher temperatures

Section 19.6

1. (d) less, less
2. (a) product-favored at equilibrium
3. (b) false

Section 19.7

1. (c) -2155 kJ/mol-rxn
2. (a) -225 kJ/mol-rxn
3. (c) 23 kJ/mol-rxn

Chapter 20

Section 20.1

1. (a) CuS
2. (d) $4\,H^+ + 3\,e^- + NO_3^- \rightarrow NO + 2\,H_2O$
3. (b) $12\,OH^- + Br_2 \rightarrow 2\,BrO_3^- + 6\,H_2O + 10\,e^-$

Section 20.2

1. (b) Electrons transfer from Cd to Ni.
2. (a) Cd is the anode and is negative.
3. (b) NO_3^- ions move from the Ni half-cell to the Cd half-cell, and K^+ ions move from the Cd half-cell to the Ni half-cell.

Section 20.3

1. (b) Lead(IV) oxide is reduced.
2. (b) Sulfuric acid is consumed.

Section 20.4

1. (a) 1.562 V
2. (d) Mg
3. (a) ii and iv

Section 20.5

(a) 0.47 V

Section 20.6

(b) 6.3×10^{16}

Section 20.7

(d) Ag^+

Section 20.8

(d) 1450 seconds

Chapter 21

Section 21.2

1. (d) Ca_2O_3
2. (d) tetraphosphorus decaoxide
3. (b) $+3$
4. (d) $+5$

Section 21.3

1. (a) neon
2. (c) the high temperature reaction of methane and water

Section 21.4

1. (c) high melting point (>400 °C)
2. (a) Li^+
3. (c) two Na^+ ions and one O_2^{2-} ion

Section 21.5

1. (c) gypsum, $CaSO_4 \cdot 2H_2O$
2. (c) converting slaked lime, $Ca(OH)_2$, to lime

Section 21.6

1. (c) third
2. (d) dissolve in acid and in base

Section 21.7

1. (c) SiO_2
2. (c) +4

Section 21.8

1. (c) between 2 and 3
2. (b) Solutions of ammonia are acidic.
3. (c) +3

Section 21.9

1. (c) +3
2. (d) All electrons in O_2 are paired.

Section 21.10

1. (b) Cl_2
2. (c) F_2 is prepared industrially by electrolysis of aqueous NaF.

Chapter 22

Section 22.1

1. (e) +7
2. (b) Atomic radii that are similar to the 5th period transition elements.

Section 22.2

1. (b) Copper is reduced; sulfur is oxidized.
2. (b) iron oxide

Section 22.3

1. (b) 6
2. (d) +3
3. (b) $Na_4[Fe(C_2O_4)_3]$
4. (b) pentaamminehydroxochromium(III) chloride

Section 22.4

1. (b) $Ni(H_2O)_4(C_2O_4)$
2. (b) $Fe(en)_2(CN)_2$
3. (b) There are two geometric isomers, one of which has an optical isomer.
4. (d) 3

Section 22.5

1. (b) high-spin $[Mn(NH_3)_6]^{2+}$
2. (a) square-planar $[PtCl_4]^{2-}$

Section 22.6

(c) $[CrF_6]^{3-}$

Section 22.7

(d) the anion in Zeise's salt, $[Pt(\eta^2\text{-}C_2H_4)Cl_3]^-$

Chapter 23

Section 23.2

1. (a) alpha radiation
2. (b) 7 α and 4 β
3. (c) $^{90}_{38}Sr \rightarrow ^{90}_{39}Y + \beta$

Section 23.3

(c) $^{56}_{26}Fe$

Section 23.4

1. (a) 20%
2. (d) 1/32

Section 23.5

(c) electrons

Section 23.6

(a) $^{93}_{37}Rb$

Q Answers to Selected Interchapter Study Questions

The Chemistry of Fuels and Energy Resources

1. (a) From methane: $H_2O(g) + CH_4(g) \rightarrow$
    $$3\ H_2(g) + CO(g)$$

    100. g $CH_4(1$ mol $CH_4/16.043$ g)
    (3 mol H_2/mol CH_4)(2.016 g H_2/1 mol H_2)
    = 37.7 g of H_2 produced

    (b) From petroleum: $H_2O(g) + CH_2(\ell) \rightarrow$
    $$2\ H_2(g) + CO\ (g)$$

    100. g $CH_2(1$ mol $CH_2/14.026$ g CH_2)
    (2 mol H_2/1 mol CH_2)(2.016 g H_2/1 mol H_2)
    = 28.7 g H_2 produced

    (c) From coal: $H_2O(g) + C(s) \rightarrow H_2(g) + CO(g)$

    100. g $C(1$ mol $C/12.011$ g $C)(1$ mol H_2/mole C)
    (2.016 g H_2/1 mol H_2) = 16.8 g H_2 produced

3. 70. lb $(453.6$ g/lb$)(33$ kJ/g$) = 1.0 \times 10^6$ kJ

5. Assume burning oil produces 43 kJ/g (the value for crude petroleum in Table 1)

    7.0 gal$(3.785$ L/gal$)(1000$ cm^3/L$)(0.8$ g/cm^3)
    $(43$ kJ/g$) = 0.9 \times 10^6$ kJ. Uncertainty in the numbers is one significant figure. This value is close to the value for the energy obtained by burning from 70 kg of coal (calculated in Question 3.)

7. (a) Isooctane: $C_8H_{18}(\ell) + 25/2\ O_2(g) \rightarrow$
    $$8\ CO_2(g) + 9\ H_2O(\ell)$$

    $\Delta_r H° = (8$ mol CO_2/1 mol-rxn$)\Delta_f H°[CO_2(g)]$
    $+ (9$ mol H_2O/1 mol-rxn$)\Delta_f H°[H_2O(\ell)]$
    $- \{(1$ mol C_8H_{18}/1 mol-rxn$)\Delta_f H°[C_8H_{18}(\ell)]$
    $+ 25/2$ mol O_2/1 mol-rxn$)\Delta_f H°[O_2(g)]\}$
    $= (8$ mol CO_2/1 mol-rxn$)(-393.509$ kJ/mol $CO_2)$
    $+ (9$ mol H_2O/1 mol-rxn$)(-285.83$ kJ/mol $H_2O)$
    $- \{(1$ mol C_8H_{18}/1 mol-rxn$)(-259.3$ kJ/mol $C_8H_{18})$
    $+ 25/2$ mol O_2/1 mol-rxn$)(0$ kJ/mol $O_2)\}$
    $= -5461.2$ kJ/mol-rxn
    -5461.2 kJ/mol-rxn $(1$ mol-rxn/1 mol $C_8H_{18})$
    $(1$ mol $C_8H_{18}/114.230$ g $C_8H_{18})(1000$ g/1 kg$)$
    $= -47,809$ kJ/kg C_8H_{18}

Ethanol: $C_2H_5OH(\ell) + 3\ O_2(g) \rightarrow$
$$2\ CO_2(g) + 3\ H_2O(\ell)$$

$\Delta_r H° = (2$ mol CO_2/1 mol-rxn$)\Delta_f H°[CO_2(g)]$
$+ (3$ mol H_2O/1 mol-rxn$)\Delta_f H°[H_2O(\ell)]$
$- \{(1$ mol C_2H_5OH/1 mol-rxn$)\Delta_f H°[C_2H_5OH(\ell)]$
$+ 3$ mol O_2/1 mol-rxn$)\Delta_f H°[O_2(g)]\}$
$= (2$ mol CO_2/1 mol-rxn$)(-393.509$ kJ/mol $CO_2)$
$+ (3$ mol H_2O/1 mol-rxn$)(-285.83$ kJ/mol $H_2O)$
$- \{(1$ mol C_2H_5OH/1 mol-rxn$)(-277.0$ kJ/mol
$C_2H_5OH) + 3$ mol O_2/1 mol-rxn$)(0$ kJ/mol $O_2)\} =$
-1367.5 kJ/mol-rxn
-1367.5 kJ/mol-rxn $(1$ mol-rxn/1 mol $C_2H_5OH)$
$(1$ mol $C_2H_5OH/46.069$ g $C_2H_5OH)(1000$ g/1 kg$) =$
$-29,684$ kJ/kg C_2H_5OH

Isooctane releases more energy per kilogram.

(b) Isooctane: 1.00 kg C_8H_{18} $(1000$ g/1 kg$)(1$ mol
$C_8H_{18}/114.230$ g $C_8H_{18})(8$ mol CO_2/1 mol $C_8H_{18})$
= 70.0 mol CO_2

Ethanol: 1.00 kg C_2H_5OH $(1000$ g/1 kg$)(1$ mol
$C_2H_5OH/46.069$ g $C_2H_5OH)(2$ mol CO_2/1 mol
$C_2H_5OH) = 43.4$ mol CO_2

Ethanol produces less CO_2 per kilogram.

(c) On the basis of this simplistic comparison, there is not a clear winner. Isooctane releases more energy per kilogram but also releases more CO_2 per kilogram.

9. The factor for converting kW-h to kJ is 1 kW-h = 3600 kJ

    $(940$ kW-h/yr$)(3600$ kJ/kW-h$) = 3.4 \times 10^6$ kJ/yr
    $(940$ kW-h/yr$)$ $(1$ yr/12 months$)($\$0.08$/kW-h$) = $ \$ 6.3

11. First, calculate $\Delta_r H°$ for the reaction $CH_3OH(\ell) +$
    $1.5\ O_2(g) \rightarrow CO_2(g) + 2\ H_2O(\ell)$, using enthalpies
    of formation $(\Delta_r H° = -726.8$ kJ/mol-rxn$)$. Use
    molar mass and density to calculate energy per liter
    $[-726.8$ kJ/mol-rxn $(1$ mol-rxn/32.04 g$)(787$ g/L$) =$
    -17.9×10^3 kJ/L$]$. Then use the kW-h to kJ
    conversion factor from Question 9 to obtain the answer
    $[(17.9 \times 10^3$ kJ/L$)(1$ kW-h/3600 kJ$) = 4.96$ kW-h/L$]$.

13. Area of parking lot = 325 m $\times$ 50.0 m $= 1.63 \times 10^4$ m^2

    2.6×10^7 J/m$^2(1.63 \times 10^4$ m$^2) = 4.2 \times 10^{11}$ J

15. Energy per gallon of gas $= (48.0$ kJ/g$)(0.737$ g/cm$^3)$
    $(1000$ cm^3/L$)(3.785$ L/gal$) = 1.34 \times 10^5$ kJ/gal

    Energy to travel 1 mile = 1.00 mile $(1$ gal/55.0 mile$)$
    $(1.34 \times 10^5$ kJ/gal$) = 2430$ kJ

Milestones in the Development of Chemistry and the Modern View of Atoms and Molecules

1. Atoms are not solid, hard, or impenetrable. They do have mass (an important aspect of Dalton's hypothesis), and we now know that atoms are in rapid motion at all temperatures above absolute zero (the kinetic-molecular theory).

3. mass e/mass $p = 9.109383 \times 10^{-28}$ g/1.672622×10^{-24} g $= 5.446170 \times 10^{-4}$. (Mass of p and e obtained from Table 2.1, page 53.) The proton is 1,834 times more massive than an electron. Thomson's estimate was off by a factor of about 2.

The Chemistry of Life: Biochemistry

1. (a)

(b)

(c) The zwitterionic form is the predominant form at physiological pH.

3.

5.

7. (a) The structure of ribose is given in Figure 12.

(b) Adenosine

(c) Adenosine-5′-monophosphate

9. The sequences differ in the positions of attachments of the phosphate to deoxyribose on adjacent units. Consider the A-T attachments. In ATGC, the phosphate links the 3′ position on A to the 5′ position on T. In CGTA, the phosphate links the 5′ position on A to the 3′ position on T.

11. (a) 5′-GAATCGCGT-3′
(b) 5′-GAAUCGCGU-3′
(c) 5′-UUC-3′, 5′-CGA-3′, and 5′-ACG-3′
(d) glutamic acid, serine, and arginine

13. (a) In transcription, a strand of RNA complementary to the segment of DNA is constructed.
(b) In translation, an amino acid sequence is constructed based on the information in a mRNA sequence.

15. The four-ring structure present in all steroids is given in Figure 17a.

17. (a) false   (b) true   (c) true   (d) true

19. (a) $6 \, CO_2(g) + 6 \, H_2O(\ell) \rightarrow C_6H_{12}O_6(s) + 6 \, O_2(g)$

$\Delta_r H° = \Sigma n \Delta_f H°(\text{products}) -$
$$\Sigma n \Delta_f H°(\text{reactants})$$

$\Delta_r H° = (1 \text{ mol } C_6H_{12}O_6/\text{mol-rxn})$
$[\Delta_f H°(C_6H_{12}O_6)] - (6 \text{ mol } H_2O/\text{mol-rxn})$
$[\Delta_f H°(H_2O)] - (6 \text{ mol } CO_2/\text{mol-rxn})$
$[\Delta_f H°(CO_2)]$

$\Delta_r H° = (1 \text{ mol } C_6H_{12}O_6/\text{mol-rxn})$
$(-1273.3 \text{ kJ/mol } C_6H_{12}O_6) - (6 \text{ mol } H_2O/\text{mol-rxn})$
$(-285.8 \text{ kJ/mol } H_2O) - (6 \text{ mol } CO_2/\text{mol-rxn})$
$(-393.5 \text{ kJ/mol } CO_2)$

$\Delta_r H° = +2{,}803 \text{ kJ/mol-rxn}$

(b) $(2803 \text{ kJ/mol})(1 \text{ mol}/6.022 \times 10^{23} \text{ molecules})$
$(1000 \text{ J}/1 \text{ kJ}) = 4.655 \times 10^{-18} \text{ J/molecule}$

(c) $\lambda = 650 \text{ nm } (1 \text{ m}/10^9 \text{ nm}) = 6.50 \times 10^{-7} \text{ m}$

$E = hc/\lambda = (6.626 \times 10^{-34} \text{ J} \cdot \text{s})$
$(3.00 \times 10^8 \text{ m} \cdot \text{s}^{-1})/(6.50 \times 10^{-7} \text{ m})$
$= 3.06 \times 10^{-19} \text{ J}$

(d) The energy per photon is less than the amount required per molecule of glucose; therefore, multiple photons must be absorbed.

The Chemistry of Modern Materials

1. Figure 14b: 5.0 mm/1 mm = 5; magnification is 5×

   Figure 14c: 5.0 mm/20 μm = 5.0 mm/$(20 \times 10^{-3} \text{ mm})$ = 250; magnification is 250×

   Figure 14d: 5.0 mm/500 nm = 5.0 mm/$(5 \times 10^{-4} \text{ mm})$ = 10,000; magnification = 10,000×

3. The amount of light falling on a single solar cell = 925 W/m^2 $[(1 \text{ m}^2/10^4 \text{ cm}^2)(1.0 \text{ cm}^2/\text{cell})$ = 0.093 W/cell.] Using the conversion factor 1 W = 1 J/s, the energy incident on the cell is $(0.093 \text{ W/cell})(1 \text{ J/W} \cdot \text{s})(60 \text{ sec/min})$ = 5.6 J/(min · cell). At 25% efficiency, the energy absorbed for each cell is 1.4 J/min.

5. Pewter consists of 91% Sn, 7.5% Sb, and 1.5% Cu. The densities of these elements (from www.ptable.com and converted to units of g/cm^3) are 7.310 g/cm^3 for Sn, 6.697 g/cm^3 for Sb, and 8.920 g/cm^3 for Cu.

   Density of pewter = $0.91(7.310 \text{ g/cm}^3) + 0.075$ $(6.697 \text{ g/cm}^3) + 0.015(8.920 \text{ g/cm}^3) = 7.3 \text{ g/cm}^3$

7. Density of aerogel (from Question 6) = 0.0019 g/cm^3

   Volume = 180 cm × 150 cm × 0.20 cm = $5.4 \times 10^3 \text{ cm}^3$

   Mass aerogel needed = $5.4 \times 10^3 \text{ cm}^3 (0.0019 \text{ g/cm}^3)$ = 10. g

The Chemistry of the Environment

1. $[Na^+] = 0.460 \text{ mol/L}$, $[Cl^-] = 0.550 \text{ mol/L}$; a larger amount of chloride than sodium ion is present in a sample of seawater.

3. The amount of NaCl is limited by the amount of sodium present. From a 1.0-L sample of seawater, a maximum of 0.460 mol NaCl could be obtained. The mass of this amount of NaCl is 26.9 g $[(0.460 \text{ mol/L})$ $(1.00 \text{ L})(58.43 \text{ g NaCl}/1 \text{ mol NaCl}) = 26.9 \text{ g}]$.

5. For gases, ppm refers to numbers of particles, and hence to mole fractions (see footnote to Table 1). Gas pressure exerted is directly proportional to mole fraction. Thus, 40,000 ppm water vapor would exert a pressure of 40,000/1,000,000 of one atmosphere, or 30.4 mm Hg (0.040 × 760 mm Hg). This would be the case at a little over 29 °C, at 100% humidity.

7. The concentration of Mg^{2+} in seawater is 52 mmol/L (Table 2). Assuming that all this is converted to Mg metal, one would expect to obtain 1.3 g from 1.0 L of seawater [0.052 mol (24.31 g/mol) = 1.3 g]. To obtain 100 kg of Mg, 79,000 L of seawater [100. kg (1000 g/kg)(1 L/1.3 g) = 7.9×10^4 L] would be needed.

9. (a) Only 92% of the ice is submerged, and the water displaced by ice (the volume of ice under the surface of water) is 23 cm^3 (0.92 × 25 cm^3 = 23 cm^3). Thus, the liquid level in the graduated cylinder will be 123 mL.

   (b) Melting 25 cm^3 of ice will produce 23 mL of liquid water [25 cm^3 ice (0.92 g H_2O/cm^3 ice) (1.0 cm^3 liquid H_2O/g H_2O) = 23 cm^3 liquid H_2O]. The water level will be 123 mL (the same as in (a)); that is, the water level won't rise as the ice melts).

R Answers to Selected Study Questions

Chapter 1

1.1 (a) C, carbon
(b) K, potassium
(c) Cl, chlorine
(d) P, phosphorus
(e) Mg, magnesium
(f) Ni, nickel

1.3 (a) Ba, barium
(b) Ti, titanium
(c) Cr, chromium
(d) Pb, lead
(e) As, arsenic
(f) Zn, zinc

1.5 (a) Na (element) and NaCl (compound)
(b) Sugar (compound) and carbon (element)
(c) Gold (element) and gold chloride (compound)

1.7 (a) Physical property
(b) Chemical property
(c) Chemical property
(d) Physical property
(e) Physical property
(f) Physical property

1.9 (a) Physical (colorless liquid) and chemical (burns in air)
(b) Physical (shiny metal, orange liquid) and chemical (reacts with bromine)

1.11 Mechanical energy is used to move the lever, which in turn moves gears. The device produces electrical energy and radiant energy.

1.13 (a) Kinetic energy
(b) Potential energy
(c) Potential energy
(d) Potential energy

1.15 (a) Qualitative: blue-green color, solid physical state
Quantitative: density = 2.65 g/cm^3 and mass = 2.5 g
(b) Density, physical state, and color are intensive properties, whereas mass is an extensive property.
(c) Volume = 0.94 cm^3

1.17 Observation c is a chemical property.

1.19 Calcium, Ca; fluorine, F

The crystals are cubic in shape because the atoms are arranged in cubic structures.

1.21 Heterogeneous mixture

The iron can be separated from the sand using a magnet.

1.23 Physical changes: a, b, d
Chemical changes: c

1.25 The macroscopic view is the photograph of NaCl, and the particulate view is the drawing of the ions in a cubic arrangement. The structure of the compound at the particulate level determines the properties that are observed at the macroscopic level.

1.27 The density of the plastic is less than that of CCl$_4$, so the plastic will float on the liquid CCl$_4$. Aluminum is more dense than CCl$_4$, so aluminum will sink when placed in CCl$_4$.

1.29 (a) Mixture
(b) Mixture
(c) Element
(d) Compound

1.31

1.33 The three liquids will form three separate layers with hexane on the top, water in the middle, and perfluorohexane on the bottom. The HDPE will float at the interface of the hexane and water layers. The PVC will float at the interface of the water and perfluorohexane layers. The Teflon will sink to the bottom of the cylinder.

1.35 HDPE will float in ethylene glycol, water, acetic acid, and glycerol.

1.37 The sample's density and melting point could be compared to those of pure silver.

1.39 If too much sugar is excreted, the density of the urine would be higher than normal. If too much water is excreted, the density would be lower than normal.

1.41 (a) Solid potassium metal reacts with liquid water to produce gaseous hydrogen and a homogeneous mixture (solution) of potassium hydroxide in liquid water.
(b) The reaction is a chemical change.
(c) The reactants are potassium and water. The products are hydrogen gas and a water (aqueous) solution of potassium hydroxide. Heat and light are also evolved.
(d) Among the qualitative observations are (i) the reaction is violent, and (ii) heat and light (a purple flame) are produced.

1.43 The balloons containing helium and neon will float in air.

1.45 Physical change

Let's Review: The Tools of Quantitative Chemistry

1 298 K

3 (a) 289 K
(b) 97 °C
(c) 310 K (3.1×10^2 K)

5 42,195 m; 26.219 miles

7 5.3 cm^2; 5.3×10^{-4} m^2

9 250. cm^3; 0.250 L, 2.50×10^{-4} m^3; 0.250 dm^3

11 2.52×10^3 g

13 555 g

15 (c) zinc

17 5.0×10^6 J

19 170 kcal is equivalent to 710 kJ, which is considerably greater than 280 kJ.

21 (a) Method A with all data included:
average = 2.4 g/cm^3
Method B with all data included:
average = 3.480 g/cm^3
For B, the 5.811 g/cm^3 data point can be excluded because it is more than twice as large as all other points for Method B. Using only the first three points, average = 2.703 g/cm^3
(b) Method A: error = 0.3 g/cm^3 or about 10%
Method B: error = 0.001 g/cm^3 or about 0.04%
(c) Method A: standard deviation = 0.2 g/cm^3
Method B (including all data points):
standard deviation = 1.554 g/cm^3
Method B (excluding the 5.811 g/cm^3 data point):
standard deviation = 0.002 g/cm^3
(d) Method B's average value is both more precise and more accurate so long as the 5.811 g/cm^3 data point is excluded.

23 (a) 5.4×10^{-2} g, two significant figures
(b) 5.462×10^3 g, four significant figures
(c) 7.92×10^{-4} g, three significant figures
(d) 1.6×10^3 mL, two significant figures

25 (a) 9.44×10^{-3}
(b) 5694
(c) 11.9
(d) 0.122

27

Slope: 0.1637 g/kernel
The slope represents the average mass of a popcorn kernel.
Mass of 20 popcorn kernels = 3.370 g
There are 127 kernels in a sample with a mass of 20.88 g.

29 (a) $y = -4.00x + 20.00$
(b) $y = -4.00$

31 $C = 0.0823$

33 $T = 295$

35 0.197 nm; 197 pm

37 (a) 7.5×10^{-6} m; (b) 7.5×10^3 nm; (c) 7.5×10^6 pm

39 50. mg procaine hydrochloride

41 The volume of the marbles is 99 mL − 61 mL = 38 mL. This yields a density of 2.5 g/cm^3.

43 (a) 0.178 nm^3; 1.78×10^{-22} cm^3
(b) 3.87×10^{-22} g
(c) 9.68×10^{-23} g

45 Your normal body temperature (about 98.6 °F) is 37 °C. As this is higher than gallium's melting point, the metal will melt in your hand.

47 (a) 15%
(b) 3.63×10^3 kernels

49 8.0×10^4 kg of sodium fluoride per year

51 245 g sulfuric acid

53 (a) 272 mL ice
(b) The ice cannot be contained in the can.

55 7.99 g/cm^3

57 (a) 8.7 g/cm^3

(b) The metal is probably cadmium, but the calculated density is close to that of cobalt, nickel, and copper. Further testing should be done on the metal.

59 0.0927 cm

61 (a) 1.143×10^{21} atoms; 76.4% of the lattice is filled with atoms; 23.6% of the lattice is open space.

Atoms are spheres. When spheres are packed together, they touch only at certain points, therefore leaving spaces in the structure.

(b) Four atoms

63 Al, aluminum

65

Spectrophotometric analysis of copper

$y = 248x + 0.002$

When absorbance $= 0.635$, concentration $= 2.55 \times 10^{-3} \text{ g/L} = 2.55 \times 10^{-3} \text{ mg/mL}$

67 Average $= 5.24\%$, standard deviation $= 0.05\%$

Seven of the ten values fall within the region $5.19 \le x \le 5.29$

Chapter 2

2.1 Atoms contain the following fundamental particles: protons ($+1$ charge), neutrons (zero charge), and electrons (-1 charge). Protons and neutrons are in the nucleus of an atom. Electrons are the least massive of the three particles.

2.3 The electron cloud would extend around $1 \times 10^{-13} \text{ cm} = 1 \text{ fm}$.

2.5 (a) $^{27}_{12}\text{Mg}$
(b) $^{48}_{22}\text{Ti}$
(c) $^{62}_{30}\text{Zn}$

2.7

Element	Electrons	Protons	Neutrons
^{24}Mg	12	12	12
^{119}Sn	50	50	69
^{232}Th	90	90	142
^{13}C	6	6	7
^{63}Cu	29	29	34
^{205}Bi	83	83	122

2.9 $^{16}\text{O}/^{12}\text{C} = 1.3329$

2.11 $^{57}_{27}\text{Co}, ^{58}_{27}\text{Co}, ^{60}_{27}\text{Co}$

2.13 Protium: one proton, one electron
Deuterium: one proton, one neutron, one electron
Tritium: one proton, two neutrons, one electron

2.15 ^{205}Tl is more abundant than ^{203}Tl. The atomic mass of thallium is closer to 205 than to 203.

2.17 $(0.0750)(6.015121) + (0.9250)(7.016003) = 6.94$

2.19 (c), about 50%. Actual percent $^{107}\text{Ag} = 51.839\%$

2.21 $^{69}\text{Ga}, 60.12\%; ^{71}\text{Ga}, 39.88\%$

2.23

	Symbol	Atomic No.	Atomic Mass	Group	Period	
Titanium	Ti	22	47.867	4B(IUPAC 4)	4	Metal
Thallium	Tl	81	204.3833	3A(IUPAC 13)	6	Metal

2.25 Eight elements: periods 2 and 3. 18 elements: periods 4 and 5. 32 elements: period 6.

2.27 (a) Nonmetals: C, Cl
(b) Main group elements: C, Ca, Cl, Cs
(c) Lanthanides: Ce
(d) Transition elements: Cr, Co, Cd, Ce, Cm, Cu, Cf
(e) Actinides: Cm, Cf
(f) Gases: Cl

2.29 Metals: Na, Ni, Np
Metalloids: None in this list
Nonmetals: N, Ne

2.31 Molecular formula: H_2SO_4.
Structural formula:

$$O-\overset{\overset{\displaystyle O}{|}}{\underset{\underset{\displaystyle O-H}{|}}{S}}-O-H$$

The structure is not flat. The O atoms are arranged around the sulfur at the corners of a tetrahedron. The hydrogen atoms are connected to two of the oxygen atoms.

2.33 Molecular formula for asparagine, $C_4H_8N_2O_3$
Structural formula:

2.35 (a) Mg^{2+}
(b) Zn^{2+}
(c) Ni^{2+}
(d) Ga^{3+}

2.37 (a) Ba^{2+}
(b) Ti^{4+}

(c) PO_4^{3-}
(d) HCO_3^-
(e) S^{2-}
(f) ClO_4^-
(g) Co^{2+}
(h) SO_4^{2-}

2.39 K loses one electron per atom to form a K^+ ion. It has the same number of electrons as an Ar atom.

2.41 Ba^{2+} and Br^- ions. The compound's formula is $BaBr_2$.

2.43 (a) Two K^+ ions and one S^{2-} ion
(b) One Co^{2+} ion and one SO_4^{2-} ion
(c) One K^+ ion and one MnO_4^- ion
(d) Three NH_4^+ ions and one PO_4^{3-} ion
(e) One Ca^{2+} ion and two ClO^- ions
(f) One Na^+ ion and one $CH_3CO_2^-$ ion

2.45 Co^{2+} gives CoO and Co^{3+} gives Co_2O_3.

2.47 (a) $AlCl_2$ should be $AlCl_3$ (based on an Al^{3+} ion and three Cl^- ions).
(b) KF_2 should be KF (based on a K^+ ion and an F^- ion).
(c) Ga_2O_3 is correct.
(d) MgS is correct.

2.49 (a) Potassium sulfide
(b) Cobalt(II) sulfate
(c) Ammonium phosphate
(d) Calcium hypochlorite

2.51 (a) $(NH_4)_2CO_3$
(b) CaI_2
(c) $CuBr_2$
(d) $AlPO_4$
(e) $AgCH_3CO_2$

2.53 Compounds with Na^+: Na_2CO_3 (sodium carbonate) and NaI (sodium iodide). Compounds with Ba^{2+}: $BaCO_3$ (barium carbonate) and BaI_2 (barium iodide).

2.55 The force of attraction is stronger in NaF than in NaI because the distance between ion centers is smaller in NaF (235 pm) than in NaI (322 pm).

2.57 (a) Nitrogen trifluoride
(b) Hydrogen iodide
(c) Boron triiodide
(d) Phosphorus pentafluoride

2.59 (a) SCl_2
(b) N_2O_5
(c) $SiCl_4$
(d) B_2O_3

2.61 (a) 67 g Al
(b) 0.0698 g Fe
(c) 0.60 g Ca
(d) 1.32×10^4 g Ne

2.63 (a) 1.9998 mol Cu
(b) 0.0017 mol Li
(c) 2.1×10^{-5} mol Am
(d) 0.250 mol Al

2.65 Of these elements, He has the smallest molar mass, and Fe has the largest molar mass. Therefore, 1.0 g of

He has the largest number of atoms in these samples, and 1.0 g of Fe has the smallest number of atoms.

2.67 0.02 mol H < 0.0597 mol P < 0.0996 mol Ca < 0.259 mol O

2.69 (a) 159.7 g/mol
(b) 117.2 g/mol
(c) 176.1 g/mol

2.71 (a) 290.8 g/mol
(b) 249.7 g/mol

2.73 (a) 1.53 g
(b) 4.60 g
(c) 4.60 g
(d) 1.48 g

2.75 Amount of SO_3 = 12.5 mol
Number of molecules = 7.52×10^{24} molecules
Number of S atoms = 7.52×10^{24} atoms
Number of O atoms = 2.26×10^{25} atoms

2.77 4×10^{21} molecules

2.79 (a) 86.60% Pb and 13.40% S
(b) 81.71% C and 18.29% H
(c) 79.96% C, 9.394% H, and 10.65% O

2.81 66.46% copper in CuS. 15.0 g of CuS is needed to obtain 10.0 g of Cu.

2.83 $C_4H_6O_4$

2.85 (a) CH, 26.0 g/mol; C_2H_2
(b) CHO, 116.1 g/mol; $C_4H_4O_4$
(c) CH_2, 112.2 g/mol, C_8H_{16}

2.87 Empirical formula, CH; molecular formula, C_2H_2

2.89 Empirical formula, C_3H_4; molecular formula, C_9H_{12}

2.91 Empirical and molecular formulas are both $C_8H_8O_3$

2.93 XeF_2

2.95 ZnI_2

2.97

Symbol	^{58}Ni	^{33}S	^{20}Ne	^{55}Mn
Protons	28	16	10	25
Neutrons	30	17	10	30
Electrons	28	16	10	25
Name	Nickel	Sulfur	Neon	Manganese

2.99

S	N
B	I

2.101 (a) 1.0552×10^{-22} g for 1 Cu atom
(b) 6.286×10^{-22} dollars for 1 Cu atom

2.103 (a) Strontium
(b) Zirconium

(c) Carbon
(d) Arsenic
(e) Iodine
(f) Magnesium
(g) Krypton
(h) Sulfur
(i) Germanium or arsenic

2.105 (a) 0.25 mol U
(b) 0.50 mol Na
(c) 10 atoms of Fe

2.107 40.157 g H_2 (b) < 103.0 g C (c) < 182 g Al (f) < 210 g Si (d) < 212.0 g Na (e) < 351 g Fe (a) < 650 g Cl_2 (g)

2.109 (a) Atomic mass of O = 15.873 u; Avogadro's number = 5.9802×10^{23} particles per mole
(b) Atomic mass of H = 1.00798 u; Avogadro's number = 6.0279×10^{23} particles per mole

2.111 $(NH_4)_2CO_3$, $(NH_4)_2SO_4$, $NiCO_3$, $NiSO_4$

2.113 All of these compounds have one atom of some element plus three Cl atoms. The highest mass percent of chlorine will occur in the compound having the lightest central element. Here, that element is B, so BCl_3 should have the highest mass percent of Cl (90.77%).

2.115 The molar mass of adenine ($C_5H_5N_5$) is 135.13 g/mol. 3.0×10^{23} molecules represents 67 g. Thus, 3.0×10^{23} molecules of adenine has a larger mass than 40.0 g of the compound.

2.117 1.7×10^{21} molecules of water

2.119 245.75 g/mol. Mass percent: 25.86% Cu, 22.80% N, 5.742% H, 13.05% S, and 32.55% O. In 10.5 g of compound there are 2.72 g Cu and 0.770 g H_2O.

2.121 Empirical formula of malic acid: $C_4H_6O_5$

2.123 $Fe_2(CO)_9$

2.125 (a) $C_7H_5NO_3S$

(b) 6.82×10^{-4} mol saccharin
(c) 21.9 mg S

2.127 (a) NaClO, ionic
(b) BI_3
(c) $Al(ClO_4)_3$, ionic
(d) $Ca(CH_3CO_2)_2$, ionic
(e) $KMnO_4$, ionic
(f) $(NH_4)_2SO_3$, ionic
(g) KH_2PO_4, ionic
(h) S_2Cl_2
(i) ClF_3
(j) PF_3

2.129 (a) Empirical formula = molecular formula = CF_2O_2
(b) Empirical formula = C_5H_4; molecular formula = $C_{10}H_8$

2.131 Empirical formula and molecular formula = $C_5H_{14}N_2$

2.133 $C_9H_7MnO_3$

2.135 68.42% Cr; 1.2×10^3 kg Cr_2O_3

2.137 Empirical formula = ICl_3; molecular formula = I_2Cl_6

2.139 7.35 kg of iron

2.141 (d) Na_2MoO_4

2.143 5.52×10^{-4} mol $C_{21}H_{15}Bi_3O_{12}$; 0.346 g Bi

2.145 The molar mass of the compound is 154 g/mol. The unknown element is carbon.

2.147 $n = 2.19 \times 10^3$

2.149 (a) 2.3×10^{14} g/cm^3
(b) 3.34×10^{-3} g/cm^3
(c) The nucleus is much more dense than the space occupied by the electrons.

2.151 (a) 0.0130 mol Ni
(b) NiF_2
(c) Nickel(II) fluoride

2.153 Formula is $MgSO_4 \cdot 7\,H_2O$

2.155 Volume = 3.0 cm^3; length of side = 1.4 cm

2.157 (c) The calculated mole ratio is 0.78 mol H_2O per mol $CaCl_2$. The student should heat the crucible again and then reweigh it. More water might be driven off.

2.159 (a) $m/Z = 50$ is $^{12}C^1H_3^{35}Cl^+$; $m/Z = 52$ is $^{12}C^1H_3^{37}Cl^+$ The height of the line at $m/Z = 52$ is about 1/3 the height of the line at $m/Z = 50$ because the abundance of ^{37}Cl is about 1/3 that of ^{35}Cl.
(b) $^{13}C^1H_3^{35}Cl^+$ (a small portion of this peak is also due to $^{12}C^2H^1H_2^{35}Cl^+$)

2.161 Required data: density of iron (d), molar mass of iron (b), Avogadro's number (c)

$$1.00\ cm^3 \left(\frac{7.87\ g}{1\ cm^3}\right)\left(\frac{1\ mol}{55.85\ g}\right)\left(\frac{6.02 \times 10^{23}\ atoms}{1\ mol}\right) = 8.49 \times 10^{22}\ atoms\ Fe$$

2.163 (a) Barium would be more reactive than calcium, so a more vigorous evolution of hydrogen should occur.
(b) Reactivity increases on descending the periodic table, at least for Groups 1A and 2A.

2.165 When words are written with the pink, hydrated compound, the words are not visible. However, when heated, the hydrated salt loses water to form anhydrous $CoCl_2$, which is deep blue. The words are then visible.

Applying Chemical Principles: Argon—An Amazing Discovery

1. 162.18 cm^3

3. % Abundance ^{40}Ar = 99.600%
Atomic mass of ^{40}Ar = 39.963 u

Chapter 3

3.1 (a) $2\ Al(s) + Fe_2O_3(s) \rightarrow 2\ Fe(\ell) + Al_2O_3(s)$

So much energy is released as heat in this reaction that the iron formed is in the liquid state.

(b) $C(s) + H_2O(g) \rightarrow CO(g) + H_2(g)$

(c) $SiCl_4(\ell) + 2\ Mg(s) \rightarrow Si(s) + 2\ MgCl_2(s)$

3.3 (a) $4\ Cr(s) + 3\ O_2(g) \rightarrow 2\ Cr_2O_3(s)$

(b) $Cu_2S(s) + O_2(g) \rightarrow 2\ Cu(s) + SO_2(g)$

(c) $C_6H_5CH_3(\ell) + 9\ O_2(g) \rightarrow 4\ H_2O(\ell) + 7\ CO_2(g)$

3.5 (a) $Fe_2O_3(s) + 3\ Mg(s) \rightarrow 3\ MgO(s) + 2\ Fe(s)$

Reactants = iron(III) oxide, magnesium

Products = magnesium oxide, iron

(b) $AlCl_3(s) + 3\ NaOH(aq) \rightarrow$
$$Al(OH)_3(s) + 3\ NaCl(aq)$$

Reactants = aluminum chloride, sodium hydroxide

Products = aluminum hydroxide, sodium chloride

(c) $2\ NaNO_3(s) + H_2SO_4(aq) \rightarrow$
$$Na_2SO_4(s) + 2\ HNO_3(aq)$$

Reactants = sodium nitrate, sulfuric acid

Products = sodium sulfate, nitric acid

(d) $NiCO_3(s) + 2\ HNO_3(aq) \rightarrow$
$$Ni(NO_3)_2(aq) + CO_2(g) + H_2O(\ell)$$

Reactants = nickel(II) carbonate, nitric acid

Products = nickel(II) nitrate, carbon dioxide, water

3.7 The reaction involving HCl is more product-favored at equilibrium.

3.9 Electrolytes are compounds whose aqueous solutions conduct electricity. Given an aqueous solution containing a strong electrolyte and another aqueous solution containing a weak electrolyte at the same concentration, the solution containing the strong electrolyte (such as NaCl) will conduct electricity much better than the one containing the weak electrolyte (such as acetic acid).

3.11 (a) $CuCl_2$

(b) $AgNO_3$

(c) All are water-soluble.

3.13 (a) K^+ and OH^- ions

(b) K^+ and SO_4^{2-} ions

(c) Li^+ and NO_3^- ions

(d) NH_4^+ and SO_4^{2-} ions

3.15 (a) Soluble, Na^+ and CO_3^{2-} ions

(b) Soluble, Cu^{2+} and SO_4^{2-} ions

(c) Insoluble

(d) Soluble, Ba^{2+} and Br^- ions

3.17 $CdCl_2(aq) + 2\ NaOH(aq) \rightarrow$
$$Cd(OH)_2(s) + 2\ NaCl(aq)$$
$Cd^{2+}(aq) + 2\ OH^-(aq) \rightarrow Cd(OH)_2(s)$

3.19 (a) $NiCl_2(aq) + (NH_4)_2S(aq) \rightarrow NiS(s) + 2\ NH_4Cl(aq)$

$Ni^{2+}(aq) + S^{2-}(aq) \rightarrow NiS(s)$

(b) $3\ Mn(NO_3)_2(aq) + 2\ Na_3PO_4(aq) \rightarrow$
$$Mn_3(PO_4)_2(s) + 6\ NaNO_3(aq)$$
$3\ Mn^{2+}(aq) + 2\ PO_4^{3-}(aq) \rightarrow Mn_3(PO_4)_2(s)$

3.21 $HNO_3(aq) + H_2O(\ell) \rightarrow H_3O^+(aq) + NO_3^-(aq)$

3.23 $H_2C_2O_4(aq) + H_2O(\ell) \rightarrow H_3O^+(aq) + HC_2O_4^-(aq)$

$HC_2O_4^-(aq) + H_2O(\ell) \rightarrow H_3O^+(aq) + C_2O_4^{2-}(aq)$

3.25 $MgO(s) + H_2O(\ell) \rightarrow Mg(OH)_2(s)$

3.27 (a) Acetic acid reacts with magnesium hydroxide to give magnesium acetate and water.

$2\ CH_3CO_2H(aq) + Mg(OH)_2(s) \rightarrow$
$$Mg(CH_3CO_2)_2(aq) + 2\ H_2O(\ell)$$

(b) Perchloric acid reacts with ammonia to give ammonium perchlorate

$HClO_4(aq) + NH_3(aq) \rightarrow NH_4ClO_4(aq)$

3.29 $Ba(OH)_2(aq) + 2\ HNO_3(aq) \rightarrow$
$$Ba(NO_3)_2(aq) + 2\ H_2O(\ell)$$

3.31 $HNO_3(aq) + H_2O(\ell) \rightleftharpoons H_3O^+(aq) + NO_3^-(aq)$

Brønsted acids: $HNO_3(aq)$ and $H_3O^+(aq)$

Brønsted bases: $H_2O(\ell)$ and $NO_3^-(aq)$

HNO_3 is a strong acid; therefore, this reaction is product-favored at equilibrium.

3.33 $H_2O(\ell) + HBr(aq) \rightleftharpoons H_3O^+(aq) + Br^-(aq)$

Water accepts H^+ from $HBr(aq)$

$H_2O(\ell) + NH_3(aq) \rightleftharpoons OH^-(aq) + NH_4^+(aq)$

Water donates H^+ to $NH_3(aq)$

3.35 (a) $(NH_4)_2CO_3(aq) + Cu(NO_3)_2(aq) \rightarrow$
$$CuCO_3(s) + 2\ NH_4NO_3(aq)$$
$CO_3^{2-}(aq) + Cu^{2+}(aq) \rightarrow CuCO_3(s)$

(b) $Pb(OH)_2(s) + 2\ HCl(aq) \rightarrow PbCl_2(s) + 2\ H_2O(\ell)$

$Pb(OH)_2(s) + 2\ H_3O^+(aq) + 2\ Cl^-(aq) \rightarrow$
$$PbCl_2(s) + 4\ H_2O(\ell)$$

(c) $BaCO_3(s) + 2\ HCl(aq) \rightarrow$
$$BaCl_2(aq) + H_2O(\ell) + CO_2(g)$$
$BaCO_3(s) + 2\ H_3O^+(aq) \rightarrow$
$$Ba^{2+}(aq) + 3\ H_2O(\ell) + CO_2(g)$$

(d) $2\ CH_3CO_2H(aq) + Ni(OH)_2(s) \rightarrow$
$$Ni(CH_3CO_2)_2(aq) + 2\ H_2O(\ell)$$
$2\ CH_3CO_2H(aq) + Ni(OH)_2(s) \rightarrow$
$$Ni^{2+}(aq) + 2\ CH_3CO_2^-(aq) + 2\ H_2O(\ell)$$

3.37 (a) $AgNO_3(aq) + KI(aq) \rightarrow AgI(s) + KNO_3(aq)$

$Ag^+(aq) + I^-(aq) \rightarrow AgI(s)$

(b) $Ba(OH)_2(aq) + 2\ HNO_3(aq) \rightarrow$
$$Ba(NO_3)_2(aq) + 2\ H_2O(\ell)$$
$OH^-(aq) + H_3O^+(aq) \rightarrow 2\ H_2O(\ell)$

(c) $2\ Na_3PO_4(aq) + 3\ Ni(NO_3)_2(aq) \rightarrow$
$$Ni_3(PO_4)_2(s) + 6\ NaNO_3(aq)$$
$2\ PO_4^{3-}(aq) + 3\ Ni^{2+}(aq) \rightarrow Ni_3(PO_4)_2(s)$

3.39 (a) $HNO_2(aq) + OH^-(aq) \rightarrow NO_2^-(aq) + H_2O(\ell)$

(b) $Ca(OH)_2(s) + 2\ H_3O^+(aq) \rightarrow$
$$Ca^{2+}(aq) + 4\ H_2O(\ell)$$

3.41 $FeCO_3(s) + 2\ HNO_3(aq) \rightarrow$
$$Fe(NO_3)_2(aq) + CO_2(g) + H_2O(\ell)$$
Iron(II) carbonate reacts with nitric acid to give iron(II) nitrate, carbon dioxide, and water.

3.43 $(NH_4)_2S(aq) + 2\ HBr(aq) \rightarrow 2\ NH_4Br(aq) + H_2S(g)$
Ammonium sulfide reacts with hydrobromic acid to give ammonium bromide and hydrogen sulfide.

3.45 (a) Br = +5 and O = −2
(b) C = +3 each and O = −2
(c) F = −1
(d) Ca = +2 and H = −1
(e) H = +1, Si = +4, and O = −2
(f) H = +1, S = +6, and O = −2

3.47 (a) Oxidation–reduction
Zn is oxidized from 0 to +2, and N in NO_3^- is reduced from +5 to +4 in NO_2.
(b) Acid–base reaction
(c) Oxidation–reduction
Calcium is oxidized from 0 to +2 in $Ca(OH)_2$, and H is reduced from +1 in H_2O to 0 in H_2.

3.49 (a) O_2 is the oxidizing agent (as it always is), so C_2H_4 is the reducing agent. In this process, C_2H_4 is oxidized, and O_2 is reduced.
(b) Si is oxidized from 0 in Si to +4 in $SiCl_4$. Cl_2 is reduced from 0 in Cl_2 to −1 in Cl^-. Si is the reducing agent, and Cl_2 is the oxidizing agent.

3.51 (a) Acid–base
$Ba(OH)_2(aq) + 2\ HCl(aq) \rightarrow$
$$BaCl_2(aq) + 2\ H_2O(\ell)$$
(b) Gas-forming
$2\ HNO_3(aq) + CoCO_3(s) \rightarrow$
$$Co(NO_3)_2(aq) + H_2O(\ell) + CO_2(g)$$
(c) Precipitation
$2\ Na_3PO_4(aq) + 3\ Cu(NO_3)_2(aq) \rightarrow$
$$Cu_3(PO_4)_2(s) + 6\ NaNO_3(aq)$$

3.53 (a) Precipitation
$MnCl_2(aq) + Na_2S(aq) \rightarrow MnS(s) + 2\ NaCl(aq)$
$Mn^{2+}(aq) + S^{2-}(aq) \rightarrow MnS(s)$
(b) Precipitation
$K_2CO_3(aq) + ZnCl_2(aq) \rightarrow ZnCO_3(s) + 2\ KCl(aq)$
$CO_3^{2-}(aq) + Zn^{2+}(aq) \rightarrow ZnCO_3(s)$

3.55 (a) $CuCl_2(aq) + H_2S(aq) \rightarrow$
$$CuS(s) + 2\ HCl(aq)\ \text{precipitation}$$
(b) $H_3PO_4(aq) + 3\ KOH(aq) \rightarrow$
$$3\ H_2O(\ell) + K_3PO_4(aq)$$
acid–base
(c) $Ca(s) + 2\ HBr(aq) \rightarrow H_2(g) + CaBr_2(aq)$
oxidation–reduction and gas-forming
(d) $MgCl_2(aq) + 2\ NaOH(aq) \rightarrow$
$$Mg(OH)_2(s) + 2\ NaCl(aq)$$
precipitation

3.57 (a) $Ca(OH)_2(s) + 2\ HBr(aq) \rightarrow$
$$2\ H_2O(\ell) + CaBr_2(aq)$$
(b) $MgCO_3(s) + 2\ HNO_3(aq) \rightarrow$
$$Mg(NO_3)_2(aq) + CO_2(g) + H_2O(\ell)$$
(c) $BaCl_2(aq) + Na_2SO_4(aq) \rightarrow$
$$BaSO_4(s) + 2\ NaCl(aq)$$
(d) $NH_3(g) + H_2O(\ell) \rightarrow NH_4^+(aq) + OH^-(aq)$

3.59 (a) $CO_2(g) + 2\ NH_3(g) \rightarrow NH_2CONH_2(s) + H_2O(\ell)$
(b) $UO_2(s) + 4\ HF(aq) \rightarrow UF_4(s) + 2\ H_2O(\ell)$
$UF_4(s) + F_2(g) \rightarrow UF_6(s)$
(c) $TiO_2(s) + 2\ Cl_2(g) + 2\ C(s) \rightarrow TiCl_4(\ell) + 2\ CO(g)$
$TiCl_4(\ell) + 2\ Mg(s) \rightarrow Ti(s) + 2\ MgCl_2(s)$

3.61 (a) NaBr, KBr, or other alkali metal bromides; Group 2A bromides; other metal bromides except AgBr, Hg_2Br_2, and $PbBr_2$
(b) $Al(OH)_3$ and transition metal hydroxides
(c) Alkaline earth carbonates ($CaCO_3$) or transition metal carbonates ($NiCO_3$)
(d) Metal nitrates are generally water-soluble [e.g., $NaNO_3$, $Ni(NO_3)_2$].
(e) CH_3CO_2H, other acids containing the $-CO_2H$ group

3.63 Water soluble: $Cu(NO_3)_2$, $CuCl_2$. Water-insoluble: $CuCO_3$, $Cu_3(PO_4)_2$

3.65 $2\ H_3O^+(aq) + Mg(OH)_2(s) \rightarrow 4\ H_2O(\ell) + Mg^{2+}(aq)$
Spectator ion, NO_3^-. Acid–base reaction.

3.67 (a) Cl_2 is reduced (to Cl^-) and Br^- is oxidized (to Br_2).
(b) Cl_2 is the oxidizing agent and Br^- is the reducing agent.

3.69 (a) $MgCO_3(s) + 2\ H_3O^+(aq) \rightarrow$
$$CO_2(g) + Mg^{2+}(aq) + 3\ H_2O(\ell)$$
Chloride ion (Cl^-) is the spectator ion.
(b) Gas-forming reaction

3.71 (a) H_2O, NH_3, NH_4^+, and OH^- (and a trace of H_3O^+)
weak Brønsted base
(b) H_2O, CH_3CO_2H, $CH_3CO_2^-$, and H_3O^+ (and a trace of OH^-)
weak Brønsted acid
(c) H_2O, Na^+, and OH^- (and a trace of H_3O^+)
strong Brønsted base
(d) H_2O, H_3O^+, and Br^- (and a trace of OH^-)
strong Brønsted acid

3.73 (a) $K_2CO_3(aq) + 2\ HClO_4(aq) \rightarrow$
$$2\ KClO_4(aq) + CO_2(g) + H_2O(\ell)$$

gas-forming

Potassium carbonate and perchloric acid react to form potassium perchlorate, carbon dioxide, and water

$$CO_3^{2-}(aq) + 2\ H_3O^+(aq) \rightarrow CO_2(g) + 3\ H_2O(\ell)$$

(b) $FeCl_2(aq) + (NH_4)_2S(aq) \rightarrow$
$$FeS(s) + 2\ NH_4Cl(aq)$$

precipitation

Iron(II) chloride and ammonium sulfide react to form iron(II) sulfide and ammonium chloride

$$Fe^{2+}(aq) + S^{2-}(aq) \rightarrow FeS(s)$$

(c) $Fe(NO_3)_2(aq) + Na_2CO_3(aq) \rightarrow$
$$FeCO_3(s) + 2\ NaNO_3(aq)$$

precipitation

Iron(II) nitrate and sodium carbonate react to form iron(II) carbonate and sodium nitrate

$$Fe^{2+}(aq) + CO_3^{2-}(aq) \rightarrow FeCO_3(s)$$

(d) $3\ NaOH(aq) + FeCl_3(aq) \rightarrow$
$$3\ NaCl(aq) + Fe(OH)_3(s)$$

precipitation

Sodium hydroxide and iron(III) chloride react to form sodium chloride and iron(III) hydroxide

$$3\ OH^-(aq) + Fe^{3+}(aq) \rightarrow Fe(OH)_3(s)$$

3.75 (a) $NaOH$
(b) $MgCl_2$
(c) KI
(d) NH_4Cl

3.77 (a) NH_3
(b) CH_3CO_2H, HF

3.79 $2\ H_3O^+(aq) + S^{2-}(aq) \rightarrow H_2S(g) + 2\ H_2O(\ell)$

$H_2S(g) + Pb^{2+}(aq) + 2\ H_2O(\ell) \rightarrow$
$$PbS(s) + 2\ H_3O^+(aq)$$

3.81 (a) Reactants: Na(+1), I(−1), H(+1), S(+6), O(−2), Mn(+4)

Products: Na(+1), S(+6), O(−2), Mn(+2), I(0), H(+1)

(b) The oxidizing agent is MnO_2, and NaI is oxidized. The reducing agent is NaI, and MnO_2 is reduced.

(c) Based on the picture, the reaction is product-favored.

(d) Sodium iodide, sulfuric acid, and manganese(IV) oxide react to form sodium sulfate, manganese(II) sulfate, and water.

3.83 Among the reactions that could be used are the following:

$MgCO_3(s) + 2\ HCl(aq) \rightarrow$
$$MgCl_2(aq) + CO_2(g) + H_2O(\ell)$$

$MgS(s) + 2\ HCl(aq) \rightarrow MgCl_2(aq) + H_2S(g)$

$MgSO_3(s) + 2\ HCl(aq) \rightarrow$
$$MgCl_2(aq) + SO_2(g) + H_2O(\ell)$$

In each case, the resulting solution could be evaporated to obtain the desired magnesium chloride.

3.85 The Ag^+ was reduced (to silver metal), and the glucose was oxidized (to $C_6H_{12}O_7$). The Ag^+ is the oxidizing agent, and the glucose is the reducing agent.

3.87 Weak electrolyte test: Compare the conductivity of a solution of lactic acid and that of an equal concentration of a strong acid. The conductivity of the lactic acid solution should be significantly less.

Reversible reaction: The fact that lactic acid is an electrolyte indicates that the reaction proceeds in the forward direction. To test whether the ionization is reversible, one could prepare a solution containing as much lactic acid as it will hold and then add a strong acid (to provide H_3O^+). If the reaction proceeds in the reverse direction, this will cause some lactic acid to precipitate.

3.89 (a) Several precipitation reactions are possible:

i. $BaCl_2(aq) + H_2SO_4(aq) \rightarrow$
$$BaSO_4(s) + 2\ HCl(aq)$$

ii. $BaCl_2(aq) + Na_2SO_4(aq) \rightarrow$
$$BaSO_4(s) + 2\ NaCl(aq)$$

iii. $Ba(OH)_2(aq) + H_2SO_4(aq) \rightarrow$
$$BaSO_4(s) + 2\ H_2O(\ell)$$

(b) Gas-forming reaction:

$BaCO_3(s) + H_2SO_4(aq) \rightarrow$
$$BaSO_4(s) + CO_2(g) + H_2O(\ell)$$

3.91 $NiC_8H_{14}N_4O_4$

3.93 (a) Reactants: As: +3; S: −2; N: +5

Products: As: +5; S: 0; N: +2

(b) Ag_3AsO_4

Applying Chemical Principles: Superconductors

1. In this case, because you know that Cu has an implied subscript of 1, divide the number of moles of each element determined by the number of moles of Cu. $x = 0.15$; Formula = $La_{1.85}Ba_{0.15}CuO_4$

3. One formula unit of the compound contains two Cu^{2+} ions and one Cu^{3+} ion.

5. $0.011\ g\ O_2$

Chapter 4

4.1 $4.5\ mol\ O_2$; $310\ g\ Al_2O_3$

4.3 $22.7\ g\ Br_2$; $25.3\ g\ Al_2Br_6$

4.5 (a) CO_2, carbon dioxide, and H_2O, water
(b) $CH_4(g) + 2\ O_2(g) \rightarrow CO_2(g) + 2\ H_2O(\ell)$
(c) $102\ g\ O_2$
(d) $128\ g$ products

4.7

Equation	2 PbS(s)	+ 3 O₂(g)	→ 2 PbO(s)	+ 2 SO₂(g)

Equation	$2\,PbS(s)$	$+\ 3\,O_2(g)$	$\rightarrow\ 2\,PbO(s)$	$+\ 2\,SO_2(g)$
Initial (mol)	2.50	3.75	0	0
Change (mol)	−2.50	$-\tfrac{3}{2}(2.50)$ = −3.75	$+\tfrac{2}{2}(2.50)$ = +2.50	$+\tfrac{2}{2}(2.50)$ = +2.50
Final (mol)	0	0	2.50	2.50

The amounts table shows that 2.50 mol of PbS requires $\tfrac{3}{2}(2.50) = 3.75$ mol of O_2 and produces 2.50 mol of PbO and 2.50 mol of SO_2.

4.9 (a) Balanced equation: $4\,Cr(s) + 3\,O_2(g) \rightarrow 2\,Cr_2O_3(s)$
(b) 0.175 g of Cr is equivalent to 0.00337 mol

Equation	$4\,Cr(s)$	$+\ 3\,O_2(g)$	$\rightarrow$	$2\,Cr_2O_3(s)$
Initial (mol)	0.00337	0.00252 mol		0
Change (mol)	−0.00337	$-\tfrac{3}{4}(0.00337)$ = −0.00252		$\tfrac{2}{4}(0.00337)$ = +0.00168
Final (mol)	0	0		0.00168

The 0.00168 mol Cr_2O_3 produced corresponds to 0.256 g Cr_2O_3.
(c) 0.081 g O_2

4.11 0.11 mol of Na_2SO_4 and 0.62 mol of C are mixed. Sodium sulfate is the limiting reactant. Therefore, 0.11 mol of Na_2S is formed, or 8.2 g.

4.13 F_2 is the limiting reactant.

4.15 (a) CH_4 is the limiting reactant.
(b) 375 g H_2
(c) Excess $H_2O = 1390$ g

4.17 (a) $2\,C_6H_{14}(\ell) + 19\,O_2(g) \rightarrow 12\,CO_2(g) + 14\,H_2O(g)$
(b) O_2 is the limiting reactant. Products are 187 g of CO_2 and 89.2 g of H_2O.
(c) 154 g of hexane remains
(d)

Equation	$2\,C_6H_{14}(\ell)$	$+\ 19\,O_2(g)$	$\rightarrow\ 12\,CO_2(g)$	$+\ 14\,H_2O(g)$
Initial (mol)	2.49	6.72	0	0
Change (mol)	−0.707	−6.72	+4.24	+4.95
Final (mol)	1.78	0	4.24	4.95

4.19 $(332\ g/407\ g)100\% = 81.6\%$

4.21 (a) 14.3 g $Cu(NH_3)_4SO_4$
(b) 88.3% yield

4.23 91.9% hydrate

4.25 84.3% $CaCO_3$

4.27 1.467% Tl_2SO_4

4.29 Empirical formula = CH

4.31 Empirical formula = CH_2;
molecular formula = C_5H_{10}

4.33 Empirical formula = CH_3O;
molecular formula = $C_2H_6O_2$

4.35 $Ni(CO)_4$

4.37 $[Na_2CO_3] = 0.254$ M; $[Na^+] = 0.508$ M;
$[CO_3^{2-}] = 0.254$ M

4.39 0.494 g $KMnO_4$

4.41 5.08×10^3 mL

4.43 (a) 0.50 M NH_4^+ and 0.25 M SO_4^{2-}
(b) 0.246 M Na^+ and 0.123 M CO_3^{2-}
(c) 0.056 M H_3O^+ and 0.056 M NO_3^-

4.45 A mass of 1.06 g of Na_2CO_3 is required. After weighing out this quantity of Na_2CO_3, transfer it to a 500.-mL volumetric flask. Rinse any solid from the neck of the flask while filling the flask with distilled water. Dissolve the solute in water. Add water until the bottom of the meniscus of the water is at the top of the scribed mark on the neck of the flask. Thoroughly mix the solution.

4.47 0.0750 M

4.49 Method (a) is correct. Method (b) gives an acid concentration of 0.15 M.

4.51 0.00340 M

4.53 $[H_3O^+] = 10^{-pH} = 4.0 \times 10^{-4}$ M; the solution is acidic.

4.55 HNO_3 is a strong acid, so $[H_3O^+] = 0.0013$ M. pH = 2.89.

4.57

	pH	$[H_3O^+]$	Acidic/Basic
(a)	1.00	0.10 M	Acidic
(b)	10.50	3.2×10^{-11} M	Basic
(c)	4.89	1.3×10^{-5} M	Acidic
(d)	7.64	2.3×10^{-8} M	Basic

4.59 268 mL

4.61 210 g NaOH and 190 g Cl_2

4.63 174 mL of $Na_2S_2O_3$ solution

4.65 1.50×10^3 mL of $Pb(NO_3)_2$ solution

4.67 44.6 mL

4.69 1.052 M HCl

4.71 104 g/mol

4.73 12.8% Fe

4.75

Calibration plot for dye
$y = 115000x + 0.1785$

(a) Slope = 1.2×10^5 M⁻¹; y-intercept = 0.18 M
(b) 3.0×10^{-6} M

4.77 (a) Products = $CO_2(g)$ and $H_2O(g)$
(b) $2 C_6H_6(\ell) + 15 O_2(g) \rightarrow 12 CO_2(g) + 6 H_2O(g)$
(c) 49.28 g O_2
(d) 65.32 g products (= sum of C_6H_6 mass and O_2 mass)

4.79 0.28 g arginine, 0.21 g ornithine

4.81 (a) Titanium(IV) chloride, water, titanium(IV) oxide, hydrogen chloride
(b) 4.60 g H_2O
(c) 10.2 TiO_2, 18.6 g HCl

4.83 8.33 g NaN_3

4.85 Mass percent saccharin = 75.92%

4.87 SiH_4

4.89 C_3H_2O

4.91 1.85 kg H_2SO_4

4.93 The calculated molar mass of the metal is 1.2×10^2 g/mol. The metal is probably tin (118.67 g/mol).

4.95 479 kg Cl_2

4.97 66.5 kg CaO

4.99 1.27 g C_4H_8 (44.4%) and 1.59 g C_4H_{10} (55.6%)

4.101 62.2% Cu_2S and 26.8% CuS

4.103 (a) $MgCO_3(s) + 2 H_3O^+(aq) \rightarrow$
$CO_2(g) + Mg^{2+}(aq) + 2 H_2O(\ell)$
(b) Gas-forming reaction
(c) 0.15 g

4.105 15.0 g of $NaHCO_3$ require 1190 mL of 0.15 M acetic acid. Therefore, acetic acid is the limiting reactant. (Conversely, 125 mL of 0.15 M acetic acid requires only 1.58 g of $NaHCO_3$.) 1.54 g of $NaCH_3CO_2$ produced.

4.107 3.13 g $Na_2S_2O_3$, 96.8%

4.109 (a) pH = 0.979
(b) $[H_3O^+]$ = 0.0028 M; the solution is acidic.
(c) $[H_3O^+]$ = 2.1×10^{-10} M; the solution is basic.
(d) The new solution's concentration is 0.102 M HCl; the pH = 0.990

4.111 The concentration of hydrochloric acid is 2.92 M; the pH is −0.465

4.113 1.56 g of $CaCO_3$ required; 1.00 g $CaCO_3$ remain; 1.73 g $CaCl_2$ produced.

4.115 Volume of water in the pool = 7.6×10^4 L

4.117 (a) Au, gold, has been oxidized and is the reducing agent.
O_2, oxygen, has been reduced and is the oxidizing agent.
(b) 26 L NaCN solution

4.119 % Atom economy = 49.81%

4.121 The concentration of Na_2CO_3 in the first solution prepared is 0.0275 M, in the second solution prepared the concentration of Na_2CO_3 is 0.00110 M.

4.123 (a) First reaction: oxidizing agent = Cu^{2+} and reducing agent = I^-
Second reaction: oxidizing agent = I_3^- and reducing agent = $S_2O_3^{2-}$
(b) 67.3% copper

4.125 $x = 6$; $Cr(NH_3)_6Cl_3$.

4.127 11.48% 2,4-D

4.129 3.3 mol H_2O/mol $CaCl_2$

4.131 (a) Slope = 2.06×10^5; y-intercept = 0.024
(b) 1.20×10^{-4} g/L
(c) 0.413 mg PO_4^{3-}

4.133 The total mass of the beakers and products after reaction is equal to the total mass before the reaction (167.170 g) because no gases were produced in the reaction and there is conservation of mass in chemical reactions.

4.135 The balanced chemical equation indicates that the stoichiometric ratio of HCl to Zn is 2 mol HCl/1 mol Zn. In each reaction, there is 0.100 mol of HCl present. In reaction 1, there is 0.107 mol of Zn present. This gives a 0.93 mol HCl/mol Zn ratio, indicating that HCl is the limiting reactant. In reaction 2, there is 0.050 mol of Zn, giving a 2.0 mol HCl/mol Zn ratio. This indicates that the two reactants are present in exactly the correct stoichiometric ratio. In reaction 3, there is 0.020 mol of Zn, giving a 5.0 mol HCl/mol Zn ratio. This indicates that the HCl is present in excess and that the zinc is the limiting reactant.

4.137 If both students base their calculations on the amount of HCl solution pipeted into the flask (20 mL), then the second student's result will be (e), the same as the first student's. However, if the HCl concentration is calculated using the diluted solution volume, student 1 will use a volume of 40 mL, and student 2 will use a volume of 80 mL in the calculation. The second student's result will be (c), half that of the first student's.

4.139 (a) % Atom economy = 44.15%
(b) Theoretical yield of maleic anhydride = 1.26×10^3 g; % yield = 77.4%
The theoretical yield of carbon dioxide from 1.00 kg of benzene is 1.13 kg.

Applying Chemical Principles: Antacids

1. $NaHCO_3$, $KHCO_3$, and $CaCO_3$

3. (a) $Mg(OH)_2(s) + 2 HCl(aq) \rightarrow MgCl_2(aq) + 2 H_2O(\ell)$
(b) 110. mg $Mg(OH)_2$

5. Rolaids neutralizes the greatest quantity of acid.

Chapter 5

5.1 The system is the part of the universe being studied. The surroundings are everything else in the universe that can exchange matter and/or energy with the system. A system and its surroundings are said to be in thermal equilibrium if they can exchange energy with each other but are at the same temperature; therefore, there is no net transfer of energy as heat from one to the other.

5.3 (a) Exothermic
(b) Endothermic
(c) Endothermic
(d) Endothermic

5.5 $0.140 \, J/g \cdot K$

5.7 $2.44 \, kJ$

5.9 $32.8 \, °C$

5.11 $20.7 \, °C$

5.13 $47.8 \, °C$

5.15 $0.40 \, J/g \cdot K$

5.17 $330 \, kJ$

5.19 $49.3 \, kJ$

5.21 $273 \, J$

5.23 $9.97 \times 10^5 \, J$

5.25 Reaction is exothermic because $\Delta_r H°$ is negative. The heat evolved is $2.38 \, kJ$.

5.27 $-3.3 \times 10^4 \, kJ$

5.29 $\Delta H = -56 \, kJ/mol \, CsOH$

5.31 $0.52 \, J/g \cdot K$

5.33 $\Delta_r H = +23 \, kJ/mol\text{-rxn}$

5.35 $-297 \, kJ/mol \, SO_2$

5.37 $-3.09 \times 10^3 \, kJ/mol \, C_6H_5CO_2H$

5.39 $0.236 \, J/g \cdot K$

5.41 (a) $\Delta_r H° = -126 \, kJ/mol\text{-rxn}$
(b)

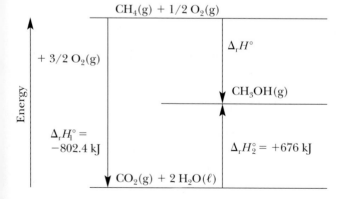

5.43 $\Delta_r H° = +90.3 \, kJ/mol\text{-rxn}$

5.45 $C(s) + 2 \, H_2(g) + 1/2 \, O_2(g) \rightarrow CH_3OH(\ell)$
$\Delta_f H° = -238.4 \, kJ/mol$

5.47 (a) $2 \, Cr(s) + 3/2 \, O_2(g) \rightarrow Cr_2O_3(s)$
$\Delta_f H° = -1134.7 \, kJ/mol$
(b) $2.4 \, g$ is equivalent to $0.046 \, mol$ of Cr. This will produce $26 \, kJ$ of energy transferred as heat.

5.49 (a) $\Delta H° = -24 \, kJ$ for $1.0 \, g$ of phosphorus
(b) $\Delta H° = -18 \, kJ$ for $0.20 \, mol \, NO$
(c) $\Delta H° = -16.9 \, kJ$ for the formation of $2.40 \, g$ of $NaCl(s)$
(d) $\Delta H° = -1.8 \times 10^3 \, kJ$ for the oxidation of $250 \, g$ of iron

5.51 (a) $\Delta_r H° = -906.2 \, kJ$
(b) The heat evolved is $133 \, kJ$ for the oxidation of $10.0 \, g$ of NH_3

5.53 (a) $\Delta_r H° = +161.6 \, kJ/mol\text{-rxn}$; the reaction is endothermic.
(b)

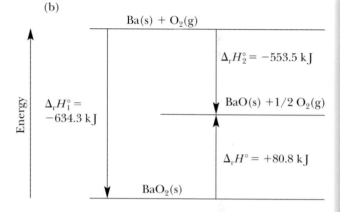

5.55 $\Delta_f H° = +77.7 \, kJ/mol$ for naphthalene

5.57 (a) Exothermic: a process in which energy is transferred as heat from a system to its surroundings. (The combustion of methane is exothermic.)

Endothermic: a process in which energy is transferred as heat from the surroundings to the system. (Ice melting is endothermic.)
(b) System: the object or collection of objects being studied. (A chemical reaction—the system—taking place inside a calorimeter—the surroundings.)

Surroundings: everything outside the system that can exchange mass or energy with the system. (The calorimeter and everything outside the calorimeter comprise the surroundings.)
(c) Specific heat capacity: the quantity of energy that must be transferred as heat to raise the temperature of 1 gram of a substance 1 kelvin. (The specific heat capacity of water is $4.184 \, J/g \cdot K$.)
(d) State function: a quantity that is characterized by changes that do not depend on the path chosen to go from the initial state to the final state. (Enthalpy and internal energy are state functions.)
(e) Standard state: the most stable form of a substance in the physical state that exists at a pressure of 1 bar and at a specified temperature. (The standard state of carbon at 25 °C is graphite.)
(f) Enthalpy change, ΔH: the energy transferred as heat at constant pressure. (The enthalpy change for melting ice at 0 °C is $6.00 \, kJ/mol$.)

(g) Standard enthalpy of formation: the enthalpy change for the formation of 1 mol of a compound in its standard state directly from the component elements in their standard states. ($\Delta_f H°$ for liquid water is -285.83 kJ/mol.)

5.59 (a) System: reaction between methane and oxygen

Surroundings: the furnace and the rest of the universe. Energy is transferred as heat from the system to the surroundings.

(b) System: water drops

Surroundings: skin and the rest of the universe

Energy is transferred as heat from the surroundings to the system

(c) System: water

Surroundings: freezer and the rest of the universe

Energy is transferred as heat from the system to the surroundings

(d) System: reaction of aluminum and iron(III) oxide

Surroundings: flask, laboratory bench, and rest of the universe

Energy is transferred as heat from the system to the surroundings.

5.61 Standard state of oxygen is gas, $O_2(g)$.

$O_2(g) \rightarrow 2\,O(g)$, $\Delta_r H° = +498.34$ kJ/mol-rxn, endothermic

$3/2\,O_2(g) \rightarrow O_3(g)$, $\Delta_r H° = +142.67$ kJ/mol-rxn

5.63 (a) Energy is transferred as heat from the surroundings to the system and as work done by the system.

(b) Energy is transferred as heat from the surroundings to the system and as work done by the system.

5.65 $\Delta H° = -0.627$ kJ

5.67 $C_{Ag} = 0.24$ J/g · K

5.69 Mass of ice melted = 75.4 g

5.71 Final temperature = 278 K (5 °C)

5.73 (a) When summed, the following equations give the balanced equation for the formation of $B_2H_6(g)$ from the elements.

$2\,B(s)\ \ +3/2\,O_2(g) \rightarrow B_2O_3(s)$	$\Delta_r H° = -1271.9$ kJ
$3\,H_2(g)+3/2\,O_2(g) \rightarrow 3\,H_2O(g)$	$\Delta_r H° = -725.4$ kJ
$B_2O_3(s)+3\,H_2O(g) \rightarrow B_2H_6(g)+3\,O_2(g)$	$\Delta_r H° = +2032.9$ kJ
$2\,B(s)\ \ +3\,H_2(g)\ \ \rightarrow B_2H_6(g)$	$\Delta_r H° = +35.6$ kJ

(b) The enthalpy of formation of $B_2H_6(g)$ is $+35.6$ kJ/mol.

(c)

(d) The formation of $B_2H_6(g)$ is endothermic.

5.75 (a) $\Delta_r H° = +131.31$ kJ
(b) Endothermic
(c) 1.0932×10^7 kJ

5.77 Assuming $CO_2(g)$ and $H_2O(\ell)$ are the products of combustion:

$\Delta_r H°$ for isooctane is -5461.3 kJ/mol or -47.81 kJ per gram.

$\Delta_r H°$ for liquid methanol is -726.77 kJ/mol or -22.682 kJ per gram.

5.79 (a) Adding the equations as they are given in the question results in the desired equation for the formation of $SrCO_3(s)$. The calculated $\Delta_r H° = -1220.$ kJ/mol.

(b)

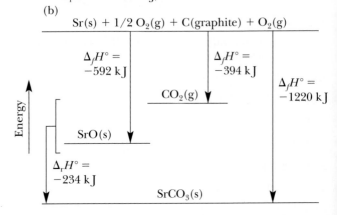

5.81 $\Delta_r H° = -305.3$ kJ

5.83 $C_{Pb} = 0.121$ J/g · K

5.85 $\Delta_r H = -69$ kJ/mol AgCl

5.87 36.0 kJ evolved per mol of NH_4NO_3

5.89 The standard enthalpy change, $\Delta_r H°$, is -352.88 kJ. The quantity of magnesium needed is 0.43 g.

5.91 (a) Exothermic
(b) Exothermic

5.93 The enthalpy change for each of the three reactions below is known or can be measured by calorimetry. The three equations sum to give the enthalpy of formation of $CaSO_4(s)$.

$$Ca(s) + 1/2\ O_2(g) \rightarrow CaO(s) \quad \Delta_rH° = \Delta_fH°$$
$$= -635.09\ kJ$$

$$1/8\ S_8(s) + 3/2\ O_2(g) \rightarrow SO_3(g) \quad \Delta_rH° = \Delta_fH°$$
$$= -395.77\ kJ$$

$$CaO(s) + SO_3(g) \rightarrow CaSO_4(s) \quad \Delta_rH° = -402.7\ kJ$$
$$Ca(s) + 1/8\ S_8(s) + 2\ O_2(g) \rightarrow CaSO_4(s) \quad \Delta_rH° = \Delta_fH°$$
$$= -1433.6\ kJ$$

5.95

Metal	Molar Heat Capacity (J/mol · K)
Al	24.2
Fe	25.1
Cu	24.5
Au	25.4

All the metals have a molar heat capacity of 24.8 ± 0.5 J/mol · K. Therefore, assuming the molar heat capacity of Ag is 24.8 J/mol · K, its specific heat capacity is 0.230 J/g · K. This is very close to the experimental value of 0.236 J/g · K.

5.97 120 g of CH_4 required (assuming $H_2O(g)$ as product)

5.99 1.6×10^{11} kJ released to the surroundings. This is equivalent to 3.8×10^4 tons of dynamite.

5.101 (a)

(b) *cis*-2-butene: $\Delta_fH° = -7.6$ kJ/mol

trans-2-butene: $\Delta_fH° = -10.8$ kJ/mol

1-butene: $\Delta_fH° = -0.6$ kJ/mol

(c)

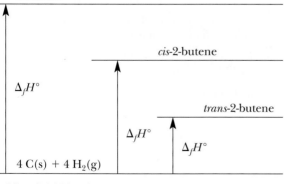

(d) -3.4 kJ/mol-rxn

5.103 (a) -726 kJ/mol Mg
(b) 25.0 °C

5.105 (a) Methane
(b) Methane
(c) -279 kJ
(d) $CH_4(g) + 1/2\ O_2(g) \rightarrow CH_3OH(\ell)$

5.107 (a) Metal heated = 100.0 g of Al; metal cooled = 50.0 g of Au; final temperature = 26 °C
(b) Metal heated = 50.0 g of Zn; metal cooled = 50.0 g of Al; final temperature = 21 °C

5.109 $w = -(1.0\ L \cdot atm)(0.36\ L - 0\ L) = -0.36\ L\ atm = -36\ J$

Thus, 36 J of work is done by the system on the surroundings.

Applying Chemical Principles: Gunpowder

1. (a) $\Delta_rH° = -567.9$ kJ/mol-rxn
(b) $\Delta H° = -2.10$ kJ

3. (a) $4\ C_3H_5N_3O_9(\ell) \rightarrow 12\ CO_2(g) + 6\ N_2(g) + 10\ H_2O(g) + O_2(g)$
(b) $\Delta_fH° = -3.70 \times 10^2$ kJ/mol

Chapter 6

6.1 (a) Microwaves
(b) Red light
(c) Infrared

6.3 (a) Green light has a higher frequency than amber light
(b) 5.04×10^{14} s^{-1}

6.5 Frequency = 6.0×10^{14} s^{-1}; energy per photon = 4.0×10^{-19} J; energy per mol of photons = 2.4×10^5 J

6.7 Frequency = 7.5676×10^{14} s^{-1}; energy per photon = 5.0144×10^{-19} J; 302 kJ/mol of photons

6.9 In order of increasing energy: FM station < microwaves < yellow light < x-rays

6.11 Light with a wavelength as long as 600 nm would be sufficient. This is in the visible region.

6.13 (a) The light of shortest wavelength has a wavelength of 253.652 nm.
(b) Frequency = 1.18190×10^{15} s^{-1}. Energy per photon = 7.83139×10^{-19} J/photon.
(c) The lines at 404 nm (violet) and 436 nm (blue) are in the visible region of the spectrum.

6.15 The color is violet. $n_{initial} = 6$ and $n_{final} = 2$

6.17 (a) 10 lines possible
(b) Highest frequency (highest energy), $n = 5$ to $n = 1$
(c) Longest wavelength (lowest energy), $n = 5$ to $n = 4$

6.19 (a) $n = 3$ to $n = 2$
(b) $n = 4$ to $n = 1$. The energy levels are progressively closer at higher levels, so the energy difference from $n = 4$ to $n = 1$ is greater than from $n = 5$ to $n = 2$.

6.21 Wavelength $= 102.6$ nm and frequency $= 2.923 \times 10^{15}$ s^{-1}. Light with these properties is in the ultraviolet region.

6.23 Wavelength $= 0.29$ nm

6.25 The wavelength is 2.2×10^{-25} nm. (Calculated from $\lambda = h/m \cdot v$, where m is the ball's mass in kg and v is the velocity.) To have a wavelength of 5.6×10^{-3} nm, the ball would have to travel at 1.2×10^{-21} m/s.

6.27 (a) $n = 4$, $\ell = 0, 1, 2, 3$
(b) When $\ell = 2$, $m_\ell = -2, -1, 0, 1, 2$
(c) For a 4s orbital, $n = 4$, $\ell = 0$, and $m_\ell = 0$
(d) For a 4f orbital, $n = 4$, $\ell = 3$, and $m_\ell = -3, -2, -1, 0, 1, 2, 3$

6.29 Set 1: $n = 4$, $\ell = 1$, and $m_\ell = -1$
Set 2: $n = 4$, $\ell = 1$, and $m_\ell = 0$
Set 3: $n = 4$, $\ell = 1$, and $m_\ell = +1$

6.31 Four subshells. (The number of subshells in a shell is always equal to n.)

6.33 (a) ℓ must have a value no greater than $n - 1$.
(b) When $\ell = 0$, m_ℓ can only equal 0.
(c) When $\ell = 0$, m_ℓ can only equal 0.

6.35 (a) None. The quantum number set is not possible. When $\ell = 0$, m_ℓ can only equal 0.
(b) 3 orbitals
(c) 11 orbitals
(d) 1 orbital

6.37 (a) $m_s = 0$ is not possible. m_s may only have values of $\pm 1/2$.
One possible set of quantum numbers: $n = 4$, $\ell = 2$, $m_\ell = 0$, $m_s = +1/2$
(b) m_ℓ cannot equal -3 in this case. If $\ell = 1$, m_ℓ can only be $-1, 0,$ or 1.
One possible set of quantum numbers: $n = 3$, $\ell = 1$, $m_\ell = -1$, $m_s = -1/2$
(c) $\ell = 3$ is not possible in this case. The maximum value of ℓ is $n - 1$.
One possible set of quantum numbers: $n = 3$, $\ell = 2$, $m_\ell = -1$, $m_s = +1/2$

6.39 2d and 3f orbitals cannot exist. The $n = 2$ shell consists only of s and p subshells. The $n = 3$ shell consists only of s, p, and d subshells.

6.41 (a) For 2p: $n = 2$, $\ell = 1$, and $m_\ell = -1, 0,$ or $+1$
(b) For 3d: $n = 3$, $\ell = 2$, and $m_\ell = -2, -1, 0, +1,$ or $+2$
(c) For 4f: $n = 4$, $\ell = 3$, and $m_\ell = -3, -2, -1, 0, +1, +2,$ or $+3$

6.43 4d

6.45 (a) 2s has 0 nodal surfaces that pass through the nucleus ($\ell = 0$).
(b) 5d has 2 nodal surfaces that pass through the nucleus ($\ell = 2$).
(c) 5f has three nodal surfaces that pass through the nucleus ($\ell = 3$).

6.47 (a) Correct
(b) Incorrect. The intensity of a light beam is independent of frequency and is related to the number of photons of light with a certain energy.
(c) Correct

6.49 Considering only angular nodes (nodal surfaces that pass through the nucleus):

s orbital	0 nodal surfaces through the nucleus
p orbitals	1 nodal surface or plane passing through the nucleus
d orbitals	2 nodal surfaces or planes passing through the nucleus
f orbitals	3 nodal surfaces or planes passing through the nucleus

6.51

ℓ Value	Orbital Type
3	f
0	s
1	p
2	d

6.53 Considering only angular nodes (nodal surfaces that pass through the nucleus):

Orbital Type	Number of Orbitals in a Given Subshell	Number of Nodal Surfaces
s	1	0
p	3	1
d	5	2
f	7	3

6.55 (a) Green light
(b) Red light has a wavelength of 680 nm, and green light has a wavelength of 500 nm.
(c) Green light has a higher frequency than red light.

6.57 (a) Wavelength $= 0.35$ m
(b) Energy $= 0.34$ J/mol
(c) Violet light (with $\lambda = 420$ nm) has an energy of 280 kJ/mol of photons.
(d) Violet light has an energy (per mol of photons) that is 840,000 times greater than a mole of photons from a cell phone.

6.59 The ionization energy for He$^+$ is 5248 kJ/mol. This is four times the ionization energy for the H atom.

6.61 $1s < 2s = 2p < 3s = 3p = 3d < 4s$
In the H atom orbitals in the same shell (e.g., 2s and 2p) have the same energy.

6.63 Frequency $= 2.836 \times 10^{20}$ s^{-1} and wavelength $= 1.057 \times 10^{-12}$ m

6.65 260 s or 4.3 min

6.67 (a) Size and energy
(b) ℓ
(c) More
(d) 7 (when $\ell = 3$ these are f orbitals)
(e) One orbital
(f) (Left to right) d, s, and p
(g) $\ell = 0, 1, 2, 3, 4$
(h) 16 orbitals ($1s$, $3p$, $5d$, and $7f$) ($= n^2$)
(i) Paramagnetic

6.69 (a) Drawing (a) is a ferromagnetic solid, (b) is a diamagnetic solid, and (c) is a paramagnetic solid.
(b) Substance (a) would be most strongly attracted to a magnet, whereas (b) would be least strongly attracted.

6.71 The pickle glows because it was made by soaking a cucumber in brine, a concentrated solution of NaCl. The sodium atoms in the pickle are excited by the electric current and release energy as yellow light as they return to the ground state. Excited sodium atoms are the source of the yellow light you see in fireworks and in certain kinds of street lighting.

6.73 (a) $\lambda = 0.0005$ cm $= 5$ μm
(b) The left side is the higher energy side, and the right side is the lower energy side.
(c) The interaction with O—H requires more energy.

6.75 (c)

6.77 An experiment can be done that shows that the electron can behave as a particle, and another experiment can be done to show that it has wave properties. (However, no single experiment shows both properties of the electron.) The modern view of atomic structure is based on the wave properties of the electron.

6.79 (a) and (b)

6.81 Radiation with a wavelength of 93.8 nm is sufficient to raise the electron to the $n = 6$ quantum level (see Figure 6.10). There should be 15 emission lines involving transitions from $n = 6$ to lower energy levels. (There are five lines for transitions from $n = 6$ to lower levels, four lines for $n = 5$ to lower levels, three for $n = 4$ to lower levels, two lines for $n = 3$ to lower levels, and one line for $n = 2$ to $n = 1$.) Wavelengths for many of the lines are given in Figure 6.10. For example, there will be an emission involving an electron moving from $n = 6$ to $n = 2$ with a wavelength of 410.2 nm.

6.83 (a) Group 7B (IUPAC Group 7); Period 5
(b) $n = 5$, $\ell = 0$, $m_\ell = 0$, $m_s = +1/2$
(c) $\lambda = 8.79 \times 10^{-12}$ m; $\nu = 3.41 \times 10^{19}$ s^{-1}
(d) (i) HTcO$_4$(aq) + NaOH(aq) $\rightarrow$
$\quad\quad\quad\quad\quad$ H$_2$O(ℓ) + NaTcO$_4$(aq)
(ii) 8.5×10^{-3} g NaTcO$_4$ produced;
$\quad$ 1.8×10^{-3} g NaOH needed
(e) 0.28 mg NaTcO$_4$; 0.00015 M

Applying Chemical Principles: Chemistry of the Sun

1. $\nu = 5.102 \times 10^{14}$ s^{-1}

3. For $\lambda = 589.00$ nm, $E = 3.3726 \times 10^{-19}$ J
    For $\lambda = 589.59$ nm, $E = 3.3692 \times 10^{-19}$ J
    $\Delta E = 3.4 \times 10^{-22}$ J

5. Balmer series: G', F, C (as marked on the spectrum)

Chapter 7

7.1 (a) Phosphorus: $1s^2 2s^2 2p^6 3s^2 3p^3$

$\quad$ $1s$ $\quad$ $2s$ $\quad$ $2p$ $\quad\quad$ $3s$ $\quad$ $3p$

The element is in the third period in Group 5A. Therefore, it has five electrons in the third shell.
(b) Chlorine: $1s^2 2s^2 2p^6 3s^2 3p^5$

$\quad$ $1s$ $\quad$ $2s$ $\quad$ $2p$ $\quad\quad$ $3s$ $\quad$ $3p$

The element is in the third period and in Group 7A. Therefore, it has seven electrons in the third shell.

7.3 (a) Chromium: $1s^2 2s^2 2p^6 3s^2 3p^6 3d^5 4s^1$
(b) Iron: $1s^2 2s^2 2p^6 3s^2 3p^6 3d^6 4s^2$

7.5 (a) Arsenic: $1s^2 2s^2 2p^6 3s^2 3p^6 3d^{10} 4s^2 4p^3$; [Ar]$3d^{10} 4s^2 4p^3$
(b) Krypton: $1s^2 2s^2 2p^6 3s^2 3p^6 3d^{10} 4s^2 4p^6$;
[Ar]$3d^{10} 4s^2 4p^6$ = [Kr]

7.7 (a) Tantalum: This is the third element in the transition series in the sixth period. Therefore, it has a core equivalent to Xe plus two $6s$ electrons, 14 $4f$ electrons, and three electrons in $5d$: [Xe]$4f^{14} 5d^3 6s^2$
(b) Platinum: This is the eighth element in the transition series in the sixth period. Therefore, it is predicted to have a core equivalent to Xe plus two $6s$ electrons, 14 $4f$ electrons, and eight electrons in $5d$: [Xe]$4f^{14} 5d^8 6s^2$. In reality, its actual configuration (Table 7.3) is [Xe]$4f^{14} 5d^9 6s^1$.

7.9 Americium: [Rn]$5f^7 7s^2$ (see Table 7.3)

7.11 (a) 2
(b) 1
(c) None (because ℓ cannot equal n)

7.13 Magnesium: $1s^2 2s^2 2p^6 3s^2$

[Ne]

$3s$

Quantum numbers for the two electrons in the $3s$ orbital:

$n = 3$, $\ell = 0$, $m_\ell = 0$, and $m_s = +1/2$
$n = 3$, $\ell = 0$, $m_\ell = 0$, and $m_s = -1/2$

7.15 Gallium: $1s^2 2s^2 2p^6 3s^2 3p^6 3d^{10} 4s^2 4p^1$

$$3d \qquad 4s \qquad 4p$$

Quantum numbers for the $4p$ electron:

$n = 4$, $\ell = 1$, $m_\ell = -1, 0,$ or $+1$, and $m_s = +\frac{1}{2}$ or $-\frac{1}{2}$

7.17 (a) Mg^{2+} ion

$$1s \quad 2s \qquad 2p$$

(b) K^+ ion

$$1s \quad 2s \qquad 2p \qquad 3s \qquad 3p$$

(c) Cl^- ion (Note that both Cl^- and K^+ have the same configuration; both are equivalent to Ar.)

$$1s \quad 2s \qquad 2p \qquad 3s \qquad 3p$$

(d) O^{2-} ion

$$1s \quad 2s \qquad 2p$$

7.19 (a) V (paramagnetic; three unpaired electrons)

$$[Ar] \qquad 3d \qquad 4s$$

(b) V^{2+} ion (paramagnetic, three unpaired electrons)

$$[Ar] \qquad 3d \qquad 4s$$

(c) V^{5+} ion. This ion has an electron configuration equivalent to argon, [Ar]. It is diamagnetic with no unpaired electrons.

7.21 (a) Manganese

$$[Ar] \qquad 3d \qquad 4s$$

(b) Mn^{4+}

$$[Ar] \qquad 3d \qquad 4s$$

(c) The 4^+ ion is paramagnetic to the extent of three unpaired electrons.

(d) 3

7.23 Increasing size: C < B < Al < Na < K

7.25 (a) Cl^-
  (b) Al
  (c) In

7.27 (c)

7.29 (a) Largest radius, Na
  (b) Most negative electron attachment enthalpy: O
  (c) Ionization energy: Na < Mg < P < O

7.31 (a) Increasing ionization energy: S < O < F. S is less than O because the IE decreases down a group. F is greater than O because IE generally increases across a period.
  (b) Largest IE: O. IE decreases down a group.
  (c) Most negative electron attachment enthalpy: Cl. Electron attachment enthalpy becomes more negative across the periodic table and on ascending a group.
  (d) Largest size: O^{2-}. Negative ions are larger than their corresponding neutral atoms. F^- is thus larger than F. O^{2-} and F^- are isoelectronic, but the O^{2-} ion has only eight protons in its nucleus to attract the 10 electrons, whereas the F^- has nine protons, making the O^{2-} ion larger.

7.33 Uranium configuration: $[Rn]5f^3 6d^1 7s^2$

$$5f \qquad 6d \qquad 7s$$

Uranium(IV) ion, U^{4+}: $[Rn]5f^2$

$$5f \qquad 6d \qquad 7s$$

Both U and U^{4+} are paramagnetic.

7.35 (a) Atomic number = 20
  (b) Total number of s electrons = 8
  (c) Total number of p electrons = 12
  (d) Total number of d electrons = 0
  (e) The element is Ca, calcium, a metal.

7.37 (a) Valid. Possible elements are Li and Be.
  (b) Not valid. The maximum value of ℓ is $(n - 1)$.
  (c) Valid. Possible elements are B through Ne.
  (d) Valid. Possible elements are Y through Cd.

7.39 (a) Neodymium, Nd: $[Xe]4f^4 6s^2$ (Table 7.3)

$$[Xe] \qquad 4f \qquad 5d \qquad 6s$$

Iron, Fe: $[Ar]3d^6 4s^2$

$$[Ar] \qquad 3d \qquad 4s$$

Boron, B: $[He]2s^2 2p^1$

$$[He] \qquad 2s \qquad 2p$$

(b) All three elements have unpaired electrons and so should be paramagnetic.

(c) Neodymium(III) ion, Nd^{3+}: $[Xe]4f^3$

$$[Xe] \qquad 4f \qquad 5d \qquad 6s$$

Iron(III) ion, Fe^{3+}: $[Ar]3d^5$

$$3d \qquad 4s$$

Both neodymium(III) and iron(III) have unpaired electrons and are paramagnetic.

7.41 $K < Ca < Si < P$

7.43 (a) Metal
(b) B
(c) A
(d) A
(e) Rb_2Se

7.45 In^{4+}: Indium has three outer shell electrons and so is unlikely to form a 4^+ ion.

Fe^{6+}: Although iron has eight electrons in its $3d$ and $4s$ orbitals, ions with a 6^+ charge are highly unlikely. The ionization energy is too large.

Sn^{5+}: Tin has four outer shell electrons and so is unlikely to form a 5^+ ion.

7.47 (a) Se
(b) Br^-
(c) Na
(d) N
(e) N^{3-}

7.49 (a) Na
(b) C
(c) $Na < Al < B < C$

7.51 (a) Cobalt
(b) Paramagnetic
(c) Four unpaired electrons

7.53 (a) 0.421 g
(b) Paramagnetic; two unpaired electrons
(c) 99.8 mg; the nickel powder is paramagnetic and will stick to a magnet.

7.55 Li has three electrons ($1s^2 2s^1$) and Li^+ has only two electrons ($1s^2$). The ion is smaller than the atom because there are only two electrons to be held by three protons in the ion. Also, an electron in a larger orbital has been removed. Fluorine atoms have nine electrons and nine protons ($1s^2 2s^2 2p^5$). The anion, F^-, has one additional electron, which means that 10 electrons must be held by only nine protons, and so the ion is larger than the atom.

7.57 Element 1 comes from Group 4A (IUPAC Group 14). The first two IEs correspond to removing electrons from a p subshell. With the third IE, there is a fairly large jump in IE corresponding to removing an electron from an s subshell. The fourth electron removed comes from the same s subshell and therefore does not increase the IE by as much. None of the IEs are large enough to correspond to removing an electron from a lower energy level.

Element 2 comes from Group 3A (IUPAC Group 13). There is a large change in IE between the third and fourth IEs. The first three IEs correspond to removing electrons from the same energy level. The large jump at the fourth IE corresponds to having to remove the electron from a lower energy level.

7.59 Most stable: (d). The two electrons are in separate orbitals, following Hund's rule, and are of the same spin.

Least stable: (a). In this case the electrons violate both Hund's rule and the Pauli exclusion principle.

7.61 $K\ (1s^2 2s^2 2p^6 3s^2 3p^6 4s^1) \rightarrow K^+\ (1s^2 2s^2 2p^6 3s^2 3p^6)$
$K^+\ (1s^2 2s^2 2p^6 3s^2 3p^6) \rightarrow K^{2+}\ (1s^2 2s^2 2p^6 3s^2 3p^5)$

The first ionization is for the removal of an electron from the valence shell of electrons. The second electron, however, is removed from the $3p$ subshell. This subshell is significantly lower in energy than the $4s$ subshell, and considerably more energy is required to remove this second electron.

7.63 (a) In going from one element to the next across the period, the effective nuclear charge increases slightly and the attraction between the nucleus and the electrons increases.
(b) The size of fourth period transition elements, for example, is a reflection of the size of the $4s$ orbital. As d electrons are added across the series, protons are added to the nucleus. Adding protons should lead to a decreased atom size, but the effect of the protons is balanced by repulsions of the $3d$ electrons and $4s$ electrons, and the atom size is changed little.

7.65 Among the arguments for a compound composed of Mg^{2+} and O^{2-} are the following:
(a) Chemical experience suggests that all Group 2A elements form 2^+ cations, and that oxygen is typically the O^{2-} ion in its compounds.
(b) Other alkaline earth elements form oxides such as BeO, CaO, and BaO.

A possible experiment is to measure the melting point of the compound. An ionic compound such as NaF (with ions having 1^+ and 1^- charges) melts at 990 °C, whereas a compound analogous to MgO, CaO, melts at a much higher temperature (2580 °C).

7.67 (a) The effective nuclear charge increases, causing the valence orbital energies to become more negative on moving across the period.
(b) As the valence orbital energies become more negative, it is increasingly difficult to remove an electron from the atom, and the IE increases. Toward the end of the period, the orbital energies have become so negative that removing an electron requires significant energy. Instead, the effective nuclear charge has reached the point that the atom forms a negative ion, in line with the more negative electron attachment enthalpy for elements on the right side of the periodic table.
(c) The valence orbital energies are in the order:

Li (-520.0 kJ) < Be (-899.3 kJ) > B (-800.8 kJ) < C (-1029 kJ)

This means it is more difficult to remove an electron from Be than from either Li or B. The energy is more negative for C than for B, so it is more difficult to remove an electron from C than from B.

7.69 The size declines across this series of elements while their mass increases. Thus, the mass per volume, the density, increases.

7.71 (a) Element 113: $[Rn]5f^{14}6d^{10}7s^27p^1$
Element 115: $[Rn]5f^{14}6d^{10}7s^27p^3$
(b) Element 113 is in Group 3A (with elements such as boron and aluminum), and element 115 is in Group 5A (with elements such as nitrogen and phosphorus).
(c) Americium ($Z = 95$) + argon ($Z = 18$) = element 113

7.73 (a) Sulfur electron configuration

$1s$ $2s$ $2p$ $3s$ $3p$

(b) $n = 3$, $\ell = 1$, $m_\ell = 1$, and $m_s = +1/2$
(c) S has the smallest ionization energy and O has the smallest radius.
(d) S is smaller than the S^{2-} ion.
(e) 584 g SCl_2
(f) 10.0 g of SCl_2 is the limiting reactant, and 11.6 g of $SOCl_2$ can be produced.
(g) $\Delta_fH°[SCl_2(g)] = -17.6$ kJ/mol

7.75 (a) Z* for F is 5.20; Z* for Ne is 5.85. The effective nuclear charge increases from O to F to Ne. As the effective nuclear charge increases, the atomic radius decreases, and the first ionization energy increases.
(b) Z* for a $3d$ electron in Mn is 5.6; for a $4s$ electron it is only 3.6. The effective nuclear charge experienced by a $4s$ electron is much smaller than that experienced by a $3d$ electron. A $4s$ electron in Mn is thus more easily removed.

Applying Chemical Principles: The Not-So-Rare Earths

1. (a) Sm^{3+}: $[Xe]4f^5$
(b) $4\ Sm(s) + 3\ O_2(g) \rightarrow 2\ Sm_2O_3(s)$

3. (a) $[Xe]$
$4f$ $5d$ $6s$

(b) The most common oxidation state is +3, corresponding to the loss of the two $6s$ and one $5d$ electrons. The electron configuration of Gd^{3+} is $[Xe]4f^7$.

5. $\nu = 4.90 \times 10^{14}$ s^{-1}; $E = 3.25 \times 10^{-19}$ J/photon

Chapter 8

8.1. (a) Group 6A, six valence electrons
(b) Group 3A, three valence electrons
(c) Group 1A, one valence electron
(d) Group 2A, two valence electrons
(e) Group 7A, seven valence electrons
(f) Group 6A, six valence electrons

8.3 Group 4A, four bonds
Group 5A, three bonds (for a neutral compound)
Group 6A, two bonds (for a neutral compound)
Group 7A, one (for a neutral compound)

8.5 (a) NF_3, 26 valence electrons

:F—N—F:
     |
    :F:

(b) ClO_3^-, 26 valence electrons

[:O—Cl—O:]⁻
       |
      :O:

(c) HOBr, 14 valence electrons

H—O—Br:

(d) SO_3^{2-}, 26 valence electrons

[:O—S—O:]²⁻
      |
     :O:

8.7 (a) $CHClF_2$, 26 valence electrons

    H
    |
:Cl—C—F:
    |
   :F:

(b) CH_3CO_2H, 24 valence electrons

  H :O:
  | ‖
H—C—C—O—H
  |
  H

(c) CH_3CN, 16 valence electrons

    H
    |
H—C—C≡N:
    |
    H

(d) H_2CCCH_2, 16 valence electrons

  H   H
  | |
H—C=C=C—H

8.9 (a) SO_2, 18 valence electrons

:O—S=O: ⟷ O=S—O:

(b) HNO_2, 18 valence electrons

H—O—N=O

(c) SCN^-, 16 valence electrons

[S=C=N]⁻ ⟷ [:S≡C—N:]⁻ ⟷ [:S—C≡N]⁻

8.11 (a) BrF_3, 28 valence electrons

    :F:
    |
    Br—F:
    |
    :F:

(b) I_3^-, 22 valence electrons

(c) XeO_2F_2, 34 valence electrons

(d) XeF_3^+, 28 valence electrons

8.13 (a) N = 0; H = 0
(b) P = +1; O = −1
(c) B = −1; H = 0
(d) All are zero.

8.15 (a) N = +1; O = 0
(b) The central N is 0. The singly bonded O atom is −1, and the doubly bonded O atom is 0.

$$\left[:\ddot{O}-\ddot{N}=\ddot{O} \right]^- \longleftrightarrow \left[\ddot{O}=\ddot{N}-\ddot{O}: \right]^-$$

(c) N and F are both 0.
(d) The central N atom is +1, one of the O atoms is −1, and the other two O atoms and the H atom are all 0.

$$\overset{0}{H-\ddot{O}}-\overset{+1}{N}=\overset{0}{\ddot{O}}$$
$$\underset{-1}{:\ddot{O}:}$$

8.17 (a) Electron-pair geometry around N is tetrahedral. Molecular geometry is trigonal-pyramidal.

$$:\ddot{C}l-\underset{H}{\overset{|}{N}}-H$$

(b) Electron-pair geometry around O is tetrahedral. Molecular geometry is bent.

$$:\ddot{C}l-\ddot{O}-\ddot{C}l:$$

(c) Electron-pair geometry around C is linear. Molecular geometry is linear.

$$\left[\ddot{S}=C=\ddot{N} \right]^-$$

(d) Electron-pair geometry around O is tetrahedral. The molecular geometry is bent.

$$H-\ddot{O}-\ddot{F}:$$

8.19 (a) Electron-pair geometry around C is linear. Molecular geometry is linear.

$$\ddot{O}=C=\ddot{O}$$

(b) Electron-pair geometry around N is trigonal-planar. Molecular geometry is bent.

$$\left[:\ddot{O}-\ddot{N}=\ddot{O} \right]^-$$

(c) Electron-pair geometry around O is trigonal-planar. Molecular geometry is bent.

$$\ddot{O}=\ddot{O}-\ddot{O}:$$

(d) Electron-pair geometry around Cl atom is tetrahedral. Molecular geometry is bent.

$$\left[:\ddot{O}-\ddot{C}l-\ddot{O}: \right]^-$$

All have two atoms attached to the central atom. As the bond and lone pairs vary, the electron-pair geometries vary from linear to tetrahedral, and the molecular geometries vary from linear to bent.

8.21 (a) Electron-pair geometry around Cl is trigonal-bipyramidal. Molecular geometry is linear.

$$\left[:\ddot{F}-\ddot{C}l-\ddot{F}: \right]^-$$

(b) Electron-pair geometry around Cl is trigonal-bipyramidal. Molecular geometry is T-shaped.

$$:\ddot{F}-\underset{:\ddot{F}:}{\overset{|}{C}l}-\ddot{F}:$$

(c) Electron-pair geometry around Cl is octahedral. Molecular geometry is square-planar.

$$\left[:\ddot{F}-\underset{:\ddot{F}:}{\overset{:\ddot{F}:}{\overset{|}{C}l}}-\ddot{F}: \right]^-$$

(d) Electron-pair geometry around Cl is octahedral. Molecular geometry is a square-pyramidal.

$$:\ddot{F}\diagdown\underset{:\ddot{F}}{\overset{:\ddot{F}:}{\overset{|}{C}l}}\diagup\ddot{F}:$$

8.23 (a) Ideal O—S—O angle = 120°
(b) 120°
(c) 120°
(d) H—C—H = 109° and C—C—N angle = 180°

8.25 1 = 120°; 2 = 109°; 3 = 120°; 4 = 109°; 5 = 109°

The chain cannot be linear because the first two carbon atoms in the chain have bond angles of 109° and the final one has a bond angle of 120°. These bond angles do not lead to a linear chain.

8.27

$$\overset{\longrightarrow}{\underset{+\delta \quad -\delta}{C-O}} \qquad \overset{\longrightarrow}{\underset{+\delta \quad -\delta}{C-N}}$$

CO is more polar

$$\overset{\longrightarrow}{\underset{+\delta \quad -\delta}{P-Cl}} \qquad \overset{\longrightarrow}{\underset{+\delta \quad -\delta}{P-Br}}$$

PCl is more polar

$$\overset{\longrightarrow}{\underset{+\delta \quad -\delta}{B-O}} \qquad \overset{\longrightarrow}{\underset{+\delta \quad -\delta}{B-S}}$$

BO is more polar

$$\overset{\longrightarrow}{\underset{+\delta \quad -\delta}{B-F}} \qquad \overset{\longrightarrow}{\underset{+\delta \quad -\delta}{B-I}}$$

BF is more polar

8.29 (a) CH and CO bonds are polar.
   (b) The CO bond is most polar, and O is the most negative atom.

8.31 (a) OH^-: The formal charge on O is -1 and on H it is 0.
   (b) BH_4^-: Even though the formal charge on B is -1 and on H is 0, H is slightly more electronegative than B. The four H atoms are therefore more likely to bear the -1 charge of the ion. The BH bonds are polar with the H atom the negative end.
   (c) The CH and CO bonds are all polar (but the C—C bond is not). The negative charge in the CO bonds lies on the O atoms.

8.33 Structure C is most reasonable. The charges are as small as possible, and the negative charge resides on the more electronegative atom.

$$\overset{-2}{:\!\ddot{N}}\!-\!\overset{+1}{N}\!\equiv\!\overset{+1}{O:} \longleftrightarrow \overset{-1}{\ddot{N}}\!=\!\overset{+1}{N}\!=\!\overset{0}{\ddot{O}} \longleftrightarrow \overset{0}{:\!N}\!\equiv\!\overset{+1}{N}\!-\!\overset{-1}{\ddot{O}:}$$
$$\quad\;\; A \qquad\qquad\quad B \qquad\qquad\quad C$$

8.35 Lewis structures:

   (a) These species are isoelectronic.
   (b) Each has two major resonance structures.
   (c) In HCO_3^-, the H, C, and O attached to the H all have a formal charge of 0. Each of the other oxygen atoms has a formal charge of $-1/2$.
   In HNO_3, the same formal charges are present as in HCO_3^- except that the central N has a formal charge of $+1$.
   (d) HNO_3 is much more acidic than HCO_3^-. This is due, in part, to simple electrostatics. It is much easier to remove a positively charge species (H^+) from a neutral species (HNO_3) than from a negatively charged one (HCO_3^-).

8.37 (a)

   (b) If an H^+ ion were to attack NO_2^-, it would attach to an O atom because the O atoms bear the negative charge in this ion.
   (c)

   The structure on the left is strongly favored because all of the atoms have zero formal charge, whereas the structure on the right has a -1 formal charge on one oxygen and a $+1$ formal charge on the other.

8.39 (i)   The most polar bonds are in H_2O (because O and H have the largest difference in electronegativity).
   (ii) Not polar: CO_2 and CCl_4
   (iii) The F atom is more negatively charged.

8.41 (a) $BeCl_2$, nonpolar linear molecule
   (b) HBF_2, polar trigonal-planar molecule with F atoms on the negative end of the dipole and the H atom on the positive end.
   (c) CH_3Cl, polar tetrahedral molecule. The Cl atom is on the negative end of the dipole and the three H atoms are on the positive side of the molecule.
   (d) SO_3, a nonpolar trigonal-planar molecule

8.43 (a) Two C—H bonds, bond order is 1; 1 C=O bond, bond order is 2.
   (b) Three S—O single bonds, bond order is 1.
   (c) Two nitrogen–oxygen double bonds, bond order is 2.
   (d) One N=O double bond, bond order is 2; one N—Cl bond, bond order is 1.

8.45 (a) B—Cl
   (b) C—O
   (c) P—O
   (d) C=O

8.47 NO bond orders: 2 in NO_2^+, 1.5 in NO_2^-; 1.33 in NO_3^-. The NO bond is longest in NO_3^- and shortest in NO_2^+.

8.49 The CO bond in carbon monoxide is a triple bond, so it is both shorter and stronger than the CO double bond in H_2CO.

8.51 Using bond dissociation enthalpy data, $\Delta_rH° \approx -44$ kJ/mol-rxn. Using $\Delta_fH°$ data, $\Delta_rH° = -45.9$ kJ/mol-rxn.

8.53 $\Delta_rH = -126$ kJ

8.55 O—F bond dissociation energy = 192 kJ/mol

8.57

Element	Number of Valence Electrons
Li	1
Ti	4
Zn	2
Si	4
Cl	7

8.59 SeF_4, BrF_4^-, XeF_4

8.61

   Bond order = 3/2

8.63 To estimate the enthalpy change, we need bond dissociation enthalpies for the following bonds: O=O, H—H, and H—O.

ΔH to break bonds ≈ 498 kJ (for O=O) + 2×436 kJ (for H—H) = $+1370$ kJ

ΔH evolved when bonds are made $\approx 4 \times 463$ kJ (for O—H) = -1852 kJ

$\Delta_rH \approx -482$ kJ

8.65 All the species in the series have 16 valence electrons and all are linear.

(a) $\ddot{O}=C=\ddot{O} \longleftrightarrow :\ddot{O}-C\equiv O: \longleftrightarrow :O\equiv C-\ddot{O}:$

(b)

$$\left[\ddot{N}=N=\ddot{N}\right]^- \longleftrightarrow \left[:\ddot{N}-N\equiv N:\right]^- \longleftrightarrow \left[:N\equiv N-\ddot{N}:\right]^-$$

(c)

$$\left[\ddot{O}=C=\ddot{N}\right]^- \longleftrightarrow \left[:\ddot{O}-C\equiv N:\right]^- \longleftrightarrow \left[:O\equiv C-\ddot{N}:\right]^-$$

8.67 The N—O bonds in NO_2^- have a bond order of 1.5, whereas in NO_2^+ the bond order is 2. The shorter bonds (110 pm) are the NO bonds with the higher bond order (in NO_2^+), whereas the longer bonds (124 pm) in NO_2^- have a lower bond order.

8.69 The F—Cl—F bond angle in ClF_2^+, which has a tetrahedral electron-pair geometry, is approximately 109°.

$$\left[:\ddot{F}-\ddot{Cl}-\ddot{F}:\right]^+$$

The ClF_2^- ion has a trigonal-bipyramidal electron-pair geometry with F atoms in the axial positions and the lone pairs in the equatorial positions. Therefore, the F—C—F angle is 180°.

$$\left[:\ddot{F}-\ddot{Cl}-\ddot{F}:\right]^-$$

8.71 An H^+ ion will attach to an O atom of SO_3^{2-} and not to the S atom. The O atoms each have a formal charge of −1, whereas the S atom formal charge is +1.

$$\left[:\ddot{O}-\ddot{S}-\ddot{O}: \atop \quad :\ddot{O}:\right]^{2-}$$

8.73 (a) Calculation from bond dissociation enthalpies: $\Delta_rH° = -1070$ kJ/mol-rxn; $\Delta H° = -535$ kJ/mol CH_3OH

(b) Calculation from thermochemical data: $\Delta_rH° = -1352.3$ kJ/mol-rxn; $\Delta H° = -676$ kJ/mol CH_3OH

8.75 (a)

$$\left[:C\equiv N-\ddot{O}:\right]^- \longleftrightarrow \left[\ddot{C}=N=\ddot{O}\right]^- \longleftrightarrow \left[:\ddot{C}-N\equiv O:\right]^-$$
$$\quad {-1} \ {+1} \ {-1} \qquad\qquad {-2} \ {+1} \ \ 0 \qquad\qquad {-3} \ {+1} \ {+1}$$

(b) The first resonance structure is the most reasonable because oxygen, the most electronegative atom, has a negative formal charge, and the unfavorable negative charge on the least electronegative atom, carbon, is smallest.

(c) This species is so unstable because carbon, the least electronegative element in the ion, has a negative formal charge. In addition, all three resonance structures have an unfavorable charge distribution.

8.77

$$:\!-\!\overset{\textstyle F}{\underset{\textstyle F}{Xe}} \Big\rangle 120° \qquad F\!-\!\overset{\textstyle F}{\underset{\textstyle F}{Cl}} \Big\rangle 120°$$

(a) XeF_2 has three lone pairs around the Xe atom. The electron-pair geometry is trigonal-bipyramidal. Because lone pairs require more space than bond pairs, it is better to place the lone pairs in the equator of the bipyramid where the angles between them are 120°.

(b) Like XeF_2, ClF_3 has a trigonal-bipyramidal electron-pair geometry, but with only two lone pairs around the Cl. These are again placed in the equatorial plane where the angle between them is 120°.

8.79 (a) Angle 1 = 109°; angle 2 = 120°; angle 3 = 109°; angle 4 = 109°; and angle 5 = 109°

(b) The O—H bond is the most polar bond.

8.81 $\Delta_rH = +146$ kJ $= 2 (\Delta H_{C-N}) + \Delta H_{C=O} - [\Delta H_{N-N} + \Delta H_{C\equiv O}]$

8.83 (a) Two C—H bonds and one O=O are broken and two O—C bonds and two H—O bonds are made in the reaction. $\Delta_rH = -318$ kJ. The reaction is exothermic.

(b) Both hydroxyacetone and acetone are polar.

(c) The O—H hydrogen atoms are the most positive in dihydroxyacetone.

8.85 (a) The C=C bond is stronger than the C—C bond.

(b) The C—C single bond is longer than the C=C double bond.

(c) Ethylene is nonpolar, whereas acrolein is polar.

(d) The reaction is exothermic ($\Delta_rH = -45$ kJ).

8.87 $\Delta_rH = -211$ kJ

8.89 Methanol is a polar solvent. Methanol contains two bonds of significant polarity, the C—O bond and the O—H bond. The C—O—H atoms are in a bent configuration, leading to a polar molecule. Toluene contains only carbon and hydrogen atoms, which have similar electronegativites and which are arranged in tetrahedral or trigonal planar geometries, leading to a molecule that is largely nonpolar.

8.91 (a)

$$H-\overset{\textstyle H}{\underset{\textstyle H}{C}}-\overset{\textstyle\ }{\underset{\textstyle\ }{S}}-\overset{\textstyle H}{\underset{\textstyle H}{C}}-H$$

The bond angles are all approximately 109°.

(b) The sulfur atom should have a slight partial negative charge, and the carbons should have slight partial positive charges. The molecule has a bent shape and is polar.

(c) 1.6×10^{18} molecules

8.93 (a) $P_4 + 6 Cl_2 \rightarrow 4 PCl_3$

(b) $\Delta_rH = -1206.9$ kJ/mol-rxn

(c) Bonds broken: 6 mol P—P, 6 mol Cl—Cl
Bonds formed: 12 mol P—Cl
$\Delta H_{P-Cl} = 322$ kJ/mol; the value in Table 8.9 is 326 kJ/mol

8.95 (a) Odd electron molecules: BrO (13 electrons)

(b) $Br_2(g) \rightarrow 2\ Br(g)$ $\Delta_rH = +193$ kJ
   $2\ Br(g) + O_2(g) \rightarrow 2\ BrO(g)$ $\Delta_rH = +96$ kJ
   $BrO(g) + H_2O(g) \rightarrow HOBr(g) + OH(g)$
   $\Delta_rH = 0$ kJ

(c) $\Delta_fH\ [HOBr(g)] = -101$ kJ/mol

(d) The reactions in part (b) are endothermic (or thermal-neutral for the third reaction), and the enthalpy of formation in part (c) is exothermic.

Applying Chemical Principles: Linus Pauling and Electronegativity

1. Using average bond dissociation enthalpies:
   $\chi_{Cl} - \chi_H = 0.98$
   Acording to Figure 8.11, $\chi_{Cl} - \chi_H = 1.0$

3. $\chi_S = 2.55$

Chapter 9

9.1 The electron-pair and molecular geometry of $CHCl_3$ are both tetrahedral. Each C—Cl bond is formed by the overlap of an sp^3 hybrid orbital on the C atom with a $3p$ orbital on a Cl atom to form a sigma bond. A C—H sigma bond is formed by the overlap of an sp^3 hybrid orbital on the C atom with an H atom $1s$ orbital.

9.3

Both the N and the O are sp^3 hybridized. One of the sp^3 orbitals on the N overlaps with one of the sp^3 hybrid orbitals on the O.

9.5

The electron-pair and molecular geometries are both trigonal-planar. The carbon atom is sp^2 hybridized. The σ bond between the C and O is formed by the overlap of an sp^2 hybrid orbital on C with an sp^2 hybrid orbital on O. The π bond is formed by the overlap of a $2p$ orbital on C with a $2p$ orbital on O.

9.7

	Electron-Pair Geometry	Molecular Geometry	Hybrid Orbital Set
(a)	Trigonal-planar	Trigonal-planar	sp^2
(b)	Linear	Linear	sp
(c)	Tetrahedral	Tetrahedral	sp^3
(d)	Trigonal-planar	Trigonal-planar	sp^2

9.9 (a) C, sp^3; O, sp^3

(b) CH_3, sp^3; middle C, sp^2; CH_2, sp^2

(c) CH_2, sp^3; CO_2H, sp^2; N, sp^3

9.11 (a) Electron-pair geometry is octahedral. Molecular geometry is octahedral. Si: sp^3d^2

(b) Electron-pair geometry is trigonal-bipyramidal. Molecular geometry is seesaw. Se: sp^3d

(c) Electron-pair geometry is trigonal-bipyramidal. Molecular geometry is linear. I: sp^3d

(d) Electron-pair geometry is octahedral. Molecular geometry is square-planar. Xe: sp^3d^2

9.13 There are 32 valence electrons in both HPO_2F_2 and its anion. Both have a tetrahedral molecular geometry, so the P atom in both is sp^3 hybridized.

9.15 The C atom is sp^2 hybridized. Two of the sp^2 hybrid orbitals are used to form C—Cl σ bonds, and the third is used to form the C—O σ bond. The p orbital not used in the C atom hybrid orbitals is used to form the CO pi bond.

9.17 The electron-pair geometry around S is tetrahedral, and the molecular geometry is trigonal-pyramidal. The S atom is sp^3 hybridized.

9.19

cis isomer   trans isomer

9.21 H_2^+ ion: $(\sigma_{1s})^1$. Bond order is 0.5. The bond in H_2^+ is weaker than in H_2 (bond order $=1$).

9.23 MO diagram for C_2^{2-} ion

$$\underline{\qquad} \; \sigma^*_{2p}$$

$$\underline{\qquad} \; \underline{\qquad} \; \pi^*_{2p}$$

$$\underline{\uparrow\downarrow} \; \sigma_{2p}$$

$$\underline{\uparrow\downarrow} \; \underline{\uparrow\downarrow} \; \pi_{2p}$$

$$\underline{\uparrow\downarrow} \; \sigma^*_{2s}$$

$$\underline{\uparrow\downarrow} \; \sigma_{2s}$$

The ion has 10 valence electrons (isoelectronic with N_2). There are one net σ bond and two net π bonds, for a bond order of 3. The bond order increases by 1 on going from C_2 to C_2^{2-}. The ion is not paramagnetic.

9.25 O_2: (core electrons)$(\sigma_{2s})^2(\sigma^*_{2s})^2(\sigma_{2p})^2(\pi_{2p})^4(\pi^*_{2p})^2$
O_2^{2-}: (core electrons)$(\sigma_{2s})^2(\sigma^*_{2s})^2(\sigma_{2p})^2(\pi_{2p})^4(\pi^*_{2p})^4$
(a) O_2 is paramagnetic; O_2^{2-} is diamagnetic.
(b) O_2 has one net σ bond and one net π bond. O_2^{2-} has one net σ bond.
(c) O_2 bond order = 2; O_2^{2-} bond order = 1
(d) The bond length in O_2 is shorter than that in O_2^{2-}.

9.27 Shortest, N_2; longest, Li_2

9.29 (a) ClO has 13 valence electrons
$$[\text{core}] (\sigma_s)^2 (\sigma^*_s)^2 (\pi_p)^4 (\sigma_p)^2 (\pi^*_p)^3$$
(b) π^*_p
(c) Diamagnetic
(d) There are net 1 σ bond and 0.5 π bonds; bond order is 1.5.

9.31
$$\left[\begin{array}{c} :\ddot{F}: \\ | \\ :\ddot{F}-Al-\ddot{F}: \\ | \\ :\ddot{F}: \end{array} \right]^-$$

The electron pair and molecular geometries are both tetrahedral. The Al atom is sp^3 hybridized, so the Al—F bonds are formed by overlap of an Al sp^3 orbital with a p orbital on each F atom. The formal charge on each of the fluorines is 0, and that on the Al is -1. This is not a reasonable charge distribution because the less electronegative atom, aluminum, has the negative charge.

9.33

Molecule/Ion	O—S—O Angle	Hybrid Orbitals
SO_2	120°	sp^2
SO_3	120°	sp^2
SO_3^{2-}	109°	sp^3
SO_4^{2-}	109°	sp^3

9.35
$$\left[:\ddot{O}-\ddot{N}=\ddot{O}: \right]^- \longleftrightarrow \left[:\ddot{O}=\ddot{N}-\ddot{O}: \right]^-$$

The electron-pair geometry is trigonal-planar. The molecular geometry is bent (or angular). The O—N—O angle will be about 120°, the average N—O bond order is 3/2, and the N atom is sp^2 hybridized.

9.37 The resonance structures of N_2O, with formal charges, are shown here.

$$\overset{-2}{:\ddot{N}}-\overset{+1}{N}\equiv\overset{+1}{O}: \longleftrightarrow \overset{-1}{N}=\overset{+1}{N}=\overset{0}{\ddot{O}} \longleftrightarrow :\overset{0}{N}\equiv\overset{+1}{N}-\overset{-1}{\ddot{O}}:$$

$$\qquad A \qquad\qquad\qquad B \qquad\qquad\qquad C$$

The central N atom is sp hybridized in all structures. The two sp hybrid orbitals on the central N atom are used to form N—N and N—O σ bonds. The two p orbitals not used in the N atom hybridization are used to form the required π bonds.

9.39 (a) All three have the formula C_2H_4O. They are usually referred to as structural isomers.
(b) *Ethylene oxide:* Both C atoms are sp^3 hybridized.
Acetaldehyde: The CH_3 carbon atom has sp^3 hybridization, and the other C atom is sp^2 hybridized.
Vinyl alcohol: Both C atoms are sp^2 hybridized.
(c) *Ethylene oxide:* 109°
Acetaldehyde: 109°
Vinyl alcohol: 120°
(d) All are polar.
(e) Acetaldehyde has the strongest CO bond, and vinyl alcohol has the strongest C—C bond.

9.41 (a) CH_3 carbon atom: sp^3
C=N carbon atom: sp^2
N atom: sp^2
(b) C—N—O bond angle = 120°

9.43 (a) $C(1) = sp^2$; $O(2) = sp^3$; $N(3) = sp^3$; $C(4) = sp^3$; $P(5) = sp^3$
(b) Angle A = 120°; angle B = 109°; angle C = 109°; angle D = 109°
(c) The P—O and O—H bonds are most polar ($\Delta\chi = 1.3$).

9.45 (a) C=O bond is most polar.
(b) 18 σ bonds and five π bonds
(c)

trans isomer   *cis* isomer

(d) All C atoms are sp^2 hybridized.
(e) All bond angles are 120°.

9.47 (a) The Sb in SbF_5 is sp^3d hybridized, whereas it is sp^3d^2 hybridized in SbF_6^-.
(b) The molecular geometry of the H_2F^+ ion is bent or angular, and the F atom is sp^3 hybridized.

$$\left[:\overset{\textstyle |}{\ddot{F}}\text{---}_{\cdots\text{H}}^{\text{H}} \right]^-$$

9.49 (a) The peroxide ion has a bond order of 1.

$$\left[:\overset{..}{\underset{..}{O}}-\overset{..}{\underset{..}{O}}:\right]^{2-}$$

(b) [Core electrons]$(\sigma_{2s})^2(\sigma^*_{2s})^2(\sigma_{2p})^2(\pi_{2p})^4(\pi^*_{2p})^4$
This configuration also leads to a bond order of 1.

(c) Both theories lead to a diamagnetic ion with a bond order of 1.

9.51 Paramagnetic diatomic molecules: B_2 and O_2

Bond order of 1: Li_2, B_2, F_2; bond order of 2: C_2 and O_2; highest bond order: N_2

9.53 CN has nine valence electrons.
[core electrons]$(\sigma_{2s})^2(\sigma^*_{2s})^2(\pi_{2p})^4(\sigma_{2p})^1$
(a) HOMO, σ_{2p}
(b, c) Bond order = 2.5 (0.5 σ bond and 2 π bonds)
(d) Paramagnetic

9.55 (a) All C atoms are sp^3 hybridized.
(b) About 109°
(c) Polar
(d) The six-membered ring cannot be planar, owing to the tetrahedral C atoms of the ring. The bond angles are all 109°.

9.57 (a) The geometry about the boron atom is trigonal-planar in BF_3 but tetrahedral in $H_3N{-}BF_3$.
(b) Boron is sp^2 hybridized in BF_3 but sp^3 hybridized in $H_3N{-}BF_3$.
(c) Yes
(d) The ammonia molecule is polar with the N atom partially negative. While the BF_3 molecule is non-polar overall, each of the B—F bonds is polarized such that the B has a partial positive charge. The partially negative N in NH_3 is attracted to the partially positive B in BF_3.
(e) One of the lone pairs on the oxygen of H_2O can form a coordinate covalent bond with the B in BF_3. The resulting compound would be (the lone pairs on the F's not shown):

$$\text{H}-\overset{..}{\underset{..}{O}}-\overset{\overset{\text{H}\quad\text{F}}{|\quad\ |}}{\underset{|}{B}}-\text{F}$$
$$\text{F}$$

9.59 (a) NH_2^-: electron-pair geometry = tetrahedral, molecular geometry = bent, hybridization of N = sp^3

SO_3: electron-pair geometry = molecular geometry = trigonal-planar, hybridization of S = sp^2

(b)

$$\left[\begin{array}{c}:\overset{..}{O}:\\ \text{H} \quad | \\ \text{H}{\blacktriangleleft}\text{N}{-}\text{S}{\equiv}\overset{..}{O}: \\ \overset{..}{\underset{..}{O}}: \end{array}\right]^{-}$$

The bond angles around the N and the S are all approximately 109°.

(c) The N does not undergo any change in its hybridization; the S changes from sp^2 to sp^3.
(d) The SO_3 is the acceptor of an electron pair in this reaction. The electrostatic potential map confirms this to be reasonable because the sulfur has a partial positive charge.

9.61

$$\left[\begin{array}{c}\text{H}\quad:\overset{..}{O}:\\ |\quad\ \ \| \\ \text{H}{-}\text{C}{-}\text{C}{-}\overset{..}{\underset{..}{O}}: \\ | \\ \text{H}\end{array}\right]^{-} \longleftrightarrow \left[\begin{array}{c}\text{H}\quad:\overset{..}{O}:\\ |\quad\ \ | \\ \text{H}{-}\text{C}{-}\text{C}{=}\overset{..}{O} \\ | \\ \text{H}\end{array}\right]^{-}$$

Hybridization of C in $-CO_2^-$ is sp^2

C—C bond: overlap of sp^2 hybrid orbital on the carbon of $-CO_2^-$ with sp^3 hybrid orbital on the other C.

C—O σ bond of C=O double bond: overlap of sp^2 hybrid orbital on C with sp^2 hybrid orbital on O

C—O π bond of C=O double bond: overlap of p orbital on C with p orbital on O

C—O single bond: The Lewis structure by itself would make it appear this bond is formed by the overlap of an sp^2 hybrid orbital on C with an sp^3 hybrid orbital on O. In the resonance hybrid, however, this oxygen would also have sp^2 hybridization.

9.63 $\overset{..}{O}{=}\overset{..}{S}{-}\overset{..}{\underset{..}{O}}: \longleftrightarrow :\overset{..}{\underset{..}{O}}{-}\overset{..}{S}{=}\overset{..}{O}$

MO theory pictures one net σ bond for each S—O linkage plus a contribution from π bonding. The π bonding in this molecule will be similar to that in O_3 discussed in the text. There will be two electrons in a π bonding MO and two electrons in a π non-bonding MO. This gives an overall bond order of 1 for the π bonding in the entire molecule and therefore a net π bond order of 0.5 for each S—O linkage. The total bond order for each S—O linkage is therefore 1.5 (1 from σ bonding, 0.5 from π bonding).

9.65 A C atom may form, at most, four hybrid orbitals (sp^3). The minimum number is two, for example, the sp hybrid orbitals used by carbon in CO. Carbon has only four valence orbitals, so it cannot form more than four hybrid orbitals.

9.67 (a) C, sp^2; N (predicted based on Lewis structure), sp^3
(b) The amide or peptide link has two resonance structures (shown here with formal charges on the O and N atoms). Structure B is less favorable, owing to the separation of charge.

$$\begin{array}{cc}:\overset{0}{O}: & :\overset{..}{\underset{..}{O}}:^- \\ \| & | \\ \underset{R}{\overset{C}{\diagdown}}\underset{\quad \text{A R}}{\overset{..0}{\underset{N}{\diagup}}}^{\text{H}} \longleftrightarrow \underset{R}{\overset{C}{\diagdown}}\underset{\quad \text{B R}}{\overset{+}{\underset{N}{\diagup}}}^{\text{H}}\end{array}$$

(c) The fact that the amide link is planar indicates that structure B has some importance and that the N of the peptide linkage is sp^2 hybridized.

The principal sites of positive charge are the nitrogen in the amide linkage and the hydrogen of the —O—H group. The principal regions of negative charge are oxygen atoms and the nitrogen of the free $-NH_2$ group.

9.69 MO theory is better to use when explaining or understanding the effect of adding energy to molecules. A molecule can absorb energy and an electron can thus be promoted to a higher level. Using MO theory, one can see how this can occur. Additionally, MO theory is a better model to use to predict whether a molecule is paramagnetic.

9.71 Lowest energy = orbital C < orbital B < orbital A = highest energy

9.73 B surrounded by three electron pairs: electron-pair geometry = molecular geometry = trigonal planar; hybridization = sp^2; formal charge = 0

B surrounded by four electron pairs; electron-pair geometry = molecular geometry = tetrahedral; hybridization = sp^3; formal charge = -1

9.75 HF has a bond order of 1. HF_2^- has a bond order of 1 for the entire three-center-four-electron bond and thus a 0.5 bond order per H—F linkage. It should therefore be easier to break the bond in HF_2^-, leading to a smaller bond enthalpy for HF_2^- than for HF.

9.77 (a) BrF_5

(b) square pyramidal molecular geometry; sp^3d^2 hybridization

(c) The square pyramidal structure is polar, so this is consistent with a dipole moment being present for the molecule.

9.79 (a) empirical formula = Br_2O

$$:\!\ddot{Br}\!-\!\ddot{O}\!-\!\ddot{Br}\!:$$

The O should have sp^3 hybrid orbitals.

(b) 13 valence electrons; $(\sigma_s)^2(\sigma^*_s)^2(\pi_p)^4(\sigma_p)^2(\pi^*_p)^3$

$HOMO = \pi^*_p$

Applying Chemical Principles: Probing Molecules with Photoelectron Spectroscopy

1. Metal

3. σ_{2p}

5. The 15.6 eV and 16.7 eV ejected electrons came from bonding orbitals. Removing an electron from a bonding orbital weakens the bond and thus results in a longer bond length. The 18.6 eV ejected electron comes from an antibonding orbital.

Chapter 10

10.1 Heptane

10.3 C_5H_{12} and $C_{14}H_{30}$ are alkanes.

10.5 3-Ethyl-2-methylhexane

CH$_3$—CH—CH—CH$_2$—CH$_2$—CH$_3$ with CH$_3$ and CH$_2$CH$_3$ substituents

2,3,3,4-Tetramethylpentane

CH$_3$—CH—C—CH—CH$_3$ with CH$_3$, CH$_3$, CH$_3$ and CH$_3$ substituents

Other possibilities include 2,2,3,4-tetramethylpentane, 3-ethyl-2,2-dimethylpentane, 3-ethyl-2,3-dimethylpentane, and 3-ethyl-2,4-dimethylpentane.

10.7 2,3-Dimethylbutane

10.9 (a) 2,3-Dimethylhexane

CH$_3$—CH—CH—CH$_2$—CH$_2$—CH$_3$ with CH$_3$ and CH$_3$ substituents

(b) 2,3-Dimethyloctane

CH$_3$—CH—CH—CH$_2$—CH$_2$—CH$_2$—CH$_2$—CH$_3$ with CH$_3$ and CH$_3$ substituents

(c) 3-Ethylheptane

CH$_3$—CH$_2$—CH—CH$_2$—CH$_2$—CH$_2$—CH$_3$ with CH$_2$CH$_3$ substituent

(d) 3-Ethyl-2-methylhexane

CH$_3$—CH—CH—CH$_2$—CH$_2$—CH$_3$ with CH$_3$ and CH$_2$CH$_3$ substituents

10.11

H$_3$C—C(H)(CH$_3$)—CH$_2$CH$_2$CH$_2$CH$_2$CH$_3$ 2-methylheptane

CH$_3$CH$_2$CH$_2$—C(H)(CH$_3$)—CH$_2$CH$_2$CH$_3$ 4-methylheptane

CH$_3$CH$_2$—C*(H)(CH$_3$)—CH$_2$CH$_2$CH$_2$CH$_3$ 3-methylheptane. The C atom with an asterisk is chiral.

10.13 Chair form of cyclohexane:

Axial hydrogens are shown in red; equatorial hydrogens are shown in blue.

10.15

CH$_3$CH$_2$CH$_2$—C(H)(CH$_2$CH$_3$)—CH$_2$CH$_2$CH$_3$ 4-ethylheptane. The compound is not chiral.

CH$_3$CH$_2$—C(H)(CH$_2$CH$_3$)—CH$_2$CH$_2$CH$_2$CH$_3$ 3-ethylheptane. Not chiral.

10.17 C_4H_{10}, butane: a low-molar-mass fuel gas at room temperature and pressure. Slightly soluble in water.

$C_{12}H_{26}$, dodecane: a colorless liquid at room temperature. Expected to be insoluble in water but quite soluble in nonpolar solvents.

10.19

cis-4-methyl-2-hexene

trans-4-methyl-2-hexene

10.21 (a)

1-pentene

2-methyl-2-butene

2-methyl-1-butene

cis-2-pentene

3-methyl-1-butene

trans-2-pentene

(b) H_2C-CH_2, H_2C, CH_2, CH_2

cyclopentane

10.23 (a) 1,2-Dibromopropane, $CH_3CHBrCH_2Br$
(b) Pentane, C_5H_{12}

10.25 The three alkenes are 1-butene, cis-2-butene, and trans-2-butene. The reaction with 1-butene is shown below:

$$C=C \ (H, H / H, CH_2CH_3) + HBr \longrightarrow CH_3CHCH_2CH_3 \ (Br)$$

10.27 Four isomers are possible.

cis-1-chloropropene

2-chloropropene

trans-1-chloropropene

3-chloro-1-propene

10.29

$$C=C \ (H, H / H, CH_2CH_2CH_2CH_3) + H_2 \longrightarrow CH_3CH_2CH_2CH_2CH_2CH_3$$

Hydrogenation is often carried out in the presence of a metal catalyst (Pt, Pd, Rh). Hydrogenation is often carried out in the food industry to convert liquid oils to solids and to make them less susceptible to spoilage.

10.31

m-dichlorobenzene

p-bromotoluene

10.33

$$\text{benzene} \xrightarrow{CH_3CH_2Cl/AlCl_3} \text{ethylbenzene} (CH_2CH_3)$$

10.35

$$\xrightarrow{CH_3Cl/AlCl_3}$$

1,2,4-trimethylbenzene

10.37 (a) 1-Propanol, primary
(b) 1-Butanol, primary
(c) 2-Methyl-2-propanol, tertiary
(d) 2-Methyl-2-butanol, tertiary

10.39 (a) Ethylamine, $CH_3CH_2NH_2$
(b) Dipropylamine, $(CH_3CH_2CH_2)_2NH$

$$CH_3CH_2CH_2-\underset{\underset{H}{|}}{N}-CH_2CH_2CH_3$$

(c) Butyldimethylamine

$$CH_3CH_2CH_2CH_2-\underset{\underset{CH_3}{|}}{N}-CH_3$$

(d) Triethylamine

$$CH_3CH_2-\underset{\underset{CH_2CH_3}{|}}{N}-CH_2CH_3$$

10.41 (a) 1-Butanol, $CH_3CH_2CH_2CH_2OH$
(b) 2-Butanol

$$CH_3CH_2-\underset{\underset{H}{|}}{\overset{\overset{OH}{|}}{C}}-CH_3$$

(c) 2-Methyl-1-propanol

$$CH_3-\underset{\underset{CH_3}{|}}{\overset{\overset{H}{|}}{C}}-CH_2OH$$

(d) 2-Methyl-2-propanol

$$CH_3-\underset{\underset{CH_3}{|}}{\overset{\overset{OH}{|}}{C}}-CH_3$$

10.43 (a) $C_6H_5NH_2(aq) + HCl(aq) \rightarrow (C_6H_5NH_3)Cl(aq)$
(b) $(CH_3)_3N(aq) + H_2SO_4(aq) \rightarrow$
$$[(CH_3)_3NH]HSO_4(aq)$$

10.45 (a)
$$CH_3CH_2CH_2-\underset{\underset{CH_3}{|}}{\overset{\overset{CH_3}{|}}{CH}}-\overset{\overset{O}{\|}}{C}-OH$$

(b)
$$CH_3CH_2-\underset{\underset{CH_3}{|}}{\overset{\overset{CH_3}{|}}{CH}}-\overset{\overset{O}{\|}}{C}-CH_3$$

(c)
$$OH-\overset{\overset{O}{\|}}{C}-CH_2CH_2-\overset{\overset{O}{\|}}{C}-OH$$

(d)
$$NH_2CH_2CH_2-\overset{\overset{O}{\|}}{C}-OH$$

10.47

$$CH_3-\overset{\overset{O}{\|}}{C}-CH_2CH_2CH_3$$

$$H-\overset{\overset{O}{\|}}{C}-CH_2CH_2CH_2CH_2CH_3$$

$$CH_3CH_2CH_2CH_2-\overset{\overset{O}{\|}}{C}-OH$$

10.49 (a) Acid, 3-methylpentanoic acid
(b) Ester, methyl propanoate
(c) Ester, butyl acetate (or butyl ethanoate)
(d) Acid, p-bromobenzoic acid

10.51 (a) Pentanoic acid

$$CH_3CH_2CH_2CH_2-\overset{\overset{O}{\|}}{C}-OH$$

(b) 2-Octanol

$$H_3C-\underset{\underset{H}{|}}{\overset{\overset{OH}{|}}{C}}-CH_2CH_2CH_2CH_2CH_2CH_3$$

10.53 Step 1: Oxidize 1-propanol to propanoic acid.

$$CH_3CH_2-\underset{\underset{H}{|}}{\overset{\overset{H}{|}}{C}}-OH \xrightarrow{\text{oxidizing agent}} CH_3CH_2-\overset{\overset{O}{\|}}{C}-OH$$

Step 2: Combine propanoic acid and 1-propanol.

$$CH_3CH_2-\overset{\overset{O}{\|}}{C}-OH + CH_3CH_2-\underset{\underset{H}{|}}{\overset{\overset{H}{|}}{C}}-OH \xrightarrow{-H_2O}$$

$$CH_3CH_2-\overset{\overset{O}{\|}}{C}-O-CH_2CH_2CH_3$$

10.55 Sodium acetate, $NaCH_3CO_2$, and 1-butanol, $CH_3CH_2CH_2CH_2OH$

10.57 (a) Trigonal-planar
(b) 120°
(c) The molecule is chiral. There are four different groups around the carbon atom marked 2.
(d) The acidic H atom is the H attached to the CO_2H (carboxyl) group.

10.59
$$CH_3CH_2CH_2\overset{\overset{O}{\|}}{C}NHCH_3$$

This compound is an amide.
$$CH_3CH_2CH_2CO_2H + CH_3NH_2 \rightarrow$$
$$CH_3CH_2CH_2CONHCH_3 + H_2O$$

10.61 (a) Alcohol; (b) amide; (c) acid; (d) ester

10.63 (a) Prepare polyvinyl acetate (PVA) from vinylacetate.

(b) Three units of PVA:

(c) Hydrolysis of polyvinyl acetate will yield polyvinyl alcohol.

10.65 Illustrated here is a segment of a copolymer composed of two units of 1,1–dichloroethylene and two units of chloroethylene.

10.67

(a)

cis isomer   trans isomer

(b)

10.69

cyclohexane   methylcyclopentane

$CH_3CH=CHCH_2CH_2CH_3$

2-hexene
Other isomers are possible by
moving the double bond and
with a branched chain.

The three structures shown above are not chiral, but
some chiral isomers do exist.

10.71

10.73 (a)

(b)

10.75

10.77 (a) 2, 3-Dimethylpentane

(b) 3, 3-Diethylpentane

(c) 3-Ethyl-2-methylpentane

(d) 3-Ethylhexane

10.79

1,1-Dichloropropane

1,2-Dichloropropane

1,3-Dichloropropane

2,2-Dichloropropane

10.81

1,2,3-trimethylbenzene   1,2,4-trimethylbenzene   1,3,5-trimethylbenzene

10.83 Replace the carboxylic acid group with an H atom.

10.85 (a)

butane (not chiral)

(b)

10.87

(a)

$$H_2C-O-\overset{\overset{\displaystyle O}{\|}}{C}(CH_2)_{10}CH_3$$
$$HC-O-\overset{\overset{\displaystyle O}{\|}}{C}(CH_2)_{10}CH_3$$
$$H_2C-O-\overset{\overset{\displaystyle O}{\|}}{C}(CH_2)_{10}CH_3$$

$$H_2C-O-\overset{\overset{\displaystyle O}{\|}}{C}(CH_2)_{10}CH_3$$
$$HC-O-\overset{\overset{\displaystyle O}{\|}}{C}(CH_2)_{10}CH_3 \quad + \ 3\ NaOH \longrightarrow$$
$$H_2C-O-\overset{\overset{\displaystyle O}{\|}}{C}(CH_2)_{10}CH_3$$

$$\begin{array}{c}H_2C-OH\\|\\HC-OH\\|\\H_2C-OH\end{array} \ + \ 3 \left[CH_3(CH_2)_{10}\overset{\overset{\displaystyle O}{\|}}{C}O^- \right] Na+$$

(b)

$$H_2C-O-\overset{\overset{\displaystyle O}{\|}}{C}(CH_2)_{10}CH_3$$
$$HC-O-\overset{\overset{\displaystyle O}{\|}}{C}(CH_2)_{10}CH_3 \quad + \ 3\ CH_3OH \longrightarrow$$
$$H_2C-O-\overset{\overset{\displaystyle O}{\|}}{C}(CH_2)_{10}CH_3$$

$$\begin{array}{c}H_2C-OH\\|\\HC-OH\\|\\H_2C-OH\end{array} \ + \ 3 \ \ CH_3(CH_2)_{10}\overset{\overset{\displaystyle O}{\|}}{C}OCH_2$$

10.89

10.91 (a)

$$H-\overset{\overset{\displaystyle H}{|}}{\underset{\underset{\displaystyle H}{|}}{C}}-\overset{\overset{\displaystyle }{}}{C}=\overset{\overset{\displaystyle }{}}{C}-H \xrightarrow{+HBr} H-\overset{\overset{\displaystyle H}{|}}{\underset{\underset{\displaystyle H}{|}}{C}}-\overset{\overset{\displaystyle Br}{|}}{\underset{\underset{\displaystyle H}{|}}{C}}-\overset{\overset{\displaystyle H}{|}}{\underset{\underset{\displaystyle H}{|}}{C}}-H$$

2-bromopropane

(b)

$$H_3C-\overset{\overset{\displaystyle H}{|}}{\underset{\underset{\displaystyle H}{|}}{C}}-\overset{\overset{\displaystyle CH_3}{|}}{C}=\overset{\overset{\displaystyle H}{}}{C}-H \xrightarrow{+H_2O} H_3C-\overset{\overset{\displaystyle H}{|}}{\underset{\underset{\displaystyle H}{|}}{C}}-\overset{\overset{\displaystyle CH_3}{|}}{\underset{\underset{\displaystyle OH}{|}}{C}}-\overset{\overset{\displaystyle H}{|}}{\underset{\underset{\displaystyle H}{|}}{C}}-H$$

2-methyl-2-butanol

(c)

$$H_3C-\overset{\overset{\displaystyle H}{}}{C}=\overset{\overset{\displaystyle CH_3}{|}}{C}-\overset{\overset{\displaystyle H}{|}}{\underset{\underset{\displaystyle H}{|}}{C}}-H \xrightarrow{+H_2O} H_3C-\overset{\overset{\displaystyle H}{|}}{\underset{\underset{\displaystyle H}{|}}{C}}-\overset{\overset{\displaystyle CH_3}{|}}{\underset{\underset{\displaystyle OH}{|}}{C}}-\overset{\overset{\displaystyle H}{|}}{\underset{\underset{\displaystyle H}{|}}{C}}-H$$

The product is the same for parts (b) and (c).

10.93 Compound (b), acetaldehyde, and (c), ethanol, produce acetic acid when oxidized.

10.95 Cyclohexene, a cyclic alkene, will add Br_2 readily (to give $C_6H_{10}Br_2$).

Benzene, however, needs much more stringent conditions to react with bromine; then Br_2 will substitute for H atoms on benzene and not add to the ring.

10.97 (a) The compound is either propanone, a ketone, or propanal, an aldehyde.

(b) The ketone will not undergo oxidation, but the aldehyde will be oxidized to the acid, $CH_3CH_2CO_2H$. Thus, the unknown is likely propanal.

(c) Propanoic acid

10.99 2-Propanol will react with an oxidizing agent such as $KMnO_4$ (to give the ketone), whereas methyl ethyl ether ($CH_3OC_2H_5$) will not react. In addition, the alcohol should be more soluble in water than the ether.

10.101

X = 3,3-dimethyl-1-pentene

+H₂O

Y = 3,3-dimethyl-2-pentanol   3,3-dimethyl-2-pentanone

10.103

methane   four single bonds

formaldehyde   one double bond and
                 two single bonds

allene   two double bonds

acetylene   one single bond and one
                 triple bond

10.105 (a) Cross-linking makes the material very rigid and inflexible.
(b) The OH groups give the polymer a high affinity for water.
(c) Hydrogen bonding allows the chains to form coils and sheets with high tensile strength.

10.107 (a) Ethane enthalpy of combustion = −47.51 kJ/g
Ethanol enthalpy of combustion = −26.82 kJ/g
(b) The enthalpy change for the combustion of ethanol is less negative than for ethane, so partially oxidizing ethane to form ethanol decreases the amount of energy per gram available from the combustion of the substance.

10.109 (a) Empirical formula, CHO
(b) Molecular formula, $C_4H_4O_4$
(c)

(d) All four C atoms are sp^2 hybridized.
(e) 120°

Applying Chemical Principles: Biodiesel— An Attractive Fuel for the Future?

1. $C_{13}H_{27}CO_2CH_3(\ell) + 43/2\ O_2(g) \rightarrow$
$$15\ CO_2(g) + 15\ H_2O(g)$$

3. Hexadecane ($\Delta H° = -9951.2$ kJ/mol) provides more energy per mole of fuel than methyl myristate ($\Delta H° = -8759.1$ kJ/mol).

    Hexadecane ($\Delta H° = -3.4 \times 10^4$ kJ/L) also provides more energy per liter of fuel than methyl myristate ($\Delta H° = -3.1 \times 10^4$ kJ/L).

Chapter 11

11.1 (a) 0.58 atm
(b) 0.59 bar
(c) 59 kPa

11.3 (a) 0.754 bar
(b) 650 kPa
(c) 934 kPa

11.5 2.70×10^2 mm Hg

11.7 3.7 L

11.9 250 mm Hg

11.11 3.2×10^2 mm Hg

11.13 9.72 atm

11.15 (a) 75 mL O_2
(b) 150 mL NO_2

11.17 0.919 atm

11.19 $V = 2.9$ L

11.21 1.9×10^6 g He

11.23 3.7×10^{-4} g/L

11.25 34.0 g/mol

11.27 57.5 g/mol

11.29 Molar mass = 74.9 g/mol; B_6H_{10}

11.31 0.039 mol H_2; 0.096 atm; 73 mm Hg

11.33 170 g NaN_3

11.35 1.7 atm O_2

11.37 4.1 atm H_2; 1.6 atm Ar; total pressure = 5.7 atm

11.39 (a) 0.30 mol halothane/1 mol O_2
(b) 3.0×10^2 g halothane

11.41 (a) CO_2 has the higher kinetic energy.
(b) The root mean square speed of the H_2 molecules is greater than the root mean square speed of the CO_2 molecules.
(c) The number of CO_2 molecules is greater than the number of H_2 molecules [$n(CO_2) = 1.8n(H_2)$].
(d) The mass of CO_2 is greater than the mass of H_2.

11.43 Average speed of CO_2 molecule $= 3.65 \times 10^4$ cm/s

11.45 Average speed increases (and molar mass decreases) in the order $CH_2F_2 < Ar < N_2 < CH_4$.

11.47 (a) F_2 (38 g/mol) effuses faster than CO_2 (44 g/mol).
(b) N_2 (28 g/mol) effuses faster than O_2 (32 g/mol).
(c) C_2H_4 (28.1 g/mol) effuses faster than C_2H_6 (30.1 g/mol).
(d) $CFCl_3$ (137 g/mol) effuses faster than $C_2Cl_2F_4$ (171 g/mol).

11.49 36 g/mol

11.51 P from the van der Waals equation $= 26.0$ atm
P from the ideal gas law $= 30.6$ atm

11.53 (a) Standard atmosphere: 1 atm; 760 mm Hg; 101.325 kPa; 1.013 bar
(b) N_2 partial pressure: 0.780 atm; 593 mm Hg; 79.1 kPa; 0.791 bar
(c) H_2 pressure: 131 atm; 9.98×10^4 mm Hg; 1.33×10^4 kPa; 133 bar
(d) Air: 0.333 atm; 253 mm Hg; 33.7 kPa; 0.337 bar

11.55 $T = 290.$ K or 17 °C

11.57 $2\ C_4H_9SH(g) + 15\ O_2(g) \rightarrow$
$\qquad 8\ CO_2(g) + 10\ H_2O(g) + 2\ SO_2(g)$

Total pressure $= 37.3$ mm Hg. Partial pressures: $CO_2 = 14.9$ mm Hg, $H_2O = 18.6$ mm Hg, and $SO_2 = 3.73$ mm Hg.

11.59 4 mol

11.61 Ni is the limiting reactant; 1.31 g $Ni(CO)_4$

11.63 (a, b) Sample 4 (He) has the largest number of molecules and sample 3 (H_2 at 27 °C and 760 mm Hg) has the fewest number of molecules.
(c) Sample 2 (Ar)

11.65 8.54 g $Fe(CO)_5$

11.67 S_2F_{10}

11.69 (a) 28.7 g/mol $\simeq$ 29 g/mol
(b) X of $O_2 = 0.17$ and X of $N_2 = 0.83$

11.71 Molar mass $= 86.4$ g/mol. The gas is probably ClO_2F.

11.73 (d) is not correct. The rate of effusion is really inversely proportional to the square root of a gas's molar mass.

11.75 1.3×10^2 g/mol

11.77 $n(He) = 0.0128$ mol

11.79 Weight percent $KClO_3 = 69.1\%$

11.81 (a) $NO_2 < O_2 < NO$
(b) $P(O_2) = 75$ mm Hg
(c) $P(NO_2) = 150$ mm Hg

11.83 $P(NH_3) = 69$ mm Hg and $P(F_2) = 51$ mm Hg
Pressure after reaction $= 17$ mm Hg

11.85 At 20 °C, there is 7.8×10^{-3} g H_2O/L. At 0 °C, there is 4.6×10^{-3} g H_2O/L.

11.87 The mixture contains 0.22 g CO_2 and 0.77 g CO.
$P(CO_2) = 0.22$ atm; $P(O_2) = 0.12$ atm; $P(CO) = 1.22$ atm

11.89 The formula of the iron compound is $Fe(CO)_5$.

11.91 (a) $P(B_2H_6) = 0.0160$ atm
(b) $P(H_2) = 0.0320$ atm, so $P_{total} = 0.0480$ atm

11.93 Amount of $Na_2CO_3 = 0.00424$ mol
Amount of $NaHCO_3 = 0.00951$ mol
Amount of CO_2 produced $= 0.0138$ mol
Volume of CO_2 produced $= 0.343$ L

11.95 Decomposition of 1 mol of $Cu(NO_3)_2$ should give 2 mol NO_2 and $\frac{1}{2}$ mol of O_2. Total actual amount $= 4.72 \times 10^{-3}$ mol of gas.
(a) Average molar mass $= 41.3$ g/mol
(b) Mole fractions: $X(NO_2) = 0.666$ and $X(O_2) = 0.334$
(c) Amount of each gas: 3.13×10^{-3} mol NO_2 and 1.57×10^{-3} mol O_2. The ratio of these amounts is 1.99 mol NO_2/mol O_2. This is different from the 4 mol NO_2/mol O_2 ratio expected from the reaction.
(d) If some NO_2 molecules combine to form N_2O_4, the apparent mole fraction of NO_2 would be smaller than expected ($= 0.8$). As this is the case, it is apparent that some N_2O_4 has been formed (as is observed in the experiment).

11.97 (a) M $= 138$ g/mol; the unknown compound is P_2F_4.
(b) M $= 1.4 \times 10^2$ g/mol; this is consistent with the result obtained in part (a).

11.99 (a) 10.0 g of O_2 represents more molecules than 10.0 g of CO_2. Therefore, O_2 has the greater partial pressure.
(b) The average speed of the O_2 molecules is greater than the average speed of the CO_2 molecules.
(c) The gases are at the same temperature and so have the same average kinetic energy.

11.101 (a) $P(C_2H_2) > P(CO)$
(b) There are more molecules in the C_2H_2 container than in the CO container.

11.103 (a) Not a gas. A gas would expand to an infinite volume.
(b) Not a gas. A density of 8.2 g/mL is typical of a solid.
(c) Insufficient information
(d) Gas

11.105 (a) There are more molecules of H_2 than atoms of He.
(b) The mass of He is greater than the mass of H_2.

11.107 The speed of gas molecules is related to the square root of the absolute temperature, so a doubling of the temperature will lead to an increase of about $(2)^{1/2}$ or 1.4.

Applying Chemical Principles:
The Goodyear Blimp

1. 0.164 g/L

3. Mass of passengers + ballast = 5.75×10^5 g = 575 kg

Chapter 12

12.1 (a) Dipole–dipole interactions (and hydrogen bonds)
(b) Induced dipole–induced dipole forces
(c) Dipole–dipole interactions (and hydrogen bonds)

12.3 (a) Induced dipole–induced dipole forces
(b) Induced dipole–induced dipole forces
(c) Dipole–dipole forces
(d) Dipole–dipole forces (and hydrogen bonding)

12.5 The predicted order of increasing strength is $CH_4 < Ne < CO < CCl_4$. In this case, prediction agrees with reality. The boiling points are Ne (-246 °C) < CO (-192 °C) < CH_4 (-162 °C) < CCl_4 (77 °C).

12.7 (c) HF; (d) acetic acid; (f) CH_3OH

12.9 (a) LiCl. The Li^+ ion is smaller than Cs^+ (Figure 7.12), which makes the ion–ion forces of attraction stronger in LiCl.
(b) $Mg(NO_3)_2$. The Mg^{2+} ion is smaller than the Na^+ ion (Figure 7.12), and the magnesium ion has a 2+ charge (as opposed to 1+ for sodium). Both of these effects lead to stronger ion–ion forces of attraction in magnesium nitrate.
(c) $NiCl_2$. The nickel(II) ion has a larger charge than Rb^+ and is considerably smaller. Both effects mean that there are stronger ion–ion forces of attraction in nickel(II) chloride.

12.11 $q = +90.1$ kJ

12.13 (a) Water vapor pressure is about 150 mm Hg at 60 °C. (Appendix G gives a value of 149.4 mm Hg at 60 °C.)
(b) 600 mm Hg at about 93 °C
(c) At 70 °C, ethanol has a vapor pressure of about 520 mm Hg, whereas that of water is about 225 mm Hg.

12.15 At 30 °C, the vapor pressure of ether is about 590 mm Hg. (This pressure requires 0.23 g of ether in the vapor phase at the given conditions, so there is sufficient ether in the flask.) At 0 °C, the vapor pressure is about 160 mm Hg, so some ether condenses when the temperature declines.

12.17 (a) O_2 (-183 °C) (bp of N_2 = -196 °C)
(b) SO_2 (-10 °C) (CO_2 sublimes at -78 °C)
(c) HF ($+19.7$ °C) (HI, -35.6 °C)
(d) GeH_4 (-90.0 °C) (SiH_4, -111.8 °C)

12.19 (a) CS_2, about 620 mm Hg; CH_3NO_2, about 80 mm Hg
(b) CS_2, induced dipole–induced dipole forces; CH_3NO_2, dipole–dipole forces
(c) CS_2, about 46 °C; CH_3NO_2, about 100 °C
(d) About 39 °C
(e) About 34 °C

12.21 (a) 80.1 °C
(b) At about 48 °C, the liquid has a vapor pressure of 250 mm Hg.
The vapor pressure is 650 mm Hg at 75 °C.
(c) 33.5 kJ/mol (from slope of plot)

12.23 No, CO cannot be liquefied at room temperature because the critical temperature is lower than room temperature.

12.25 The layer of molecules on the surface of a liquid is harder to break through than the bulk liquid. The energy needed to break through this skin is the surface tension. An application of surface tension is that it is possible to float a paperclip on the surface of water, but if the paperclip breaks through the surface, it will sink. Surface tension results from intermolecular forces because molecules in the interior of a liquid interact through intermolecular forces with molecules all around them, but molecules on the surface have intermolecular forces only with molecules at or below the surface layer and thus feel a net inward force of attraction.

12.27 This phenomenon results from capillary action. The water is attracted to —OH groups in the paper. As a result of these adhesive forces, some water molecules begin to move up the paper. Other water molecules remain in contact with these water molecules by means of cohesive forces. A stream of water molecules thus moves up the paper.

12.29 Ar < CO_2 < CH_3OH

12.31 Li^+ ions are smaller than Cs^+ ions (78 pm and 165 pm, respectively; see Figure 7.12). Thus, there will be a stronger attractive force between Li^+ ion and water molecules than between Cs^+ ions and water molecules.

12.33 (a) 350 mm Hg
(b) Ethanol (lower vapor pressure at every temperature)
(c) 84 °C
(d) CS_2, 46 °C; C_2H_5OH, 78 °C; C_7H_{16}, 99 °C
(e) CS_2, gas; C_2H_5OH, gas; C_7H_{16}, liquid

12.35 Molar enthalpy of vaporization increases with increasing intermolecular forces: C_2H_6 (14.69 kJ/mol; induced dipole) < HCl (16.15 kJ/mol; dipole) < CH_3OH (35.21 kJ/mol, hydrogen bonds). (The molar enthalpies of vaporization here are given at the boiling point of the liquid.)

12.37 5.49×10^{19} atoms/m^3

12.39 (a) 70.3 °C

(b)

Using the equation for the straight line in the plot

$$\ln P = -3885\ (1/T) + 17.949$$

we calculate that $T = 312.6$ K (39.5 °C) when $P = 250$ mm Hg. When $P = 650$ mm Hg, $T = 338.7$ K (65.5 °C).

(c) Calculated $\Delta_{vap}H = 32.3$ kJ/mol

12.41 (a) When the can is inverted in cold water, the water vapor pressure in the can, which was approximately 760 mm Hg, drops rapidly—say, to 9 mm Hg at 10 °C. This creates a partial vacuum in the can, and the can is crushed because of the difference in pressure inside the can and the pressure of the atmosphere pressing down on the outside of the can.

(b)

Before heating   After heating

12.43 Acetone and water can interact by hydrogen bonding.

12.45 Ethylene glycol's viscosity will be greater than ethanol's, owing to the greater hydrogen-bonding capacity of glycol.

12.47 (a) Water has two OH bonds and two lone pairs, whereas the O atom of ethanol has only one OH bond (and two lone pairs). More extensive hydrogen bonding is likely for water.

(b) Water and ethanol interact extensively through hydrogen bonding, so the volume is expected to be slightly smaller than the sum of the two volumes.

12.49 Two pieces of evidence for $H_2O(\ell)$ having considerable intermolecular attractive forces:

(a) Based on the boiling points of the Group 6A hydrides (Figure 12.6), the boiling point of water should be approximately −80 °C. The actual boiling point of 100 °C reflects the significant hydrogen bonding that occurs.

(b) Liquid water has a specific heat capacity that is higher than almost any other liquid. This reflects the fact that a relatively larger amount of energy is necessary to overcome intermolecular forces and raise the temperature of the liquid.

12.51 (a) HI, hydrogen iodide

(b) The large iodine atom in HI leads to a significant polarizability for the molecule and thus to a large dispersion force.

(c) The dipole moment of HCl (1.07 D, Table 8.7) is larger than for HI (0.38 D).

(d) HI. See part (b).

12.53 A gas can be liquefied at or below its critical temperature. The critical temperature for CF_4 (−45.7 °C) is below room temperature (25 °C), so it cannot be liquefied at room temperature.

12.55 Hydrogen bonding is most likely at the O—H group at the "right" end of the molecule, and at the C=O and N—H groups in the amide group (—NH—CO—).

12.57 Boiling point, enthalpy of vaporization, volatility, surface tension

12.59 The more branching in the hydrocarbons, the lower the boiling point. This implies weaker induced dipole–induced dipole forces. Greater branching results in a more compact shape with less surface area available for contact and therefore smaller induced dipole–induced dipole forces.

12.61 $F_2 < Cl_2 < Br_2 < I_2$

$He < Ne < Ar < Kr < Xe$

Molar mass and boiling point correlate with these orders.

12.63 The boiling point of the water in the pressure cooker is 121 °C.

12.65 Using the equation of the line from Question 12.64, $P = 9.8$ atm.

12.67 (a) There will be water in the tube in equilibrium with its vapor, but almost all of the water will be present as liquid water.

(b) 760. mm Hg

(c) 10.4 cm^3

(d) 0.0233 g H_2O

Applying Chemical Principles: Chromatography

1. (a) The 1,5-pentanediol is most attracted to the mobile phase. The primary attractive force is hydrogen bonding. Dipole–dipole forces and dispersion forces are also present.
    (b) The propyl ethyl ether is most attracted to the stationary phase by dispersion forces but there are also some dipole–induced dipole interactions.
    (c) The molecules will elute in the following order (first to last): 1,5-pentanediol, 1-pentanol, and propyl ethyl ether.

Chapter 13

13.1 Two possible unit cells are illustrated here. The simplest formula is AB_8.

13.3 Ca^{2+} ions at eight corners = 1 net Ca^{2+} ion

O²⁻ ions in six faces = 3 net O^{2-} ions

Ti^{4+} ion in center of unit cell = 1 net Ti^{4+} ion

Formula = $CaTiO_3$

13.5 (a) There are eight O^{2-} ions at the corners and one in the center for a net of two O^{2-} ions per unit cell. There are four Cu ions in the interior in tetrahedral holes. The ratio of ions is Cu_2O.
    (b) The oxidation number of copper must be +1.

13.7 Calcium atom radius = 197 pm

13.9 There are three ways the edge dimensions can be calculated:
    (a) Calculate mass of unit cell (= 1.103×10^{-21} g/uc)

   Calculate volume of unit cell from mass (= 3.53×10^{-22} cm³/uc)

   Calculate edge length from volume (= 707 pm)
    (b) Assume I^- ions touch along the cell diagonal (◀ Check Your Understanding 13.1) and use I^- radius to find the edge length. Radius I^- = 220 pm

   Edge = $4(220 \text{ pm})/2^{1/2}$ = 622 pm
    (c) Assume the I^- and K^+ ions touch along the cell edge (page 593)

   Edge = $2 \times I^-$ radius + $2 \times K^+$ radius = 706 pm

   Methods (a) and (c) agree. It is apparent that the sizes of the ions are such that the I^- ions cannot touch along the cell diagonal.

13.11 The 1000 $2s$ orbitals will combine to form 1000 molecular orbitals. In the lowest energy state, 500 of these will be populated by pairs of electrons, and 500 will be empty.

13.13 In metals, thermal energy causes some electrons to occupy higher-energy orbitals in the band of molecular orbitals. For each electron promoted, two singly occupied levels result: a negative electron above the Fermi level and a positive hole below the Fermi level. Electrical conductivity results because in the presence of an electric field, these negative electrons will move toward the positive side of the field and the positive holes will move toward the negative side.

13.15 In carbon the band gap is too large for electrons to move up in energy from the valence band to the conduction band, whereas in silicon the band gap is small enough to permit this.

13.17 An intrinsic semiconductor is one that naturally can have electrons move across the band gap, whereas an extrinsic semiconductor requires the addition of dopants in order for it to conduct.

13.19 Increasing lattice energy: RbI < LiI < LiF < CaO

13.21 As the ion–ion distance decreases, the force of attraction between ions increases. This should make the lattice more stable, and more energy should be required to melt the compound.

13.23 $\Delta_f H° = -607$ kJ/mol

13.25 (a) Eight C atoms per unit cell. There are eight corners (= 1 net C atom), six faces (= 3 net C atoms), and four internal C atoms
    (b) Face-centered cubic (fcc) with C atoms in the tetrahedral holes

13.27 Type of solid: particles, forces of attraction
    (a) Metallic: metal atoms, metallic bonding
    (b) Ionic: ions, ion–ion interactions
    (c) Molecular: molecules, covalent bonds within the molecules and intermolecular forces between the molecules
    (d) Network: extended network of covalently bonded atoms, covalent bonds
    (e) Amorphous: covalently bonded networks with no long-range regularity, covalent bonds

13.29 Substance: type of solid, particles, forces, property
    (a) Gallium arsenide: network, covalently bonded atoms, covalent bonds, semiconductor
    (b) Polystyrene: amorphous, covalent bonds within the polymer molecules and dispersion forces between the polymer molecules, thermal insulator
    (c) Silicon carbide: network, covalently bonded atoms, covalent bonds, very hard material
    (d) Perovskite: ionic, Ca^{2+} and TiO_3^{2-} ions, ion–ion interactions, high melting point

13.31 q (for fusion) = -1.97 kJ; q (for melting) = $+1.97$ kJ

13.33 (a) The density of liquid CO_2 is less than that of solid CO_2.
(b) CO_2 is a gas at 5 atm and 0 °C.
(c) Critical temperature = 31 °C, so CO_2 cannot be liquefied at 45 °C.

13.35 q (to heat the liquid) = 9.4×10^2 kJ
q (to vaporize NH_3) = 1.6×10^4 kJ
q (to heat the vapor) = 8.8×10^2 kJ
q_{total} = 1.8×10^4 kJ

13.37 O_2 phase diagram. (i) Note the slight positive slope of the solid–liquid equilibrium line. It indicates that the density of solid O_2 is greater than that of liquid O_2. (ii) Using the diagram here, the vapor pressure of O_2 at 77 K is between 150 and 200 mm Hg.

13.39 Radius of silver = 145 pm

13.41 1.356×10^{-8} cm (literature value is 1.357×10^{-8} cm)

13.43 Mass of 1 CaF_2 unit calculated from crystal data = 1.2963×10^{-22} g. Divide molar mass of CaF_2 (78.077 g/mol) by mass of 1 CaF_2 to obtain Avogadro's number. Calculated value = 6.0230×10^{23} CaF_2/mol.

13.45 Diagram A leads to a surface coverage of 78.5%. Diagram B leads to 90.7% coverage.

13.47 (a) The lattice can be described as an fcc lattice of Si atoms with Si atoms in one half of the tetrahedral holes.
(b) There are eight Si atoms in the unit cell.
Mass of unit cell = 3.731×10^{-22} g
Volume of unit cell = 1.602×10^{-22} cm³
Density = 2.329 g/cm³ (which is the same as the literature value)

In the Si unit cell we cannot assume the atoms touch along the edge or along the face diagonal. Instead, we know that the Si atoms in the tetrahedral holes are bonded to the Si atoms at the corner.

Distance = 1/2 (cell diagonal) = 384 pm

Distance across cell face diagonal = 768 pm
Sin (109.5°/2) = 0.817 = (384 pm/2)/(Si-Si distance)
Distance from Si in tetrahedral hole to face or corner Si = 235 pm
Si radius = 118 pm
Table 7.8 gives Si radius as 117 pm

13.49 (a) Mg^{2+} ions are in $\frac{1}{8}$ of the eight possible tetrahedral holes, and Al^{3+} ions are in $\frac{1}{2}$ of the four available octahedral holes.
(b) Fe^{2+} ions are in $\frac{1}{8}$ of the eight possible tetrahedral holes, and Cr^{3+} ions are in $\frac{1}{2}$ of the four available octahedral holes.

13.51 8.5×10^2 nm

13.53 Germanium has a smaller band gap, so it has a higher conductivity.

13.55 Because boron is electron deficient in comparison to carbon, this is a p-type semiconductor.

13.57 Lead sulfide has the same structure as sodium chloride, not the same structure as ZnS. There are four Pb^{2+} ions and four S^{2-} ions per unit cell, a 1:1 ratio that matches the compound formula.

13.59 (a) $BBr_3(g) + PBr_3(g) + 3\,H_2(g) \rightarrow$
$$BP(s) + 6\,HBr(g)$$
(b) If B atoms are in an fcc lattice, then the P atoms must be in $\frac{1}{2}$ of the tetrahedral holes. (In this way it resembles Si in Question 13.47.)
(c) Unit cell volume = 1.092×10^{-22} cm³
Unit cell mass = 2.775×10^{-22} g
Density = 2.54 g/cm³
(d) The solution to this problem is identical to Question 13.47. In the BP lattice, the cell face diagonal is 676 pm. Therefore, the calculated BP distance is 207 pm.

13.61 Assuming the spheres are packed in an identical way, the water levels are the same. A face-centered cubic lattice, for example, uses 74% of the available space, regardless of the sphere size.

Applying Chemical Principles: Tin Disease

1. β-Tin has four atoms in the unit cell. α-Tin has eight atoms in the unit cell.

3. The length of each side is 649.0 pm.

Chapter 14

14.1 (a) Concentration (m) = 0.0434 m
(b) Mole fraction of acid = 0.000781
(c) Weight percent of acid = 0.509%

14.3 NaI: 0.15 m; 2.2%; X = 2.7 × 10^{-3}
CH$_3$CH$_2$OH: 1.1 m; 5.0%; X = 0.020
C$_{12}$H$_{22}$O$_{11}$: 0.15 m; 4.9%; X = 2.7 × 10^{-3}

14.5 2.65 g Na$_2$CO$_3$; X(Na$_2$CO$_3$) = 3.59 × 10^{-3}

14.7 220 g glycerol; 5.7 m

14.9 16.2 m; 37.1%

14.11 Molality = 2.6 × 10^{-5} m (assuming that 1 kg of seawater is equivalent to 1 kg of solvent)

14.13 (b) and (c)

14.15 $\Delta_{soln}H°$ for LiCl = −36.9 kJ/mol. This is an exothermic enthalpy of solution, as compared with the very slightly endothermic value for NaCl.

14.17 Above about 40 °C the solubility increases with temperature; therefore, add more NaCl and raise the temperature.

14.19 2 × 10^{-3} g O$_2$

14.21 1130 mm Hg or 1.49 bar

14.23 35.0 mm Hg

14.25 X(H$_2$O) = 0.869; 16.7 mol glycol; 1040 g glycol

14.27 Calculated boiling point = 84.2 °C

14.29 ΔT_{bp} = 0.808 °C; solution boiling point = 62.51 °C

14.31 Molality = 8.60 m; 28.4%

14.33 Molality = 0.195 m; ΔT_{fp} = fp = −0.362 °C

14.35 (a) ΔT_{fp} = −0.348 °C; fp = −0.348 °C
(b) ΔT_{bp} = +0.0959 °C; bp = 100.0959 °C
(c) Π = 4.58 atm

The osmotic pressure is large and can be measured with a small experimental error.

14.37 Molar mass = 6.0 × 10^3 g/mol

14.39 Molar mass = 360 g/mol; C$_{20}$H$_{16}$Fe$_2$

14.41 Molar mass = 150 g/mol

14.43 Molar mass = 170 g/mol

14.45 Freezing point = −24.6 °C

14.47 0.08 m CaCl$_2$ < 0.1 m NaCl < 0.04 m Na$_2$SO$_4$ < 0.1 sugar

14.49 (a) BaCl$_2$(aq) + Na$_2$SO$_4$(aq) →
$$BaSO_4(s) + 2\ NaCl(aq)$$
(b) Initially, the BaSO$_4$ particles form a colloidal suspension.
(c) Over time, the particles of BaSO$_4$(s) grow and precipitate.

14.51 Molar mass = 110 g/mol

14.53 (a) Increase in vapor pressure of water
0.20 m Na$_2$SO$_4$ < 0.50 m sugar < 0.20 m KBr < 0.35 m ethylene glycol
(b) Increase in boiling point
0.35 m ethylene glycol < 0.20 m KBr < 0.50 m sugar < 0.20 m Na$_2$SO$_4$

14.55 (a) 0.456 mol DMG and 11.4 mol ethanol; X(DMG) = 0.0385
(b) 0.869 m
(c) VP ethanol over the solution at 78.4 °C = 730.7 mm Hg
(d) bp = 79.5 °C

14.57 For ammonia: 23 m; X(NH$_3$) = 0.29; 28%

14.59 0.592 g Na$_2$SO$_4$

14.61 (a) 0.20 m KBr; (b) 0.10 m Na$_2$CO$_3$

14.63 Freezing point = −11 °C

14.65 4.0 × 10^2 g/mol

14.67 4.7 × 10^{-4} mol/kg

14.69 (a) Molar mass = 4.9 × 10^4 g/mol
(b) ΔT_{fp} = −3.8 × 10^{-4} °C

14.71 $\Delta_{soln}H°$ [Li$_2$SO$_4$] = −28.0 kJ/mol
$\Delta_{soln}H°$ [LiCl] = −36.9 kJ/mol
$\Delta_{soln}H°$ [K$_2$SO$_4$] = +23.7 kJ/mol
$\Delta_{soln}H°$ [KCl] = +17.2 kJ/mol

Both lithium compounds have exothermic enthalpies of solution, whereas both potassium compounds have endothermic values. Consistent with this is the fact that lithium salts (LiCl) are often more water-soluble than potassium salts (KCl) (see Figure 14.11).

14.73 X(benzene in solution) = 0.67 and X(toluene in solution) = 0.33

$$P_{total} = P_{toluene} + P_{benzene} = 7.3\ \text{mm Hg} + 50.\ \text{mm Hg}$$
$$= 57\ \text{mm Hg}$$

$$X(\text{toluene in vapor}) = \frac{7.3\ \text{mm Hg}}{57\ \text{mm Hg}} = 0.13$$

$$X(\text{benzene in vapor}) = \frac{50.\ \text{mm Hg}}{57\ \text{mm Hg}} = 0.87$$

14.75 i = 1.7. That is, there is 1.7 mol of ions in solution per mole of compound.

14.77 (a) Calculate the number of moles of ions in 10^6 g H_2O: 550. mol Cl^-; 470. mol Na^+; 53.1 mol Mg^{2+}; 9.42 mol SO_4^{2-}; 10.3 mol Ca^{2+}; 9.72 mol K^+; 0.84 mol Br^-. Total moles of ions = 1.103×10^3 per 10^6 g water. This gives ΔT_{fp} of -2.05 °C.

(b) $\Pi = 27.0$ atm. This means that a minimum pressure of 27 atm would have to be used in a reverse osmosis device.

14.79 (a) $i = 2.06$

(b) There are approximately two particles in solution, so $H^+ + HSO_4^-$ best represents H_2SO_4 in aqueous solution.

14.81 Mass of $N_2O = 0.53$ g; concentration = 1.1×10^3 ppm

14.83 The best method would be to shine a laser through the liquid and look for the Tyndall effect. Some other properties of colloids that could be utilized are that the dispersed material in a colloid will either not crystallize or crystallize only with difficulty and will either not diffuse across a membrane or do so much more slowly than a true solute.

14.85 The calculated molality at the freezing point of benzene is 0.47 m, whereas it is 0.99 m at the boiling point. A higher molality at the higher temperature indicates more molecules are dissolved. Therefore, assuming benzoic acid forms dimers like acetic acid (Figure 12.7), dimer formation is more prevalent at the lower temperature. In this process two molecules become one entity, lowering the number of separate species in solution and lowering the molality.

14.87 Molar mass in benzene = 1.20×10^2 g/mol; molar mass in water = 62.4 g/mol. The actual molar mass of acetic acid is 60.1 g/mol. In benzene, the molecules of acetic acid form "dimers." That is, two molecules form a single unit through hydrogen bonding. See Figure 12.7 on page 556.

14.89 (a) Molar mass = 97.6 g/mol; empirical formula, BF_2, and molecular formula, B_2F_4

(b)

14.91 The strength of the interactions goes inversely with the size of the ion. Thus, Be^{2+} is most strongly hydrated, and Ca^{2+} is least strongly hydrated.

14.93 Colligative properties depend on the number of ions or molecules in solution. Each mole of $CaCl_2$ provides 1.5 times as many ions as each mole of NaCl.

14.95 Benzene is a nonpolar solvent. Thus, ionic substances such as $NaNO_3$ and NH_4Cl will certainly not dissolve. However, naphthalene is also nonpolar and resembles benzene in its structure; it should dissolve very well. (A chemical handbook gives a solubility of 33 g naphthalene per 100 g benzene.) Diethyl ether is weakly polar but is miscible to some extent with benzene.

Water is a polar solvent. The ionic compounds, $NaNO_3$ and NH_4Cl, are both soluble in water ($NaNO_3$ solubility (at 25 °C) = 91 g per 100 g water; NH_4Cl solubility (at 25 °C) = 40 g per 100 g water. The slightly polar compound diethyl ether is soluble to a small extent in water (about 6 g per 100 g water at 25 °C). Nonpolar naphthalene is not soluble in water (solubility at 25 °C = 0.003 g per 100 g water).

14.97 The C—C and C—H bonds in hydrocarbons are nonpolar or weakly polar and tend to make such dispersions hydrophobic (water-hating). The C—O and O—H bonds in starch present opportunities for hydrogen bonding with water. Hence, starch is expected to be more hydrophilic.

14.99 [NaCl] = 1.0 M and $[KNO_3]$ = 0.88 M. The KNO_3 solution has a higher solvent concentration, so solvent will flow from the KNO_3 solution to the NaCl solution.

14.101 (a) $X(C_2H_5OH) = 0.051$; $X(H_2O) = 0.949$

(b) $P(C_2H_5OH)$ over mixture = 38 mm Hg; $P°(H_2O)$ calculated by linear interpolation using the vapor pressures at 78 °C and 79 °C = 334.2 mm Hg; $P(H_2O)$ over mixture = 317 mm Hg

(c) $X(C_2H_5OH) = 0.11$; $X(H_2O) = 0.89$

(d) The mole fraction of ethanol increased from 0.051 to 0.11, a factor of 2.2 times. Weight percent of $C_2H_5OH = 24\%$

14.103 The molality of the 5.00% NaCl solution is 0.901 m. Assuming no dissociation, this leads to ΔT_{fp}(calculated) = -1.68 °C and $i = 1.82$. The molality of the 5.00% Na_2SO_4 solution is 0.371 m, ΔT_{fp}(calculated) = -0.689 °C, and $i = 1.97$. These values are consistent with the trends seen in Table 14.4. As the concentration of the ionic solute increases, the value of i continues to decrease for both solutes, and rate of decrease is falling for both solutes. In the case of NaCl, this value is leveling off quite a bit. In the case of Na_2SO_4, it is continuing to decrease by significant amounts. Interestingly, the value of i for Na_2SO_4 has now fallen below 2 and is getting closer to that for NaCl.

14.105 This does not lend credence to this story. The reported lowest temperature for a NaCl solution corresponds to a temperature of 2.372 °F. The temperature of 0 °F is still below this.

Applying Chemical Principles: Distillation

1. X(hexane) = 0.59

3. Mass percent (hexane) = 18%

Chapter 15

15.1 (a) $-\dfrac{1}{2}\dfrac{\Delta[O_3]}{\Delta t} = \dfrac{1}{3}\dfrac{\Delta[O_2]}{\Delta t}$

(b) $-\dfrac{1}{2}\dfrac{\Delta[HOF]}{\Delta t} = \dfrac{1}{2}\dfrac{\Delta[HF]}{\Delta t} = \dfrac{\Delta[O_2]}{\Delta t}$

15.3 $\dfrac{1}{3}\dfrac{\Delta[O_2]}{\Delta t} = -\dfrac{1}{2}\dfrac{\Delta[O_3]}{\Delta t}$ or $\dfrac{\Delta[O_2]}{\Delta t} = -\dfrac{2}{3}\dfrac{\Delta[O_2]}{\Delta t}$

so $\Delta[O_3]/\Delta t = -1.0 \times 10^{-3}$ mol/L·s.

15.5 (a) The graph of [B] (product concentration) versus time shows [B] increasing from zero. The line is curved, indicating the rate changes with time; thus the rate depends on concentration. Rates for the four 10-s intervals are as follows: 0–10 s, 0.0326 mol/L·s; from 10–20 s, 0.0246 mol/L·s; 20–30 s, 0.0178 mol/L·s; 30–40 s, 0.0140 mol/L·s.

(b) $-\dfrac{\Delta[A]}{\Delta t} = \dfrac{1}{2}\dfrac{\Delta[B]}{\Delta t}$ throughout the reaction

In the interval 10–20 s, $\dfrac{\Delta[A]}{\Delta t} = -0.0123 \dfrac{mol}{L \cdot s}$

(c) Instantaneous rate when [B] = 0.750 mol/L

$= \dfrac{\Delta[B]}{\Delta t} = 0.0163 \dfrac{mol}{L \cdot s}$

15.7 The reaction is second order in A, first order in B, and third order overall.

15.9 (a) Rate = $k[NO_2][O_3]$
(b) If $[NO_2]$ is tripled, the rate triples.
(c) If $[O_3]$ is halved, the rate is halved.

15.11 (a) The reaction is second order in [NO] and first order in $[O_2]$.

(b) Rate = $1/2 \dfrac{-\Delta[NO]}{\Delta t} = k[NO]^2[O_2]$

(c) $k = 13$ $L^2/mol^2 \cdot s$

(d) Rate = 1.4×10^{-5} mol/L·s

(e) When $-\Delta[NO]/\Delta t = 1.0 \times 10^{-4}$ mol/L·s, $\Delta[O_2]/\Delta t = 5.0 \times 10^{-5}$ mol/L·s and $\Delta[NO_2]/\Delta t = 1.0 \times 10^{-4}$ mol/L·s.

15.13 (a) Rate = $-(1/2)\Delta[NO]/\Delta t = k[NO]^2[O_2]$
(b) 25. $L^2/mol^2 \cdot h$
(c) Rate = 8.5×10^{-9} mol/L·h

15.15 $k = 3.73 \times 10^{-3}$ min^{-1}

15.17 5.0×10^2 min

15.19 (a) 153 min
(b) 1790 min

15.21 97 s

15.23 39 s

15.25 (a) $t_{1/2} = 10,000$ s (b) 34,000 s

15.27 1.87 g azomethane remains, 0.063 g N_2 formed

15.29 Fraction of ^{64}Cu remaining = 0.030

15.31 The straight line obtained in a graph of $\ln[N_2O]$ versus time indicates a first-order reaction.

$k = (-slope) = 0.0127$ min^{-1}

The rate when $[N_2O] = 0.035$ mol/L is 4.4×10^{-4} mol/L·min.

15.33 The graph of $1/[NO_2]$ versus time gives a straight line, indicating the reaction is second order with respect to $[NO_2]$ (see Table 15.1 on page 686). The slope of the line is k, so $k = 1.1$ L/mol·s.

15.35 $-\Delta[C_2F_4]/\Delta t = k[C_2F_4]^2 = (0.04$ L/mol·s$)[C_2F_4]^2$

15.37 Activation energy = 102 kJ/mol

15.39 $k = 0.3$ s^{-1}

15.41

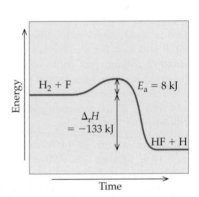

15.43 (a) Rate = $k[NO_3][NO]$
(b) Rate = $k[Cl][H_2]$
(c) Rate = $k[(CH_3)_3CBr]$

15.45 (a) The second step; (b) Rate = $k[O_3][O]$

15.47 (a) NO_2 is a reactant in the first step and a product in the second step. CO is a reactant in the second step. NO_3 is an intermediate, and CO_2 is a product. NO is a product.
(b) Reaction coordinate diagram

15.49 Doubling the concentration of A will increase the rate by a factor of 4 because the concentration of A appears in the rate law as $[A]^2$. Halving the concentration of B will halve the rate The net result is that the rate of the reaction will double.

15.51 After measuring pH as a function of time, one could then calculate pOH and then $[OH^-]$. Finally, a plot of $1/[OH^-]$ versus time would give a straight line with a slope equal to k.

15.53 72 s represents two half-lives, so $t_{1/2} = 36$ s.

15.55 (a) A plot of $1/[C_2F_4]$ versus time indicates the reaction is second order with respect to $[C_2F_4]$. The rate law is Rate $= k[C_2F_4]^2$.

(b) The rate constant (= slope of the line) is about 0.045 L/mol · s. (The graph does not allow a very accurate calculation.)

(c) Using $k = 0.045$ L/mol · s, the concentration after 600 s is 0.03 M (to one significant figure).

(d) Time = 2000 s [using k from part (b)].

15.57 (a) A plot of $1/[NH_4NCO]$ versus time is linear, so the reaction is second order with respect to NH_4NCO.

(b) Slope $= k = 0.0109$ L/mol · min.

(c) $t_{1/2} = 200.$ min

(d) $[NH_4NCO] = 0.0997$ mol/L

15.59 Mechanism 2

15.61 $k = 0.0176$ h^{-1} and $t_{1/2} = 39.3$ h

15.63 (a) After 125 min, 0.251 g remains. After 145, 0.144 g remains.

(b) Time = 43.9 min

(c) Fraction remaining = 0.016

15.65 The rate equation for the slow step is Rate $= k[O_3][O]$. The equilibrium constant, K, for step 1 is $K = [O_2][O]/[O_3]$. Solving this for [O], we have $[O] = K[O_3]/[O_2]$. Substituting the expression for [O] into the rate equation we find

Rate $= k[O_3]\{K[O_3]/[O_2]\} = kK[O_3]^2/[O_2]$

15.67 The slope of the ln k versus $1/T$ plot is -6370. From slope $= -E_a/R$, we derive $E_a = 53.0$ kJ/mol.

15.69 Estimated time at 90 °C = 4.76 min

15.71 After 30 min (one half-life), $P_{HOF} = 50.0$ mm Hg and $P_{total} = 125.0$ mm Hg. After 45 min, $P_{HOF} = 35.4$ mm Hg and $P_{total} = 132$ mm Hg.

15.73 (a) Reaction is first order in NO_2NH_2 and -1 for H_3O^+. In a buffered solution, $[H_3O]^+$ is constant, so the reaction has an apparent order of 1.

(b, c) Mechanism 3

In step 1, $K = k_4/k_4'$
$= [NO_2NH^-][H_3O^+]/[NO_2NH_2]$

Rearrange this and substitute into the rate law for the slow step.

Rate $= k_5[NO_2NH^-] = k_5K[NO_2NH_2]/[H_3O^+]$

This is the same as the experimental rate law, where the overall rate constant $k = k_5K$.

(d) Addition of OH^- ions will shift the equilibrium in step 1 (by reacting with H_3O^+) to produce a larger concentration of NO_2NH^-, the reactant in the rate-determining step.

15.75 (a) Average rate for $t = 0$ to $t = 15$ is about 4.7×10^{-5} M/s. For $t = 100$ s to 125 s, the average rate is about 1.6×10^{-5} M/s. The rate slows because the rate of the reaction is dependent on the concentration of reactant and this concentration is declining with time.

(b) Instantaneous rate at 50 s is about 2.7×10^{-5} M/s.

(c) A plot of ln (concentration) versus time is a straight line with an equation of $y = -0.010x - 5.2984$. The slope, which is equal to $-k$, is -0.010, so $k = 0.010$ s^{-1}.

(d) From the data the half-life is 69.3 s, and the same value comes from the relation $t_{1/2} = $ ln $2/k$.

15.77 A plot of 1/Rate versus 1/[S] gives the equation

1/Rate $= 94 \, (1/[S]) + 7.5 \times 10^4$

so Rate$_{max} = 1/(7.5 \times 10^4)$
$= 1.3 \times 10^{-5}$ M min^{-1}.

15.79 The finely divided rhodium metal will have a significantly greater surface area than the small block of metal. This leads to a large increase in the number of reaction sites and vastly increases the reaction rate.

15.81 (a) False. The reaction may occur in a single step but this does not have to be true.

(b) True

(c) False. Raising the temperature increases the value of k.

(d) False. Temperature has no effect on the value of E_a.

(e) False. If the concentrations of both reactants are doubled, the rate will increase by a factor of 4.

(f) True

15.83 (a) True

(b) True

(c) False. As a reaction proceeds, the reactant concentration decreases and the rate decreases.

(d) False. It is possible to have a one-step mechanism for a third-order reaction if the slow, rate-determining step is termolecular.

15.85 (a) Decrease   (d) No change

(b) Increase   (e) No change

(c) No change   (f) No change

15.87 (a) There are three mechanistic steps.

(b) The overall reaction is exothermic.

Applying Chemical Principles: Kinetics and Mechanisms: A 70-Year-Old Mystery Solved

1. (a) 207 kJ/mol photons

(b) 792 nm

3. The probability of three particles colliding simultaneously with the correct geometry for a successful reaction is low.

Chapter 16

16.1 (a) $K = \dfrac{[H_2O]^2[O_2]}{[H_2O_2]^2}$

(b) $K = \dfrac{[CO_2]}{[CO][O_2]^{1/2}}$

(c) $K = \dfrac{[CO]^2}{[CO_2]}$

(d) $K = \dfrac{[CO_2]}{[CO]}$

16.3 $Q = (2.0 \times 10^{-8})^2/(0.020) = 2.0 \times 10^{-14}$
$Q < K$, so the reaction proceeds to the right.

16.5 $Q = 1.0 \times 10^3$, so $Q > K$ and the reaction is not at equilibrium. It proceeds to the left to convert products to reactants.

16.7 $K = 1.2$

16.9 (a) $K = 0.025$
(b) $K = 0.025$
(c) The amount of solid does not affect the equilibrium.

16.11 (a) $[COCl_2] = 0.00308$ M; $[CO] = 0.0071$ M
(b) $K = 140$

16.13 [isobutane] = 0.024 M; [butane] = 0.010 M

16.15 $[I_2] = 6.14 \times 10^{-3}$ M; $[I] = 4.79 \times 10^{-3}$ M

16.17 $[COBr_2] = 0.107$ M; $[CO] = [Br_2] = 0.143$ M
57.1% of the $COBr_2$ has decomposed.

16.19 (b)

16.21 (e) $K_2 = 1/(K_1)^2$

16.23 $K = 13.7$

16.25 (a) Equilibrium shifts to the right
(b) Equilibrium shifts to the left
(c) Equilibrium shifts to the right
(d) Equilibrium shifts to the left

16.27 Equilibrium concentrations are the same under both circumstances: [butane] = 1.1 M and [isobutane] = 2.9 M.

16.29 $K = 3.9 \times 10^{-4}$

16.31 For decomposition of $COCl_2$, $K = 1/(K$ for $COCl_2$ formation) $= 1/(6.5 \times 10^{11}) = 1.5 \times 10^{-12}$

16.33 $K = 4$

16.35 Q is less than K, so the system shifts to form more isobutane.
At equilibrium, [butane] = 0.86 M and [isobutane] = 2.14 M.

16.37 The second equation has been reversed and multiplied by 2.
(c) $K_2 = 1/K_1^2$

16.39 (a) No change (d) Shifts right
(b) Shifts left   (e) Shifts right
(c) No change

16.41 (a) The equilibrium will shift to the left on adding more Cl_2.
(b) K is calculated (from the quantities of reactants and products at equilibrium) to be 0.0470. After Cl_2 is added, the concentrations are: $[PCl_5]$ = 0.0199 M, $[PCl_3]$ = 0.0231 M, and $[Cl_2]$ = 0.0403 M.

16.43 $K_p = 0.215$

16.45 (a) Fraction dissociated = 0.15
(b) Fraction dissociated = 0.189. If the pressure decreases, the equilibrium shifts to the right, increasing the fraction of N_2O_4 dissociated.

16.47 $[NH_3] = 0.67$ M; $[N_2] = 0.57$ M; $[H_2] = 1.7$ M; P_{total} = 180 atm

16.49 (a) $[NH_3] = [H_2S] = 0.013$ M
(b) $[NH_3] = 0.027$ M and $[H_2S] = 0.0067$ M

16.51 $P(NO_2) = 0.37$ atm and $P(N_2O_4) = 0.96$ atm; P(total) = 1.33 atm

16.53 (a) $K_p = K_c = 56$. Because 2 mol of reactant gases gives 2 mol of product gases, Δn does not change and $K_p = K_c$ (◀ page 726).
(b, c) Initial $P(H_2) = P(I_2) = 2.6$ atm and $P_{total} = 5.2$ atm
At equilibrium, $P(H_2) = P(I_2) = 0.54$ atm and $P(HI) = 4.1$ atm. Therefore, $P_{total} = 5.2$ atm. The initial total pressure and the equilibrium total pressure are the same owing to the reaction stoichiometry. Percent dissociation = 69%

16.55 $P(CO) = 0.0010$ atm

16.57 1.7×10^{18} O atoms

16.59 Glycerin concentration should be 1.7 M

16.61 (a) $K_p = 0.20$
(b) When initial $[N_2O_4]$ = 1.00 atm, the equilibrium pressures are $[N_2O_4]$ = 0.80 atm and $[NO_2]$ = 0.40 atm. When initial $[N_2O_4]$ = 0.10 atm, the equilibrium pressures are $[N_2O_4]$ = 0.050 atm and $[NO_2]$ = 0.10 atm. The percent dissociation is now 50.%. This is in accord with Le Chatelier's principle: If the initial pressure of the reactant is smaller, the equilibrium shifts to the right, increasing the fraction of the reactant dissociated. [This might be clearer if you imagine beginning with the equilibrium system in the case when the initial pressure of N_2O_4 was 1.00 atm and then increasing the volume tenfold (obtaining the same equilibrium system as starting with 0.10 atm N_2O_4). Le Chatelier's principle predicts a shift in the direction that has a greater number of gas molecules. See also Question 16.45.]

16.63 (a) The flask containing $(H_3N)B(CH_3)_3$ will have the largest partial pressure of $B(CH_3)_3$.

(b) $P[B(CH_3)_3] = P(NH_3) = 2.1$ and $P[(H_3N)B(CH_3)_3] = 1.0$ atm

$P_{total} = 5.2$ atm

Percent dissociation = 69%

16.65 (a) As more KSCN is added, Le Chatelier's principle predicts more of the red complex ion $[Fe(H_2O)_5(SCN)]^+$ will form.

(b) Adding Ag^+ ions leads to a precipitate of AgSCN, thus removing SCN^- ions from solution. The equilibrium shifts left, dropping the concentration of the red complex ion.

16.67 (a) False. The magnitude of K is always dependent on temperature.

(b) True

(c) False. The equilibrium constant for a reaction is the reciprocal of the value of K for its reverse.

(d) True

(e) False. $\Delta n = 1$, so $K_p = K_c(RT)$

16.69 (a) Product-favored, $K \gg 1$

(b) Reactant-favored, $K \ll 1$

(c) Product-favored, $K \gg 1$

16.71 Begin with an equilibrium system containing $^{14}N_2$, H_2, and $^{14}NH_3$. Introduce some $^{15}N_2$ and allow the system to equilibrate. The presence of $^{15}NH_3$ indicates that the forward reaction has occurred. In addition, the presence of $^{15}N^{14}N$ indicates that the reverse reaction has occurred. Further evidence of the reverse reaction occurring could be obtained by carrying out another trial in which $^{15}NH_3$ is added to the initial equilibrium mixture. The presence of $^{15}N^{14}N$ or $^{15}N_2$ indicates that the reverse reaction is occurring. (A similar set of experiments could be run using ^2H instead of ^{15}N.)

Applying Chemical Principles: Trivalent Carbon

1. (a) Concentration (molality) = -0.542 °C/ -5.12 °C/m = 0.106 mol dimer/kg benzene

Amount dimer = (0.106 mol dimer/kg benzene) (0.0100 kg benzene) = 1.06×10^{-3} mol dimer

Molar mass of dimer = 0.503 g/1.06×10^{-3} mol = 475 g/mol

(b) Each molecule of the dimer that decomposes produces two monomer particles, increasing the total number of moles of particles in solution. When the mass of the dimer is divided by the moles of particles, the calculated molar mass is too low.

3. [Monomer] = 0.0045 M, [dimer] = 0.0503 M

5. (b) Triphenylmethyl radical

Chapter 17

17.1 (a) CN^-, cyanide ion

(b) SO_4^{2-}, sulfate ion

(c) F^-, fluoride ion

17.3 (a) $H_3O^+(aq) + NO_3^-(aq)$; $H_3O^+(aq)$ is the conjugate acid of H_2O, and $NO_3^-(aq)$ is the conjugate base of HNO_3.

(b) $H_3O^+(aq) + SO_4^{2-}(aq)$; $H_3O^+(aq)$ is the conjugate acid of H_2O, and $SO_4^{2-}(aq)$ is the conjugate base of HSO_4^-.

(c) $H_2O + HF$; H_2O is the conjugate base of H_3O^+, and HF is the conjugate acid of F^-.

17.5 Brønsted acid: $HC_2O_4^-(aq) + H_2O(\ell) \rightleftharpoons H_3O^+(aq) + C_2O_4^{2-}(aq)$

Brønsted base: $HC_2O_4^-(aq) + H_2O(\ell) \rightleftharpoons H_2C_2O_4(aq) + OH^-(aq)$

17.7

	Acid (A)	Base (B)	Conjugate Base of A	Conjugate Acid of B
(a)	HCO_2H	H_2O	HCO_2^-	H_3O^+
(b)	H_2S	NH_3	HS^-	NH_4^+
(c)	HSO_4^-	OH^-	SO_4^{2-}	H_2O

17.9 $[H_3O^+] = 1.8 \times 10^{-4}$ M; acidic

17.11 HCl is a strong acid, so $[H_3O^+]$ = concentration of the acid. $[H_3O^+] = 0.0075$ M and $[OH^-] = 1.3 \times 10^{-12}$ M. pH = 2.12.

17.13 $Ba(OH)_2$ is a strong base, so $[OH^-] = 2 \times$ concentration of the base.

$[OH^-] = 3.0 \times 10^{-3}$ M; pOH = 2.52; and pH = 11.48

17.15 (a) The strongest acid is HCO_2H (largest K_a) and the weakest acid is C_6H_5OH (smallest K_a).

(b) The strongest acid (HCO_2H) has the weakest conjugate base.

(c) The weakest acid (C_6H_5OH) has the strongest conjugate base.

17.17 (c) HClO, the weakest acid in this list (Table 17.3), has the strongest conjugate base.

17.19 $CO_3^{2-}(aq) + H_2O(\ell) \rightarrow HCO_3^-(aq) + OH^-(aq)$

17.21 Highest pH, Na_2S; lowest pH, $AlCl_3$ (which gives the weak acid $[Al(H_2O)_6]^{3+}$ in solution)

17.23 $pK_a = 4.19$

17.25 $K_a = 3.0 \times 10^{-10}$; in Table 17.3, this acid falls between hexaaquairon(II) ion and the hydrogen carbonate ion.

17.27 2-Chlorobenzoic acid is the stronger acid; it has the smaller pK_a value.

17.29 $K_b = 7.1 \times 10^{-12}$

17.31 $K_b = 6.3 \times 10^{-5}$

17.33 $CH_3CO_2H(aq) + HCO_3^-(aq) \rightleftharpoons$
$$CH_3CO_2^-(aq) + H_2CO_3(aq)$$

Equilibrium lies predominantly to the right because CH_3CO_2H is a stronger acid than H_2CO_3.

17.35 (a) Left; NH_3 and HBr are the stronger base and acid, respectively.
   (b) Left; PO_4^{3-} and CH_3CO_2H are the stronger base and acid, respectively.
   (c) Right; $[Fe(H_2O)_6]^{3+}$ and HCO_3^- are the stronger acid and base, respectively.

17.37 (a) $OH^-(aq) + HPO_4^{2-}(aq) \rightleftharpoons$
$$H_2O(\ell) + PO_4^{3-}(aq)$$
   (b) OH^- is a stronger base than PO_4^{3-}, so the equilibrium will lie to the right.

17.39 (a) $CH_3CO_2H(aq) + HPO_4^{2-}(aq) \rightleftharpoons$
$$CH_3CO_2^-(aq) + H_2PO_4^-(aq)$$
   (b) CH_3CO_2H is a stronger acid than $H_2PO_4^-$, so the equilibrium will lie to the right.

17.41 (a) 2.1×10^{-3} M; (b) $K_a = 3.5 \times 10^{-4}$

17.43 $K_b = 6.6 \times 10^{-9}$

17.45 (a) $[H_3O^+] = 1.6 \times 10^{-4}$ M
   (b) Moderately weak; $K_a = 1.1 \times 10^{-5}$

17.47 $[CH_3CO_2^-] = [H_3O^+] = 1.9 \times 10^{-3}$ M and $[CH_3CO_2H] = 0.20$ M

17.49 $[H_3O^+] = [CN^-] = 3.2 \times 10^{-6}$ M; $[HCN] = 0.025$ M; pH $= 5.50$

17.51 $[NH_4^+] = [OH^-] = 1.6 \times 10^{-3}$ M; $[NH_3] = 0.15$ M; pH $= 11.22$

17.53 $[OH^-] = 0.010$ M; pH $= 12.01$; pOH $= 1.99$

17.55 pH $= 3.25$

17.57 $[H_3O^+] = 1.1 \times 10^{-5}$ M; pH $= 4.98$

17.59 $[HCN] = [OH^-] = 3.3 \times 10^{-3}$ M; $[H_3O^+] = 3.0 \times 10^{-12}$ M; $[Na^+] = 0.441$ M

17.61 $[H_3O^+] = 1.5 \times 10^{-9}$ M; pH $= 8.81$

17.63 (a) The reaction produces acetate ion, the conjugate base of acetic acid. The solution is weakly basic. pH is greater than 7.
   (b) The reaction produces NH_4^+, the conjugate acid of NH_3. The solution is weakly acidic. pH is less than 7.
   (c) The reaction mixes equal molar amounts of strong base and strong acid. The solution will be neutral. pH will be 7.

17.65 (a) pH $= 1.17$; (b) $[SO_3^{2-}] = 6.2 \times 10^{-8}$ M

17.67 (a) $[OH^-] = [N_2H_5^+] = 9.2 \times 10^{-5}$ M; $[N_2H_6^{2+}] = 8.9 \times 10^{-16}$ M
   (b) pH $= 9.96$

17.69 HOCN should be a stronger acid than HCN because the H atom in HOCN is attached to the more electronegative O atom. The electron attachment enthalpy of OCN is thus more negative than that of CN, thus stabilizing the conjugate base that forms and making the ionization of HOCN more product-favored.

17.71 The S atom is surrounded by four highly electronegative O atoms. These help stabilize the conjugate base that needs to form so that the negative charge is more readily accepted.

17.73 (a) Lewis base
   (b) Lewis acid
   (c) Lewis base (owing to lone pair of electrons on the N atom)

17.75 CO is a Lewis base in its reactions with transition metal atoms. It donates a lone pair of electrons on the C atom.

17.77 pH $= 2.671$

17.79 Both $Ba(OH)_2$ and $Sr(OH)_2$ dissolve completely in water to provide M^{2+} and OH^- ions. 2.50 g $Sr(OH)_2$ in 1.00 L of water gives $[Sr^{2+}] = 0.021$ M and $[OH^-] = 0.041$ M. The concentration of OH^- is reflected in a pH of 12.61.

17.81 $H_2S(aq) + CH_3CO_2^-(aq) \rightleftharpoons$
$$CH_3CO_2H(aq) + HS^-(aq)$$

The equilibrium lies to the left and favors the reactants.

17.83 $[X^-] = [H_3O^+] = 3.0 \times 10^{-3}$ M; $[HX] = 0.007$ M; pH $= 2.52$

17.85 $K_a = 1.4 \times 10^{-5}$; $pK_a = 4.86$

17.87 pH $= 5.84$

17.89 (a) Ethylamine is a stronger base than ethanolamine.
   (b) For ethylamine, the pH of the solution is 11.82.

17.91 pH $= 7.66$

17.93 Acidic: $NaHSO_4$, NH_4Br, $FeCl_3$
   Neutral: $KClO_4$, $NaNO_3$, LiBr
   Basic: Na_2CO_3, $(NH_4)_2S$, Na_2HPO_4
   Highest pH: $(NH_4)_2S$, lowest pH: $NaHSO_4$

17.95 $K_{net} = K_{a1} \times K_{a2} = 3.8 \times 10^{-6}$

17.97 For the reaction $HCO_2H(aq) + OH^-(aq) \rightarrow H_2O(\ell) + HCO_2^-(aq)$, $K_{net} = K_a$ (for HCO_2H) $\times [1/K_w] = 1.8 \times 10^{10}$

17.99 To double the percent ionization, you must dilute 100 mL of solution to 400 mL.

17.101 $H_2O > H_2C_2O_4 > HC_2O_4^- = H_3O^+ > C_2O_4^{2-} > OH^-$

17.103 Measure the pH of 0.1 M solutions of the three bases. The solution containing the strongest base will have the highest pH. The solution having the weakest base will have the lowest pH.

17.105 The possible cation–anion combinations are NaCl (neutral), NaOH (basic), NH_4Cl (acidic), NH_4OH (basic), HCl (acidic), and H_2O (neutral).

   A $= H^+$ solution; B $= NH_4^+$ solution; C $= Na^+$ solution; Y $= Cl^-$ solution; Z $= OH^-$ solution

17.107 $K_a = 3.0 \times 10^{-5}$

17.109 (a) Aniline is both a Brønsted and a Lewis base. As a proton acceptor it gives $C_6H_5NH_3^+$. The N atom can also donate an electron pair to give a Lewis acid–base adduct, $F_3B \leftarrow NH_2C_6H_5$.

      (b) pH = 7.97

17.111 Water can both accept a proton (a Brønsted base) and donate a lone pair (a Lewis base). Water can also donate a proton (Brønsted acid), but it cannot accept a pair of electrons (and act as a Lewis acid).

17.113 (a) HOCl is the strongest acid (smallest pK_a and largest K_a), and HOI is the weakest acid.

      (b) Cl is more electronegative than Br or I, so the OCl^- anion is more stable than the other two oxoanions.

17.115 (a) $HClO_4 + H_2SO_4 \rightleftharpoons ClO_4^- + H_3SO_4^+$

      (b) The O atoms on sulfuric acid have lone pairs of electrons that can be used to bind to an H^+ ion.

$$H-\overset{\ddot{}}{\underset{\ddot{}}{O}}-\overset{\overset{:\ddot{O}:}{|}}{\underset{\underset{:\ddot{O}:}{|}}{S}}-\overset{\ddot{}}{\underset{\ddot{}}{O}}-H$$

17.117 (a) $\left[:\ddot{I}-\ddot{I}-\ddot{I}: \right]^-$

      (b) $I^-(aq)$ [Lewis base] $+ I_2(aq)$ [Lewis acid] $\rightarrow$ $I_3^-(aq)$

17.119 (a) For the weak acid HA, the concentrations at equilibrium are $[HA] = C_0 - \alpha C_0$, $[H_3O^+] = [A^-] = \alpha C_0$. Putting these into the usual expression for K_a we have $K_a = \alpha^2 C_0/(1-\alpha)$.

      (b) For 0.10 M NH_4^+, $\alpha = 7.5 \times 10^{-5}$ (reflecting the fact that NH_4^+ is a much weaker acid than acetic acid).

17.121 (a) Add the three equations.

$$NH_4^+(aq) + H_2O(\ell) \rightleftharpoons NH_3(aq) + H_3O^+(aq)$$
$$K_1 = K_w/K_b$$
$$CN^-(aq) + H_2O(\ell) \rightleftharpoons HCN(aq) + OH^-(aq)$$
$$K_2 = K_w/K_a$$
$$H_3O^+(aq) + OH^-(aq) \rightleftharpoons 2\,H_2O(\ell) \quad K_3 = 1/K_w$$
$$\overline{NH_4^+(aq) + CN^-(aq) \rightleftharpoons NH_3(aq) + HCN(aq)}$$
$$K_{net} = K_1K_2K_3 = K_w/K_aK_b$$

      (b) The salts NH_4CN, $NH_4CH_3CO_2$, and NH_4F have K_{net} values of 1.4, 3.1×10^{-5}, and 7.7×10^{-7}, respectively. Only in the case of NH_4CN is the base (the cyanide ion) strong enough to remove a proton from the ammonium ion and produce a significant concentration of products.

      (c) NH_4CN: basic, K_b of $CN^- > K_a$ of NH_4^+

      $NH_4CH_3CO_2$: neutral, K_b of $CH_3CO_2^- = K_a$ of NH_4^+

      NH_4F: acidic, K_b of F^- is less than K_a of NH_4^+

Applying Chemical Principles: The Leveling Effect, Nonaqueous Solvents, and Superacids

1. $HClO_4$ ($K = 5 \times 10^{-6}$) $> H_2SO_4$ ($K = 2 \times 10^{-7}$) $>$ HCl (K $= 2 \times 10^{-9}$)

3. $NH_2^-(aq) + H_2O(\ell) \rightleftharpoons NH_3(aq) + OH^-(aq)$
The reaction is product-favored at equilibrium.

5. (a) $2\,NH_3 \rightleftharpoons NH_4^+ + NH_2^-$

      (b) The strongest acid is NH_4^+; the strongest base is NH_2^-.

      (c) HCl is a stronger acid than NH_4^+, so HCl will be completely ionized. The solution will be a strong conductor.

      (d) $O^{2-} + NH_3 \rightleftharpoons OH^- + NH_2^-$
The reaction is product-favored at equilibrium.

Chapter 18

18.1 (a) Decrease pH; (b) increase pH; (c) no change in pH

18.3 pH = 9.25

18.5 pH = 4.38

18.7 pH = 9.12; pH of buffer is lower than the pH of the original solution of NH_3(pH = 11.17).

18.9 4.7 g

18.11 pH = 4.92

18.13 (a) pH = 3.59; (b) $[HCO_2H]/[HCO_2^-]$ = 0.45

18.15 (b) $NH_3 + NH_4Cl$

18.17 The buffer must have a ratio of 0.51 mol NaH_2PO_4 to 1 mol Na_2HPO_4. For example, dissolve 0.51 mol NaH_2PO_4 (61 g) and 1.0 mol Na_2HPO_4 (140 g) in some amount of water.

18.19 (a) pH = 4.95; (b) pH = 5.05

18.21 (a) pH = 9.55; (b) pH = 9.50

18.23 (a) Original pH = 5.62

      (b) $[Na^+]$ = 0.0323 M, $[OH^-]$ = 1.5×10^{-3} M, $[H_3O^+]$ = 6.5×10^{-12} M, and $[C_6H_5O^-]$ = 0.0308 M

      (c) pH = 11.19

18.25 (a) Original NH_3 concentration = 0.0154 M

      (b) At the equivalence point $[H_3O^+]$ = 1.9×10^{-6} M, $[OH^-]$ = 5.3×10^{-9} M, $[NH_4^+]$ = 6.25×10^{-3} M.

      (c) pH at equivalence point = 5.73

18.27 The titration curve begins at pH = 13.00 and drops slowly as HCl is added. Just before the equivalence point (when 30.0 mL of acid has been added), the curve falls steeply. The pH at the equivalence point is exactly 7. Just after the equivalence point, the curve flattens again and begins to approach the final pH of just over 1.0. The total volume at the equivalence point is 60.0 mL.

18.29 (a) Starting pH = 11.12
(b) pH at equivalence point = 5.28
(c) pH at midpoint (half-neutralization point) = 9.25
(d) Methyl red, bromcresol green
(e)

Acid (mL)	Added pH
5.00	9.85
15.0	9.08
20.0	8.65
22.0	8.39
30.0	2.04

18.31 See Figure 18.10 on page 828.
(a) Thymol blue or bromphenol blue
(b) Phenolphthalein
(c) Methyl red; thymol blue

18.33 (a) Silver chloride, $AgCl$; lead(II) chloride, $PbCl_2$
(b) Zinc carbonate, $ZnCO_3$; zinc sulfide, ZnS
(c) Iron(II) carbonate, $FeCO_3$; iron(II) oxalate, FeC_2O_4

18.35 (a) and (b) are soluble, (c) and (d) are insoluble.

18.37 (a) $AgCN(s) \rightarrow Ag^+(aq) + CN^-(aq)$,
$K_{sp} = [Ag^+][CN^-]$
(b) $NiCO_3(s) \rightarrow Ni^{2+}(aq) + CO_3^{2-}(aq)$,
$K_{sp} = [Ni^{2+}][CO_3^{2-}]$
(c) $AuBr_3(s) \rightarrow Au^{3+}(aq) + 3\ Br^-(aq)$,
$K_{sp} = [Au^{3+}][Br^-]^3$

18.39 $K_{sp} = (1.9 \times 10^{-3})^2 = 3.6 \times 10^{-6}$

18.41 $K_{sp} = 4.37 \times 10^{-9}$

18.43 $K_{sp} = 1.4 \times 10^{-15}$

18.45 (a) 9.2×10^{-9} M; (b) 2.2×10^{-6} g/L

18.47 (a) 2.4×10^{-4} M; (b) 0.018 g/L

18.49 Only 2.1×10^{-4} g dissolves.

18.51 (a) $PbCl_2$; (b) FeS; (c) $Fe(OH)_2$

18.53 Solubility in pure water = 1.0×10^{-6} mol/L; solubility in 0.010 M SCN^- = 1.0×10^{-10} mol/L

18.55 (a) Solubility in pure water = 2.2×10^{-6} mg/mL
(b) Solubility in 0.020 M $AgNO_3$ = 1.0×10^{-12} mg/mL

18.57 (a) PbS
(b) Ag_2CO_3
(c) $Al(OH)_3$

18.59 $Q < K_{sp}$, so no precipitate forms.

18.61 $Q > K_{sp}$; $Zn(OH)_2$ will precipitate.

18.63 $[OH^-]$ must exceed 1.0×10^{-5} M.

18.65 Using K_{sp} for $Zn(OH)_2$ and K_f for $[Zn(OH)_4]^{2-}$, K_{net} for
$$Zn(OH)_2(s) + 2\ OH^-(aq) \rightleftharpoons [Zn(OH)_4]^{2-}(aq)$$
is 1×10^1. This indicates that the reaction is definitely product-favored.

18.67 K_{net} for $AgCl(s) + 2\ NH_3(aq) \rightleftharpoons [Ag(NH_3)_2]^+(aq) + Cl^-(aq)$ is 2.0×10^{-3}. When all the AgCl dissolves, $[Ag(NH_3)_2^+] = [Cl^-] = 0.050$ M. To achieve these concentrations, $[NH_3]$ must be 1.12 M. Therefore, the amount of NH_3 added must be 2×0.050 mol/L (to react with the AgCl) plus 1.12 mol/L (to achieve the proper equilibrium concentration). The total is 1.22 mol/L NH_3.

18.69 (a) Solubility in pure water = 1.3×10^{-5} mol/L or 0.0019 g/L.
(b) K_{net} for $AgCl(s) + 2\ NH_3(aq) \rightleftharpoons [Ag(NH_3)_2]^+(aq) + Cl^-(aq)$ is 2.0×10^{-3}. When using 1.0 M NH_3, the concentrations of species in solution are $[Ag(NH_3)_2]^+ = [Cl^-] = 0.041$ M and so $[NH_3] = 1.0 - 2(0.041)$ M or about 0.9 M. The amount of AgCl dissolved is 0.041 mol/L or 5.88 g/L.

18.71 (a) $NaBr(aq) + AgNO_3(aq) \rightarrow$
$NaNO_3(aq) + AgBr(s)$
(b) $2\ KCl(aq) + Pb(NO_3)_2(aq) \rightarrow$
$2\ KNO_3(aq) + PbCl_2(s)$

18.73 $Q > K_{sp}$, so $BaSO_4$ precipitates.

18.75 $[H_3O^+] = 1.9 \times 10^{-10}$ M; pH = 9.73

18.77 $BaCO_3 < Ag_2CO_3 < Na_2CO_3$

18.79 Original pH = 8.62; dilution will not affect the pH.

18.81 (a) 0.100 M acetic acid has a pH of 2.87. Adding sodium acetate slowly raises the pH.
(b) Adding $NaNO_3$ to 0.100 M HNO_3 has no effect on the pH.
(c) In part (a), adding the conjugate base of a weak acid creates a buffer solution. In part (b), HNO_3 is a strong acid, but its conjugate base (NO_3^-) is so weak that the base has no effect on the complete ionization of the acid.

18.83 (a) pH = 4.13
(b) 0.6 g of $C_6H_5CO_2H$
(c) 8.2 mL of 2.0 M HCl should be added

18.85 $K = 2.1 \times 10^6$; yes, AgI forms

18.87 (a) $[F^-] = 1.3 \times 10^{-3}$ M
(b) $[Ca^{2+}] = 2.9 \times 10^{-5}$ M

18.89 (a) $PbSO_4$ will precipitate first.
(b) $[Pb^{2+}] = 5.1 \times 10^{-6}$ M

18.91 When $[CO_3^{2-}] = 0.050$ M, $[Ca^{2+}] = 6.8 \times 10^{-8}$ M. This means only 6.8×10^{-4} % of the ions remain, or that essentially all of the calcium ions have been removed.

18.93 (a) Add H_2SO_4, precipitating $BaSO_4$ and leaving $Na^+(aq)$ in solution.
(b) Add HCl or another source of chloride ion. $PbCl_2$ will precipitate, but $NiCl_2$ is water-soluble.

18.95 (a) $BaSO_4$ will precipitate first.
(b) $[Ba^{2+}] = 1.8 \times 10^{-7}$ M

18.97 (a) pH = 2.81
(b) pH at equivalence point = 8.72
(c) pH at the midpoint = pK_a = 4.62
(d) Phenolphthalein
(e) After 10.0 mL, pH = 4.39.
After 20.0 mL, pH = 5.07.
After 30.0 mL, pH = 11.84.
(f) A plot of pH versus volume of NaOH added would begin at a pH of 2.81, rise slightly to the midpoint at pH = 4.62, and then begin to rise more steeply as the equivalence point is approached (when the volume of NaOH added is 27.0 mL). The pH rises vertically through the equivalence point, and then begins to level off above a pH of about 11.0.

18.99 The K_b value for ethylamine (4.27×10^{-4}) is found in Appendix I.
(a) pH = 11.89
(b) Midpoint pH = 10.63
(c) pH = 10.15
(d) pH = 5.93 at the equivalence point
(e) pH = 2.13
(f) Titration curve

(g) Alizarin or bromcresol purple (see Figure 18.10)

18.101 110 mL NaOH

18.103 Add dilute HCl, say 1 M HCl, to a solution of the salts. Both AgCl and $PbCl_2$ will precipitate, but Cu^{2+} ions will stay in solution (as $CuCl_2$ is water-soluble). Decant off the copper-containing solution to leave a precipitate of white AgCl and $PbCl_2$. Lead(II) chloride $(K_{sp} = 1.7 \times 10^{-5})$ is much more soluble than AgCl $(K_{sp} = 1.8 \times 10^{-10})$. Warming the precipitates in water will dissolve the $PbCl_2$ and leave the AgCl as a white solid.

18.105 $Cu(OH)_2$ will dissolve in a nonoxidizing acid such as HCl, whereas CuS will not.

18.107 When Ag_3PO_4 dissolves slightly, it produces a small concentration of the phosphate ion, PO_4^{3-}. This ion is a strong base and hydrolyzes to HPO_4^{2-}. As this reaction removes the PO_4^{3-} ion from equilibrium with Ag_3PO_4, the equilibrium shifts to the right, producing more PO_4^{3-} and Ag^+ ions. Thus, Ag_3PO_4 dissolves to a greater extent than might be calculated from a K_{sp} value (unless the K_{sp} value was actually determined experimentally).

18.109 (a) Base is added to increase the pH. The added base reacts with acetic acid to form more acetate ions in the mixture. Thus, the fraction of acid declines and the fraction of conjugate base rises (i.e., the ratio $[CH_3CO_2H]/[CH_3CO_2^-]$ decreases) as the pH rises.
(b) At pH = 4, acid predominates (85% acid and 15% acetate ions). At pH = 6, acetate ions predominate (95% acetate ions and 5% acid).
(c) At the point the lines cross, $[CH_3CO_2H]$ = $[CH_3CO_2^-]$. At this point pH = pK_a, so pK_a for acetic acid is 4.74.

18.111 (a) C—C—C angle, 120°; O—C=O, 120°; C—O—H, 109°; C—C—H, 120°
(b) Both the ring C atoms and the C in CO_2H are sp^2 hybridized.
(c) $K_a = 1 \times 10^{-3}$
(d) 10%
(e) pH at half-way point = pK_a = 3.0; pH at equivalence point = 7.3

Applying Chemical Principles: Everything That Glitters

1. 2.9×10^2 mL

3. $[Au^+] = 1.1 \times 10^{-38}$ M. Yes, the conclusion is reasonable; less than one free Au^+ ion is present per liter of solution.

5. $2 NaAu(CN)_2(aq) + Zn(s) \rightarrow 2 Au(s) + Na_2Zn(CN)_4(aq)$

Chapter 19

19.1 (a) For a given substance at a given temperature, a gas always has a greater entropy than the liquid. Matter and energy are more dispersed.
(b) Liquid water at 50 °C
(c) Ruby
(d) One mole of N_2 at 1 bar

19.3 (a) $\Delta_r S° = +12.7$ J/K · mol-rxn. Entropy increases.
(b) $\Delta_r S° = -102.55$ J/K · mol-rxn. Significant decrease in entropy.
(c) $\Delta_r S° = +93.3$ J/K · mol-rxn. Entropy increases.
(d) $\Delta_r S° = -129.7$ J/K · mol-rxn. The solution has a smaller entropy (with H^+ forming H_3O^+ and hydrogen bonding occurring) than HCl in the gaseous state.

19.5 (a) $\Delta_r S° = +9.3$ J/K · mol-rxn
(b) $\Delta_r S° = -293.97$ J/K · mol-rxn

19.7 (a) $\Delta_r S° = -507.3$ J/K · mol-rxn; entropy declines as a gaseous reactant is incorporated in a solid compound.
(b) $\Delta_r S° = +313.25$ J/K · mol-rxn; entropy increases as five molecules (three of them in the gas phase) form six molecules of products (all gases).

19.9 $\Delta S°$(system) $= -134.18$ J/K · mol-rxn; $\Delta H°$(system) $=$ -662.75 kJ/mol-rxn; $\Delta S°$(surroundings) $= +2222.9$ J/K · mol-rxn; $\Delta S°$(universe) $= +2088.7$ J/K · mol-rxn. The reaction is spontaneous under standard conditions.

19.11 $\Delta S°$(system) $= +163.3$ J/K · mol-rxn; $\Delta H°$(system) $=$ $+285.83$ kJ/mol-rxn; $\Delta S°$(surroundings) $= -958.68$ J/K · mol-rxn; $\Delta S°$(universe) $= -795.4$ J/K · mol-rxn

The reaction is not spontaneous because the overall entropy change in the universe is negative. The reaction is disfavored by energy dispersal.

19.13 (a) Type 2. The reaction is enthalpy-favored but entropy-disfavored. It is more favorable at low temperatures.
(b) Type 4. This endothermic reaction is not favored by the enthalpy change nor is it favored by the entropy change. It is not spontaneous under standard conditions at any temperature.

19.15 (a) $\Delta_r H° = -438$ kJ/mol-rxn; $\Delta_r S° = -201.7$ J/K · mol-rxn; $\Delta_r G° = -378$ kJ/mol-rxn. The reaction is product-favored at equilibrium and is enthalpy-driven.
(b) $\Delta_r H° = -86.61$ kJ/mol-rxn; $\Delta_r S° = -79.4$ J/K · mol-rxn; $\Delta_r G° = -62.9$ kJ/mol-rxn. The reaction is product-favored at equilibrium. The enthalpy change favors the reaction.

19.17 (a) $\Delta_r H° = +116.7$ kJ/mol-rxn; $\Delta_r S° = +168.0$ J/K · mol-rxn; $\Delta_f G° = +66.6$ kJ/mol
(b) $\Delta_r H° = -425.93$ kJ/mol-rxn; $\Delta_r S° = -154.6$ J/K · mol-rxn; $\Delta_f G° = -379.82$ kJ/mol
(c) $\Delta_r H° = +17.51$ kJ/mol-rxn; $\Delta_r S° = +77.95$ J/K · mol-rxn; $\Delta_f G° = -5.73$ kJ/mol

The reactions in (b) and (c) are predicted to be spontaneous under standard conditions.

19.19 (a) $\Delta_r G° = -817.54$ kJ/mol-rxn; product-favored
(b) $\Delta_r G° = +256.6$ kJ/mol-rxn; reactant-favored
(c) $\Delta_r G° = -1101.14$ kJ/mol-rxn; product-favored

19.21 $\Delta_f G°$ [$BaCO_3(s)$] $= -1134.4$ kJ/mol

19.23 (a) $\Delta_r H° = +66.2$ kJ/mol-rxn; $\Delta_r S° = -121.62$ J/K · mol-rxn; $\Delta_r G° = +102.5$ kJ/mol-rxn

Both the enthalpy and the entropy changes indicate the reaction is not spontaneous. There is no temperature at which it will become spontaneous. This is a case like that in the right panel in Figure 19.11 and is a Type 4 reaction (Table 19.1). As the temperature increases, the reaction becomes even more reactant-favored (the value of $\Delta_r G°$ becomes more positive).
(b) $\Delta_r H° = -221.05$ kJ/mol-rxn; $\Delta_r S° = +179.1$ J/K · mol-rxn; $\Delta_r G° = -283.99$ kJ/mol-rxn

The reaction is favored by both enthalpy and entropy and is product-favored at all temperatures. This is a case like that in the left panel in Figure 19.11 and is a Type 1 reaction. As the temperature increases, the reaction becomes even more product-favored (the value of $\Delta_r G°$ becomes more negative).

(c) $\Delta_r H° = -179.0$ kJ/mol-rxn; $\Delta_r S° = -160.2$ J/K · mol-rxn; $\Delta_r G° = -131.4$ kJ/mol-rxn

The reaction is favored by the enthalpy change but disfavored by the entropy change. The reaction becomes less product-favored as the temperature increases; it is a case like the line with a negative slope in the middle panel of Figure 19.11.
(d) $\Delta_r H° = +822.2$ kJ/mol-rxn; $\Delta_r S° = +181.28$ J/K · mol-rxn; $\Delta_r G° = +768.08$ kJ/mol-rxn

The reaction is not favored by the enthalpy change but favored by the entropy change. The reaction becomes more product-favored as the temperature increases; it is a case like the line with a positive slope in the middle panel of Figure 19.11.

19.25 (a) $\Delta_r S° = +174.75$ J/K · mol-rxn; $\Delta_r H° = +116.94$ kJ/mol-rxn
(b) $\Delta_r G° = +64.87$ kJ/mol-rxn. The reaction is not spontaneous under standard conditions at 298 K.
(c) As the temperature increases, $\Delta_r S°$ becomes more important, so $\Delta_r G°$ can become negative at a sufficiently high temperature.

19.27 $K = 6.8 \times 10^{-16}$. Note that K is very small and that $\Delta G°$ is positive. Both indicate a process that is reactant-favored at equilibrium.

19.29 $\Delta_r G° = -100.24$ kJ/mol-rxn and $K_p = 3.6 \times 10^{17}$. Both the free energy change and K indicate a process that is product-favored at equilibrium.

19.31 (a) $HBr(g)$
(b) $NH_4Cl(aq)$
(c) $C_2H_4(g)$
(d) $NaCl(g)$

19.33 $\Delta_r G° = -98.9$ kJ/mol-rxn. The reaction is spontaneous under standard conditions and therefore product-favored at equilibrium. It is enthalpy-driven.

19.35 $\Delta_r H° = -1428.66$ kJ/mol-rxn; $\Delta_r S° = +47.1$ J/K · mol-rxn; $\Delta S°$(universe) $= +4840$ J/K · mol-rxn. Combustion reactions are spontaneous, and this is confirmed by the sign of $\Delta S°$(universe).

19.37 (a) The reaction occurs spontaneously and is product-favored. Therefore, $\Delta S°$(universe) is positive and $\Delta_r G°$ is negative. The reaction is likely to be exothermic, so $\Delta_r H°$ is negative, and $\Delta S°$(surroundings) is positive. $\Delta S°$(system) is expected to be negative because two moles of gas form one mole of solid. The calculated values are as follows:

$\Delta S°$(system) $= -284.2$ J/K · mol-rxn

$\Delta_r H° = -176.34$ kJ/mol-rxn

$\Delta S°$(surroundings) $= +591.45$ J/K · mol-rxn

$\Delta S°$(universe) $= +307.3$ J/K · mol-rxn

$\Delta_r G° = -91.64$ kJ/mol-rxn
(b) $K_p = 1.2 \times 10^{16}$

19.39 $K_p = 1.3 \times 10^{29}$ at 298 K ($\Delta G° = -166.1$ kJ/mol-rxn). The reaction is already extremely product-favored at 298 K. A higher temperature would make the reaction less product-favored because $\Delta_r S°$ has a negative value (-242.3 J/K · mol-rxn).

19.41 At the boiling point, $\Delta G° = 0 = \Delta H° - T\Delta S°$.

Here $\Delta S° = \Delta H°/T = 112$ J/K · mol-rxn at 351.15 K.

19.43 $\Delta_r S°$ is $+137.2$ J/K · mol-rxn. A positive entropy change means that raising the temperature will increase the product favorability of the reaction (because $T\Delta S°$ will become more negative).

19.45 The reaction is exothermic, so $\Delta_r H°$ should be negative. Also, a gas and an aqueous solution are formed, so $\Delta_r S°$ should be positive. The calculated values are $\Delta_r H° = -183.32$ kJ/mol-rxn (with a negative sign as expected) and $\Delta_r S° = -7.7$ J/K · mol-rxn

The entropy change is slightly negative, not positive as predicted. The reason for this is the negative entropy change upon dissolving NaOH. Apparently the OH^- ions in water hydrogen-bond with water molecules, an effect that also leads to a small, negative entropy change.

19.47 $\Delta_r H° = +126.03$ kJ/mol-rxn; $\Delta_r S° = +78.2$ J/K · mol-rxn; and $\Delta_r G° = +103$ kJ/mol-rxn. The reaction is not predicted to be spontaneous under standard conditions and therefore is not product-favored at equilibrium.

19.49 $\Delta_r G°$ from K value = 4.87 kJ/mol-rxn

$\Delta_r G°$ from free energies of formation = 4.73 kJ/mol-rxn

19.51 $\Delta_r G° = -2.27$ kJ/mol-rxn

19.53 (a) $\Delta_r G° = +141.82$ kJ/mol-rxn, so the reaction is not spontaneous.
(b) $\Delta_r H° = +197.86$ kJ/mol-rxn; $\Delta_r S° = +187.95$ J/K · mol-rxn

$T = \Delta_r H°/\Delta_r S° = 1052.7$ K or 779.6 °C
(c) $\Delta_r G°$ at 1500 °C (1773 K) = -135.4 kJ/mol-rxn

K_p at 1500 °C = 1×10^4

19.55 $\Delta_r S° = -459.0$ J/K · mol-rxn; $\Delta_r H° = -793$ kJ/mol-rxn;

$\Delta_r G° = -657$ kJ/mol-rxn

The reaction is spontaneous under standard conditions and therefore product-favored at equilibrium. It is enthalpy-driven.

19.57 (a) $\Delta_r G°$ at 80.0 °C = $+0.14$ kJ/mol-rxn

$\Delta_r G°$ at 110.0 °C = -0.12 kJ/mol-rxn

Rhombic sulfur is more stable than monoclinic sulfur at 80 °C, but the reverse is true at 110 °C.
(b) $T = 370$ K or about 96 °C. This is the temperature at which the two forms are at equilibrium under standard conditions.

19.59 $\Delta_r G°$ at 298 K = 22.64 kJ/mol; reaction is not product-favored at equilibrium.

It does become product-favored above 469 K (196 °C).

19.61 $\Delta_f G°$ [HI(g)] = -10.9 kJ/mol

19.63 (a) $\Delta_r G° = +194.8$ kJ/mol-rxn and $K = 6.68 \times 10^{-11}$
(b) The reaction is not spontaneous under standard conditions at 727 °C; it is reactant-favored at equilibrium.
(c) Keep the pressure of CO as low as possible (by removing it during the course of the reaction).

19.65 $K_p = P_{Hg(g)}$ at any temperature

$K_p = 1$ at 620.3 K or 347.2 °C when $P_{Hg(g)} = 1.000$ bar

T when $P_{Hg(g)} = (1/760)$ bar is 398.3 K or 125.2 °C.

19.67 (a) True
(b) False. Whether an exothermic system is spontaneous also depends on the entropy change for the system.
(c) False. Reactions with $+\Delta_r H°$ and $+\Delta_r S°$ are spontaneous at higher temperatures.
(d) True

19.69 Dissolving a solid such as NaCl in water is a spontaneous process. Thus, $\Delta G° < 0$. If $\Delta H° = 0$, then the only way the free energy change can be negative is if $\Delta S°$ is positive. Generally the entropy change is the important factor in forming a solution.

19.71 $2\ C_2H_6(g) + 7\ O_2(g) \rightarrow 4\ CO_2(g) + 6\ H_2O(g)$
(a) Not only is this an exothermic combustion reaction, but there is also an increase in the number of molecules of gases from reactants to products. Therefore, we would predict a positive value for $\Delta S°$ for both the system and the surroundings and thus for the universe as well.
(b) The exothermic reaction has $\Delta_r H° < 0$. Combined with a positive $\Delta S°$(system), the value of $\Delta_r G°$ is negative.
(c) The value of K_p is likely to be much greater than 1. Further, because $\Delta S°$(system) is positive, the value of K_p will be even larger at a higher temperature. (See the left panel of Figure 19.11.)

19.73 Reaction 1: $\Delta_r S_1° = -80.7$ J/K · mol-rxn

Reaction 2: $\Delta_r S_2° = -161.60$ J/K · mol-rxn

Reaction 3: $\Delta_r S_3° = -242.3$ J/K · mol-rxn

$\Delta_r S_1° + \Delta_r S_2° = \Delta_r S_3°$; entropy is a state function.

19.75 (a) $\Delta_r H° = -352.88$ kJ/mol-rxn and $\Delta_r S° = +21.31$ J/K · mol-rxn. Therefore, at 298 K, $\Delta_r G° = -359.23$ kJ/mol-rxn.
(b) 4.84 g of Mg is required.

19.77 (a) $N_2H_4(\ell) + O_2(g) \rightarrow 2\ H_2O(\ell) + N_2(g)$

O_2 is the oxidizing agent and N_2H_4 is the reducing agent.

(b) $\Delta_r H° = -622.29$ kJ/mol-rxn and $\Delta_r S° = +4.87$ J/K · mol-rxn. Therefore, at 298 K, $\Delta_r G° = -623.77$ kJ/mol-rxn.

(c) 0.0027 K

(d) 7.5 mol O_2

(e) 4.8×10^3 g solution

(f) 7.5 mol $N_2(g)$ occupies 170 L at 273 K and 1.0 atm of pressure.

19.79 Iodine dissolves readily, so the process is spontaneous and $\Delta G°$ must be less than zero. Because $\Delta H° = 0$, the process is entropy-driven.

19.81 $CH_3OH(g) \rightarrow C(s,\ \text{graphite}) + 2\ H_2(g) + 1/2\ O_2(g)$

(a) The spontaneity increases as temperature increases.

(b) There is no temperature between 400 K and 1000 K at which the decomposition is spontaneous.

19.83 (a, b)

Temperature (K)	$\Delta_r G°$ (kJ/mol)	K
298.0 K	−32.74	5.5×10^5
800.0 K	+72.9	2×10^{-5}
1300. K	+184.0	4.0×10^{-8}

(c) The largest mole fraction of NH_3 in an equilibrium mixture will be at 298 K.

Applying Chemical Principles: Are Diamonds Forever?

1. $C(\text{diamond}) \rightarrow C(\text{graphite})$

(a) $\Delta_r G° = -2.900$ kJ/mol-rxn; $K = 3.22$

(b) $\Delta_r H° = -1.8$ kJ/mol-rxn; $\Delta_r S° = 3.2$ J/K · mol-rxn $= 0.0032$ kJ/K · mol; $\Delta_r G° = -5.0$ kJ/mol-rxn; $K = 1.8$

Though still favoring graphite, the equilibrium has shifted more toward diamond.

(c) Greater pressures favor the formation of diamond, which is more dense than graphite.

(d) The rate of reaction is negligibly slow at room temperature.

Chapter 20

20.1 (a) $Cr(s) \rightarrow Cr^{3+}(aq) + 3\ e^-$

Cr is a reducing agent; this is an oxidation reaction.

(b) $AsH_3(g) \rightarrow As(s) + 3\ H^+(aq) + 3\ e^-$

AsH_3 is a reducing agent; this is an oxidation reaction.

(c) $VO_3^-(aq) + 6\ H^+(aq) + 3\ e^- \rightarrow$
$$V^{2+}(aq) + 3\ H_2O(\ell)$$

$VO_3^-(aq)$ is an oxidizing agent; this is a reduction reaction.

(d) $2\ Ag(s) + 2\ OH^-(aq) \rightarrow$
$$Ag_2O(s) + H_2O(\ell) + 2e^-$$

Silver is a reducing agent; this is an oxidation reaction.

20.3 (a) $Ag(s) \rightarrow Ag^+(aq) + e^-$

$e^- + NO_3^-(aq) + 2\ H^+(aq) \rightarrow NO_2(g) + H_2O(\ell)$

$Ag(s) + NO_3^-(aq) + 2\ H^+(aq) \rightarrow$
$$Ag^+(aq) + NO_2(g) + H_2O(\ell)$$

(b) $2[MnO_4^-(aq) + 8\ H^+(aq) + 5\ e^- \rightarrow$
$$Mn^{2+}(aq) + 4\ H_2O(\ell)]$$

$5[HSO_3^-(aq) + H_2O(\ell) \rightarrow$
$$SO_4^{2-}(aq) + 3\ H^+(aq) + 2\ e^-]$$

$2\ MnO_4^-(aq) + H^+(aq) + 5\ HSO_3^-(aq) \rightarrow$
$$2\ Mn^{2+}(aq) + 3\ H_2O(\ell) + 5\ SO_4^{2-}(aq)$$

(c) $4[Zn(s) \rightarrow Zn^{2+}(aq) + 2\ e^-]$

$2\ NO_3^-(aq) + 10\ H^+(aq) + 8\ e^- \rightarrow$
$$N_2O(g) + 5\ H_2O(\ell)$$

$4\ Zn(s) + 2\ NO_3^-(aq) + 10\ H^+(aq) \rightarrow$
$$4\ Zn^{2+}(aq) + N_2O(g) + 5\ H_2O(\ell)$$

(d) $Cr(s) \rightarrow Cr^{3+}(aq) + 3\ e^-$

$3\ e^- + NO_3^-(aq) + 4\ H^+(aq) \rightarrow$
$$NO(g) + 2\ H_2O(\ell)$$

$Cr(s) + NO_3^-(aq) + 4\ H^+(aq) \rightarrow$
$$Cr^{3+}(aq) + NO(g) + 2\ H_2O(\ell)$$

20.5 (a) $2[Al(s) + 4\ OH^-(aq) \rightarrow Al(OH)_4^-(aq) + 3\ e^-]$

$3[2\ H_2O(\ell) + 2\ e^- \rightarrow H_2(g) + 2\ OH^-(aq)]$

$2\ Al(s) + 2\ OH^-(aq) + 6\ H_2O(\ell) \rightarrow$
$$2\ Al(OH)_4^-(aq) + 3\ H_2(g)$$

(b) $2[CrO_4^{2-}(aq) + 4\ H_2O(\ell) + 3\ e^- \rightarrow$
$$Cr(OH)_3(s) + 5\ OH^-(aq)]$$

$3[SO_3^{2-}(aq) + 2\ OH^-(aq) \rightarrow$
$$SO_4^{2-}(aq) + H_2O(\ell) + 2\ e^-]$$

$2\ CrO_4^{2-}(aq) + 3\ SO_3^{2-}(aq) + 5\ H_2O(\ell) \rightarrow$
$$2\ Cr(OH)_3(s) + 3\ SO_4^{2-}(aq) + 4\ OH^-(aq)$$

(c) $Zn(s) + 4\ OH^-(aq) \rightarrow [Zn(OH)_4]^{2-}(aq) + 2\ e^-$
$Cu(OH)_2(s) + 2\ e^- \rightarrow Cu(s) + 2\ OH^-(aq)$

$Zn(s) + 2\ OH^-(aq) + Cu(OH)_2(s) \rightarrow$
$\qquad\qquad [Zn(OH)_4]^{2-}(aq) + Cu(s)$

(d) $3[HS^-(aq) + OH^-(aq) \rightarrow S(s) + H_2O(\ell) + 2\ e^-]$
$ClO_3^-(aq) + 3\ H_2O(\ell) + 6\ e^- \rightarrow$
$\qquad\qquad Cl^-(aq) + 6\ OH^-(aq)$

$3\ HS^-(aq) + ClO_3^-(aq) \rightarrow$
$\qquad\qquad 3\ S(s) + Cl^-(aq) + 3\ OH^-(aq)$

20.7 Electrons flow from the Cr electrode to the Fe electrode. Negative ions move via the salt bridge from the Fe/Fe^{2+} half-cell to the Cr/Cr^{3+} half-cell (and positive ions move in the opposite direction).

Anode (oxidation): $Cr(s) \rightarrow Cr^{3+}(aq) + 3\ e^-$

Cathode (reduction): $Fe^{2+}(aq) + 2\ e^- \rightarrow Fe(s)$

20.9 (a) Oxidation: $Fe(s) \rightarrow Fe^{2+}(aq) + 2\ e^-$
Reduction: $O_2(g) + 4\ H^+(aq) + 4\ e^- \rightarrow 2\ H_2O(\ell)$
Overall: $2\ Fe(s) + O_2(g) + 4\ H^+(aq) \rightarrow$
$\qquad\qquad 2\ Fe^{2+}(aq) + 2\ H_2O(\ell)$
(b) Anode, oxidation: $Fe(s) \rightarrow Fe^{2+}(aq) + 2\ e^-$
Cathode, reduction: $O_2(g) + 4\ H^+(aq) + 4\ e^- \rightarrow$
$\qquad\qquad 2\ H_2O(\ell)$
(c) Electrons flow from the negative anode (Fe) to the positive cathode (site of the O$_2$ half-reaction). Negative ions move through the salt bridge from the cathode compartment in which the O$_2$ reduction occurs to the anode compartment in which Fe oxidation occurs (and positive ions move in the opposite direction).

20.11 (a) All are primary batteries, not rechargeable.
(b) Dry cells and alkaline batteries have Zn anodes and are primary batteries. Ni-Cd batteries have a cadmium anode and are rechargeable.
(c) Dry cells have an acidic environment, whereas the environment is alkaline for alkaline and Ni-Cd cells.

20.13 (a) $E^\circ_{cell} = -1.298$ V; not product-favored
(b) $E^\circ_{cell} = -0.51$ V; not product-favored
(c) $E^\circ_{cell} = -1.023$ V; not product-favored
(d) $E^\circ_{cell} = +0.028$ V; product-favored

20.15 (a) $Sn^{2+}(aq) + 2\ Ag(s) \rightarrow Sn(s) + 2\ Ag^+(aq)$
$E^\circ_{cell} = -0.94$ V; not product-favored
(b) $3\ Sn^{4+}(aq) + 2\ Al(s) \rightarrow 3\ Sn^{2+}(aq) + 2\ Al^{3+}(aq)$
$E^\circ_{cell} = +1.81$ V; product-favored
(c) $2\ ClO_3^-(aq) + 10\ Ce^{3+}(aq) + 12\ H^+(aq) \rightarrow$
$\qquad\qquad Cl_2(aq) + 10\ Ce^{4+}(aq) + 6\ H_2O(\ell)$
$E^\circ_{cell} = -0.14$ V; not product-favored
(d) $3\ Cu(s) + 2\ NO_3^-(aq) + 8\ H^+(aq) \rightarrow$
$\qquad\qquad 3\ Cu^{2+}(aq) + 2\ NO(g) + 4\ H_2O(\ell)$
$E^\circ_{cell} = +0.62$ V; product-favored

20.17 (a) Al
(b) Zn and Al
(c) $Fe^{2+}(aq) + Sn(s) \rightarrow Fe(s) + Sn^{2+}(aq)$; reactant-favored
(d) $Zn^{2+}(aq) + Sn(s) \rightarrow Zn(s) + Sn^{2+}(aq)$; reactant-favored

20.19 Best reducing agent, Cr(s) (Use Appendix M.)

20.21 Ag$^+$

20.23 See Example 20.5
(a) F$_2$, most readily reduced
(b) F$_2$ and Cl$_2$

20.25 $E^\circ_{cell} = +0.3923$ V. When $[Zn(OH)_4^{2-}] = [OH^-] = 0.025$ M and $P(H_2) = 1.0$ bar, $E_{cell} = 0.345$ V.

20.27 $E^\circ_{cell} = +1.563$ V and $E_{cell} = +1.58$ V

20.29 $E^\circ_{cell} = +1.563$ V. When $E_{cell} = 1.48$ V, $n = 2$, and $[Zn^{2+}] = 1.0$ M, the concentration of Ag$^+$ = 0.040 M.

20.31 (a) $\Delta_r G^\circ = -29.0$ kJ; $K = 1 \times 10^5$
(b) $\Delta_r G^\circ = +89$ kJ; $K = 3 \times 10^{-16}$

20.33 E°_{cell} for $AgBr(s) \rightarrow Ag^+(aq) + Br^-(aq)$ is -0.7281.
$K_{sp} = 4.9 \times 10^{-13}$

20.35 $K_{formation} = 2 \times 10^{25}$

20.37 See Figure 20.19. Electrons from the battery or other source enter the cathode where they are transferred to Na$^+$ ions, reducing the ions to Na metal. Chloride ions move toward the positively charged anode where an electron is transferred from each Cl$^-$ ion, and Cl$_2$ gas is formed.

20.39 O$_2$ from the oxidation of water is more likely than F$_2$. See Example 20.10.

20.41 See Example 20.10.
(a) Cathode: $2\ H_2O(\ell) + 2\ e^- \rightarrow H_2(g) + 2\ OH^-(aq)$
(b) Anode: $2\ Br^-(aq) \rightarrow Br_2(\ell) + 2\ e^-$

20.43 Mass of Ni = 0.0334 g

20.45 Time = 2300 s or 38 min

20.47 Time = 250 h

20.49 (a) $UO_2^+(aq) + 4\ H^+(aq) + e^- \rightarrow$
$\qquad\qquad U^{4+}(aq) + 2\ H_2O(\ell)$
(b) $ClO_3^-(aq) + 6\ H^+(aq) + 6\ e^- \rightarrow$
$\qquad\qquad Cl^-(aq) + 3\ H_2O(\ell)$
(c) $N_2H_4(aq) + 4\ OH^-(aq) \rightarrow$
$\qquad\qquad N_2(g) + 4\ H_2O(\ell) + 4\ e^-$
(d) $ClO^-(aq) + H_2O(\ell) + 2\ e^- \rightarrow$
$\qquad\qquad Cl^-(aq) + 2\ OH^-(aq)$

20.51 (a, c) The electrode at the right is a magnesium anode. (Magnesium metal supplies electrons and is oxidized to Mg^{2+} ions.) Electrons pass through the wire to the silver cathode, where Ag^+ ions are reduced to silver metal. Nitrate ions move via the salt bridge from the $AgNO_3$ solution to the $Mg(NO_3)_2$ solution (and Na^+ ions move in the opposite direction). A salt bridge is needed to maintain electrical neutrality in each half-cell and to complete the electrical circuit.

(b) Anode: $Mg(s) \rightarrow Mg^{2+}(aq) + 2 e^-$

Cathode: $Ag^+(aq) + e^- \rightarrow Ag(s)$

Net reaction: $Mg(s) + 2 Ag^+(aq) \rightarrow$
$$Mg^{2+}(aq) + 2 Ag(s)$$

20.53 (a) For 1.7 V:
Use chromium as the anode to reduce $Ag^+(aq)$ to $Ag(s)$ at the cathode. The cell potential is $+1.71$ V.

(b) For 0.5 V:
(i) Use copper as the anode to reduce silver ions to silver metal at the cathode. The cell potential is $+0.46$ V.
(ii) Use silver as the anode to reduce chlorine to chloride ions. The cell potential would be $+0.56$ V. (In practice, this setup is not likely to work well because the product would be insoluble silver chloride.)

20.55 (a) $Zn^{2+}(aq)$ (c) $Zn(s)$
(b) $Au^+(aq)$ (d) $Au(s)$
(e) Yes, $Sn(s)$ will reduce Cu^{2+}.
(f) No, $Ag(s)$ can only reduce $Au^+(aq)$.
(g) Cu^{2+}, Ag^+ and Au^+
(h) $Ag^+(aq)$ can oxidize Cu, Sn, Co, and Zn.

20.57 (a) The cathode is the site of reduction, so the half-reaction must be $2 H^+(aq) + 2 e^- \rightarrow H_2(g)$. This is the case with the following half-reactions: $Cr^{3+}(aq)|Cr(s)$, $Fe^{2+}(aq)|Fe(s)$, and $Mg^{2+}(aq)|Mg(s)$.
(b) Choosing from the half-cells in part (a), the reaction of $Mg(s)$ and $H^+(aq)$ would produce the most positive potential (2.37 V), and the reaction of H_2 with Cu^{2+} would produce the least positive potential ($+0.337$ V).

20.59 8.1×10^5 g Al

20.61 (a) $E°_{anode} = -0.268$ V
(b) $K_{sp} = 2 \times 10^{-5}$

20.63 $\Delta_r G° = -409$ kJ

20.65 6700 kWh; 820 kg Na; 1300 kg Cl_2

20.67 Ru^{2+}, $Ru(NO_3)_2$

20.69 9.5×10^6 g Cl_2 per day

20.71 Anode: $2 H_2O(\ell) \rightarrow O_2(g) + 4 H^+(aq) + 4 e^-$
Cathode: $Cu^{2+}(aq) + 2 e^- \rightarrow Cu(s)$

20.73 The rate of the reaction with H_2O is more rapid than the rate of the reaction with NO_3^-.
Products formed at anode: $O_2(g)$ and $H^+(aq)$
Anode half-reaction: $2 H_2O(\ell) \rightarrow$
$$O_2(g) + 4 H^+(aq) + 4 e^-$$

20.75 Under standard conditions, the spontaneous reaction is $Hg^{2+}(aq) + 2 Fe^{2+}(aq) \rightarrow Hg(\ell) + 2 Fe^{3+}(aq)$ with $E° = 0.084$ V.

Under the conditions present, $E = -0.244$ V. The reaction is not spontaneous in the same direction as under standard conditions but in the opposite direction: $Hg(\ell) + 2 Fe^{3+}(aq) \rightarrow Hg^{2+}(aq) + 2 Fe^{2+}(aq)$. Under these conditions, the anode for the spontaneous reaction is the $Hg(\ell)|Hg^{2+}(aq, 0.020 M)$ electrode and the measured voltage will be 0.244 V.

20.77 $E° = 0.771$ V. When $[H^+] = 1.0 \times 10^{-7}$ M, $E = 1.185$ V. The reaction is more favorable at a lower $[H^+]$ (higher pH). The reaction is thus less favorable at lower pH.

20.79 (a) See Figure 20.5
In this case, both electrodes are made of silver metal. On one side, the solution contains 1.0×10^{-5} M Ag^+ and on the other the solution contains 1.0 M Ag^+. The cathode is the electrode on the side that has the 1.0 M Ag^+ solution [half-reaction: $Ag^+(aq) + e^- \rightarrow Ag(s)$], and the anode is the electrode on the side that has the 1.0×10^{-5} M Ag^+ solution [half-reaction: $Ag(s) \rightarrow Ag^+(aq) + e^-$). Connecting the two electrodes is a wire. Electrons flow through the wire from the anode to the cathode. A salt bridge also connects the two compartments.
(b) $E = 0.30$ V

20.81 (a) $K = 3.4 \times 10^{-10}$; reactant-favored at equilibrium
(b) $K = 3.0$; product-favored at equilibrium

20.83 (a) $\Delta_r G° = -3.6 \times 10^2$ kJ/mol-rxn
(b) $\Delta_r G° = -79$ kJ/mol-rxn

20.85 (a) $2[Ag^+(aq) + e^- \rightarrow Ag(s)]$
$C_6H_5CHO(aq) + H_2O(\ell) \rightarrow$
$$C_6H_5CO_2H(aq) + 2 H^+(aq) + 2 e^-$$

$2Ag^+(aq) + C_6H_5CHO(aq) + H_2O(\ell) \rightarrow$
$$C_6H_5CO_2H(aq) + 2 H^+(aq) + 2 Ag(s)$$

(b) $3[CH_3CH_2OH(aq) + H_2O(\ell) \rightarrow$
$$CH_3CO_2H(aq) + 4 H^+(aq) + 4 e^-]$$
$2[Cr_2O_7^{2-}(aq) + 14 H^+(aq) + 6 e^- \rightarrow$
$$2 Cr^{3+}(aq) + 7 H_2O(\ell)]$$

$3 CH_3CH_2OH(aq) +$
$$2 Cr_2O_7^{2-}(aq) + 16 H^+(aq) \rightarrow$$
$$3 CH_3CO_2H(aq) + 4 Cr^{3+}(aq) + 11 H_2O(\ell)$$

20.87 (a) 0.974 kJ/g
(b) 0.60 kJ/g
(c) The silver-zinc battery produces more energy per gram of reactants.

20.89 (a) $2 NO_3^-(aq) + 3 Mn^{2+}(aq) + 2 H_2O(\ell) \rightarrow$
$$2 NO(g) + 3 MnO_2(s) + 4 H^+(aq)$$
$3 MnO_2(s) + 4 H^+(aq) + 2 NH_4^+(aq) \rightarrow$
$$N_2(g) + 3 Mn^{2+}(aq) + 6 H_2O(\ell)$$
(b) $E°$ for reduction of NO_3^- with Mn^{2+} is -0.27 V.
$E°$ for oxidation of NH_4^+ with MnO_2 is $+1.50$ V.

20.91 (a) $Fe^{2+}(aq) + 2 e^- \rightarrow Fe(s)$
$2[Fe^{2+}(aq) \rightarrow Fe^{3+}(aq) + e^-]$
$3 Fe^{2+}(aq) \rightarrow Fe(s) + 2 Fe^{3+}(aq)$
(b) $E°_{cell} = -1.21$ V; not product-favored
(c) $K = 1 \times 10^{-41}$

20.93 (a)

wire

(b) Anode: $Cd(s) \rightarrow Cd^{2+}(aq) + 2 e^-$
Cathode: $Ni^{2+}(aq) + 2 e^- \rightarrow Ni(s)$
Net: $Cd(s) + Ni^{2+}(aq) \rightarrow Cd^{2+}(aq) + Ni(s)$
(c) The anode is negative and the cathode is positive.
(d) $E°_{cell} = E°_{cathode} - E°_{anode} =$
$(-0.25$ V$) - (-0.40$ V$) = +0.15$ V
(e) Electrons flow from anode (Cd) to cathode (Ni).
(f) Positive ions move from the anode compartment to the cathode compartment. Anions move in the opposite direction.
(g) $K = 1 \times 10^5$
(h) $E_{cell} = 0.21$ V; yes, the net reaction is still the same.
(i) 480 h

20.95 0.054 g Au

20.97 I^- is the strongest reducing agent of the three halide ions. Iodide ion reduces Cu^{2+} to Cu^+, forming insoluble $CuI(s)$.
$2 Cu^{2+}(aq) + 4 I^-(aq) \rightarrow 2 CuI(s) + I_2(aq)$

20.99 (a) 92 g HF required; 230 g CF_3SO_2F and 9.3 g H_2 isolated
(b) H_2 is produced at the cathode.
(c) 48 kWh

20.101 290 h

20.103 (a) 3.6 mol glucose and 22 mol O_2
(b) 86 mol electrons
(c) 96 amps
(d) 96 watts

Applying Chemical Principles: Sacrifice!

1. An insulator will prevent the flow of electrons from the zinc to copper, preventing zinc from keeping the copper reduced.

3. (e) chromium

5. (a) $Cu(OH)_2(s) + 2 e^- \rightarrow Cu(s) + 2 OH^-(aq)$
(b) $Zn(s) + 2 OH^-(aq) \rightarrow Zn(OH)_2(s) + 2 e^-$
(c) $Cu(OH)_2(s) + Zn(s) \rightarrow Cu(s) + Zn(OH)_2(s)$
(d) $E = 0.89$ V

Chapter 21

21.1 $4 Li(s) + O_2(g) \rightarrow 2 Li_2O(s)$
$Li_2O(s) + H_2O(\ell) \rightarrow 2 LiOH(aq)$
$2 Ca(s) + O_2(g) \rightarrow 2 CaO(s)$
$CaO(s) + H_2O(\ell) \rightarrow Ca(OH)_2(s)$

21.3 These are the elements of Group 3A: boron, B; aluminum, Al; gallium, Ga; indium, In; and thallium, Tl.

21.5 $2 Na(s) + Cl_2(g) \rightarrow 2 NaCl(s)$
The reaction is exothermic and the product is ionic. See Figure 1.2.

21.7 The product, NaCl, is a colorless solid and is soluble in water. Other alkali metal chlorides have similar properties.

21.9 Calcium will not exist in the earth's crust because the metal reacts with water.

21.11 Increasing basicity: $CO_2 < SiO_2 < SnO_2$

21.13 (a) $2 Na(s) + Br_2(\ell) \rightarrow 2 NaBr(s)$
(b) $2 Mg(s) + O_2(g) \rightarrow 2 MgO(s)$
(c) $2 Al(s) + 3 F_2(g) \rightarrow 2 AlF_3(s)$
(d) $C(s) + O_2(g) \rightarrow CO_2(g)$

21.15 $2 H_2(g) + O_2(g) \rightarrow 2 H_2O(g)$
$H_2(g) + Cl_2(g) \rightarrow 2 HCl(g)$
$3 H_2(g) + N_2(g) \rightarrow 2 NH_3(g)$

21.17 $CH_4(g) + H_2O(g) \rightarrow CO(g) + 3 H_2(g)$
$\Delta_r H° = +206.2$ kJ; $\Delta_r S° = +214.7$ J/K; $\Delta_r G° = +142.2$ kJ (at 298 K).

21.19 Step 1: $2 SO_2(g) + 4 H_2O(\ell) + 2 I_2(s) \rightarrow$
$2 H_2SO_4(\ell) + 4 HI(g)$
Step 2: $2 H_2SO_4(\ell) \rightarrow$
$2 H_2O(\ell) + 2 SO_2(g) + O_2(g)$
Step 3: $4 HI(g) \rightarrow 2 H_2(g) + 2 I_2(g)$
Net: $2 H_2O(\ell) \rightarrow 2 H_2(g) + O_2(g)$

21.21 $2 Na(s) + F_2(g) \rightarrow 2 NaF(s)$
$2 Na(s) + Cl_2(g) \rightarrow 2 NaCl(s)$
$2 Na(s) + Br_2(\ell) \rightarrow 2 NaBr(s)$
$2 Na(s) + I_2(s) \rightarrow 2 NaI(s)$
The alkali metal halides are white, crystalline solids. They have high melting and boiling points, and they are soluble in water.

21.23 (a) $2 Cl^-(aq) + 2 H_2O(\ell) \rightarrow$
$Cl_2(g) + H_2(g) + 2 OH^-(aq)$
(b) If this were the only process used to produce chlorine, the mass of Cl_2 reported for industrial production would be 0.88 times the mass of NaOH produced (2 mol NaCl, 117 g, would yield 2 mol NaOH, 80 g, and 1 mol Cl_2, 70 g). The amounts quoted indicate a Cl_2 to NaOH mass ratio 0.96. Chlorine is presumably also prepared by other routes than this one.

21.25 $2 \text{ Mg(s)} + \text{O}_2(\text{g}) \rightarrow 2 \text{ MgO(s)}$

$3 \text{ Mg(s)} + \text{N}_2(\text{g}) \rightarrow \text{Mg}_3\text{N}_2(\text{s})$

21.27 CaCO_3 is used in agriculture to neutralize acidic soil, to prepare CaO for use in mortar, and in steel production.

$\text{CaCO}_3(\text{s}) + \text{H}_2\text{O}(\ell) + \text{CO}_2(\text{g}) \rightarrow$
$$\text{Ca}^{2+}(\text{aq}) + 2 \text{ HCO}_3^-(\text{aq})$$

21.29 $1.4 \times 10^6 \text{ g SO}_2$

21.31

$\text{B}_3\text{O}_6{}^{3-}$

$\text{B}_2\text{O}_5{}^{4-}$

21.33 (a) $2 \text{ B}_5\text{H}_9(\text{g}) + 12 \text{ O}_2(\text{g}) \rightarrow 5 \text{ B}_2\text{O}_3(\text{s}) + 9 \text{ H}_2\text{O}(\text{g})$
   (b) Enthalpy of combustion of $\text{B}_5\text{H}_9 = -4341.2 \text{ kJ/mol}$. This is more than double the enthalpy of combustion of B_2H_6.
   (c) Enthalpy of combustion of $\text{C}_2\text{H}_6(\text{g})$ [to give $\text{CO}_2(\text{g})$ and $\text{H}_2\text{O}(\text{g})$] $= -1428.7 \text{ kJ/mol}$. C_2H_6 produces 47.5 kJ/g, whereas diborane produces much more (73.7 kJ/g).

21.35 $2 \text{ Al(s)} + 6 \text{ HCl(aq)} \rightarrow$
$$2 \text{ Al}^{3+}(\text{aq}) + 6 \text{ Cl}^-(\text{aq}) + 3 \text{ H}_2(\text{g})$$

$2 \text{ Al(s)} + 3 \text{ Cl}_2(\text{g}) \rightarrow 2 \text{ AlCl}_3(\text{s})$

$4 \text{ Al(s)} + 3 \text{ O}_2(\text{g}) \rightarrow 2 \text{ Al}_2\text{O}_3(\text{s})$

21.37 $2 \text{ Al(s)} + 2 \text{ OH}^-(\text{aq}) + 6 \text{ H}_2\text{O}(\ell) \rightarrow$
$$2 \text{ Al(OH)}_4{}^-(\text{aq}) + 3 \text{ H}_2(\text{g})$$

Volume of H_2 obtained from 13.2 g Al = 18.4 L

21.39 $\text{Al}_2\text{O}_3(\text{s}) + 3 \text{ H}_2\text{SO}_4(\text{aq}) \rightarrow \text{Al}_2(\text{SO}_4)_3(\text{s}) + 3 \text{ H}_2\text{O}(\ell)$

Mass of H_2SO_4 required = 860 g and mass of Al_2O_3 required = 298 g.

21.41 Pyroxenes have as their basic structural unit an extended chain of linked SiO_4 tetrahedra. The ratio of Si to O is 1:3.

21.43 This structure has a six-member ring of Si atoms with O atom bridges. Each Si also has two O atoms attached. The basic unit is $\text{SiO}_3{}^{2-}$, and the overall charge is -12 in $[(\text{SiO}_3)_6]^{-12}$. (Electron lone pairs are omitted in the following structure.)

21.45 Consider the general decomposition reaction:

$$\text{N}_x\text{O}_y \rightarrow {}^x/_2 \text{ N}_2 + {}^y/_2 \text{ O}_2$$

The value of $\Delta G°$ can be obtained for all N_xO_y molecules because $\Delta_r G° = -\Delta_f G°$. These data show that the decomposition reaction is spontaneous for all of the nitrogen oxides. All are unstable with respect to decomposition to the elements.

Compound	$-\Delta_f G°$ (kJ/mol)
NO(g)	-86.58
NO_2	-51.23
N_2O	-104.20
N_2O_4	-97.73

21.47 $\Delta_r H° = -114.4 \text{ kJ/mol-rxn}$; exothermic $\Delta_r G° = -70.7 \text{ kJ/mol-rxn}$, product-favored at equilibrium

21.49 (a) $\text{N}_2\text{H}_4(\text{aq}) + \text{O}_2(\text{g}) \rightarrow \text{N}_2(\text{g}) + 2 \text{ H}_2\text{O}(\ell)$
   (b) $1.32 \times 10^3 \text{ g}$

21.51 (a) Oxidation number = $+3$
   (b) Diphosphorous acid ($\text{H}_4\text{P}_2\text{O}_5$) should be a diprotic acid (losing the two H atoms attached to O atoms).

21.53 (a) $3.5 \times 10^3 \text{ kg SO}_2$
   (b) $4.1 \times 10^3 \text{ kg Ca(OH)}_2$

21.55

disulfide ion

21.57 $E°_{\text{cell}} = E°_{\text{cathode}} - E°_{\text{anode}} = +1.44 \text{ V} - (+1.51 \text{ V}) = -0.07 \text{ V}$

The reaction is not product-favored under standard conditions.

21.59 $\text{Cl}_2(\text{aq}) + 2 \text{ Br}^-(\text{aq}) \rightarrow 2 \text{ Cl}^-(\text{aq}) + \text{Br}_2(\ell)$

Cl_2 is the oxidizing agent, Br^- is the reducing agent; $E°_{\text{cell}} = 0.28 \text{ V}$.

21.61 The reaction consumes $4.32 \times 10^8 \text{ C}$ to produce $8.51 \times 10^4 \text{ g F}_2$.

21.63

Element	Appearance	State
Na, Mg, Al	Silvery metal	Solids
Si	Black, shiny metalloid	Solid
P	White, red, and black allotropes; nonmetal	Solid
S	Yellow nonmetal	Solid
Cl	Pale green nonmetal	Gas
Ar	Colorless nonmetal	Gas

21.65 (a) $2 K(s) + Cl_2(g) \rightarrow 2 KCl(s)$

$Ca(s) + Cl_2(g) \rightarrow CaCl_2(s)$

$2 Ga(s) + 3 Cl_2(g) \rightarrow 2 GaCl_3(s)$

$Ge(s) + 2 Cl_2(g) \rightarrow GeCl_4(\ell)$

$2 As(s) + 3 Cl_2(g) \rightarrow 2 AsCl_3(\ell)$

(AsCl$_5$ has been prepared but is not stable.)

(b) KCl and CaCl$_2$ are ionic; the other products are covalent.

(c) The electron-pair and molecular geometries of GaCl$_3$ are both trigonal-planar; the electron-pair geometry of AsCl$_3$ is tetrahedral, and its molecular geometry is trigonal-pyramidal.

21.67 (a) $2 KClO_3(s) \rightarrow 2 KCl(s) + 3 O_2(g)$

(b) $2 H_2S(g) + 3 O_2(g) \rightarrow 2 H_2O(g) + 2 SO_2(g)$

(c) $2 Na(s) + O_2(g) \rightarrow Na_2O_2(s)$

(d) $P_4(s) + 3 KOH(aq) + 3 H_2O(\ell) \rightarrow$
$\qquad\qquad\qquad PH_3(g) + 3 KH_2PO_2(aq)$

(e) $NH_4NO_3(s) \rightarrow N_2O(g) + 2 H_2O(g)$

(f) $2 In(s) + 3 Br_2(\ell) \rightarrow 2 InBr_3(s)$

(g) $SnCl_4(\ell) + 2 H_2O(\ell) \rightarrow SnO_2(s) + 4 HCl(aq)$

21.69 1.4×10^5 metric tons

21.71 Mg: $\Delta_r G° = +64.9$ kJ

Ca: $\Delta_r G° = +131.40$ kJ

Ba: $\Delta_r G° = +219.4$ kJ

Relative tendency to decompose:
$MgCO_3 > CaCO_3 > BaCO_3$

21.73 (a) $\Delta_f G°$ should be more negative than $(-95.1 \text{ kJ}) \times n$.

(b) Ba, Pb, Ti

21.75 O—F bond energy = 190 kJ/mol

21.77 (a) N_2O_4 is the oxidizing agent (N is reduced from +4 to 0 in N_2), and $H_2NN(CH_3)_2$ is the reducing agent.

(b) 1.3×10^4 kg N_2O_4 is required. Product masses: 5.7×10^3 kg N_2; 4.9×10^3 kg H_2O; 6.0×10^3 kg CO_2.

21.79 $\Delta_r H° = -257.78$ kJ. This reaction is entropy-disfavored, however, with $\Delta_r S° = -963$ J/K because of the decrease in the number of moles of gases. Combining these values gives $\Delta_r G° = +29.19$ kJ, indicating that under standard conditions at 298 K the reaction is not spontaneous. (The reaction has a favorable $\Delta_r G°$ at temperatures less than 268 K, indicating that further research on this system might be worthwhile. Note that at that temperature water is a solid.)

21.81 $A = B_2H_6$; $B = B_4H_{10}$; $C = B_5H_{11}$; $D = B_5H_9$; $E = B_{10}H_{14}$

21.83 48.6 kiloamps

21.85

The ring is not expected to be planar because a tetrahedral electron-pair geometry is predicted for each atom in the ring.

21.87 $\Delta_r G° = -834.28$ kJ/mol-rxn, therefore the reaction is product-favored at equilibrium at 298 K.

$\Delta_r S° = -149.9$ J/K · mol-rxn at 298 K. Because this is negative, the reaction will be less product-favored at high temperatures.

21.89 (a) $2 CH_3Cl(g) + Si(s) \rightarrow (CH_3)_2SiCl_2(\ell)$

(b) 0.823 atm

(c) 12.2 g

21.91 $5 N_2H_5^+(aq) + 4 IO_3^-(aq) \rightarrow$
$\qquad 5 N_2(g) + 2 I_2(aq) + H^+(aq) + 12 H_2O(\ell)$

$E°_{net} = 1.43$ V

21.93 (a) Br_2O_3

(b) The structure of Br_2O is reasonably well known. Several possible structures for Br_2O_3 can be imagined, but experiment confirms the structure below.

21.95 (a) The NO bond with a length of 114.2 pm is a double bond. The other two NO bonds (with a length of 121 pm) have a bond order of 1.5 (as there are two resonance structures involving these bonds).

(b) $K = 1.90$; $\Delta_r S° = 141$ J/K · mol-rxn

(c) $\Delta_f H° = 82.9$ kJ/mol

21.97 The flask contains a fixed number of moles of gas at the given pressure and temperature. One could burn the mixture because only the H_2 will combust; the argon is untouched. Cooling the gases from combustion would remove water (the combustion product of H_2) and leave only Ar in the gas phase. Measuring its pressure in a calibrated volume at a known temperature would allow one to calculate the amount of Ar that was in the original mixture.

21.99 Generally, a sodium fire can be extinguished by smothering it with sand. The worst choice is to use water (which reacts violently with sodium to give H_2 gas and NaOH).

21.101 Nitrogen is a relatively unreactive gas, so it will not participate in any reaction typical of hydrogen or oxygen. The most obvious property of H_2 is that it burns, so attempting to burn a small sample of the gas would immediately confirm or deny the presence of H_2. If O_2 is present, it can be detected by allowing it to react as an oxidizing agent. There are many reactions known with low-valent metals, especially transition metal ions in solution, that can be detected by color changes.

21.103 3.5 kW-h

21.105 The reducing ability of the Group 3A metals declines considerably on descending the group, with the largest drop occurring on going from Al to Ga. The reducing ability of gallium and indium are similar, but another large change is observed on going to thallium. In fact, thallium is most stable in the +1 oxidation state. This same tendency for elements to be more stable with lower oxidation numbers is seen in Groups 4A (Ge and Pb) and 5A (Bi).

Applying Chemical Principles: Van Arkel Triangles and Bonding

1. (a) CuZn is metallic.
   (b) GaAs and BP are semiconductors. As and B are metalloids; Ga and P are not. In both compounds, only one element is a metalloid.
   (c) Mg_3N_2 and $SrBr_2$ are ionic. Both are composed of a metal combined with a nonmetal.
   (d) Covalent bonding
   (e) SBr_2 and C_3N_4 are covalent. Both elements in the compounds are nonmetallic.

Chapter 22

22.1 (a) Cr^{3+}: $[Ar]3d^3$, paramagnetic
   (b) V^{2+}: $[Ar]3d^3$, paramagnetic
   (c) Ni^{2+}: $[Ar]3d^8$, paramagnetic
   (d) Cu^+: $[Ar]3d^{10}$, diamagnetic

22.3 (a) Fe^{3+}: $[Ar]3d^5$, isoelectronic with Mn^{2+}
   (b) Zn^{2+}: $[Ar]3d^{10}$, isoelectronic with Cu^+
   (c) Fe^{2+}: $[Ar]3d^6$, isoelectronic with Co^{3+}
   (d) Cr^{3+}: $[Ar]3d^3$, isoelectronic with V^{2+}

22.5 (a) $Cr_2O_3(s) + 2\ Al(s) \rightarrow Al_2O_3(s) + 2\ Cr(s)$
   (b) $TiCl_4(\ell) + 2\ Mg(s) \rightarrow Ti(s) + 2\ MgCl_2(s)$
   (c) $2\ [Ag(CN)_2]^-(aq) + Zn(s) \rightarrow$
       $2\ Ag(s) + [Zn(CN)_4]^{2-}(aq)$
   (d) $3\ Mn_3O_4(s) + 8\ Al(s) \rightarrow 9\ Mn(s) + 4\ Al_2O_3(s)$

22.7 Monodentate: CH_3NH_2, CH_3CN, N_3^-, Br^-

   Bidentate: en, phen (see Figure 22.14)

22.9 (a) Mn^{2+}; (b) Co^{3+}; (c) Co^{3+}; (d) Cr^{2+}

22.11 $[Ni(en)(NH_3)_3(H_2O)]^{2+}$

22.13 (a) $Ni(en)_2Cl_2$ (en = $H_2NCH_2CH_2NH_2$)
   (b) $K_2[PtCl_4]$
   (c) $K[Cu(CN)_2]$
   (d) $[Fe(NH_3)_4(H_2O)_2]^{2+}$

22.15 (a) Diaquabis(oxalato)nickelate(II) ion
   (b) Dibromobis(ethylenediamine)cobalt(III) ion
   (c) Amminechlorobis(ethylenediamine)cobalt(III) ion
   (d) Diammineoxalatoplatinum(II)

22.17 (a) $[Fe(H_2O)_5OH]^{2+}$
   (b) Potassium tetracyanonickelate(II)
   (c) Potassium diaquabis(oxalato)chromate(III)
   (d) $(NH_4)_2[PtCl_4]$

22.19

Only one structure possible. (N—N is the bidentate ethylenediamine ligand.)

22.21 (a) Fe^{2+} is a chiral center.
   (b) Co^{3+} is not a chiral center.
   (c) Co^{3+} is not a chiral center.
   (d) No. Square-planar complexes are never chiral.

22.23 (a) $[Mn(CN)_6]^{4-}$: d^5, low-spin Mn^{2+} complex is paramagnetic (one unpaired electron).

   $\underline{\uparrow\downarrow}\ \underline{\uparrow\downarrow}\ \underline{\uparrow}$

   (b) $[Co(NH_3)_6]^{3+}$: d^6, low-spin Co^{3+} complex is diamagnetic.

   $\underline{\uparrow\downarrow}\ \underline{\uparrow\downarrow}\ \underline{\uparrow\downarrow}$

   (c) $[Fe(H_2O)_6]^{3+}$: d^5, low-spin Fe^{3+} complex is paramagnetic [one unpaired electron; same as part (a)].
   (d) $[Cr(en)_3]^{2+}$: d^4, Cr^{2+} complex is paramagnetic (two unpaired electrons).

   $\underline{\uparrow\downarrow}\ \underline{\uparrow}\ \underline{\uparrow}$

22.25 (a) Fe^{2+}, d^6, paramagnetic, four unpaired electrons
(b) Co^{2+}, d^7, paramagnetic, three unpaired electrons
(c) Mn^{2+}, d^5, paramagnetic, five unpaired electrons
(d) Zn^{2+}, d^{10}, diamagnetic, zero unpaired electrons

22.27 (a) 6
(b) Octahedral
(c) +2
(d) Four unpaired electrons (high spin)
(e) Paramagnetic

22.29 With four ligands, complexes of the d^8 Ni^{2+} ion can be either tetrahedral or square-planar. The CN^- ligand is at one end of the spectrochemical series and leads to a large ligand field splitting, whereas Cl^- is at the opposite end and often leads to complexes with small orbital splitting. With ligands such as CN^- the complex will be square-planar (and for a d^8 ion it will be diamagnetic). With a weak field ligand (Cl^-) the complex will be tetrahedral and, for the d^8 ion, two electrons will be unpaired, giving a paramagnetic complex.

22.31 The light absorbed is in the green region of the spectrum (page 1043). Therefore, the light transmitted—which is the color of the solution—is magenta.

22.33 (a) The Mn^+ ion in this complex has six d electrons. Each CO contributes two electrons, giving a total of 18 for the complex ion.
(b) The $C_5H_5^-$ ligand contributes six electrons, CO and PR_3 each contribute two electrons, for a total of 10 electrons for the ligands. The cobalt is effectively a Co^+ ion and contributes eight d electrons. The total is 18 electrons.
(c) The $C_5H_5^-$ ligand contributes six electrons, each CO contributes two electrons, for a total of 12 electrons for the ligands. The manganese is effectively a Mn^+ ion and contributes six d electrons. The total is 18 electrons.

22.35 Determine the magnetic properties of the complex. Square-planar Ni^{2+} (d^8) complexes are diamagnetic, whereas tetrahedral complexes are paramagnetic.

22.37 Fe^{2+} has a d^6 configuration. Low-spin octahedral complexes are diamagnetic, whereas high-spin octahedral complexes of this ion have four unpaired electrons and are paramagnetic.

22.39 Square-planar complexes most often arise from d^8 transition metal ions. Therefore, it is likely that $[Ni(CN)_4]^{2-}$ (Ni^{2+}) and $[Pt(CN)_4]^{2-}$ (Pt^{2+}) are square planar. (See also Study Question 22.29.)

22.41 Two geometric isomers are possible.

22.43 Absorbing at 425 nm means the complex is absorbing light in the blue-violet end of the spectrum. Therefore, red and green light are transmitted, and the complex appears yellow (see Figure 22.27).

22.45 (a) Mn^{2+}; (b) 6; (c) octahedral; (d) 5; (e) paramagnetic; (f) *cis* and *trans* isomers exist.

22.47 Name: tetraamminedichlorocobalt(III) chloride

cis   trans

22.49 $[Co(en)_2(H_2O)Cl]^{2+}$

22.51

mer   *fac*

trans chlorides   *cis* chlorides

22.53

H_2O and NH_3
cis, chiral

H_2O *cis* and
NH_3 *trans*,
not chiral

H_2O *trans* and
NH_3 *cis*, not
chiral

22.55 In $[Mn(H_2O)_6]^{2+}$ and $[Mn(CN)_6]^{4-}$, Mn has an oxidation number of +2 (Mn is a d^5 ion).

$[Mn(H_2O)_6]^{2+}$ $[Mn(CN)_6]^{4-}$
paramagnetic,   paramagnetic,
5 unpaired e^- 1 unpaired e^-

This shows that Δ_o for CN^- is greater than for H_2O.

22.57 (a) Ammonium tetrachlorocuprate(II)

(b) Hexacarbonylmolybdenum(0)

(c) $[Cr(H_2O)_4Cl_2]Cl$

(d) $[Co(H_2O)(NH_2CH_2CH_2NH_2)_2(SCN)](NO_3)_2$

22.59 (a) The light absorbed is in the orange region of the spectrum (page 1043). Therefore, the light transmitted (the color of the solution) is blue or cyan.

(b) Using the cobalt(III) complexes in Table 22.3 as a guide, we might place CO_3^{2-} between F^- and the oxalato ion, $C_2O_4^{2-}$.

(c) Δ_o is small, so the complex should be high spin and paramagnetic.

22.61

$$\overset{\frown}{N \quad O} = H_2N—CH_2—CO_2^-$$

enantiometric pair

enantiometric pair

enantiometric pair

22.63 (a) In complexes such as $M(PR_3)Cl_2$ the metal is Ni^{2+} or Pd^{2+}, both of which are d^8 metal ions. If an Ni^{2+} complex is paramagnetic it must be tetrahedral, whereas the Pd^{2+} must be square planar. (A d^8 metal complex cannot be diamagnetic if it has a tetrahedral structure.)

Tetrahedral Ni^{2+} complex, paramagnetic

Square-planar Pd^{2+} complex, diamagnetic

(b) A tetrahedral Ni^{2+} complex cannot have isomers, whereas a square-planar complex of the type $M(PR_3)_2Cl_2$ can have *cis* and *trans* isomers. (See page 1035.)

22.65 A, dark violet isomer: $[Co(NH_3)_5Br]SO_4$

B, violet-red isomer: $[Co(NH_3)_5(SO_4)]Br$

$[Co(NH_3)_5Br]SO_4(aq) + BaCl_2(aq) \rightarrow$
$[Co(NH_3)_5Br]Cl_2(aq) + BaSO_4(s)$

22.67 (a) There is 5.41×10^{-4} mol of $UO_2(NO_3)_2$, and this provides 5.41×10^{-4} mol of U^{n+} ions on reduction by Zn. The 5.41×10^{-4} mol U^{n+} requires 2.16×10^{-4} mol MnO_4^- to reach the equivalence point. This is a ratio of 5 mol of U^{n+} ions to 2 mol MnO_4^- ions. The 2 mol MnO_4^- ions require 10 mol of e^- (to go to Mn^{2+} ions), so 5 mol of U^{n+} ions provide 10 mol e^- (on going to 5 UO_2^{2+} ions, with a uranium oxidation number of +6). This means the U^{n+} ion must be U^{4+}.

(b) $Zn(s) \rightarrow Zn^{2+}(aq) + 2 e^-$

$\underline{UO_2^{2+}(aq) + 4 H^+(aq) + 2 e^- \rightarrow}$
$\quad\quad\quad\quad U^{4+}(aq) + 2 H_2O(\ell)$

$UO_2^{2+}(aq) + 4 H^+(aq) + Zn(s) \rightarrow$
$\quad U^{4+}(aq) + 2 H_2O(\ell) + Zn^{2+}(aq)$

(c) $5[U^{4+}(aq) + 2 H_2O(\ell) \rightarrow$
$\quad\quad\quad UO_2^{2+}(aq) + 4 H^+(aq) + 2 e^-]$

$\underline{2[MnO_4^-(aq) + 8 H^+(aq) + 5 e^- \rightarrow}$
$\quad\quad\quad Mn^{2+}(aq) + 4 H_2O(\ell)]$

$5 U^{4+}(aq) + 2 MnO_4^-(aq) + 2 H_2O(\ell) \rightarrow$
$\quad 5 UO_2^{2+}(aq) + 4 H^+(aq) + 2 Mn^{2+}(aq)$

22.69

Ion	$K_{formation}$ (ammine complexes)
Co^{2+}	1.3×10^5
Ni^{2+}	5.5×10^8
Cu^{2+}	2.1×10^{13}
Zn^{2+}	2.9×10^9

The data for these hexaammine complexes do, indeed, verify the Irving-Williams series. In the book *Chemistry of the Elements* (N. N. Greenwood and A. Earnshaw: 2nd edition, p. 908, Oxford, England, Butterworth-Heinemann, 1997), it is stated: "the stabilities of corresponding complexes of the bivalent ions of the first transition series, irrespective of the particular ligand involved, usually vary in the Irving-Williams order, . . . , which is the reverse of the order for the cation radii. These observations are consistent with the view that, at least for metals in oxidation states +2 and +3, the coordinate bond is largely electrostatic. This was a major factor in the acceptance of the crystal field theory."

22.71 Wilkinson's catalyst and the EAN rule.

Step 1: Rhodium-containing reactant. Each PR_3 ligand donates two electrons as does the Cl^- ligand. The Rh^+ ion has 8 d electrons. Total electrons = 16.

Step 1: Rhodium-containing product. Assuming that the H ligand is H^-, each donates two electrons, as do Cl^- and the two PR_3 ligands. The metal center is Rh^{3+}, a d^6 metal ion. Total electrons = 18.

Step 2: The product has 16 electrons because one PR_3 ligand has been dissociated.

Step 3: The product has 18 electrons. The two-electron donor ligand CH_2CH_2 has replaced the dissociated PR_3 ligand.

Step 4: The product has 16 electrons. There are three anionic, two-electron donor ligands (Cl^-, H^-, and $CH_3CH_2^-$), two two-electron donor PR_3 ligands, and an Rh^{3+} ion (d^6).

Step 5: The product has 14 electrons. It is an Rh^+ complex (d^8) with two PR_3 ligands (two electrons each) and one Cl^- (two electrons). (It is likely a solvent molecule fills the vacant site here to give a transient, 16-electron complex.)

Step 6: The product is once again the active, 16-electron catalyst.

Applying Chemical Principles: Green Catalysts

1. Coordination number = 5

3. Dentate

5. Square-planar

Chapter 23

23.1 Each answer is in the format: person(s); experiment; significance.
(a) Becquerel; potassium uranyl sulfate caused an image to appear on a photographic plate; this opened up a new area of study.
(b) Marie and Pierre Curie; separated these elements from pitchblende; discovery of new elements based on radioactivity.
(c) Rutherford; bombarded ^{14}N with α particles and found protons and ^{17}O among products; human-caused transmutation of one element into another.
(d) Fermi; absorption of a neutron by a nucleus with subsequent release of a γ ray; production of more nuclei and the use of this process to produce many of the radioisotopes used in medicine.
(e) Hahn and Strassman, experiment explained by Meitner; bombarded a sample of uranium with neutrons and detected barium in products; nuclear fission is used in atomic bombs and in nuclear energy plants.

23.3 Binding energy per nucleon is determined by first calculating the mass defect for an isotope, converting the mass defect to binding energy (using $E = mc^2$) and then dividing the binding energy by the mass number of the nucleus.

23.5 Nuclear reactions are carried out in a laboratory by hitting a nucleus with a particle. Various particles have been used: α particles, protons, neutrons, and the nuclei of other atoms. In producing transuranium elements, this last method is used; the particles are usually accelerated to high energy in a particle accelerator.

23.7 While an organism lives, the percentage of carbon that is ^{14}C in the organism will equal the percentage in the atmosphere. When the organism dies, it no longer replenishes the ^{14}C. By measuring the activity of ^{14}C in the organism, comparing it to the ambient ^{14}C activity, and using first-order kinetics, it is possible to determine how long ago the organism stopped taking in ^{14}C (died). Limitations: (1) The method assumes that the amount of ^{14}C in the atmosphere has remained constant, whereas it has varied by as much as 10%. (2) ^{14}C dating cannot be used to date an object less than 100 or more than about 40,000 years old. (3) The accuracy of ^{14}C dating is about ± 100 years.

23.9 A radioactive decay series occurs when a radioactive isotope decays to form another radioactive isotope. The series continues until a nonradioactive isotope is formed. Uranium ore contains radium and polonium because these elements are formed in the radioactive decay series of uranium.

23.11 (a) $^{56}_{28}Ni$; (b) $^{1}_{0}n$; (c) $^{32}_{15}P$; (d) $^{97}_{43}Tc$; (e) $^{0}_{-1}\beta$; (f) $^{0}_{1}e$ (positron)

23.13 (a) $^{0}_{-1}\beta$; (b) $^{87}_{37}Rb$; (c) $^{4}_{2}\alpha$; (d) $^{226}_{88}Ra$; (e) $^{0}_{-1}\beta$; (f) $^{24}_{11}Na$

23.15 $^{235}_{92}U \rightarrow {}^{231}_{90}Th + {}^{4}_{2}\alpha$

$^{231}_{90}Th \rightarrow {}^{231}_{91}Pa + {}^{0}_{-1}\beta$

$^{231}_{91}Pa \rightarrow {}^{227}_{89}Ac + {}^{4}_{2}\alpha$

$^{227}_{89}Ac \rightarrow {}^{227}_{90}Th + {}^{0}_{-1}\beta$

$^{227}_{90}Th \rightarrow {}^{223}_{88}Ra + {}^{4}_{2}\alpha$

$^{223}_{88}Ra \rightarrow {}^{219}_{86}Rn + {}^{4}_{2}\alpha$

$^{219}_{86}Rn \rightarrow {}^{215}_{84}Po + {}^{4}_{2}\alpha$

$^{215}_{84}Po \rightarrow {}^{211}_{82}Pb + {}^{4}_{2}\alpha$

$^{211}_{82}Pb \rightarrow {}^{211}_{83}Bi + {}^{0}_{-1}\beta$

$^{211}_{83}Bi \rightarrow {}^{211}_{84}Po + {}^{0}_{-1}\beta$

$^{211}_{84}Po \rightarrow {}^{207}_{82}Pb + {}^{4}_{2}\alpha$

23.17 (a) $^{198}_{79}Au \rightarrow {}^{198}_{80}Hg + {}^{0}_{-1}\beta$
(b) $^{222}_{86}Rn \rightarrow {}^{218}_{84}Po + {}^{4}_{2}\alpha$
(c) $^{137}_{55}Cs \rightarrow {}^{137}_{56}Ba + {}^{0}_{-1}\beta$
(d) $^{110}_{49}In \rightarrow {}^{110}_{48}Cd + {}^{0}_{1}e$

23.19 (a) $^{80}_{35}Br$ has a high neutron/proton ratio of 45/35. Beta decay will allow the ratio to decrease: $^{80}_{35}Br \rightarrow ^{80}_{36}Kr + ^{0}_{-1}\beta$.

(b) Alpha decay is likely: $^{240}_{98}Cf \rightarrow ^{236}_{96}Cm + ^{4}_{2}\alpha$

(c) Cobalt-61 has a high n/p ratio, so beta decay is likely:

$$^{61}_{27}Co \rightarrow ^{61}_{28}Kr + ^{0}_{-1}\beta$$

(d) Carbon-11 has only five neutrons, so K-capture or positron emission may occur:

$$^{11}_{6}C + ^{0}_{-1}e \rightarrow ^{11}_{5}B$$
$$^{11}_{6}C \rightarrow ^{11}_{5}B + ^{0}_{1}e$$

23.21 Generally beta decay will occur when the n/p ratio is high, whereas positron emission will occur when the n/p ratio is low.

(a) Beta decay: $^{20}_{9}F \rightarrow ^{20}_{10}Ne + ^{0}_{-1}\beta$

$$^{3}_{1}H \rightarrow ^{3}_{2}He + ^{0}_{-1}\beta$$

(b) Positron emission

$$^{22}_{11}Na \rightarrow ^{22}_{10}Ne + ^{0}_{1}\beta$$

23.23 Binding energy per mole of nucleons for ^{11}B = 6.70×10^8 kJ

Binding energy per mole of nucleons for ^{10}B = 6.26×10^8 kJ

23.25 8.256×10^8 kJ/mol nucleons

23.27 7.700×10^8 kJ/mol nucleons

23.29 0.781 micrograms

23.31 (a) $^{131}_{53}I \rightarrow ^{131}_{54}Xe + ^{0}_{-1}\beta$
(b) 0.075 micrograms

23.33 9.5×10^{-4} mg

23.35 (a) $^{222}_{86}Rn \rightarrow ^{218}_{84}Po + ^{4}_{2}\alpha$
(b) Time = 8.87 d

23.37 (a) 15.8 y; (b) 88%

23.39 $^{239}_{94}Pu + ^{4}_{2}\alpha \rightarrow ^{240}_{95}Am + ^{1}_{1}H + 2 ^{1}_{0}n$

23.41 $^{48}_{20}Ca + ^{242}_{94}Pu \rightarrow ^{287}_{114}Uuq + 3 ^{1}_{0}n$

23.43 (a) $^{115}_{48}Cd$; (b) $^{7}_{4}Be$; (c) $^{4}_{2}\alpha$; (d) $^{63}_{29}Cu$

23.45 $^{10}_{5}B + ^{1}_{0}n \rightarrow ^{7}_{3}Li + ^{4}_{2}\alpha$

23.47 Time = 4.4×10^{10} y

23.49 If $t_{1/2}$ = 14.28 d, then $k = 4.854 \times 10^{-2}$ d^{-1}. If the original disintegration rate is 3.2×10^6 dpm, then (from the integrated first order rate equation), the rate after 365 d is 0.065 dpm. The plot will resemble Figure 23.5.

23.51 (a) $^{238}_{92}U + ^{1}_{0}n \rightarrow ^{239}_{92}U + \gamma$
(b) $^{239}_{92}U \rightarrow ^{239}_{93}Np + ^{0}_{-1}\beta$
(c) $^{239}_{93}Np \rightarrow ^{239}_{94}Pu + ^{0}_{-1}\beta$
(d) $^{239}_{94}Pu + ^{1}_{0}n \rightarrow 2 ^{1}_{0}n + $ energy + other nuclei

23.53 About 2700 years old

23.55 Plot ln(activity) versus time. The slope of the plot is $-k$, the rate constant for decay. Here, $k = 0.0050$ d^{-1}, so $t_{1/2} = 140$ d.

23.57 Time = 1.9×10^9 y

23.59 Energy obtained from 1.000 lb (452.6 g) of ^{235}U = 4.1×10^{10} kJ

Mass of coal required = 1.6×10^3 ton (or about 3 million pounds of coal)

23.61 27 fish tagged fish out of 5250 fish caught represents 0.51% of the fish in the lake. Therefore, 1000 fish put into the lake represent 0.51% of the fish in the lake, or 0.51% of 190,000 fish.

23.63 (a) The mass decreases by 4 units (with an $^{4}_{2}\alpha$ emission) or is unchanged (with a $^{0}_{-1}\beta$ emission), so the only masses possible are 4 units apart.

(b) ^{232}Th series, $m = 4n$; ^{235}U series $m = 4n + 3$

(c) ^{226}Ra and ^{210}Bi, $4n + 2$ series; ^{215}At, $4n + 3$ series; ^{228}Th, $4n$ series

(d) Each series is headed by a long-lived isotope (in the order of 10^9 years, the age of the Earth). The $4n + 1$ series is missing because there is no long-lived isotope in this series. Over geologic time, all the members of this series have decayed completely.

23.65 (a) ^{231}Pa isotope belongs to the ^{235}U decay series (see Question 23.63b).

(b) $^{235}_{92}U \rightarrow ^{231}_{90}Th + ^{4}_{2}\alpha$

$$^{231}_{90}Th \rightarrow ^{231}_{91}Pa + ^{0}_{-1}\beta$$

(c) Pa-231 is present to the extent of 1 part per million. Therefore, 1 million grams of pitchblende need to be used to obtain 1 g of Pa-231.

(d) $^{231}_{91}Pa \rightarrow ^{227}_{89}Ac + ^{4}_{2}\alpha$

23.67 Pitchblende contains $^{238}_{92}U$ and $^{235}_{92}U$. Thus, both radium and polonium isotopes must belong to either the $4n + 2$ or $4n + 3$ decay series. Furthermore, the isotopes must have sufficiently long half-lives in order to survive the separation and isolation process. These criteria are satisfied by ^{226}Ra and ^{210}Po.

Applying Chemical Principles: The Age of Meteorites

1. $^{87}_{37}Rb \rightarrow ^{87}_{38}Sr + ^{0}_{-1}\beta$

3. $k = 1.42 \times 10^{-11}$ y^{-1}

5. Age of meteorite = 2.80×10^9 y

Index/Glossary

PHYSICAL AND CHEMICAL CONSTANTS

Avogadro's number $N = 6.0221415 \times 10^{23}/\text{mol}$
Electronic charge $e = 1.60217653 \times 10^{-19}\ \text{C}$
Faraday's constant $F = 9.6485338 \times 10^{4}\ \text{C/mol electrons}$
Gas constant $R = 8.314472\ \text{J/K} \cdot \text{mol}$
     $= 0.082057\ \text{L} \cdot \text{atm/K} \cdot \text{mol}$

π $\pi = 3.1415926536$
Planck's constant $h = 6.6260693 \times 10^{-34}\ \text{J} \cdot \text{sec}$
Speed of light $c = 2.99792458 \times 10^{8}\ \text{m/sec}$
  (in a vacuum)

USEFUL CONVERSION FACTORS AND RELATIONSHIPS

Length
SI unit: Meter (m)
1 kilometer $= 1000$ meters
        $= 0.62137$ mile
1 meter $= 100$ centimeters
1 centimeter $= 10$ millimeters
1 nanometer $= 1.00 \times 10^{-9}$ meter
1 picometer $= 1.00 \times 10^{-12}$ meter
    1 inch $= 2.54$ centimeter (exactly)
1 Ångstrom $= 1.00 \times 10^{-10}$ meter

Mass
SI unit: Kilogram (kg)
1 kilogram $= 1000$ grams
   1 gram $= 1000$ milligrams
   1 pound $= 453.59237$ grams $= 16$ ounces
    1 ton $= 2000$ pounds

Volume
SI unit: Cubic meter (m³)
1 liter (L) $= 1.00 \times 10^{-3}\ \text{m}^3$
         $= 1000\ \text{cm}^3$
         $= 1.056710$ quarts
1 gallon $= 4.00$ quarts

Energy
SI unit: Joule (J)
1 joule $= 1\ \text{kg} \cdot \text{m}^2/\text{s}^2$
      $= 0.23901$ calorie
      $= 1\ \text{C} \times 1\ \text{V}$
1 calorie $= 4.184$ joules

Pressure
SI unit: Pascal (Pa)
1 pascal $= 1\ \text{N/m}^2$
        $= 1\ \text{kg/m} \cdot \text{s}^2$
1 atmosphere $= 101.325$ kilopascals
          $= 760\ \text{mm Hg} = 760\ \text{torr}$
          $= 14.70\ \text{lb/in}^2$
          $= 1.01325$ bar
1 bar $= 10^5\ \text{Pa}$ (exactly)

Temperature
SI unit: kelvin (K)
0 K $= -273.15\ °\text{C}$
K $= °\text{C} + 273.15°\text{C}$
? $°\text{C} = (5\ °\text{C}/9\ °\text{F})(°\text{F} - 32\ °\text{F})$
? $°\text{F} = (9\ °\text{F}/5\ °\text{C})(°\text{C}) + 32\ °\text{F}$

LOCATION OF USEFUL TABLES AND FIGURES